Discovering Algebra

An Investigative Approach

SECOND EDITION

Jerald Murdock

Ellen Kamischke

Eric Kamischke

DISCOVERING

MATHEMATICS™

Key Curriculum Press
Innovators in Mathematics Education

Project Editor
Elizabeth DeCarli

Project Administrator
Aaron Madrigal

Student Edition Editor
Josephine Noah

Editorial Assistant
Brady Golden

Mathematics Consultant and Writer
Larry Copes

Teacher Consultants
Jennifer North Morris,
William Putnam

Accuracy Checker
Dudley Brooks

Editorial Production Supervisor
Christine Osborne

Production Editor
Kristin Ferraioli

Copy Editor
Mary Roybal

Production Director
McKinley Williams

Production Supervisor
Ann Rothenbuhler

Cover Designers
Jill Kongabel, Marilyn Perry

Text Designer
Jenny Somerville

Art Editor
Jason Luz

Technical Art
Precision Graphics,
Interactive Composition Corporation

Photo Editor
Margee Robinson

Compositor and Prepress
Interactive Composition Corporation

Printing
Webcrafters, Inc.

———————————————

Textbook Product Manager
James Ryan

Executive Editor
Casey FitzSimons

Publisher
Steven Rasmussen

®The Geometer's Sketchpad, Dynamic Geometry, and Key Curriculum Press are registered trademarks of Key Curriculum Press. ™Sketchpad is a trademark of Key Curriculum Press.

™Fathom Dynamic Data and the Fathom logo are trademarks of KCP Technologies.

All other trademarks are held by their respective owners.

Key Curriculum Press
1150 65th Street
Emeryville, CA 94608
510-595-7000
editorial@keypress.com
www.keypress.com

Printed in the United States of America

10 9 8 7 6 5 4   12 11 10 09 08

ISBN 978-1-55953-785-8

Discovering Algebra Acknowledgments

Mathematical Content Reviewers

Larry Copes, Grove Heights, Minnesota

David Rasmussen, Neil's Harbour, Nova Scotia

First Edition Reviewers

Mathematical Content Reviewers

Bill Medigovich, San Francisco, California

Mary Jean Winter, Michigan State University, East Lansing, Michigan

Equity Reviewers

Edward Castillo, Sonoma State University, Rohnert Park, California

Genevieve Lau, Skyline College, San Bruno, California

Charlene Morrow, Mount Holyoke College, South Hadley, Massachusetts

Arthur Powell, Rutgers University, Newark, New Jersey

William Yslas Velez, University of Arizona, Tucson, Arizona

Social Sciences and Humanities Reviewers

Ann Lawrence, Middletown, Connecticut

Karen Michalowicz, The Langley School, McLean, Virginia

Science Reviewers

Andrey Aristov, Loyola High School, Los Angeles, California

Matthew Weinstein, Macalester College, St. Paul, Minnesota

Laura Whitlock, Ph.D., Sonoma Center for Innovative Education in Science, Rohnert Park, California

Cooperative Learning Consultant

Michael Serra, San Francisco, California

Second Edition Development Reviewers

Dean F. Brown, Mira Mesa High School, San Diego, California

Ronda Davis, Sandia High School, Albuquerque, New Mexico

Fred Decovsky, Teaneck High School, Teaneck, New Jersey

Pamela Weber Harris, Kyle, Texas

Judy Hicks, Ralston Valley High School, Arvada, Colorado

Carla James, Marietta High School, Marietta, Georgia

Greg Ladner, Hong Kong International School, Hong Kong

Fernando A. Rizo, J. M. Hanks High School, El Paso, Texas

Julie L. Sirmon, Marietta High School, Marietta, Georgia

Ted C. Widersky, Madison Metropolitan School District, Madison, Wisconsin

First Edition Development Reviewers

Tina Barbieri, Palm Beach Day School, Palm Beach, Florida

Tom Beatini, Glen Rock Junior/Senior High School, Glen Rock, New Jersey

Marlys Brimmer, Ridgeview High School, Bakersfield, California

Martha Brown, Prince George's County Schools, Upper Marlboro, Maryland

Lois Burke, Charlottesville High School, Charlottesville, Virginia

Barbara Close, Palm Beach Day School, Palm Beach, Florida

Judy Cubillo, Northgate High School, Walnut Creek, California

Dave Damcke, Jefferson High School, Portland, Oregon

Pennie DeHoff, Tucson, Arizona

Larry Deis, El Molino High School, Forestville, California

Genie Dunn, Killian Senior High School, Miami, Florida

Patty Flowers, Humboldt High School, Humboldt, Tennessee

Claudia Gary, Amphitheater High School, Tucson, Arizona

Pamela Harris, Southwest Texas State University, San Marcos, Texas

Rachel Henning, Mims Elementary School, Mission, Texas

Murrel Hoover, South Charleston High School, South Charleston, West Virginia

Carolyn Jordan, Franklin High School, Stockton, California

Larry Lucas, Haskell Indian Nations University, Lawrence, Kansas

Bill Marthinsen, Piedmont High School, Piedmont, California

Jane Moore, Mariposa Middle School, Mariposa, California

John Oppedisano, Jefferson High School, Portland, Oregon

Luis Ortiz Franco, Chapman University, Orange, California

Marilyn Peak, Spencer County High School, Taylorsville, Kentucky

Debbie Preston, Keystone School, San Antonio, Texas

Darlene Pugh, Malta High School, Malta, Montana

Oran Pyle, Mariposa County High School, Mariposa, California

Beth Schlesinger, San Diego, California

Rick Shanley, Collegiate School, New York, New York

Phil Smith, Wayne High School, Fort Wayne, Indiana

Denise Tenanty, Masconomet High School, Topsfield, Massachusetts

Lisa Usher, San Pedro Math, Science, Technology Center, San Pedro, California

Dick Vinetz, Grant High School, Van Nuys, California

Preliminary Edition Field-test Participants

Jacqueline Abubakari, Arbor Middle School, Decatur, Georgia

Marjorie Ader, Platte Canyon High School, Bailey, Colorado

Doug Alford, South Orange Middle School, South Orange, New Jersey

Maelynn Anderson, Skyview High School, Vancouver, Washington

Jim Barys, Wachusett Regional High School, Holden, Massachusetts

Ellen Basile, Maplewood Middle School, Maplewood, New Jersey

Candice Beattys, South Orange and Maplewood Middle School, South Orange, New Jersey

Lanna Bell, The Lexington School, Lexington, Kentucky

Brian Boyd, Oakwood High School, Dayton, Ohio

Jeffrey Choppin, Benjamin Banneker Academic High School, Washington, D.C.

Jan Christianson, Hong Kong International School, Hong Kong

Mary Ann Clark, The Langley School, McLean, Virginia

Cel Cowan, Hamlin High School, Hamlin, Texas

Pat Cusick, Hong Kong International School, Hong Kong

Howard David, Amherst Regional High School, Amherst, Massachusetts

Carol DeCuzzi, Audubon Junior-Senior High School, Audubon, New Jersey

Cathy Doll, Henry County High School, New Castle, Kentucky

Bill Dolyniuk, Woodside Elementary School, Woodside, California

Marilyn Eglovitch, Maplewood Middle School, Maplewood, New Jersey

Janine Evans, Hong Kong International School, Hong Kong

Patty Flowers, Humboldt High School, Humboldt, Tennessee

Sy Friedman, Amherst Regional High School, Amherst, Massachusetts

Jennifer Gardner, Arrowsmith Academy, Berkeley, California

Janet Gibson, Denver City High School, Denver City, Texas

Steve Gile, Kingsburg High School, Kingsburg, California

Kara Granger, Northwestern High School, Hyattsville, Maryland

Kevin Harris, Pennridge Central Middle School, Perkasie, Pennsylvania

Carol Hattan, Skyview High School, Vancouver, Washington

Susan Heinrich, Hong Kong International School, Hong Kong

Edna Horton Flores, Kenwood Academy, Chicago, Illinois

Marilyn Howard, University School at Tulsa University, Tulsa, Oklahoma

Steven Isaak, Green Valley High School, Henderson, Nevada

Nancy Jameson, Rowland Hall–St. Mark's School, Salt Lake City, Utah

Mary Jensen, Friday Harbor High School, Friday Harbor, Washington

Patty Kincaid, Sheldon High School, Eugene, Oregon

Norman Krumpe, Oakwood High School, Dayton, Ohio

Bill Manchester, Amherst Regional High School, Amherst, Massachusetts

John Moran, Amherst Regional High School, Amherst, Massachusetts

Kristin Muldowney, Hong Kong International School, Hong Kong

David Mullins, Amherst Regional High School, Amherst, Massachusetts

Paul Myers, Woodward Academy, College Park, Georgia

Wayne Nirode, Troy High School, Troy, Ohio

Ken Nossardi, C. K. McClatchy High School, Sacramento, California

Paul Peelle, Amherst Regional High School, Amherst, Massachusetts

Doris Peim, South Orange Middle School, South Orange, New Jersey

Benita Pfeiffer, Hong Kong International School, Hong Kong

Wakako Rohlich, Amherst Regional High School, Amherst, Massachusetts

Ken Rohrs, Hong Kong International School, Hong Kong

Alison Ruebusch, Catlin-Gabel School, Portland, Oregon

Debi Rydeski, Columbia High School, Burbank, Washington

Rick Shanley, The Collegiate School, New York, New York

Rebecca Simpson, Green Mountain High School, Lakewood, Colorado

Janet Taylor, Hong Kong International School, Hong Kong

Denise Tenanty, Masconomet High School, Topsfield, Massachusetts

Tim Voegeli, Fairmont High School, Kettering, Ohio

Gladys Whitehead, Prince George's County Public Schools, Upper Marlboro, Maryland

Karla Wiggins, South Orange Middle School, South Orange, New Jersey

June Wilby, Amherst Regional High School, Amherst, Massachusetts

Cher Williams, Onalaska High School, Onalaska, Washington

Cheryl Wright, Amherst Regional High School, Amherst, Massachusetts

A Note from the Publisher

The mathematics we learn and teach in school is evolving to address the needs of today's students, driven by new discoveries in mathematics and science, new research on learning, changing societal needs, and the use of more advanced technologies in work and in education. The algebra you find in this book won't look exactly like the algebra you may have seen in older textbooks. It covers the same topics and includes lots of familiar equations, but the mathematics in *Discovering Algebra* also works with data from the physical and social sciences, emphasizes techniques for data analysis, and uses technology tools such as graphing calculators to help visualize and explore important concepts. And we have included important new mathematics in this text to better prepare students for the educational and career opportunities they'll find in our fast-changing world.

For more than 30 years, Key Curriculum Press has developed mathematics materials for schools. Over the years, in spite of the changes in mathematics and mathematics education, we have found one truth that has not changed: Students learn mathematics best when they understand the concepts behind it. With this in mind, Key Curriculum Press created the *Discovering Mathematics* series, which begins with this book, *Discovering Algebra: An Investigative Approach*. Through the investigations that are the heart of the series, students discover many important mathematical principles themselves. In the process, they develop deep understanding and become confident and excited about their abilities to continue exploring, discovering, and learning mathematics.

Many years of research, thoughtful work, and class testing have gone into the development of *Discovering Algebra*. Over the course of ten years, thousands of teachers and hundreds of thousands of students have used this curriculum to enhance their classroom experience and learning. *Discovering Algebra* has been proven successful time and time again. For this second edition, we asked teachers across the country what they would like to see more of, and we surveyed the mathematics standards of all states and many districts to be sure that we'd meet diverse needs. This has resulted in a textbook that teaches students what they need to know in a manner that ensures both deep conceptual understanding and ability to demonstrate knowledge on all kinds of assessments.

Also with this new edition, we've enhanced the computer-based resources available. Students, parents, tutors, and teachers who have Internet access at school, in the library, or at home can take advantage of the online version of the textbook. And at www.keymath.com/DA you'll find Dynamic Algebra Explorations to help you interactively investigate certain algebra topics, web links you can use to learn more about connections between math and other subjects, and downloadable versions of calculator notes, condensed lessons, and worksheets to help you practice skills.

If you are a student, we hope that, as you work through this course, you gain knowledge for a lifetime. If you are parent, we hope you enjoy watching your student develop mathematical power. If you are a teacher, we hope you find that *Discovering Algebra* makes a positive impact in your classroom. Whoever you are, we wish you success and urge you to continue your involvement and interest in mathematics.

Steven Rasmussen, President
Key Curriculum Press

Contents

CHAPTER 0

Fractions and Fractals   1

A Note to Teachers from the Authors

Jerald Murdock

Ellen Kamischke

Eric Kamischke

Mathematics, like art, literature, philosophy, or music, is a journey toward finding beauty and meaning in our chaotic world through the discovery and celebration of patterns. Just as poetry is much more than the rhyming text on a greeting card, mathematics is more than exercises and symbols. The paths you and your students are embarking on are rich with mathematical investigations and applications that encourage exploration of ideas, data, patterns, and relationships. Also, in *Discovering Algebra,* algebra blends seamlessly with geometry, data analysis, discrete mathematics, and statistics.

Discovering Algebra helps you rethink algebra and redefine what a good mathematics teacher can do in today's classroom. This *Teacher's Edition* can help you guide and encourage better learning of important mathematics—mathematics that students can immediately make sense of and use. This curriculum is influenced by our experience with students, teachers, the National Council of Teachers of Mathematics (NCTM) *Principles and Standards for School Mathematics,* recent projects funded by the National Science Foundation (NSF), and insights of contemporary curriculum leaders.

Scientific research has shown that students learn new material by connecting it to what they already know in order to develop their own understanding. *Discovering Algebra* actively engages students in both guided and open-ended mathematical explorations that help them make connections. Students' algebra experiences will help them develop proficiency at problem solving and symbolic manipulation, while giving them the conceptual power to articulate why a procedure works.

Students who complete *Discovering Algebra* begin to build the comprehensive mathematical knowledge base they need to move on to higher-level mathematics courses. The skills learned in this course can be the foundation to succeed in a wide range of careers, and to participate in the world as creative and productive citizens. Several recent studies conducted using *Discovering Algebra* support our belief that it is the right curriculum if your school or district values an investigative, technology-rich curriculum that prepares students for success both on exams and in life. You can find more information about the research supporting *Discovering Algebra* at www.keypress.com.

Since 1993, we have had the good fortune of working with Key Curriculum Press, a leading-edge publisher that provides educational software and materials to meet needs not satisfied by traditional publishers. Key seeks authors who are also teachers to guarantee that materials will work when they reach the classroom. Key published our *Advanced Algebra Through Data Exploration* in 1998, the first edition of *Discovering Algebra* in 2002, and *Discovering Advanced Algebra* in 2004. This new edition of *Discovering Algebra* has been developed and shaped by what we learned in writing our previous texts, by extensive classroom testing and student and teacher suggestions, and by the expertise of reviewers and Key editors. We know that you'll find *Discovering Algebra* to be a thoughtful and high-quality curriculum that serves the needs of both you and your students.

Jerald Murdock
Ellen Kamischke
Eric Kamischke

You are about to embark on an exciting mathematical journey. The goal of your trip is to reach the point at which you have gathered the skills, tools, confidence, and mathematical power to participate fully as a productive citizen in a changing world. Your life will always be full of important decision-making situations, and your ability to use mathematics and algebra can help you make informed decisions. You need skills that can evolve and adapt to new situations. You need to be able to interpret and make decisions based on numerical information, and to find ways to solve problems that arise in real life, not just in textbooks. On this journey you will make connections between algebra and the world around you.

You're going to discover and learn much useful algebra along the way. Learning algebra is more than learning facts and theories and memorizing procedures. We hope you also discover the pleasure involved in mathematics and in learning "how to do mathematics." Success in algebra is a gateway to many varied career opportunities.

With your teacher as a guide, you will learn algebra by doing mathematics. You will make sense of important algebraic concepts, learn essential algebraic skills, and discover how to use algebra. This requires a far bigger commitment than just "waiting for the teacher to show you" or studying "worked-out examples."

During this journey, successful learning will come from your personal involvement, which will often come about when you work with others in small groups. Talk about algebra, share ideas, and learn from and with the members of your group. Work and communicate with others to strengthen your understanding of the mathematical concepts presented in this book. To gain respect in your role as a teamplayer, respect differences among group members, listen carefully when others are sharing their ideas, stay focused during the process, be responsible and respectful, and share your own ideas and suggestions.

A graphing calculator, data-collection devices, and powerful modeling tools like The Geometer's Sketchpad® and Fathom Dynamic Data™ software are tools that help you explore new ideas and investigate and answer questions that come up along the way. Learning to appropriately use technology and being able to interpret its output will prepare you to successfully use new technologies in the future. Throughout the text you can refer to **Calculator Notes,** available from your teacher or at www.keymath.com/DA, for information that will help you use the graphing calculator. You'll also find **Dynamic Algebra Explorations** and many other resources at www.keymath.com/DA.

The text itself is your guidebook, leading you to explore questions and giving you the opportunity to ponder. Read the book carefully, with paper, pencil, and calculator close at hand. Work through the **Examples** and answer the questions that are asked along the way. Perform the **Investigations** as you travel through the course, being careful when making measurements and collecting data. Keep your data and calculations neat and accurate so that your work will be easier and the concepts clearer in the long run. Some **Exercises** require a great deal of thought. Don't give up. Make a solid attempt at each problem that is assigned. Sometimes you will need to fill in details later, after you discuss a problem in class or with your group.

Your notebook will serve as a record of your travels. In it, record your notes, answers to questions in the text, and solutions to your homework problems. You may also want to keep a journal of your personal impressions along the way. You can place some of your especially notable accomplishments in a portfolio, which will serve as a "photo album" of the highlights of your trip. Collect pieces of work in your portfolio as you go, and refine the contents as you make progress on your journey. Each chapter ends with a feature called **Assessing What You've Learned.** This feature gives suggestions for organizing your notebook, writing in your journal, updating your portfolio, and otherwise reflecting on what you have learned.

You should expect struggles and hard work along your path. Yet, as your algebra skills grow, you'll overcome obstacles and be rewarded with a deeper understanding of mathematics, an increased confidence in your own problem-solving abilities, and the opportunity to be creative. Features called **Project, Improving Your . . . Skills,** and **Take Another Look** give you special opportunities to creatively apply and extend your learning. We hope that your journey through *Discovering Algebra* will be a meaningful and rewarding experience.

And now it is time to begin. You are about to discover some pretty fascinating things.

Features of the Student Edition

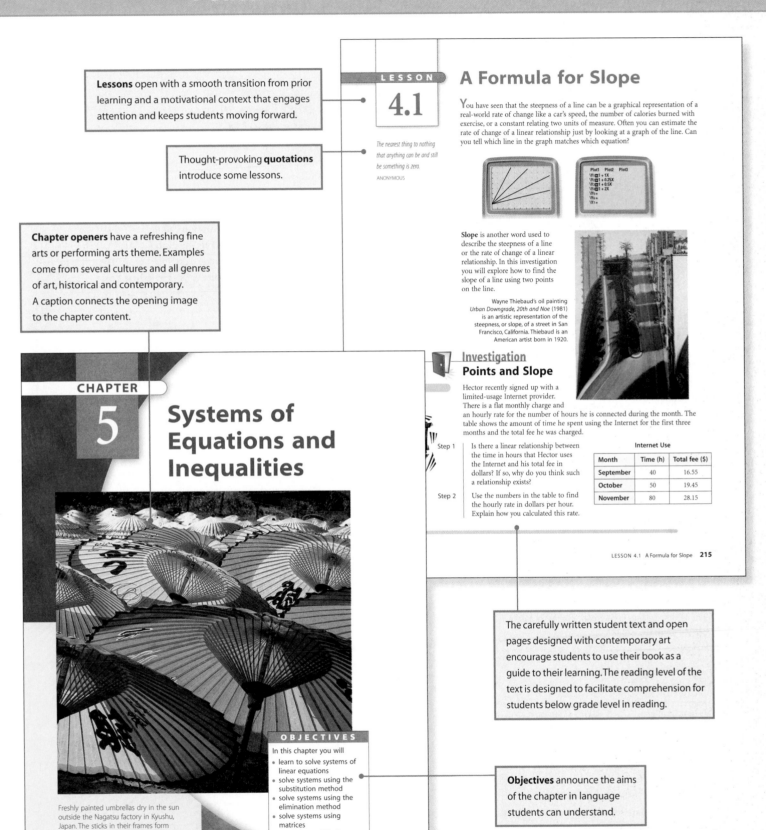

Lessons open with a smooth transition from prior learning and a motivational context that engages attention and keeps students moving forward.

Thought-provoking quotations introduce some lessons.

Chapter openers have a refreshing fine arts or performing arts theme. Examples come from several cultures and all genres of art, historical and contemporary. A caption connects the opening image to the chapter content.

LESSON

4.1

The nearest thing to nothing that anything can be and still be something is zero.
ANONYMOUS

A Formula for Slope

You have seen that the steepness of a line can be a graphical representation of a real-world rate of change like a car's speed, the number of calories burned with exercise, or a constant relating two units of measure. Often you can estimate the rate of change of a linear relationship just by looking at a graph of the line. Can you tell which line in the graph matches which equation?

```
Plot1  Plot2  Plot3
\Y1■1 + 1X
\Y2■1 + 0.25X
\Y3■1 + 0.5X
\Y4■1 + 2X
\Y5=
\Y6=
\Y7=
```

Slope is another word used to describe the steepness of a line or the rate of change of a linear relationship. In this investigation you will explore how to find the slope of a line using two points on the line.

Wayne Thiebaud's oil painting *Urban Downgrade, 20th and Noe* (1981) is an artistic representation of the steepness, or slope, of a street in San Francisco, California. Thiebaud is an American artist born in 1920.

Investigation
Points and Slope

Hector recently signed up with a limited-usage Internet provider. There is a flat monthly charge and an hourly rate for the number of hours he is connected during the month. The table shows the amount of time he spent using the Internet for the first three months and the total fee he was charged.

Step 1 Is there a linear relationship between the time in hours that Hector uses the Internet and his total fee in dollars? If so, why do you think such a relationship exists?

Step 2 Use the numbers in the table to find the hourly rate in dollars per hour. Explain how you calculated this rate.

Internet Use

Month	Time (h)	Total fee ($)
September	40	16.55
October	50	19.45
November	80	28.15

LESSON 4.1 A Formula for Slope **215**

CHAPTER

5

Systems of Equations and Inequalities

Freshly painted umbrellas dry in the sun outside the Nagatsu factory in Kyushu, Japan. The sticks in their frames form intersecting lines like the graphs of linear equations. Where do you see only two lines intersecting at a point? Where do several lines intersect?

OBJECTIVES

In this chapter you will
- learn to solve systems of linear equations
- solve systems using the substitution method
- solve systems using the elimination method
- solve systems using matrices
- graph inequalities in one and two variables
- solve systems of linear inequalities

The carefully written student text and open pages designed with contemporary art encourage students to use their book as a guide to their learning. The reading level of the text is designed to facilitate comprehension for students below grade level in reading.

Objectives announce the aims of the chapter in language students can understand.

Investigation
Beam Strength

You will need

- graph paper
- uncooked spaghetti
- several books
- a plastic cup
- string
- pennies

How strong do the beams in a ceiling have to be? How do bridge engineers select beams to support traffic? In this investigation you will collect data and find a linear model to determine the strength of various "beams" made of spaghetti.

Step 1	Make two stacks of books of equal height. Punch holes on opposite sides of the cup and tie the string through the holes.
Step 2	Follow the Procedure Note for a beam made from one strand of spaghetti. Record the maximum load (the number of pennies) that this beam will support.
Step 3	Repeat Step 2 for beams made from two, three, four, five, and six strands of spaghetti.

Procedure Note

1. Hang your c
of your spag
2. Support the
the stacks o
it overlaps e
about 1 inch
book on eac
the beam in
3. Put pennies
at a time, u
breaks.

Step 4	Plot your data on your calculator. Let x represent the number of strands of spaghetti, and let y represent the maximum load. Sketch the plot on paper too.
Step 5	Use a strand of spaghetti to visualize a line that you think fits the sketch. Choose two points on the line. Note the coordinates of the Calculate the slope of the line between the two points.
Step 6	Use the slope, b, that you found in Step 5 to graph the equation y calculator. Why is this line parallel to the direction the points indi too low or too high to fit the data?
Step 7	Using the spaghetti strand on your sketch, estimate a good y-inter the equation $y = a + bx$ better fits your data. On your calculator, equation $y = a + bx$ in place of $y = bx$. Adjust your estimate for have a line of fit.
Step 8	In Step 5, everyone started with a visual model that went through In your group, compare all final lines. Did everyone end up with Do you think a line of fit must go through at least two data point line better than the others?

keymath.com/DA

[▶The graphs of growth defined by repeated multiplication share certain characteristics. You can use the **Dynamic Algebra Exploration** at www.keymath.com/DA to explore these graphs and to solve some of the exercises in this lesson.◀]

It is helpful to think of a constant multiplier, like 1.05 in Example A, as a sum. The plus sign in $1 + 0.05$ shows that the pattern increases and 0.05 is the percent growth per year, written as a decimal. When a balance or population decreases, say, by 15% during a given time period, you write the constant multiplier as a difference, for example, $1 - 0.15$. The subtraction sign shows that the pattern decreases and 0.15 is the percent decrease per time period, written as a decimal.

Example B uses a proportion and a constant multiplier to calculate a marked-down price.

EXAMPLE B

Birdbaths at the Feathered Friends store are marked down 35%. What is the cost of a birdbath that was originally priced $34.99? What is the cost if the birdbath is marked down 35% a second time?

▶ **Solution**

If an item is marked down 35%, then it must retain $100 - 35$ percent of its original price. That is, it will cost 65% of the original price. In Chapter 2, you learned how to set up a proportion using 65% and the ratio of cost, C, to original price.

Cost   Part of the original price retained in sale price

$$\frac{C}{34.99} = \frac{100 - 35}{100}$$ Write a proportion.

The original price   The whole original price

$$C = \frac{100 - 35}{100} \cdot 34.99$$ Multiply by 34.99 to undo the division.

$$C \approx 22.74$$ Multiply and divide, and round to the nearest hundredth.

So the cost after the 35% markdown is $22.74.

You can set up a proportion again to find the cost after the second markdown. Or, you can solve this problem using a constant multiplier. The cost after one 35% markdown is calculated like this:

$$34.99(1 - 0.35) \approx 22.74$$

The exercise sets are developmental and begin with opportunities for self-testing of new material in **Practice Your Skills.** These exercises involve direct applications of what students have learned through the investigation and examples.

Graphing calculator use is modeled in the examples. Students use calculators in nearly all the investigations. Exercises requiring a graphing calculator are called out. Screen captures demonstrate the functionalities available to students, including tables, graphs, and operations on lists. Because calculator notes with keystroke-level instructions are provided separately, the page text remains uncluttered and the sense of the mathematics remains paramount over keystroke details. The calculator notes allow *Discovering Algebra* to be used with different calculators and with new calculators as they become available.

...described in the investigation. ◄]

EXERCISES

You will need your graphing calculator for Exercises **4–7** and **9**.

Practice Your Skills

1. Decide whether each expression is positive or negative without using your calculator. Then check your answer with your calculator.

a. $-35(44) + 23$ **b.** $(-14)(-36) - 32$ **c.** $25 - \frac{152}{12}$

d. $50 - 23(-12)$ **e.** $\frac{-12 - 38}{15}$ **f.** $24(15 - 76)$

2. List the terms of each number sequence of *y*-coordinates for the points shown on each graph. Then write a recursive routine to generate each sequence.

Reason and Apply offers more challenging exercises that develop reasoning and transfer of knowledge. These exercises often include several steps that build on each other. They may also require students to combine information from earlier chapters with what they have just learned.

...2b and d.

...e in 4a and b on

Reason and Apply

5. APPLICATION In the Empire State Building the long... shaft reaches the 86th floor, 1050 ft above ground l... Another elevator takes visitors from the 86th floor... observation area on the 102nd floor, 1224 ft above... level. For more information about the Empire State... see www.keymath.com/DA .

a. Write a recursive routine that gives the height ab... ground level for each of the first 86 floors. Tell w... starting value and the rule mean in terms of the...

b. Write a recursive routine that gives the heights o... 86 through 102. Tell what the starting value and... mean in this routine.

c. When you are 531 ft above ground level, what fl... are you on?

d. When you are on the 90th floor, how high up ar... you are 1137 ft above ground level, what floor ar...

6. The diagram at right shows a sequence of gray and... each layered under the previous one.

a. Explain how the sequence 1, 3, 5, 7, . . . is related... these squares. @

b. Write a recursive routine that gives the sequence...

c. Use your routine to predict the number of additi... you need to enlarge this diagram by one... and column. Explain how you found your answe...

d. What is the 20th number in the sequence 1, 3, 5,...

e. The first term in the sequence is 1, and the seco... term is the number 95? Explain how you found...

7. Imagine a tilted L-shaped puzzle piece made from... units. Add puzzle pieces in the corner of each "L" t... design. In a second figure, the two pieces "share" tw... 14 toothpicks instead of 16.

Figure 1   Figure 2

a. As you did in the investigation, make a table wit... the number of toothpicks, perimeter, and area of...

b. Write a recursive routine that will produce the n... of the table.

c. Find the number of toothpicks, perimeter, and a...

d. Find the perimeter and area of the figure made f...

Review keeps previously learned skills from falling out of use, especially those that will be needed in upcoming lessons.

Review

11. At a family picnic, your cousin tells you that he always has a hard time remembering how to compute percents. Write him a note explaining what percent means. Use these problems as examples of how to solve the different types of percent problems, with an answer for each.

a. 8 is 15% of what number? @   **b.** 15% of 18.95 is what number?
c. What percent of 64 is 326?   **d.** 10% of what number is 40?

12. APPLICATION Carl has been keeping a record of his gas purchases for his new car. Each time he buys gas, he fills the tank completely. Then he records the number of gallons he bought and the miles since the last fill-up. Here is his record:

a. Copy and complete the table by calculating the ratio of miles per gallon for each purchase.

b. What is the average rate of miles per gallon so far?

c. The car's tank holds 17.1 gallons. To the nearest mile, how far should Carl be able to go without running out of gas?

d. Carl is planning a trip across the United States. He estimates that the trip will be 4230 miles. How many gallons of gas can Carl expect to buy?

Carl's Purchases

Miles traveled	Gallons	miles gallon
363	16.2	
342	15.1	
285	12.9	

Hints and answers to selected exercises can be found in the back of the student text.

Consumer
CONNECTION

Many factors influence the rate at which cars use gas, including size, age, and driving conditions. Advertisements for new cars often give the average mpg for city traffic (slow, congested) and highway traffic (fast, free flowing). These rates help consumers make an informed purchase. For more information about fuel economy, see the links at www.keymath.com/DA .

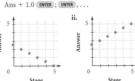 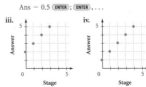

13. Match each recursive routine to a graph below. Explain how you made your decision and tell what assumptions you made.

a. 2.5 ENTER
Ans + 0.5 ENTER ; ENTER , . . .

b. 1.0 ENTER
Ans + 1.0 ENTER ; ENTER , . . .

c. 2.0 ENTER
Ans + 1.0 ENTER ; ENTER , . . .

d. 2.5 ENTER
Ans − 0.5 ENTER ; ENTER , . . .

As they read about and investigate patterns and relationships, students will learn to move easily between **multiple representations:** tables, graphs, recursive routines, equations, and words.

Graphs and other technical art are carefully designed for clarity and emphasis.

i.   ii.   iii.   iv.

(Answer vs. Stage graphs)

Activity Day is a chance for students to solidify what they have learned by carrying out a fun activity. No new material is introduced, so student groups have a chance to spend more time experimenting. And there is more time for groups to share their results and learn from what other students have discovered.

The **Chapter Review** begins with a summary of the new mathematical ideas. The exercises are similar to those in the lesson and those that will appear on the Chapter Test. A more extensive **Mixed Review** is provided every four chapters.

Boldface terms can be found in the **glossary** at the back of the student text.

Connections highlight how the mathematics applies to students' lives—in the workplace or in the fields of science, history, technology, and the arts.

Activity Day

Variation with a Bicycle

The Tour de France is a demanding bicycle race through France and several other countries. For 23 days, cyclists ride approximately 3500 kilometers on steep mountain roads before crossing the finish line in Paris. The cyclists rely on their knowledge of gear shifting and bicycle speeds.

Many bicycles have several speeds or gears. In a low gear, it's easier to pedal uphill. In a high gear, it's harder to pedal, but you can go faster on flat surfaces and down hills. When you change gears, the chain shifts from one sprocket to another. In this activity you will discover the relationships among the bicycle's gears, the teeth on the sprockets, how fast you pedal, and how fast the bike goes.

Activity

The Wheels Go Round and Round

You will need
- a meterstick or metric tape measure
- a multispeed bicycle

In Steps 1–5, you'll analyze the effect of the rear sprockets.

Rear sprocket assemblies

Tooth

Crankshaft

Front sprocket assemblies

Proportional Reasoning and Variation

> **Procedure Note**
>
> **Changing Gears**
> You'll collect data with the bike upside down. You may be able to change gears in this position—rotate the pedals and crankshaft a few times. If you have to turn the bike right side up to change gears, then turn it upside down before you observe and record data.

Procedure Notes help keep students working independently and simplify steps.

CHAPTER 4 REVIEW

In Chapter 3, you learned how to write equations in intercept form, $y = a + bx$. In this chapter, you learned how to calculate **slope** using the slope formula, $b = \frac{y_2 - y_1}{x_2 - x_1}$. You also used the slope formula to derive another form for a linear equation—the **point-slope form.** The point-slope form, $y = y_1 + b(x - x_1)$, is the equation of a line through point (x_1, y_1) with slope b. You learned that this form is very useful in real-world situations when the starting value is not on the y-axis.

You investigated equivalent forms of expressions and equations using tables and graphs. You used the **distributive property** of multiplication over addition and the **commutative** and **associative** properties of addition and multiplication to write point-slope equations in intercept form.

You investigated several methods of finding a **line of fit,** and you discovered how to use the first and third quartiles from the five-number summaries of x- and y-values in a data set to write a linear model for data based on **Q-points.**

Small cameos from the chapter pictures remind students where an idea was first presented.

EXERCISES

You will need your graphing calculator for Exercises **3, 4,** and **9.**

ⓐ Answers are provided for all exercises in this set.

1. The slope of the line between $(2, 10)$ and $(x_2, 4)$ is -3. Find the value of x_2.

2. Give the slope and the y-intercept for each equation.
   a. $y = -4 - 3x$ **b.** $2x + 7 = y$ **c.** $38x - 10y = 24$

3. Line a and line b are shown on the graph at right. Name the slope and the y-intercept, and write the equation of each line. Check your equations by graphing on your calculator.

line a

wers

---

ating with a rate, so...
...e several sentences explaining which of these methods you prefer and why.

History
CONNECTION

The Panama Canal allows ships to cross the strip of land between the Atlantic and Pacific Oceans. Before the canal was completed in 1913, ships had to sail thousands of miles around the dangerous Cape Horn, even though only 50 mi separate the two oceans. Learn more about famous canals at **www.keymath.com/DA** .

Panama Canal route

Equator

SOUTH AMERICA

Tropic of Capricorn

Route before 1913

Atlantic Ocean

Pacific Ocean

Cape Horn

A ship passes through the Panama Canal.

Assessing What You've Learned
GIVING A PRESENTATION

Making presentations is an important career skill. Most jobs require workers to share information, to help orient new coworkers, or to represent the employer to clients. Making a presentation to the class is a good way to develop your skill at organizing and delivering your ideas clearly and in an interesting way. Most teachers will tell you that they have learned more by trying to teach something than they did simply by studying it in school.

Here are some suggestions to make your presentation go well:

▶ Work with a group. Acting as a panel member might make you less ner~ giving a talk on your own. Be sure the role of each panel member is clea~ the work and the credit are equally shared.

▶ Choose the topic carefully. You can summarize the results of an investig~ research for a project and present what you've learned and how it conne~ chapter, or give your own thinking on Take Another Look or Improving~ Reasoning Skills.

▶ Prepare thoroughly. Outline your presentation and think about what you~ say on each point. Decide how much detail to give, but don't try to mem~ whole sentences. Illustrate your presentation with models, a poster, a ha~ overhead transparencies. Prepare these visual aids ahead of time and de~ when to introduce them.

▶ Speak clearly. Practice talking loudly and clearly. Show your interest in t~

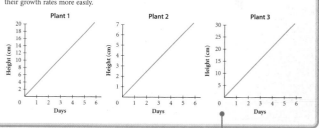

project
THE GOLDEN RATIO

In this project you'll research the amazing number mathematicians call the **golden ratio.** (There are plenty of books and web sites on the topic. Find links at www.keymath.com/DA .) Your project should include

▶ Basic information on the golden ratio, such as its exact value, why it represents a mathematically "ideal" ratio, and how to construct a golden rectangle. (Its length-to-width ratio is the golden ratio.)

▶ Some history of the golden ratio, including its role in ancient Greek architecture.

▶ At least one other interesting mathematical fact about the golden ratio, such as its relationship to the Fibonacci sequence or its own reciprocal.

▶ A report on where to find the golden ratio in the environment, architecture, or art. List items and their measurements or include prints from photographs, art, or architecture on which you have drawn the golden rectangle.

THE GEOMETER'S SKETCHPAD

Once you've learned how to construct the golden ratio, The Geometer's Sketchpad is an ideal tool for further exploration. You can create a Custom Tool for dividing segments into the golden ratio, and then use this tool to help you construct the golden rectangle or even the golden spiral.

19. Consider the equation $2(x - 6) = -5$.

    a. Solve the equation.

    b. Show how you can check your result by substituting it into th~

20. APPLICATION Amber makes $6 an hour at a sandwich shop. She wants to know how many hours she needs to work to save $500 in her bank account. On her first paycheck, she notices that her net pay is about 75% of her gross~

    a. How many hours must she work to earn $500 in gross pay?

    b. How many hours must she work to earn $500 in net pay?

TAKE ANOTHER LOOK

1. The picture at right is a **contour map.** This type of map reveals the character of the terrain. All points on an **isometric line** are the same height in feet above sea level. The graph below shows how the hiker's walking speed changes as she covers the terrain on the dotted-line trail shown on the map.

    a. What quantities are changing in the graph and in the map?

    b. How does each display reveal rate of change?

    c. How could you measure distance on each display?

    d. What would the graph sketch of this hike look like if distance were plotted on the vertical axis instead of speed?

    e. What do these two displays tell you when you study them together?

Sediment layers form contour lines in the Grand Canyon.

2. You've learned that a rational number is a number that can be written as a ratio of two integers. Every rational number can also be written in an equivalent decimal form. In Lesson 2.1, you learned how to convert fractions into decimal form. In some cases the result was a *terminating decimal,* and in other cases the result was a *repeating decimal,* in which a digit or group of digits repeated.

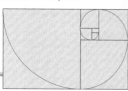

IMPROVING YOUR REASONING SKILLS

Did these plants grow at the same rate? If not, which plant was tallest on Day 4? Which plant took the most time to reach 8 cm? Redraw the graphs so that you can compare their growth rates more easily.

An **overview** of the chapter contents appears first in the interleaf pages that open each chapter of the Teacher's Edition.

Using This Chapter will tell you which lessons deal with topics that might not be required for your algebra curriculum.

Resources available for the chapter, including calculator notes, worksheet and transparency masters, and technology demonstrations, are listed here.

Materials for the chapter are summarized in this list.

CHAPTER 3

Linear Equations

Overview

In Chapter 3, students use equations to model linear growth and graphs of straight lines and learn the balancing method for solving equations. This chapter builds toward the concept of *function*, which is formalized in Chapter 8.

Lesson 3.1 begins the development of linear growth with the study of recursive sequences. In **Lesson 3.2**, students encounter linear plots. These two ideas are combined through the notion of "walking instructions" to study motion in **Lesson 3.3**. The ideas of starting value and rate of change are formalized in **Lesson 3.4** with the intercept form of a line.

In **Lesson 3.5**, students study rates of change further, using input-output tables that foreshadow the study of functions. **Lesson 3.6** demonstrates the balancing technique for solving equations. In the Activity Day, **Lesson 3.7**, students model real-world data with their linear equations.

The Mathematics

Linearity

Having a *constant rate of change* is a primary characteristic of linearity. You start somewhere and advance by the same amount at each step. This kind of change is represented by a recursive sequence, easily generated on a calculator.

-15 ENTER — Start with -15.
Ans $+10$ ENTER — Add 10 to the answer.
ENTER ; ENTER — Continue to add 10 to each answer.

A constant rate of change produces linear growth, though the values will be shrinking instead of growing if the rate of change is negative.

A second way to think about linearity is through equations that relate variables. Students begin to use, write, and make sense of the intercept form of the equation of a line, $y = a + bx$. Seeing and using multiple representations help students connect the recursive sequence start value with a and its constant rate of change with b. The calculator steps

for the recursive sequence above are equiva[...]
the equation $y = -15 + 10x$, when the init[...]
x-value is 0.

The traditional *slope-intercept form*, $y = mx$ [...]
mentioned in Lesson 4.2. In Lesson 4.3, stud[...]
will see the *point-slope form*, $y = y_1 + b(x$ [...]

A third way to think about linearity is throu[...]
graphs. Indeed, the term *linearity* comes fro[...]
fact that the associated graphs are (straight)[...]
Students have seen linear graphs before—in [...]
points, the graph of $y = x$ for comparing est[...]
with actual distances in Chapter 1, and dire[...]
variations $y = kx$ in Chapter 2.

The new forms of equations of a line indica[...]
ways of thinking of the graph. For example, [...]
intercept form $y = a + bx$ allows students to [...]
by starting at point $(0, a)$ and moving vertica[...]
b units for each unit they move across from [...]
to right. This process reflects the constant ra[...]
change of linear growth and the recursive se[...]
Later, in Chapter 8, students will discover th[...]
point-slope equation $y = y_1 + b(x - x_1)$ rep[...]
a vertical shift of y_1 and a horizontal shift of [...]

Most data sets from real-world situations w[...]
linear trend aren't exactly linear. Lesson 3.7 p[...]
an activity for finding an equation that mod[...]
of data points that lie close to but not on a s[...]
line. Students will learn more about lines of [...]
Chapter 4.

Solving Equations

Many real-life situations call for predicting [...]
linear growth will reach a certain value. Way[...]
making that prediction reflect the three way[...]
thinking about linearity—constant rate of c[...]
equations that relate variables, and graphs.

From the *constant-rate-of-change* perspective [...]
can run the recursive routine until it reaches [...]
desired output, counting input steps as you g[...]
mount a flagpole 75 ft up on a building, what [...]
would you go to if the building's basement fl[...]
15 ft below the ground and its floors are 10 ft [...]

CHAPTER 3 INTERLE[...]

Just run the sequence -15 ENTER ; Ans $+ 10$;
ENTER ; ENTER ; ... until you get to 75 ft.
To undo those steps and get back to the number of floors, you can subtract -15 and divide by 10, the distance between floors.

This undoing process took place with equations in Chapter 2: If $10x - 15 = 75$, you can "get back to" x by adding 15 to 75 and then dividing by 10. The equation can also be solved using the metaphor of an equation as a pan balance. To keep it balanced, you do the same thing to both sides.

The third approach to linearity, *graphs*, also provides a means of solving equations. You can graph the data points on a graphing calculator and then use the trace feature to approximate the input value for the desired output value. Using the calculator's table features is another way to approximate a solution.

Using This Chapter

Lesson 3.1 is essential because recursive sequences will be used throughout the book. Solving by undoing is emphasized until the introduction of the balancing method in Lesson 3.6. If you must skip a lesson, you could skip the activity day, Lesson 3.7. No new material is presented, and the rope tying is done again in Lesson 5.2.

Resources

Discovering Algebra Resources

Teaching and Worksheet Masters
  Lessons 3.2, 3.5, 3.6

Calculator Notes 0D, 1J, 2A, 2C, 3A, 3B, 3C, 3D

Sketchpad Demonstrations
  Lessons 3.1, 3.5, 3.6

Fathom Demonstrations
  Lessons 3.1, 3.2, 3.4, 3.7

CBL Demonstrations
  Lesson 3.5

Dynamic Algebra Explorations online
  Lessons 3.1, 3.2

Assessment Resources
  Quiz 1 (Lessons 3.1–3.3)
  Quiz 2 (Lessons 3.4–3.6)
  Chapter 3 Test
  Chapter 3 Constructive Assessment Options
  Chapters 1 to 3 Exam

More Practice Your Skills for Chapter 3

Condensed Lessons for Chapter 3

Other Resources

Play It Again Sam: Recurrence Equations and Recursion in Mathematics and Computer Science by Rochelle Wilson Meyer and Walter Meyer.

For complete references to this and other resources see www.keypress.com/DA.

- boxes of toothpicks
- graph paper
- colored pencils
- 4 m measuring tapes, metersticks, or ropes
- motion sensors
- stopwatches or watches with second hands
- 300 pennies or other markers
- washers, *optional*
- paper cups (three per group)
- pieces of rope of different lengths (around 1 m) and thickness (two per group)

Pacing Guide

	day 1	day 2	day 3	day 4	day 5	day 6	day 7	day 8	day 9	day 10
standard	3.1	3.2	3.2	3.3	quiz, 3.4	3.5	3.6	3.7	review	assessment
enriched	3.1	3.2	3.2	3.3, project	quiz, 3.4	3.5	3.6	3.7	review, TAL	assessment
block	3.1, 3.2	3.2, 3.3, project	3.4, 3.5	3.6, quiz	3.7, review	assessment, mixed review	exam			

	day 11	day 12
standard	mixed review	exam
enriched	mixed review	exam

157B CHAPTER 3 INTERLEAF Linear Equations

The Mathematics gives a survey that places the mathematics of the chapter in context and discusses mathematical topics in greater depth or at a higher level than is presented in the student text.

Pacing Guides let you see at a glance which lessons will require two days and when you might give a quiz or enrich your curriculum with a project.

Planning helps you complete lesson plans, gather materials, and prepare worksheets, transparencies, calculator notes, and technology demonstrations.

The **Lesson Outline** helps you structure the class period and lets you know whether you should plan to spend two days on the lesson.

Teaching gives practical help in guiding the investigation, facilitating student sharing, evaluating student progress, and explaining new mathematical ideas.

One Step is for classes experienced at investigating. It is an alternative to the more guided several-step investigation.

Help is keyed to the **steps** of the investigation.

LESSON
2.3

PLANNING

LESSON OUTLINE

One day:
20 min Investigation
10 min Sharing
10 min Examples
5 min Closing
5 min Exercises

MATERIALS

- yardsticks or tape measures (one per group)
- metersticks or metric tape measures (one per group)
- Calculator Note 1K

TEACHING

As they convert between different measurement units in this lesson, students use ratios called *conversion factors*. Products of several conversion factors can be set up to do more complicated conversions, in a process called *dimensional analysis*.

The name *Système Internationale* is French for the *International System* of measurement units. The SI is used in most science texts.

Guiding the Investigation

One Step

[Ask] "In as many ways as possible, decide how many centimeters are equivalent to an inch." As you circulate, encourage thinking beyond measuring the yardstick with the meterstick.

Step 1 Be sure students understand how to read the inch markings. Often the fractional parts of an inch give students trouble.

LESSON
2.3

Proportions and Measurement Systems

Have you ever visited another country? If so, you needed to convert your money to theirs and perhaps some of your measurement units to theirs as well. Many countries use the units of the Système Internationale, or SI, known in the United States as the metric system.

So, instead of selling gasoline by the gallon, they sell it by the liter. Distance signs are in kilometers rather than in miles, and vegetables are sold by the kilo (kilogram) rather than by the pound.

Cultural
CONNECTION

To learn more about measurements used in other countries, as well as historical measurement units, see the links at www.keymath.com/DA

Vegetables are sold at a French market.

Investigation
Converting Centimeters to Inches

You will need
- a yardstick or tape measure
- a meterstick or metric tape measure

In this investigation you will find a ratio to help you convert inches to centimeters and centimeters to inches. Then you will use this ratio in a proportion to convert some measurements from the system standard in the United States to measurements in the metric system, and vice versa.

Step 1 Measure the length or width on each of six different-sized objects, such as a pencil, a book, your desk, or your calculator. For each object, record the inch measurement and the centimeter measurement in a table like this:

Inches to Centimeters

Object	Measurement in inches	Measurement in centimeters

Step 2 Enter the measurements in inches into your calculator's list L1 and the measurements in centimeters into L2. Into list L3 enter the ratio of centimeters to inches, $\frac{L_2}{L_1}$, and let your calculator fill in the ratio values. [▶ See **Calculator Note 1K**. ◀]

Step 3 How do the ratios of centimeters to inches compare for the different measurements? If one of the ratios is much different from the others, recheck your measurements. Ratios should be about $\frac{2.54 \text{ cm}}{1 \text{ in.}}$.

LESSON OBJECTIVES

- Review the English measurement system and the metric system
- Convert measurement units using conversion factors
- Convert measurement units using dimensional analysis
- Learn and use the term *rate*

NCTM STANDARDS

CONTENT		PROCESS	
✔	Number	✔	Problem Solving
✔	Algebra	✔	Reasoning
	Geometry	✔	Communication
✔	Measurement	✔	Connections
	Data/Probability	✔	Representation

108 CHAPTER 2 Proportional Reasoning and Variation

The **Lesson Objectives** help you know what students should gain from the lesson.

The **National Council of Teachers of Mathematics Standards** addressed by this lesson are listed. The NCTM Principles as they apply to this book are discussed on page xxvii.

CHAPTER
2

Proportional Reasoning and Variation

Murals are just one of the many art forms around us that come to life with the help of ratios and proportions. To plan a mural, the artist draws sketches on paper, then uses ratio to enlarge the image to the size of the final work.

OBJECTIVES

In this chapter you will
- use proportional reasoning to understand problem situations
- learn what rates are and use them to make predictions
- study how quantities vary directly and inversely
- use equations and graphs to represent variation
- solve real-world problems using variation
- review the rules for order of operations
- describe number tricks using algebraic expressions
- solve equations using the undoing method

CHAPTER 2 OBJECTIVES

- Learn to set up and solve proportions in which a variable represents an unknown number
- Use proportions to help make predictions from data gathered for the capture-recapture method
- Change measurement units through conversion factors and dimensional analysis
- Use direct variation equations and their graphs to solve real-world problems
- Learn the basic inverse variation equations
- Use inverse variation equations and their graphs to solve real-world problems
- Investigate the direct and inverse variations between gear selection and wheel speeds on a multispeed bicycle
- Review or learn the rules governing order of operations
- Use calculator list operations to investigate the concepts *variables*, *terms*, and *expressions*
- Write and evaluate algebraic expressions
- Solve equations using the undoing method

Most students have constructed pictures using enlargement grids; they capture the drawing fragment within the small square and transfer it to the large square. **[Ask]** "If the artist first worked on paper that was about 18 inches by 24 inches, what did he or she have to multiply by to create a large drawing to transfer the image to the building?" [Reasonable answers are between 25 and 35.] Sketches for modern murals can be projected on a wall, which also involves an enlargement by a ratio.

You might also **[Ask]** "How are the real students like their images on the mural?" [The ratios of corresponding lengths are all the same, or the corresponding pairs of lengths are proportional. The images are about 3 times the height of a student. They look a lot bigger because they appear to have a volume of about 3^3 times that of a student.]

Objectives for the teacher summarize the objectives stated at the beginning of each lesson.

Suggestions on how to use the fine-art image to introduce the chapter are given here, as well as more information about the specific image or the area of the arts it represents. Questions for class discussion are also suggested.

CHAPTER 2 Proportional Reasoning and Variation **95**

---

xxiii

Step 1 Request that a few students show you how they found the numbers in their tables.

Step 2 Make sure students notice the word *new*.

Step 3 [Ask] "Why is the number being multiplied by 3 each time?" One answer is below Step 4 in the text.

SHARING IDEAS

While visiting groups, ask one student to copy onto a transparency the group's table from Step 1. Select other students to share their approaches to Steps 2 and 4. During reporting time, encourage participation, but probe for explanations. Ask for a correct definition of *exponent*. Ask why exponents are useful to elicit the point that they reduce writing when a single number is being multiplied many times.

Assessing Progress

As you watch students contribute to groups or to the whole class, look for understanding of multiplication and the symbols used to indicate multiplication as well as ideas that were new in the previous lesson: recursive procedure, fractal, Sierpiński triangle, congruent figures, and order of operations.

EXAMPLE

[Language] The term *exponent* is defined in the student text, but some students may be more familiar with the expression *raising a number to a power*.

The example leads into a discussion of exponents. Call students' attention to the picture and question in the text.

Model good mathematical language to help students learn what terms mean. For example, use the word *factor* in context. Point out how the text answers your earlier question about a correct definition of *exponent* by saying that the

You can write the symbol for multiplication in different ways. For example, you can write 3×3 as $3 \cdot 3$ or $(3)(3)$ or $3(3)$. All of these expressions have the same meaning. Each expression equals 9.

EXAMPLE | Describe how the number of new upward-pointing triangles is growing in this fractal.

Stage 0
1 triangle

Stage 1
6 triangles

Stage 2
36 triangles

Stage 3
216 triangles

▶ **Solution** | At Stage 1, the six new upward-pointing triangles are numbered. At Stage 2, six new upward-pointing triangles are formed in each numbered Stage 1 triangle. At Stage 2, there are $6 \cdot 6$ or 36 new triangles. At Stage 3, six triangles are formed in each new upward-pointing Stage 2 triangle, so there are $36 \cdot 6$ or 216 new upward-pointing triangles.

Another way to look at the number of new upward-pointing triangles at each stage is shown in the table below.

Stage number	Number of new upward-pointing triangles		
	Total	Repeated multiplication	Exponent form
1	6	6	6^1
2	36	$6 \cdot 6$	6^2
3	216	$36 \cdot 6$ or $6 \cdot 6 \cdot 6$	6^3

The last number in each row of the table is a 6 followed by a small raised number. The small number, called an **exponent**, shows how many 6's are multiplied together. An exponent shows the number of times that 6 is a factor. What is the pattern between the stage number and the exponent?

Do you think the pattern applies to Stage 0? Put the number 6^0 into your calculator. [▶ See **Calculator Note 0B** to learn how to enter exponents. ◀] Does the result fit the pattern?

How many upward-pointing triangles are there at Stage 4? According to the pattern, there should be 6^4. That's 1296 triangles! It is a lot easier to use the exponent pattern than to count all those triangles.

exponent tells "how many 6's are multiplied together." [Alert] The phrase "how many times you multiply a number by itself" is not strictly correct; 6^2 is not 6 multiplied by itself twice.

As part of the fractal design development, students are introduced to the concept of zero as an exponent. Detailed coverage of zero and negative exponents appears in Chapter 6.

Closing the Lesson

Remind students of the main ideas of this lesson. Numbers being multiplied together are **factors**. An **exponent** is a raised number that tells how many times a number is used as a factor.

[Ask] "Why are exponents useful?" [They save a lot of multiplication and writing when the triangles become complicated.]

Step 6 The mean of the sample data is 1993.6.

Step 5 no year occurs most often. How many modes does your data set have? What are they? Does your mode have to be a whole number? Modes will vary but must be a whole number; the sample data have mode 1998. Draw a square around the year corresponding to the mode(s) on the number line of your dot plot. Label each value "mode."

Step 6 Find the sum of the mint years of all your pennies and divide by the number of pennies. The result is called the mean. What is the mean of your data set?

Step 7 Show where the mean falls on your dot plot's number line. Draw an arrowhead under it and write the number you got in Step 6. Label it "mean."

Step 8 Now enter your data into a calculator list, and use your calculator to find the mean and the median. Are they the same as what you found using pencil and paper? [▶ Refer to **Calculator Note 1A** to check the settings on your calculator. See **Calculator Notes 1B and 1C** to enter data into lists and find the mean and median. ◀]

Save the dot plot you created. You will use it in Lesson 1.3.

Measures of Center

Mean
The mean is the sum of the data values divided by the number of data items. The result is often called the average.

Median
For an odd number of data items, the median is the middle value when the data values are listed in order. If there is an even number of data items, then the median is the average of the two middle values.

Mode
The mode is the data value that occurs most often. Data sets can have two modes (bimodal) or more. Some data sets have no mode.

Each measure of center has its advantages. The mean and the median may be quite different, and the mode, if it exists, may or may not be useful. You will have to decide which measure is most meaningful for each situation.

EXAMPLE | This data set shows the number of people who attended a movie theater over a period of 16 days.

{14, 23, 10, 21, 7, 80, 32, 30, 92, 14, 26, 21, 38, 20, 35, 21}

a. Find the measures of center.

b. The theater's management wants to compare its attendance to that of other theaters in the area. Which measure of center best represents the data?

Moviegoers wear special glasses to watch 3-D movies. To learn about 3-D glasses, see the links at www.keymath.com/DA.

the words would be *promedia* (mean), *intermedio* (median), and *el más común* (mode).

As you ask groups to copy their dot plots onto transparencies, include some with an even number of data points and others with an odd number. If possible, include one whose data have outliers and one with bimodal data.

[Ask] "When are the mean, median, and mode close to being equal?" [with single-modal data that have good symmetry about the mean] Refer to the box "Measures of Center" in the text. Ask students to explain in their own words how to find each measure of center. You might point out that the word *mode* starts like *most*; the mode is the number that occurs most often.

Step 1 [Alert] Make sure students label their number line, title the plot, and show the units.

Step 2 [Alert] Watch that students mark their number line with all years, not just the ones for which they have pennies.

Step 2 Medians will vary; the Pennies Sample Data worksheet has median 1995. The median does not need to be a whole number; it may have decimal part 0.5. Both orderings give the same median.

Step 3 Be sure that students don't simply call the median the average of the minimum and the maximum. Refer them to the Procedure Note.

Step 4 "No mode" is relative to the size of the data set. If you have 1000 distinct data values, having five to ten modes may be worthwhile information. But if you have only 12 data values, having five modes is not very informative.

Step 6 Students can use the symbol ⇝ to indicate a "break" in the x-axis between extreme outliers and the rest of the pennies.

Step 7 [Link] You might mention that if the horizontal number line were a beam and the data points were weights, the balance point would be at the mean.

If you're saving Step 8 for a second day on this lesson, collect handwritten data for later entry into calculators.

Step 8 [Language] The word *mode* has several meanings, as does the word *mean*. [Alert] Watch for confusion about the word *mode*; the mode on the graphing calculator (Calculator Note 1A) is not related to the statistical mode of a data set.

SHARING IDEAS

[ELL] Ask students to translate *mean*, *median*, and *mode* into their first language. In Spanish

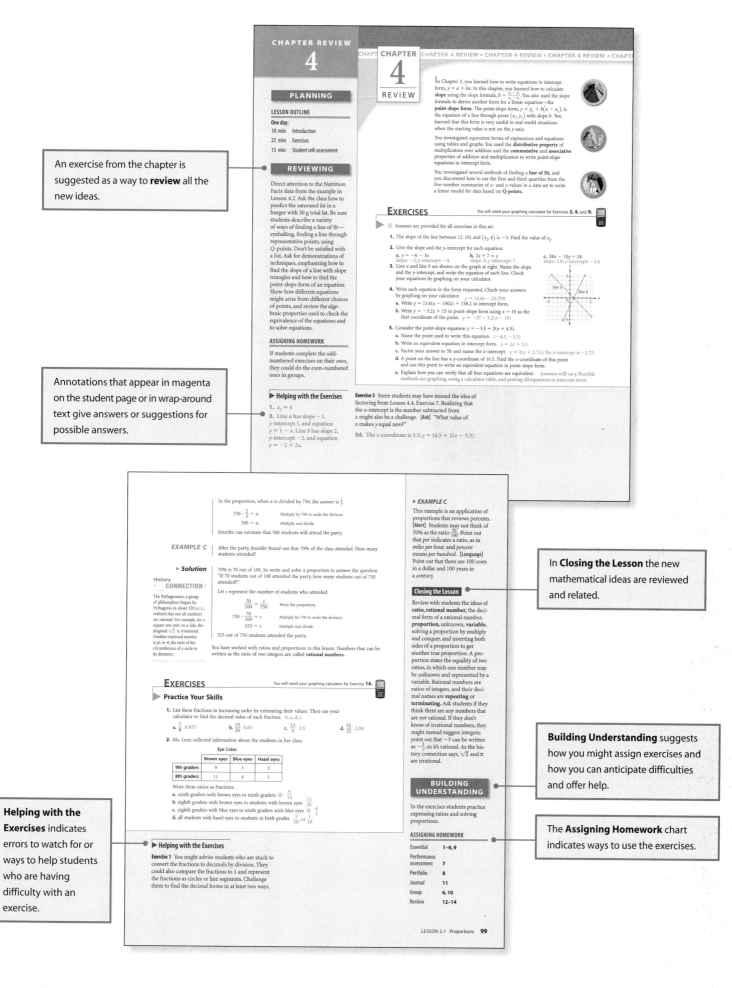

An exercise from the chapter is suggested as a way to **review** all the new ideas.

Annotations that appear in magenta on the student page or in wrap-around text give answers or suggestions for possible answers.

Helping with the Exercises indicates errors to watch for or ways to help students who are having difficulty with an exercise.

In **Closing the Lesson** the new mathematical ideas are reviewed and related.

Building Understanding suggests how you might assign exercises and how you can anticipate difficulties and offer help.

The **Assigning Homework** chart indicates ways to use the exercises.

CHAPTER REVIEW
4

PLANNING

LESSON OUTLINE

One day:
10 min   Introduction
25 min   Exercises
15 min   Student self-assessment

REVIEWING

Direct attention to the Nutrition Facts data from the example in Lesson 4.2. Ask the class how to predict the saturated fat in a burger with 50 g total fat. Be sure students describe a variety of ways of finding a line of fit—eyeballing, finding a line through representative points, using Q-points. Don't be satisfied with a list. Ask for demonstrations of techniques, emphasizing how to find the slope of a line with slope triangles and how to find the point-slope form of an equation. Show how different equations might arise from different choices of points, and review the algebraic properties used to check the equivalence of the equations and to solve equations.

ASSIGNING HOMEWORK

If students complete the odd-numbered exercises on their own, they could do the even-numbered ones in groups.

▶ **Helping with the Exercises**

1. $x_2 = 4$
3. Line a has slope -1, y-intercept 1, and equation $y = 1 - x$. Line b has slope 2, y-intercept -2, and equation $y = -2 + 2x$.

CHAPTER 4 REVIEW • CHAPTER 4 REVIEW • CHAPTER 4 REVIEW • CHAPTER

CHAPTER
4
REVIEW

In Chapter 3, you learned how to write equations in intercept form, $y = a + bx$. In this chapter, you learned how to calculate **slope** using the slope formula, $b = \frac{y_2 - y_1}{x_2 - x_1}$. You also used the slope formula to derive another form for a linear equation—the **point-slope form.** The point-slope form, $y = y_1 + b(x - x_1)$, is the equation of a line through point (x_1, y_1) with slope b. You learned that this form is very useful in real-world situations when the starting value is not on the y-axis.

You investigated equivalent forms of expressions and equations using tables and graphs. You used the **distributive property** of multiplication over addition and the **commutative** and **associative** properties of addition and multiplication to write point-slope equations in intercept form.

You investigated several methods of finding a **line of fit**, and you discovered how to use the first and third quartiles from the five-number summaries of x- and y-values in a data set to write a linear model for data based on Q-points.

EXERCISES

You will need your graphing calculator for Exercises **3, 4,** and **9.**

@ Answers are provided for all exercises in this set.

1. The slope of the line between $(2, 10)$ and $(x_2, 4)$ is -3. Find the value of x_2.

2. Give the slope and the y-intercept for each equation.
   a. $y = -4 - 3x$ **b.** $2x + 7 = y$ **c.** $38x - 10y = 24$
   slope: -3; y-intercept: -4 slope: 2; y-intercept: 7   slope: 3.8; y-intercept: -2.4

3. Line a and line b are shown on the graph at right. Name the slope and the y-intercept, and write the equation of each line. Check your equations by graphing on your calculator.

4. Write each equation in the form requested. Check your answers by graphing on your calculator. $y = 13.6x - 25,709$
   a. Write $y = 13.6(x - 1902) + 158.2$ in intercept form.
   b. Write $y = -5.2x + 15$ in point-slope form using $x = 10$ as the first coordinate of the point. $y = -37 - 5.2(x - 10)$

5. Consider the point-slope equation $y = -3.5 + 2(x + 4.5)$.
   a. Name the point used to write this equation. $(-4.5, -3.5)$
   b. Write an equivalent equation in intercept form. $y = 2x + 5.5$
   c. Factor your answer to 5b and name the x-intercept. $y = 2(x + 2.75)$; the x-intercept is -2.75.
   d. A point on the line has a y-coordinate of 16.5. Find the x-coordinate of this point and use this point to write an equivalent equation in point-slope form.
   e. Explain how you can verify that all four equations are equivalent.   Answers will vary. Possible methods are graphing, using a calculator table, and putting all equations in intercept form.

Exercise 5 Some students may have missed the idea of factoring from Lesson 4.4, Exercise 7. Realizing that the x-intercept is the number subtracted from x might also be a challenge. [**Ask**] "What value of x makes y equal zero?"

5d. The x-coordinate is 5.5; $y = 16.5 + 2(x - 5.5)$.

In the proportion, when a is divided by 750, the answer is $\frac{2}{3}$.

$750 \cdot \frac{2}{3} = a$ Multiply by 750 to undo the division.

$500 = a$ Multiply and divide.

Jennifer can estimate that 500 students will attend the party.

EXAMPLE C | After the party, Jennifer found out that 70% of the class attended. How many students attended?

▶ **Solution**

70% is 70 out of 100. So write and solve a proportion to answer the question "If 70 students out of 100 attended the party, how many students out of 750 attended?"

Let s represent the number of students who attended.

$\frac{70}{100} = \frac{s}{750}$ Write the proportion.

$750 \cdot \frac{70}{100} = s$ Multiply by 750 to undo the division.

$525 = s$ Multiply and divide.

525 out of 750 students attended the party.

You have worked with ratios and proportions in this lesson. Numbers that can be written as the ratio of two integers are called **rational numbers.**

History
CONNECTION

The Pythagoreans, a group of philosophers begun by Pythagoras in about 520 B.C.E., realized that not all numbers are rational. For example, for a square one unit on a side, the diagonal $\sqrt{2}$ is *irrational.* Another irrational number is pi, or π, the ratio of the circumference of a circle to its diameter.

EXERCISES

You will need your graphing calculator for Exercise **14.**

▶ **Practice Your Skills**

1. List these fractions in increasing order by estimating their values. Then use your calculator to find the decimal value of each fraction.   b, a, d, c
   a. $\frac{7}{8}$ 0.875   **b.** $\frac{13}{20}$ 0.65   **c.** $\frac{13}{5}$ 2.6   **d.** $\frac{52}{25}$ 2.08

2. Ms. Lenz collected information about the students in her class.

Eye Color

	Brown eyes	Blue eyes	Hazel eyes
9th graders	9	3	2
8th graders	11	4	1

Write these ratios as fractions.
   a. ninth graders with brown eyes to ninth graders   @ $\frac{9}{14}$
   b. eighth graders with brown eyes to students with brown eyes $\frac{11}{20}$
   c. eighth graders with blue eyes to ninth graders with blue eyes   @ $\frac{4}{3}$
   d. all students with hazel eyes to students in both grades $\frac{3}{30}$, or $\frac{1}{10}$

▶ **Helping with the Exercises**

Exercise 1 You might advise students who are stuck to convert the fractions to decimals by division. They could also compare the fractions to 1 and represent the fractions as circles or line segments. Challenge them to find the decimal forms in at least two ways.

▶ *EXAMPLE C*

This example is an application of proportions that reviews percents. [**Alert**] Students may not think of 70% as the ratio $\frac{70}{100}$. Point out that *per* indicates a ratio, as in *miles per hour,* and *percent* means *per hundred.* [**Language**] Point out that there are 100 *cents* in a dollar and 100 years in a *century.*

Closing the Lesson

Review with students the ideas of **ratio, rational number,** the decimal form of a rational number, **proportion,** unknown, **variable,** solving a proportion by multiply and conquer, and inverting both sides of a proportion to get another true proportion. A proportion states the equality of two ratios, in which one number may be unknown and represented by a variable. Rational numbers are ratios of integers, and their decimal names are **repeating** or **terminating.** Ask students if they think there are any numbers that are *not* rational. If they don't know of irrational numbers, they might instead suggest integers; point out that -3 can be written as $-\frac{3}{1}$, so it's rational. As the history connection says, $\sqrt{2}$ and π are irrational.

BUILDING UNDERSTANDING

In the exercises students practice expressing ratios and solving proportions.

ASSIGNING HOMEWORK

Essential	1–6, 9
Performance assessment	7
Portfolio	8
Journal	11
Group	6, 10
Review	12–14

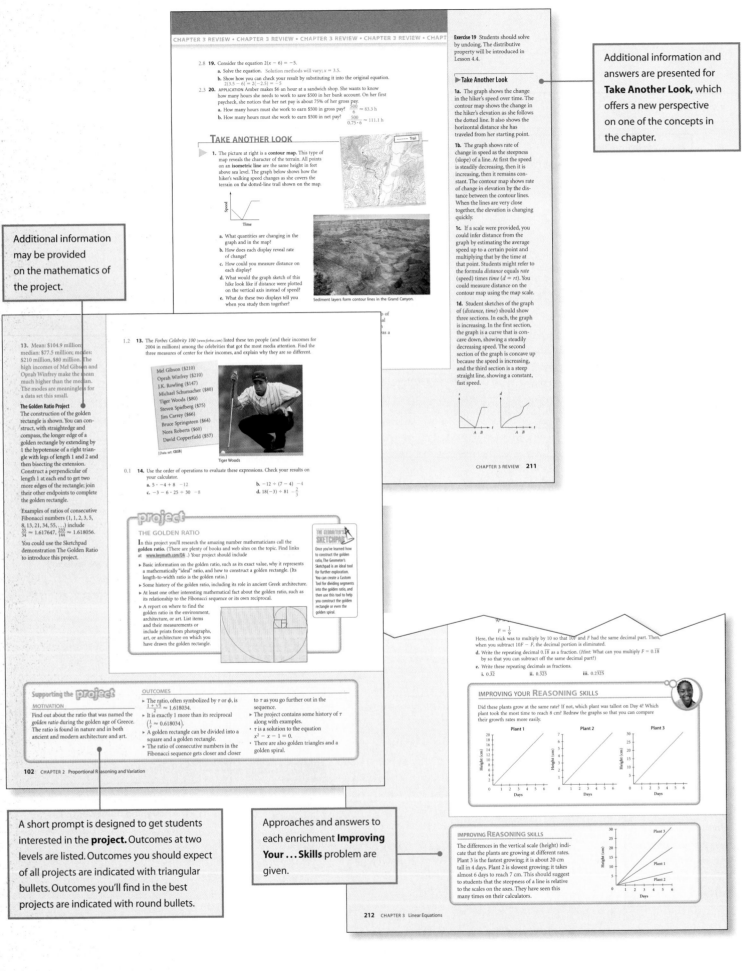

Additional information and answers are presented for **Take Another Look,** which offers a new perspective on one of the concepts in the chapter.

Additional information may be provided on the mathematics of the project.

A short prompt is designed to get students interested in the **project.** Outcomes at two levels are listed. Outcomes you should expect of all projects are indicated with triangular bullets. Outcomes you'll find in the best projects are indicated with round bullets.

Approaches and answers to each enrichment **Improving Your … Skills** problem are given.

2.8 **19.** Consider the equation $2(x - 6) = -5$.
 a. Solve the equation. Solution methods will vary; $x = 3.5$.
 b. Show how you can check your result by substituting it into the original equation. $2(3.5 - 6) = 2(-2.5) = -5$

2.3 **20. APPLICATION** Amber makes $6 an hour at a sandwich shop. She wants to know how many hours she needs to work to save $500 in her bank account. On her first paycheck, she notices that her net pay is about 75% of her gross pay.
 a. How many hours must she work to earn $500 in gross pay? $\frac{500}{6} \approx 83.3$ h
 b. How many hours must she work to earn $500 in net pay? $\frac{500}{0.75 \cdot 6} \approx 111.1$ h

TAKE ANOTHER LOOK

1. The picture at right is a **contour map.** This type of map reveals the character of the terrain. All points on an **isometric line** are the same height in feet above sea level. The graph below shows how the hiker's walking speed changes as she covers the terrain on the dotted-line trail shown on the map.

 a. What quantities are changing in the graph and in the map?
 b. How does each display reveal rate of change?
 c. How could you measure distance on each display?
 d. What would the graph sketch of this hike look like if distance were plotted on the vertical axis instead of speed?
 e. What do these two displays tell you when you study them together?

Sediment layers form contour lines in the Grand Canyon.

Exercise 19 Students should solve by undoing. The distributive property will be introduced in Lesson 4.4.

▶ **Take Another Look**

1a. The graph shows the change in the hiker's speed over time. The contour map shows the change in the hiker's elevation as she follows the dotted line. It also shows the horizontal distance she has traveled from her starting point.

1b. The graph shows rate of change in speed as the steepness (slope) of a line. At first the speed is steadily decreasing, then it is increasing, then it remains constant. The contour map shows rate of change in elevation by the distance between the contour lines. When the lines are very close together, the elevation is changing quickly.

1c. If a scale were provided, you could infer distance from the graph by estimating the average speed up to a certain point and multiplying that by the time at that point. Students might refer to the formula *distance* equals *rate* (speed) times *time* ($d = rt$). You could measure distance on the contour map using the map scale.

1d. Student sketches of the graph of (*distance, time*) should show three sections. In each, the graph is increasing. In the first section, the graph is a curve that is concave down, showing a steadily decreasing speed. The second section of the graph is concave up because the speed is increasing, and the third section is a steep straight line, showing a constant, fast speed.

CHAPTER 3 REVIEW **211**

13. Mean: $104.9 million; median: $77.5 million; modes: $210 million, $80 million. The high incomes of Mel Gibson and Oprah Winfrey make the mean much higher than the median. The modes are meaningless for a data set this small.

The Golden Ratio Project
The construction of the golden rectangle is shown. You can construct, with straightedge and compass, the longer edge of a golden rectangle by extending by 1 the hypotenuse of a right triangle with legs of length 1 and 2 and then bisecting the extension. Construct a perpendicular of length 1 at each end to get two more edges of the rectangle; join their other endpoints to complete the golden rectangle.

Examples of ratios of consecutive Fibonacci numbers (1, 1, 2, 3, 5, 8, 13, 21, 34, 55, ...) include $\frac{55}{34} \approx 1.617647$, $\frac{233}{144} \approx 1.618056$.

You could use the Sketchpad demonstration The Golden Ratio to introduce this project.

1.2 **13.** The *Forbes Celebrity 100* (www.forbes.com) listed these ten people (and their incomes for 2004 in millions) among the celebrities that got the most media attention. Find the three measures of center for their incomes, and explain why they are so different.

Mel Gibson ($210)
Oprah Winfrey ($210)
J.K. Rowling ($147)
Michael Schumacher ($80)
Tiger Woods ($80)
Steven Spielberg ($75)
Jim Carrey ($66)
Bruce Springsteen ($64)
Nora Roberts ($60)
David Copperfield ($57)

[Data set: **CELEB**]

Tiger Woods

0.1 **14.** Use the order of operations to evaluate these expressions. Check your results on your calculator.
 a. $5 \cdot -4 + 8$ -12
 b. $-12 \div (7 - 4)$ -4
 c. $-3 - 6 \cdot 25 \div 30$ -8
 d. $18(-3) \div 81$ $-\frac{2}{3}$

project

THE GOLDEN RATIO

In this project you'll research the amazing number mathematicians call the **golden ratio.** (There are plenty of books and web sites on the topic. Find links at www.keymath.com/DA .) Your project should include

▶ Basic information on the golden ratio, such as its exact value, why it represents a mathematically "ideal" ratio, and how to construct a golden rectangle. (Its length-to-width ratio is the golden ratio.)
▶ Some history of the golden ratio, including its role in ancient Greek architecture.
▶ At least one other interesting mathematical fact about the golden ratio, such as its relationship to the Fibonacci sequence or its own reciprocal.
▶ A report on where to find the golden ratio in the environment, architecture, or art. List items and their measurements or include prints from photographs, art, or architecture on which you have drawn the golden rectangle.

THE GEOMETER'S SKETCHPAD
Once you've learned how to construct the golden ratio, The Geometer's Sketchpad is an ideal tool for further exploration. You can create a Custom Tool for dividing segments into the golden ratio, and then use this tool to help you construct the golden rectangle or even the golden spiral.

Supporting the project

MOTIVATION
Find out about the ratio that was named the *golden ratio* during the golden age of Greece. The ratio is found in nature and in both ancient and modern architecture and art.

OUTCOMES
▶ The ratio, often symbolized by τ or ϕ, is $\frac{1 + \sqrt{5}}{2} \approx 1.618034$.
▶ It is exactly 1 more than its reciprocal $\left(\frac{1}{\tau} \approx 0.618034\right)$.
▶ A golden rectangle can be divided into a square and a golden rectangle.
▶ The ratio of consecutive numbers in the Fibonacci sequence gets closer and closer

to τ as you go further out in the sequence.
● The project contains some history of τ along with examples.
● τ is a solution to the equation $x^2 - x - 1 = 0$.
● There are also golden triangles and a golden spiral.

102 CHAPTER 2 Proportional Reasoning and Variation

$F = \frac{1}{9}$
Here, the trick was to multiply by 10 so that $10F$ and F had the same decimal part. Then, when you subtract $10F - F$, the decimal portion is eliminated.
 d. Write the repeating decimal $0.\overline{18}$ as a fraction. (*Hint:* What can you multiply $F = 0.\overline{18}$ by so that you can subtract off the same decimal part?)
 e. Write these repeating decimals as fractions.
  i. $0.\overline{32}$ **ii.** $0.\overline{325}$ **iii.** $0.2\overline{325}$

IMPROVING YOUR REASONING SKILLS

Did these plants grow at the same rate? If not, which plant was tallest on Day 4? Which plant took the most time to reach 8 cm? Redraw the graphs so that you can compare their growth rates more easily.

IMPROVING REASONING SKILLS

The differences in the vertical scale (height) indicate that the plants are growing at different rates. Plant 3 is the fastest growing; it is about 20 cm tall in 4 days. Plant 2 is slowest growing; it takes almost 6 days to reach 7 cm. This should suggest to students that the steepness of a line is relative to the scales on the axes. They have seen this many times on their calculators.

212 CHAPTER 3 Linear Equations

NCTM Principles and Standards 2000

As part of the Key Curriculum Press *Discovering Mathematics* series, *Discovering Algebra: An Investigative Approach* exemplifies the *Principles and Standards for School Mathematics* set forth by the National Council of Teachers of Mathematics (NCTM) in 2000.

The Equity Principle

Excellence in mathematics education requires equity—high expectations and strong support for all students. (*Principles and Standards for School Mathematics.* Reston, Virginia: National Council of Teachers of Mathematics, 2000, page 12.)

Discovering Algebra grew out of the belief that all students—not just a select few—are capable of learning mathematics. Research shows that most learning takes place while students are actively engaged in the learning process. That's why *Discovering Algebra* is structured around investigations and activities. Through these experiences, students who may have difficulty memorizing formulas or doing calculations come to understand algebra concepts, see relationships, and explain and apply them.

Different students, however, need a variety of experiences. Some need extra skills practice; *Discovering Algebra* provides that. Others learn from puzzles and different perspectives; *Discovering Algebra*'s Improving Your Reasoning Skills and Take Another Look sections provide such challenges. Some students face learning disabilities or language barriers, while others learn quickly and can explore further. This *Discovering Algebra Teacher's Edition* provides advice for accommodating such differences, partly through [Alert], [Language], and [ELL] prompts and through [Ask] prompts that help clarify or challenge.

The Curriculum Principle

A curriculum is more than a collection of activities: it must be coherent, focused on important mathematics, and well articulated across the grades. (NCTM *Principles and Standards,* page 14.)

The investigations and activities in *Discovering Algebra* are coherently organized and carefully crafted. They promote an intuitive understanding of algebra concepts and objects. Only after students come to understand a concept through experience are they introduced to the appropriate symbols and given opportunities to practice mechanics and problem solving.

Moreover, the investigations help students focus on a major mathematical idea in each lesson. The central idea is summarized in each lesson's closing in the *Discovering Algebra Teacher's Edition.*

This algebra course does not stand alone. *Discovering Algebra* is part of the Key Curriculum Press *Discovering Mathematics* series, which articulates a three-year high school curriculum that includes the most important ideas of algebra and geometry.

As part of this series, *Discovering Algebra* ties algebra to other mathematical topics. It introduces data analysis techniques, it enhances proportional reasoning in several contexts, it provides geometric investigations of topics from coordinate geometry, it revisits properties of arithmetic before generalizing them to algebraic principles, and it strengthens reasoning skills.

The *Principles* state (p. 15), " . . . teachers also need to be able to adjust [the curriculum] and take advantage of opportunities to move lessons in unanticipated directions." To help you maintain this flexibility, this *Discovering Algebra Teacher's Edition* includes ideas of the form "If students ask . . . then you might . . . ."

The Teaching Principle

Effective mathematics teaching requires understanding what students know and need to learn and then challenging and supporting them to learn it well. (NCTM *Principles and Standards,* page 16.)

The *Discovering Algebra Teacher's Edition* assumes that you are a creative professional and don't just follow a script. It supports four primary aspects of professional teaching outlined in the *Principles:*

Your mathematical understanding is supported by the essay titled The Mathematics in each chapter interleaf of the *Discovering Algebra Teacher's Edition.* Each essay summarizes the mathematical content of chapter, places it in historical context, and relates new material to what your students already know.

The *Discovering Algebra Teacher's Edition* helps you **create an effective learning environment** by offering advice throughout. For example, later in this introduction you can find tested ideas about how to promote inquiry through cooperative learning.

While interacting with students, you may encounter confusion or questions that hint at a misunderstanding. The commentary in *Discovering Algebra Teacher's Edition* alerts you to common comprehension issues, suggests reasons why they arise, and proposes questions (with an [Ask] prompt) and alternative representations that you might use to help the students.

Occasional advice about **analysis and reflection** on your teaching helps save you time in engaging in these important activities.

The Learning Principle

Students must learn mathematics with understanding, actively building new knowledge from experience and prior knowledge. (NCTM Principles and Standards, page 20.)

To achieve deep understanding, students need to connect new ideas to old ones in personal ways. To make those connections, *Discovering Algebra* uses simple, hands-on investigations in age-appropriate contexts.

The investigations of *Discovering Algebra* require students to make sense of numbers, algebraic expressions, patterns, functions, solution procedures, and answers. They encourage the use of multiple representations—numerical, graphical, symbolic, and verbal. Thus, the investigations lead to deep understanding through active engagement. Working and communicating with their peers strengthen students' understanding of concepts and help them build on their prior knowledge.

Moreover, *Discovering Algebra* takes students beyond learning algebra. First, it helps students learn to be resourceful, flexible problem solvers. Students develop ways of thinking about mathematics. They become open to new ideas, examining alternatives, dealing with real data and the uncertainties they introduce, thinking critically, and working independently.

Second, the text empowers students. The investigations ask students to develop their mathematical power by exploring, verbalizing and writing their reactions, using graphs to illustrate data, and drawing conclusions. Students are also empowered because the technology helps them hurdle some unproductive paper-and-pencil barriers. Many students feel more in control as they decide when and how to use appropriate technology to inform their mathematics conjectures by manipulating, investigating, and summarizing data. More students will thus enjoy a successful journey through one of the most important gateways to their future.

The Technology Principle

Technology is essential in teaching and learning mathematics; it influences the mathematics that is taught and enhances students' learning. (NCTM Principles and Standards, page 24.)

Technology is not a substitute for conceptual understanding, but it is one way to help deepen that understanding. Technological tools allow students to get beyond algorithmic barriers and focus on concepts. Graphing calculators and dynamic software are tools for exploring and investigating—tools that encourage students to ask "What if . . ." questions because it's easy to pursue them; tools that let students focus on decision making, reflection, reasoning, and problem solving; tools that erase artificial lines separating algebra, geometry, and precalculus.

Discovering Algebra was written to make powerful use of graphing calculators. For virtually every investigation, students use calculators in addition to paper and pencil. Extensive calculator notes for various graphing calculators aid students as they learn to use the calculator. These notes also include help for students as they use motion sensors (Texas Instrument's CBL 2 or CBR, or Casio's EA-100 probe-based data collector) to explore, graph, and make sense of time/distance/rate situations.

Suggestions for projects include some that students can do with The Geometer's Sketchpad or Fathom Dynamic Data software. To help students make connections, *Discovering Algebra* includes numerous exercises from situations all over the world. Links at www.keymath.com/DA lead students to websites related to those situations and help students collect and update data. Dynamic Algebra Explorations at www.keymath.com/DA give students the opportunity to explore using dynamic sketches online. And *Discovering Algebra Technology Demonstrations* contains Fathom, Sketchpad, CBL 2, and CBR demonstrations designed to replace or extend specific investigations and exercises.

The Assessment Principle

Assessment should support the learning of important mathematics and furnish useful information to both teachers and students. (NCTM Principles and Standards, page 22.)

Often the focus of teaching is on final assessment: quizzes and tests with right or wrong answers. But also important is ongoing assessment of how students are thinking, so they can see how well they're learning and you can modify your teaching. *Discovering Algebra* supports both kinds of assessment.

During investigations you'll assess through observation as you move around the classroom and as students present ideas. In this *Discovering Algebra Teacher's Edition,* each lesson includes a section that lists what you can assess as you observe students as they work or present ideas. The list includes concepts and skills from earlier lessons, as well as visualization, problem solving, and group work. On pages xxx–xxxi of this introduction you can find advice about assessing group work. This formative assessment leads to adjustments of your pedagogical plans and strategies.

Students can learn from self-assessment as well. Ideas for self-assessment appear at the end of each chapter of the student book. The *Discovering Algebra Assessment Resources* ancillary includes quizzes and tests (with answers) for skill assessment, and constructive assessments (with rubrics) to evaluate deeper understanding. The *TestCheck™: Test Generator and Worksheet Builder™* allows you to create customized written and online assessments.

The Content and Process Standards

Each lesson addresses many of the NCTM content and process standards. At the beginning of each lesson, the *Discovering Algebra Teacher's Edition* lists the relevant standards.

Teaching with *Discovering Algebra*

In today's society, everyone, not just those who are good at mathematics, must understand algebraic concepts and be able to work with technology. Changes in society and changing expectations of employers have required changes in the algebra curriculum. *Discovering Algebra* answers that need for change. It teaches a range of skills more applicable to today, it works toward building technological understanding, it connects algebra to other areas of math, and it encourages an informal understanding of algebraic ideas.

Michael T. Battista of Kent State University writes that algebra teaching should

> focus on the basic skills of today, not those of 40 years ago. Problem solving, reasoning, justifying ideas, making sense of complex situations, and learning new ideas independently—not paper-and-pencil computation—are now critical skills for all Americans. In the Information Age and the Web era, obtaining the facts is not the problem; analyzing and making sense of them is. ("The Mathematical Miseducation of America's Youth," *The Phi Delta Kappan.* February, 1999.)

Toward that end, *Discovering Algebra* can help you teach a practical blend of technology-related and paper-and-pencil problem-solving skills. With the assistance of graphing calculators, your students can study new and different algebraic topics and apply them in our technologically rich society.

Discovering Algebra uses technology, along with applications, to foster a deeper understanding of algebraic ideas. The explorations emphasize symbol sense, algebraic manipulations, and conceptual understandings. The investigative process encourages the use of multiple representations—numerical, graphical, symbolic, and verbal—to deepen understanding for all students and to serve a variety of learning styles. Explorations from multiple perspectives help students simplify and understand what formerly were difficult algebraic abstractions. Investigations actively engage students as they make personal and meaningful connections to the mathematics they discover.

Discovering Algebra contains many connections to other areas of mathematics, especially geometry and statistics. Moreover, because lessons are based on cooperative learning, students have opportunities to share meaningful links to work they have completed in the past.

Traditional algebra teaches skills and ideas before examples and applications. The investigative approach works the other way. Interesting questions and simple hands-on investigations precede the introduction of formulas and symbolic representations. By providing meaningful contexts for students, the investigations motivate relevant algebraic concepts and processes. Moreover, these investigations are accessible. They use inexpensive and readily available materials, require little prerequisite technical knowledge, and follow simple procedures. Students can conduct them with a minimum of direction and intervention from you.

Teaching with *Discovering Algebra* decreases the time students spend on rote memorization, teacher exposition, and extended periods of paper-and-pencil drill. It changes the rules for what is expected of students and what they should expect of their teacher. Thus, teaching from *Discovering Algebra* requires nontraditional thinking and behavior and a nontraditional classroom. Success depends on your sensitivity, patience, enthusiasm, and determination.

Using Technology

Discovering Algebra makes extensive use of graphing calculators to capitalize on these strengths:

- Graphing calculators can generate many examples quickly, allowing students to focus on the meaning of and patterns in the results rather than on getting those results alone. Scatter plots and families of graphs make patterns easier to see, especially for students who tend to avoid more abstract mathematics.

- Students gain experience interpreting the output of technology, an important skill in today's world. *Discovering Algebra* helps students focus on the meaning of the numbers and expressions they enter into a calculator and of the results they generate. Finding meaning in numbers, variables, expressions, tables, and graphs is a year-long challenge for everyone. As the teacher, you will ask for the real-world meaning of things such as a term in a sequence, the slope of a line, the *y*-intercept, and possible outcomes.

- With a calculator, students can take on more realistic problems, which may require more difficult computations. Students can explore variables that actually vary and functions that describe real-world phenomena.

- The graphing calculator allows some students to hurdle error-plagued paper-and-pencil barriers. Even students who enter this course with poor computational and manipulation skills will find that, through their graphing calculator screens, they can visualize mathematical processes and concepts that previously eluded them.

- Many students will want to perform more than one calculation on their graphing calculators. They will ask, "But what if we changed just this one thing?" Routine exercises become open-ended ongoing mathematical explorations, initiated by students.

Cooperative Learning

Students with a wide range of backgrounds flourish in a course that catches their interest. *Discovering Algebra*'s emphasis on technology can help generate that interest. Having students work on investigations within small cooperative groups can engage them even more. The investigations in *Discovering Algebra* encourage students to plan together, brainstorm, determine and organize tasks, and communicate their individual and collective results.

If you haven't already experienced the power of teaching with cooperative groups, you might have several questions: Why use groups? How big should they be? How do I decide group membership? How often do they change? Do they require tables? How do I teach group cooperative skills? How should a class period be structured? How do I behave as a teacher?

Cooperative learning has many benefits:

- Students learn and practice the essential life skill of working with others. In a cooperative learning environment, the group cooperative skills are an integral part of the curriculum.

- Students are exposed to more ideas for solving problems. In solving challenging problems, "two heads are better than one."

- Students who are good in social situations can gain confidence in their mathematical abilities, even if they were previously unsuccessful in mathematics.

- Students understand an idea more deeply if they have to articulate it for someone else.

- Students learn to solve more complex problems than they could if they didn't have a group to contribute different areas of expertise.

- Groups working in a supportive atmosphere can provide quicker feedback on ideas than a single teacher could offer.

- Some students will be more willing to contribute to a small group than to a full class, thus practicing oral communication skills.

Groups of two, three, or four are usually best. If you or your students are new to group work, you might start with pairs. Later you can move to groups of four, with groups of three as needed to make it come out evenly. Most investigations in *Discovering Algebra* are appropriate for groups of three or four.

How do you assign groups? At first, assign them randomly. As you get to know the students, think about who works well with whom. Mixing abilities usually works, but putting the strongest and weakest students together can frustrate both. Keep student groups together long enough for the members to get to know each other, but change group assignments for variety and for a healthy dynamic. You might reorganize the groups at the beginning of each chapter.

(continued)

(Cooperative Learning continued)

Appropriate furniture helps facilitate group behavior. Tables work well because they allow students plenty of work space. But you can have an effective cooperative setting with desks also. Be sure that the desktops are brought together to form as close to a single surface as possible.

Discuss the reasons for working in groups. In the working world, people often work in groups, consult others for help, and rely on others to complete part of a large project. The ability to work with a group is a valuable skill. Try to counter some students' ideas that learning is competitive, that a course is about delivering information that only the teacher knows, or that stronger students have to slow down to teach weaker students.

Develop with your students some specific guidelines to follow for productive work. These might include the following: be considerate, listen without interrupting, ask questions when needed, help others in the group, and make sure everyone in the group understands the ideas well enough to present them to the class.

Appropriate assignments, such as the investigations in *Discovering Algebra,* are important for group work. Some assignments include problems that elicit many ideas, while others have tasks that group members can divide among themselves.

Hold each group fully accountable. End each group session with presentations to the class. You won't have time for all groups to present each time, but each student should be prepared.

Hold individuals responsible for group participation. Make part of the individual grade dependent on how that person contributes to the group. Several days a week, as you move around the room, carry a copy of the roll and record a plus or minus sign for participation. Make these marks part of each student's grade.

As the course progresses, you might extend your observation sheet to include items such as contributing ideas, asking questions, giving directions, actively listening, expressing support, encouraging members to participate, summarizing, talking through problems, and justifying viewpoints. Let your students know when you are looking for specific contribution skills, so that they can learn from the assessment.

Trust the group process. Allow plenty of time for the group to correct mistakes. If a student asks you a question, turn it back to the group. If some students are causing behavior problems, try to facilitate a group solution: Review the guidelines with the group or help students clarify their roles. In some cases you will need to call a student aside for a discussion of poor behavior. When you do so, also talk with the other group members individually about your expectations. Sometimes it helps to point out that the groups will change and that students will have a chance to work with a different set of classmates soon.

Promoting Inquiry

The investigations in *Discovering Algebra* encourage students to inquire about relevant ideas and issues beyond the bounds of the course. Students have legitimate opportunities to experiment, hypothesize, measure, analyze, test, talk, write, explain, and justify their ideas. In short, they engage in real mathematics.

Inquiry-based classes go beyond engaging students in activities. They place students in the role of researchers. The quality of students' investigations is linked to the quality of their own inquiries. The motivation for pursuing answers to their own questions is very strong. In fact, it conforms to the old educational maxim, "Don't answer questions that students haven't asked." Being flexible challenges you and your students in several ways. An inquiry-based classroom requires several things from both you and your students.

- First, it challenges everyone to develop skills of problem posing as well as problem solving. Encourage the posing of new problems during Sharing and Closing. You can foster problem posing by using question openers such as those listed in the box.

- Second, develop a list of inquiry questions that includes some specific to the lesson you're ready to do next. Use those suggested in this *Teacher's Edition* for that lesson as well as questions based on The Mathematics section of the teaching notes before each chapter. What questions does each lesson answer? Where did these questions arise in previous lessons?

- Third, students must take responsibility for their own learning and see that learning is an active, not a passive, process. *Discovering Algebra*'s cooperative investigations are chosen for their value as vehicles to promote activity and help students construct their own knowledge. The interaction, discussion, questions, suggestions, and ideas that students offer while working in groups can benefit all members. Some students want more from you than to help them help themselves. It is not the way they have played the learning game. But it is the way a work environment runs. Their grades in the course, like their evaluations in the workplace, must take into account how well they're learning to do research in a team, not just the results of that research.

- Fourth, you have to play the role of an experienced co-researcher rather than someone with all the answers. Don't give too many hints. Give encouragement for good thinking, not just for right answers. Treat right answers as discussion topics until the class, the research team, agrees on them. As soon as you acknowledge a right answer, you often shut off thinking about that problem, even if students don't understand the answer. You will find that if you provide answers and explanations too quickly, students may continue to expect and depend on your answers.

- Fifth, students must not conceive of mathematics as a collection of facts and procedures. Many mathematical investigations, such as those in *Discovering Algebra*, don't have just one answer, and rarely is there only one valid approach to a solution. Justification of ideas and problem solving become more important than the actual answers. The goal is that students experience mathematics as a process of finding and connecting ideas. Let students know that the thinking and problem-solving skills they develop can serve them in all aspects of their lives. They are learning more than algebra.

- Sixth, as you plan, be flexible in responding to students' ideas. Spend planning time thinking of how students might respond to the problem under investigation. This *Teacher's Edition* can help you anticipate places where students may need help and suggest good questions that will keep students thinking.

Inquiry Question Openers

What happens if …?	What's the largest/smallest …?
What if not …?	What are the properties of …?
Why …?	What other …?
How many …?	How do you know …?
In general, …?	Is it always true that …?
What do we mean by …?	Is it possible …?
Is there a relationship …?	How can you …?
Under what conditions …?	Is there a similarity between …?

Teaching with Cooperative Groups

If you are new to the investigative approach, the change of role may be the most difficult part of learning to create an inquiry-based classroom. You may be comfortable with situations in which you are the center of attention, following a standard script. Now you need to be a leader at problem solving. You will constantly be making professional judgments in response to student contributions.

Don't assume that an emphasis on process over product leads to "anything goes." In fact, sloppy thinking is no more acceptable now than before. Indeed, careful thinking is a major goal of the course. Trust that everything in mathematics can be justified logically and that almost all conflicts between intuition and logic can be resolved on the side of logic.

How can you make your classroom student-centered? You need to keep the focus of your classroom on the students while continuing to be a role model and facilitator. After you give groups a few minutes to settle down and get started (a good time to take attendance), move among groups, observing carefully, encouraging as necessary. As you observe the working groups, sit down if possible so that attention isn't drawn to you. Say little. Don't be too quick to jump in and correct errors. If the other students in the group don't catch a common error, have a student present that error later so that the entire class can learn from it. If students ask you a question, reflect it back to the group. During student presentations, sit down and watch. Keep in mind that if you take the stage or answer a question, many students will stop thinking about that question. In the material presented with each chapter, this *Teacher's Edition* gives suggestions about particular difficulties students might have and how to respond to them.

As you listen to functioning groups, plan how to make use of students' ideas during Sharing. Who should present what? What questions should be asked and what points can you make in response? Through watching the groups at work, you can decide which of their approaches should be shared with the whole class and in what order. For example, you might decide that a group that actually constructed the next stage of a fractal design and counted areas should show their picture first, a student who used the area formula for triangles should describe that formula next, and a pair that found a pattern in the numbers should present last. Look for individuals who seem to understand various key steps particularly well. Be sensitive to the fact that sometimes students with poor calculation skills have creative ideas in problem solving. Keep in mind the suggestions for Sharing from this *Discovering Algebra Teacher's Edition*.

To facilitate good group work, go to any groups that don't seem to be on task. If joining them doesn't refocus them, ask about their progress. If they think they've finished the task, look at their work, ask questions, make suggestions, and challenge them to extend it. If they say they're stuck, ask one of them to describe what they've done, and ask others for their ideas about it. If they're not cooperating, remind them of the group process guidelines. Praise good group work and good thinking, even if it's not yet "on the right track."

Structuring the Class Period

The order of events in a class period can vary with the lesson, with your class's growing experience in independent learning, and according to how students are responding. If they're lethargic, have them act out the investigation. If they're overly excited, channel the energy into their investigation.

This *Teacher's Edition* includes suggested times for these stages of each lesson:

Introduction (5–10 minutes): Set the context for the investigation. Pose the problem and be sure the terms are clear. Many lessons in *Discovering Algebra* include examples to help students learn techniques and see the steps involved in solving real-world problems.

Investigation (15–50 minutes): Students work in groups while you observe, encourage, and craft plans for the rest of the class period. For some of the longer investigations, the Pacing Guide recommends spending two days on the lesson. The section Using This Chapter in the teacher pages that begin each chapter can help you decide which lessons you can skip, depending on the requirements of your curriculum, to allow more time for other lessons.

Sharing (10 minutes): Selected students report to the class. You lead the asking of questions, elaborate on students' ideas, and praise good work. Lead into further examples.

Closing (5 minutes): Remind students of the main mathematical ideas and where they arose in the lesson. If cooperative learning is new to your students, you might lead a quick discussion on how the groups are functioning, what they can improve on, and what they do well. Or ask students to write briefly about what they learned or what they're confused about.

Exercises (5–10 minutes): Assign and begin work on the exercises.

For most lessons, the *Discovering Algebra Teacher's Edition* includes a section marked **One Step,** which offers an alternative to the several-step investigation and perhaps to some examples. You can use the one-step approach for classes that have already become experienced at investigations. Even if your class needs more guidance at the beginning of the course, read through these alternatives to keep in view your goal of helping your students become more independent investigators. This will help you become better at finding "teachable moments" in students' ideas and experiences.

Communicating

Over the last decade, teachers and researchers have become aware that the ability to read mathematics and other technical material and to effectively communicate ideas not only enhances students' understanding of the concepts but improves their other language abilities as well.

The authors have taken care to make *Discovering Algebra* readable. Students will read the steps of an investigation, the real-world contexts of the exercises, and other parts of the text. Ideally you won't tell them what they can read in the textbook, and you'll point out that they can use the textbook as a resource.

As you embark on teaching the course, be sensitive to students' inexperience in reading mathematics and, perhaps, English. You can take steps to help. Ask a student to read a brief passage or instruction aloud. If one student in the class or a group reads an instruction or problem aloud, the others (especially auditory learners) might benefit from hearing it. Don't ask students to read aloud anything that they haven't first read silently. You might, for example, ask all students to read through the instructions to themselves and then ask a student in each group to read it aloud. You might suggest that a group rotate readers counterclockwise to be sure everyone gets a turn.

It is also helpful to ask students to paraphrase. After one student reads aloud, ask another student to restate the instruction or problem in different words. Once they read a passage, help struggling students by emphasizing main ideas and relating them to what students have learned.

(continued)

Assessing

Assessment is your way of getting feedback about how well your students are learning. Students want to know how well they are doing, too. The materials accompanying *Discovering Algebra* support a variety of methods for assessing both processes and results.

While you circulate among groups or watch students' presentations, engage in informal assessment of students' previous learning. Each lesson's Assessing Progress section in the *Discovering Algebra Teacher's Edition* provides ideas of what to look for. Also, during class, note how effectively the lesson is proceeding. This allows you to make adjustments as you go. Throughout the *Teacher's Edition* you can find ideas for what to look for. You can also assess group process skills as described earlier in the Cooperative Learning section. And because *Discovering Algebra* emphasizes mathematics as a journey, journals can be especially useful for assessment.

You will also use more intentionally focused activities to evaluate students' learning. *Discovering Algebra Assessment Resources* includes two versions of quizzes and tests and several Constructive Assessment options for each chapter, as well as unit tests and a final exam. If you feel that in-class examinations don't allow you to assess the depth of students' understanding, you can use the projects in *Discovering Algebra* for assessment. Or you might have students prepare portfolios of their best work. The *Teacher's Edition* lists exercises that you might assign for this purpose. At the end of each chapter of the student text, the section Assessing What You've Learned contains suggestions for student self-assessment. These will give you and your students additional feedback on their learning.

You can find more details about assessment in the front matter for *Assessment Resources*.

(*Communicating continued*)

The real-life contexts of the material will help motivate the reading and enhance critical-thinking skills as students solve problems that relate to things they understand. If students are having trouble understanding an exercise they read, reemphasize the mathematical concepts involved in solving the problems. It is crucial that students recognize the underlying mathematical concepts and how they apply to certain situations.

Students can often increase their comprehension of a chapter if they outline the chapter and list the objectives and main ideas in their notebooks.

Writing and speaking clearly are also important. The process of deciding what to say or write deepens students' understanding of the ideas. As the old saying goes, "Writing is nature's way of telling us what we don't understand." The same holds true for careful speaking.

Critique students' writing and speaking to deepen their understanding. Cultivate in your students the habit of reflecting on what they are saying and writing. Encourage them not to turn in their scratch paper for a homework assignment, but to write up a careful presentation of their answer and its justification. When you grade homework or critique a presentation, ask for clarification of vague expressions or murky logic.

Encourage students to use graphics in communicating, both orally and in writing. They can create overhead transparencies, use computer graphics programs, or use the linking software that accompanies graphing calculators to incorporate graphical illustrations into oral presentations and written reports.

The *Discovering Algebra Teacher's Edition* includes many ideas for planning. For each chapter and lesson it lists objectives and materials and outlines how to spend class time. The commentary on the lesson includes alerts, based on teachers' experience, about difficulties students might have (but may not be able to articulate) and suggestions for how you might respond to them.

But every class is different. Don't limit your planning to reading through these comments. Think about each chapter and lesson with your own students and schedule in mind.

Planning a Chapter

To allow flexibility to meet your class's needs, each chapter of *Discovering Algebra* contains more material than most classes will have time to do. Although all the investigations are valuable, you probably won't be able to explore all of them to the same depth. Complete those you choose to do in class and have students share their findings. You may choose to work through an investigation as a whole class or even omit an investigation because of time constraints. Ask yourself, "What do my students need at this time?" The section Using This Chapter on the page before each student chapter in the *Teacher's Edition* can help you decide what you might skip.

You need to think about your students' strengths and weaknesses in planning individual lessons as well. Work through the investigation, asking yourself how your students will respond to it and how you can facilitate. If you have time, ask friends and colleagues to think out loud about how they'd do the investigation.

Planning a Lesson

While planning lessons, keep in mind that the approach of this course is different from what you may be used to. Instead of telling students everything they need to know before they embark on the investigation (and then retelling them as they work), the approach here is to have students encounter the mathematical ideas during the investigation. Later those ideas can be formalized with a name and definition. Remember that your role is to help students discover mathematics, in both the processes and the content of the journey.

Part of planning involves deepening your own understanding of the mathematics. Some may believe that if students have to figure out the mathematics themselves, you don't need to know the mathematics very well. Such a belief doesn't take into account the intellectual level of an investigation-based classroom. Students working collaboratively in groups will find themselves on many paths that you haven't explored before. Students with calculators in their hands may raise "What if . . ." questions that astound you. Even though your role is no longer to provide answers, you need to keep encouraging and challenging the students. To do so, you need to understand the mathematical ideas very well. Reading The Mathematics section in the pages before each new student chapter will help you.

Planning Assignments

In planning homework assignments, be aware that *Discovering Algebra* contains many more exercises than most classes will have time to work on. Select those you think can generate interest among your own students and can satisfy your curriculum goals. At times you may want to assign different exercises to different groups or individuals and follow them with classroom presentations. The Assigning Homework chart for each lesson offers some guidance about the appropriateness of the exercises for particular goals.

When hard-working students return to class with questions, consider asking them

to continue working on the assignment and turn it in the following day.

Although careful planning is necessary, don't let it get in the way of your teaching. Planning should not mean preparing a script you have to follow. What students do with technology-enhanced investigations can be different from what you anticipated. Each day you'll need to adjust your plans for the next few days. The farther you can see ahead, the better you'll be able to decide how to balance allowing students to explore and answer their own questions with getting the class through the course.

The *Discovering Algebra Teacher's Edition* outlines how to teach each lesson over one or two periods of 50 minutes. These outlines are only guidelines; your period may be 45 minutes or 90 minutes. Moreover, prepare yourself to move faster or more slowly according to how well your class is learning.

The Pacing Options chart indicates the days per lesson for several schedules:

- a block schedule, in which there are fewer, longer class periods each week
- a standard one-year algebra course, covering all the essential lessons
- an enriched course, in which students cover all the topics and the projects

If you are teaching a two-year beginning algebra class, you can spend one day on the investigation and a second day on the exercises for each lesson.

Pacing Guide for Block Schedules

Chapter	day 1	day 2	day 3	day 4	day 5	day 6	day 7	day 8	day 9
0	0.1	0.2, 0.3	0.4	0.5, review	assessment				
1	1.1, 1.2	1.2, 1.3	1.4, project	quiz, 1.5	1.6	1.7, project	1.8, review	assessment	
2	2.1, 2.2	2.3, 2.4	quiz, 2.5	2.6, 2.7	2.8, review	assessment			
3	3.1, 3.2	3.2, 3.3, project	3.4, 3.5	3.6, quiz	3.7, review	assessment, mixed review	exam		
4	4.1, 4.2	4.2, 4.3	4.4	quiz, 4.5	4.6	project, 4.7	4.8	review, assessment	
5	5.1	5.2	5.3	5.4, quiz	5.5, 5.6	5.7, review	assessment		
6	6.1, 6.2	6.2, 6.3	6.4, 6.5	6.6	quiz, 6.7	6.8, review	assessment		
7	7.1	7.2, 7.3	7.4	quiz, 7.5	7.6, review	assessment, mixed review	exam		
8	8.1	8.2, 8.3	quiz, 8.4	8.5, 8.6	quiz, 8.7	review, assessment			
9	9.1, 9.2	quiz, 9.3	9.4, 9.5	quiz, 9.6, 9.7	9.8, review	assessment			
10	10.1, 10.2	quiz, 10.3, 10.4	10.5	10.6, quiz	review, assessment				
11	11.1, 11.2	11.3, 11.4	11.5, quiz	11.6	11.7	11.8, quiz, review	assessment	mixed review	final exam

Pacing Options

Pacing Guide for a Standard Course

Chapter	day 1	day 2	day 3	day 4	day 5	day 6	day 7	day 8	day 9	day 10
0	0.1	0.1	0.2	0.3	0.4	0.5	review	assessment		

Chapter	day 1	day 2	day 3	day 4	day 5	day 6	day 7	day 8	day 9	day 10
1	1.1	1.2	1.2	1.3	1.4	quiz, 1.5	1.5	1.6	1.6	1.7

day 11	day 12	day 13	day 14
1.8	1.8	review	assessment

Chapter	day 1	day 2	day 3	day 4	day 5	day 6	day 7	day 8	day 9	day 10
2	2.1	2.2	2.3	2.4	quiz, 2.5	2.5	2.6	2.7	2.8	review

day 11
assessment

Chapter	day 1	day 2	day 3	day 4	day 5	day 6	day 7	day 8	day 9	day 10
3	3.1	3.2	3.2	3.3	quiz, 3.4	3.5	3.6	3.7	review	assessment

day 11	day 12
mixed review	exam

Chapter	day 1	day 2	day 3	day 4	day 5	day 6	day 7	day 8	day 9	day 10
4	4.1	4.2	4.2	4.3	4.4	4.4, quiz	4.5	4.6	4.6	4.7

day 11	day 12	day 13	day 14
quiz, 4.8	4.8	review	assessment

Chapter	day 1	day 2	day 3	day 4	day 5	day 6	day 7	day 8	day 9	day 10
5	5.1	5.2	5.2	5.3	5.3	5.4	5.4	quiz, 5.5	5.6	5.7

day 11	day 12
quiz, review	assessment

Pacing Guide for a Standard Course (continued)

Chapter	day 1	day 2	day 3	day 4	day 5	day 6	day 7	day 8	day 9	day 10
6	6.1	6.2	6.2	quiz, 6.3	6.4	6.5	6.6	6.6	quiz, 6.7	6.7
	day 11	**day 12**	**day 13**							
	6.8	review	assessment							

Chapter	day 1	day 2	day 3	day 4	day 5	day 6	day 7	day 8	day 9	day 10
7	7.1	7.1	7.2	quiz, 7.3	7.4	7.5	7.5	7.6	review	assessment
	day 11	**day 12**								
	mixed review	exam								

Chapter	day 1	day 2	day 3	day 4	day 5	day 6	day 7	day 8	day 9	day 10
8	8.1	8.1	8.2	quiz, 8.3	8.4	8.5	8.5, quiz	8.6	8.7, quiz	review
	day 11									
	assessment									

Chapter	day 1	day 2	day 3	day 4	day 5	day 6	day 7	day 8	day 9	day 10
9	9.1	9.2	quiz, 9.3	9.3	9.4	9.5	quiz, 9.6	9.6	9.7	9.8
	day 11	**day 12**								
	review	assessment								

Chapter	day 1	day 2	day 3	day 4	day 5	day 6	day 7	day 8	day 9
10	10.1	10.2	quiz, 10.3	10.4	10.5	10.5	10.6, quiz	review	assessment

Chapter	day 1	day 2	day 3	day 4	day 5	day 6	day 7	day 8	day 9	day 10
11	11.1	11.2	11.3, quiz	11.4	11.5	11.5	quiz, 11.6	11.6	11.7	11.7
	day 11	**day 12**	**day 13**	**day 14**	**day 15**					
	11.8	review	assessment	mixed review	final exam					

Pacing Options

Pacing Guide for an Enriched Course

Chapter	day 1	day 2	day 3	day 4	day 5	day 6	day 7	day 8	day 9	day 10
0	0.1	0.2	0.3, project	0.4	0.5	review, TAL	assessment			

	day 1	day 2	day 3	day 4	day 5	day 6	day 7	day 8	day 9	day 10
1	1.1	1.2	1.2	1.3	1.4, project	quiz, 1.5	1.5	1.6	1.6	1.7, project

	day 11	day 12	day 13	day 14
	1.8	1.8	review, TAL	assessment

	day 1	day 2	day 3	day 4	day 5	day 6	day 7	day 8	day 9	day 10
2	2.1	project	2.2	2.3	2.4	quiz, 2.5	2.6	2.7	2.8	review, TAL

	day 11
	assessment

	day 1	day 2	day 3	day 4	day 5	day 6	day 7	day 8	day 9	day 10
3	3.1	3.2	3.2	3.3, project	quiz, 3.4	3.5	3.6	3.7	review, TAL	assessment

	day 11	day 12
	mixed review	exam

	day 1	day 2	day 3	day 4	day 5	day 6	day 7	day 8	day 9	day 10
4	4.1	project, 4.2	4.2	4.3	4.4	4.4, quiz	4.5	4.6	4.6, project	4.7

	day 11	day 12	day 13	day 14
	quiz, 4.8	4.8	review, TAL	assessment

	day 1	day 2	day 3	day 4	day 5	day 6	day 7	day 8	day 9	day 10
5	5.1	5.2	5.2	5.3	5.3	5.4	5.4	quiz, 5.5, project	5.6	5.7

	day 11	day 12
	review, TAL	assessment

Pacing Guide for an Enriched Course (continued)

Chapter	day 1	day 2	day 3	day 4	day 5	day 6	day 7	day 8	day 9	day 10
6	6.1	6.2	6.2, project	quiz, 6.3	6.4	6.5	6.6	6.6	quiz, 6.7	6.7, project
	day 11	**day 12**	**day 13**							
	6.8	review, TAL	assessment							

Chapter	day 1	day 2	day 3	day 4	day 5	day 6	day 7	day 8	day 9	day 10
7	7.1	7.1, project	7.2	quiz, 7.3	7.4	7.5	7.5	7.6	review, TAL	assessment
	day 11	**day 12**								
	mixed review	exam								

Chapter	day 1	day 2	day 3	day 4	day 5	day 6	day 7	day 8	day 9	day 10
8	8.1	8.1, project	8.2	quiz, 8.3	8.4	8.5	quiz, 8.6	8.7	project, quiz	review, TAL
	day 11									
	assessment									

Chapter	day 1	day 2	day 3	day 4	day 5	day 6	day 7	day 8	day 9	day 10
9	9.1	9.2	quiz, 9.3	9.3	9.4	9.5	quiz, project	9.6	9.7	9.8
	day 11	**day 12**								
	review, TAL	assessment								

Chapter	day 1	day 2	day 3	day 4	day 5	day 6	day 7	day 8	day 9
10	10.1	10.2, project	quiz, 10.3	10.4	10.5	10.5	10.6, quiz	review, TAL	assessment

Chapter	day 1	day 2	day 3	day 4	day 5	day 6	day 7	day 8	day 9	day 10
11	11.1	11.2	11.3, quiz	11.4, project	11.5	11.5, project	quiz, 11.6	11.6	11.7	11.7
	day 11	**day 12**	**day 13**	**day 14**	**day 15**					
	11.8	review, TAL	assessment	mixed review	final exam					

Materials List

Material	Quantity	Material	Quantity
balls	1 per group	markers	
beans, red	$\frac{1}{4}$ cup per group	masking tape	
beans, white	1 cup per group	metersticks	
blank transparencies		motion sensors, *optional*	1 per group
books on a variety of topics (for analysis)	2 books per group	multiple-speed bicycle	1 per group or 1 per class for demonstration
books (for stacking)	4 per group	nickels, *optional*	9 per group
books, notebooks, or cardboard (for ramps)	1 per group	objects that roll (such as pencils and soda cans)	1 per group
bucket or other object to pass	1 per class	packets of colored candies	1 per group
cables for linking calculators		paper bags	1 per group
centimeter graph paper		paper clips (one size)	4 per group
centimeter rulers	2 per group	paper cups	1 per group
chalk or long rope (for number line), *optional*	1 per class	paper plates	1 per group
compasses or circle templates	1 per group	patty paper, *optional*	
computer with CD-ROM to download data and programs, *optional*		pennies (not new)	100 per group
counters (small, flat objects such as lentils or flat candies)	100 per group	plastic cups (5 oz size)	1 per group
dice	1 per student pair	poster board	
empty coffee cans	1 per group	poster paper	
empty soda cans	1 per group	protractors	1 per group
graph paper		ropes—different thicknesses and lengths (each about 1 m long)	2 per group
large marbles	1 per group	rubber bands (identical)	300 per class

Material	Quantity	Material	Quantity
rulers	1 per student	toothpicks	about 50 per group
scissors (or awls)	1 per group	toy figures	1 per group
small boxes, *optional*	1 per group	transparency markers	1 per group
stopwatches, or watches or clocks with second hand	1 per group	uncooked spaghetti	1 box per group
straightedges	1 per student	video camera, *optional*	
string	several 24 cm lengths per group	washers, *optional*	10 per group
tables and chairs	1 each per group	yardsticks	1 per group
tape			

0

Fractions and Fractals

Overview

In Chapter 0, students look both backward and forward. They deepen their understanding of fractions, integers, and exponents by using them to solve problems about fractals. The fractions reviewed here are especially useful in the book's theme of data analysis. Also, in fractals students see the idea of recursion. Recursion will help students understand rates of change—constant rate of change in Chapters 2 through 4 (in which they learn to set up and solve linear equations) and nonlinear change in Chapters 6 through 9. Fractals and other recursive procedures appear in *Discovering Geometry.* Recursion, data analysis and rates of change are major themes of *Discovering Advanced Algebra.*

In **Lesson 0.1,** fractions are reviewed in the context of comparing areas within fractal drawings. **Lessons 0.2** and **0.3** review exponents as a tool for counting features and segment lengths of a fractal at various stages in its generation. **Lesson 0.4** extends to algebraic expressions the notion of recursion, which will be used throughout the text; it also reviews operations with signed numbers. In **Lesson 0.5,** students practice making careful measurements.

The Mathematics

Fractions and Integers

To work successfully with equations and probability, students need confidence with fractions, both common and decimal, as well as with integers. Students should understand equivalent fractions and their use in finding common denominators. They should realize that multiplying by a fraction less than 1 makes a quantity smaller, while dividing by that same fraction makes it larger. They need to know how fractions and integers relate to each other and to the number line.

The decimals displayed on a calculator usually conceal some of the patterns that common fractions reveal, so an ability to use and understand both forms of fractions is important.

Fractals and Recursion

A procedure is *iterative* if it does the same thing repeatedly in a systematic way. One example of iteration is finding 3% of a bank balance and adding it to the balance, then doing it again for each resulting balance.

A *recursive* procedure is a special kind of iterative procedure; to get the next result, it uses the result of the previous step (or steps). One example is adding 3% to a bank balance and then doing the same procedure to the resulting balance again and again.

The fractals in this chapter are geometric shapes generated by recursive procedures; that is, they're formed by a procedure that uses each stage to produce the next one. For a true mathematical fractal, the recursive procedure is applied infinitely. Every fractal also has the property that a part of it is a shrunken version of the whole figure. That is, fractals are *self-similar*. Self-similarity is possible only because fractals are generated through infinitely many stages.

Many fractals were developed about 100 years ago, but not in an attempt to model reality. Rather, mathematicians were testing the implications of new mathematical definitions. Some mathematicians applied infinite processes to line segments to obtain what they called "curves" with unusual properties, such as passing through every point in a square. For example, the Koch curve of Lesson 0.3 was first proposed in 1906 by the Swedish mathematician Neils Fabian Helge von Koch as a curve on which every point is a "corner." (*Koch* is pronounced "KawCK," where *CK* is the sound made in Scottish or German by putting the tongue in the position of *k* while pronouncing *h*.)

Other mathematicians wanted nothing to do with these "monsters." Charles Hermite wrote, "I turn away with fear and horror from this lamentable sore." This extreme case illustrates disagreement over mathematics.

Only about a quarter century ago, Benoit Mandelbrot of IBM was looking for a mathematical way to represent natural phenomena whose appearance is irregular due to fragmentation and

turbulence. The squares and triangles of traditional mathematics don't look like clouds and mountains, but these "monsters" do. He began calling them fractals because they were "fractured." He also found that, in a very real sense, they had fractional dimensions. Indeed, fractal models have since been used in many areas, including anatomy (arteries and veins, lungs, the brain), topography (coastlines, watersheds), graphs of the stock market, and even linguistics (patterns of word use). Research is finding new areas where fractal models are useful.

Generating fractals is just one example of using a recursive procedure. Lesson 0.4 offers a glimpse of the many other types of recursion in mathematics.

Using This Chapter

You can use this chapter at the beginning of the school year even if your classes have not yet stabilized. Success with *Discovering Algebra* does not depend on detailed coverage of this chapter, so you may decide to use only the first three lessons or perhaps only the last two. The chapter reviews fractions, integers, and exponents in the new context of fractals, so don't skip this chapter if your students need practice with these topics.

Even if you cannot do every investigation, do as many as your time and situation permit. In this chapter the investigations are specially designed to help students prepare for the rest of the course. Students less experienced in investigating and group work will benefit from engaging in at least a part of each one.

Throughout this chapter, you will notice balloons with hints for students on how to use the text successfully. Encourage students to read these.

Resources

Discovering Algebra Resources

Teaching and Worksheet Masters
   Lessons 0.1–0.5

Programs and Data CD

Calculator Notes 0A, 0B, 0C, 0D, 0E, 0F, 0G, 0H

Sketchpad Demonstration
   Lesson 0.3

Fathom Demonstration
   Lesson 0.4

Dynamic Algebra Explorations online
   Lessons 0.3–0.5

Assessment Resources
   Chapter 0 Test
   Chapter 0 Constructive Assessment Options

More Practice Your Skills for Chapter 0

Condensed Lessons for Chapter 0

Other Resources

Fractals: A Toolkit of Dynamics Activities by Robert Devaney, Jonathan Choate, and Alice Foster.

Iteration: A Toolkit of Dynamics Activities by Robert Devaney, Jonathan Choate, and Alice Foster.

Fractals for the Classroom, Parts One and Two by Heinz-Otto Peitgen et al.

Students may enjoy experimenting with fractal-drawing computer programs.

For complete references to these and other resources see www.keypress.com/DA.

For complete references to these and other resources see www.keypress.com/DA.

Materials

- dice
- centimeter rulers
- blank transparencies
- transparency markers

Pacing Guide

	day 1	day 2	day 3	day 4	day 5	day 6	day 7	day 8	day 9	day 10
standard	0.1	0.1	0.2	0.3	0.4	0.5	review	assessment		
enriched	0.1	0.1	0.2	0.3, project	0.4	0.5	review, TAL	assessment		
block	0.1	0.2, 0.3	0.4	0.5, review	assessment					

0 Fractions and Fractals

You have probably seen designs like this—you may even have heard the word *fractal* used to describe them. Complex fractals are created by infinitely repeating simple processes; some are created with basic geometric shapes such as triangles or squares. With fractals, mathematicians and scientists can model the formation of clouds, the growth of trees, and human blood vessels.

OBJECTIVES

In this chapter you will
- investigate numeric, algebraic, and geometric patterns
- review operations with fractions
- review operations with positive and negative numbers
- use exponents to represent repeated multiplication
- explore designs called fractals
- learn to use this book as a tool

This fractal is generated by a much more complex procedure than those used for fractal designs in the chapter. You might ask students what patterns they see. They may see similar shapes, but the patterns aren't completely regular. Mention that fractals are generated by a regular process that produces apparent randomness and that they'll be seeing such processes (called *chaotic*) in this chapter.

The fractal in this picture, called a Julia set, is generated by considering each point within a circle, moving it to another point determined by evaluating an equation at that point, then moving that to another point by taking the result and using it to again evaluate the equation, and so on, repeatedly. The starting point is colored according to how fast the successive points are moving away from it. (For this fractal, the operation on a point is given by considering the point as a complex number z and then moving it to the point $z^4 + z - 0.4 + 0.04i$.)

LESSON

0.1

The Same yet Smaller

A procedure that you do over and over, each time building on the previous stage, is **recursive.** You'll see recursion used in many different ways throughout this book. In this lesson you'll draw a **fractal** design using a recursive procedure. After you draw the design, you'll work with fractions to examine its parts.

> Words in **bold** type are important mathematical terms. They may be new to you, so they will be explained in the text. You can also find a definition in the glossary.

> Investigations are a very important part of this course. Often you'll discover new concepts in an investigation, so be sure to take an active role.

Investigation
Connect the Dots

You will need
- a ruler
- the worksheet Connect the Dots

   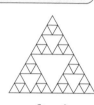

| Stage 0 | Stage 1 | Stage 2 | Stage 3 |

Step 1 Examine the figures above. The starting figure is the Stage 0 figure. To create the Stage 1 figure, you join the *midpoints* of the sides of the triangle. You can locate the midpoints by counting dots to find the middle of each side. The Stage 1 figure has three small upward-pointing triangles. See if you can find all three.

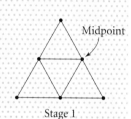

Midpoint

Stage 1

If your class is less independent, here are some ideas for more guidance.

Step 1 [ELL] Be sure all students, especially ELL students, understand what a *midpoint* of a line segment is.

LESSON OBJECTIVES

- Review conventional order of operations
- Review midpoint of a line segment
- Review equivalent fractions
- Practice arithmetic operations on fractions
- Learn to use the calculator with fractions
- Recognize a pattern in a fractal design and describe the recursive procedure that created it
- Become familiar with congruent figures

PLANNING

LESSON OUTLINE

First day:

15 min	Getting started
30 min	Investigation
5 min	Closing

Second day:

15 min	Sharing
10 min	Examples
10 min	Closing
15 min	Exercises

MATERIALS

- rulers (one per student)
- Connect the Dots or isometric dot paper (W)
- Calculator Note 0A

TEACHING

This lesson emphasizes equivalent fractions and arithmetic operations on fractions.

 Guiding the Investigation

After forming groups, talk a little bit about fractals. Then display the Connect the Dots worksheet.

One Step

If your students are experienced at investigations, you might simply ask "What's the sum of the areas of all upward-pointing triangles at the next stage of this figure?" and let them go to work. They must figure out the generating rule, how to find the areas of the triangles, and how to calculate the desired sum. You can remind individuals or groups of the mathematical ideas being reviewed, handing out Calculator Note 0A and More Practice Your Skills sheets as needed.

Step 2   At Stage 2, line *segments* connect the midpoints of the sides of the three upward-pointing triangles that showed up at Stage 1. What do you notice when you compare Stage 1 and Stage 2?

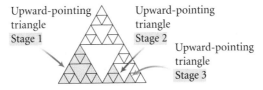

Upward-pointing triangle **Stage 1**

Upward-pointing triangle **Stage 2**

Upward-pointing triangle **Stage 3**

Step 3   How many new upward-pointing triangles are there in the Stage 3 figure?   27

Step 4   On your worksheet, create the Stage 4 figure. A blank triangle is provided. Connect the midpoints of the sides of the large triangle, and continue connecting the midpoints of the sides of each smaller upward-pointing triangle at every stage. How many small upward-pointing triangles are in the Stage 4 figure?   81

Stage 4

Step 5   What would happen if you continued to further stages? Describe any patterns you've noticed in drawing these figures.

> Most words in *italic* are words you may have seen before or that you can probably figure out. Some italicized words are defined in the glossary.

You have been using a *recursive rule*. The rule is "Connect the midpoints of the sides of each upward-pointing triangle."

If you could continue this process forever, you would create a fractal called the *Sierpiński triangle*. At each stage the small upward-pointing triangles are *congruent*—the same shape and size.

> This marker shows a convenient stopping place.

Step 6   If the Stage 0 figure has an area equal to 1, what is the area of one new upward-pointing triangle at Stage 1? $\frac{1}{4}$

Step 7   How many different ways are there to find the combined area of the smallest upward-pointing triangles at Stage 1? For example, you could write the *addition expression* $\frac{1}{4} + \frac{1}{4} + \frac{1}{4}$. Write at least two other expressions to find this area. Use as many different operations (like addition, subtraction, multiplication, or division) as you can. $3 \times \frac{1}{4}$ or $1 - \frac{1}{4}$ or $(1 \div 4) \times 3$

Step 8   What is the area of one of the smallest upward-pointing triangles at Stage 2? How do you know? $\frac{1}{4}$ of $\frac{1}{4}$ is $\frac{1}{16}$

Step 9   How many smallest upward-pointing triangles are there at Stage 2? What is the combined area of these triangles? $9; \frac{9}{16}$

Step 10   Repeat Steps 8 and 9 for Stage 3. $\frac{1}{64}$ $\left(\text{or } \frac{1}{4} \text{ of } \frac{1}{16}\right); 27; \frac{27}{64}$

Step 11   If the Stage 0 figure has an area of 8, what is the combined area of

     a. One smallest upward-pointing triangle at Stage 1, plus one smallest upward-pointing triangle at Stage 2? $2\frac{1}{2}$

NCTM STANDARDS

CONTENT		PROCESS	
✓	Number	✓	Problem Solving
	Algebra	✓	Reasoning
✓	Geometry		Communication
✓	Measurement	✓	Connections
	Data/Probability	✓	Representation

Step 2 Possible answers: Each upward-pointing triangle in Stage 1 contains three upward-pointing triangles in Stage 2. The large downward-pointing triangle remains unchanged from Stage 1 to Stage 2. Stage 2 has three smaller versions of Stage 1.

Step 4 Be sure students understand how to count dots to find the midpoint of a side.

Some students may skip the actual construction of the Stage 4 figure. Encourage them, but be sure they don't dominate their groups and prevent the more visual and kinesthetic learners from creating the pattern for themselves.

Step 5 [Link] In geometry class, students will learn how to prove that the new triangles formed at any stage are congruent.

Step 5 Possible answers: At each stage, three new upward-pointing triangles are formed in each upward-pointing triangle. Quickly the new triangles become very small, and the number of new triangles becomes very large.

Step 7 Help students see a variety of ways to write the combined area. [Ask] "How much less than the whole are the three upward-pointing triangles at Stage 1?" Plan for several approaches to be presented later.

Step 8 [Alert] Watch for difficulties in calculating these areas. [Ask] "How does the smallest triangle at each stage relate to the smallest triangle at the previous stage?"

Step 11 [Alert] Watch for difficulties in determining the sizes of the triangles. Point out that the area of the smallest triangle at Stage 1 is one-fourth the area of the Stage 0 triangle.

b. Two smallest upward-pointing triangles at Stage 2, minus one smallest upward-pointing triangle at Stage 3? $\frac{7}{8}$

c. One smallest upward-pointing triangle at Stage 1, plus three smallest upward-pointing triangles at Stage 2, plus nine smallest upward-pointing triangles at Stage 3? $4\frac{5}{8}$

Step 12 Make up one problem like those in Step 11, and exchange it with a partner to solve.

This marker means the investigation is done.

The Polish mathematician Waclaw Sierpiński created his triangle in 1916. But the word *fractal* wasn't used until nearly 60 years later, when Benoit Mandelbrot drew attention to recursion that occurs in nature. Trees, ferns, and even the coastlines of continents can be examined as real-life fractals.

EXAMPLE A

Examples are important learning tools. Have your pencil in hand when you study the solution to an example. Try to do the problem before reading the solution. Work out any calculations in the solution so that you're sure you understand them.

Evan designed an herb garden. He divided each side of his garden into thirds and connected the points. He planted oregano in the labeled sections. If the whole garden has an area of 1, what is the area of one oregano section? What is the total area planted in oregano?

▶ Solution

Sometimes you will find questions in a solution. Try to answer these questions before you continue reading.

Because there are nine equal-size sections, each oregano section is one-ninth of the garden's area. To find the total area planted in oregano, you can either add $\frac{1}{9} + \frac{1}{9} = \frac{2}{9}$ or multiply $2 \times \frac{1}{9} = \frac{2}{9}$. So the oregano is planted in sections with a total area equal to $\frac{2}{9}$ of the garden. Can you explain how each expression represents the area?

Let's examine some features of Evan's garden in more detail. You can think of Evan's garden as a Stage 1 figure with six identical upward-pointing triangles that each have an area of $\frac{1}{9}$.

What is the area of one small upward-pointing triangle at Stage 2?

Stage 0

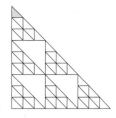

Stage 1

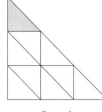

Stage 2

This feature will help you connect algebra to the people who continue to develop and use it.

History
CONNECTION

Benoit Mandelbrot (b 1924) first used the word *fractal* in 1975 to describe irregular patterns in nature. You can link to a biography of Mandelbrot at www.keymath.com/DA .

At Stage 2, nine smaller triangles are formed in each upward-pointing triangle from Stage 1. The shaded triangle in Stage 2 has an area that is $\frac{1}{9}$ of the Stage 1 shaded triangle. This equals $\frac{1}{9}$ of $\frac{1}{9}$, which you can write as $\frac{1}{9} \times \frac{1}{9}$, which is equal to $\frac{1}{81}$.

To find combined areas, you'll be adding, subtracting, and multiplying fractions. When there are more than two operations in an expression, it can be difficult to know where to start. To avoid confusion, all mathematicians have agreed to use the **order of operations.**

Order of Operations

1. Evaluate all expressions within parentheses.
2. Evaluate all powers.
3. Multiply and divide from left to right.
4. Add and subtract from left to right.

Go to the calculator notes whenever you see this icon. The calculator notes explain how to use your graphing calculator. You can get these notes from your teacher or at www.keymath.com/DA .

You should be able to do the calculations in this lesson with pencil and paper. Many calculators are programmed to give answers in fraction form, so use a calculator to check your answers.
[▶ 🖳 See **Calculator Note 0A.** ◀]

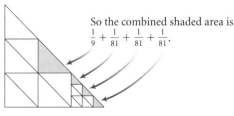

EXAMPLE B

If the largest triangle has an area of 1, what is the combined area of the shaded triangles?

▶ **Solution**

The area of the larger shaded triangle is $\frac{1}{9}$.

The area of each smaller triangle is $\frac{1}{9} \times \frac{1}{9}$, or $\frac{1}{81}$.

So the combined shaded area is
$\frac{1}{9} + \frac{1}{81} + \frac{1}{81} + \frac{1}{81}$.

Notice that $\frac{1}{81} + \frac{1}{81} + \frac{1}{81} = \frac{3}{81}$, so the combined area is $\frac{1}{9} + \frac{3}{81}$.

ORDER OF OPERATIONS

Students need to understand order of operations, whether they are doing arithmetic by hand or entering it into the calculator. **[Alert]** Many students who have learned the mnemonic PEMDAS for the order of operations mistakenly believe that multiplication must be done before division, and addition before subtraction. Lesson 2.7 looks at these ideas again.

The diver has not followed the correct order of operations in getting dressed. The trunks should have been put on before the wet suit.

▶ ***EXAMPLE B***

Example B offers another opportunity to discuss adding and simplifying fractions. Before adding fractions, students must find a common denominator. **[Ask]** "Why is $\frac{12}{81}$ the same as $\frac{4}{27}$?" **[Language]** Make sure students can use the phrases *equivalent fractions* and *fraction reduced to lowest terms* in discussing this question.

Closing the Lesson

Mention the new mathematical ideas. **Fractal** designs are produced by **recursive** procedures; at each stage congruent figures are formed. The calculator can give answers as fractions, and patterns are often easier to see when the answers are given as fractions. The **order of operations** clarifies the steps when evaluating an expression.

Invite students to look for patterns in clothing or architecture while at school and on their way home and to try to see self-similarities as they look outdoors.

In these exercises, students are looking for patterns and practicing the skills of multiplying and dividing fractions, adding and subtracting fractions, using a common denominator, and reducing fractions.

ASSIGNING HOMEWORK

Essential	2–5, 7, 8, 11
Performance assessment	10
Portfolio	5
Journal	6, 8
Group	7, 9, 10
Review	12, 13

▶ Helping with the Exercises

Exercise 1 [Alert] Students may need help finding the denominator for fractional parts of a figure, especially when the figure is not divided into parts of equal size.

Students may still not understand equivalent fractions. Remind them that the value of a fraction does not change if the numerator and the denominator are multiplied or divided by the same number, as in $\frac{1}{4} = \frac{1 \times 4}{4 \times 4} = \frac{4}{16}$.

1c. $\frac{3}{5}$; $\frac{1}{25} + \frac{1}{25} + \frac{1}{25} + \frac{1}{25} + \frac{1}{25} + \frac{1}{25} + \frac{1}{25} + \frac{1}{25} + \frac{1}{25} + \frac{1}{25} + \frac{1}{25} + \frac{1}{25} + \frac{1}{25} + \frac{1}{25} + \frac{1}{25}$ or $15 \times \frac{1}{25}$

1d. $\frac{7}{625}$; $\frac{1}{625} + \frac{1}{625} + \frac{1}{625} + \frac{1}{625} + \frac{1}{625} + \frac{1}{625} + \frac{1}{625}$ or $7 \times \frac{1}{625}$

To add fractions, you need a *common denominator*. Because nine of the smallest triangles (each with area of $\frac{1}{81}$) fit into a triangle with area of $\frac{1}{9}$, you can write $\frac{1}{9}$ as $\frac{9}{81}$. So you can rewrite the combined area as $\frac{9}{81} + \frac{3}{81}$, which equals $\frac{12}{81}$, or $\frac{4}{27}$ in *lowest terms*.

Think of another way to get the same answer. Check your method with a classmate to see if he or she agrees with you.

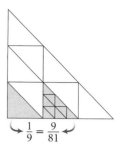

$$\frac{1}{9} = \frac{9}{81}$$

> Notice that you're asked to rework a problem. Check your method and your answer by sharing them with a classmate. Working together is a powerful learning strategy.

Nature
CONNECTION

The smallest leaves of a fern look very similar to the whole fern. This is an example of self-similarity in nature.

In the Sierpiński triangle, the design in any upward-pointing triangle looks just like any other upward-pointing triangle and just like the whole figure—they differ only in size. Objects like this are called **self-similar.** Self-similarity is an important feature of fractals, and you can find many examples of self-similarity in nature.

> This tells you which exercises you'll need a graphing calculator for. You should always have a four-function calculator available as you work the exercises.

EXERCISES

You will need your graphing calculator for Exercises **1, 2,** and **4.**

▶ Practice Your Skills

> If an exercise has an ⓐ, you can find an answer in Selected Answers and Hints at the back of the book. If an exercise has an ⓗ, you'll find a hint.

Do the calculations in Exercises 1 and 2 with paper and pencil. Check your work with a calculator.

> In the Practice Your Skills exercises, you will practice basic skills that you'll need to solve exercises in the Reason and Apply section.

1. Find the total shaded area in each triangle. Write two expressions for each problem, one using addition and the other using multiplication. Assume that the area of each Stage 0 triangle is 1.

a. ⓐ

b.

c.

d. ⓐ

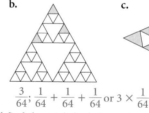 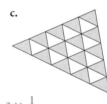 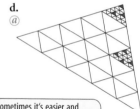

$\frac{1}{8}$; $\frac{1}{16} + \frac{1}{16}$ or $2 \times \frac{1}{16}$ $\frac{3}{64}$; $\frac{1}{64} + \frac{1}{64} + \frac{1}{64}$ or $3 \times \frac{1}{64}$

2. Write an expression and find the total shaded area in each triangle. Assume that the area of each Stage 0 triangle is 1.

> Sometimes it's easier and faster to do a calculation by hand than with a calculator.

a. ⓐ

b.

c. ⓐ

d.

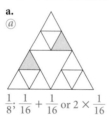 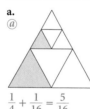 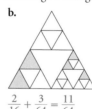 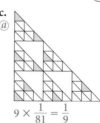 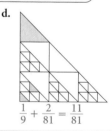

$\frac{1}{4} + \frac{1}{16} = \frac{5}{16}$ $\frac{2}{16} + \frac{3}{64} = \frac{11}{64}$ $9 \times \frac{1}{81} = \frac{1}{9}$ $\frac{1}{9} + \frac{2}{81} = \frac{11}{81}$

3. The first stages of a Sierpiński-like triangle are shown below.

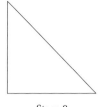 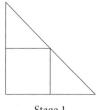 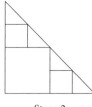 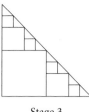

Stage 0　　　　　Stage 1　　　　　Stage 2　　　　　Stage 3

　a. Draw Stage 4 of this pattern. You might find it easiest to start with a triangle that is about 8 cm or 4 in. along the bottom. ⓐ

　b. If the Stage 0 triangle has an area of 64, what is the area of the square at Stage 1? ⓗ　32

　c. At Stage 2, what is the area of the squares combined? ⓐ　48

　d. At Stage 3, what is the area of the squares combined?　56

4. Do each calculation, then check your results with a calculator. Set your calculator to give answers in fraction form.

　a. $\frac{1}{3} + \frac{2}{9}$　$\frac{5}{9}$　　　　**b.** $\frac{3}{4} + \frac{1}{2} + \frac{1}{3}$　$\frac{19}{12}$　　　　**c.** $\frac{2}{5} \times \frac{3}{7}$　$\frac{6}{35}$　　　　**d.** $2 - \frac{4}{9}$

　　　　　　　　　　　　　　　　　　　　　　　　　　　　　　　　　　　　　　　$\frac{14}{9}$ or $1\frac{5}{9}$

▶ Reason and Apply

5. Suppose the area of the original large triangle in the fractal design at right is equal to 1. Copy the figure and shade parts to show each area.

　a. $\frac{1}{4}$　　　　**b.** $\frac{3}{16}$ ⓗ　　　　**c.** $\frac{5}{16}$　　　　**d.** $1 - \frac{7}{16}$

6. You have been introduced to the Sierpiński triangle. What are some aspects of this triangle that make it a fractal?

7. Look at the Sierpiński-like pattern in the squares.

　　Stage 0　　　　　Stage 1　　　　　Stage 2

The exercises in this book may be different from what you're used to. There may be fewer exercises, but you'll probably have to put more time into each one.

　a. Describe in detail the recursive rule used to create this pattern.

　b. Carefully draw the next stage of the pattern.

　c. Suppose the Stage 0 figure represents a square carpet. The new squares drawn at each stage represent holes that have been cut out of the carpet. If the Stage 0 carpet has an area of 1, what is the total area of the holes at Stages 1 to 3?

　d. What is the area of the remaining carpet at each stage?

7a. Sample description: Divide each side of the square into thirds, and connect those points with lines parallel to the sides. A square is formed in the middle. Erase everything except the center square. To get the next stage, do the same thing in all eight squares formed around the middle square.

7b.

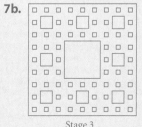

Stage 3

7c. $\frac{1}{9}$; $\frac{17}{81}$; $\frac{217}{729}$　　　　**7d.** $\frac{8}{9}$; $\frac{64}{81}$; $\frac{512}{729}$

Exercise 3 Students can use dot paper or start with edges of length 8 cm or 4 in. to make finding the midpoint easy.

3a.

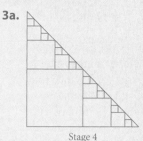

Stage 4

Exercise 4 [Ask] "For which parts of this exercise do you need to find a common denominator?"

5. sample answers:

5a.

5b.

5c.

5d.

6. Answers should include creation by a repetitive process, and smaller parts look like the whole.

Exercise 7a [ELL] Be sure students can use the term *parallel*.
[Alert] Watch for inexact statements here.

[Ask] "If you want to subtract a fraction from 1, what might you change 1 into?" [Any fraction whose numerator equals its denominator is equivalent to 1.]

8. Suppose the area of the original large triangle at right is 8.

  a. Write a division expression to find the area of one of the shaded triangles. What is the area? ⓐ $8 \div 4 = 2$

  b. What fraction of the total area is each shaded triangle? Use this fraction in a multiplication expression to find the area of one of the shaded triangles. ⓐ $8 \times \frac{1}{4} = 2$

  c. What is the difference between dividing by 4 and multiplying by $\frac{1}{4}$? ⓐ

  d. Write a multiplication expression using the fraction $\frac{3}{4}$ to find the combined shaded area. ⓐ $8 \times \frac{3}{4} = 6$

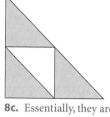

8c. Essentially, they are the same.

9. Suppose the original large triangle below has an area of 12.

9b. sample answers:

$12 \times \frac{9}{16} = 6\frac{3}{4}$;

$(12 \div 16) \times 9 = 6.75$

  a. What fraction of the area is shaded? $\frac{9}{16}$

  b. Find the combined area of the shaded triangles. Write two different expressions you could use to find this area.

10. Suppose the original large triangle at right has an area of 24. $\frac{1}{9}$

  a. What fraction of the area is the shaded triangle at the top? $\frac{1}{81}$

  b. What fraction of the area is each smallest shaded triangle?

  c. What is the total shaded area? Can you find two ways to calculate this area? $11\frac{5}{9}$; $\left(\frac{4}{9} \times 24\right) + \left(\frac{3}{81} \times 24\right)$ or $24 \times \left(\frac{4}{9} + \frac{3}{81}\right)$

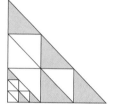

11. Rewrite each expression below using fractions. Then draw a Sierpiński triangle and shade the area described. In each case the Stage 0 triangle has an area of 32.

  a. $\frac{1}{4}$ of $\frac{1}{4}$ of 32 ⓐ $\frac{1}{4} \times \frac{1}{4} \times 32 = \frac{32}{16} = 2$

  b. $\frac{3}{4}$ of $\frac{1}{4}$ of $\frac{1}{4}$ of 32

  c. $\frac{1}{2}$ of $\frac{1}{2}$ of $\frac{1}{4}$ of 32 $\frac{1}{2} \times \frac{1}{2} \times \frac{1}{4} \times 32 = \frac{32}{16} = 2$

> You may need to refer back to examples or to work you did in an investigation as you work on an exercise.

▶ Review

12. Assume the area of your desktop equals 1. Your math book covers $\frac{1}{4}$ of your desktop, your calculator covers $\frac{1}{16}$ of your desktop, and your scrap paper covers $\frac{1}{32}$ of your desktop. What total area is covered by these objects? Write an addition expression and then give your answer as a single fraction in lowest terms. ⓗ $\frac{1}{4} + \frac{1}{16} + \frac{1}{32} = \frac{11}{32}$

13. Use the information from Exercise 12 to find the area of your desk that is *not* covered by these materials. Write a subtraction expression and then give your answer as a single fraction in lowest terms. $1 - \frac{11}{32} = \frac{21}{32}$

More and More

Did you notice that at each stage of a Sierpiński design, you have more to draw than in the previous stage? The new parts get smaller, but the number of them increases quickly. Let's examine these patterns more closely.

A strong positive mental attitude will create more miracles than any wonder drug.

PATRICIA NEAL

 ## Investigation
How Many?

Explore how quickly the number of new triangles grows using multiplication repeatedly. Look for a pattern to help you *predict* the number of new triangles at each stage without counting them.

Stage 0 Stage 1 Stage 2 Stage 3 Stage 4

Step 1 Look at the fractal designs. Count the number of new upward-pointing triangles for Stages 0 to 4. Make a table like this to record your work. 1; 3; 9; 27; 81

Stage	Number of new upward-pointing triangles
0	1
1	

 Throughout this course you'll record results in a table. Tables provide a useful way to keep track of your work and see patterns develop.

Step 2 How does the number of new triangles compare to the number of new triangles at the previous stage? Each time the stage is increased by 1, the number of triangles is multiplied by 3.

Step 3 Using your answer to Step 2, find how many new upward-pointing triangles are at Stages 5, 6, and 7. 243; 729; 2187

Step 4 Explain how you could find the number of upward-pointing triangles at Stage 15 without counting. Use the answer for Stage 7, that is, 2187, and multiply it by 3 eight times.

At each stage, three new upward-pointing triangles are drawn in each of the upward-pointing triangles from the previous stage. How is this the same as repeatedly multiplying by 3? At each stage, there are 3 times the number of new upward-pointing triangles as at the previous stage.

NCTM STANDARDS

CONTENT		PROCESS	
✔	Number	✔	Problem Solving
	Algebra	✔	Reasoning
✔	Geometry	✔	Communication
	Measurement	✔	Connections
	Data/Probability	✔	Representation

LESSON OBJECTIVES

- Review the repeated multiplication model for exponents
- Learn a precise definition of *exponent*
- Generalize a growth pattern into a symbolic expression involving exponents

---

PLANNING

LESSON OUTLINE

One day:

10 min	Introduction
20 min	Investigation, Sharing
5 min	Example
5 min	Closing
10 min	Exercises

MATERIALS

- How Many? (T)
- Calculator Note 0B

TEACHING

In this lesson students use exponents to model the rapidly changing numbers and sizes of parts between one stage of a fractal design and the next.

Guiding the Investigation

Once students are in their groups, put up the How Many? transparency. Remind the class of the meanings of *recursive procedure* and *fractal*, and elicit the idea that the number of parts in the Sierpiński triangle increases rapidly from one stage to the next.

One Step

[Ask] "How many upward-pointing triangles will Stage 15 have?" As you visit groups, remind students of exponential notation as needed and help them enter exponents on their calculators. If some students are proficient with the calculator, encourage peer teaching.

Step 1 Request that a few students show you how they found the numbers in their tables.

Step 2 Make sure students notice the word *new*.

Step 3 **[Ask]** "Why is the number being multiplied by 3 each time?" One answer is below Step 4 in the text.

SHARING IDEAS

While visiting groups, ask one student to copy onto a transparency the group's table from Step 1. Select other students to share their approaches to Steps 2 and 4. During reporting time, encourage participation, but probe for explanations. Ask for a correct definition of *exponent*. Ask why exponents are useful to elicit the point that they reduce writing when a single number is being multiplied many times.

Assessing Progress

As you watch students contribute to groups or to the whole class, look for understanding of multiplication and the symbols used to indicate multiplication as well as ideas that were new in the previous lesson: recursive procedure, fractal, Sierpiński triangle, congruent figures, and order of operations.

EXAMPLE

[Language] The term *exponent* is defined in the student text, but some students may be more familiar with the expression *raising a number to a power*.

The example leads into a discussion of exponents. Call students' attention to the picture and question in the text.

Model good mathematical language to help students learn what terms mean. For example, use the word *factor* in context. Point out how the text answers your earlier question about a correct definition of *exponent* by saying that the

You can write the symbol for multiplication in different ways. For example, you can write 3×3 as $3 \cdot 3$ or $(3)(3)$ or $3(3)$. All of these expressions have the same meaning. Each expression equals 9.

EXAMPLE | Describe how the number of new upward-pointing triangles is growing in this fractal.

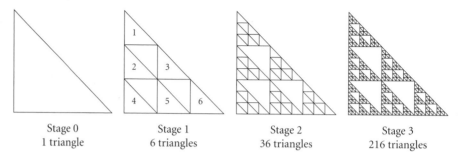

| Stage 0 | Stage 1 | Stage 2 | Stage 3 |
| 1 triangle | 6 triangles | 36 triangles | 216 triangles |

▶ **Solution** | At Stage 1, the six new upward-pointing triangles are numbered. At Stage 2, six new upward-pointing triangles are formed in each numbered Stage 1 triangle. At Stage 2, there are $6 \cdot 6$ or 36 new triangles. At Stage 3, six triangles are formed in each new upward-pointing Stage 2 triangle, so there are $36 \cdot 6$ or 216 new upward-pointing triangles.

Another way to look at the number of new upward-pointing triangles at each stage is shown in the table below.

Stage number	Number of new upward-pointing triangles		
	Total	Repeated multiplication	Exponent form
1	6	6	6^1
2	36	$6 \cdot 6$	6^2
3	216	$36 \cdot 6$ or $6 \cdot 6 \cdot 6$	6^3

The last number in each row of the table is a 6 followed by a small raised number. The small number, called an **exponent,** shows how many 6's are multiplied together. An exponent shows the number of times that 6 is a **factor.** What is the pattern between the stage number and the exponent?

Do you think the pattern applies to Stage 0? Put the number 6^0 into your calculator. [▶☐ See **Calculator Note 0B** to learn how to enter exponents. ◀] Does the result fit the pattern?

How many upward-pointing triangles are there at Stage 4? According to the pattern, there should be 6^4. That's 1296 triangles! It is a lot easier to use the exponent pattern than to count all those triangles.

exponent tells "how many 6's are multiplied together." **[Alert]** The phrase "how many times you multiply a number by itself" is not strictly correct; 6^2 is not 6 multiplied by itself twice.

As part of the fractal design development, students are introduced to the concept of zero as an exponent. Detailed coverage of zero and negative exponents appears in Chapter 6.

Closing the Lesson

Remind students of the main ideas of this lesson. Numbers being multiplied together are **factors.** An **exponent** is a raised number that tells how many times a number is used as a factor.

[Ask] "Why are exponents useful?" [They save a lot of multiplication and writing when the triangles become complicated.]

EXERCISES

You will need your graphing calculator for Exercise **4.**

▶ Practice Your Skills

1. Write each multiplication expression in exponent form.

a. $5 \times 5 \times 5 \times 5$ @ 5^4 **b.** $7 \times 7 \times 7 \times 7 \times 7$ 7^5

c. $3 \cdot 3 \cdot 3 \cdot 3 \cdot 3 \cdot 3 \cdot 3$ 3^7 **d.** $2(2)(2)$ 2^3

2. Rewrite each expression as a repeated multiplication in three ways: using $\times$, $\cdot$, and parentheses.

a. 3^4 @   **b.** 5^6 **c.** $\left(\frac{1}{2}\right)^3$

3. Write each number with an exponent other than 1. For example, $125 = 5^3$.

a. 27 @ 3^3 **b.** 32 2^5 **c.** 625 5^4 **d.** 343 7^3

4. Do the calculations. Check your results with a calculator.

a. $\frac{2}{3} \cdot 12$ 8   **b.** $\frac{1}{3} + \frac{3}{5}$ $\frac{14}{15}$ **c.** $\frac{3}{4} - \frac{1}{8}$ $\frac{5}{8}$

d. $5 - \frac{2}{7}$ $\frac{33}{7}$ or $4\frac{5}{7}$ **e.** $\frac{1}{4} \cdot \frac{1}{4} \cdot 8$ $\frac{1}{2}$ **f.** $\frac{3}{64} + \frac{3}{16} + \frac{3}{4}$ $\frac{63}{64}$

▶ Reason and Apply

5. Another type of fractal drawing is called a "tree." Study Stages 0 to 3 of this tree:

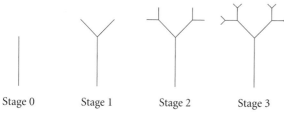

Stage 0   Stage 1   Stage 2   Stage 3

> Homework helps you reinforce what you've learned in the lesson and develops your understanding of new ideas.

a. At Stage 1, two new branches are growing from the trunk. How many new branches are there at Stage 2? At Stage 3? 4 or 2^2; 8 or 2^3

b. How many new branches are there at Stage 5? Write your answer in exponent form. 2^5

6. Another fractal tree pattern is shown below.

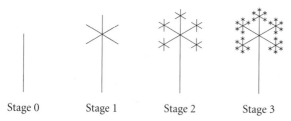

Stage 0   Stage 1   Stage 2   Stage 3

a. At Stage 1, five new branches are growing. How many new branches are there at Stage 2? @ 25 or 5^2

2a. $3 \times 3 \times 3 \times 3$; $3 \cdot 3 \cdot 3 \cdot 3$; $3(3)(3)(3)$

2b. $5 \times 5 \times 5 \times 5 \times 5 \times 5$; $5 \cdot 5 \cdot 5 \cdot 5 \cdot 5 \cdot 5$; $5(5)(5)(5)(5)(5)$

2c. $\frac{1}{2} \times \frac{1}{2} \times \frac{1}{2}$; $\frac{1}{2} \cdot \frac{1}{2} \cdot \frac{1}{2}$; $\frac{1}{2}\left(\frac{1}{2}\right)\left(\frac{1}{2}\right)$

To help make the idea of self-similarity more real to students, you might request that students bring in a self-similar object from nature or a written description of a self-similar object other than a fractal.

b. How many new branches are there at Stage 3? 125 or 5^3

c. How many new branches are there at Stage 5? Write your answer in exponent form. 5^5

7. At Stage 1 of this pattern, there is one square hole. At Stage 2, there are eight new square holes.

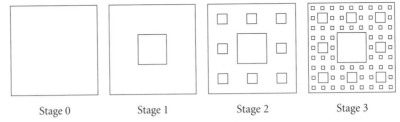

Stage 0   Stage 1   Stage 2   Stage 3

a. How many new square holes are there at Stage 3? 64

b. If you drew the Stage 4 figure, how many new square holes would you have to draw? 512

c. Write the answers to 7a and b in exponent form. ⓐ 8^2; 8^3

d. How many new square holes would you have to draw in the Stage 7 figure? 262,144 or 8^6

e. Describe the relationship between the stage number and the exponent for these figures. The exponent is always one less than the stage number.

f. Will the pattern you described in 7e work for the Stage 1 figure? Why or why not?
yes; because $8^0 = 1$

8. Study Stages 0 to 3 of this fractal "weed" pattern. At Stage 1, two new branches are created.

Stage 0   Stage 1   Stage 2   Stage 3

a. How many new branches are created at Stage 2? ⓐ10

b. How many new branches are created at Stage 3? 50

c. You can write the expression $2 \cdot 5^1$ to represent the number of new branches in the Stage 2 figure. Write similar expressions to represent the number of new branches in Stages 3 to 5.

d. How do the 2 and the 5 in each expression relate to the figure? ⓗ

Patterns like the "weed" in Exercise 8 can be used to create very realistic computer-generated plants, like the "seaweed" shown here. Graphic designers can use fractal routines to create realistic-looking trees and other natural features.

8c. Stage 3: $2 \cdot 5^2$; Stage 4: $2 \cdot 5^3$; Stage 5: $2 \cdot 5^4$

8d. The 2 is the number of new branches at Stage 1. The 5 is the number of smaller segments created in Stage 1. At each subsequent stage, new branches are added by multiplying by 5 again.

12   CHAPTER 0 Fractions and Fractals

9. Look again at this familiar fractal design.

     Stage 0   Stage 1   Stage 2   Stage 3

a. Make a table like this to calculate and record the area of one shaded triangle in each figure.

Stage number	Area of one shaded triangle	Total area of the shaded triangles
0	1	1
1		

b. Record the combined shaded area of each figure in your table.

c. Describe at least two patterns you discovered.

▶ Review

10. Ethan deposits $2 in a bank account on the first day, $4 on the second day, and $8 on the third day. He will continue to double the deposit each day. How much will he deposit on the eighth day? Write your answer as repeated multiplication separated by dots, in exponent form, and as a single number.
$2 \cdot 2 \cdot 2 \cdot 2 \cdot 2 \cdot 2 \cdot 2 \cdot 2 = 2^8 = 256$ or $256

11. Write a word problem that illustrates $\frac{3}{4} \cdot \frac{1}{5}$, and find the answer.

12. The large triangles below each have an area of 1. Find the total shaded area in each.

a.

$\frac{21}{64}$

b.
ⓐ

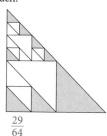

$\frac{29}{64}$

9b.

Stage	One triangle	Total area of the shaded triangles
1	$\frac{1}{4}$	$\frac{3}{4}$
2	$\frac{1}{16}$	$9 \cdot \frac{1}{16}$ or $\frac{3}{4} \cdot \frac{3}{4} = \frac{9}{16}$
3	$\frac{1}{64}$	$\frac{3}{4} \cdot \frac{9}{16} = \frac{27}{64}$

9c. The area of one shaded triangle is $\frac{1}{4}$ the area of one of the previous shaded triangles. The total area of the shaded triangles in each figure is $\frac{3}{4}$ the shaded area in the previous figure.

11. One possibility: The restaurant had $\frac{3}{4}$ of a pie left. Five people wanted pie. After cutting the pie into fifths, how much of the pie did each person get? $\frac{3}{20}$

LESSON

0.3

Shorter yet Longer

In fractals like the Sierpiński triangle, new enclosed shapes are formed at each stage. Not all fractals are formed this way. One example is the *Koch curve*, which is not a smooth curve, but a set of connected line segments. It was introduced in 1906 by the Swedish mathematician Niels Fabian Helge von Koch. As you explore the Koch curve, you'll continue to work with exponents.

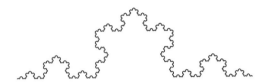

The number of distinct scales of length of natural patterns is for all practical purposes infinite.

BENOIT MANDELBROT

PLANNING

LESSON OUTLINE

One day:

25 min Investigation

10 min Sharing

5 min Closing

10 min Exercises

MATERIALS

- How Long Is This Fractal? (T), *optional*
- How Long Is This Fractal? (W), *optional*
- Calculator Note 0B
- Sketchpad demonstration Fractal Length, *optional*

TEACHING

In this lesson the familiar idea of perimeter is extended to include the perimeter of a fractal.

 Guiding the Investigation

The Sketchpad demonstration Fractal Length can be used as a replacement or a supplement to the investigation.

Display the How Long Is This Fractal? transparency.

Remind the class that fractals are useful in describing nature, especially irregular shapes such as coastlines. Point out three stages in the generation of the Koch curve, so-named for its inventor. (See page 1A for pronunciation of Koch.) Mathematicians of the early 1900s extended the notion of a curve to shapes like the Koch curve as they searched for one-dimensional figures that had unusual properties such as having a sharp turn at every point.

Investigation
How Long Is This Fractal?

Study how the Koch curve develops. One way to discover a fractal's recursive rule is to determine what happens from Stage 0 to Stage 1. Once you know the rule, you can build, or generate, later stages of the figure.

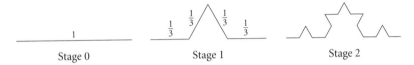

Stage 0   Stage 1   Stage 2

Step 1 | Make and complete a table like this for Stages 0 to 2 of the Koch curve shown. How do the lengths change from stage to stage? If you don't see a pattern, try writing the total lengths in different forms.

Stage number	Number of segments	Length of each segment	Total length (Number of segments times length of segments)	
			Fraction form	Decimal form
0	1	1	1	1
1	4	$\frac{1}{3}$	$\frac{4}{3}$	1.33
2	16	$\frac{1}{9}$	$\frac{16}{9}$	1.78

Look at Stages 0 and 1. Describe the curve's recursive rule so that someone could re-create the curve from your description.

Predict the total length at Stage 3.
Good estimate: "more than 2."
Find the length of each small segment at Stage 3 and the total length of the Stage 3 figure.

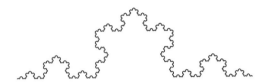

Stage 3

Use exponents to rewrite your numbers in the column labeled "Total length, Fraction form" for Stages 0 to 3. $1; \frac{4^1}{3^1}; \frac{4^2}{3^2}; \frac{4^3}{3^3}$

Step 2 Remove the middle third of each segment, then create the other two sides of an equilateral triangle that would have that removed segment as a base. **Step 2**

Step 3

Step 4 At Stage 3, there **Step 4** are 64 segments. Each segment has length $\frac{1}{27}$, so the total length **Step 5** is $\frac{64}{27}$ or about 2.37.

One Step

[Ask] "What's the total length of the Koch curve at Stage 4?" After students have produced satisfactory results, you might ask a similar question about Stage 17 of the fractal in the example.

Step 1 Students might change all improper fractions to mixed numbers. Suggest that the improper forms often make it easier to see patterns. If necessary, point out that though the individual pieces get shorter, the total length increases.

LESSON OBJECTIVES

- Practice multiplication of fractions
- Extend exponent concepts to include fractions as bases
- Learn the concept of a curve created from line segments
- Think about confined infinity to gain an informal intuition about the concept of limit

| Step 6 | Predict the Stage 4 lengths. *Predictions will vary. Actual length is $\frac{4^4}{3^4}$ or $\frac{256}{81}$.* |
| Step 7 | Koch was attempting to create a "curve" that was nothing but corners. Do you think he succeeded? If the curve is formed recursively for many stages, what would happen to its length? *Answers will vary. Students should notice that the length continues to increase.* |

At later stages the Koch curve looks smoother and smoother. But, if you magnify a section at a later stage, it is just as jagged as at Stage 1. Mandelbrot named these figures *fractals* based on the Latin word *fractus,* meaning broken or irregular.

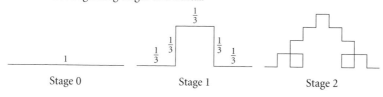

EXAMPLE

Look at these beginning stages of a fractal:

$$\text{Stage 0} \qquad \text{Stage 1} \qquad \text{Stage 2}$$

a. Describe the fractal's recursive rule.

b. Find its length at Stage 2.

c. Write an expression for its length at Stage 17.

[▶ See the next few stages of this fractal using the **Dynamic Algebra Exploration** at **www.keymath.com/DA** .◀]

When you see this icon, check out the Dynamic Algebra Explorations at **www.keymath.com/DA** These will help you look at mathematical ideas in a new or different way.

keymath.com/DA

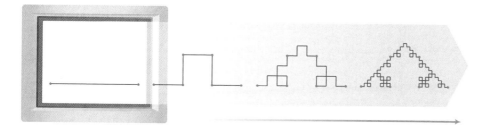

Step 5 Point out that exponents mean repeated multiplication, whether the base is a fraction or an integer. Students may wonder why multiplying by fractions is giving larger results. Remind them that now they are multiplying by fractions larger than 1.

Step 6 Challenge students who are finding this exploration easy to write an expression for Stage 17 lengths. If all students can do this, you need not work through the example later.

SHARING IDEAS

A student with a good table in Step 1 might prepare a transparency for presentation, to be added to by a student with a good answer to Step 5. An imprecisely stated rule in Step 2 might help illustrate the amount of care needed in stating such rules. Someone could then show an answer to Step 6, and you could encourage students to develop their ideas about the questions in Step 7.

Ask students where else they've seen exponents used. They might mention units such as ft^2 on signs for office space, or scientific notation, which will come up in Chapter 6.

Encourage discussion about the paradoxical notion that the perimeter increases while the rectangular space containing the curve does not.

Assessing Progress
While watching students contribute to groups or to the whole class, note which students seem most and least comfortable with the principal ideas reviewed in this lesson: fraction multiplication and exponents representing repeated multiplication.

Refer students to the picture and questions in the text. **[Ask]** "What's another way to express the recursive rule given in the first part of the solution?" [The rule could be improved; it doesn't say whether the square goes out or in.]

You might use the term *for each* in the replacement: For each segment of the previous stage, there are five new segments, so you multiply the number of segments by 5. **[Link]** Students will use *for each* and multiplication when applying the *counting principle* in Chapter 10. (If for each of m ways of accomplishing a task there are n ways of accomplishing another task, then there are m times n ways of accomplishing the two tasks.)

Closing the Lesson

Briefly say something about each new mathematical idea. A Koch curve can be generated from a line segment by a recursive rule. The changing lengths of the curves can be represented by exponents on fractions.

▶ **Solution**

Don't forget to think through the solution and answer any questions.

a. You compare Stage 0 and Stage 1 to get the recursive rule. To get Stage 1, you divide the Stage 0 segment into thirds. Build a square on the middle third and remove the bottom. So the recursive rule is "To get to the next stage, divide each segment from the previous stage into thirds and build a bottomless square on the middle third."

b. To find the length of the fractal at Stage 2, you'll start by looking at its length at Stage 1. The Stage 1 figure has 5 segments. Each segment is $\frac{1}{3}$ long. So the total length at Stage 1 is $5 \cdot \frac{1}{3}$. You can rewrite this as $\frac{5}{3}$.

At Stage 2, you replace each of the five Stage 1 segments with five new segments. So the Stage 2 figure has $5 \cdot 5$, or 5^2 segments.

Each Stage 1 segment is $\frac{1}{3}$ long, and each Stage 2 segment is $\frac{1}{3}$ of that. So each Stage 2 segment is $\frac{1}{3} \cdot \frac{1}{3}$, or $\left(\frac{1}{3}\right)^2$ long.

So at Stage 2 there are 5^2 segments, each $\left(\frac{1}{3}\right)^2$ long. The total length at Stage 2 is $5^2 \cdot \left(\frac{1}{3}\right)^2$. You can rewrite this as $\left(\frac{5}{3}\right)^2$.

c. Do you see the connection between the stage number and the exponent? At each stage, you replace every segment from the previous stage with five new segments. The length of each new segment is $\frac{1}{3}$ the length of a segment at the previous stage. By Stage 17, you've done this 17 times. The Stage 17 figure is $\left(\frac{5}{3}\right)^{17}$ long.

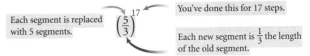

Each segment is replaced with 5 segments.

You've done this for 17 steps.

Each new segment is $\frac{1}{3}$ the length of the old segment.

To compare total lengths, it's often easiest to express each length as a decimal rounded to the hundreds place.

Stage number	Number of segments	Length of each segment	Total length (Number of segments times length of segments)	
			Fraction form	Decimal form
0	1	1	$1 \cdot 1$	1.00
1	$1 \cdot 5 = 5^1$	$1 \cdot \frac{1}{3} = \left(\frac{1}{3}\right)^1$	$5^1 \cdot \left(\frac{1}{3}\right)^1 = \left(\frac{5}{3}\right)^1$	1.67
2	$5 \cdot 5 = 5^2$	$\frac{1}{3} \cdot \frac{1}{3} = \left(\frac{1}{3}\right)^2$	$5^2 \cdot \left(\frac{1}{3}\right)^2 = \left(\frac{5}{3}\right)^2$	2.78
⋮	⋮	⋮	⋮	⋮
17	5^{17}	$\left(\frac{1}{3}\right)^{17}$	$5^{17} \cdot \left(\frac{1}{3}\right)^{17} = \left(\frac{5}{3}\right)^{17}$	5907.84

You will need your graphing calculator for Exercises **1, 3, 4, 5, 6, 7,** and **8.**

Practice Your Skills

1. Evaluate each expression. Write your answer as a fraction and as a decimal, rounded to the nearest hundredth. Remember, if the third digit to the right of the decimal is 5 or higher, round up.

a. $\dfrac{5^3}{2^3}$ $\dfrac{125}{8}$; 15.63   **b.** $\left(\dfrac{5}{3}\right)^2$ @ $\dfrac{25}{9}$; 2.78   **c.** $\left(\dfrac{7}{3}\right)^4$ $\dfrac{2401}{81}$; 29.64   **d.** $\left(\dfrac{9}{4}\right)^3$ $\dfrac{729}{64}$; 11.39

2. The fractal from the example is shown below. How much longer is the figure at Stage 2 than at Stage 1? Using the table on the previous page, find your answer as a fraction and as a decimal rounded to the nearest hundredth. $\dfrac{5^2}{3^2} - \dfrac{5}{3} = \dfrac{10}{9}$ or $2.78 - 1.67 = 1.11$

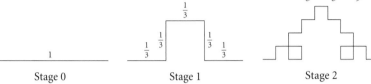

Stage 0   Stage 1   Stage 2

3. At what stage does the figure above first exceed a length of 10? $\left(\dfrac{5}{3}\right)^4 \approx 7.72$; $\left(\dfrac{5}{3}\right)^5 \approx 12.86$; Stage 5

4. Evaluate each expression and check your results with a calculator.

a. $\dfrac{1}{5} + \dfrac{3}{4}$ $\dfrac{19}{20}$ **b.** $3^2 + 2^4$ 25   **c.** $\dfrac{2}{3} \cdot \left(\dfrac{6}{5}\right)^2$ $\dfrac{72}{75}$ or $\dfrac{24}{25}$ **d.** $4^3 - \dfrac{2}{5}$ $\dfrac{318}{5}$ or $63\dfrac{3}{5}$

Reason and Apply

5. The Stage 0 figure below has a length of 1. At Stage 1, each segment has a length of $\dfrac{1}{4}$.

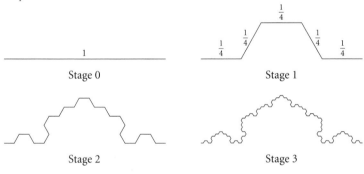

Stage 0   Stage 1

Stage 2   Stage 3

a. Complete a table like the one on the next page by calculating the lengths of the figure at Stages 2 and 3. Give each answer as a fraction in multiplication form, as a fraction in exponent form, and as a decimal rounded to the nearest hundredth. Try to figure out the total lengths at Stages 2 and 3 without counting. ⓗ

5b. Stage 5: $\left(\frac{5}{4}\right)^5 \approx 3.05$;

Stage 11: $\left(\frac{5}{4}\right)^{11} \approx 11.64$

Exercise 6 [Alert] Watch for difficulties in handling exponents and fraction reduction at the same time. Suggest that it's easier to use exponents with smaller numbers than with larger ones, so it's usually better to do fraction reduction before exponentiation.

b. Which is the first stage to have a length greater than 3? A length greater than 10?

Stage number	Total length		
	Multiplication form	**Exponent form**	**Decimal form**
0	1	1^0	1
1	$5 \cdot \frac{1}{4} = \frac{5}{4}$	$\left(\frac{5}{4}\right)^1$	1.25
2	$5 \cdot 5 \cdot \frac{1}{4} \cdot \frac{1}{4} = \frac{25}{16}$	$5^2 \cdot \left(\frac{1}{4}\right)^2 = \left(\frac{5}{4}\right)^2$	1.56
3	$5 \cdot 5 \cdot 5 \cdot \frac{1}{4} \cdot \frac{1}{4} \cdot \frac{1}{4} = \frac{125}{64}$	$5^3 \cdot \left(\frac{1}{4}\right)^3 = \left(\frac{5}{4}\right)^3$	1.95

6. The Stage 0 figure below has a length of 1.

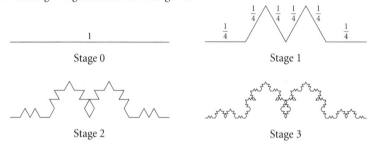

Stage 0   Stage 1

Stage 2   Stage 3

a. Complete a table like the one below by calculating the total length of the figure at each stage shown above. Give each answer as a fraction in multiplication form, as a fraction in exponent form, and as a decimal rounded to the nearest hundredth.

Stage number	Total length		
	Multiplication form	**Exponent form**	**Decimal form**
0	1	1^0	1
1	$6 \cdot \frac{1}{4} = \frac{6}{4} = \frac{3}{2}$	$6^1 \cdot \left(\frac{1}{4}\right)^1 = \left(\frac{6}{4}\right)^1 = \left(\frac{3}{2}\right)^1$	1.5
2	$6 \cdot 6 \cdot \frac{1}{4} \cdot \frac{1}{4} = \frac{36}{16} = \frac{9}{4}$	$6^2 \cdot \left(\frac{1}{4}\right)^2 = \left(\frac{6}{4}\right)^2 = \left(\frac{3}{2}\right)^2$	2.25
3	$6 \cdot 6 \cdot 6 \cdot \frac{1}{4} \cdot \frac{1}{4} \cdot \frac{1}{4}$ $= \frac{216}{64} = \frac{27}{8}$	$6^3 \cdot \left(\frac{1}{4}\right)^3 = \left(\frac{6}{4}\right)^3 = \left(\frac{3}{2}\right)^3$	3.38

b. At what stage does the figure have a length of $\frac{243}{32}$?   Stage 5

c. At what stage is the length closest to 100?   Stage 11: $\left(\frac{6}{4}\right)^{11} \approx 86.50$

7. The Stage 0 figure below has a length of 1.

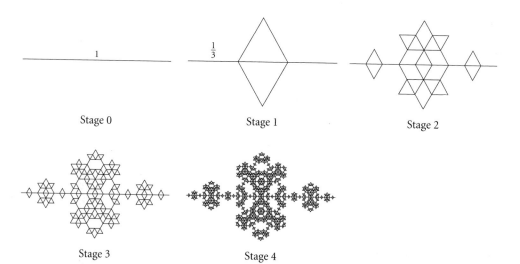

Stage 0   Stage 1   Stage 2

Stage 3   Stage 4

a. Complete a table like the one below by calculating the total length of each stage. Give each answer as a fraction in multiplication form, as a fraction in exponent form, and as a decimal number rounded to the nearest hundredth. Figure out the lengths of Stages 3 and 4 without counting.

Stage number	Total length		
	Multiplication form	Exponent form	Decimal form
0	1	1^0	1
1	$7 \cdot \frac{1}{3} = \frac{7}{3}$	$7^1 \cdot \left(\frac{1}{3}\right)^1 = \left(\frac{7}{3}\right)^1$	2.33
2	$7 \cdot 7 \cdot \frac{1}{3} \cdot \frac{1}{3} = \frac{49}{9}$	$7^2 \cdot \left(\frac{1}{3}\right)^2 = \left(\frac{7}{3}\right)^2$	5.44
3	$7 \cdot 7 \cdot 7 \cdot \frac{1}{3} \cdot \frac{1}{3} \cdot \frac{1}{3} = \frac{343}{27}$	$7^3 \cdot \left(\frac{1}{3}\right)^3 = \left(\frac{7}{3}\right)^3$	12.70
4	$7 \cdot 7 \cdot 7 \cdot 7 \cdot \frac{1}{3} \cdot \frac{1}{3} \cdot \frac{1}{3} \cdot \frac{1}{3} = \frac{2401}{81}$	$7^4 \cdot \left(\frac{1}{3}\right)^4 = \left(\frac{7}{3}\right)^4$	29.64

b. At what stage does the figure have a length of $\frac{16,807}{243}$?   Stage 5

c. Will the figure ever have a length of 168? If so, at what stage? If not, why not?

No; Stage 6 has a length of slightly more than 161, and Stage 7 has a length of over 376.

8. The figures below look a little more complicated than others you have seen because parts overlap. The Stage 0 figure has a length of 1.

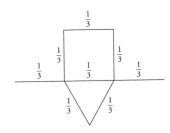

_____
1

Stage 0

Stage 1

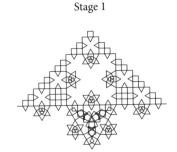

Stage 2

Stage 3

a. Complete a table like the one below by calculating the total length of the Stage 2 and Stage 3 figures shown above.

Stage number	Total length		
	Multiplication form	**Exponent form**	**Decimal form**
0	1	1^0	1
1	$8 \cdot \frac{1}{3} = \frac{8}{3}$	$8^1 \cdot \left(\frac{1}{3}\right)^1 = \left(\frac{8}{3}\right)^1$	2.67
2	$8 \cdot 8 \cdot \frac{1}{3} \cdot \frac{1}{3} = \frac{64}{9}$	$8^2 \cdot \left(\frac{1}{3}\right)^2 = \left(\frac{8}{3}\right)^2$	7.11
3	$8 \cdot 8 \cdot 8 \cdot \frac{1}{3} \cdot \frac{1}{3} \cdot \frac{1}{3} = \frac{512}{27}$	$8^3 \cdot \left(\frac{1}{3}\right)^3 = \left(\frac{8}{3}\right)^3$	18.96

b. Look at how the lengths of the figures grow with each stage. Estimate how long the length will be at Stage 4. Then calculate this value. Estimates will vary; $\left(\frac{8}{3}\right)^4$ or about 50.

c. At what stage does your calculator begin to use a different notation for the length? After 23 stages, many calculators resort to scientific notation or get an overflow error.

▶ **Review**

> Whenever possible it's a good idea to try to estimate your answer before calculating it. Estimating will help you determine whether your calculated answer is reasonable.

9. Write $\frac{14}{5}$ as a decimal. 2.8

10. What is $\frac{8}{3} - \frac{4}{9} \cdot \frac{3}{1}$? $\frac{4}{3}$, or $1\frac{1}{3}$

11. Look at the fractal "cross" pattern below. At each stage, new line segments are drawn through the existing segments to create crosses.

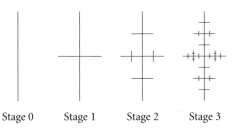

Stage 0   Stage 1   Stage 2   Stage 3

    a. How many new segments are drawn at Stage 2? @   4

    b. How many new segments are drawn at Stage 3?   16

    c. How many new segments would be drawn at Stage 4?   64

    d. Use exponents to represent the number of new segments drawn at Stages 2 to 4. $4^1, 4^2, 4^3$

    e. In general, how is the exponent related to the stage number for Stages 2 to 4? Does this rule apply to Stage 1?   The exponent is 1 less than the stage number; for Stage 1, $4^0 = 1$.

INVENT A FRACTAL!

Recursive procedures can produce surprising and even beautiful results. Consider these two fractals. (The top one was "invented" by student Andrew Riley!) Would you have expected that the Stage 1 figures would lead to the higher-stage figures?

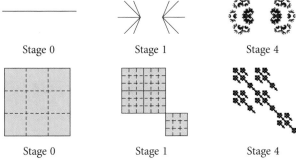

Stage 0   Stage 1   Stage 4

Stage 0   Stage 1   Stage 4

Invent your own fractal. You can start with a line segment, as in the Koch curve or Andrew's fractal. Or try a two-dimensional shape like Stage 0 of the Sierpiński triangle or the square in the "kite" above. Your project should include

▶ A drawing of your fractal at Stages 0, 1, 2, and 3 (and possibly higher).

▶ A written description of the recursive rule that generates the fractal.

▶ A table that shows how one aspect of the figure changes. Consider area, length, or the number of holes or branches at each stage.

▶ A written explanation of how to continue your table for higher stages.

> **THE GEOMETER'S SKETCHPAD**
>
> The Geometer's Sketchpad® was used to create these fractals. Sketchpad™ has several tools to help you create fractals. With Sketchpad, you can quickly and easily create the Sierpiński triangle, the Koch curve, and more. Learn how to use Sketchpad and create your own fractals!

Supporting the project

MOTIVATION

To pique student interest, ask "What recursive rule did Andrew Riley use to create his fractal?" (See the side column for a complete description of Riley's process.)

OUTCOMES

▶ The written description is sufficient to produce the fractal illustrated.

▶ The table clearly shows how one aspect of the figure changes at each stage.

▶ The student uses correct mathematical language to explain how to continue the table.

• The student extends the fractal and table to stages beyond Stage 3.

Invent a Fractal! Project

This is the recursive process that created the first fractal pattern:

Divide a segment into thirds and remove the middle third. Call the four endpoints 1, 2, 3, and 4.

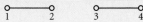

Rotate point 1 about point 2 by 45° and −45° and then rotate point 2 about point 1 by 45° and −45°. Do the same operations on the segment joining points 3 and 4.

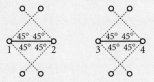

Now draw segments between point 2 and the four newly created points above and below it, and between point 3 and the four newly created points above and below it.

Then repeat the process on each of the ten segments above.

For instructions on how to create fractals, see *Exploring Geometry with The Geometer's Sketchpad.*

Going Somewhere?

Leslie was playing miniature golf with her friends. First she hit the ball past the hole. Then she hit it back, but it went too far and missed again. She kept hitting the ball closer, but it still missed the hole. Finally she got so close that the ball fell in.

Some number processes also get closer and closer to a final target, until the result is so close that the number rounds off to the target value or answer. You'll explore processes like these while reviewing operations with positive and negative numbers.

Investigation
A Strange Attraction

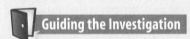

keymath.com/DA

Step 1 Each member of your group takes one of these four expressions.

$$2 \cdot \Box + 1 \qquad 3 \cdot \Box - 4 \qquad -2 \cdot \Box + 3 \qquad -3 \cdot \Box - 1$$

Step 2 As a group, choose a starting number. Record your expression and starting number in a table like the one shown.

Original expression:		
Starting number (at Stage 0):		
Stage number	Input	Result
1		

Step 3 Put your starting number in the box, and do the computation. This process is called **evaluating the expression,** and the result is the **value of the expression.** Be sure to follow the order of operations. Check your answer with a calculator, and record it in the table as your first result. [▶ ▢ See **Calculator Note 0C** to learn about the difference between the negative key and the subtraction key. ◀]

Step 4 Take the result you got from Step 3, put it in the box in your expression, and evaluate your expression again. Place your new answer in the table as your second result.

Step 5 Continue this recursive process using your result from the previous stage. Evaluate your expression. Each time, record the new result in your table. Do this ten times.

Step 6 | Draw a number line and scale it so that you can show the first five results from your table. Plot the first result from your table, and draw an arrow to the next result to show how the value of the expression changes. For example,

Step 7 | How do the results in your group compare?

Step 8 | Repeat Steps 1 to 6 with one of the expressions below.

$$0.5 \cdot \square - 3 \qquad 0.2 \cdot \square + 1 \qquad -0.5 \cdot \square + 3 \qquad -0.2 \cdot \square - 2$$

Step 9 | How do the results in your group compare? Do the results of these expressions differ from the results of your first expression? Students starting with the same expression will see that it tends toward the same specific value: -6, 1.25, 2, and $-\frac{5}{3}$, respectively.

In this investigation you explored what happens when you recursively evaluate an expression. First you selected a starting number to put into your expression, then you evaluated it. Then you put your result back into the same expression and evaluated it again. Calculators, like computers, are good tools for doing these repetitive operations.

EXAMPLE A | What happens when you evaluate the expression $0.5 \cdot \square - 2$ recursively with different starting numbers?

▶ **Solution** | Randomly choosing the starting number 1 gives

> Have your pencil and calculator in hand as you work through the solution to this example.

Original expression: $0.5 \cdot \square - 2$

Starting number: 1

Input	Result
1	$0.5 \cdot (1) - 2 = 0.5 - 2 = -1.5$
-1.5	$0.5 \cdot (-1.5) - 2 = -0.75 - 2 = -2.75$
-2.75	$0.5 \cdot (-2.75) - 2 = -1.375 - 2 = -3.375$
-3.375	$0.5 \cdot (-3.375) - 2 = -1.6875 - 2 = -3.6875$
-3.6875	$0.5 \cdot (-3.6875) - 2 = -1.84375 - 2 = -3.84375$

NCTM STANDARDS

CONTENT		PROCESS	
✓	Number		Problem Solving
✓	Algebra	✓	Reasoning
	Geometry		Communication
	Measurement	✓	Connections
	Data/Probability	✓	Representation

LESSON OBJECTIVES

- Practice arithmetic operations on signed numbers
- Work on recognizing patterns
- Extend the idea of recursion to algebraic expressions
- Learn to evaluate an expression recursively on the calculator
- Become familiar with the phrases *value of an expression* and *evaluating an expression*
- Learn the concept of an attractor

Steps 6–9 These steps give surprising results and are a good small-group activity.

You might demonstrate recursion on the calculator at this point. Sometimes recursion on a graphing calculator is called *home-screen iteration. Iteration* is a fancy word for repetition. Recursion is a special case of iteration.

Step 7 Students starting with the same expression will see the same patterns. The first two expressions will increase without bounds if students start with a number above -1 for the first or above 2 for the second. Those expressions will decrease toward negative infinity if students start with numbers below -1 or 2, respectively. The last two expressions will oscillate in ever-widening swings.

Step 9 If students choose the starting values -6, 1.25, 2, and $-\frac{5}{3}$, respectively, the result will be a fixed point. Any other starting value will result in convergence toward -6, 1.25, 2, and $-\frac{5}{3}$.

SHARING IDEAS

For each expression in Step 8, call on a different group to report its results. Make a table for the class. **[Ask]** "How might you predict from the expression the number that's being approached? Under what conditions will the process approach a number?"

Ask students to explain how the recursion is like the work they did with fractal drawing. Students may compare the attractor encountered in these later expressions to the confined infinity they saw before, thus deepening their intuitive feeling for mathematical limits.

Assessing Progress

As you listen to students contribute to groups or to the whole class, check that they understand the concepts reviewed in this lesson: operations on signed numbers, recursion, and order of operations.

► **EXAMPLE A**

► **EXAMPLE A**

This example is good to use if some students haven't grasped the details of a convergent case. Make sure students notice that the result of the previous iteration is inserted into the calculation for the next iteration. In this example any starting value will iterate toward a single value, −4.

► **EXAMPLE B**

This example shows an expression for which there are two attractors (−1 and 2) instead of just one. Some starting values lead to one of those attractors, and other starting values lead to the other. The values −1 and 2 are fixed points.

The Fathom demonstration Recursive Formulas can be used as a replacement for Examples A and B.

Each result of the recursion seems to get closer to a certain number. If you continue the process a few more times, you'll get approximately −3.9219, then −3.9609, then −3.9805. What do you think will happen after even more recursions?

Using 6 as a starting number in the same expression, you get

Original expression: 0.5 • ☐ − 2	
Starting number:	6
Input	Result
6	0.5(6) − 2 = 1
1	0.5(1) − 2 = −1.5
−1.5	0.5(−1.5) − 2 = −2.75
−2.75	0.5(−2.75) − 2 = −3.375
−3.375	0.5(−3.375) − 2 = −3.6875

Again the values seem to get closer to one number, perhaps −4. If any starting number that you try (other than −4) eventually gets closer and closer to −4, then −4 is called an **attractor** for this expression.

Now try using −4 as the starting number.

Using −4 as the starting number gives

$$0.5 \cdot (-4) - 2 = -2 - 2 = -4$$

Because you get back exactly what you started with, −4 is also called a **fixed point** for the expression $0.5 \cdot \square - 2$.

Evaluating expressions recursively does not always lead to an attractor value. Some expressions continue to grow larger when evaluated recursively, whereas others are difficult, or even impossible, to recognize.

EXAMPLE B | What happens when you evaluate the expression $\square^2 - 2$ recursively with different starting numbers?

► **Solution** | Randomly choosing 1 as a starting number:

$$(1)^2 - 2 = 1 - 2 = -1$$
$$(-1)^2 - 2 = 1 - 2 = -1$$
$$(-1)^2 - 2 = 1 - 2 = -1$$

The results are all −1's, so −1 is an attractor value for this expression. On a number line the results look like this:

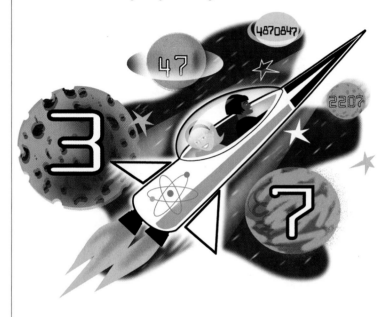

Choosing 3 as a starting number:

$$(3)^2 - 2 = 9 - 2 = 7$$

$$(7)^2 - 2 = 49 - 2 = 47$$

$$(47)^2 - 2 = 2209 - 2 = 2207$$

In this case the results get larger and larger.

Choosing −2 as a starting number:

$$(-2)^2 - 2 = 4 - 2 = 2$$

$$(2)^2 - 2 = 4 - 2 = 2$$

So 2 is another attractor value for this expression.

Choose any starting number, and either you'll get a series of repeating −1's or 2's, or the values will get farther apart at each stage.

With enough practice you may be able to predict the attractor values for some simple expressions without actually doing any computations. But as you try this process with more complex expressions, the results are less predictable.

Remind students that as they have explored recursion on expressions, they have used recursion on their calculator and have **evaluated an expression** and found the **value of an expression.**

They have also learned two new mathematical terms, **fixed point** and **attractor.** Emphasize the closing paragraph in the student text.

If your students need more practice with operations on integers, you can assign a worksheet from More Practice Your Skills.

BUILDING UNDERSTANDING

Doing recursion on a calculator is a useful skill for many of these exercises. See *Exploring Algebra 1 with The Geometer's Sketchpad* for additional practice and demonstrations of integer arithmetic.

ASSIGNING HOMEWORK

Essential	1–6, 8, 9
Performance assessment	8
Portfolio	10, 11
Journal	5
Group	7, 9
Review	12–15

▶ Helping with the Exercises

Exercises 1 and 4 You might use colored tiles to model positive and negative integers. Some teachers also use tile spacers, which are shaped like a "plus" sign. Break off two ends to create a "minus" sign.

Exercise 5 Students may not know the term *absolute value* and may refer to "the number without its sign" in their answers.

5a. Add the two absolute values. The result will be a negative number.

5b. Subtract the number with the smaller absolute value from the number with the larger absolute value. The sign of the answer is the sign of the number with the larger absolute value.

5c. Subtracting a negative number is the same as adding a positive number, so you just add the two absolute values. The result will be a positive number.

5d. Subtracting a negative number is the same as adding a positive number, so the problem actually involves adding a negative number and a positive number.

EXERCISES

You will need your graphing calculator for Exercises **1, 2, 3, 9,** and **10.**

▶ Practice Your Skills

1. Do each calculation and use a calculator to check your results. Then use a number line to illustrate your answer.

   a. $-4 + 7$ 3
   b. $5 + -8$ -3
   c. $-2 - 5$ -7
   d. $-6 - (-3)$ -3

2. Do each calculation and use a calculator to check your results.

   a. $-2 \cdot 5$ -10
   b. $6 \cdot -4$ -24
   c. $-3 \cdot -4$ 12
   d. $-12 \div 3$ -4
   e. $36 \div -6$ -6
   f. $-50 \div -5$ 10

3. Do the following calculations. Check your results by entering the expression into your calculator exactly as it is shown.

   a. $5 \cdot -4 - 2 \cdot -6$ -8
   b. $3 + -4 \cdot 7$ -25
   c. $-2 - 5 \cdot (6 + -3)$ -17
   d. $(-3 - 5) \cdot -2 + 9 \cdot -3$ -11

4. Match each number-line diagram to the expression it illustrates. State the value of each expression.

   a. $8 + -6$ i; 2
   b. $-8 + -6$ iv; -14
   c. $8 - (-6)$ ii; 14
   d. $-8 - 6$ iii; -14
   e. $-8 - (-6)$ v; -2

▶ Reason and Apply

5. Explain how to do each operation described below, and state whether the result is a positive or a negative number.
   a. adding two negative numbers
   b. adding a negative number and a positive number @
   c. subtracting a negative number from a positive number
   d. subtracting a negative number from a negative number
   e. multiplying a negative number by a positive number

5e. Multiply the two absolute values. When you multiply two numbers with different signs, the result is a negative number.

f. multiplying two negative numbers

g. dividing a positive number by a negative number

h. dividing two negative numbers

6. Pete Repeat was recursively evaluating this expression starting with 2.

$$-0.2 \cdot \square - 4$$

a. Check his first two stages and explain what, if anything, he did wrong. @

$$-0.2 \cdot 2 - 4 = 0.4 - 4 = -3.6$$
$$-0.2 \cdot -3.6 - 4 = -0.72 - 4 = -4.72$$

b. Redo Pete's first two stages and do two more.

c. Now do three recursions starting with -1. $-3.8, -3.24, -3.352$

d. Do you think this expression has an attractor value? Explain.

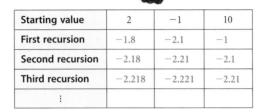

7. To tell whether an expression has an attractor value, you often have to look at the results of several different starting values.

a. Evaluate this expression for different starting values.

$$0.1 \cdot \square - 2$$

Record the results for several recursions (stages) in a table like the one shown. @

Starting value	2	-1	10
First recursion	-1.8	-2.1	-1
Second recursion	-2.18	-2.21	-2.1
Third recursion	-2.218	-2.221	-2.21
⋮			

b. Based on your table, do you think this expression reaches an attractor value in the long run? If so, what is it? If not, why not? @ yes; about -2.222

c. If you found an attractor in 7b, use your calculator to see if substituting that value in the expression gives it back to you. Entering -2.222222222222 as a starting value returns the same value as an answer.

8. Investigate this expression.

$$-2 \cdot \square + 1$$

a. Evaluate the expression for different starting values. Record your results in a table like the one shown.

Starting value	2	-1	10
First recursion	-3	3	-19
Second recursion	7	-5	39
Third recursion	-13	11	-77
⋮			

b. Based on your table, do you think this expression reaches an attractor value in the long run? If so, what is it? If not, why not? No; the values get farther and farther apart.

c. Try the starting value $\frac{1}{3}$. What is the result? What is the value $\frac{1}{3}$ called for this expression? @ The result is $\frac{1}{3}$. The value $\frac{1}{3}$ is a fixed point for this expression.

9. Use a calculator to investigate the behavior of these expressions.
[▶ 🖥 See **Calculator Note 0D** to learn how to do recursion quickly on your calculator. ◀]

keymath.com/DA

a. Use recursion to evaluate each expression many times, and record the attractor value you get after many recursions.

   i. $0.5 \cdot \square + 6$ @ 12   **ii.** $0.5 \cdot \square - 8$ -16 **iii.** $0.5 \cdot \square - 4$ -8

b. Describe any connections you see between the numbers in the original expressions and their attractor values. @

c. Create an expression that has an attractor value of 6. One possibility is $0.5 \cdot \square + 3$.

5f. Multiply the two absolute values. When you multiply two numbers with the same sign, the result is a positive number.

5g. Divide the two absolute values. When you divide two numbers with different signs, the result is a negative number.

5h. Divide the two absolute values. When you divide two numbers with the same sign, the result is a positive number.

Exercise 6 Here students check and then correct some common errors. Problems like this appear throughout the text and give students practice in looking for mistakes.

6a. In the first recursion, he should get $-0.2 \cdot 2 = -0.4$, not $+0.4$. His arithmetic when evaluating $0.4 - 4$ was correct. In the second recursion, he used the wrong value (-3.6 instead of -4.4) because of his previous error. His arithmetic was also incorrect, because $-0.2 \cdot -3.6 = +0.72$, not -0.72. His arithmetic when evaluating $-0.72 - 4$ was correct.

6b. $-4.4, -3.12, -3.376,$ -3.3248

6d. Yes; the calculations seem to be approaching a value close to -3.3.

Exercise 9 Students need Calculator Note 0D.

9b. When the coefficient of the box is 0.5, the attractor value is twice the constant. In general the attractor value is

$$\frac{constant\ term}{1 - coefficient\ of\ the\ box}$$

10b. When the coefficient is 0.2, the attractor value is 1.25 times the constant. In general the attractor value is

$$\frac{constant\ term}{1 - coefficient\ of\ the\ box}$$

10. Use a calculator to investigate the behavior of the expressions below.

i. $0.2 \cdot \square + 6$ 7.5 or $\frac{15}{2}$ **ii.** $0.2 \cdot \square - 8$ -10 **iii.** $0.2 \cdot \square + 5$ 6.25

a. Use recursion to evaluate each expression many times, and record its attractor value.

b. Describe any connections you see between the numbers in the original expressions and the attractor values.

c. Create an expression that has an attractor value of 2.25.   One possibility is $0.2 \cdot \square + 1.8$.

11. How is the recursion process like drawing the Sierpiński triangle in Lesson 0.1, or like creating the Koch curve in Lesson 0.3? All involve repeating a process. Each time, the result becomes the starting value or figure for the next repetition.

12. Determine the missing value in each equation.

a. $-3(-5) + 6 = \boxed{21}$

b. $0.2(-14) - (-3) = \square$ @ 0.2

c. $\boxed{13} + \frac{2}{3}(-9) = 7$

d. $\frac{\boxed{3}}{0.5} - 6 = 0$ @

Review

13. What is $4 - 12 \div 4 \cdot \frac{1}{2} - 5^2$? -22.5, or $-22\frac{1}{2}$

14. Find $(-3 \cdot -4) - (-4 \cdot 2)$. 20

15. What is $\frac{3}{8} - \frac{1}{2} + \left(\frac{3}{4}\right)^2$? $\frac{7}{16}$

IMPROVING YOUR REASONING SKILLS

As the Koch curve develops, the length of each segment decreases as the number of segments increases.

As you draw higher stages, the length of individual segments approaches, or gets closer and closer to, what number? What number does the number of line segments approach? Is it possible to draw the "finished" fractal? Why or why not? What would its total length be?

Now consider this pattern of polygons inscribed in circles:

As you draw higher and higher stages, what does the length of each polygon side approach? What number does the number of sides approach? Is it possible to draw the "finished" polygon? If so, what would it look like? What would the total perimeter of the polygon be? Is this pattern recursive? Is the result a fractal? Why or why not?

IMPROVING REASONING SKILLS

This activity builds on an analogy between forming fractals and approximating a circle with polygons. Like fractal designs, this figure lays some groundwork for the idea of limit. Students should realize that the polygon with "infinitely many sides" is the circle itself and that the area between the inscribed polygon and the circle approaches 0 as the number of sides increases.

Although the process shown for generating regular polygons isn't recursive (no stage builds on the previous one), it could be made so, for example, by repeatedly doubling the number of sides. Some students may believe that the resulting circle is a fractal because it's the result of an infinite sequence of recursive operations. Others may argue that it's not a fractal because it's not self-similar.

Out of Chaos

If you looked at the results of 100 rolls of a die, would you expect to find a pattern in the numbers? You might expect each number to appear about one-sixth of the time. But you probably wouldn't expect to see a pattern in when, for example, a 5 appears. The 5 appears **randomly,** without order. You could not create a method to predict exactly when or how often a 5 appears.

Many irregular and chaotic-seeming events can be seen in nature, and occur in life. In this lesson you'll take a look at trying to understand some of these irregularities. As you explore seemingly random patterns, you'll review some measurement and fraction ideas.

Nothing in nature is random....
A thing appears random only
through the incompleteness
of our knowledge.
BARUCH SPINOZA

Investigation
A Chaotic Pattern?

What happens if you use a random process recursively to determine where you draw a point? Would you expect to see a pattern?

Work with a partner. One partner rolls the die. The other measures distance and marks points.

You will need

● a die
● a centimeter ruler
● a blank transparency and marker
● the worksheet A Chaotic Pattern?

keymath.com/DA

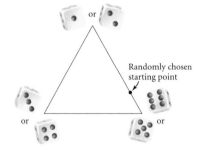

Randomly chosen starting point

For best results, measure as accurately as you can.

Step 1 | Mark any point on the triangle as your starting point.

Step 2 | Roll the die.

Step 3 | In centimeters, measure the distance from your point to the corner, or *vertex,* labeled with the number on the die. Take half of the distance, and place a small dot at this midpoint. This is your new point.

Step 4 | Repeat Steps 2 and 3 until you've rolled the die 20 times. Then switch roles with your partner and repeat the process 20 times.

Step 5 | How is this process recursive? Answers should indicate that the result from one step becomes the input for the next step.

Step 6 | Describe the arrangement of dots on your paper.

Step 7 | What would have happened if you had numbered the vertices of the triangle 1 and 3, 2 and 5, and 4 and 6? Answers should indicate that the result would be the same.

Step 6 Answers should mention that some areas show lots of dots while others remain empty. Some might mention Sierpiński's triangle.

Step 2 [Language] *Die* is singular; *dice* is plural.

Step 3 [Language] Use the term *vertex* for a corner of the triangle and *vertices* for the plural.

These four steps take about 10 minutes to complete. Student results will look pretty chaotic at this point, although students may notice a lack of dots in the centers of their triangles. To keep students

motivated, you might remind them that larger collections of data often show more obvious patterns than smaller sets. Hint that they will eventually see an unexpected pattern.

Step 5 The process is recursive because at each stage students are building on the point that results from the previous stage.

PLANNING

LESSON OUTLINE

One day:

35 min	Investigation, Sharing
5 min	Example
5 min	Closing
5 min	Exercises

MATERIALS

● dice (one die per pair)
● centimeter rulers or rulers cut from the Centimeter Rulers transparency (one per pair)
● transparencies and erasable transparency markers (one per pair)
● A Chaotic Pattern? (W, one per pair)
● Calculator Notes 0E, 0F, 0G, 0H
● Programs and Data CD, *optional*

TEACHING

In this lesson students discover that a fractal is an attractor of a random recursive process.

 Guiding the Investigation

Every class will benefit from following the steps in the text. Organize students into pairs. Give each pair of students the worksheet, a transparency, and a transparency marker.

Steps 1–4 You might want to demonstrate the first several steps in the Chaos game on the board or an overhead projector, explaining the random element of rolling a fair die. Model careful measurement and care in remembering the location of the last dot marked. Be sure students follow the direction to switch tasks after the first 20 points are marked.

Step 9 As students add more layers of transparencies, they will begin to see a familiar pattern appear. It can be very exciting to see the Sierpiński triangle appearing out of the chaotic mass of dots. The Sierpiński triangle is an attractor for the Chaos game.

Step 10 Students need Calculator Notes 0E, 0F, and 0G. The Chaos program is also available on the Programs and Data CD and at www.keymath.com.

Step 11 You might challenge students to try various shapes and fractions and report their results.

SHARING IDEAS

Most reporting in this lesson takes place during the investigation. You need not push for deep understanding of the two terms defined here informally: *random* and *predict*. They will be used again later.

[Ask] "Did the game result in a random pattern?" [No; the process was random, but the overall result is predictable.]

You might mention that, technically, the Chaos game is misnamed; mathematical chaos is the production of seemingly random patterns by methods that are not random.

The random generation of the Sierpiński triangle gives experience with careful measurement and more practice with fraction multiplication and recursion.

Assessing Progress

To complete the investigation, students need to know what is meant by the vertex of a triangle and the midpoint of a segment. They must also be able to multiply fractions or decimals to find the midpoint of the segment between the vertex of the triangle and a point. They should understand that the Chaos game uses recursion and that the resulting Sierpiński triangle is an attractor.

Step 8 | Place a transparency over your worksheet. Use a transparency marker and mark the vertices of the triangle. Carefully trace your dots onto the transparency.

Step 9 | When you finish, place your transparency on an overhead projector. Align the vertices of your triangle with the vertices of your classmates' triangles. This allows you to see the results of many rolls of a die. Describe what happens when you combine everyone's points. How is this like the result in other recursion processes? Is the result as random as you expected? Explain.

Step 9 Because the position of a dot is used as input for determining the next dot, the process is recursive.

A *random* process can produce ordered-looking results while an orderly process can produce random-looking results. Mathematicians use the term *chaotic* to describe systematic, nonrandom processes that produce results that look random. Chaos theory helps scientists understand the turbulent flow of water, the mixing of chemicals, and the spread of an oil spill. They often use computers to do these calculations. Your calculator can repeat steps quickly, so you can use the calculator to plot thousands of points.

Step 10 | Enter the Chaos program into your calculator. [▶ 🖥 See **Calculator Note 0E** for the program. To learn how to link calculators, see **Calculator Note 0F.** To learn how to enter a program, see **Calculator Note 0G.**◄]

The program randomly "chooses" one vertex of the triangle as a starting point. It "rolls" an imaginary die and plots a new point halfway to the vertex it chose. The program rolls the die 999 more times. It does this a lot faster than you can.

Step 11 | Run the program. Select an equilateral (equal-sided) triangle as your shape. When the program "asks" for the fraction of the distance to move, enter $\frac{1}{2}$ or 0.5. It will take a while to plot all 1000 points, so be patient.

Step 12 | What do you see on your calculator screen, and how does it compare to your class's combined transparency image? Answers should mention Sierpiński's triangle and the similarity to the combined points for the class transparencies.

Most people are surprised that after plotting many points, a familiar figure appears. When an orderly result appears out of a random process like this one, the figure is a *strange attractor*. No matter where you start, the points "fall" toward this shape. Many fractal designs, like the Sierpiński triangles on your calculator screen, are also strange attractors. Accurate measurements are essential to seeing a strange attractor form. In the next example, practice your measurement skills with a centimeter ruler.

Science
CONNECTION

The growth and movement of an oil spill may appear random, but scientists can use chaos theory to predict its boundaries. This can aid restraint and cleanup. Learn more about the application of chaos theory with the Internet links at **www.keymath.com/DA** .

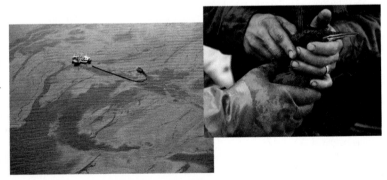

LESSON OBJECTIVES

- Practice multiplication with fractions and decimals
- Deepen understanding of recursion and attractors
- Practice careful measuring skills
- Review the meaning of a vertex of a triangle
- Learn to link calculators to transfer a program
- Learn to run a calculator program

NCTM STANDARDS

CONTENT		PROCESS	
	Number		Problem Solving
	Algebra	✔	Reasoning
✔	Geometry		Communication
✔	Measurement	✔	Connections
	Data/Probability	✔	Representation

EXAMPLE

Find point C one-third of the way from A to B. Give the distance from A to C in centimeters.

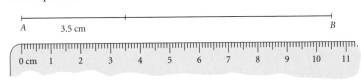

A   B

▶ **Solution**

> Have your ruler handy so that you can check the measurements. Use your calculator to check the computations.

Measuring segment AB shows that it is about 10.5 cm long. (Check this.) Find one-third of this length.

$$\frac{1}{3} \cdot 10.5 = \frac{10.5}{3} \qquad \text{Multiply by } \tfrac{1}{3} \text{ or divide by 3.}$$
$$= 3.5 \qquad \text{Divide.}$$

Place a point 3.5 cm from A.

A   3.5 cm   B

0 cm   1   2   3   4   5   6   7   8   9   10   11

EXERCISES

You will need your graphing calculator for Exercises **4, 5, 6, 7,** and **10**.

▶ **Practice Your Skills**

1. Estimate the length of each segment in centimeters. Then measure and record the length to the nearest tenth of a centimeter.

   a. A   B   @   8.0 cm

   b. C   D   4.3 cm

   c. E   F   7.2 cm

2. Use a ruler to draw a segment that fits each description.

   a. one-third of a segment 8.4 cm long   2.8 cm segment

   b. three-fourths of a segment 7.6 cm long   5.7 cm segment

   c. two-fifths of a segment 12.7 cm long   about 5.1 cm segment

3. Mark two points on your paper. Label them A and B. Draw a segment between the two points.

   a. Mark a point two-thirds of the way from A to B and label it C.

   b. Mark a point two-thirds of the way from C to B and label it D.

   c. Mark a point two-thirds of the way from D to A and label it E.

   d. Which two points are closest together? Does it matter how long your original segment was?   points D and B; no

4. Do these calculations. Check your results with a calculator.

   a. $-2 + 5 - (-7)$ 10   **b.** $(-3)^2 - (-2)^3$ 17   **c.** $\frac{3}{5} + \frac{-2}{3}$ $\frac{-1}{15}$ **d.** $-0.2 \cdot 20 + 15$ 11

   e. $4 - 6(-2)$ 16   **f.** $7 - 4(2 - 5)$ 19   **g.** $-2\frac{1}{3} - 4\frac{1}{6}$ $-6\frac{1}{2}$

3a–c. Answers should look proportional to this:

A   E   C   D   B

This example will be especially useful to students who are having difficulties with measurement and fractions. Using a marked number line might help students.

Closing the Lesson

As needed, briefly say something about the importance of measuring carefully. Make sure no questions remain about the new calculator skills of transferring programs between calculators and running a calculator program.

BUILDING UNDERSTANDING

Like the investigation, this set of exercises includes generating fractals by hand as well as with the calculator program.

ASSIGNING HOMEWORK

Essential	1–3, 6
Performance assessment	5
Portfolio	7
Journal	8
Group	4, 5
Review	9–11

▶ **Helping with the Exercises**

Exercise 1 [Alert] Watch for confusion about the meaning of rounding to the nearest tenth of a centimeter.

Exercise 3 To students having difficulty with the level of abstraction, you might suggest assuming a distance such as 27 from A to B and then finding the distance of every point from A.

Exercise 5 Any triangle can be used to make a Sierpiński-like triangle in this way. Students can use Calculator Note 0H for 5b.

Reason and Apply

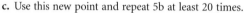

[▶️ You'll need the program in **Calculator Note 0E** for Exercises 5–8. ◀]

5. Draw a large right triangle on your paper. You can use the corner of a piece of paper or your book to help draw the right angle numbered 2. Number the vertices as shown.

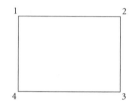

  a. Choose a point anywhere on your triangle. This is your starting point.

  b. On your calculator, enter RandInt(1,3) to randomly select a vertex. [▶️ See **Calculator Note 0H** for help with this. ◀] Measure from your point to the chosen vertex. Mark a new point halfway from your point to the vertex.

  c. Use this new point and repeat 5b at least 20 times.

  d. Describe any pattern you see forming. @ The resulting figure should slightly resemble a right-angle Sierpiński triangle.

  e. Run the Chaos program for Exercise 5 to see what happens when you plot 1000 points.

6. Draw a large square or rectangle on your paper. Number the vertices from 1 to 4 as shown.

  a. Choose a point anywhere on your figure. This is your starting point.

  b. In order to choose a vertex to move toward, flip two different coins, such as a nickel and a penny. Use this scheme to determine the vertex:

Nickel	Penny	Vertex number
H	H	1
H	T	2
T	H	3
T	T	4

a–d. The resulting figure should slightly resemble the Sierpiński carpet from Lesson 0.1, Exercise 7.

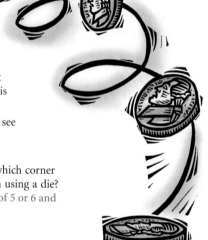

Measure the distance between your starting point and the chosen vertex. Mark a new point two-thirds of the distance to the vertex. Use this point and repeat the process at least 20 times.

  c. Run the calculator simulation for Exercise 6 to see what happens when you plot 1000 points. (h)

  d. Describe any pattern you see forming.

  e. How could you have used a die to determine which corner to move toward? What problems are there with using a die? Answers will vary. You could ignore any rolls of 5 or 6 and move toward corner 1, 2, 3, or 4 on those rolls.

Exercise 6e [Language] Make sure students know that *die* is the singular of *dice*.

7. Experiment with the calculator program for each game description. For each, use the shape and fraction given. The program will start with a point inside the shape, randomly choose a vertex, and plot a point a fraction of the distance to the vertex. Describe your results and draw a sketch if possible.

    a. square, $\frac{1}{2}$ @

    b. equilateral triangle, $\frac{2}{3}$

    c. square, $\frac{3}{4}$

    d. right triangle, $\frac{2}{5}$

8. Suppose you are going to play a chaos game on a pentagon. Describe a process that would tell you which corner to move toward on each move.   Possible answers: Use a die and ignore rolls of 6, or choose one of five playing cards to indicate the move. The answer should describe a process by which all corners are equally likely to be chosen.

▶ Review

9. Draw a segment that is 12 cm in length. Find and label a point that is two-thirds the distance from one of the endpoints.   Point should divide segment into an 8 cm and a 4 cm segment.

10. Use a calculator to investigate the behavior of the expressions below.

    i. $-0.5 \cdot \square + 3$ @ 2   **ii.** $-0.5 \cdot \square + 6$ 4   **iii.** $-0.5 \cdot \square - 9$ -6

    a. Use recursion to evaluate each expression many times and record its attractor value.

    b. Describe any connections you see between the numbers in the original expressions and the attractor values. @ The attractor is two-thirds of the constant.

    c. Create an expression that has an attractor value of -10. One possibility is $-0.5 \cdot \square - 15$.

11. Look at the fractal below. The Stage 0 figure has a length of 1.

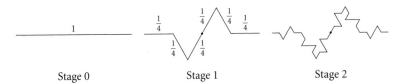

Stage 0   Stage 1   Stage 2

Complete a table like the one below for Stages 0 to 2. Use any patterns you notice to extend the table for Stages 3 and 4.

Stage number	Total length		
	Multiplication form	Exponent form	Decimal form
0	1	1^0	1
1	$6 \cdot \frac{1}{4}$	$6^1 \cdot \left(\frac{1}{4}\right)^1 = \left(\frac{6}{4}\right)^1 = \left(\frac{3}{2}\right)^1$	1.5
2	$6 \cdot 6 \cdot \frac{1}{4} \cdot \frac{1}{4}$	$6^2 \cdot \left(\frac{1}{4}\right)^2 = \left(\frac{6}{4}\right)^2 = \frac{9}{4}$	2.25

11.

Stage number	Total length		
	Multiplication form	Exponent form	Decimal form
3	$6 \cdot 6 \cdot 6 \cdot \left(\frac{1}{4}\right) \cdot \left(\frac{1}{4}\right) \cdot \left(\frac{1}{4}\right)$	$6^3 \cdot \left(\frac{1}{4}\right)^3 = \left(\frac{6}{4}\right)^3 = \frac{27}{8}$	3.38
4	$6 \cdot 6 \cdot 6 \cdot 6 \cdot \left(\frac{1}{4}\right) \cdot \left(\frac{1}{4}\right) \cdot \left(\frac{1}{4}\right) \cdot \left(\frac{1}{4}\right)$	$6^4 \cdot \left(\frac{1}{4}\right)^4 = \left(\frac{6}{4}\right)^4 = \frac{81}{16}$	5.06

Exercise 7 The calculator allows entering either common fractions or decimal fractions at the "Enter a fraction" step.

7a. This game fills the entire square.

7b. This game creates a small Sierpiński triangle at each corner of the triangle.

7c. This game creates four small Sierpiński carpets, one at each corner of the square.

7d. This game creates a pattern like the Sierpiński triangle.

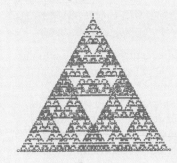

PLANNING

LESSON OUTLINE

One day:

5 min   Introduction

30 min   Exercises

15 min   Student self-assessment

REVIEWING

Direct students' attention to the table of lengths generated in the example on page 16. **[Ask]** "What expression could you evaluate recursively to generate the column of lengths?" If students try to use the last column, help them see that the patterns will be easier to find from the fourth column. You may need to remind students of how fractions and exponents are being used and that a recursive pattern needs a starting number (in this case, 1). The recursive rule is $\frac{5}{3} \cdot \boxed{}$. This might look simpler than the recursive expressions they worked with in Lesson 0.4, but it is different and therefore may be confusing. Be sure all students can use it to generate the sequence of lengths $1, \frac{5}{3}, \left(\frac{5}{3}\right)^2$, $\left(\frac{5}{3}\right)^3$, and so on.

As a challenge, ask students to consider the same fractal patterns but with the left segment $\left(\text{length } \frac{1}{3}\right)$ removed from Stage 0. Each length will be $\frac{1}{3}$ less than before: $\frac{2}{3}, \frac{5}{3} - \frac{1}{3}, \left(\frac{5}{3}\right)^2 - \frac{1}{3}, \left(\frac{5}{3}\right)^3 - \frac{1}{3}$, and so on. The challenge is to get an expression that can be applied recursively so that each length is obtained from the previous length. As a hint, suggest that students first add $\frac{1}{3}$ to get the term back to that in the earlier sequence. Then they'll multiply that by $\frac{5}{3}$ and subtract $\frac{1}{3}$ from the total to get $\left(\boxed{} + \frac{1}{3}\right)\left(\frac{5}{3}\right) - \frac{1}{3}$. They can check

In this chapter you saw many instances of how you can start with a figure or a number, apply a mathematical rule, get a result, then apply the same rule to the result. This is called **recursion**, and it led you to find patterns in the results. When the recursive rule involved multiplication, you used an **exponent** as a shorthand way to show repeated multiplication.

Patterns in the results of recursion were often easier to see when you left them as common fractions. To add and subtract fractions, you needed a common denominator. You also needed to round decimals and measure lengths.

To **evaluate expressions** with any kind of numbers, you needed to know the **order of operations** that mathematicians use. The order is (1) evaluate what is in parentheses, (2) evaluate all powers, (3) multiply and divide as needed, and (4) add and subtract as needed. You used your knowledge of operations (add, subtract, multiply, divide, raise to a power) to write several expressions that gave the same number. Having an expression for the recursive rule helps you predict a value later in a sequence without figuring out all the values in between.

In this chapter you also got a peek at some mathematics that are new even to mathematicians, including **fractals** like the Sierpiński triangle, chaos, and strange attractors. You had to think about **random** processes and whether the long-term outcome of these processes was truly random.

EXERCISES

You will need your graphing calculator for Exercise **7**.

@ Answers are provided for all exercises in this set.

1. Match equivalent expressions.

  a. $\frac{1}{9} + \frac{1}{9} + \frac{1}{9}$ iii   **i.** $\frac{35}{81}$

  b. $\frac{1}{9} + \frac{1}{9} + \frac{1}{3}$ v   **ii.** $\frac{10}{27}$

  c. $\frac{2}{9} + \frac{1}{9} + \frac{1}{27}$ ii   **iii.** $3 \times \frac{1}{9}$

  d. $\frac{4}{9} + \frac{2}{27} + \frac{3}{81}$ iv   **iv.** $\frac{12}{27} + \frac{2}{27} + \frac{1}{27}$

  e. $\frac{2}{81} + \frac{1}{3} + \frac{2}{27}$ i   **v.** $2 \times \left(\frac{1}{9}\right) + \frac{1}{3}$

2. Evaluate these expressions.

  a. $2 \times (24 + 12)$ 72   **b.** $2 + 24 \times 12$ 290   **c.** $2 - 24 + 12$ -10

  d. $(2 + 24) \times 12$ 312   **e.** $(2 + 24) \div 12$ $2.1\overline{6}$ **f.** $2 - (24 + 12)$ -34

3. Write a multiplication expression equivalent to each expression below in exponent form.

a. $\left(\frac{1}{3}\right)^3$ $\frac{1}{3}\times\frac{1}{3}\times\frac{1}{3}$

b. $\left(\frac{2}{3}\right)^4$ $\frac{2}{3}\times\frac{2}{3}\times\frac{2}{3}\times\frac{2}{3}$

c. $(1.2)^2$ 1.2×1.2

d. 16^5 $16\times16\times16\times16\times16$

e. 2^7 $2\times2\times2\times2\times2\times2\times2$

4. Write an addition expression that gives the combined total of shaded areas in each figure. Then evaluate the expression. The area of each figure is originally 1.

a.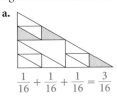

$\frac{1}{16}+\frac{1}{16}+\frac{1}{16}=\frac{3}{16}$

b.

$\frac{1}{9}+\frac{1}{9}+\frac{1}{81}+\frac{1}{81}=\frac{20}{81}$

c.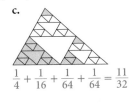

$\frac{1}{4}+\frac{1}{16}+\frac{1}{64}+\frac{1}{64}=\frac{11}{32}$

5. Draw the next stage of each fractal design below. Then describe the recursive rule for each pattern in words.

a.

Stage 0   Stage 1   Stage 2

b.

Stage 0   Stage 1   Stage 2

c.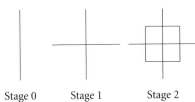

Stage 0   Stage 1   Stage 2

d.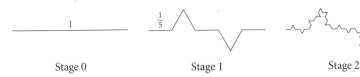

Stage 0   Stage 1   Stage 2

6. Look at the figures below.

Stage 0   Stage 1   Stage 2

a. Complete a table like the one on the next page.

that this expression generates the sequence $\frac{2}{3}, \frac{5}{3}-\frac{1}{3}, \left(\frac{5}{3}\right)^2-\frac{1}{3}, \left(\frac{5}{3}\right)^3-\frac{1}{3}, \ldots$ without necessarily simplifying to $\frac{2}{9}+\frac{5}{3}\cdot\square$, which requires students to apply the distributive property to expressions containing variables.

ASSIGNING HOMEWORK

If you plan to assess students individually, then they should work individually on these exercises. You can help students who have been having difficulty.

5a.

Stage 3

A branch is added at the midpoint of each of the newest segments, with half the length, at a 45° clockwise rotation.

5b.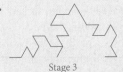

Stage 3

A "bottomless" equilateral triangle is built on the "right" half of segments.

5c.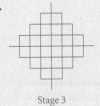

Stage 3

Each new segment is crossed at its midpoint by a centered perpendicular segment of equal length.

5d.

Stage 3

Each unshaded square is divided horizontally and vertically to create four congruent squares; the bottom-right square is shaded.

▶ Take Another Look

Some students will find the first three questions simple. They should work on them anyway because they'll find the rest of the activity easier if they're in the mode of recording results in a table.

The behavior of numbers raised to a power depends on the kinds of numbers involved, as described in the table at the bottom of this page.

The questions about increasing denominators give students an opportunity to think about numbers more broadly than they might be used to. The statement "If the denominator of a fraction increases, the value of the fraction decreases" is true for positive fractions written with both numerator and denominator positive. For negative fractions—written with only the numerator negative—increasing the denominator makes the magnitude of the fraction decrease, thereby moving it closer to zero. Because the fraction moves to the right along the number line, it becomes greater.

Students might find the questions about numerators most difficult because they require generating data rather than using algebra. (Students will learn how to solve proportions in Chapter 2.)

If the denominator is positive, then for $\dfrac{\bigcirc}{\square}^3$ to be smaller than $\square^3$ the numerator would have to be less than $\square^6$. For $\dfrac{\bigcirc}{\square}^3$ to be greater than $\square^3$, the numerator would need to be greater than $\square^6$. If the denominator is negative, the cases are reversed.

With $\dfrac{\bigcirc}{\square}^4$, the numerator would be compared to $\square^8$.

	Total length		
Stage number	Multiplication form	Exponent form	Decimal form
0	1	1	1
1	$7 \cdot \left(\dfrac{1}{5}\right)$	$7^1 \cdot \left(\dfrac{1}{5}\right)^1 = \left(\dfrac{7}{5}\right)^1 = \dfrac{7}{5}$	1.4
2	$7 \cdot 7 \cdot \left(\dfrac{1}{5}\right) \cdot \left(\dfrac{1}{5}\right)$	$7^2 \cdot \left(\dfrac{1}{5}\right)^2 = \left(\dfrac{7}{5}\right)^2 = \dfrac{49}{25}$	1.96

b. If you were to draw Stage 20, what expression could you write with an exponent to represent the total length? Evaluate this expression using your calculator, and round the answer to the nearest hundredth. $\left(\dfrac{7}{5}\right)^{20} \approx 836.68$

7. Investigate the behavior of the expression below. Use recursion to evaluate the expression several times for different starting values. You may want to record your recursions in a table. Does the expression appear to have an attractor value?

$0.4 \cdot \square + 3$ The attractor is 5.

TAKE ANOTHER LOOK

▶
- If a number gets larger when it is raised to a power, what kind of number is it?
- If a number gets smaller when it is raised to a power, what kind of number is it?
- What numbers stay the same when they are raised to a power?

To investigate these questions, choose positive and negative numbers, zero, and positive and negative fractions to put in the box and evaluate the expressions

$\square^3$ and $\square^4$

You may want to use a table like the one at right to save your results.

You know that if the denominator of a fraction increases, the value of the fraction decreases. Why is that? Are there any exceptions?

Look again at your results for the expression $\square^3$.

What would the numerator of the fraction have to be so that

$\dfrac{\bigcirc}{\square}^3$ is smaller than $\square^3$? Greater than $\square^3$?

Now do the same thing with $\dfrac{\bigcirc}{\square}^4$.

Display your results in a table.

$\square$	$\square^3$
1	$1^3 = 1$
2	$2^3 = 8$

Number in box	Exponent of 3 (or any odd integer greater than 1)	Exponent of 4 (or any even integer greater than 0)
Positive number greater than 1	bigger	bigger
Negative number less than -1	smaller (negative yet farther from 0)	bigger (becomes positive)
0 or 1	stays the same	stays the same
-1	stays the same	bigger (becomes 1)
Positive fraction between 0 and 1	smaller (positive yet closer to 0)	smaller (positive yet closer to 0)
Negative fraction between 0 and -1	bigger (negative yet closer to 0)	bigger (becomes positive)

Assessing What You've Learned

BEGIN A PORTFOLIO

If you look up "assess" in a dictionary, you'll find that it means to estimate or judge the value of something. The value you've gained by the end of a chapter is not what you studied, it's what you remember and what you've gained confidence in. There are ideas you may not remember, but you will be able to reconstruct them when you meet similar situations. That's mathematical confidence.

One way to hold on to the value you've gained is to start a portfolio. Like an artist's portfolio, a mathematics portfolio shows off what you can do. It also collects work that you found interesting or rewarding (even if it isn't a masterpiece!). It also reminds you of ideas worth pursuing. The fractal designs that you figured out or invented are worth collecting and showing. Your study of patterns in fractals is a rich example of investigative mathematics that is also a good reference for how to work with fractions and exponents.

Choose one or more pieces of your work for your portfolio. Your teacher may have specific suggestions. Document each piece with a paragraph that answers these questions:

▶ What is this piece an example of?
▶ Does it represent your best work? Why else did you choose it?
▶ What mathematics did you learn or gain confidence in with this work?
▶ How would you improve the piece if you wanted to redo it?

Portfolios are an ongoing and ever-changing display of your work and growth. As you finish other chapters, remember to update your portfolio with new work.

If you want to give a test, you can use either Form A or Form B of the Chapter Test, or you can use Constructive Assessment items. Using the Test Generator CD, you can create an alternate version of the test or combine some items from Form A or Form B with Constructive Assessment items.

In this chapter students have gained familiarity with the investigative method, improved their facility with the graphing calculator, and looked for and analyzed patterns. All these skills will be developed further throughout the course.

Students have reviewed fractions, exponents, and integers. For students who are having trouble adding or multiplying fractions, provide extra practice with the More Practice Your Skills worksheets.

The important new mathematical ideas are fractals and recursion. Because students will see recursion again, emphasize this idea as you review the chapter.

FACILITATING SELF-ASSESSMENT

To help students complete the portfolio described in Assessing What You've Learned, suggest that they consider for evaluation their work on Lesson 0.1, Exercise 5; Lesson 0.2, Exercise 6; Lesson 0.3, Exercise 6; Lesson 0.4, Exercises 10 and 11; and Lesson 0.5, Exercise 7.

TESTING

If many students missed much of this introductory chapter, you may choose not to give a test and simply regard the chapter as diagnostic.

You have several other options for assessing students' learning. You might use the chapter project, ask students to present the results of the calculator program for different polygons, or evaluate their portfolios. (See Assessing What You've Learned at the end of the chapter.)

Because investigative skills and group work are essential to *Discovering Algebra*, be sure to evaluate these skills as well as mathematical understanding.

Data Exploration

Overview

In **Lesson 1.1,** students learn about bar graphs and dot plots. In **Lesson 1.2,** they see the measures of center—mean, median, and mode. **Lesson 1.3** introduces five-number summaries and box plots. **Lesson 1.4** presents histograms and stem-and-leaf plots. On the activity day, **Lesson 1.5,** students state a conjecture on how two books differ and collect data to verify their conjecture. In **Lesson 1.6,** students graph scatter plots of two-variable data. The goals of **Lesson 1.7** are to practice estimation skills and to understand the meaning of points on the coordinate plane in comparison with the graph of $y = x$. **Lesson 1.8** introduces matrices as an extension of data tables.

Data sets have three important characteristics: center, spread, and shape. Chapter 1 focuses on describing center and spread. Descriptions of shape are addressed in Lesson 1.4, Exercise 10; in several exercises in Chapter 10; and in *Discovering Advanced Algebra*.

The Mathematics

If a data set is numerical, then several mathematical representations help summarize the data, display the data set, or make it easier to work with.

Statistics

Some representations of data are numbers, called *statistics*. Some statistics are measures of center; others are measures of spread.

The mean, median, and mode are measures of center. The *mean* (often called *average*) is the most commonly used, but *outliers* (extreme, atypical points) on one end of the data set can distort the mean's usefulness as a measure of center. The *median*, or middle value, is a better measure of center in that case. The *mode* or modes give the most commonly occurring value(s), the ones "most likely" to be picked at random.

Other useful statistics describe the spread of the data, or the density of data points in various regions. The *range* is a single number giving the difference between the *maximum* value and the *minimum* value. The first and third *quartiles* (boundaries of the quarters) are the medians of the two halves of the data set. Also useful in describing the spread is the *interquartile range*, or IQR, which is the difference between the third and first quartiles. Perhaps the most useful way to measure spread is by a *five-number summary*, which lists the minimum, first quartile, median, third quartile, and maximum. It shows the range and concentration of the data.

Graphs

Graphic displays make one- and two-variable data sets easier to understand.

For some one-variable data sets, it works best to group data into categories that aren't numerical. If a single picture or icon represents a specific number of data points in a category, the graph is called a *pictograph*. In contrast, a *bar graph* represents the data values in each category using a single bar whose length is proportional to the number of points.

The best grouping in other one-variable data sets is by numbers, either single numbers or intervals of numbers. The analog of a bar graph is a *histogram*, in which bins over different intervals are adjacent. If the categories are single numbers, then a graph with rows or columns of dots, called a *dot plot*, might best represent the data. If the data set consists of numbers that are categorized by their first digit or digits, a *stem-and-leaf plot* may be preferable, with the remaining digits of each number listed on the other side of a bar next to the first digit(s).

All of these graphs of one-variable data sets aid intuition about the measures of center and give some indication of spread. For a better indication

of spread, a *box-and-whisker plot* parallels the five-number summary of the data.

Two-variable data sets consist of ordered pairs of data. A *scatter plot* is a graph of the points whose coordinates are given by the data set. For comparison (and later as a model), a scatter plot is often augmented by a line, such as the graph of $y = x$.

Matrices

Another way to display two-variable data is in a table. The mathematical abstraction of a table, a *matrix* (plural, *matrices*), is a useful tool for combining data sets. You can enter the data values from a table into a graphing calculator as a matrix, and the calculator can perform matrix operations such as multiplying a matrix by a constant and adding, subtracting, and multiplying matrices.

Using This Chapter

Exploring data offers many opportunities to use algebra and see its applications, but if data representations aren't part of your required curriculum, you could skip over some of these lessons and return to them later. Include at least parts of Lessons 1.3 and 1.6, however, because students will need to understand scatter plots, five-number summaries, and graphing on the coordinate plane. Use Lesson 1.8 only if your curriculum requires that students study matrices. If you skip some lessons, be sure to present the associated calculator skills when they are required later.

Resources

Discovering Algebra Resources

Teaching and Worksheet Masters
   Lessons 1.1–1.4, 1.6–1.8

Programs and Data CD

Calculator Notes 0H, 1A, 1B, 1C, 1D, 1E, 1F, 1G, 1H, 1I, 1J, 1K, 1L, 1M, 1N, 1P (for TI-73 only, 1Q, 1R)

Sketchpad Demonstration
   Lesson 1.8

Fathom Demonstrations
   Lessons 1.1–1.4

CBR Demonstration
   Lesson 1.6

Dynamic Algebra Explorations online
   Lessons 1.2, 1.3

Assessment Resources
   Quiz 1 (Lessons 1.1, 1.2)
   Quiz 2 (Lessons 1.3, 1.4)
   Quiz 3 (Lessons 1.6–1.8)
   Chapter 1 Test
   Chapter 1 Constructive Assessment Options

More Practice Your Skills for Chapter 1

Condensed Lessons for Chapter 1

Other Resources

www.keypress.com/DA

Materials

- watch or clock with second hand
- 250–300 pennies (not new)
- graph paper
- centimeter rulers
- a variety of books
- colored pencils or pens
- poster paper
- ramps (books, notebooks, or cardboard)
- assortment of objects that roll
- metersticks or tape measures
- motion sensors, *optional*

Pacing Guide

	day 1	day 2	day 3	day 4	day 5	day 6	day 7	day 8	day 9	day 10
standard	1.1	1.2	1.2	1.3	1.4	quiz, 1.5	1.5	1.6	1.6	1.7
enriched	1.1	1.2	1.2	1.3	1.4, project	quiz, 1.5	1.5	1.6	1.6	1.7, project
block	1.1, 1.2	1.2, 1.3	1.4, project	quiz, 1.5	1.6	1.7, project, 1.8	1.8, review	assessment		

	day 11	day 12	day 13	day 14	day 15	day 16	day 17	day 18	day 19	day 20
standard	1.8	1.8	review	assessment						
enriched	1.8	1.8	review, TAL	assessment						

1 Data Exploration

- Learn to calculate (on paper and by calculator), interpret, and compare statistics representing a one-variable data set: *minimum, maximum, range, mean, median, mode, quartiles, interquartile range, five-number summary, outliers*

- Learn to create (on paper and by calculator), interpret, and compare graphical displays of a one-variable data set: *pictograph, bar graph, dot plot, stem-and-leaf plot, histogram, box plot*

- Learn to create (on paper and by calculator) and analyze scatter plot displays of a two-variable data set along with the line $y = x$

- Learn to represent two-variable data with a matrix, multiply the matrix by a number, add and subtract matrices, and multiply a matrix by a column matrix

- Gain experience making conjectures about a data set and testing them with appropriate statistical and graphical methods

- Use the terminology of statistics and graphs to present conclusions of a study of data

- Improve ability to work with others on a mathematical problem

You are surrounded by information in many forms—in pictures, in graphs, in words, and in numbers. This information can influence what you eat, what you buy, and what you think of the world around you. This photo collage by Robert Silvers shows a lot of information.

OBJECTIVES

In this chapter you will

- interpret and compare a variety of graphs
- find summary values for a data set
- draw conclusions about a data set based on graphs and summary values
- review how to graph points on a plane
- organize and compute data with matrices

The picture illustrates how individual pieces of information can contribute to a larger meaning. You might **[Ask]** "What do you think this artist is trying to say about the population of the United States?" You could mention the census (taken every ten years) and ask students what attributes displayed in the photo might be counted in the census. You might even use the photo as a fictitious data set and have students summarize the data (such as by counting gender, ethnicity, or approximate age) to characterize the artist's idea about the population.

Bar Graphs and Dot Plots

I've always felt rock and roll was very, very wholesome music.

ARETHA FRANKLIN

This **pictograph** shows the number of CDs sold at Sheri's music store in one day. Can you tell just by looking which *type* sold the most? How many CDs of this type were sold? Rock; 16

This specific information, the kind Sheri may later use to make decisions, is sometimes called **data.** You use data every day when you answer questions like "Where is the cheapest place to buy a can of soda?" or "How long does it take to walk from class to the lunchroom?"

In this lesson you'll interpret and create graphs. Throughout the chapter, you'll learn more ways to organize and represent data.

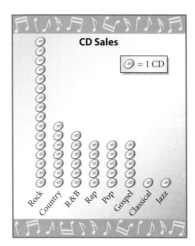

CD Sales

= 1 CD

Rock Country R&B Rap Pop Gospel Classical Jazz

EXAMPLE

Joaquin's school posts a pictograph showing how many students celebrate their birthdays each month. Here is part of this pictograph. Create a table of data and a **bar graph** from the pictograph.

Number of Birthdays in Each Month

Birth month

January

February

March

April

= 5 students

▶ **Solution**

This table lists the birthday data.

Number of Birthdays in Each Month

Jan	Feb	Mar	Apr
15	10	0	25

In the pictograph, there are three figures for January. Each figure represents five students. So 3 × 5 gives 15.

NCTM STANDARDS

CONTENT		PROCESS	
✔	Number	✔	Problem Solving
	Algebra	✔	Reasoning
	Geometry		Communication
	Measurement	✔	Connections
✔	Data/Probability	✔	Representation

LESSON OBJECTIVES

• Create a pictograph, bar graph, and dot plot of a data set

• Calculate the minimum, maximum, and range of a data set

• Interpret pictographs, bar graphs, and dot plots

• Decide the appropriateness of bar graphs and dot plots for a given data set

PLANNING

LESSON OUTLINE

One day:

10 min	Introduction
5 min	Example
15 min	Investigation
5 min	Sharing
5 min	Closing
10 min	Exercises

MATERIALS

• clock or watch with a second hand

• Pulse Rate Sample Data (W), *optional*

• Calculator Notes 1Q, 1R for TI-73 only

• Fathom demonstration Pulse Rates, *optional*

TEACHING

Mention the term *data* and how a set of data can be represented by a graph. **[Ask]** "What does the graph of CD data truly say about sales at any given store?" The fictional graph describing CD sales depicts some data published by the Recording Industry Association of America. Students might visit the site (and others like it) to acquire realistic data for creating other graphs. They can find links to RIAA's original data at www.keymath.com/DA.

EXAMPLE

[ELL] Make sure that students understand the word *category*. You may want to do this example with students lining up as a human pictograph or as an activity in which students write their birthdays on sticky notes and build a pictograph of their birthday data.

Mention the term *pictograph*. Each picture or icon in a pictograph may represent several data points.

You might start a list of new terms for this chapter and display them on a "wall of words."

Point out that the original data of names and birthdays are not recoverable from the pictograph.

If students are using TI-73 graphing calculators, they can use notes 1Q and 1R and draw calculator pictographs and bar graphs.

Guiding the Investigation

The Fathom demonstration Pulse Rates can be used as a replacement for the investigation.

Mention that *beats per minute* is abbreviated *bpm* in this lesson. Some students may know this abbreviation from music. You can also relate this to ratios and rates as $\frac{beats}{minute}$.

One Step

If your students are experienced investigators, use One Step instead of Steps 1 to 6. Ask students to collect a data set of pulse rates and to try to represent that set with graphs. Encourage a variety of representations. After a few students have shared their ideas, give a name to each standard representation. As students move into the main part of the investigation, mention that you'll be constructing a graph that's not a bar graph for data giving pulse rates. In general, try to avoid telling students things they can figure out.

Step 1 Sample data are provided on the Pulse Rate Sample Data worksheet and can also be downloaded from the Programs and Data CD or from www.keymath.com/DA. However, most students will prefer actively collecting the data themselves. [Alert] Students who have trouble locating a pulse in the neck can try the wrist. You

Career
CONNECTION

There are over 120,000 paramedics in the United States. Schooling can require up to 2,000 hours of classes and ongoing training after high school. Paramedics need to be able to read values from graphs and to make decisions based on numerical data.

This bar graph shows the same data. The height of a bar shows the total in that **category,** in this case, a particular month. You use the *scale* on the *vertical axis* to measure the height of each bar. The vertical axis extends slightly past the greatest number of birthdays in any one month, so the data do not go beyond the scale.

Bar graphs gather data into categories and make it easy to present a lot of information in a compact form. In a bar graph you can quickly compare the quantities for each category.

In a **dot plot** each item of numerical data is shown above a number line or *horizontal axis*. Dot plots make it easy to see gaps and clusters in the data set, as well as how the data **spreads** along the axis.

In the investigation you'll gather and plot data about pulse rates. People's pulse rates vary, but a healthy person at rest usually has a pulse rate between certain values. A pulse that is too fast or too slow could tell a paramedic that a person needs immediate care.

Investigation
Picturing Pulse Rates

You will need
- a watch or clock with a second hand

Use the Procedure Note to learn how to take your pulse. Practice a few times to make sure you have an accurate reading.

Step 1 Start with pulse-rate data for 10 to 20 students.

Step 2 Find the **minimum** (lowest) and **maximum** (highest) values in the pulse-rate data. The minimum and maximum describe the spread of the data. For example, you could say, "The pulse rates are between 56 and 96 bpm."

Based on your data, do you think a paramedic would consider a pulse rate of 80 bpm to be "normal"? What about a pulse rate of 36 bpm? 80 bpm is "normal," while 36 bpm is too low.

Step 3 Construct a number line with the minimum value near the left end. Select a scale and label equal **intervals** until you reach the maximum.

Step 4 Put a dot above the number line for each data value. When a data value occurs more than once, stack the dots.

Number of Birthdays in Each Month

Procedure Note

How to Take Your Pulse
1. Find the pulse in your neck.
2. Count the number of beats for 15 seconds.
3. Multiply the number of beats by 4 to get the number of beats per minute (bpm). This number is your pulse rate.

might also suggest that one person in a group serve as timer while the others count their pulses.

Coordinate the compiling of data into a class set. Without comment, skip students who show discomfort in volunteering; they may be generally self-conscious or have a medical condition. Record the data where everyone can see them.

Step 3 [Alert] Some students may need to be reminded of how to draw a number line. Point out the one on the next page.

Step 4 You might remind students that they are creating a dot plot here. Dot plots can be made with X's instead of dots.

Here is an example for the data set {56, 60, 60, 68, 76, 76, 96}. Your line will probably have different minimum and maximum values.

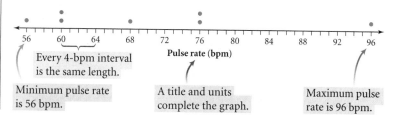

Every 4-bpm interval is the same length.

Pulse rate (bpm)

Minimum pulse rate is 56 bpm.

A title and units complete the graph.

Maximum pulse rate is 96 bpm.

The **range** of a data set is the difference between the maximum and minimum values. The data on the example graph have a range of $96 - 56$, or 40 bpm.

Step 5 Most likely, the range will be greater than 12; the minimum and maximum.

Step 5 The *Physicians' Desk Reference* lists the normal resting pulse rate for adult men as 70 to 72 bpm and for women as 78 to 82 bpm. **[Alert]** Some students may use the word *range* in the phrase "the range is from 56 to 96 bpm." The maximum and minimum values help describe the spread of the data, but emphasize that in statistics the range is a single number—the maximum minus the minimum.

Step 6 Clustering would help a paramedic identify a normal range. Factors such as age affect pulse, and a single class's data comprise too small a sample. Also, factors such as whether your class data were collected immediately after jogging in place for 3 min will affect whether your data are more or less representative of all people.

Step 7 Students may be reluctant to do the kind of thinking requested here, but it's important for them to think about data-gathering techniques that can produce unreliable results.

[ELL] Many students have trouble pronouncing *statistics*. Don't insist on correct pronunciation.

SHARING IDEAS

Good steps to ask students to present: Steps 4, 5, 6. Encourage presenters to use standard terminology, especially *dot plot, minimum, maximum,* and *range.*

[Ask] "Why are the class data points multiples of 4?" [The one-minute data came from multiplying 15-second data by 4.] This anticipates Exercise 5c.

Assessing Progress

Observe students' contributions to the lesson so you can assess their abilities to order and multiply whole numbers and their familiarity with the number line.

Step 5 What is the range of your data? Suppose a paramedic says normal pulse rates have a range of 12. Is this range more or less than your range? What information is the paramedic not telling you when she mentions the range of 12?

Step 6 For your class data, are there data values between which a lot of points cluster? What do you think these clusters would tell a paramedic? What factors might affect whether your class's data is more or less representative of all people?

Step 7 How could you change your data-collection method to make it appear that your class's pulse rates are much higher than they really are? You could ask your classmates to exercise before collecting the pulse data, or you could ask them either to hold their breath or to breathe very fast.

History CONNECTION

The word *statistics* was first used in the late 18th century to mean the collection of data about a state or country. To learn about the history of statistics, see www.keymath.com/DA .

Statistics is a word used many ways. We sometimes refer to data we collect and the results we get as *statistics*. For example, you could collect pulse-rate statistics from thousands of people and then determine a "normal" pulse-rate. The single value you calculate to be "normal" could also be called a statistic.

Statistics can help us describe a population or generalize what is "normal." However, data are sometimes collected or reported in ways that can be misleading. You'll learn more about statistics and their usefulness in this chapter.

EXERCISES

▶ Practice Your Skills

1. Angelica has taken her pulse 11 times in the last six hours. Her results are 69, 92, 64, 78, 80, 82, 86, 93, 75, 80, and 80 beats per minute. Find the maximum, minimum, and range of the data. ⓗ max: 93 bpm; min: 64 bpm; range: 93 bpm − 64 bpm = 29 bpm

2. The table shows the percentages of the most common elements found in the human body. Make a bar graph to display the data.

Elements in the Human Body

Oxygen	Carbon	Hydrogen	Nitrogen	Calcium	Phosphorus	Other
65%	18%	10%	3%	2%	1%	1%

Closing the Lesson

Reiterate the main ideas of this lesson: A **data** set consists of information. Sometimes the data can be grouped into **categories** and represented visually, perhaps by a **pictograph**, a **dot plot**, or a **bar graph**, all of which show the number of data points in each category. Sometimes the data are numerical. In that case, the data set might be represented by numbers called **statistics.** The **minimum** and **maximum** values are statistics; so is the **range,** which is a single number that is the maximum minus the minimum.

2.

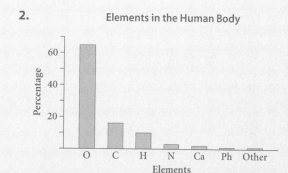

Elements in the Human Body

The exercises provide practice with finding the range of a data set and with reading and creating bar graphs and dot plots.

ASSIGNING HOMEWORK

Essential	1–6
Performance assessment	7, 9
Portfolio	3
Journal	8
Group	6–9
Review	10–13

▶ **Helping with the Exercises**

Exercise 3 [ELL] Some students will benefit from definitions of *horizontal* (like the horizon) and *vertical*. **[Ask]** "Is there a reason for the order of categories on the vertical axis?" [They are listed by increasing distance from the sun.]

[Ask] "How many more satellites does Neptune have than Mars?" [Six more, four times as many, or three times more are all correct answers.] Encourage a variety of legitimate responses. Show students that some mathematics questions have more than one answer and answers often can be arrived at in more than one way.

Exercise 4 You might use this exercise as a class activity, with students gathering their own data.

Exercise 4a Encourage students to place numbers on the number line in a proportional way.

Exercise 4c Students may simply add the times. Be sure they see why they must multiply time by number of students before adding.

Exercise 4d This question might be review. Students who don't remember what *average* means will be introduced to it as *mean* in Lesson 1.2.

3. Use this bar graph to answer each question.

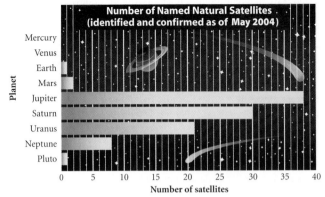

Number of Named Natural Satellites (identified and confirmed as of May 2004)

(Solar System Dynamics Group, *ssd.jpl.nasa.gov*)

a. Which planet has the most satellites? Jupiter

b. What does this graph tell you about Mercury and Venus? Mercury and Venus have no satellites.

c. How many more satellites does Jupiter have than Neptune? 30

d. Saturn has how many times as many satellites as Mars? 15 times

4. This table shows how long it takes the students in one of Mr. Matau's math classes to get to school.

a. Construct a dot plot to display the data. Your number line should show time in minutes. @

b. How many students are in this class? 30

c. What is the combined time for Mr. Matau's students to travel to school? ⓗ 241 min

d. What is the average travel time for Mr. Matau's students to get to school? $\frac{241}{30} \approx 8$ min

Travel Time to School

Time (min)	Number of students
1	2
3	2
5	6
6	1
8	6
10	7
12	3
14	2
15	1

▶ **Reason and Apply**

5. This graph is a dot plot of Angelica's pulse-rate data.

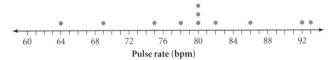

Pulse rate (bpm)

a. What pulse rate appeared most often? 80 bpm

b. What is the range of Angelica's data? 29 bpm

c. If your class followed the directions for the investigation, your pulse rates should be multiples of four. Angelica's are not. How do you think she took her pulse? She counted her pulse for 1 full minute.

d. How would your data change if everyone in your class had taken his or her pulse for a full minute? How would the dot plot be different? Any whole number could occur, not just multiples of 4.

e. Do you think medical professionals measure pulse rates for 1 minute or 15 seconds? Why? a full minute, sometimes longer; to ensure accuracy

4a. Travel Time to School

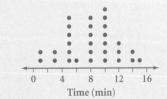

Time (min)

Exercise 5e Watch for different interpretations of the question "Why?": as asking either why "you think" something (one answer: "I've seen them") or why the professionals measure pulse rates the way they do (one answer: "to save time"). Encourage a range of thoughtful responses; the question is intended to keep students thinking.

6. Each graph below displays information from a recent class survey. Determine which graph best represents each description:

a. number of people living in students' homes iii

b. students' heights in inches ii

c. students' pulse rates in beats per minute iv

d. number of working television sets in students' homes @ i

i.
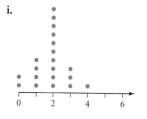

ii.
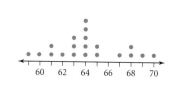

iii.
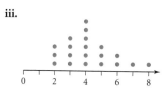

iv.
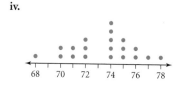

7. Reporter "Scoop" Presley of the school paper polled 20 students about their favorite type of music—classical, pop/rock, R&B, rap, or country. He delivered his story to his editor, Rose, just under the deadline. Rose discovered that Scoop, in his haste, had ripped the page with the bar graph showing his data. The vertical scale and one category were missing! Unfortunately, the only thing Scoop could remember was that three students had listed R&B as their favorite type. Reconstruct the graph so that it includes the vertical axis and the missing category with the correct count.

3 in classical

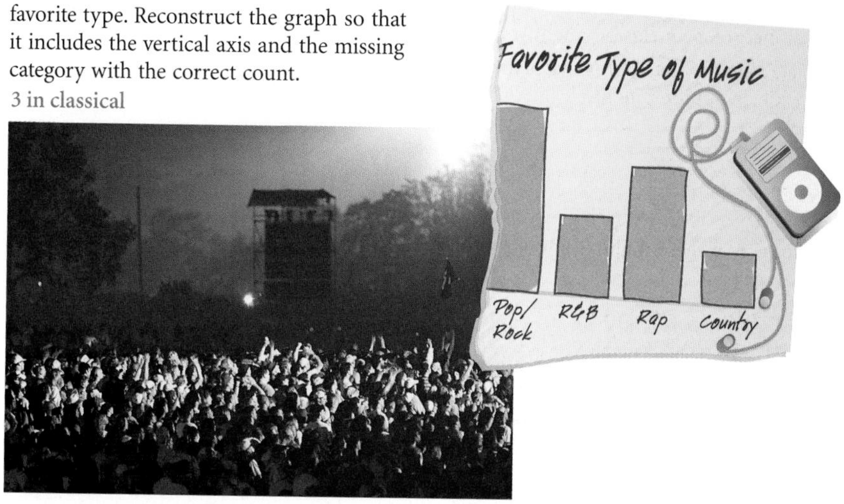

8. Suppose you collect information on how each person in your class gets to school. Would you use a bar graph or a dot plot to show the data? Explain why you think your choice would be the better graph for this information. @ a bar graph; because the information falls into categories, is not numerical data, and cannot be scaled on a number line

Exercise 6 [Alert] Students may misinterpret 6a to mean "number of other kids (not people) in families in general," in which case the value 0 might be legitimate. To distinguish between sets, suggest that students also consider the modes. A class of unusually tall students might justifiably switch 6b and 6c.

Exercise 7 [Alert] Students may have difficulty dealing with all the information at once. Be patient. One reason this is a good exercise for groups is that the groups are more likely to be self-correcting than an individual student, so you don't have to intervene as much.

9a. possible answer: Jonesville's Varsity Basketball Team

9b. possible answer: Jonesville's Kindergarten Class and Their Teacher

9c. possible answer: Jonesville's Algebra Class

9d. possible answers: Group A: "Everyone in the school is very tall"; Group B: "Almost everyone in the school is very short"; Group C: "Jonesville School is a high school only."

9e. Answers will vary.

9. These three graphs represent heights, in inches, of a sample of students from Jonesville School, which has students in kindergarten to 12th grade. Each sample was taken from a particular class or group of students.

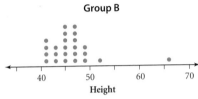

Group A

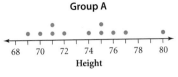

Group B

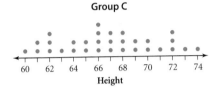

Group C

a. Guess at a more descriptive title for the Group A graph. (*Hint:* Think about different groups or classes in your school, such as clubs, sports teams, or grade levels.) @

b. Guess at a more descriptive title for the Group B graph.

c. Guess at a more descriptive title for the Group C graph.

d. If the title on each graph above was "Sample Heights from Jonesville School," what incorrect conclusion might you draw from each graph?

e. Create a graph that approximates the heights of a class or group in your school. Provide an appropriate title.

▶ Review

0.2   **10.** Rewrite each of these multiplication expressions using exponents.

a. $10 \times 10 \times 10 \times 10$ 10^4

b. $2 \cdot 2 \cdot 2 \cdot 5 \cdot 5 \cdot 5 \cdot 5 \cdot 5 \cdot 5$ $2^3 \cdot 5^6$

c. $\dfrac{3^2(3^4)}{8(8)(8)}$ $\dfrac{3^6}{8^3}$

0.1   **11.** Use the order of operations to evaluate each expression.

a. $7 + (3 \cdot 2) - 4$ 9

b. $8 + 2 - 4 \cdot 12 \div 16$ 7

c. $1 - 2 \cdot 3 + 4 \div 5$ -4.2

d. $1 - (2 \cdot 3 + 4) \div 5$ @ -1

e. $1^2 \cdot 3 + (4 \div 5)$ 3.8

Exercise 11 Especially if you skipped Lesson 0.1, be ready to describe the conventional order of operations.

12. The early Egyptian *Ahmes Papyrus* (1650 B.C.) shows how to use a doubling method to divide 696 by 29. (George Joseph, *The Crest of the Peacock*, 2000, pp. 61–66)

Doubles of 29	58	116	**232**	**464**	928
Doubles of 1	2	4	**8**	**16**	32

Double the divisor (29) until you go past the dividend (696). Find doubles of 29 that sum to 696: 232 + 464 = 696. Then sum the corresponding doubles of 1: 8 + 16 = 24. So, 696 divided by 29 is 24.

Doubles of 225	450	900	1800	3600	7200
Doubles of 1	2	4	8	16	32

a. Divide 4050 by 225 with this method. @ 18;

b. Divide 57 by 6 with this method. (*Hint:* Use doubles and halves.)

0.1 **13.** Write an addition expression that gives the combined total of the shaded area. Then evaluate the expression. The area of the large triangle is 1.

 $\frac{1}{16} + \frac{1}{16} + \frac{1}{4} = \frac{3}{8}$

IMPROVING YOUR REASONING SKILLS

Janet and JoAnn used the same data set of high and low temperatures for cities in a month in early spring. Which graph shows the low temperatures better? Is either graph better for showing the differences between high and low temperatures?

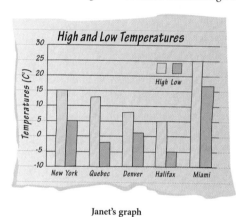

Janet's graph

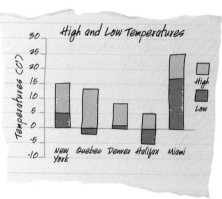

JoAnn's graph

Exercise 12b Because doubles of 6 add to 54, a half of 6 must also be used.

IMPROVING REASONING SKILLS

Students may find that JoAnn's graph illustrates low temperatures better than Janet's, because negative values fall under the axis. JoAnn's choice of how to mark the graph makes it hard to compare the low temperatures. However, the side-by-side feature of Janet's graph allows easy comparison between high and low temperatures.

12b. $9\frac{1}{2}$;

Doubles of 6	6	12	24	48	96
Doubles of 1	1	2	4	8	16

Half of 6	3
Half of 1	$\frac{1}{2}$

Summarizing Data with Measures of Center

"Americans watch an average of four hours of television each day."

"Half of the participants polled had five or more people living in their home."

"When graduating seniors were asked how many colleges they applied to, the most frequent answer they gave was three."

Statements like these try to say what is typical. They summarize a lot of data with one number called a **measure of center** or **measure of central tendency.** The first statement uses the **mean,** or *average*. The second statement uses the **median,** or middle value. The third statement uses the **mode,** or most frequent value.

Investigation
Making "Cents" of the Center

In this investigation you learn to find the mean, median, and mode of a data set. You may have learned about these measures of center in a past mathematics class.

You will need

• 20 to 30 pennies

Step 1 Sort your pennies by mint year. Make a dot plot of the years.

Step 2 Put your pennies in a single line from oldest to newest. Find the median, or middle value. Does the median have to be a whole-number year? Why or why not? Would you get the same median if you arranged the pennies from newest to oldest?

Step 3 On your dot plot, circle the dot or dots that represent the median. Write the value you got in Step 2 beside the circled dot(s), and label the value "median."

Step 4 Now stack pennies with the same mint year. The year of the tallest stack is called the mode. If there are two tall stacks, your data set is **bimodal.** If every stack had two pennies in it, you might say there is "no mode" because

> ### Procedure Note
> **Finding the Median**
> If you have an odd number of pennies, the median is the year on the middle penny. If you have an even number of pennies, add the dates on the two pennies closest to the middle and divide by two.

LESSON OBJECTIVES

• Calculate the *mean, median,* and *mode* of a data set, noting *outliers*

• Enter data into calculator lists

• Given a list of data, use a calculator to find the mean and the median

• Compare and interpret the three measures of center

• Explain the effects of outliers on the mean and the median

NCTM STANDARDS

CONTENT		PROCESS	
✔	Number	✔	Problem Solving
	Algebra	✔	Reasoning
	Geometry		Communication
	Measurement	✔	Connections
✔	Data/Probability	✔	Representation

no year occurs most often. How many modes does your data set have? What are they? Does your mode have to be a whole number? Modes will vary but must be a whole number; the sample data have mode 1998.

Step 5 Draw a square around the year corresponding to the mode(s) on the number line of your dot plot. Label each value "mode."

Step 6 The mean of the sample data is 1993.6.

Step 6 Find the sum of the mint years of all your pennies and divide by the number of pennies. The result is called the mean. What is the mean of your data set?

Step 7 Show where the mean falls on your dot plot's number line. Draw an arrowhead under it and write the number you got in Step 6. Label it "mean."

Step 8 Now enter your data into a calculator list, and use your calculator to find the mean and the median. Are they the same as what you found using pencil and paper? [▶ 🖳] Refer to **Calculator Note 1A** to check the settings on your calculator. See **Calculator Notes 1B and 1C** to enter data into lists and find the mean and median. ◀]

Save the dot plot you created. You will use it in Lesson 1.3.

Measures of Center

Mean
The mean is the sum of the data values divided by the number of data items. The result is often called the average.

Median
For an odd number of data items, the median is the middle value when the data values are listed in order. If there is an even number of data items, then the median is the average of the two middle values.

Mode
The mode is the data value that occurs most often. Data sets can have two modes (bimodal) or more. Some data sets have no mode.

keymath.com/DA

Each measure of center has its advantages. The mean and the median may be quite different, and the mode, if it exists, may or may not be useful. You will have to decide which measure is most meaningful for each situation.

EXAMPLE

This data set shows the number of people who attended a movie theater over a period of 16 days.

{14, 23, 10, 21, 7, 80, 32, 30, 92, 14, 26, 21, 38, 20, 35, 21}

a. Find the measures of center.

b. The theater's management wants to compare its attendance to that of other theaters in the area. Which measure of center best represents the data?

Moviegoers wear special glasses to watch 3-D movies. To learn about 3-D glasses, see the links at www.keymath.com/DA .

---

the words would be *promedia* (*mean*), *intermedio* (*median*), and *el más común* (*mode*).

As you ask groups to copy their dot plots onto transparencies, include some with an even number of data points and others with an odd number. If possible, include one whose data have outliers and one with bimodal data.

[Ask] "When are the mean, median, and mode close to being equal?" [with single-modal data that have good symmetry about the mean] Refer to the box "Measures of Center" in the text. Ask students to explain in their own words how to find each measure of center. You might point out that the word *mode* starts like *most;* the mode is the number that occurs most often.

Step 1 [Alert] Make sure students label their number line, title the plot, and show the units.

Step 2 [Alert] Watch that students mark their number line with all years, not just the ones for which they have pennies.

Step 2 Medians will vary; the Pennies Sample Data worksheet has median 1995. The median does not need to be a whole number; it may have decimal part 0.5. Both orderings give the same median.

Step 3 Be sure that students don't simply call the median the average of the minimum and the maximum. Refer them to the Procedure Note.

Step 4 "No mode" is relative to the size of the data set. If you have 1000 distinct data values, having five to ten modes may be worthwhile information. But if you have only 12 data values, having five modes is not very informative.

Step 6 Students can use the symbol ⫪ to indicate a "break" in the x-axis between extreme outliers and the rest of the pennies.

Step 7 [Link] You might mention that if the horizontal number line were a beam and the data points were weights, the balance point would be at the mean.

If you're saving Step 8 for a second day on this lesson, collect handwritten data for later entry into calculators.

Step 8 [Language] The word *mode* has several meanings, as does the word *mean*. **[Alert]** Watch for confusion about the word *mode;* the mode on the graphing calculator (Calculator Note 1A) is not related to the statistical mode of a data set.

SHARING IDEAS

[ELL] Ask students to translate *mean, median,* and *mode* into their first language. In Spanish

If there are outliers in one or more data sets, mention the term as the outliers show up. **[Ask]** "Is there ever a case in which outliers do *not* affect the mean?" [when they are equidistant on opposite sides of the mean]

Assessing Progress

By observing students' contributions, you can assess their skills at organizing data, ordering numbers, rounding, counting, and critical and creative thinking.

MEASURES OF CENTER

[Ask] "Which is the best measure of center?" Encourage discussion that focuses on "For what purposes?" For example, the mean is good for summarizing heights or miles per gallon; the median is good for income or the cost of a home; the mode is good for shoe sizes if selling shoes.

[Ask] "What statistics besides measures of center might be used to describe the differences among these data sets?" You can review *maximum, minimum,* and *range,* and in a fast-moving class you might introduce the notion of quartiles to lead into Lesson 1.3.

EXAMPLE

The Fathom demonstration Measures of Center can be used as a replacement for the example.

Talk through this example to help students understand how an outlier can affect the mean. You might comment on the mid-twentieth-century moviegoers who are wearing special glasses to view a three-dimensional movie.

Solution a The mean indicates that if the attendance were distributed evenly over the 16 days, approximately 30 people would have attended each day.

Solution b The median and mode are more appropriate for comparison purposes, but using the mean in an advertisement would make the theater seem more popular than it is.

▶ *Solution*

a. The mean is approximately 30 people.

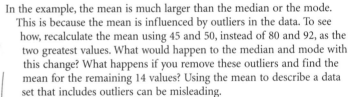

$$\frac{14 + 23 + 10 + 21 + 7 + 80 + 32 + 30 + 92 + 14 + 26 + 21 + 38 + 20 + 35 + 21}{16} = 30.25$$

number of data values   the mean

The median is 22 people.

data values listed in order

7, 10, 14, 14, 20, 21, 21, 21, 23, 26, 30, 32, 35, 38, 80, 92

The median is in the middle, or halfway between 21 and 23.

The most frequent value, 21 people, is the only mode.

b. To determine which measure of center best summarizes the data, look for patterns in the data and look at the shape of the graph.

Attendance (number of people)

The dot plot clearly shows that, except for two items, the data are clustered between 7 and 38. The items with values 80 and 92 are far outside the range of most of the data and are called **outliers.**

Either the median, 22, or the mode, 21, could be used by the management to compare this theater's attendance to that of other theaters. The management could say, "Attendance was about 21 or 22 people per day over a 16-day period." The mean, 30, is too far to the right of most of the data to be the best measure of center. Yet the theater's management might prefer to use the mean of 30 in an advertisement. Why?

In the example, the mean is much larger than the median or the mode. This is because the mean is influenced by outliers in the data. To see how, recalculate the mean using 45 and 50, instead of 80 and 92, as the two greatest values. What would happen to the median and mode with this change? What happens if you remove these outliers and find the mean for the remaining 14 values? Using the mean to describe a data set that includes outliers can be misleading.

With the outliers 45 and 50, the mean is approximately 25; the median and mode are the same. With the outliers removed, the mean is approximately 22, the median is 21, and the mode stays the same.

If students use a calculator list for the theater data, it will be easy for them to change values and recalculate the mean.

Closing the Lesson

The mathematical ideas of this lesson concern the three primary **measures of center,** also called **measures of central tendency.** The **mean** is the sum of the values divided by the number of values. The **median** is the middle value or the mean of the two middle values. The **mode** or modes are the most common value(s). **Outliers** are values unusually far from the middle; they have a strong influence on the mean but not on the median.

Ask students to save their handwritten penny data and dot plots for use in Lesson 1.3.

EXERCISES

▶ Practice Your Skills

1. Find the mean, median, and mode for each data set.

   a. {1, 5, 7, 3, 5, 9, 6, 8, 10} @

   b. {6, 1, 3, 9, 2, 7, 3, 4, 8, 8}

   c. {12, 6, 11, 7, 18, 5, 2, 21} @

   d. {10, 10, 20, 20, 20, 25}

2. Find the mean, median, and mode for each dot plot.

   a.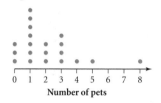

   mean: $\frac{65}{15} \approx 4.3$;
   median: 4;
   no mode

   b.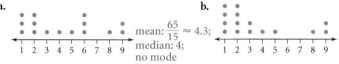

   mean: $\frac{53}{15} \approx 3.5$;
   median: 2;
   modes: 1, 2

3. Students were asked how many pets they had. Their responses are shown in the dot plot below.

   a. How many students were surveyed? 20   b. What is the range of answers? 8

   c. What was the most common answer? 1

4. This graph gives the lift heights and vertical drops of the five tallest roller coasters at Cedar Point Amusement Park in Ohio in September 2004.

   a. Find the mean and median for the lift heights. @   mean: 262.2 ft; median: 215 ft

   b. Find the mean and median for the vertical drops. mean: 251.2 ft; median: 206 ft

This is the first hill of the Mean Streak at Cedar Point.

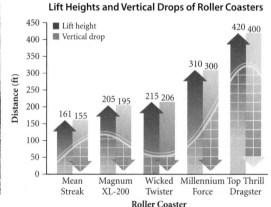

(Cedar Point Amusement Park, *www.cedarpoint.com*)

5. If you purchase 16 grocery items at an average cost of $1.14, what is your grocery bill?
   Explain how you found the total bill. $18.24; if you multiply the mean by the number of items, you get the sum of the items.

Exercises 6 and 12 The data for these exercises can be downloaded from the Programs and Data CD or from www.keymath.com/DA.

Exercise 6 In finding the median, students must first put the heights in order.

Exercise 6b Students may ask if, instead of finding the median, they can just eliminate outliers before finding the mean. Encourage this kind of questioning. The *trimmed mean* statistic is the mean of the middle 90% of data. In this exercise it would be the mean of all values except the highest and lowest.

6a. mean: 97.485 m; median: 60 m
6b. Median; the mean is affected by the extreme value 525.

Exercise 7 This exercise takes Exercise 5 another step. Students might solve it by multiplying and then subtracting, or by guess-and-check. Encourage them to try more than one approach.

7. The first three averaged 53 s each; together they took 159 s. The total time for the whole team must be 50(5) or 250 s. The two remaining members must have a total of 250 − 159 or 91 s. So the last two members must average 91 ÷ 2 or 45.5 s each.

8. The mean, 83.8, is lower than all but one of his scores; the median, 88, is more representative.

Reason and Apply

6. An ocean wave caused by an earthquake, landslide, or volcano is called a tsunami. The heights of the 20 tallest tsunamis on record are given below. The December 26, 2004 Indian Ocean tsunami, which caused the most damage and loss of life of any tsunami in recorded history, had a maximum height of about 27 m.

Tallest Tsunamis

Location	Year	Height (m)	Location	Year	Height (m)
Lomblen Island, Indonesia	1979	120	Merak, Java, Indonesia	1883	35
Valdez Inlet, Alaska	1964	70	Lituya Bay, Alaska	1880	60
Lituya Bay, Alaska	1958	525	Lituya Bay, Alaska	1853	120
Amorgos, Greece	1956	30.6	Shimabara, Japan	1792	55
Unimak Island, Alaska	1946	35	Ishigaki Island, Japan	1771	85.4
Nachi River, Japan	1944	200	Sado Island, Japan	1741	90
Lituya Bay, Alaska	1936	150	Bering Island, Russia	1737	60
Disenchantment Bay, Alaska	1905	35	Hila, Indonesia	1674	100
Lituya Bay, Alaska	1899	60	West Coast Patmos, Greece	1650	30.5
Shirahama, Japan	1896	38.2	West Coast Patmos, Greece	1650	50

(National Geophysical Data Center, *www.ngdc.noaa.gov*) [Data set: **TSUHT**]

(*The Hollow of the Deep-Sea Wave Off Kanagawa* by Katsushika Hokusai/Minneapolis Institute of Art Acc. No. 74.1.230)

Many of the data sets in this book are available for you to download onto your graphing calculator.

  a. Calculate the mean and median for the height data.
  b. Which measure of center is most appropriate for the height data? Explain your reasoning.

7. The first three members of the stilt-walking relay team finished their laps of the race with a mean time of 53 seconds per lap. What mean time for the next two members will give an overall team mean of 50 seconds per lap? ⓗ

8. Noah scored 88, 92, 85, 65, and 89 on five tests in his history class. Each test was worth 100 points. Noah's teacher usually uses the mean to calculate each student's overall score. How might Noah argue that the median is a better measure of center for his test scores?

9. At a state political rally, a speaker announced, "We should raise test scores so that all students are above the state median." Analyze this statement.

10. This table gives information about ten of the largest saltwater fish species in the world. The approximate mean weight of these fish is 1527.4 lb.

a. Explain how to use the mean to find an approximate total weight for these ten fish. What is the total weight? @

b. The median weight of these fish is about 1449 lb. Assuming that no two weights are the same, what does the median tell you about the individual weights of the fish? @

c. The range of weights is 1673 lb, and the minimum weight is 991 lb. What is the weight of the great white shark, the largest fish caught? 2664 lb

Largest Saltwater Fish Species

Species	Location where caught
Swordfish	Chile
Bluefin tuna	Nova Scotia
Great white shark	South Australia
Atlantic blue marlin	Brazil
Greenland shark	Norway
Black marlin	Peru
Hammerhead shark	Florida
Tiger shark	California
Pacific blue marlin	Hawaii
Mako shark	Mauritius

(International Game Fish Association, in *The Top 10 of Everything 2001*, p. 41)

11. Create a set of data that fits each description.

a. The mean age of a family is 19 years, and the median age is 12 years. There are five people in the family. ⓗ   sample answer: {8, 10, 12, 32, 33} years

b. Six students in the Mathematics Club compared their family sizes. The mode was five people, and the median was four people.

c. The points scored by the varsity football team in the last seven games have a mean of 20, a median of 21, and a mode of 27 points.
sample answer: {7, 14, 20, 21, 24, 27, 27} points

12. This data set represents the ages of the 20 highest-paid athletes in the United States in June 2004, in decreasing order of salary. (Forbes, *www.forbes.com*)
[Data set: **ATHPY**]

{28, 35, 28, 41, 32, 28, 34, 29, 28, 25, 31, 29, 39, 32, 31, 19, 27, 29, 74, 34}

a. Make a dot plot of these data.

b. Give the mean, median, and mode for the data. @   mean: 32.65; median: 30; mode: 28

c. Which measure of center best summarizes the data? Explain your reasoning. @

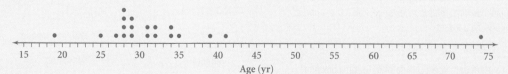

▶ **Review**

1.1 **13.** Fifteen students gave their ages in months.

168   163   142   163   165   164   167   153   149   173   163   179   155   162   162

a. Would you use a bar graph, pictograph, or dot plot to display these data? Explain. @

b. Create the graph you chose in 13a.

0.5 **14.** Use this segment to measure or calculate in 14a–c.

a. What is the length in centimeters of the segment? 12 cm

b. Draw a segment that is $\frac{2}{3}$ as long as this segment. What is the length of your new segment? 8 cm

c. Draw a segment that is $\frac{1}{5}$ as long as the original segment. What is the length of this new segment? 2.4 cm

12a.   **Highest-Paid Athletes**

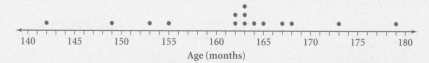

13b. Answers may vary.   **Student Ages**

Exercise 9 Encourage critical thinking. Students might critique the statement in several ways: Not all scores can be above the median, because the median is the middle score; the speaker may be urging that all scores in a city or county should be above the state median, which is possible; or the students themselves can't be above the median, only their scores can.

9. Answers will vary. If the speaker is talking about the entire state, this cannot occur. All scores cannot be greater than the middle score. In fact, exactly half of the scores will be above the median and half will be below.

10a. Multiply the mean by 10; together they weigh approximately 15,274 lb.

10b. Five of the fish caught weigh 1449 lb or less, and five weigh 1449 lb or more.

Exercise 11 Students working together on this exercise can help stimulate ideas and be self-correcting. Students may not know how to handle the freedom of creating their own set of numbers. Encourage a variety of responses, including creative use of outliers, but watch for errors. If some students are completely baffled, suggest starting with a set of points all of which are the mean, then adjusting them to keep the mean the same but to change to the desired median, and finally adjusting them to achieve the desired mode without changing the other two measures of center.

11b. sample answer: {2, 3, 3, 5, 5, 5} people

12c. The median is probably best; the mean is distorted by one extremely high value.

13a. A dot plot may be most appropriate for the numeric data. However, if each value was translated into years (divide by 12), you could make a bar graph or pictograph with ages as categories.

Exercise 14 Students may need help with this exercise if you skipped Chapter 0.

PLANNING

LESSON OUTLINE

One day:

10 min	Introduction, Example
20 min	Investigation
10 min	Sharing
5 min	Closing
5 min	Exercises

MATERIALS

- Dot Plot for Pennies (W or T), *optional*
- Box Plot for Pennies (T), *optional*
- Calculator Note 1D
- Fathom demonstration Five-Number Summaries and Dot Plots, *optional*

TEACHING

Ask students to read the introduction. Point out that the five numbers include three medians: of the whole data set, of the upper half, and of the lower half.

EXAMPLE

The five-number summary represents the spread of a data set better than minimum, maximum, and range alone.

[Ask] "What are the measures of center of this data set?" [mean: about 675; median: 416] "Do measures of center give you enough information to describe a data set?" Elicit the idea that measures of center don't describe the distribution, or spread, of data points.

Have students read the example to themselves. **[Ask]** "What do you observe in the data set?" Pool their observations. Add your own to the list as they seem to fit. Include in the list things listed at the bottom of page 53.

To talk sense is to talk quantities. It is no use saying a nation is large—how large?

ALFRED NORTH WHITEHEAD

Five-Number Summaries and Box Plots

Michael Jordan is regarded as one of the all-time best athletes. He played in more than 1,000 basketball games, scored more than 32,000 points, was the National Basketball Association (NBA) Most Valuable Player five times, and helped the Chicago Bulls win six NBA championships. During his last season, he scored almost three times as many points as the next highest scorer on his team. Does any measure of center give a complete description of how the Bulls scored as a team? A **five-number summary** could give a better picture. It uses five boundary points: the minimum and the maximum, the median, the **first quartile** (the median of the first half), and the **third quartile** (the median of the second half).

Points Scored by Chicago Bulls Players Who Played over 40 Games (1997–98 Season)

Chicago Bulls	Total points scored	Chicago Bulls	Total points scored
Michael Jordan	2357	Steve Kerr	376
Toni Kukoc	984	Dennis Rodman	375
Scottie Pippen	841	Randy Brown	288
Ron Harper	764	Jud Buechler	198
Luc Longley	663	Bill Wennington	167
Scott Burrell	416		

(National Basketball Association, *www.nba.com*)

Michael Jordan

EXAMPLE Find the five-number summary for the number of points scored by the Chicago Bulls during the 1997–98 season (use the table above).

▶ **Solution**

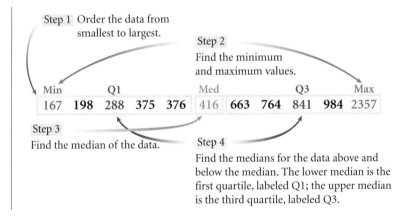

Step 1 Order the data from smallest to largest.

Step 2 Find the minimum and maximum values.

Min		Q1			Med		Q3		Max
167	198	288	375	376	416	663	764	841	984	2357

Step 3 Find the median of the data.

Step 4 Find the medians for the data above and below the median. The lower median is the first quartile, labeled Q1; the upper median is the third quartile, labeled Q3.

LESSON OBJECTIVES

- Calculate *quartiles, interquartile range*, and a *five-number summary* of a data set
- Create a *box plot* of a data set
- Given a list of data, use a calculator to graph a box plot
- Interpret box plots
- Decide the appropriateness of a box plot for a given data set
- Formally define *outlier*

NCTM STANDARDS

CONTENT		PROCESS	
✔	Number		Problem Solving
	Algebra	✔	Reasoning
	Geometry	✔	Communication
	Measurement	✔	Connections
✔	Data/Probability	✔	Representation

The five-number summary is 167, 288, 416, 841, 2357. This is the minimum, first quartile, median, third quartile, and maximum in order from smallest to largest. The first quartile, median, and third quartile divide the data into four equal groups. Each of the four groups has the same number of values, in this case two.

A five-number summary helps you better understand the spread of the data along the number line. It also helps you compare different sets of data. A **box plot** is a visual way to show a five-number summary. This box plot shows the data for the 1997–98 Bulls.

Points scored

Notice how the box plot shows the spread of data and Michael Jordan as an extreme outlier. Can you find the five-number summary values in this box plot? Can you see why this type of graph is sometimes called a **box-and-whisker plot?** In the next investigation you'll see how to use the five-number summary to construct a box plot.

Investigation
Pennies in a Box

You will need

• your dot plot from Investigation: Making "Cents" of the Center

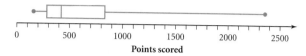

Year

The illustrations are examples only. Your box plot should look different.

Step 1 | Find the five-number summary values for your penny data.

Step 2 | Place a clean sheet of paper over your dot plot and trace the number line. Using the same scale will help you compare your dot plot and box plot.

Step 3 | Find the median value on your number line and draw a short vertical line segment just above it. Repeat this process for the first quartile and the third quartile.

Min   Q1   Med   Q3   Max

Step 4 | Place dots above your number line to represent the minimum and maximum values from your dot plot.

This worker is counting and bagging pennies at the U.S. Mint in Denver, Colorado.

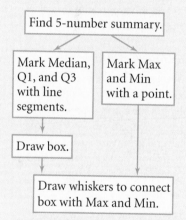

Guiding the Investigation

After groups have gathered, be sure students have their dot plots from the investigation in Lesson 1.2. You can provide a copy of the sample to any group that doesn't have its own data set.

One Step

If your class is experienced at investigations, ask them to figure out a way of graphing the five-number summary of their pennies data. During sharing time, introduce the ideas of box plot and interquartile range and have students make box plots on their calculators.

Steps 1–6 [ELL] Students might benefit from making a flow chart of the process of making a box plot.

Find 5-number summary.

Mark Median, Q1, and Q3 with line segments.

Mark Max and Min with a point.

Draw box.

Draw whiskers to connect box with Max and Min.

Step 3 If the median falls between two data points, then the lower point is considered part of the lower half of the data and the upper point part of the upper half.

• The mean is affected by an outlier (Jordan).

• The data are in order from largest to smallest.

• The median does not illustrate the wide spread of the data.

• There is no mode.

• The box plot shows the number-line position better than the table does.

• You can't tell the number of data points from the box plot.

• Quartiles are not quarters but rather the boundary values of the quarters.

• The five-number summary and box plot show the spread of data better than range does.

Step 6 [ELL] Be sure students understand the word *symmetric*. A box plot is symmetric when the first and last pairs of consecutive numbers in the five-number summary have the same difference, and the second and third pairs do as well. You might challenge students to come up with a data set that has a symmetric box plot.

Step 7 Calculator Note 1D gives instructions for making a box plot on a calculator. Don't clear out the penny list if it's still there from Lesson 1.2.

Step 7 Students should compare the relative size of the box and whiskers to determine whether the plots are equivalent.

Step 9 Answers to 9a and the first part of 9b will depend on the data set. You might rephrase 9c to ask about percents as well as fractions, as a review.

SHARING IDEAS

You can compare box plots if you ask all students to use the same length for a unit on their number line (such as 1 cm for 1 yr). Ask several groups of students to put their box plots on transparencies, and then overlay them for comparison.

[Ask] "What if you had 10,000 pennies and you wanted to show how many were minted in various years?" Discussion of this question can lead into the idea of histograms in Lesson 1.4.

Students might wonder how the IQR is used. **[Ask]** "Can we use the IQR to define outliers?" This question is answered in Exercise 10, so you need only encourage discussion here.

Assessing Progress

From your observations during the lesson, you can assess students' facility at finding the median and their understanding of dot plots and spread.

Step 5 Draw a rectangle with ends at the first and third quartiles. This is the "box." Finally, draw horizontal segments that extend from each end of the box to the minimum and maximum values. These are the "whiskers."

Step 6 Compare your dot plot and box plot. On which graph is it easier to locate the five-number summary? Which graph helps you to see the spread of data better?

Step 6 The five-number summary is clearly displayed by a box plot; the dot plot shows the actual data; both show the spread.

Remember that the first quartile, median, and third quartile divide the data items into four equal groups. Although each section has the same number of data items, your boxes and whiskers may vary in length. Some box plots will be more *symmetric* than others. When would that happen?

Step 7 Enter your penny mint years into list L_1, and draw a calculator box plot. [▶ 🖥] Follow the procedure outlined in **Calculator Note 1D**. ◀ Does your calculator box plot look equivalent to the plot you drew by hand?

Step 8 Use the trace function on your calculator. What values are displayed as you trace the box plot? Are the five-number summary values the same as those you found before? The five-number summary values shown should be the same as calculated previously.

The difference between the first quartile and third quartile is the **interquartile range, or IQR.** Like the range, the interquartile range helps describe the spread in the data.

Step 9 Complete this investigation by answering these questions.

a. What are the range and IQR of your data?

b. How many pennies fall between the first and third quartiles of the graph? What fraction of the total number of pennies is this number? Will this fraction always be the same? Explain. about $\frac{1}{2}$

c. Under what conditions will exactly $\frac{1}{4}$ of the pennies be in each whisker of the box plot? The number of data points must be a multiple of 4.

keymath.com/DA

[▶ You can explore relationships between a data set and its box plot using the **Dynamic Algebra Exploration** at www.keymath.com/DA . ◀]

Box plots are a good way to compare two data sets. These box plots summarize the final test scores for two of Ms. Werner's algebra classes. Use what you have learned to compare these two graphs. Which class has the greater range of scores? Which has the greater IQR? In which class did the greatest fraction of students score above 80?

Notice that neither graph shows the number of students in the class or the individual scores. If knowing each data value is important, then a box plot is not the best choice to display your data.

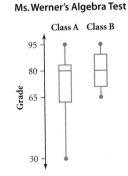

Ms. Werner's Algebra Test

Closing the Lesson

Point out the two box plots showing test scores. Vertical plots, with low numbers on the bottom, foreshadow the coordinate system in Lesson 1.6. If you have time, ask students to write a comparison of the two box plots. Class A has the greatest range and the greatest IQR. In both classes, half the class scored above 80.

This lesson shows how to describe the spread of a data set more completely than with just the range.

Statistically, the **five-number summary** includes the **first quartile,** Q1 (the median of the first half of the data values), and the **third quartile,** Q3 (the median of the second half), as well as the minimum, maximum, and median of the whole data set. The **interquartile range, or IQR,** is given by Q3−Q1. Graphically, these five numbers can be represented in a **box plot** (or **box-and-whisker plot**) in which vertical lines at Q3 and Q1 form two sides of a box, from which whiskers extend to the minimum and maximum. The box plot also has a vertical line at the median.

EXERCISES

Practice Your Skills

1. Find the five-number summary for each data set.
   a. {5, 5, 8, 10, 14, 16, 22, 23, 32, 32, 37, 37, 44, 45, 50} ⓐ 5, 10, 23, 37, 50
   b. {10, 15, 20, 22, 25, 30, 30, 33, 34, 36, 37, 41, 47, 50} 10, 22, 31.5, 37, 50
   c. {44, 16, 42, 20, 25, 26, 14, 37, 26, 33, 40, 26, 47} ⓐ 14, 22.5, 26, 41, 47
   d. {47, 43, 35, 34, 32, 21, 17, 16, 11, 9, 5, 5} 5, 10, 19, 34.5, 47

2. Sketch each graph on your own paper.

   i.
   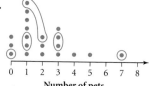
   Number of pets

   ii.
   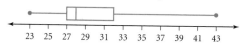
   Pulse rate (bpm)

   a. Circle the points that represent the five-number summary values. If two data points are needed to calculate the median, first quartile, or third quartile, draw a circle around both points.
   b. List the five-number summary values for each data set. ⓐ i. 0, 1, 1.5, 3, 7; ii. 64, 75, 80, 86, 93

3. Give the five-number summary and create a box plot for the listed values.
   {2, 6, 4, 9, 1, 6, 4, 7, 2, 8, 5, 6, 9, 3, 6, 7, 5, 4, 8}

4. Which data set matches this box plot? (More than one answer may be correct.) a, d

   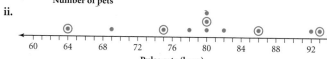

   a. {23, 25, 26, 28, 28, 28, 28, 30, 31, 33, 41, 43}
   b. {23, 23, 24, 25, 26, 27, 29, 30, 31, 33, 41, 43}
   c. {23, 27, 28, 28, 33, 43}
   d. {23, 27, 28, 28, 29, 32, 43}

5. Check your vocabulary by answering these questions.
   a. How does the term *quartile* relate to how data values are grouped when using a five-number summary? ⓐ
   b. What is the name for the difference between the minimum and maximum values in a five-number summary? ⓐ the range
   c. What is the name for the difference between the third quartile and first quartile in a five-number summary? the interquartile range, or IQR
   d. How are outliers of a data set related to the whiskers of its box plot? Outliers are at or near the minimum and maximum values, which are the endpoints of the whiskers.

▶ Helping with the Exercises

Exercise 3 Students may have trouble deciding how to mark the axis. Point out that the maximum and minimum values determine the endpoints. It is not necessary to extend the number line beyond these points, nor is it wrong to do so.

3. 1, 4, 6, 7, 9

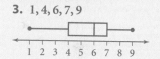

5a. Quartiles are the boundaries dividing a data set into four groups, or quarters, with the same number of values.

Exercise 6
Watch for misreading "mean score" as "median score." As a good extension, **[Ask]** "How much of this exercise could he solve if 25.5 were the median score instead of the mean?" [The missing score would have to be smaller than the median. In fact, 25.5 must be halfway between the missing score and 27, so the missing score would be 24.]

7b. The mean for the 1997–98 Bulls is about 675 points, and the mean for the 2003–04 Bulls is about 564 points; the medians are 416 points and 360 points, respectively. The means are both much higher than the medians because both teams have a few players who score very high. However, the 1997–98 mean is much higher than the 2003–04 mean because Michael Jordan scored so many total points.

7c. The median probably best represents the total-points-scored data for the 1997–98 Bulls. Students can justify choosing either the mean or the median for the 2003–04 Bulls. As a team owner, you might think the mean better reflects your team's talents.

7d. The box for the 2003–04 Bulls is longer, indicating that more of the team members are grouped toward the center. The minimum number of points scored by a player is about the same, but the maximum is much higher for the 1997–98 Bulls.

The Fathom demonstration Five-Number Summaries and Box Plots can be used as a replacement for Exercise 7. If you use Fathom, or other statistical software with your students, you might mention that there is more than one way to define quartile. Students may occasionally notice a discrepancy between their own calculations and the Q1 and Q3 values calculated by the software.

Reason and Apply

6. Stu had a mean score of 25.5 on four 30-point papers in English. He remembers three scores: 23, 29, and 27.

   a. Estimate the fourth score without actually calculating it. *The prediction should be less than the mean.*

   b. Check your estimate by calculating the fourth score. *@* 23 points

   c. What is the five-number summary for this situation? 23, 23, 25, 28, 29

   d. Does it make sense to have a five-number summary for this data set? Explain why or why not. *Because there are only four values, a five-number summary may be inappropriate—the values themselves illustrate the spread of the data.*

7. **APPLICATION** Here are the points scored by the top Chicago Bulls players in the 2003–04 season.

Points Scored by Chicago Bulls Who Played over 40 Games (2003–04 Season)

Chicago Bulls	Total points scored
Jamal Crawford	1383
Eddy Curry	1070
Kirk Hinrich	915
Antonio Davis	579
Kendall Gill	539
Marcus Fizer	360
Jerome Williams	345
Eddie Robinson	343
Ronald Dupree	292
Jannero Pargo	207
Linton Johnson	173

(National Basketball Association, *www.nba.com*)
[Data sets: **BLS03**, **BLS97**]

   a. The five-number summary for the Chicago Bulls' 1997–98 season is 167, 288, 416, 841, 2357. (See the table and example at the beginning of this lesson.) Find the five-number summary for the Chicago Bulls' 2003–04 season. 173, 292, 360, 915, 1383

   b. Find and compare the measures of center for the two Chicago Bulls teams.

   c. Decide which measure of center best describes each team's performance. Explain your answer.

   d. These box plots compare the points scored by the 1997–98 Chicago Bulls players to the points scored by the 2003–04 Chicago Bulls players. Compare the two teams' performance based on what you see in the graphs.

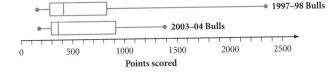

7e. Without Jordan, the range of the data is much smaller, and the box is a little shorter. If Jordan's points scored are eliminated, the 2003–04 Bulls have the higher-scoring players. There is more variation in the number of points scored by individual 2003–04 Bulls than for individual 1997–98 Bulls without Jordan.

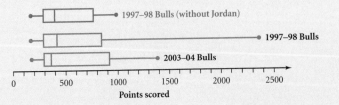

e. Remove Michael Jordan's points from the data table for the 1997–98 Chicago Bulls and make a new box plot. How does this new box plot compare to the original box plot for the 1997–98 Bulls? How does it compare to the box plot for the 2003–04 Bulls?

8. APPLICATION This table lists median weekly earnings of full-time workers by occupation and gender for 2000.

Median Weekly Earnings, 2000

Occupation	Men	Women
Managerial and professional specialty	$999	$697
Executive, administration, and managerial	995	684
Professional specialty	1001	708
Technical, sales, and admin. support	653	451
Technicians and related support	754	539
Sales occupations	683	379
Administrative support including clerical	552	455
Service occupations	405	313
Protective service	636	470
Precision production, craft, and repair	622	439
Mechanics and repairers	645	588
Operators, fabricators, and laborers	492	353
Machine operators, assemblers, and inspectors	498	353
Transportation and material moving	555	421
Handlers, equipment cleaners, helpers, and laborers	401	329
Farming, forestry, and fishing	342	288

(Bureau of Labor Statistics, *www.bls.gov*)

a. Make two box plots, one for men's salaries and one for women's salaries, above the same number line. Use them to compare the two data sets. Use the terms you have learned in this chapter. @

b. What do the data tell you about women's and men's wages for the same type of work in 2000?

c. Do the box plots help you identify characteristics of the data better than the table does? Are there any aspects of the data that are better seen in the table?

d. How could you use the box plots to explain the slogan "Equal pay for equal work"?

During World War II many women took nontraditional jobs to support war industries. Some fought for and achieved equal pay for equal work.

7e. See page 56.

Exercise 8 [ELL] Be sure students understand that the slogan "Equal pay for equal work" states that men and women in the same job should be paid the same salary. Historically, women have earned less than men.

You might have students compile their own lists of recent data from the website. **[Alert]** Students may miss the meaning of *median weekly earnings*. If needed, point out that the table shows weekly earnings. Students need to put the data in order before they can determine the summary values.

8a. For men, the mean salary is $639.56, and the five-number summary is 342, 495, 629, 718.5, 1001; for women, the mean salary is approximately $466.69, and the five-number summary is 288, 353, 445, 563.5, 708.

8b. Women received less pay than men for the same type of work.

8c. The box plots highlight the discrepancy in pay and spread of the data; however, dollar amount comparisons within a single profession are possible only in the table.

8d. Answers will vary. In 2000, gender equity did not exist for pay.

Median Weekly Earnings, 2000

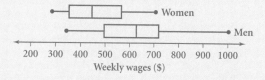

Exercise 9 [Language] The skin of a reticulated snake is covered with a pattern that resembles a net. *Reticulated* means "netlike." **[Alert]** Students may miss the fact that each data set has ten points. Or, students may say that the length of the fifth-longest snake is at the median of the ten data points. Have them create a data set in which that's not the case. The box plots aren't comparable, because the markings on the number line refer to completely different quantities: lengths and speeds.

9d. The ten longest snakes vary in length from about 8 ft to 35 ft. About half of the snakes have lengths from about 11 ft to 25 ft. Running speeds of the ten fastest mammals vary from 42 mi/h to 65 mi/h. About half of the speeds are between 43 mi/h and 50 mi/h. The cheetah appears to run much faster than most other mammals.

9e. No; the units of these data sets are different.

Exercise 10 This essential exercise defines *outlier*. Remind students that in Lesson 1.2 we saw that outliers are important in their effect on the mean. Sometimes statisticians look at the statistics (measures) of the data both with and without the data points that meet this definition of *outlier*. If you used the term *limit* in Chapter 0, be sure students realize that its use in 10d is very different.

11. One possibility is a family with ages 4, 10, 14, 39, and 43. The 14 is fixed, and the total of all ages must be 110 years.

---

9. These box plots display the recorded lengths of the ten longest snakes and the recorded running speeds for the ten fastest mammals.

Longest Snakes

5 10 15 20 25 30 35
Length (ft)

(*Factastic Book of 1001 Lists, 1999*, p. 41)

Fastest Mammals

40 45 50 55 60 65 70
Speed (mi/h)

(*The Top Ten of Everything 2004*, p. 31)

a. The longest snake in the world is believed to be the reticulated python. What is the length of this snake? @ 35 ft

b. The fifth-longest snake is the king cobra. Can you determine its length from the box plot? Explain. @ More information is needed. The length is between 17.5 and 25 ft.

c. The fastest mammal in the world is believed to be the cheetah. What is the fastest recorded speed for a cheetah? 65 mi/h

d. Explain what each box plot tells you about the spread of the data.

e. Could these two box plots be constructed above the same number line? Explain. @

f. The fifth- and sixth-fastest mammals (Grant's gazelle and Thomson's gazelle) have been recorded at the same maximum speed. About how fast can they run? @ about 47 mi/h

10. As a general rule, if the distance of a data point from the nearest end of the box is more than 1.5 times the length of the box (or IQR), then it qualifies as an outlier.

$1.5 \cdot IQR$ IQR $1.5 \cdot IQR$ Outliers

a. The five-number summary for the number of points scored by the 1997–98 Chicago Bulls players is 167, 288, 416, 841, 2357. What is 1.5 times the interquartile range? 829.5

b. What is the value of the first quartile minus 1.5 times the interquartile range? -541.5

c. What is the value of the third quartile plus 1.5 times the interquartile range? 1670.5

d. The values you found in 10b and c are the limits of outlier values. Identify any 1997–98 Chicago Bulls players who are outliers. An outlier would have to score fewer than -541.5 points or more than 1670.5 points. Michael Jordan is an outlier.

▶ **Review**

1.2 **11.** Create a data set for a family of five with a mean age of 22 years and a median age of 14.

1.1 **12.** The majority of pets in the United States are cats.

a. How many pet cats are there in the United States? Use the pictograph below. @ 76 million

b. How many fewer dogs are there? 15 million

c. If small mammals (21 million) were added to the pictograph below, how many pawprints would be drawn to represent them? ("Small mammals" includes rabbits and small rodents.) @ $10\frac{1}{2}$ pawprints

Pets in the United States

Cat

Dog

🐾 = 2 million

(Euromonitor, in *The Top 10 of Everything 2004*, pp. 40–41)

Histograms and Stem-and-Leaf Plots

This dot plot provides information about the amount of pocket money 16 students had with them on a given day. If you collect similar data for all the students in your school, you probably wouldn't want to make a dot plot because you would have too many dots. A box plot could be used to show the spread of the data set, but it wouldn't show whether you polled 16 or 600 students.

Pocket Money

Amount of pocket money ($)

A **histogram** is related to a dot plot, but is more useful than a dot plot when you have a large data set. Histograms use columns to display how data are distributed and reveal clusters and gaps in the data. Unlike bar graphs, which use categories, the data for histograms must be numeric and ordered along the horizontal axis.

This histogram shows the same data as the dot plot.

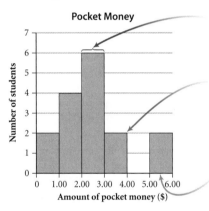

Pocket Money

Number of students

Amount of pocket money ($)

The width of each column represents an interval of $1.00. These intervals are also called **bins.**

The height of each bin shows the number of students whose money falls in that interval. This is the **frequency** of each bin.

Boundary values fall in the bin to the right. That is, this bin is $5.00 to $5.99.

All bins in a histogram have the same width, and the columns are drawn next to each other without any space between them. A gap between columns means that there is an interval with no data items that have those values. You can't name the individual values represented in a histogram, so a histogram summarizes data. You *can* determine the total number of data items. The sum of the bar heights in the histogram above tells you the total number of students.

NCTM STANDARDS

CONTENT		PROCESS	
✔	Number	✔	Problem Solving
	Algebra	✔	Reasoning
✔	Geometry		Communication
✔	Measurement	✔	Connections
✔	Data/Probability	✔	Representation

LESSON OBJECTIVES

- Create a histogram and a stem-and-leaf plot of a data set
- Given a list of data, use a calculator to graph a histogram
- Interpret histograms and stem-and-leaf plots
- Decide the appropriateness of a histogram and a stem-and-leaf plot for a given data set

LESSON OUTLINE

One day:

10 min	Introduction
20 min	Investigation
5 min	Sharing
5 min	Example
5 min	Closing
5 min	Exercises

MATERIALS

- graph paper
- centimeter rulers
- Hand-Span Sample Data (W, one copy per group), *optional*
- Calculator Note 1E
- Fathom demonstration Hand Spans, *optional*

Histograms are used for data with whole-number values, as well as for continuous, measured values.

INTRODUCTION

[ELL] Be sure students understand the meaning of the word *bin.* After forming groups, remind the class that in the previous lesson the box plot didn't show the actual numbers of pennies, as a dot plot would have. On the other hand, if they'd had lots of pennies, drawing a dot plot—with one dot per penny—would have been time-consuming. Ask for ideas of how to show the actual numbers in a large sample. Encourage a variety of suggestions.

Ask students to read through the introduction to themselves, and then have several students read it aloud.

You might mention that the word *histogram* comes from the Greek words *histo*, which means "beam," and *gram*, which means "graph."

Point out that bins are named by the boundary values. The boundary item falls in the bin to the right. For discrete values, it is possible to list both ends of each bin, such as 0–9, 10–19, 20–29. For continuous data, bins are designated by the smallest number and the number that all values in the bin are less than, such as 0–10, 10–20, 20–30. Though intervals are named differently depending on whether they represent discrete or continuous data, they are always labeled by boundary numbers.

 Guiding the Investigation

The Fathom demonstration Hand Spans can be used with class data or sample data to replace the investigation.

One Step

Ask each group to make a histogram of the hand spans of all the students in the class. Phrasing a problem so that it can be solved in several ways, or is subject to multiple interpretations, helps students understand more deeply the underlying ideas. As they work, remind them that bins need to be the same width, and let them experiment to find appropriate intervals. Pass out Calculator Note 1E to groups that finish their histograms quickly.

For classes following the steps of the investigation, you might want to take more time on the introduction. Point out that using such a long line for so few data items in this dot plot is not economical. Ask the expository questions. The histogram with $1 bins shows that most students have between $2 and $3. The histogram with 50¢ bins shows that most students

See page 722 for a sample graph for Steps 1–6.

When you construct a histogram, you have to decide what bin width works best. These histograms show the same data set but use different bin widths. Use each of the three histograms presented to answer the question "Most students had pocket money between which values?" How do the bin widths of each histogram affect your answers?

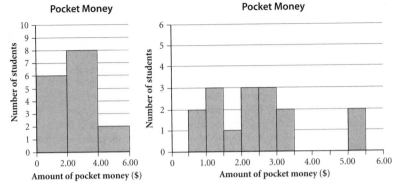

Too many bins may create an information overload. Too few bins may hide some features of the data set. As a general rule, try to have five to ten bins. Of course, there are exceptions.

 ## Investigation
Hand Spans

You will need
- graph paper
- a centimeter ruler

In this investigation you'll collect hand-span measurements and make a histogram. You'll organize the data using different bin widths and compare the results to a box plot.

Step 1   Measure your hand span in centimeters. Post your hand-span measurement in a classroom data table.

Step 2   Mark a zero point on your graph paper. Draw a horizontal axis to the right and a vertical axis up from this point.

Step 3   Scale the horizontal axis for the range of your data. Clearly divide this range into five to ten equal bins. Label the boundary values of each bin.

Step 4   Count the data items that will fall into each bin. For example, in a bin from 20 cm to 22 cm, you would count all the items with values of 20.0, 20.5, 21.0, and 21.5. Items with a value of 22.0 are counted in the next bin.

Step 5   Scale the vertical axis for **frequency,** or count, of data items. Label it from zero to at least the largest bin count.

Step 6   Draw columns showing the correct frequency of the data items for each bin.

have between $1 and $1.50, $2.00 and $2.50, or $2.50 and $3.00. The histogram with $2 bins shows that most students have between $2 and $4. Because the bin size groups the data, the tallest bars vary as the bin sizes change.

Step 1 Measurements should be made to the nearest half centimeter. Record all answers using one decimal place (for example, 20.0, 21.5). Have groups write their measurement data where everyone can see it.

Alternatively, give out the Hand-Span Sample Data worksheet.

Step 3 Bins are labeled by the smallest number that might be in the bin and the number that all values in the bin are less than, such as 20–22, 22–24. Because the hand-span measurements don't start at 0, students may want to use a broken horizontal axis.

Step 7	Enter your hand-span measurements into list L₁ of your calculator. Create several versions of the histogram using different bin widths. [▸ 🖳 See **Calculator Note 1E** for instructions on creating a histogram.◂]
Step 8	How did you select a bin width for your graph-paper histogram? Now that you have experimented with calculator bin widths, would you change the bin width of your paper graph? Write a paragraph explaining how to pick the "best" bin width.
Step 9	Add a box plot of your hand-span data to both your graph-paper and calculator versions of the histogram. What information does the histogram provide that the box plot does not? Consider gaps in the data and the shape of the histogram.

A graph that is often useful for small data sets is a **stem plot**, or **stem-and-leaf plot**. A stem plot, like a dot plot, displays each individual item. But, like a histogram, data values are grouped into intervals or bins. You need a **key** to interpret a stem plot.

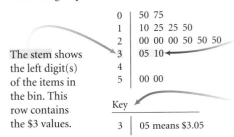

The stem shows the left digit(s) of the items in the bin. This row contains the $3 values.

```
0 | 50 75
1 | 10 25 25 50
2 | 00 00 00 50 50 50
3 | 05 10
4 |
5 | 00 00
```

The leaves show the digits that complete each value. There was one value of $3.05 and one value of $3.10.

The key helps you read the information.

Key
```
3 | 05 means $3.05
```

EXAMPLE

Use the stem-and-leaf plot to draw a histogram of the Canadian universities data.

▸ **Solution**

First, find the range of the data: 1995 − 1852 = 143 years. Then consider a "friendly" bin width. For a bin width of 10 years you'd need at least 15 bins, which is too many. For a bin width of 25 years you'd need 6 bins, which is more manageable.

You could start the first bin with the minimum value, 1852. However, it may be better to round down to 1850 so that each boundary will be a multiple of 25, and the centuries 1900 and 2000 will fall on boundaries.

Establishment Dates for Canadian Universities (1850–2000)

```
185 | 2  2  3  7
186 | 3  5
187 | 1  3  3  6  7  8
188 | 7  7
189 | 0  9
190 | 0  5  6  7  7  8
191 | 0  0  0  1  3  3  7  9
192 | 1  5
193 | 6
194 | 2  5  8
195 | 4  4  7  9
196 | 0  2  3  3  3  4  4  5  5  5  7  8  9  9
197 | 0  0  4  4  4  6  8  9
198 | 2
199 | 2  4  5
```

Key
```
197 | 3  means 1973
```

(Association of Universities and Colleges of Canada, *www.aucc.ca*)

- one axis of a bar graph represents (usually) non-numeric categories.
- All intervals in a histogram should have the same width.
- The boundaries between intervals should be easy numbers to work with.
- Five to ten bins is usually about right.
- There should be enough intervals of the right size to show the distribution.

- Wider intervals obscure gaps and clusters in the data.
- Bins should be drawn next to each other, with no space between them.
- A gap between bins indicates no data in that interval.
- A data value on the right boundary of an interval belongs in the next interval to the right.

Step 7 The calculator note instructs students to use a broken horizontal axis "Xmin equal to or slightly less than minimum of data." Suggest that they try using Xmin = 0 for comparison. In most histograms, the first bin begins at a multiple of the bin width.

Also suggest that when they have a histogram on the graphics screen, they use the calculator's trace function and note the endpoints of the intervals. This will demonstrate to them that boundary values are in the rightmost bin.

Step 8 For their paper histograms, students probably used the five to ten bins recommended in the instructions. For their calculator graphs, students should discover more subjective criteria, such as choosing "nice" boundary points and using a number of bins that accurately shows the distribution of the data. Paragraph write-ups will vary. Suggest that students exchange paragraphs and get peer feedback.

SHARING IDEAS

If students present to the full class as well as (or instead of) exchanging papers, they might show the results of Steps 6 and 9.

In discussing which histogram bin width is better, students may say that the histogram with wider intervals contains more data. The larger area of the bars can mislead those who are having trouble with the abstraction of the graphic representation. The difficulty is so common, yet so hard for students to articulate, that you might mention it even if nobody brings it up. **[Ask]** "Does this histogram represent more data than that one?"

As sharing takes place, you might want to compile a common list of students' observations of the important characteristics of histograms, such as these:

- Both axes of a histogram are marked with numbers, whereas

To offer further experience with histograms, this example concerns turning a stem-and-leaf plot into a histogram. For a histogram with 15 bins, draw columns around the leaves.

Students may need help to see that at least 15 bins are needed for widths of 10 years $\left(\frac{143}{10}\right.$ is more than 14$\left.\right)$ and 6 bins for a width of 25 years $\left(\frac{143}{25}\right.$ is more than 5$\left.\right)$.

As students explore different bin widths on their calculators, they should find that a bin width of 10 years looks erratic, with frequencies alternating between high and low. A bin width of 20, 25, or 30 years looks somewhat more uniform, with not too many bins. A bin width of 50 years shows an increasing trend but uses only three bins.

Assessing Progress

Your observations of students during this lesson can help you assess their skills at counting, scaling, and organizing data and their understanding of histograms.

Closing the Lesson

Summarize for the class the two kinds of graphs introduced in this lesson: **stem plots (stem-and-leaf plots)** are a way to organize the data to show shape and distribution. **Histograms** can better show these properties. They retain information about the number of data values but not the specific values. Box plots are even more of a summary. They can clearly show spread and center but not the specifics of the size and shape of the data set.

BUILDING UNDERSTANDING

In the exercises students deepen their understanding of histograms and stem plots by connecting them with ideas presented earlier in the chapter.

Count the frequency for each bin. You could use a table like this:

Bin	1850–1874	1875–1899	1900–1924	1925–1949	1950–1974	1975–1999
Frequency	9	7	15	5	23	7

Then create your histogram.

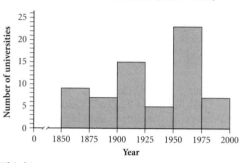

Establishment Dates for Canadian Universities (1850–2000)

This histogram may or may not use the best bin width. Use your calculator to experiment with other bin widths for the data. Which bin width do you think highlights the spread of the data? Which do you feel highlights the clustering of data? Does one bin width show an increasing trend?

When making a histogram, you may need to experiment with different bin widths. You may wish to change your minimum value as you do this so that it is a multiple of the bin width.

EXERCISES

You will need your graphing calculator for Exercise **6.**

▶ Practice Your Skills

1. Maive surveyed people attending matinee and evening ballet performances. She made the two graphs below showing the ages of attendees whom she surveyed.

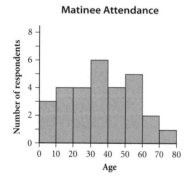

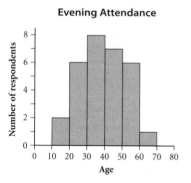

a. How many people did she survey at each performance? ⓗ matinee: 29; evening: 30

ASSIGNING HOMEWORK

Essential	1–7, 10
Performance assessment	1, 7, 11, 12
Portfolio	6, 10
Journal	8, 9, 11
Group	6, 8, 12
Review	13, 14

b. At which performance did the ages of survey respondents vary more? matinee

c. How many children younger than 10 responded to the survey at the evening performance? @ none

d. What can you say about the number of 15-year-olds surveyed at the matinee? The number is less than or equal to 4.

2. Thirty students participated in a 20-problem mathematics competition. Here are the numbers of problems they got correct:

{12, 7, 8, 3, 5, 7, 10, 13, 7, 10, 2, 1, 11, 12, 17, 4, 11, 7, 6, 18, 14, 17, 11, 9, 1, 12, 10, 12, 2, 15}

a. Construct two histograms for the data. Use different bin widths for each.

b. What patterns do you notice in the data? What do the histograms tell you about the number of problems that students tend to get correct? One observation is that student scores tended to be in the middle of the range.

c. Give the five-number summary for the data and construct a box plot.

d. Give the mode(s) for the data. 7, 12

3. This box plot and histogram reflect the life expectancy in 2000 for countries with populations greater than 10 million.

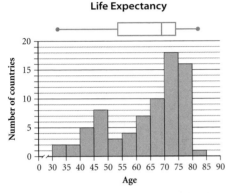

Life Expectancy

(United Nations Population Fund, in *The New York Times Almanac 2004*, pp. 475–477)

a. How many countries are represented? @ 76

b. The box that spans from the median to the third quartile of the box plot is very short. What does this mean? @

c. How many countries had life expectancies of less than 60 years? 24

d. How can you tell that no country had a life expectancy of greater than 85 years?

4. Redraw the histogram for Exercise 3, changing the bin width from 5 to 10.

5. Suppose some class members measure the lengths of their ring fingers. The measurements are 6.5, 6.5, 7.0, 6.0, 7.5, 7.0, 8.5, and 7.0 cm.

a. Identify the minimum, maximum, and range values of the data. minimum: 6.0 cm; maximum: 8.5 cm; range: 2.5 cm

b. Create a stem plot of these data values. @

4.

Life Expectancy

Number of countries vs Age (yr)

Exercise 5 On a stem-and-leaf plot, usually the first digits of numbers are on the left side of the vertical bar and later digits are on the right.

5b. Ring Finger Length

```
6 | 0  5  5
7 | 0  0  0  5
8 | 5
```

Key

```
6 | 0  means 6.0 cm
```

Exercises 2c and 2d Students may be surprised that they can't find the five-number summary from a histogram. Point out this disadvantage of histograms.

2a. possible graphs:

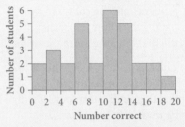

Number of Problems Correct in Math Competition

Number of Problems Correct in Math Competition

2c. 1, 6, 10, 12, 18

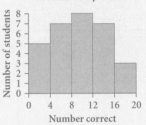

Number of Problems Correct in Math Competition

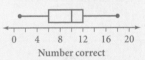

Exercise 3 The people pictured are from India, Ecuador, Kenya (Masai tribe), France, Uighur (western China), and India.

3b. Approximately $\frac{1}{4}$ of the countries had a life expectancy between approximately 69 yr and 74 yr.

3d. There are no bins to the right of 85 in the histogram. Also, the maximum point in the box plot is located at approximately 83 yr.

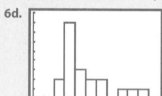
▶ Reason and Apply

6. The histogram displays the passenger-car information listed in the table.

Top 20 Selling Passenger Cars in the United States in 2002

Car	Number sold	Car	Number sold
Toyota Camry	434,145	Buick Century	163,739
Honda Accord	398,980	Pontiac Grand Am	150,818
Ford Taurus	332,690	Volkswagen Jetta	145,604
Honda Civic	131,159	Ford Mustang	138,356
Toyota Corolla	254,360	Buick LeSabre	135,916
Ford Focus	243,199	Pontiac Grand Prix	130,141
Chevrolet Cavalier	238,225	Dodge Neon	126,118
Nissan Altima	201,822	Hyundai Elantra	120,638
Chevrolet Impala	198,918	Saturn S	117,533
Chevrolet Malibu	169,377	BMW 3 Series	115,428

(Ward's Communications, in *The World Almanac and Book of Facts 2004*, p. 322) [Data set: TPCAR]

a. What does 24 on the horizontal axis represent? @

b. Explain the meaning of the first bin of this graph. @

c. List calculator window values that would produce this graph. Give your answer in brackets like this: [Xmin, Xmax, Xscl, Ymin, Ymax, Yscl]. @

d. Graph this histogram on your calculator and on graph paper.

e. Use the table and your histogram to approximate the values of a five-number summary. @

f. Graph a box plot on your calculator, and then sketch this plot above the histogram you drew in 6d.

2002 Sales

[histogram: Number of models vs. Cars sold (times 10,000)]

7. Sketch what you think a histogram looks like for each situation below. Remember to label values and units on the axes. Answers will vary.

a. The outcomes when rolling a die 100 times. @

b. The estimates of the height of the classroom ceiling made by 100 different students.

c. The ages of the next 100 people you meet in the school hallway.

d. The 100 data values used to make the box plot below. (Use a bin width of 1.)

[box plot on number line from 0 to 10]

8. Create a data set with eight data values for each graph.

a.
(ℎ)

b.
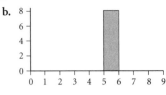

c.
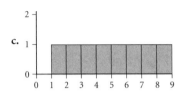

d.
(ℎ)
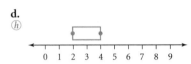

9. APPLICATION The histogram shows the results of an assessment on which 30 points were possible.

   a. How would you assign the grades A–D?

   b. Using your grading scheme, what grade would you assign the student represented by the bin farthest to the right?

   c. Write a short description explaining why your grading scheme is a "fair" distribution of grades. Include comments about the measures of center, the variability, and the shape of the distribution.

10. Chip and Dale, two algebra students, visited four different stores and recorded the prices on 1-pound bags of potato chips. They organized their data in the stem plot at right.

   a. What is the lowest price they found? @ $1.50

   b. What do the entries in the third line from the top represent?

   c. How many bags cost less than $2? 14

   d. What is the most common price? $1.99

   e. What is the range of prices for these chips? $1.09

Assessment Results

Potato Chip Prices

15	0 0 9
16	9 9
17	5 9
18	5 9
19	9 9 9 9 9
20	9
21	5 9 9 9
22	5 9 9
23	9
24	
25	9

Key

| 25 | 9   means $2.59 |

Exercise 8a If students say "The box is missing," you might say that it has been "squeezed."

8a. {1, 7, 7, 7, 7, 7, 7, 9}; the Q1 value, the median, and the Q3 value are all 7.

Exercises 8b and 8c You might point out that data may include fractions.

8b. {5, 5, 5, 5, 5, 5, 5, 5}; each value could be any number from 5 up to, but not including, 6.

8c. {1, 2, 3, 4, 5, 6, 7, 8}; these values could have any number of digits after the decimal point.

Exercise 8d Now the whiskers have been "squeezed."

8d. {2, 2, 2, 2, 2, 4, 4, 4} or {2, 2, 2, 4, 4, 4, 4, 4}; the minimum and Q1 are 2, Q3 and the maximum are 4, and the median is either 2 or 4; so the median coincides with Q1 or Q3, respectively.

9a. Perhaps the top two get As, and the next seven (down to 15 points) get Bs. Those with 9 to 15 points would get Cs, and the bottom three would get Ds. Students who score in the center (mean, median, and mode) get a C grade.

9b. The outlier gets an A.

9c. Answers will vary.

10b. chips priced $1.75 and $1.79

Exercise 11a You can introduce the terms *skewed right* (Hospital A), *skewed left* (Hospital B), *uniform* (Hospital C), and *symmetrical* or *modal* here. Students may use less technical language, such as "higher to the right" or "mounded in the middle," to describe the shapes of the graphs.

11a. Hospital A's histogram is mounded toward the left. Hospital B's histogram is mounded toward the right. Hospital C's histogram has all bins of equal height. Hospital D's histogram is mounded in the middle.

11b. Hospital A had more short waiting times and fewer long waiting times. Patients at Hospital B had fewer short waiting times and more long waiting times. An equal number of patients were in each time range at Hospital C. At Hospital D, the largest number of patients had waiting times of 20–25 min; as the waiting time gets farther from that central value, there are fewer and fewer patients.

11c. Answers will vary. No patient at Hospital B had to wait longer than 30 min, while approximately 40% of patients at Hospital A had to wait longer than 30 min. However, few patients at Hospital B waited less than 10 min, while almost 20% of patients at Hospital A waited less than 10 min.

Exercise 12 [Alert] Some students may say that Mac has more apples because his graph has more bins. Point out the different scaling on the vertical axis.

12a. Ida weighed the apples from the market, which are more uniform in weight, and Mac weighed the backyard apples, whose weights vary more widely.

12b. Mac's apples had a greater variety of weights; they were less uniform than Ida's apples.

---

11. APPLICATION Four hospital emergency rooms collected data on how long patients on a given day waited before being seen. They created these histograms:

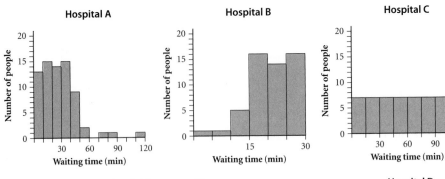

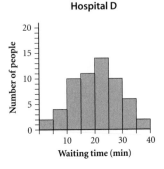

a. Describe the shape of each histogram. @

b. What do the histograms tell you about waiting times at each hospital?

c. Did patients at Hospital A generally have shorter waiting times than patients at Hospital B? Explain.

d. In an emergency, which hospital would you want to go to?

Answers will vary. Students may prefer Hospital B because all patients were seen in less than 30 min. At Hospital A, many patients were seen in less than 20 min, but some patients had to wait a very long time.

12. Mac and Ida each weighed all of the apples in a basket. One of them weighed apples bought from the farmer's market. The other weighed apples from a backyard tree. Each found they had the same number of apples and their apples had the same mean weight. They made histograms showing their apple weights.

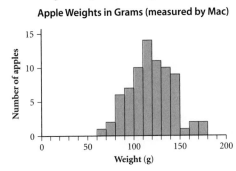 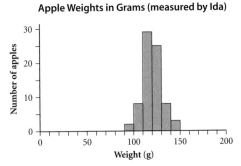

a. Who weighed the backyard apples and who weighed the purchased apples? Explain your reasoning. @

b. What differences in the two baskets of apples are indicated by the histograms?

c. What is similar about the shapes of the histograms? What might explain this similarity?

Both histograms are shaped like mounds, higher in the middle and decreasing in height toward the sides; more apples have weights near the mean, and fewer apples have weights farther from the mean.

13.

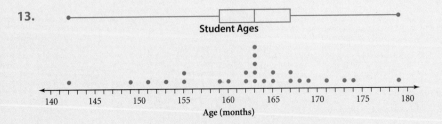

▶ Review

1.3 **13.** Re-create on your paper this dot plot representing ages (in months) for students in an algebra class. Then add a box plot of the data to your graph.

13. See page 66.

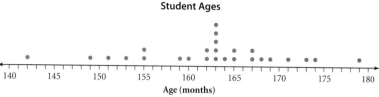

Student Ages

1.3 **14.** Create a data set of nine test scores with a five-number summary of 64, 72, 82, 82, 95 and a mean of 79. One possibility is $\{\underline{64}, 70, 74, 80, \underline{82}, \underline{82}, \underline{82}, 82, \underline{95}\}$; the underlined values are fixed.

project

COMPARE COMMUNITIES

The U.S. Bureau of the Census collects data on people from all over the United States. Citizens and governments use these data to make informed decisions and to develop programs that best serve diverse communities. Here are two box plots that use census data to compare the ages of 50 people from two communities.

Fathom™

These box plots were made with Fathom. You can use this software to work with many more people, attributes, or communities than you could by hand. Learn how to use Fathom to make a wide range of interesting graphs.

Compare Communities Project
Sample data sets are available as part of the data supplied with Fathom.

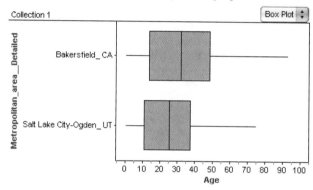

Fathom Dynamic Data™ Software lists official census data for many people in various communities. Compare two communities using three or more attributes such as gender, age, race, ancestry, marital status, education level, or income. Your project should include

▶ A graph of each attribute, for each community. You can use any type of graph from this chapter.

▶ A summary description of the attributes for each community. Compare and contrast the two communities using values like mean, median, or range.

▶ A written explanation of how you think each community could use your graphs to make decisions.

For more information on the U.S. Census, see the links at **www.keymath.com/DA** .

Supporting the project

MOTIVATION

Ask the questions: "Can you identify the median age, range, and interquartile range in each? Based on the graphs, which community might benefit more from a preschool? A senior center? What other information would help you make decisions like these?"

OUTCOMES

▶ Data are collected on individual people, not groups.
▶ The graphs are appropriate for the attributes chosen and are clearly drawn and labeled.
▶ The statistical terms are used accurately, and the comparisons are valid.

▶ Good mathematical language is used in the explanation.
• The report includes critical remarks on the census and decision-making procedures.

LESSON

1.5

Activity Day

Exploring a Conjecture

Statistics is a branch of applied mathematics dedicated to collecting and analyzing numerical data. The **data analysis** that statisticians do is used in science, government, and social services like health care. In this chapter you have learned concepts fundamental to statistics: measures of center, summary values, and types of graphs to organize and display data. Terms you have learned are in the box at left.

Each measure or graph tells part of the story. Yet having too much information for a data set might not be helpful. Statisticians, and other people who work with data, must choose which measures and graphs give the best picture for a particular situation. Carefully chosen statistics can be informative and persuasive. Poorly chosen statistics, ones that don't show important characteristics of the data set, can be accidentally or deliberately misleading.

data
measures of center
mean
median
mode
range
outlier

five-number summary
minimum
maximum
first quartile (Q1)
third quartile (Q3)
interquartile range (IQR)

pictograph
bar graph
dot plot
box-and-whisker plot
histogram
frequency
stem-and-leaf plot

Activity

The Conjecture

You will need

- two books
- graph paper
- colored pencils or pens
- poster paper

A **conjecture** is a statement that might be true but has not been proven. Your group's goal is to come up with a conjecture relating two things and to collect and analyze the numeric evidence to support your conjecture or cast doubt on it.

In this activity you'll review the measures and graphs you have learned. Along the way, you will be faced with questions that statisticians face every day.

Step 1 | Your group should select two books on different subjects or with different reading levels. Flip through the books, but do not examine them in depth. State a conjecture comparing these two books. Your conjecture should deal with a quantity that you can count or measure—for example, "The history book has more words per sentence than the math book."

PLANNING

LESSON OUTLINE

One day:

25 min	Activity
20 min	Sharing
5 min	Closing

MATERIALS

- books on a variety of topics and of assorted page size, type size, number and type of illustrations, density of print, and so on
- graph paper
- materials for making posters
- Calculator Note 0H

TEACHING

The goal here is to deepen levels of understanding rather than to encounter new material.

No homework exercises are given on activity days. You might want to assign exercises that you have skipped from previous lessons or assign a More Practice Your Skills worksheet.

Guiding the Activity

Step 1 Ask that students get your approval for their conjectures before going to Step 2. Students may suggest conjectures that are not testable because they're not quantitative—they don't involve counting or measuring. Encourage all ideas but also a careful critique of the suggestions.

Examples of testable conjectures are "The first-grade book has words with fewer syllables than the ninth-grade book" and "The chemistry book and the biology book have the same number of words per page." If students are

LESSON OBJECTIVES

- Review the statistics and graphs introduced so far
- Make conjectures about a data set and test them using appropriate statistical and graphical methods
- Use the terminology of statistics and graphs to present conclusions of a study of data

NCTM STANDARDS

CONTENT		PROCESS	
✔	Number	✔	Problem Solving
	Algebra	✔	Reasoning
	Geometry	✔	Communication
	Measurement		Connections
✔	Data/Probability	✔	Representation

Step 2 | Decide how much data you'll need to convince yourself and your group that the conjecture is true or doubtful. Design a way to choose data to count or measure. For example, you might use your calculator to randomly select a page or a sentence. [▶ 🖩 See **Calculator Note 0H** to generate random numbers.◀]

Step 3 | Collect data from both books. Be consistent in your data collection, especially if more than one person is doing the collecting. Assign tasks to each member of your group.

Step 4 | Find the measures of center, range, five-number summary, and IQR for each of the two data sets.

Step 5 | Create a dot plot or stem-and-leaf plot for each set of data.

Step 6 | Make box plots for both data sets above the same horizontal axis.

Step 7 | Make a histogram for each data set.

Be sure that you have used descriptive units for all of your measures and clearly labeled your axes and plots before going on to the next step.

Step 8 | Choose one or two of the measures and one pair of graphs that you feel give the best evidence for or against your conjecture. Prepare a brief report or a poster. Include

   a. Your conjecture.
   b. Tables showing all the data you collected.
   c. The measures and graphs that seem to support or disprove your conjecture.
   d. Your conclusion about your conjecture.

Step 9 | In Step 2, you thought about your design for data collection and you might have used random numbers. In Step 3, you practiced consistency in collecting data. In Steps 4, 5, and 6, you were asked to find many measures and graphs, even though you used only a few of these in your final argument. Write a paragraph explaining how a failure at any one of these steps might have changed your conclusion.

selecting different measures or graphs might show different distributions of data. On the other hand, two truly random samples are likely to produce equivalent results.

[Ask] "How do your graphs demonstrate the truth of your conjecture?" Try to help students realize that there may not be a single best way to represent a data set.

In the context of the report, mention the terms *sample* and *population*. Ask students why they needed to use a sample to get this data set and why their methods for getting the sample matters.

Point out how statistics and graphs can be persuasive. Also point out any examples of how they can be misleading.

Closing the Lesson

To conclude these lessons on one-variable data, you might discuss with students how statistics have become very important to society. For example, why might the first census have been taken? On a broader scale, what other fields of mathematics have been developed for governmental purposes?

having trouble making a conjecture, you might suggest, "Describe this book. Does the same description fit the other book?"

Step 2 Elicit from students how they might get a "random sample" or a "typical sample" of data.

Step 3 Point out any inconsistent data collection within a group. Group members should be measuring or counting in the same way with the same units.

Steps 4–7 Groups can divide the tasks for these steps. **[Alert]** Remind students to label their graphs. As needed, remind students that dot plots and stem plots show individual data items, that box plots help show the distribution but show no individual data items, and that histograms show how data sort into bins.

Step 8 Provide students with clear guidelines for their reports or posters. **[Alert]** Watch for weak support of conjectures.

Step 9 Selecting nonrandom data, such as using only Chapter 1 or only the first page of each chapter, would mean that if there were patterns in the books the data would not show enough variation. If a person counting occurrences of something in one book had a different definition of what an "occurrence" is from someone counting in the other book, then one of the counts could be too low and the other too high. Means and ranges could be influenced by outliers, while medians and IQR might omit significant outliers. Box plots might not show unusual distributions. Any of these things might lead students to an incorrect conclusion.

SHARING IDEAS

Ask at least one group to present its report orally, and ask the class to think about the extent to which the group justified its conclusions.

[Ask] "Could someone use the same data and reach a different conclusion?" Point out that

PLANNING

LESSON OUTLINE

First day:

25 min   Introduction, Investigation

10 min   Sharing

15 min   Begin Example

Second day:

25 min   Finish Example

10 min   Closing

15 min   Exercises

MATERIALS

- centimeter rulers (one per group)
- centimeter tape measures (one per group)
- ramps (books, notebooks or stiff pieces of cardboard, one per group)
- assortment of objects that roll (one object per group)
- graph paper
- motion sensors, *optional*
- Lab Report (W), *optional*
- Coordinate Plane (T)
- Distance from a Motion Sensor (T), *optional*
- Calculator Notes 1F, 1G, 1H, 1I *(optional)*
- CBR demonstration Out Walking Around, *optional*

TEACHING

The study of two-variable data begins with scatter plot representations and the use of letters for variables.

The Lab Report worksheet can be used if you want students to do a lab write-up for this investigation. Other lessons contain a teacher note if an investigation is recommended for a write-up.

Two-Variable Data

A **variable** is a trait or quantity whose value can change or vary. For example, birth dates will vary from person to person. In algebra, letters and symbols are used to represent variables. A person's birth date could be represented with the variable *b*, but the letter or symbol you choose doesn't matter. A data set that contains measures of only one trait or quantity is called **one-variable data.** In Lessons 1.1 to 1.5, you learned to graph and summarize one-variable data.

Statisticians often collect information on *two* variables hoping to find a relationship. For example, someone's age may affect his or her pulse rate. In this lesson you'll explore **two-variable data** and plot points to create graphs called **scatter plots.** Plotting points and identifying the location of points on a graph are important skills for algebra.

Two-variable graphs are constructed with two axes. Each axis shows possible values for one of the two variables. On the **coordinate plane,** the horizontal axis is used for values of the variable *x,* and the vertical axis is used for values of the variable *y.* The **origin** is the point where the *x*- and *y*-axes intersect. The axes divide the coordinate plane into four **quadrants.** Each point is identified with **coordinates** (*x, y*) that tell its horizontal distance *x* and vertical distance *y* from the origin. The horizontal distance of value *x* is always listed first, so (*x, y*) is called an **ordered pair.** The first coordinate is also called the **abscissa,** and the second coordinate the **ordinate.**

The coordinates tell you to move left 1 and up 2.

Investigation
Let It Roll!

You will need

- a centimeter ruler
- a centimeter tape measure
- a ramp, such as a book, notebook, or stiff piece of cardboard
- an object that rolls, such as a pencil, soda can, or toy with wheels
- graph paper

Just how far will an object roll? How does the release height of a ramp affect this distance? One way to begin to answer questions like these is to collect some data. In this investigation you'll collect two-variable data: The first variable will be the release height of the ramp, and the second variable will be the distance from the book at which the object stops rolling. A graph of these data points may help you to see a relationship between the two variables.

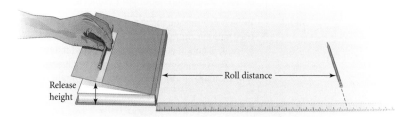

Release height

Roll distance

LESSON OBJECTIVES

- On the coordinate plane, plot points with given coordinates, and determine the coordinates of plotted points
- Represent a two-variable data set with a scatter plot
- Given a pair of calculator lists, plot points whose coordinates are in those lists
- Interpret scatter plots
- Learn and use vocabulary related to coordinates and graphs

NCTM STANDARDS

CONTENT		PROCESS	
✓	Number		Problem Solving
	Algebra	✓	Reasoning
✓	Geometry	✓	Communication
✓	Measurement	✓	Connections
✓	Data/Probability	✓	Representation

Release height (cm)	Roll distance (cm)

Step 1 Set up your experiment as shown in the diagram on the previous page. Mark the point on the ramp from which you will release your rolling object. Make sure that you have plenty of room in front of your ramp for the object to roll freely. Record the release height of the object in a table like this one.

Step 2 Release the object and let it roll to a stop. Measure the distance the object traveled from the base of the ramp to its stopping point. Record this in your table. *sample answer: 6 cm; 15 cm*

Step 3 Repeat the experiment at least five times, using a different release height each time. Record the data in your table.

Step 4 Create a set of axes on your graph paper. Label the axes as shown.

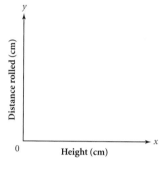

Step 6 sample answer:

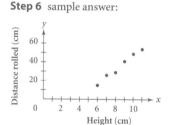

Step 5 Scale the x-axis appropriately to fit all of your height values. For example, if your largest height was 8.5 cm, you might make each grid unit represent 0.5 cm. Scale the y-axis to fit all of your roll-distance values. For example, if your longest roll length was 80 cm, you might use 10 cm for each vertical grid unit. *See Step 6.*

Step 6 Plot each piece of two-variable data from your table. Think of each row in your table as an ordered pair. Locate each point by first moving along the horizontal axis to the release-height measurement. Then move up vertically to the corresponding roll distance. Mark this point with a small dot.

Step 7 The graph is linear. The higher the release height, the farther the object will roll. An object that rolls more smoothly will have a graph with a steeper slope.

Step 7 Describe any patterns you see in the graph. Is there a relationship between the two variables?

Step 8 Enter the information from your table into two calculator lists. Make a scatter plot. The calculator display should look like the graph you drew by hand.
[▶ 🖳 See **Calculator Note 1F** to learn how to display this information on your calculator screen.◀]

may want to mark the axes with coordinates in a somewhat arbitrary way. Ask them to mark off a scale first. To do so, they can first mark the largest values of the two variables and then mark intermediate points proportionately. Because the distance rolled will be much larger than the height, the scales on the x- and y-axes could be different. This will be a new idea for some students.

Step 6 [Alert] Watch for confusion about which axis represents which variable. If asked, explain that any

variable that is a response to or outcome of a variable that you change is plotted on the vertical axis. Don't belabor the point; this investigation is not unusual in the fact that either variable might be considered the predictive variable.

Step 7 Students may say that the "points are straight." Point out that points have no length, and encourage use of the phrase "lie along a straight line" or "have a linear pattern."

 Guiding the Investigation

After students have gathered in their groups, talk through Steps 1 through 3.

Step 3 Be sure students realize that they are to release the object from the same point on the ramp each time, though that point will be at different heights above the floor.

Step 3 sample answer:

Release height (cm)	Roll distance (cm)
6	15
7	26
8	32
9	41
10	49
11	54

Steps 4–6 Ask an experienced class to gather the data and represent them in a graph. Unsuccessful attempts at several kinds of representation will motivate learning about the coordinate plane and scatter plots—from you or from each other.

Step 4 [ELL] Display the words *axis* and *axes,* and point out the singular and plural forms. If your class needs more guidance, introduce points on the coordinate plane first, relying on the lesson introduction. You might project the Coordinate Plane transparency onto a hanging map or blueprint, or have several students stand on large coordinate axes on the floor. Point out the x- and y-axes. Stress the importance of the order (first coordinate representing horizontal location, second coordinate vertical) when plotting points. **[Ask]** "What other words have the same root as *quadrant*?" [*Quad* means "four," as in *quadrangle, quadrilateral,* and *quadruplets.*]

Step 5 [ELL] Explain that the word *scale* here refers to how numbers are marked on the axes. Students

LESSON 1.6 Two-Variable Data **71**

One of the greatest difficulties students have in graphing on a calculator is setting the viewing window. If you skip the step of setting the window, the chances of seeing a graph are not very good. Help students work through Calculator Note 1F.

SHARING IDEAS

You might ask for several presentations of the results of Step 8, illustrating different slopes. **[Ask]** "Why do the graphs look different?" Encourage the class to see that different objects roll to different distances from the base of the ramp. As a consequence, the lines will vary in steepness.

Assessing Progress

By watching students' contributions, you can assess their skills with careful measurement, organized data collection, entering data into lists, considering one variable at a time, and using the term *straight line*.

EXAMPLE

If you have a second day for this lesson, the examples of motion provide opportunities for interpreting graphs in a context some students will see as relevant or fun.

If possible, use motion sensors attached to calculators. As you set up equipment, explain that remote sensors often use reflected pulses of high-pitched sound to measure distance. Try to arrange for each student to walk at least once and to operate the motion sensor. Calculator Note 1I gives instructions for reading distance with a CBL 2 or CBR. The CBR demonstration Out Walking Around gives a simple introduction to the use of a motion sensor and the WALKER program. If motion sensors aren't available, use the Distance from a Motion Sensor transparency.

[Alert] Watch for the common misinterpretation of the graph as the *path* of the motion against time, which indicates that stu-

This officer is using a radar device that measures the speed of oncoming cars.

There are many ways to collect data. Have you ever seen a police officer measuring the speed of an approaching car? Have you wondered how technicians measure the speed of a baseball pitch? Did you know that satellites collect information about Earth from distances of over 320 miles? Each of these measurements involves the use of remote sensors that collect data. In this course you may have the opportunity to work with portable sensor equipment.

EXAMPLE This scatter plot shows how the distance from a motion sensor to a person varies over a period of 6 seconds. Describe where the person is in relation to the sensor at each second.

Distance from Motion Sensor

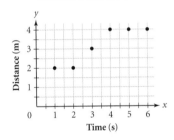

▶ **Solution** The first point (1, 2) shows that after 1 second the person was 2 meters away from the sensor.

The next point (2, 2) indicates that after 2 seconds the person was still 2 meters away.

The point (3, 3) means that after 3 seconds the person was 3 meters away.

The point (4, 4) means that at 4 seconds the person was 4 meters away. He or she remained 4 meters away until 6 seconds had passed, as indicated by the points (5, 4) and (6, 4).

Negative values of time would indicate that events had occurred before the arbitrary starting point in time.

The graph in this example is a **first-quadrant graph** because all the values are positive. A lot of real-world data is described with only positive numbers, so first-quadrant graphs are very useful. However, you could graph the person's distances in front of the sensor as positive values and his or her distances *behind* the sensor as negative values. This would require more than one quadrant to show the data. If the graph showed negative values of time, how would you interpret this?

dents are still having trouble assimilating the abstraction of the graph of distance. Repeatedly emphasize how the plot represents time and distance. It is not a map of north-south versus east-west. **[Ask]** "What other scenarios may give rise to the same distance values at seconds 4, 5, and 6?" [Both the sensor and the person may still be at a distance of 4 m from each other, or the person may be walking in an arc around the sensor at a 4 m radius, or both the person and the sensor may be moving in parallel 4 m apart.] Encourage creativity.

Time values might be negative if you were measuring time relative to a particular starting point—for example, time before noon and after noon.

Closing the Lesson

You can say that **two-variable data** points are described by pairs of numbers. These can be represented visually by a **scatter plot,** in which each point has one of those pairs of data as its **coordinates** on coordinate axes.

You will need your graphing calculator for Exercises **3, 5, 6, 7,** and **9.**

Practice Your Skills

1. Draw and label a coordinate plane so that the *x*-axis extends from −9 to 9 and the *y*-axis extends from −6 to 6. Represent each point below with a dot, and label the point using its letter name.

   $A(-5, -3.5)$ ⓐ $B(2.5, -5)$ ⓐ $C(5, 0)$ ⓐ $D(-1.5, 4)$ $E(0, 4.5)$

   $F(2, -3)$ $G(-4, -1)$ $H(-5, 5)$ $I(4, 3)$ $J(0, 0)$

2. Sketch a coordinate plane. Label the axes and each of the four quadrants—I, II, III, and IV. Identify the axis or quadrant location of each point described.

   a. The first coordinate is positive, and the second coordinate is 0. positive *x*-axis

   b. The first coordinate is negative, and the second coordinate is positive. Quadrant II

   c. Both coordinates are positive. Quadrant I

   d. Both coordinates are negative. Quadrant III

   e. The coordinates are (0, 0). the origin

   f. The first coordinate is 0, and the second coordinate is negative. negative *y*-axis

3. Use your calculator to practice identifying coordinates. The program POINTS will place a point randomly on the calculator screen. You identify the point by entering its coordinates to the nearest one-half. Run the program POINTS until you can easily name points in all four quadrants. [▶ 🖵 See **Calculator Note 1G.**◀]

Reason and Apply

4. This graph pictures a walker's distance from a stationary motion sensor.

   Motion Sensor Readings

   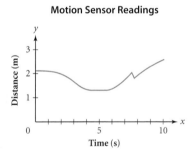

   These people are running and walking in a fund-raiser to support cancer research.

   a. How far away was the walker after 2 s? ⓐ about 2 m

   b. At what time was the walker closest to the sensor? ⓐ about 5 s

   c. Approximately how far away was the walker after 10 s? ⓐ about 2.7 m

   d. When, if ever, did the walker stop? ⓐ between 0 and 1 s, and between 4.5 and 5.5 s

---

▶ Helping with the Exercises

Graph paper will be helpful for these exercises. If you're assigning Exercise 3 and students will not be working on it in the classroom, do the linking first.

Exercise 1 The viewing window being set up could be described as $-9 \leq x \leq 9$ and $-6 \leq y \leq 6$, but students may not be familiar with inequality symbols and you may not want to start that discussion now.

You may want to note that points are sometimes given a shorthand name with capital letters. Letters and symbols can represent constants as well as variables (for example, π, or a and b in $y = a + bx$).

Exercise 2 [Alert] Watch for confusion about quadrant names here; you may need to identify them again.

Exercise 3 Load this program into your calculator so that students can acquire it through linking.

Exercise 4 [Alert] Watch for confusion about this continuous graph. The curve contains infinitely many points and shows the walker's position at each instant.

1.

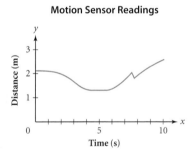

5b.

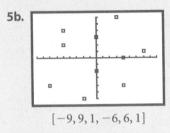

$[-9, 9, 1, -6, 6, 1]$

6. Location scenarios should include information such as *(positive, positive)* in Quadrant I, *(negative, positive)* in Quadrant II, *(negative, negative)* in Quadrant III, *(positive, negative)* in Quadrant IV, (0, *any number*) on *y*-axis, (*any number*, 0) on *x*-axis, and (0, 0) as the origin.

7a. approximate answers (the second coordinates are in millions): (1984, 280), (1985, 320), (1986, 340), (1987, 415), (1988, 450), (1989, 445), (1990, 440), (1991, 360), (1992, 370), (1993, 340), (1994, 345), (1995, 275), (1996, 225), (1997, 175), (1998, 160), (1999, 125), (2000, 75), (2001, 45), (2002, 30), (2003, 15)

7b.

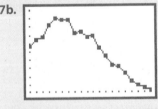

$[1984, 2003, 1, 0, 500, 50]$

7c. Answers will vary. Shipments increased until 1988 and then decreased. The introduction of compact discs may have influenced the decrease.

---

5. Look at this scatter plot.

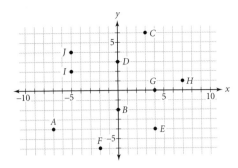

a. Name the (*x*, *y*) coordinates of each point pictured. $A(-7, -4), B(0, -2), C(3, 6), D(0, 3), E(4, -4), F(-2, -6), G(4, 0), H(7, 1), I(-5, 2), J(-5, 4)$

b. Enter the *x*-coordinates of the points you named in 5a into list L₁ and the corresponding *y*-coordinates into list L₂. Set your graphing window to the values suggested in the pictured graph, and graph a scatter plot of the points. We call this the scatter plot of (L₁, L₂).

c. Which points are on an axis? points *B, D,* and *G*

d. List the points in Quadrant I, Quadrant II, Quadrant III, and Quadrant IV.
I: *C* and *H*; II: *I* and *J*; III: *A* and *F*; IV: *E*

6. Write a paragraph explaining how to make a calculator scatter plot, and how to identify point locations in the coordinate plane.

7. APPLICATION The graph below is created by connecting the points in a scatter plot as you move left to right. [▶ 🖳 See **Calculator Note 1H** to learn how to connect a scatter plot.◀]

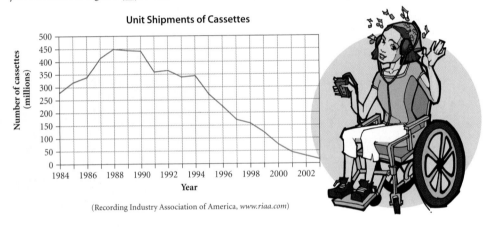

(Recording Industry Association of America, *www.riaa.com*)

a. Approximate the 20 data points represented on this graph, for which the *x*-value is the year and the *y*-value is the number of cassettes. *@*

b. Name graphing window values and create this graph on your calculator screen. If necessary, adjust your coordinates from 7a so that your graph matches the graph shown above.

c. The graph shows a pattern or trend for shipments of music cassettes. Describe any patterns you see. What do you think happened in the 1980s that would cause the patterns in this graph?

8. The data in this table show the average miles per gallon (mpg) for all U.S. automobiles during the indicated years.

a. Copy this table onto paper and calculate the years elapsed since 1960 to complete it. @

b. Graph a scatter plot on your paper of points whose *x*-value is years elapsed and whose *y*-value is miles per gallon. Carefully label and scale your axes. Give your graph a title.

c. Connect each point in your scatter plot with a line segment from left to right.

d. What is the mean mpg for these data? @ 19.5 mpg

e. Graph a horizontal line that starts on the *y*-axis at a height equal to your answer to 8d. What does the graph now show?

f. Write a short descriptive statement about any pattern you see in these data and in your graph.

Technology CONNECTION

New technologies are being developed to improve car gas mileage. Car manufacturers are now producing cars that run on electricity or a combination of gasoline and electricity. Some cars and buses run on natural gas, or even recycled vegetable oil! For more information on fuel efficiency and alternative fuels, see the links at **www.keymath.com/DA** .

Average Miles per Gallon for All U.S. Automobiles

Year	Years elapsed	mpg
1960	0	14.3
1970	10	13.5
1980	20	15.9
1990	30	20.2
1995	35	21.1
1996	36	21.2
1997	37	21.5
1998	38	21.6
1999	39	21.4
2000	40	21.9
2001	41	22.1

(U.S. Department of Transportation, *www.dot.gov*) [Data set: **AMPG**]

9. The graph at right is a hexagon whose vertices are six ordered pairs. Two of the points are (3, 0) and (1.5, 2.6). The hexagon is centered at the origin.

a. What are the coordinates of the other points? $(-1.5, 2.6), (-3, 0),$ $(-1.5, -2.6), (1.5, -2.6)$

b. Create this connected graph on your calculator. Add a few more points and line segments to make a piece of calculator art. Identify the points you added. Answers will vary.

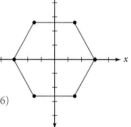

10. Xavier's dad braked suddenly to avoid hitting a squirrel as he drove Xavier to school. His speed during the trip to school is shown on the graph at right.

a. At what time did Xavier's dad apply the brakes? @ 8:06

b. What was his fastest speed during the trip? 40 mi/h

c. How long did it take Xavier to get to school? @ 12 min

d. Find one feature of this graph that you think is unrealistic. Answers will vary. That he never fully stopped during the trip to school is unusual.

Xavier's Trip to School

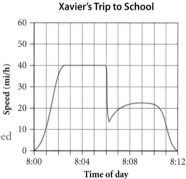

Encourage students to be suspicious about conclusions drawn from taking a mean of means. For example, if the average test score in this class is 83 and in that class is 79, the average over the two classes would not be 81 unless the classes were the same size. In Exercise 8 the mean of the means would give the average mileage of all cars over the years only if the number of gallons of gasoline used each year were the same.

Exercise 9 [Alert] Watch for difficulty in understanding that the points will be connected in the order in which they occur in the list. Encourage creativity in the art.

Exercise 10 Some students will find this exercise easy. Challenge them to find the distance traveled on the trip to school. To do so, they could estimate the mean speed for each piece of the trip and multiply by the time taken for that piece. Or they could calculate the area under the graph.

Exercise 8a In filling in the table, students may not notice that the 10-year pattern breaks with 1995.

8b.

Average Miles per Gallon for All U.S. Automobiles (since 1960)

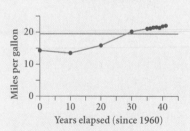

8c.

Average Miles per Gallon for All U.S. Automobiles (since 1960)

Exercise 8e [Alert] Watch for difficulty in understanding the meaning of a constant equation. The graph of the equation $y = 19.5$ consists of exactly those points whose *y*-coordinate is 19.5. Thus it's a horizontal line.

8e.

Average Miles per Gallon for All U.S. Automobiles (since 1960)

The horizontal line separates those data points that are above the mean of the averages from those that are below it.

8f. Answers will vary.

11a. One possibility is {5, 12, 14, 15, 20, 30, 47}; the underlined values are fixed.

11b. One possibility is {5, 10, 12, 13, 14, 16, 20, 30, 40, 47}; the underlined values are fixed.

11c. One possibility is {5, 10, 12, 12, 13, 14, 16, 20, 28, 32, 40, 47}; the underlined values are fixed.

12a. 476, 496, 506.5, 536, 605

12b.

Result of TIMSS

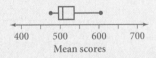

400   500   600   700
Mean scores

12c. The greatest spread is between the third quartile and the maximum, that is, the right whisker. The least spread occurs between the first quartile and the median.

12d. 40 points

12e. Scotland, England, Sweden, Lithuania, United States, Australia; Belgium, Japan, Taiwan, Hong Kong, Korea, Singapore

---

▶ **Review**

1.3 **11.** Create a data set with the specified number of items and the five-number summary values 5, 12, 15, 30, 47.

    a. 7   **b.** 10   **c.** 12

1.3 **12.** The table gives results for eighth-grade students in the 2003 Trends in International Mathematics and Science Study.

    a. Find the five-number summary for this data set.

    b. Construct a box plot for these data.

    c. Between which five-number summary values is there the greatest spread of data? The least spread?

    d. What is the interquartile range?

    e. List the countries between the first quartile and the median. List those above the third quartile.

Results of the 2003 Trends in International Mathematics and Science Study (8th Grade)

Country	Mean score	Country	Mean score
Singapore	605	Australia	505
Korea	589	United States	504
Hong Kong	586	Lithuania	502
Taiwan	585	Sweden	499
Japan	570	England	498
Belgium	537	Scotland	498
Netherlands	536	Israel	496
Estonia	531	New Zealand	494
Hungary	529	Slovenia	493
Malaysia	508	Italy	484
Latvia	508	Armenia	478
Russian Federation	508	Serbia	477
Slovakia	508	Bulgaria	476

(National Center for Education Statistics, *www.nces.ed.gov*)

IMPROVING YOUR REASONING SKILLS

A **glyph** is a symbol that presents information nonverbally. These weather glyphs show data values for several variables in one symbol. How many variables can you identify? The diagram shows data for 12 hours starting at 12:00 noon. Which characteristics would you call categorical? Which are numerical? Is it possible to show all or part of the data using one or more of the graph types you learned to use in this chapter? How would you do that? Which types of graphs have the greatest advantages in this situation? Why?

You can learn more about weather symbols and research your local weather conditions by using the Internet links at **www.keymath.com/DA** .

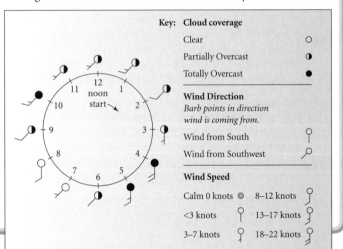

IMPROVING REASONING SKILLS

The weather glyphs show four variables: time, cloud coverage, wind direction, and wind speed. Time is definitely a numerical variable. Wind direction, cloud coverage, and wind speed, however, could be considered either numerical or categorical. Wind direction might be assigned a compass bearing. Cloud coverage could be three categories, or it could be assigned a percentage (0%, 50%, 100%) or a degree number (1, 2, 3). Wind speed is also complex because, although a specific numerical wind speed would be measured (for example, 6 knots), each is then placed in a categorical bin (for example, 3–7 knots). Students could use an array of graphs to display the data, but they may be unable to find a single type of graph to display all the information.

LESSON
1.7

Estimating

If you read Michael Crichton's book *Jurassic Park* or if you saw the movie, you may remember that the dinosaur population grows faster than expected. The characters estimate that there will be only 238 dinosaurs. But a computer inventory shows that there are actually 292 dinosaurs!

Statistics are no substitute for judgment.

HENRY CLAY

This skeleton of a *Tyrannosaurus rex* is at the Royal Tyrrell Museum in Alberta, Canada. Tyrannosaurs were among the largest carnivorous dinosaurs and measured up to 40 ft in length.

Dinosaurs in *Jurassic Park*

Species	Actual number	Estimated number	Species	Actual number	Estimated number
Tyrannosaurs	2	2	Hadrosaurs	11	11
Maiasaurs	22	21	Dilophosaurs	7	7
Stegosaurs	4	4	Pterosaurs	6	6
Triceratops	8	8	Hypsilophodontids	34	33
Procompsognathids	65	49	Euoplocephalids	16	16
Othnielia	23	16	Styracosaurs	18	18
Velociraptors	37	8	Microceratops	22	22
Apatosaurs	17	17	Total	292	238

(*Jurassic Park*, 1991, p. 164)

It is easy to see how the estimated numbers and the actual numbers compare by looking at this table. In this lesson you will learn how to make efficient comparisons of data using a scatter plot.

Investigation
Guesstimating

You will need

- a meterstick, tape measure, or motion sensor

In this investigation you will estimate and measure distances around your room. As a group, select a starting point for your measurements. Choose nine objects in the room that appear to be less than 5 m away.

Description	Actual distance (m)	Estimated distance (m)
(item 1)		
(item 2)		
(item 3)		

Step 1 | List the objects in the description column of a table like this one.

Step 2 | Estimate the distances in meters or parts of a meter from your starting point to each object. If group members disagree, find the mean of your estimates. Record the estimates in your table.

NCTM STANDARDS

CONTENT		PROCESS	
✔	Number	✔	Problem Solving
	Algebra	✔	Reasoning
✔	Geometry		Communication
✔	Measurement	✔	Connections
✔	Data/Probability	✔	Representation

LESSON OBJECTIVES

- Use a scatter plot to compare estimates with actual values
- Graph the equation $y = x$, the linear parent function
- Judge the overall accuracy of a set of estimates from a scatter plot and the graph of $y = x$
- Develop the graphing practices of scaling and plotting carefully and labeling the graph and axes

PLANNING

LESSON OUTLINE

One day:

35 min	Investigation
5 min	Closing
10 min	Exercises

MATERIALS

- tape measures, metersticks, or motion sensors
- graph paper
- Estimation Investigations (W), *optional*
- Calculator Notes 1I, 1J, 1K (*optional*)

TEACHING

USING THE QUOTE

Ask students how the quote opening the lesson relates to what they have learned in this chapter. Students should recognize that they have had to use judgment in selecting the best graphs and measures to use for analyzing the statistics they choose.

Guiding the Investigation

While students in groups are reading the opening example about dinosaurs, hand out measuring devices and graph paper. Mention that the table is organized with the estimated column on the right to make a scatter plot of the data easier to understand.

To limit confusion, you can mark observation points on the floor and ask groups to consider only objects in their region of the room.

One Step

Once a class experienced at investigations makes the table of data, ask them to compare a scatter plot of the data with the graph of the line $y = x$ and to explain what it

means for a point of the scatter plot to lie on the line.

Step 2 [ELL] Be sure students understand the word *estimate*. You can use terms like *near, close to,* and *more or less* to explain.

Show students a meterstick before they begin to estimate. Remind students to estimate and fill in the column *before* measuring.

[Alert] Make sure that students put their estimates in the estimated rather than the actual column.

Step 3 Be ready to help students who are having trouble measuring. Students using motion sensors will need Calculator Note 1I.

Step 7 Make sure students are familiar with the term *equation*. "Equation" will be defined in Lesson 2.8 in the context of solving equations.

Step 8 It is in these interpretations that the order of columns makes a difference.

You may want to discuss the terms *accuracy, error,* and *precision* with your students. A distance is measured with a *precision* of 0.1 cm, but the measurement may have an *accuracy* or *error* of 0.1, 0.4, 1.2, or more. Accuracy or error is the difference between the actual length and the estimated or measured length. Make sure students understand why their computations should not show more precision than their original measurement. **[Ask]** "Is it possible to get more accurate data by using a ruler to measure to the nearest 0.001 centimeter?"

SHARING IDEAS

Request at least two presentations of graphs. If a group did it backward from the instructions, include that group.

| Step 3 | Measure the actual distances to each object and record them in the table. |

| Step 4 | Draw coordinate axes and label actual distance on the *x*-axis and estimated distance on the *y*-axis. Use the same scale on both axes. Carefully plot your nine points. |
| Step 5 | Describe what this graph would look like if each of your estimates had been exactly the same as the actual measurement. How could you indicate this pattern on your graph? If all estimates were correct, they would lie on a diagonal line, specifically, $y = x$. |

Step 6	Make a calculator scatter plot of your data. Use your paper-and-pencil graph as a guide for setting a good graphing window.
Step 7	On your calculator, graph the line $y = x$. What does this *equation* represent? [▶ 🖥 See **Calculator Note 1J** to graph a scatter plot and an equation simultaneously.◀] estimates that are correct
Step 8	What do you notice about the points for distances that were underestimated? What about points for distances that were overestimated? Underestimates fall below the line $y = x$; overestimates are above.
Step 9	How would you recognize the point for a distance that was estimated exactly the same as its actual measurement? Explain why this point would fall where it does. Correct estimates will fall on the line $y = x$; in context the line $y = x$ represents the equation *estimate = actual*.

Throughout this course you will create useful and informative graphs. Sometimes adding other elements to a graph as a basis for comparison can help you interpret your data. In the investigation, you added the line $y = x$ to your graph. How did this help you assess your estimates? Responses should include easily identifying overestimates and underestimates.

Be aware that measurements, like those in the investigation, are approximations—they cannot be exact. You might have been able to measure with an **accuracy** of 0.1 cm, if you were careful. Often when you measure you'll decide how precise you want your measurements to be (and how precise they can be), and how much **error** is acceptable. Remember that answers calculated based on these measurements should not show more **precision** than the measurements themselves.

EXERCISES

You will need your graphing calculator for Exercises **1, 4,** and **7.**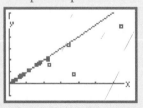

▶ **Practice Your Skills**

1. Enter the *Jurassic Park* data from page 77 into your calculator. Put actual numbers into list L1 and estimated numbers into list L2 so that each (x, y) point has the form (*actual number, estimated number*).
[Data sets: DACT, DEST]

   a. Graph a scatter plot of the data and record the window you used.

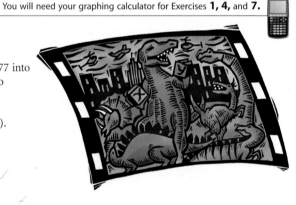

[Ask] "Do you agree with the presenters' answers to the questions in Step 8?" At an appropriate time in the discussion, write the pair (*actual, estimated*) on the board. Students need to get used to seeing (x, y) pairs set out this way. Point out that this defines x (and the *x*-axis) to stand for "actual," and y (and the *y*-axis) to stand for "estimate."

1a. The lower Ymin value allows trace numbers to appear on the calculator screen without interfering with plotted points.

$[0, 70, 10, -10, 60, 10]$

b. If *x* represents the actual number of dinosaurs and *y* the estimated number of dinosaurs, what equation represents the situation when the actual numbers equal the estimated numbers? Graph this equation on your calculator. ⓐ $y = x$

c. Are any points of the scatter plot above the line you drew in 1c? What do these points represent? No; in no case is the estimated number of dinosaurs more than the actual number.

d. Are any points of the scatter plot below the line you drew in 1c? What do these points represent? Yes; the estimated count of five different species was less than the actual count.

2. Lucia and Malcolm each estimated the weights of five different items from a grocery store. Each of Lucia's estimates was too low. Each of Malcolm's was too high. The scatter plot at right shows the (*actual weight, estimated weight*) data collected. The line drawn shows when an *estimate* is the same as the *actual* measurement.

a. Which points represent Lucia's estimates?

b. Which points represent Malcolm's estimates?

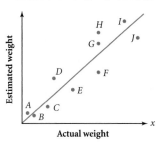

Lucia's and Malcolm's Estimates

3. These points represent student estimates of temperatures in degrees Celsius for various samples of salt water. The data are recorded in the form (*actual temperature, estimated temperature*). Which points represent overestimates and which represent underestimates? ⓗ overestimates: *B, C, D, E, G*; underestimates: *A, F, H, I*

A(27, 20)	*B*(−4, 2)	*C*(18, 22)
D(0, 3)	*E*(47, 60)	*F*(36, 28)
G(−2, 0)	*H*(33, 31)	*I*(−1, −2)

4. This graph is a scatter plot of a person's distance from a motion sensor in a 5-second time period. The line is shown only as a guide.

a. Make a table of coordinates for the points pictured on this graph.

b. Describe how you would make a scatter plot of these data points on your calculator. Name the window values you would use.

c. What is the equation of the line pictured on the graph? $y = x$

d. Was the distance between the person and the sensor increasing or decreasing?

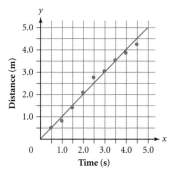

Distance from Motion Sensor

▶ **Helping with the Exercises**

Exercise 1 Be sure students understand that the ordered pair (*actual number, estimated number*) means that the estimated number is listed second.

2a. Lucia's estimates are all below the line—points *B, C, E, F,* and *J*.

2b. Malcolm's estimates are all above the line—points *A, D, G, H,* and *I*.

4a. possible approximations:

Time	0.5	1.0	1.5	2.0	2.5	3.0	3.5	4.0	4.5
Distance	0.5	0.8	1.4	2.1	2.7	3.0	3.6	3.9	4.25

4b. Answers will vary. A minimum window is [0, 5, 1, 0, 5, 1].

4d. The distance is increasing at about 1 m/s. The person may be walking away from the sensor.

Another Investigation
As an extension, you can look up the ages of current political figures, artists, musicians, film personalities, writers, or perhaps even the principal of the school! Before showing these data to the students, have them guess the age of each person. Then form (*actual age, estimated age*) pairs that students can graph and analyze. You can find some examples on the Estimation Investigations worksheets. Cover the actual data written to the right of the problem before you copy the worksheet for students.

Assessing Progress
By observing students' contributions, you can assess their skill at drawing axes and marking scales, plotting points, and making scatter plots, both on paper and on the calculator.

Closing the Lesson

If many students had difficulty using the line $y = x$, have the class read the paragraph that follows the investigation. **[Ask]** "How does the reference line help you assess your estimates?"

Reinforce the new mathematical idea that the graph of the line $y = x$ consists of all points whose coordinates are equal.

BUILDING UNDERSTANDING

In the exercises students compare estimated and actual values.

ASSIGNING HOMEWORK

Essential	1–3, 5, 7, 8
Performance assessment	3, 6, 11
Portfolio	6
Journal	4, 9
Group	11, 12
Review	12, 13

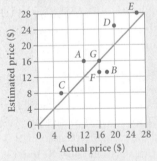
Reason and Apply

5. **APPLICATION** A group of students conducted an experiment by stretching a rubber band and letting it fly. They measured the amount of stretch (cm) in each trial and recorded it as *x*. The distance flown (cm) was measured and recorded as *y*. This scatter plot shows six trials. The numbers below the calculator screen indicate the minimum *x*, maximum *x*, *x*-scale, minimum *y*, maximum *y*, and *y*-scale of the axes.

   a. Describe any relationship you see. The more the rubber band is stretched, the farther it flies.

   b. Based on the plot, how far might the rubber band fly if they stretch it 15 cm? Answers will vary between 400 and 600 cm.

   c. How far should they stretch the rubber band if the target is at 400 cm? Answers will vary between 7 and 12 cm.

   [0, 20, 5, 0, 700, 100]

6. Copy the graph at right onto your paper.

   a. Plot a point that represents someone overestimating a $12 item by $4. Label it *A*. What are the coordinates of *A*? @ (12, 16)

   b. Plot a point that represents someone underestimating an $18 item by $5. Label it *B*. What are the coordinates of *B*? @ (18, 13)

   c. Plot and label the points *C*(6, 8), *D*(20, 25), and *E*(26, 28). Describe each point as an overestimate or underestimate. How far off was each estimate?

   d. Plot and label points *F* and *G* to represent two different estimates of an item priced at $16. Point *F* should be an underestimate of $3, and point *G* should be a perfect guess. @

   e. Where will all the points lie that represent an estimated price of $16? Describe your answer in words and show it on the graph.

   f. Where will all the points lie that picture an actual price of $16? Describe your answer in words and show it on the graph.

   g. If *x* represents the actual price and *y* represents the estimated price, where are all the points represented by the equation *y* = *x*? What do these points represent?

   Estimated Prices vs. Actual Prices

7. Recall the *Jurassic Park* data on page 77. Enter the actual numbers and estimated numbers into two calculator lists. (You may still have the data in list L₁ and list L₂ from Exercise 1.) Use list L₃ to calculate the estimated number minus the actual number for each dinosaur species. [▶ 🖳 See **Calculator Note 1K** for an explanation of how to use calculator lists in this way.◀]

   a. What information does list L₃ give you?

   b. Use list L₂ and list L₃ to create a scatter plot of points in the form (*estimated number, estimated number − actual number*). Name a graphing window that provides a good display of your scatter plot.

   c. How many points are below the *x*-axis? What would points below the *x*-axis represent?

   d. Name the coordinates of the point farthest from the *x*-axis. What do these coordinates tell you?

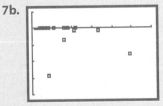

8. Draw the line for the equation $y = x$ on a coordinate grid with the x-axis labeled from -9 to 9 and the y-axis labeled from -6 to 6. Plot and label the points described.

   a. Point A with an x-coordinate of -4 and a y-coordinate 5 more than -4. $(-4, 1)$

   b. Point B with an x-coordinate of -2 and a y-coordinate 3 less than -2. $(-2, -5)$

   c. Point C with an x-coordinate of 1 and a y-coordinate 4 units above the line. $(1, 5)$

   d. Now plot several points with coordinates that are opposites (*inverses*) of each other, for example, $(-5, 5)$ or $(5, -5)$. Describe the pattern of these new points. Write an equation to describe the pattern.   Plotted points lie on the line that bisects Quadrant II and Quadrant IV; the equation $y = -x$ fits these points.

9. APPLICATION This graph shows the mean SAT verbal and mathematics scores for 50 states and the District of Columbia in 2003.

   a. Explain what it means for a point to lie on the line $y = x$.

   b. Locate the points that represent the states with the highest math scores. State two observations about their verbal scores. @

   c. Which statement is true: "More states had students with higher mathematics scores than verbal scores" or "More states had students with higher verbal scores than mathematics scores"?

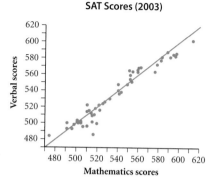

SAT Scores (2003)

(The College Board, in *The World Almanac and Book of Facts 2004*, p. 296)

10. Below is a scatter plot of points whose coordinates have the form (t, d). The variable t stands for time in seconds and d stands for distance in meters. The graph describes a person walking away from a motion sensor. The line $d = t$ is also graphed.

   a. Approximately how fast is the person moving? Explain how you know this. @

   b. Name two different half-second intervals in which the person is moving more slowly than the rate you found in 10a. @

   c. Name two different half-second intervals in which the person is moving faster than the rate you found in 10a.

   d. Name two different half-second intervals in which the person is moving at about the same rate you found in 10a. @

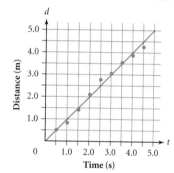

Distance from Motion Sensor

11. APPLICATION A string and meterstick were passed around a class, and each student measured the length of the string with a precision of 0.1 cm. Here are their results:

126.5 124.2 124.8 125.7 123.3 124.5 125.4 125.5 123.7 123.8 126.4
126.0 124.6 123.3 124.7 125.4 126.1 123.8 125.7 125.2 126.0 125.6

   a. What does the true length of the string probably equal? @

   b. Why are there so many different values?

   c. Sometimes you see a measurement like 47.3 ± 0.2 cm. What do you think the "± 0.2" means? @

   d. Create a measurement like the one shown in 11c, which has an accuracy or error component, to describe the length of the string. @

Exercise 12a Watch for difficulty; the median might be on an edge of the box.

13a. Rocky made several mistakes. The data values need to be organized in increasing order. The key should show actual values from the data.

13b.

13	5 8
14	2 6 7 9
15	2 5 7 7 8 8
16	2 2 4 4 5 8
17	1 3 3 3 6
18	2 4

Key

13	5 means 13.5 cm

13c. 18.4 − 13.5, or 4.9 cm

▶ **Review**

1.3   **12.** For each description, invent a seven-value data set such that all the values in the set are less than 10 and meet the conditions. *Possible answers are shown.*

    a. The box plot represents data with a median that is not inside the box. @ $\{1, 3, 3, 3, 4, 5, 6\}$

    b. The box plot represents data with an interquartile range of zero. $\{1, 4, 4, 4, 4, 4, 7\}$

    c. The box plot represents data with one outlier on the left. $\{1, 6, 6, 7, 7, 8, 9\}$

    d. The box plot has no right whisker. $\{1, 2, 3, 4, 5, 6, 6\}$

1.4   **13.** Rocky and his algebra classmates measured the circumference of their wrists in centimeters. Here are the data:

    15.2 14.7 13.8 17.3 18.2 17.6 14.6 13.5 16.5

    15.8 17.3 16.8 15.7 16.2 16.4 18.4 14.2 16.4

    15.8 16.2 17.3 15.7 14.9 15.5 17.1

    a. Rocky made the stem plot shown here. Unfortunately, he was not paying attention when these plots were discussed in class. Write a note to Rocky telling him what he did incorrectly.

    b. Make a correct stem plot of this data set.

    c. What is the range of this data set?

13	8 5
14	7 6 2 9
15	2 8 7 8 7 5
16	5 8 2 4 4 2
17	3 6 3 3 1
18	2 4

Key

10	4 means 10.4 cm

project

ESTIMATED VERSUS ACTUAL

Create a list of numerical statistics about a group of 10 to 20 people or things. You might choose ages of celebrities, average weights of animals, calories in candy bars, or average SAT scores for freshmen entering various universities. Record the actual values, and ask a friend or relative to estimate what they think the actual values might be.

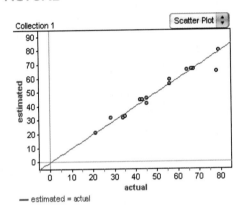

Your project should include

▶ A list of the actual and estimated values.

▶ A scatter plot of the data, with actual values on the horizontal axis and estimated values on the vertical axis. Add the line that represents when the actual values are equal to the estimated values.

▶ A description of how the data points relate to the *actual = estimated* line, and an analysis of what that says about your guesser's estimates.

▶ Any additional statistics you'd like to calculate for the actual or estimated data.

Fathom

These scatter plots were made with Fathom. You can use Fathom Dynamic Data Software to quickly and easily enter data, create various kinds of graphs, and calculate statistics. Try using Fathom for this project!

Supporting the project

MOTIVATION

Pose the questions: "How good are people at judging ages? Do people usually guess high or low?" Students can explore how well people's estimates match the actual values.

OUTCOMES

▶ The list has both actual and estimated values.

▶ The scatter plot includes data from the same two variables and the $y = x$ line.

▶ The student describes how the data relate to the $y = x$ line and gives an appropriate analysis of the guesser's estimates.

• Several additional statistics are calculated.

LESSON 1.8

Using Matrices to Organize and Combine Data

Don't agonize.
Organize.

FLORYNCE KENNEDY

Did you know that the average number of hours people work per week has been decreasing during the last 100 years? The table provides data for some countries. This table is 6 × 2 (read "six by two"), because it has six rows of countries and two columns of years. Can you identify the entry in row 2, column 1? In which row and column is the entry 37.6? 56.4; row 5, column 2

Average Weekly Working Hours

Rows are counted top to bottom.

	Country	1900	2000
row 1	Australia	47.7	35.9
row 2	Germany	56.4	30.6
row 3	France	60.1	30.8
row 4	Netherlands	64.2	26.9
row 5	United States	55.9	37.6
row 6	Britain	50.2	33.1

This entry is in row 3, column 2.

column 1   column 2

Columns are counted left to right.

During the late 1800s and early 1900s, labor unions were formed to improve working conditions. These miners may have belonged to the American Federation of Labor, one of the first unions to include African-American members.

A table is an easy way to organize data. A quicker way to organize data is to display it in a **matrix.** A matrix has rows and columns just like a table. To rewrite a table as a matrix, you simply use brackets to enclose the row and column entries. For the working-hours data, the **dimensions** of the matrix are the same as the table: 6 × 2.

In this lesson you will represent different situations with matrices and explore some matrix calculations.

EXAMPLE A

a. Form a matrix [A] from the table "Average Weekly Working Hours."

b. Verify the row and column locations of the entries 30.6, 26.9, and 50.2 in matrix [A].

c. If the average person works 50 weeks per year, what were the average yearly working-hour totals for these countries in 1900 and 2000?

NCTM STANDARDS

CONTENT		PROCESS	
✔	Number	✔	Problem Solving
	Algebra	✔	Reasoning
	Geometry		Communication
✔	Measurement	✔	Connections
✔	Data/Probability	✔	Representation

LESSON OBJECTIVES

- Use a matrix to represent a two-variable data set
- Set up a calculator matrix, enter data, and perform operations on matrices
- Multiply a matrix by a number
- Add and subtract matrices
- Multiply a matrix by an appropriate column matrix
- Understand the conditions under which two matrices can be added or multiplied

PLANNING

LESSON OUTLINE

First day:

15 min	Example A
10 min	Example B
25 min	Exercises 1–10

Second day:

30 min	Investigation
10 min	Sharing, Example C
5 min	Closing
5 min	Exercises

MATERIALS

- Pizza Prices (T)
- Calculator Notes 1L, 1M, 1N, 1P
- Sketchpad demonstration Multiplying Matrices, *optional*

TEACHING

Tables are commonly used to represent two-variable data, and matrices are mathematical abstractions of tables.

Organizing information is important in all areas of life, as the opening quote indicates. Florynce Kennedy (1916–2000) was an outspoken civil rights and equal rights advocate.

There's no universal notation for giving the dimensions of a matrix; 6 by 2, 6 × 2, and (6, 2) are all common.

EXAMPLE A

[Language] Use the term *entries* of a matrix.

[Alert] Watch for difficulty in setting up the matrix. Some students may set up a 2 × 6 matrix, thinking that the first dimension (the number of rows) is the "distance across," as on a coordinate plane.

a. Here is the 6 × 2 matrix. It is simply a table without labels.

$$[A] = \begin{bmatrix} 47.7 & 35.9 \\ 56.4 & 30.6 \\ 60.1 & 30.8 \\ 64.2 & 26.9 \\ 55.9 & 37.6 \\ 50.2 & 33.1 \end{bmatrix}$$

b. Enter the 6 × 2 matrix into your calculator. [▶ 🖳 See **Calculator Note 1L** to learn how to enter a matrix into your calculator.◀] The calculator display shows that 30.6 is located in row 2, column 2, of matrix [A]. By moving around in your editor, you see that the entry 26.9 is in row 4, column 2; 50.2 is in row 6, column 1.

c. Use your calculator to multiply [A] by 50. [▶ 🖳 See **Calculator Note 1M** to learn how to multiply a matrix by a number.◀] This new matrix shows the result of multiplying each of the original entries by 50. The new entries are the average *yearly* working hours.

As shown in the example, it is easy to operate on all the entries in a matrix with one calculation. In the next example you will learn how you can add or subtract two matrices to help you answer questions about a situation.

EXAMPLE B

Matrix [B] provides the costs of a medium pizza, medium salad, and medium drink at two different pizzerias: the Pizza Palace and Tony's Pizzeria. Matrix [C] provides the *additional* charge for large items at each pizzeria.

$$\begin{array}{cc} \text{Pizza Palace} & \text{Tony's Pizzeria} \\ \downarrow & \downarrow \end{array}$$

$$[B] = \begin{bmatrix} 8.90 & 9.10 \\ 2.35 & 2.65 \\ 1.50 & 1.60 \end{bmatrix} \begin{array}{l} \leftarrow \text{pizza} \\ \leftarrow \text{salad} \\ \leftarrow \text{drink} \end{array}$$

$$[C] = \begin{bmatrix} 2.50 & 2.25 \\ 1.00 & 1.25 \\ 0.65 & 0.50 \end{bmatrix} \begin{array}{l} \leftarrow \text{pizza} \\ \leftarrow \text{salad} \\ \leftarrow \text{drink} \end{array}$$

Write a matrix [D] displaying the costs at the Pizza Palace and at Tony's Pizzeria for a large pizza, large salad, and large drink.

▶ **Solution**   If you wanted the price of a large pizza at the Pizza Palace, you would add the
medium price and the additional charge.

$$8.90 + 2.50 = 11.40$$

The totals for matrix [D] are found by adding all corresponding entries from
matrix [B] and matrix [C]. [▶ See **Calculator Note 1N** to learn how to use your calculator
to add and subtract matrices.◀]

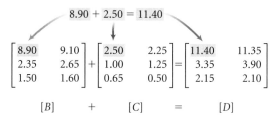

$$
\begin{bmatrix} 8.90 & 9.10 \\ 2.35 & 2.65 \\ 1.50 & 1.60 \end{bmatrix}
+
\begin{bmatrix} 2.50 & 2.25 \\ 1.00 & 1.25 \\ 0.65 & 0.50 \end{bmatrix}
=
\begin{bmatrix} 11.40 & 11.35 \\ 3.35 & 3.90 \\ 2.15 & 2.10 \end{bmatrix}
$$

$$[B] \qquad + \qquad [C] \qquad = \qquad [D]$$

Does the order in which you add these matrices make a difference? Take a
moment to calculate [B] + [C] and [C] + [B] on your calculator.

If you try adding a 6 × 2 matrix and a 3 × 2 matrix with your calculator, you'll get
an error message. This is because the matrices don't have the same dimensions, so
there is no way to match up corresponding entries to do the operations. In order
for you to add or subtract matrices, the matrices must have the same number of
rows and also the same number of columns.

Can you multiply two matrices? In this investigation you will discover why matrix
multiplication is more complicated.

Investigation
Row-by-Column Matrix Multiplication

Recall the table and matrix for large items at the Pizza Palace and Tony's Pizzeria
from Example B.

Suppose you're in charge of ordering
the food for a school club party.

$$[D] = \begin{bmatrix} 11.40 & 11.35 \\ 3.35 & 3.90 \\ 2.15 & 2.10 \end{bmatrix}$$

Large-Item Prices

	Pizza Palace	Tony's Pizzeria
Large pizza	$11.40	$11.35
Large salad	$3.35	$3.90
Large drink	$2.15	$2.10

Step 1   What will be the total cost of
4 large pizzas, 5 large salads, and
10 large drinks at the Pizza Palace? $83.85

Step 2   What will be the total cost for the same order at Tony's Pizzeria? $85.90

Step 3   Describe how you calculated the total costs. Descriptions should include
multiplying each item quantity by each cost and then adding all costs.

You may wish to display the Pizza
Prices transparency.

Guiding the Investigation

As you see, calculating the food costs for your party requires multiplication and addition. Organizing your work like this is a first step to discovering how to multiply matrices.

pizza	salad	drink	total
4 · 11.40 +	5 · 3.35 +	10 · 2.15 =	83.85
number cost	number cost	number cost	

<table>
</table>

Step 5 You might mention that a matrix of just one row or column is often called a *vector*. Be sure students write their explanations of what the matrices represent.

Step 4 Copy the calculation and replace each box with a number to find the total food cost for the same order at the Pizza Palace.

Step 6 Explanations should include that each column entry in the first matrix is multiplied by the respective row entry in the second matrix, then everything is added.

Step 5 The **row matrix** $[A]$ and **column matrix** $[B]$ contain all the information you need to calculate the total food cost at the Pizza Palace.

$$[A] = [4 \quad 5 \quad 10] \quad [B] = \begin{bmatrix} 11.40 \\ 3.35 \\ 2.15 \end{bmatrix}$$

Step 7 $\boxed{4} \cdot \boxed{11.35} + \boxed{5} \cdot \boxed{3.90}$
$+ \boxed{10} \cdot \boxed{2.10} = \boxed{85.90}$

Explain what matrix $[A]$ and matrix $[B]$ represent. $[A]$ represents the food quantities; $[B]$ represents the food costs.

Step 8 $[4 \ 5 \ 10] \begin{bmatrix} 11.35 \\ 3.90 \\ 2.10 \end{bmatrix}$
$= [85.90]$

Step 6 Enter $[A]$ and $[B]$ into your calculator and find their product, $[A] \cdot [B]$, or

$$[4 \quad 5 \quad 10] \cdot \begin{bmatrix} 11.40 \\ 3.35 \\ 2.15 \end{bmatrix}$$

Step 9 Because each column entry is multiplied by a respective row entry, the number of columns must equal the number of rows.

[▶ 🖳 See **Calculator Note 1P** to learn how to multiply two matrices.◀] Explain in detail what you think the calculator does to find this answer.

Step 7 Repeat Step 4 to find the total food cost at Tony's Pizzeria.

Step 10 Students may write the answer vertically, but don't criticize. When they do it on the calculator, they will see it as a row.

Step 8 Write the product of a row matrix and a column matrix that calculates the total food cost at Tony's Pizzeria. Use your calculator to verify that your product matches your answer to Step 7.

Step 9 Explain why the number of columns in the first matrix must be the same as the number of rows in the second matrix in order to multiply them.

Step 12 Even if both products $[A][B]$ and $[B][A]$ of two matrices are defined (that is, the matrices are square), the products are not generally equal. The products are the same only for a few special cases, such as when one of the matrices is the identity matrix $\begin{bmatrix} 1 & 0 & 0 \\ 0 & 1 & 0 \\ 0 & 0 & 1 \end{bmatrix}$.

Step 10 Predict the answer to the matrix multiplication problem below. Use your calculator to verify your answer. What is its meaning in the real-world context?

$$[4 \quad 5 \quad 10] \cdot \begin{bmatrix} 11.40 & 11.35 \\ 3.35 & 3.90 \\ 2.15 & 2.10 \end{bmatrix} = ?$$

$[83.85 \quad 85.90]$ represents the total cost at the Pizza Palace and at Tony's Pizzeria.

Step 11 Explain how to calculate the matrix multiplication in Step 10 without using calculator matrices. Explanations should include multiplying the row matrix by each column.

Step 13 [Language] Challenge students to use the language carefully: Each item in a row is multiplied by the *respective* item in the column, and the *products* are added.

Step 12 Try this matrix multiplication:

$$\begin{bmatrix} 11.40 & 11.35 \\ 3.35 & 3.90 \\ 2.15 & 2.10 \end{bmatrix} \cdot [4 \quad 5 \quad 10]$$

The dimensions do not allow multiplication.

In general, do you think $[A] \cdot [B] = [B] \cdot [A]$? Explain.

Students will need time to make the big jump from multiplying by a vector to multiplying by a larger matrix. Giving another example when you talk about Example C will help.

Step 13 Write a short paragraph explaining how to multiply two matrices.

Step 13 Answers should include the concept of multiplying rows by columns.

EXAMPLE C

Is it possible to multiply each pair of matrices? If so, what is the product? If not, why not?

a. $\begin{bmatrix} 2 & 3 & 4 \end{bmatrix} \cdot \begin{bmatrix} -1 \\ 1 \\ 5 \end{bmatrix}$

b. $\begin{bmatrix} 3 & -1 \end{bmatrix} \cdot \begin{bmatrix} 2 & 4 \\ 0 & 3 \\ 5 & -6 \end{bmatrix}$

c. $\begin{bmatrix} 3 & -1 \end{bmatrix} \cdot \begin{bmatrix} 2 & 0 & 5 \\ 4 & 7 & -6 \end{bmatrix}$

▶ **Solution**

You can only multiply matrices if the number of columns in the first matrix is equal to the number of rows in the second matrix.

a. Multiply the respective entries in the row matrix by those in the column matrix and then add the products.

$$\begin{bmatrix} 2 & 3 & 4 \end{bmatrix} \cdot \begin{bmatrix} -1 \\ 1 \\ 5 \end{bmatrix} = \begin{bmatrix} 21 \end{bmatrix}$$

$$(2 \cdot -1) + (3 \cdot 1) + (4 \cdot 5) = 21$$

b. This is not possible. There are not enough entries in the row matrix to match the three entries in each column.

c. Multiply the entries in the row matrix by the respective entries in each column. Each sum is a separate entry in the answer matrix.

Technology
CONNECTION

The development of 3-D video games uses matrices to process the graphics. For more information on the mathematics involved in video game development, see the link at
www.keymath.com/DA .

Multiply the row by each column.

You multiply a 1 × 2 matrix by a 2 × 3 matrix.

1 × 2, 2 × 3

The inside dimensions are the same so you can multiply. The 2 row entries match up with 2 column entries.

1 × 2, 2 × 3

The outside dimensions tell you the dimensions of your answer.

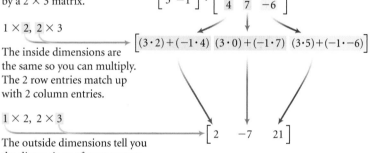

Matrix multiplication is probably too much work if all you want to do is plan a pizza party. But what if you had to manage the inventory (goods in stock) of a grocery store? Or a whole chain of grocery stores? To do this, matrix calculations carried out by a computer would be essential to your business.

second matrix; each entry of the product matrix is the sum of products of the entries in the corresponding row of the first matrix and column of the second matrix.

SHARING IDEAS

Good investigation steps to ask students to present are 3, 10, and 12. **[Ask]** "When is matrix multiplication possible?" [when the number of columns of the first matrix equals the number of rows of the second matrix]

Assessing Progress

By watching students contribute to groups or the whole class, you can assess their skill at arithmetic with decimals and keeping track of two variables at once.

EXAMPLE C

Talk through this third example if students are having difficulty in multiplying matrices. The Sketchpad demonstration Multiplying Matrices gives a geometric interpretation of matrix multiplication. This demonstration could be used as an extension of the lesson.

Another Example

Example C shows a vector and a matrix, but two matrices can be multiplied as long as the inside dimensions are the same.

A 2 × 2 matrix can be multiplied by a 2 × 3 matrix. The inside dimensions are the same. The outside dimensions indicate that the answer will be a 2 × 3 matrix.

$$\begin{bmatrix} 3 & -1 \\ 1 & 2 \end{bmatrix} \begin{bmatrix} 2 & 0 & 5 \\ 4 & 7 & -6 \end{bmatrix}$$
$$= \begin{bmatrix} 2 & -7 & 21 \\ 10 & 14 & -7 \end{bmatrix}$$

Closing the Lesson

Mention the important mathematical ideas new to this lesson. **Matrices** are abstractions of tables representing data. Their first **dimension** gives the number of rows, and their second gives the number of columns. Matrices with the same dimensions can be added, entry by entry. Matrices can be multiplied if the number of columns in the first matrix equals the number of rows in the

Practice Your Skills

Use this information for Exercises 1–8. Troy Aikman, Randall Cunningham, and
Steve Young were top-performing quarterbacks in the National Football League
throughout their careers. The rows in matrix $[A]$ and matrix $[B]$ show data for Aikman,
Cunningham, and Young, in that order. The columns show the number of passing
attempts, pass completions, touchdown passes, and interceptions, from left to right.
Matrix $[A]$ shows stats from 1992, and matrix $[B]$ shows stats from 1998.

$$[A] = \begin{bmatrix} 473 & 302 & 23 & 14 \\ 384 & 233 & 19 & 11 \\ 402 & 268 & 25 & 7 \end{bmatrix} \quad [B] = \begin{bmatrix} 315 & 187 & 12 & 5 \\ 425 & 259 & 34 & 10 \\ 517 & 322 & 36 & 12 \end{bmatrix}$$

(Sports Illustrated, *www.si.com*)

1. What does the entry in row 2, column 3, of
matrix $[A]$ tell you? @ Randall Cunningham
threw 19 touchdown passes in 1992.

2. What does the entry in row 3, column 2, of
matrix $[B]$ tell you? Steve Young made 322 pass
completions in 1998.

3. What are the dimensions of each matrix? @
3×4

4. Write a clear explanation of the procedure for
entering $[A]$ and $[B]$ into your calculator.
Answers will vary.

5. Find $[A] + [B]$. What is this matrix and what
information does it provide? @

6. Is $[A] + [B]$ equal to $[B] + [A]$? Do you think this result is always true for matrix
addition? Explain. Yes; this result should always be true if the matrices have the same dimensions.

7. Find $[B] - [A]$. What is this matrix and what information does it provide?

8. How can you use your calculator to find the average statistics for the three
quarterbacks for these two seasons? Write a matrix expression that will give
this average. $([A] + [B]) \cdot \left(\dfrac{1}{2}\right)$

▶ Reason and Apply

9. Use matrices $[A]$ and $[B]$ to write the new matrices asked for in 9a–d.

$$[A] = \begin{bmatrix} 3 & -4 & 2.5 \\ -2 & 6 & 4 \end{bmatrix} \quad [B] = \begin{bmatrix} 5 & -1 & 2 \\ -4 & 3.5 & 1 \end{bmatrix}$$

a. $[A] + [B]$ **b.** $-[A]$ @   **c.** $3 \cdot [B]$ **d.** the average of $[A]$ and $[B]$ @

10. Find the matrix $[B]$ such that this equation is valid:

$$\begin{bmatrix} -2 & 0 \\ 6 & -11.6 \\ 4.25 & 7.5 \end{bmatrix} - [B] = \begin{bmatrix} 2.8 & 2.4 \\ 2.5 & -9.4 \\ 1 & 6 \end{bmatrix} \begin{bmatrix} -4.8 & -2.4 \\ 3.5 & -2.2 \\ 3.25 & 1.5 \end{bmatrix}$$

produce an error message, because division is not
defined for matrices.

9a. $\begin{bmatrix} 8 & -5 & 4.5 \\ -6 & 9.5 & 5 \end{bmatrix}$

9b. $\begin{bmatrix} -3 & 4 & -2.5 \\ 2 & -6 & -4 \end{bmatrix}$

9c. $\begin{bmatrix} 15 & -3 & 6 \\ -12 & 10.5 & 3 \end{bmatrix}$

9d. $\begin{bmatrix} 4 & -2.5 & 2.25 \\ -3 & 4.75 & 2.5 \end{bmatrix}$

Exercise 10 Most students will find this 3×2 matrix
by thinking or guess-and-check.

11. Create a problem involving this matrix multiplication if the row matrix represents dollars and cents and the column matrix represents hours. Find the product without using your calculator's matrix menu.

$$[5.25 \quad 8.75] \cdot \begin{bmatrix} 16 \\ 30 \end{bmatrix}$$

12. APPLICATION Ms. Shurr owns three ice-cream shops and wants to know how much she made on ice-cream cone sales for one day. The number of small, medium, and large cones sold at each location and the profit for each size are contained in the tables.

Number of Cones Sold

	S	M	L
Atlanta	74	25	37
Decatur	32	38	16
Athens	120	52	34

Cone Profit

	Profit
S	$0.90
M	$1.25
L	$2.15

a. Write a quantity matrix that gives the number of each size sold at each location and a profit matrix that gives the profit for each size. What must be the same for each matrix? @

b. Without using your calculator's matrix menu, find the profit from ice-cream cones for each location. Explain how you got your answer.

c. Check your answer to 12b by using your calculator to multiply the quantity matrix [A] by the profit matrix [B]. What are the dimensions of the answer matrix?

d. What do the entries in the answer matrix tell you? Convert your matrix into a table with row and column headings so that Ms. Shurr can understand the information.

e. Try to calculate [B] · [A] on your calculator. What happens? What do you think the result means?

▶ Review

1.2 **13.** Create a data set that fits the information. ⓗ

a. Ten students were asked the number of times they had flown in an airplane. The range of data values was 7. The minimum was 0 and the mode was 2.

b. Eight students each measured the length of their right foot. The range of data values was 8.2 cm, and the maximum value was 30.4 cm. There was no mode.

1.4 **14.** Mr. Chin and Mrs. Shapiro had their classes collect data on the amount of change each student had in class on a particular day. The students graphed the data on the back-to-back stem plot at right.

a. How many students are in each class? Shapiro: 40; Chin: 41

b. Find the range of the data in each class. Shapiro: 1.35; Chin: 1.25

c. How many students had more than $1? 13

d. What do the entries in the last row represent?

e. Without adding, make an educated guess which class has the most money altogether. Explain your thinking.

f. How much money does each class have? Shapiro: $24.96; Chin: $20.34

Mrs. Shapiro's class						Mr. Chin's class					
0	0	0	0		0	0	0	0	0	5	8
		2	0		1	0	5	6			
	5	5	5		2	0	0	5	5	5	7
9	6	5	0	0	3	5	5				
			5		4	0	0	0	6		
	5	2	0	0	5	0	0	5	5	8	
	7	3	0	0	6	0	2	5	5		
		5	0		7	0	5	5	6		
	2	0	0		8						
	4	1			9						
	4	0	0		10	0	0	5			
	5	0			11	0					
6	4	1			12	1	5	5			
	5	0			13						

Key

5	4	0	0	0	6

means 45¢ in Mrs. Shapiro's class; 40¢, 40¢, 40¢, and 46¢ in Mr. Chin's class

13a. The minimum in the data set must be 0, and the maximum must be 7. Also, the data value 2 must occur more frequently than any other. A sample solution is {0, 1, 2, 2, 2, 2, 3, 4, 6, 7}.

13b. The minimum must be 22.2, and the maximum must be 30.4. No values in the list should occur more often than any other values. A sample solution is {22.2, 24.5, 25.1, 26.2, 28.3, 28.7, 29.4, 30.4}.

14d. In Mrs. Shapiro's class, one student had $1.35 and one student had $1.30.

14e. Based on the stem plot, you might expect Mrs. Shapiro's class to have more money. There are more students with more than a dollar in her class and more with less than 50¢ in Mr. Chin's class.

---

11. A possibility would be to find the labor costs of building an item using 16 hours billed at $5.25 per hour and 30 hours billed at $8.75 per hour. The product is

$$[5.25 \quad 8.75]\begin{bmatrix} 16 \\ 30 \end{bmatrix} = [346.50]$$

Exercise 12a As needed, refer students to Example C on page 87. When two matrices are multiplied, the inside dimensions must be the same (3 × 3 times 3 × 1) and the outside dimensions tell the dimensions of the answer (3 × 1).

12a. Quantity: $\begin{bmatrix} 74 & 25 & 37 \\ 32 & 38 & 16 \\ 120 & 52 & 34 \end{bmatrix}$;

profit: $\begin{bmatrix} 0.90 \\ 1.25 \\ 2.15 \end{bmatrix}$;

the number of columns in the quantity matrix must be the same as the number of rows in the profit matrix.

12b. Atlanta: 74($0.90) + 25($1.25) + 37($2.15) = $177.40; Decatur: 32($0.90) + 38($1.25) + 16($2.15) = $110.70; Athens: 120($0.90) + 52($1.25) + 34($2.15) = $246.10

12c. $\begin{bmatrix} 177.40 \\ 110.70 \\ 246.10 \end{bmatrix}$; 3 × 1

12d. The answer matrix gives the profit at each location.

	Profit
Atlanta	$177.40
Decatur	$110.70
Athens	$246.10

12e. The error message—ERR: DIM MISMATCH—means that the dimensions of the matrices in the product don't match.

CHAPTER

1

REVIEW

PLANNING

LESSON OUTLINE

One day:

5 min	Introduction
15 min	Exercises and helping individuals
15 min	Checking work and helping individuals
15 min	Student self-assessment

REVIEWING

You might use the Jurassic Park data on page 77 to review. **[Ask]** "What statistics and graphs could be used to describe this data set?" Elicit these and other responses:

For the actual or for the estimated data as a one-variable data set:

- Find measures of center, measures of spread, and the five-number summary.
- Draw a box plot; identify any outliers, and describe how they affect the measures of center.
- Draw a dot plot or stem plot.
- Construct histograms with various bins.
- Divide the dinosaurs into groups by the first letter of their names, or the length of their names, or put those whose names end in *saurus* in one group and the others in another group; then construct a bar graph or a pictograph showing how many are in each group.

Comparing the estimated and actual data sets:

- Compare the box plots, dot plots, or histograms made for the actual or for the estimated data.

In this chapter you learned how statistical measures and graphs can help you organize and make sense of **data.** You explored several different kinds of graphs—**bar graphs, pictographs, dot plots, box plots, histograms,** and **stem plots**—that can be used to represent **one-variable** data.

You analyzed the strengths and weaknesses of each kind of graph to select the most appropriate one for a given situation. A bar graph displays data that can be grouped into **categories.** Numerical data can be individually shown with a dot plot. The **spread** of data is clearly displayed with a box plot built from the **five-number summary.** A histogram uses **bins** to show the **frequency** of data and is particularly useful for large sets of data. A stem plot also groups data into intervals but maintains the identity of each data value.

You can use **measures of center** to describe a typical data value. In addition to the **mean, median,** and **mode,** statistical measures like **range, minimum, maximum, quartiles,** and **interquartile range** help you describe the spread of a data set and identify **outliers.**

You used the **coordinate plane** to compare estimates and actual values plotted on **two-variable** plots called **scatter plots.** Here, each variable is represented on a different axis, and an **ordered pair** shows the value of each variable for a single data item. You also analyzed scatter plots for situations involving the two variables *time* and *distance.* Scatter plots allowed you to find patterns in the data; sometimes these patterns could be written as an algebraic equation.

Lastly, you learned to use a **matrix** to organize data in rows and columns, very much like a table. You discovered ways to add, subtract, and multiply matrices and learned how the **dimensions** of matrices affect these computations. Computers and calculators can use matrices to calculate with large sets of data, making it easy to answer questions about the data.

EXERCISES

@ Answers are provided for all exercises in this set.

1. This data set gives the number of hours of use before each of 14 batteries required recharging: 40, 36, 27, 44, 40, 34, 42, 58, 36, 46, 52, 52, 38, 36.
   a. Find the mean, median, and mode for the data set, and explain how you found each measure.
   b. Find the five-number summary for the data set and make a box plot.

2. Seven students order onion rings. The mean number of onion rings they get is 16. The five-number summary is 9, 11, 16, 21, 22. How many onion rings might each student have been served? possible answer: {9, 11, 14, 16, 19, 21, 22}

1a. Mean: 41.5; divide the sum of the numbers by 14. Median: 40; list the numbers in ascending order and find the mean of the two middle numbers. Mode: 36; find the most frequently occurring number.

1b. 27, 36, 40, 46, 58

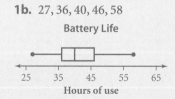

Battery Life

Hours of use

3. The table at right shows the mean annual wages earned by individuals with various levels of education in the United States in 1998.

a. Construct a bar graph for the data.

b. Between which two consecutive levels of education is there the greatest difference in mean annual wages? The smallest difference?

4. The table below shows the top ten scorers in the 2003 NCAA Women's Basketball Tournament.

a. Construct a box plot for the data.

b. Are there any outliers?

c. Which measure of center would you use to describe a typical value?

Mean Annual Wages, 1998

Level of education	Amount ($)
Did not finish high school	18,913
High school diploma only	25,257
Two-year degree (AA/AS)	33,765
Bachelor's degree (BA/BS)	45,390
Master's degree (MA/MS)	52,951
Doctorate degree	75,071

(U.S. Bureau of the Census, *www.census.gov*)

Leading Scorers in 2003 NCAA Women's Basketball Tournament

Player	Points
Diana Taurasi, Connecticut	157
Alana Beard, Duke	115
Heather Schreiber, Texas	96
Tera Bjorklund, Colorado	74
Erika Valek, Purdue	74
Plenette Pierson, Texas Tech	73
Jordan Adams, New Mexico	66
Kelly Mazzante, Penn State	66
Christi Thomas, Georgia	61
Trina Frierson, Louisiana Tech	57

(National Collegiate Athletic Association, *www.ncaa.org*)
[Data set: **NCAA3**]

After an impressive college career, Alana Beard went on to play professionally for the Washington Mystics.

5. Twenty-three students were asked how many pages they had read in a book currently assigned for class. Here are their responses: 24, 87, 158, 227, 437, 79, 93, 121, 111, 118, 12, 25, 284, 332, 181, 34, 54, 167, 300, 103, 128, 132, 345. [Data set: **BKPGS**]

a. Find the measures of center.

b. Construct histograms for two different bin widths.

c. Construct a box plot.

d. What do the histograms and the box plot tell you about this data set? Make one or two observations.

Using the data set as two-variable data:

- Construct a scatter plot of the actual numbers versus the estimated numbers; decide from the graph which species were overestimated.

- Divide the dinosaurs into groups, and construct bar graphs or pictographs showing how many overestimates occurred in each category.

As students suggest graphs, talk about the strengths and weaknesses of the various graphs for representing the data, and review how bar graphs and pictographs are used for nonnumerical categories, in contrast to dot plots, stem plots, and histograms.

ASSIGNING HOMEWORK

Students who complete Exercises 1–6 and 8–10 are reviewing all the graphical representations presented in the chapter. Assign Exercise 7 only if you covered matrices.

3a. See page 92.

3b. greatest jump: from a master's degree to a doctorate; smallest difference: from not finishing high school to a high school diploma

4a.

2003 NCAA Women's Tournament Top Scorers

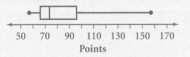

4b. 157 points (Diana Taurasi)

4c. Choices will vary; mean: 83.9; median: 73.5; modes: 66, 74.

5a. Mean: approximately 154; median: 121; there is no mode.

5b. Bin widths may vary.

Pages Read in Current Book

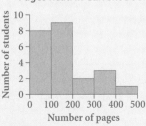

Pages Read in Current Book

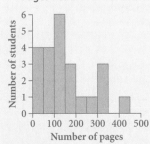

5c.

Pages Read in Current Book

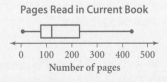

5d. Possible answer: Most of the students questioned had read fewer than 200 pages, with a fairly even distribution between 0 and 200.

6a.

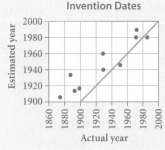

Invention Dates

6b. (1952, 1945), (1985, 1980)

6c. $y = x$, where x represents actual year and y represents estimated year

7a. $\begin{bmatrix} 5.00 & 8.00 \\ 3.50 & 4.75 \\ 3.50 & 4.00 \end{bmatrix}, \begin{bmatrix} 0.50 & 0.75 \\ 0.50 & 0.25 \\ 0.50 & 0.25 \end{bmatrix},$

$[43 \quad 81 \quad 37]$

7b. $[A] + [B] = \begin{bmatrix} 5.50 & 8.75 \\ 4.00 & 5.00 \\ 4.00 & 4.25 \end{bmatrix}$

7c. $[C] \cdot ([A] + [B])$
$= [708.5 \quad 938.5];$
matinee: \$708.50,
evening: \$938.50

8a. between points A and B

8b. Kayo was not moving; perhaps she was resting.

8c. Possible answer: Kayo started out jogging fast but had to rest for a few minutes. Then she jogged much slower until she had to rest again. She finally got the energy to jog all the way home at a steady pace without stopping.

6. Isabel made the estimates listed in the table at right for the year each item was invented.

   a. Create a scatter plot of data points with coordinates having the form (*actual year, estimated year*).

   b. Circle those points that picture an estimated year that is earlier than the actual year (underestimates).

   c. Define your variables and write the equation of a line that would represent all estimates being correct.

7. **APPLICATION** The tables below show information for the Roxy Theater. The management is considering raising the admission prices.

Invention Dates

Item	Actual year	Estimated year
Telephone	1876	1905
Color television	1928	1960
Video disk	1972	1980
Pacemaker	1952	1945
Motion picture	1893	1915
Ballpoint pen	1888	1935
Aspirin	1899	1917
Graphing calculator	1985	1980
Compact disc	1972	1990
Car radio	1929	1940

(*2000 World Almanac*, pp. 609–610)

Current Prices

	Matinee	Evening
Adult	\$5.00	\$8.00
Child	\$3.50	\$4.75
Senior	\$3.50	\$4.00

Price Increases

	Matinee	Evening
Adult	\$0.50	\$0.75
Child	\$0.50	\$0.25
Senior	\$0.50	\$0.25

Average Attendance

Adult	Child	Senior
43	81	37

   a. Convert each table to a matrix.

   b. Do a matrix calculation to find the new prices after the admission increase.

   c. Do a matrix calculation to find the total revenue of a matinee performance and of an evening performance at the new prices.

8. The graph below shows Kayo's distance over time as she jogs straight down the street in front of her home. Point A is Kayo's starting point (her home).

   a. During which time period was Kayo jogging the fastest?

   b. Explain what the jogger might have been doing during the time interval between points B and C and between points D and E.

   c. Write a brief story for this graph using all five segments.

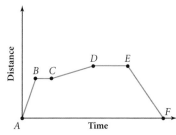

Jogger's Distance from Home

3a.

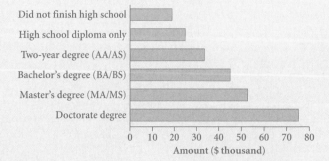

Mean Annual Wages, 1998

9. The table at right shows the approximate 2000 populations of the ten most populated cities in the United States.

   a. Write the approximate population of Chicago in 2000 as a whole number. 2,900,000

   b. Create a bar graph of the data.

   c. Create a stem plot of the data.

   d. Create a box plot of the data.

   e. Each of the graphs you have created highlights different characteristics of the data. Briefly describe what features are unique to each graph.

10. This stem-and-leaf plot shows the number of minutes of sleep for eight students. In this plot the dots represent that the interval is divided in half at 50. Use the key to fully understand how to read this graph.

416.875 min   **a.** What is the mean sleep amount?

425 min   **b.** What is the median sleep amount?

   c. What is the mode sleep amount?
   480 min

Minutes Sleeping

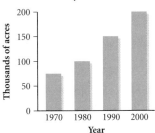

```
3  |  20
•  |  60  90
4  |  00
•  |  50  55  80  80
```

Key

```
3  |  20   means 320 minutes
•  |  60   means 360 minutes
```

The Ten Most Populated U.S. Cities, 2000

City	Population (millions)
Chicago	2.90
Dallas	1.19
Detroit	0.95
Houston	1.95
Los Angeles	3.69
New York	8.01
Philadelphia	1.52
Phoenix	1.32
San Antonio	1.14
San Diego	1.22

(U.S. Bureau of the Census, in *Time Almanac 2004*, p. 260)

TAKE ANOTHER LOOK

These two graphs display the same data set. The first graph is being presented by a citizen who argues that the city should use its budget surplus to buy land for a park. The second graph is being presented by another citizen who argues that a new park is not a high priority. Tell what position you would favor on this issue and what impact each graph has on your decision. Do you think either graph is deliberately misleading? If so, what other information would you want to know?

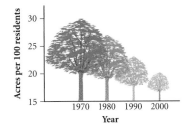

Greenspace Disappearing!

Greenspace in Our Town

Find another graphic display in a newspaper, magazine, or voter material that seems to be "engineered" to persuade the viewer to a particular point of view. Tell how the graph could be changed for a fairer presentation.

9b.

The Ten Most Populated U.S. Cities, 2000

9c.

The Ten Most Populated U.S. Cities, 2000

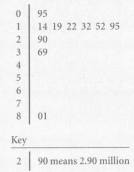

```
0 | 95
1 | 14  19  22  32  52  95
2 | 90
3 | 69
4 |
5 |
6 |
7 |
8 | 01
```

Key

```
2 | 90 means 2.90 million
```

9d.

The Ten Most Populated U.S. Cities, 2000

9e. The bar graph helps show how each city compares with the others, because they remain identified by name. The stem plot shows distribution but also shows actual values. The box plot shows distribution and a clustering between 1 and 1.4 million but does not show individual city names or populations.

▶ Take Another Look

The picture graph uses both a broken vertical axis (starting at 15) and pictures with decreasing area to exaggerate the decline of green space. The normal bar graph, on the other hand, measures only acres and ignores the ratio to the increasing population, which the first graph takes into account. Therefore, both of these bar graphs are engineered to persuade. Answers will depend on whether students think acres per person or total acres is a better measure.

ASSESSING

Through this chapter students have become more accustomed to working collaboratively and have improved their facility with graphing calculators. The principal new ideas discussed are representing data by statistics, by graphs, and by matrices.

FACILITATING SELF-ASSESSMENT

Many of the exercises students have completed could be journal entries; they are marked Journal in Assigning Homework. Students also benefit from recording their thinking about their own ideas.

To help students complete the portfolio described in Assessing What You've Learned, suggest that they consider for evaluation their work on Lesson 1.1, Exercise 3; Lesson 1.2, Exercises 10 and 11; Lesson 1.3, Exercise 8; Lesson 1.4, Exercises 6 and 10; Lesson 1.6, Exercise 8; Lesson 1.7, Exercise 6; and Lesson 1.8, Exercise 12.

TESTING

You can use either Form A or Form B of the Chapter Test, or you can use Constructive Assessment items from Assessment Resources. Using the Test Generator CD, you can create an alternate version of the test or combine some items from Form A or Form B with Constructive Assessment items.

Assessing What You've Learned

WRITE IN YOUR JOURNAL

Your course work in algebra will bring up many new ideas, and some are quite abstract. Sometimes you'll feel you have a good grip on these new ideas, other times less so.

Regular reflection on your confidence in mathematics generally, and your mastery of algebra skills in particular, will help you assess your strengths and weaknesses. Writing these reflections down will help you realize where you are having trouble, and perhaps you'll ask for help sooner. Likewise, realizing how much you know can boost your confidence. A good place to record these thoughts is in a journal—not a personal diary, but an informal collection of your feelings and observations about what you're learning. Like a travel journal that others would find interesting to read and that will help recall the details of a trip, a mathematics journal is something your teacher will want to look at and something you'll look at again later.

Here are some questions to prompt your journal writing. Your teacher might give you other ideas, but you can write in your journal any time.

▶ How is what you are learning an extension of your previous mathematics courses? How is it completely new?

▶ What are your goals for your work in algebra? What steps can you take to achieve them?

▶ Can you see ways to apply what you are learning to your everyday life? To a future career?

▶ What ideas have you found hard to understand?

UPDATE YOUR PORTFOLIO At the end of Chapter 0, you may have started a portfolio. Now would be a good time to add one or more pieces of significant work from Chapter 1. You could choose an investigation, a homework problem, or your work on a Project or Take Another Look. It might be a good idea to include a sample of every type of graph you've learned to interpret or create.

CHAPTER

2

Proportional Reasoning and Variation

Overview

In this chapter students use linear equations to represent a sequence of calculations and solve those equations by "undoing"—working backward through the inverses of the calculations. In Chapter 3, students use linear equations to model linear growth and graphs and extend their solution techniques to include balancing.

Lessons 2.1 and **2.2** begin with a review of previous work with proportions and introduce the idea of *undoing* to solve a proportion. **Lesson 2.3** moves on to linear expressions derived from measurement conversions, with an emphasis on dimensional analysis. **Lesson 2.4** introduces direct variation equations as an alternative to solving proportions; students create a scatter plot of a real data set, draw a line through the points, and find an equation in the form $y = kx$ to describe that line. **Lesson 2.5** addresses the related topic of inverse variation. Students explore both direct and indirect variations through an activity involving bicycle gears in **Lesson 2.6.** In **Lesson 2.7,** students practice the rules for order of operations by analyzing how the steps in linear expressions that describe "number tricks" undo each other to end with the same number. Then, in **Lesson 2.8,** students write linear equations to represent sequences of steps and solve those equations by undoing.

The Mathematics

Ratios and Dimensional Analysis

Traditionally, a *ratio* is a comparison of two values, such as "3 is to 2." The tradition dates back before Euclid, who defined a ratio as "a sort of relation in respect of size between two magnitudes of the same kind." Although Euclid didn't think of these magnitudes as numbers, today we often think of a ratio as a fraction. We recognize that it's something more, though: A ratio compares two values, such as

2 cups of sugar to 3 cups of flour. So in working with ratios, the measurement units, or dimensions, are important. Keeping track of these units when setting up equations that involve ratios is called *dimensional analysis*.

Proportions

A *proportion* is a statement that two ratios are equal. Four values are involved in a proportion. We say that the pairs of these values are *proportional*. Another way of thinking of a proportion—and the way that is prominent in the text—is to state that the results of two different divisions are equal.

Because a unit is attached to each value in a proportion, teachers sometimes say that the top units must be the same on both sides, as must the bottom units. But this language is unclear, as shown by Lesson 2.1, Exercise 6: A 1.5-gram ant carrying a 4-gram leaf is equivalent to a 53-kilogram algebra student carrying how many kilograms? You can write the units of the proportion as $\frac{\text{g creature}}{\text{g load}} = \frac{\text{kg creature}}{\text{kg load}}$ and $\frac{\text{g creature}}{\text{kg creature}} = \frac{\text{g load}}{\text{kg load}}$. What units are "alike"? Teachers should stress that the comparisons are alike but should not try to describe the "alikeness" in terms of units.

The term *proportion* is frequently used when one of the four values is unknown, as in the load-carrying example. In that case *solving* the proportion means finding the unknown number.

Undoing

When confronted by an equation like the proportion $\frac{2}{3} = \frac{a}{750}$, many teachers will suggest solving by cross-multiplying or by multiplying both sides by 750. Because cross-multiplying often obscures meaning, it's avoided in the text. Multiplying both sides of an equation by a number assumes a concept of an equation as a balance. In the text, this equation is solved by "multiplying by 750 to undo the division." That is, a is divided by 750, so multiplying by 750 gets back to a. This

thinking relies on an understanding that $\frac{a}{750}$ represents division. The method also lays the groundwork for the undoing approach to solving linear equations in one variable.

The undoing method for solving equations is a useful precursor to the balancing method. To use the undoing method, the student understands the equation $5x + 2 = 17$ to mean that a sequence of calculations arrives at 17: You first multiply a starting number x by 5, then add 2. To find the value of the starting number, you "undo" by working backward: You first subtract 2 from 17, then divide by 5 to get 3. This approach emphasizes that the variable represents a particular but unknown number. Although the calculations are the same as those used in solving the equation by balancing, the thought process is quite different.

This chapter builds to solving linear equations by undoing, and much of Chapter 3 uses this same technique. Solving by undoing helps students focus on the order of operations and on undoing the operations in reverse order. The balancing method is introduced in Lesson 3.6.

Using This Chapter

If your students understand ratios and proportions, you can skip some of the lessons. Be careful in making that decision, though; many students who can solve proportions are not skilled at setting them up and can't explain why their solution method works.

If students have a very good grasp of ratios and proportions, you can skip Lessons 2.1 and 2.2. Be cautious about skipping Lesson 2.3, as it emphasizes dimensional analysis and is a basis

for Lesson 2.4, which introduces direct variation as a method for solving conversion problems. Lessons 2.5 and 2.6 are optional, but at least try to work with some inverse relationships and show students the graph of an inverse variation as an example of a nonlinear graph.

Resources

Discovering Algebra Resources

Teaching and Worksheet Masters
Lessons 2.2, 2.4, 2.5, 2.7, 2.8

Calculator Notes 0A, 1B, 1F, 1J, 1K, 2A, 2B, 2C

Sketchpad Demonstration
Lesson 2.1

Fathom Demonstrations
Lessons 2.2, 2.4, 2.5

CBL 2 Demonstration
Lesson 2.5

Dynamic Algebra Explorations online
Lessons 2.2, 2.4

Assessment Resources
Quiz 1 (Lessons 2.1–2.3)
Quiz 2 (Lessons 2.4–2.5)
Quiz 3 (Lessons 2.7–2.8)
Chapter 2 Test
Chapter 2 Constructive Assessment Options

More Practice Your Skills for Chapter 2

Condensed Lessons for Chapter 2

Other Resources
www.keypress.com/DA

Materials

- paper bags
- 3–4 lb white beans
- $\frac{1}{2}$ lb red beans
- yardsticks and meter-sticks or tape measures
- graph paper
- motion sensors
- masking tape
- multispeed bicycles

Pacing Guide

	day 1	day 2	day 3	day 4	day 5	day 6	day 7	day 8	day 9	day 10	day 11
standard	2.1	2.2	2.3	2.4	quiz, 2.5	2.5	2.6	2.7	2.8	review	assessment
enriched	2.1	project	2.2	2.3	2.4	quiz, 2.5	2.6	2.7, project	2.8	review, TAL	assessment
block	2.1, 2.2	2.3, 2.4	quiz, 2.5	2.6, 2.7	2.8, review	assessment					

2 Proportional Reasoning and Variation

Murals are just one of the many art forms around us that come to life with the help of ratios and proportions. To plan a mural, the artist draws sketches on paper, then uses ratio to enlarge the image to the size of the final work.

- Learn to set up and solve proportions in which a variable represents an unknown number
- Use proportions to help make predictions from data gathered for the capture-recapture method
- Change measurement units through conversion factors and dimensional analysis
- Use direct variation equations and their graphs to solve real-world problems
- Learn the basic inverse variation equations
- Use inverse variation equations and their graphs to solve real-world problems
- Investigate the direct and inverse variations between gear selection and wheel speeds on a multispeed bicycle
- Review or learn the rules governing order of operations
- Use calculator list operations to investigate the concepts *variables*, *terms*, and *expressions*
- Write and evaluate algebraic expressions
- Solve equations using the undoing method

OBJECTIVES

In this chapter you will
- use proportional reasoning to understand problem situations
- learn what rates are and use them to make predictions
- study how quantities vary directly and inversely
- use equations and graphs to represent variation
- solve real-world problems using variation
- review the rules for order of operations
- describe number tricks using algebraic expressions
- solve equations using the undoing method

Most students have constructed pictures using enlargement grids; they capture the drawing fragment within the small square and transfer it to the large square. **[Ask]** "If the artist first worked on paper that was about 18 inches by 24 inches, what did he or she have to multiply by to create a large drawing to transfer the image to the building?" [Reasonable answers are between 25 and 35.] Sketches for modern murals can be projected on a wall, which also involves an enlargement by a ratio.

You might also **[Ask]** "How are the real students like their images on the mural?" [The ratios of corresponding lengths are all the same, or the corresponding pairs of lengths are proportional. The images are about 3 times the height of a student. They look a lot bigger because they appear to have a volume of about 3^3 times that of a student.]

LESSON
2.1

Proportions

Mathematics is not a way of hanging numbers on things so that quantitative answers to ordinary questions can be obtained. It is a language that allows one to think of extraordinary questions.

JAMES BULLOCK

When you say, "I got 21 out of 24 questions correct on the last quiz," you are comparing two numbers. The **ratio** of your correct questions to the total number of questions is 21 to 24. You can write the ratio as 21:24, or as a fraction, $\frac{21}{24}$, or as a decimal, 0.875. The fraction bar means division, so these expressions are equivalent:

EXAMPLE A | Write the ratio 210:330 in several ways.

▶ **Solution** | $\frac{210}{330}$ or $\frac{7}{11}$ 210 ÷ 330   or   7 ÷ 11

To change a common fraction into a decimal fraction, divide the numerator by the denominator.

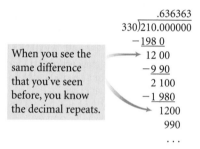

When you see the same difference that you've seen before, you know the decimal repeats.

$$\begin{array}{r} .636363 \\ 330\overline{)210.000000} \\ -198\ 0 \\ \hline 12\ 00 \\ -9\ 90 \\ \hline 2\ 100 \\ -1\ 980 \\ \hline 1200 \\ 990 \\ \cdots \end{array}$$

When you divide 21 by 24, the decimal form of the quotient ends, or **terminates.** The ratio $\frac{21}{24}$ equals 0.875 exactly. But when you divide 210 by 330 or 7 by 11, you see a **repeating decimal** pattern, 0.636363.... You can use a bar over the numerals that repeat to show a repeating decimal pattern, $\frac{7}{11} = 0.\overline{63}$. [▶ 🖳 See **Calculator Note 0A** for more about converting fractions to decimals. ◀]

PLANNING

LESSON OUTLINE

One day:

10 min	Introduction, Example A
15 min	Investigation
5 min	Sharing
10 min	Examples B, C
5 min	Closing
5 min	Exercises

MATERIALS

- Calculator Note 0A
- Sketchpad demonstration The Golden Ratio, *optional*

TEACHING

[Language] Many students need to see and hear the vocabulary words *ratio, fraction, rational number, decimal, quotient,* and *divided by*. Create a display of the words and use them often as you talk with students about their work.

The method for solving proportions presented in this lesson is easy to explain and works with other kinds of equations. Students may have learned to solve proportions using cross-multiplication. Discourage them from using cross-multiplication until they are proficient at using the undoing method introduced in the investigation.

▶ **EXAMPLE A**

[ELL] Students who learned long division outside the United States may have different methods for doing it. Ask them to show the class how they do it.

Point out that it's not the rational number itself that repeats or terminates, but only its decimal name.

LESSON OBJECTIVES

- Rename fractions as decimal numbers
- Write ratios and proportions that express relationships in data
- Solve proportions by multiplying to undo division
- Solve proportions by inverting both ratios
- Solve problems using proportions
- Review skills in working with percents

NCTM STANDARDS

CONTENT		PROCESS	
✔	Number		Problem Solving
✔	Algebra	✔	Reasoning
	Geometry		Communication
✔	Measurement		Connections
	Data/Probability	✔	Representation

A **proportion** is an equation stating that two ratios are equal. For example, $\frac{2}{3} = \frac{8}{12}$ is a proportion. You can use the numbers 2, 3, 8, and 12 to write these true proportions:

$$\frac{2}{3} = \frac{8}{12} \qquad \frac{3}{2} = \frac{12}{8} \qquad \frac{3}{12} = \frac{2}{8} \qquad \frac{12}{3} = \frac{8}{2}$$

Do you agree that these are all true equations? One way to check that a proportion is true is by finding the decimal equivalent of each side. The statement $\frac{3}{8} = \frac{2}{12}$ is not true; 0.375 is not equal to $0.1\overline{6}$.

In algebra, a **variable** can stand for an unknown number or for a set of numbers. In the proportion $\frac{2}{3} = \frac{M}{6}$, you can replace the letter M with any number, but only one number will make the proportion true. That number is unknown until the proportion is solved.

Investigation
Multiply and Conquer

You can easily guess the value of M in the proportion $\frac{2}{3} = \frac{M}{6}$. In this investigation you'll examine ways to solve a proportion for an unknown number when guessing is not easy. It's hard to guess the value of M in the proportion $\frac{M}{19} = \frac{56}{133}$.

Step 1 | Multiply both sides of the proportion $\frac{M}{19} = \frac{56}{133}$ by 19. Why can you do this? What does M equal?

Step 2 | For each equation, choose a number to multiply both ratios by to solve the proportion for the unknown number. Then multiply and divide to find the missing value.

  a. $\frac{P}{12} = \frac{132}{176} \quad P = 9$ **b.** $\frac{21}{35} = \frac{Q}{20} \quad Q = 12$

  c. $\frac{L}{30} = \frac{30}{200} \quad L = 4.5$ **d.** $\frac{130}{78} = \frac{n}{15} \quad n = 25$

Step 3 | Check that each proportion in Step 2 is true by replacing the variable with your answer.

Step 4 | In each equation in Step 2, the variables are in the numerator. Write a brief explanation of one way to solve a proportion when one of the numerators is a variable.   Answer should refer to multiplying both sides by the number under the variable.

Step 5 | The proportions you solved in Step 2 have been changed by switching the numerators and denominators. That is, the ratio on each side has been *inverted*. (You may recall that inverted fractions, like $\frac{P}{12}$ and $\frac{12}{P}$ are called *reciprocals*.) Do the solutions from Step 2 also make these new proportions true? Yes.

  a. $\frac{12}{P} = \frac{176}{132}$ **b.** $\frac{35}{21} = \frac{20}{Q}$ **c.** $\frac{30}{L} = \frac{200}{30}$ **d.** $\frac{78}{130} = \frac{15}{n}$

Step 6 | How can you use what you just discovered to help you solve a proportion that has the variable in the denominator, such as $\frac{20}{135} = \frac{12}{k}$? Why does this work? Solve the equation.

Step 6 Explanations should include the phrase "first interchange the numerators and denominators of each fraction," as well as something about equivalent proportions; $k = 81$.

After Example C, numbers that can be written as the ratio of two integers are defined as rational numbers.

Guiding the Investigation

One Step
Pose the problem: "Write out descriptions of how to find the value of M as it replaces each whole number in the proportion $\frac{8}{19} = \frac{56}{133}$." As you circulate, bring out the ideas of a proportion as an equality of ratios, of rational numbers and their decimal equivalents, and of inverting the ratios of a proportion to solve it. Avoid immediately answering questions yourself. Instead, call on students who might know the answer, or say "Have you asked your group?"

Make sure students understand how a variable is used for an unknown number in a proportion.

Step 1 Students might not see that they're undoing the division by 19. Point out that $\frac{M}{19}$ is one-nineteenth of the number M, so they're multiplying by 19 to find M.

Step 1 If both sides are equal, they remain equal when multiplied by the same number; $M = 8$.

Step 2 Students might want to reduce the fraction before they do the multiplying. Doing this will make the arithmetic easier, so it could save them time if they are not using a calculator. After they multiply, they may want to divide out some factors; emphasize that this is "legal" because they're multiplying and dividing equal numbers by the same number, and when they reduce they are removing factors that are equivalent to 1.

Step 4 You could use this as a journal prompt.

SHARING IDEAS

Have students share results of Step 2.

Using letters for unknowns may be new to students. **[Ask]** "What do the letters in the proportions represent?" [Each represents a single unknown number.] The letters are called *variables* even if they don't vary. In Chapter 1, each variable represented a variety of numbers.

Ask why the proportions in Step 5 have the same solutions as in Step 2. A mechanical answer is that you have inverted the fractions on both sides of the equation. To lead student to deeper understanding, **[Ask]** "If $\frac{6}{B} = 2$, then why will $\frac{B}{6} = \frac{1}{2}$?" Encourage students to draw segments of these lengths—and to make up their own situations—to aid their understanding of proportions.

Assessing Progress

Assess students' abilities at multiplying, finding decimal forms of rational numbers, and inverting fractions.

▶ EXAMPLE B

This is an application of proportion. Some students may be able to solve the problem without proportions. Don't discourage them, but challenge them to set up and solve a proportion. **[Ask]** "Is 2 the part or the whole? 3? 750? The unknown?" Show how the proportion can be either

$$\frac{estimate\ part}{estimate\ whole} = \frac{students\ part}{students\ whole} \text{ or}$$

$$\frac{estimate\ part}{students\ part} = \frac{estimate\ whole}{students\ whole}.$$

Step 7 | There are many ways to solve proportions. Here are three student papers each answering the question "13 is 65% of what number?" What are the steps each student followed? What other methods can you use to solve proportions?

a.
$$\frac{65}{100} = \frac{13}{x}$$
$$\frac{100}{65} = \frac{x}{13}$$
$$\frac{13}{1} \cdot \frac{100}{65} = \frac{x}{\cancel{13}} \cdot \frac{\cancel{13}}{1}$$
$$20 = x$$

b.
$$\frac{65}{100} = \frac{13}{x}$$
$$\frac{13}{\frac{65}{100}} = \frac{13}{x}$$
$$20$$
$$20 = x$$

c.
$$\frac{65}{100} = \frac{13}{x}$$
$$\frac{\cancel{100}}{1} \cdot \frac{x}{1} \cdot \frac{65}{\cancel{100}} = \frac{13}{\cancel{x}} \cdot \frac{100}{1} \cdot \frac{\cancel{x}}{1}$$
$$\frac{\cancel{65}x}{\cancel{65}} = \frac{1300}{65}$$
$$x = 20$$

In the investigation you discovered that you can solve for an unknown numerator in a proportion by multiplying both sides of the proportion by the denominator under the unknown value. You can also think of a proportion such as $\frac{M}{19} = \frac{56}{133}$ like this: "When a number is divided by 19, the result is $\frac{56}{133}$." To find the original number, you need to undo the division. Multiplying by 19 undoes the division.

EXAMPLE B | Jennifer estimates that two out of every three students will attend the class party. She knows there are 750 students in her class. Set up and solve a proportion to help her estimate how many people will attend.

▶ **Solution** | To set up the proportion, be sure both ratios make the same comparison. Use a to represent the number of students who will attend.

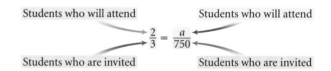

Students who will attend ⟶ $\frac{2}{3} = \frac{a}{750}$ ⟵ Students who will attend
Students who are invited ⟶ ⟵ Students who are invited

Proportions in the text are solved by undoing division to build skill at solving equations through undoing. Resist the temptation to solve by cross-multiplying or by multiplying both sides by the same thing. You might discuss cross-multiplication with your students and ask them to explain how it gives the same answer as undoing the division by multiplication.

In the proportion, when a is divided by 750, the answer is $\frac{2}{3}$.

$$750 \cdot \frac{2}{3} = a \qquad \text{Multiply by 750 to undo the division.}$$

$$500 = a \qquad \text{Multiply and divide.}$$

Jennifer can estimate that 500 students will attend the party.

EXAMPLE C | After the party, Jennifer found out that 70% of the class attended. How many students attended?

▶ **Solution**

70% is 70 out of 100. So write and solve a proportion to answer the question "If 70 students out of 100 attended the party, how many students out of 750 attended?"

Let s represent the number of students who attended.

$$\frac{70}{100} = \frac{s}{750} \qquad \text{Write the proportion.}$$

$$750 \cdot \frac{70}{100} = s \qquad \text{Multiply by 750 to undo the division.}$$

$$525 = s \qquad \text{Multiply and divide.}$$

525 out of 750 students attended the party.

You have worked with ratios and proportions in this lesson. Numbers that can be written as the ratio of two integers are called **rational numbers.**

History
CONNECTION

The Pythagoreans, a group of philosophers begun by Pythagoras in about 520 B.C.E., realized that not all numbers are rational. For example, for a square one unit on a side, the diagonal $\sqrt{2}$ is *irrational.* Another irrational number is pi, or π, the ratio of the circumference of a circle to its diameter.

EXERCISES

You will need your graphing calculator for Exercise **14.**

▶ **Practice Your Skills**

1. List these fractions in increasing order by estimating their values. Then use your calculator to find the decimal value of each fraction. b, a, d, c

   a. $\frac{7}{8}$ 0.875   b. $\frac{13}{20}$ 0.65   c. $\frac{13}{5}$ 2.6   d. $\frac{52}{25}$ 2.08

2. Ms. Lenz collected information about the students in her class.

Eye Color

	Brown eyes	Blue eyes	Hazel eyes
9th graders	9	3	2
8th graders	11	4	1

Write these ratios as fractions.
   a. ninth graders with brown eyes to ninth graders @ $\frac{9}{14}$
   b. eighth graders with brown eyes to students with brown eyes $\frac{11}{20}$
   c. eighth graders with blue eyes to ninth graders with blue eyes @ $\frac{4}{3}$
   d. all students with hazel eyes to students in both grades $\frac{3}{30}$, or $\frac{1}{10}$

▶ **Helping with the Exercises**

Exercise 1 You might advise students who are stuck to convert the fractions to decimals by division. They could also compare the fractions to 1 and represent the fractions as circles or line segments. Challenge them to find the decimal forms in at least two ways.

▶ **EXAMPLE C**

This example is an application of proportions that reviews percents. **[Alert]** Students may not think of 70% as the ratio $\frac{70}{100}$. Point out that *per* indicates a ratio, as in *miles per hour,* and *percent* means *per hundred.* **[Language]** Point out that there are 100 *cent*s in a dollar and 100 years in a *cent*ury.

Closing the Lesson

Review with students the ideas of **ratio, rational number, proportion,** unknown, **variable,** solving a proportion by multiply and conquer, and inverting both sides of a proportion to get another true proportion. A proportion states the equality of two ratios, in which one number may be unknown and represented by a variable. Rational numbers are ratios of integers with nonzero denominators and their decimal names are **repeating** or **terminating.** Ask students if they think there are any numbers that are *not* rational. If they don't know of irrational numbers, they might instead suggest integers; point out that -3 can be written as $-\frac{3}{1}$, so it's rational. As the history connection says, $\sqrt{2}$ and π are irrational.

BUILDING UNDERSTANDING

In the exercises students practice expressing ratios and solving proportions.

ASSIGNING HOMEWORK

Essential	1–6, 9
Performance assessment	7
Portfolio	8
Journal	11
Group	6, 10
Review	12–14

3. Phrases such as miles per gallon, parts per million (ppm), and accidents per 1000 people indicate ratios. Write each ratio named below as a fraction. Use a number and a unit in both the numerator and the denominator. ⓗ

a. In 2000, the McLaren was the fastest car produced. Its top speed was recorded at 240 miles per hour. ⓐ

b. Pure capsaicin, a substance that makes hot peppers taste hot, is so strong that 10 ppm in water can make your tongue blister. ⓐ

c. In 2000, women owned approximately 350 of every thousand firms in the United States. ⓐ

d. The 2000 average income in Philadelphia, Pennsylvania, was approximately \$35,500 per person. $\dfrac{35{,}500 \text{ dollars}}{1 \text{ person}}$

4. What number should you multiply by to solve for the unknown in each proportion?

a. $\dfrac{24}{40} = \dfrac{T}{30}$ ⓐ 30

b. $\dfrac{49}{56} = \dfrac{R}{32}$ 32

c. $\dfrac{M}{16} = \dfrac{87}{232}$ ⓐ 16

5. Find the value of the unknown number in each proportion.

a. $\dfrac{24}{40} = \dfrac{T}{30}$ ⓗ $T = 18$
b. $\dfrac{49}{56} = \dfrac{R}{32}$ $R = 28$
c. $\dfrac{52}{91} = \dfrac{42}{S}$ ⓐ $S = 73.5$
d. $\dfrac{100}{30} = \dfrac{7}{x}$ $x = 2.1$

e. $\dfrac{M}{16} = \dfrac{87}{232}$ $M = 6$
f. $\dfrac{6}{n} = \dfrac{62}{217}$ $n = 21$
g. $\dfrac{36}{15} = \dfrac{c}{13}$ $c = 31.2$
h. $\dfrac{220}{33} = \dfrac{60}{W}$ $W = 9$

▶ Reason and Apply

6. **APPLICATION** Write a proportion for each problem, and solve for the unknown number.

a. Leaf-cutter ants that live in Central and South America weigh about 1.5 grams (g). One ant can carry a 4 g piece of leaf that is about the size of a dime. If a person could carry proportionally as much as the leaf-cutter ant, how much could a 55 kg algebra student carry? ⓗ

b. The leaf-cutter ant is about 1.27 cm long and takes strides of 0.84 cm. If a person could take proportionally equivalent strides, what size strides would a 1.65 m tall algebra student take?

c. The 1.27 cm long ants travel up to 0.4 km from home each day. If a person could travel a proportional distance, how far would a 1.65 m tall person travel?

7. Write three other true proportions using the four values in each proportion.

a. $\dfrac{2}{5} = \dfrac{10}{25}$ ⓐ

b. $\dfrac{a}{9} = \dfrac{12}{27}$

c. $\dfrac{j}{k} = \dfrac{l}{m}$

6a. $\dfrac{4 \text{ g}}{1.5 \text{ g}} = \dfrac{x \text{ kg}}{55 \text{ kg}}$; $x = 146.\overline{6} \text{ kg}$

6b. $\dfrac{0.84 \text{ cm}}{1.27 \text{ cm}} = \dfrac{x \text{ m}}{1.65 \text{ m}}$; $x \approx 1.09 \text{ m}$

6c. $\dfrac{0.4 \text{ km}}{0.0127 \text{ m}} = \dfrac{x \text{ km}}{1.65 \text{ m}}$; $x \approx 52 \text{ km}$

7a. $\dfrac{5}{2} = \dfrac{25}{10}, \dfrac{2}{10} = \dfrac{5}{25}, \dfrac{25}{5} = \dfrac{10}{2}$

7b. $\dfrac{9}{a} = \dfrac{27}{12}, \dfrac{a}{12} = \dfrac{9}{27}, \dfrac{27}{9} = \dfrac{12}{a}$

7c. $\dfrac{k}{j} = \dfrac{m}{l}, \dfrac{j}{l} = \dfrac{k}{m}, \dfrac{m}{k} = \dfrac{l}{j}$

Capture-Recapture

The Universe is a grand book which cannot be read until one first learns to comprehend the language.... It is written in the language of mathematics.

GALILEO GALILEI

Wildlife biologists often need to know how many deer are in a national park or the size of the perch population in a large lake. It is impossible to count each deer or fish, so biologists use a method called "capture-recapture" that uses ratios to estimate the population.

To estimate a fish population, biologists first capture some of the fish and put tags on them. Then these tagged fish are returned to the lake to mingle with all of the untagged fish. The biologist allows time for the fish to mix thoroughly, captures another **sample,** and counts how many of the sample are tagged.

 ## Investigation
Fish in the Lake

You will need
- a paper bag
- white beans
- red beans

In this investigation you'll **simulate** the capture-recapture method and examine how it works.

The bag represents a lake, the white beans are the untagged fish in the lake, and the red beans will replace white beans to represent tagged fish. Your objective is to estimate the total number of fish in the lake.

Step 1 | Reach into the lake and remove a handful of fish to tag. Count and record the number of fish you removed. Replace these fish (white beans) with an equal number of tagged fish (red beans). Return the tagged fish to the lake. Set aside the extra beans.

Step 2 | Allow the fish to mingle (seal the bag and shake it). Again remove a handful of fish, count them all, and count the number of tagged fish. In a table like this, record those counts and the ratio of tagged fish to total fish in the sample.

Tagging Simulation

Sample number	Number of tagged fish	Total number of fish	Ratio of tagged fish to total fish
1			
2			

You have taken one sample by randomly capturing some of the fish. You could use this sample to estimate the number of fish in the lake, but by taking several samples, you will get a better idea of the ratio of tagged fish to total fish in the lake. Replace the fish, mix them, and repeat the sampling process four times, filling in a row of your table each time.

NCTM STANDARDS

CONTENT		PROCESS	
✓	Number	✓	Problem Solving
✓	Algebra	✓	Reasoning
	Geometry	✓	Communication
	Measurement	✓	Connections
✓	Data/Probability	✓	Representation

LESSON OBJECTIVES

- Work with the idea of sample
- Become familiar with representative samples
- Understand the capture-recapture method

PLANNING

LESSON OUTLINE

One day:
20 min	Investigation
5 min	Sharing
10 min	Examples
5 min	Closing
10 min	Exercises

MATERIALS

- paper bags with about 1 cup of white beans each (one per group)
- red beans (less than $\frac{1}{4}$ cup per group)
- Fish in the Lake Sample Data (W, T), *optional*
- Fathom demonstration Capture-Recapture, *optional*

TEACHING

Deepen students' understanding of ratio and proportion by using them in a new context: the capture-recapture (sampling) method for estimating the size of a population.

 Guiding the Investigation

Instead of beans, you might use chocolate pretzels and regular pretzels, colored macaroni and noncolored macaroni, two different varieties of shaped snack crackers, and so on, with suitable containers. Objects used for tagged and untagged fish should be the same size and weight.

Steps 1 and 2 A good number to tag is 10%.

Step 2 If asked at this point, many students will say that they don't have enough information to predict the population of fish—from a lack of understanding of ratios rather than from concern about the quality of the sampling.

Step 3 Students may choose the mean or the median or simply one of their samples that is close to one of those values. A choice is valid if the student can argue that it is representative.

Step 3 Students could choose mean, median, or mode. They could discard the largest and smallest ratio and take the mean of the other three.

Step 5 The fact that the calculator gives an answer to six decimal places doesn't mean the answer is accurate to that many places. Frequent discussion of accuracy and of reporting an appropriate number of digits is important throughout the course. In general, the number of significant digits in the answer should be the same as the smallest number of significant digits that any number in the problem has. (Whole numbers from counting are considered to have infinitely many significant digits. Whole numbers arrived at through measurement have no significant digits to the right of the decimal point.)

Step 5 The proportion will have the ratio of red beans put into the bag to the total unknown number of beans on one side and the ratio determined by the experiment on the other. If several samples are taken after thorough mixing, the estimates should be good.

SHARING IDEAS

Have one group present their results from Step 5. **[Ask]** "How representative are the samples? What can we conclude if they are

Step 4 yes, if the fish are evenly distributed in all samples and in the entire lake

keymath.com/DA

Step 3 Choose a representative ratio for the five ratios. Explain how you decided this was a representative ratio.

Step 4 If you mixed the fish well, should the fraction of tagged fish in a sample be nearly the same as the fraction of tagged fish in the lake? Why or why not?

Step 5 Write and solve a proportion to find the number of fish in the lake. (About how many beans are in your bag?) Why is this method called capture-recapture? How accurate are predictions using this method? Why?

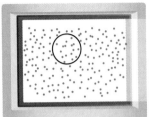
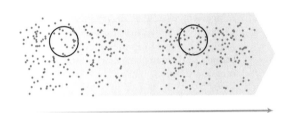

keymath.com/DA

[▶ You can use the **Dynamic Algebra Exploration** found at www.keymath.com/DA to simulate a capture-recapture situation. You'll press a button to allow the fish to swim in the lake, then you'll "capture" the fish in the circle and count the tagged and untagged ones. ◀]

You can describe the results of capture-recapture situations using percents. Here are three kinds of percent problems—finding an unknown percent, finding an unknown total, and finding an unknown part. In each case the percent equals the ratio of the part to the whole or total.

EXAMPLE A | **Finding an Unknown Percent**

In a capture-recapture process, 200 fish were tagged. From the recapture results, the game warden estimates that the lake contains 2500 fish. What percent of the fish were tagged?

Largemouth bass

Brook trout

Yellow perch

representative?" Elicit the idea that if a sample is representative, then the ratio of red to total beans in the sample should be the same as that ratio in the bag. Use, and ask students to use, the word *sample* repeatedly in discussing the capture-recapture method. In statistics, the term *population* is frequently used to describe the total, regardless of whether the items are people, other living things, or inanimate objects.

Assessing Progress

Students should be using their skills of solving proportions as well as multiplying and dividing. Assess the quality of group work as well.

▶ EXAMPLE A

This example is good for students who need a review of percents. Because the exact number of tagged fish is given, the answer is as good as the estimate of the number of fish in the lake—an estimate made from the experiment.

See page 722 for Step 5 sample data results.

▶ Solution

You know that the ratio of tagged fish (the part) to total fish in the lake (the whole) is 200 to 2500. This ratio is equivalent to the percent p of tagged fish in the sample.

$$\frac{p}{100} = \frac{200}{2500} \qquad \text{Write the proportion.}$$

$$p = \frac{200}{2500} \cdot 100 \qquad \text{Multiply by 100 to undo the division.}$$

$$p = 8 \qquad \text{Multiply and divide.}$$

In the samples used for the estimate, 8% of the fish were tagged.

EXAMPLE B

Finding an Unknown Total

In a lake with 250 tagged fish, recapture results show that 11% of the fish are tagged. About how many fish are in the lake?

▶ Solution

You can write 11% as the ratio $\frac{11}{100}$ or 11 parts to 100 (the whole). The variable will be the denominator because the unknown quantity is the whole—the total number of fish in the lake.

$$\frac{11}{100} = \frac{250}{f} \qquad \text{Write the proportion.}$$

$$\frac{100}{11} = \frac{f}{250} \qquad \text{Invert both ratios.}$$

$$250 \cdot \frac{100}{11} = f \qquad \text{Multiply by 250 to undo the division.}$$

$$2273 \approx f \qquad \text{Multiply and divide.}$$

There are about 2270 fish in the lake.

EXAMPLE C

Finding an Unknown Part

A lake is estimated to have 5000 fish after recapture experiments that showed 3% of the fish were tagged. How many fish were originally tagged?

▶ Solution

You can write 3% as the ratio $\frac{3}{100}$ or 3 parts to 100 (the whole). The variable is in the numerator because the unknown quantity is the number of tagged fish (the part).

$$\frac{t}{5000} = \frac{3}{100} \qquad \text{Write the proportion.}$$

$$t = \frac{3}{100} \cdot 5000 \qquad \text{Undo the division.}$$

$$t = 150 \qquad \text{Multiply and divide.}$$

About 150 fish were tagged.

In addition to making estimates of wildlife populations, you can use proportions to estimate quantities in many other everyday situations.

▶ *EXAMPLE B*

Also a review of percent, this example is like the investigation. Unlike Example A, the answer is an estimate.

▶ *EXAMPLE C*

This example uses a capture-recapture experiment to review the third standard type of percent problem.

Closing the Lesson

The idea of a **sample,** the representativeness of a sample, and the capture-recapture method are the principal topics to mention in closing. The capture-recapture method uses proportions to make predictions about a whole population from a sample. The quality of a prediction is determined by how representative the sample is.

EXERCISES

▶ Practice Your Skills

1. The proportion $\frac{320}{235} = \frac{g}{100}$ represents the question "320 is what percent of 235?" Write each proportion as a percent question.

    a. $\frac{24}{w} = \frac{32}{100}$ @
    32% of what number is 24?

    b. $\frac{t}{450} = \frac{48}{100}$
    48% of 450 is what number?

    c. $\frac{98}{117} = \frac{n}{100}$
    What percent of 117 is 98? or 98 is what percent of 117?

2. You can write the question "What number is 15% of 120?" as the proportion $\frac{x}{120} = \frac{15}{100}$. Write each question as a proportion.

    a. 125% of what number is 80? @ $\frac{80}{d} = \frac{125}{100}$

    b. What number is 0.25% of 46? $\frac{k}{46} = \frac{0.25}{100}$

    c. What percent of 470 is 72? $\frac{72}{470} = \frac{r}{100}$

3. There are 1582 students attending the local high school. Seventeen percent of the students are twelfth graders. How many twelfth graders are there? 269

4. **APPLICATION** Write and solve a proportion for each situation.

    a. A biologist tagged 250 fish. Then she collected another sample of 75 fish, of which 5 were tagged. How many fish would she estimate are in the lake? ⓗ

    b. A biologist estimated that there were 5500 fish in a lake in which 250 fish had been tagged. A ranger collected a sample in which there were 15 tagged fish. Approximately how many fish were in the sample the ranger collected? $\frac{250}{5500} = \frac{15}{s}$; $s = 330$ fish

keymath.com/DA

▶ Reason and Apply

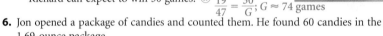

5. Marie and Richard played 47 games of backgammon last month. Marie's ratio of wins to losses was 28 to 19.

    a. Estimate the number of games you expect Marie to win if she and Richard play 12 more games. Explain your thinking. @ Marie should win over half the games.

    b. Write a proportion, and solve for Marie's expected number of wins if she and Richard play 12 more games. @

    c. Write a proportion and solve it to determine how many games she and Richard will need to play before Richard can expect to win 30 games. @ $\frac{19}{47} = \frac{30}{G}$; $G \approx 74$ games

6. Jon opened a package of candies and counted them. He found 60 candies in the 1.69-ounce package.

    a. Estimate the number of candies in a 1-pound (16-ounce) bag. Explain your thinking for this estimate. Slightly fewer than 600 pieces; 16 oz is almost 10 times 1.69 oz.

    b. Write the proportion and solve for the number of candies in a 1-pound package. Compare your approximation to your estimate in 6a.

    c. How much would 1 million candies weigh? Give your answer in pounds.

7. APPLICATION Terry and Jesse are writing a paper together. They're finished, except for proofreading the draft. Each reads the draft separately. Terry finds 24 errors, and Jesse finds 36 errors. When they compare their results, they find that they've both marked 18 of the same errors. Use the capture-recapture method to estimate the number of errors that both of them missed. (*Hint:* The error found by either student can be used as the number of tagged errors in the capture phase. The other student represents the recapture phase with the errors found by both being the tagged errors.) There are approximately six errors that they both missed.

= Leafcutter ants cut pieces of leave
carry back to their nests. They do n
eat the leaves. Instead, they chew t
up into even smaller pieces to use
fertilizer for growing a garden of
fungus that they eat. A leafcutter a
can carry a load that weighs twelve
times its own weight, but usually c
carries a load that weighs 2 to 4 tir
its weight. A roundtrip to harvest a
piece of leaf might take several ho

8. APPLICATION Fisherman Beta Hook was hired to estimate the fish population in Long Lake. She and three friends fished for a week, and in that time they caught, tagged, and released 235 bass, 147 trout, and 151 perch. Later that summer they returned and spent two weeks fishing in different parts of the lake. Here are the results:

Fish Population

	Bass	Trout	Perch
Tagged	24	15	16
Untagged	336	208	192

Bass = $\frac{360}{24} \cdot 235 = 3525$; trout = $\frac{223}{15} \cdot 147 = 2185.4$; perch = $\frac{208}{16} \cdot 151 = 1963$; total = $\frac{791}{55} \cdot 533 = 7665.5$; these values are estimates, so the total should be close to the sum of the species totals but not exactly equal to it.

Use this data to estimate the population of each of the three fish species. Then use the first-row total and the second-row total to estimate the total population. Why don't you get the same total population when you add the three different species totals?

▶ Review

2.1 **9.** The ratio of ninth graders to eighth graders in the class is 5 to 3. Write these ratios as fractions.

    a. ninth graders to eighth graders $\frac{5}{3}$

    c. eighth graders to students in the class $\frac{3}{8}$

    b. ninth graders to students in the class @ $\frac{5}{8}$

1.4 **10.** This histogram shows the ages of the first 43 presidents of the United States when they took office. (*Time Almanac 2004*, p. 112)

    a. What is a good estimate of the median age?

    b. How many presidents were younger than 50 when they took office? @ 8

    c. What ages do not represent the age of any president at inauguration? @

    d. Redraw the histogram changing the interval width from 2 to 4.

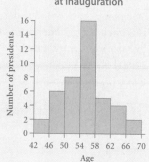

Presidents' Ages at Inauguration

0.1 **11.** On a group quiz, your group needs to calculate the answer to $12 - 2 \cdot 6 - 3$. The three other group members came up with these answers:

    Marta   57   Matt   −3   Miguel   30

Who, if anyone, is correct? What would you say to the other group members to convince them? Matt; by the order of operations, you multiply before you subtract.

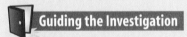
Proportions and Measurement Systems

Have you ever visited another country? If so, you needed to convert your money to theirs and perhaps some of your measurement units to theirs as well. Many countries use the units of the Système Internationale, or SI, known in the United States as the metric system.

So, instead of selling gasoline by the gallon, they sell it by the liter. Distance signs are in kilometers rather than in miles, and vegetables are sold by the kilo (kilogram) rather than by the pound.

Cultural

CONNECTION

To learn more about measurements used in other countries, as well as historical measurement units, see the links at **www.keymath.com/DA** .

Vegetables are sold at a French market.

Investigation
Converting Centimeters to Inches

You will need

- a yardstick or tape measure
- a meterstick or metric tape measure

In this investigation you will find a ratio to help you convert inches to centimeters and centimeters to inches. Then you will use this ratio in a proportion to convert some measurements from the system standard in the United States to measurements in the metric system, and vice versa.

Step 1 Measure the length or width on each of six different-sized objects, such as a pencil, a book, your desk, or your calculator. For each object, record the inch measurement and the centimeter measurement in a table like this:

Inches to Centimeters

Object	Measurement in inches	Measurement in centimeters

Step 2 Enter the measurements in inches into your calculator's list L1 and the measurements in centimeters into list L2. Into list L3 enter the ratio of centimeters to inches, $\frac{L2}{L1}$, and let your calculator fill in the ratio values. [▶ See **Calculator Note 1K.** ◀]

Step 3 How do the ratios of centimeters to inches compare for the different measurements? If one of the ratios is much different from the others, recheck your measurements. Ratios should be about $\frac{2.54 \text{ cm}}{1 \text{ in.}}$.

| Step 4 | Choose a single representative ratio of centimeters to inches. Write a sentence that explains the meaning of this ratio. 1 in. is 2.54 cm. |
| Step 5 | Using your ratio, set up a proportion and convert each length. |

  a. 215 centimeters $= x$ inches 84.6 in.

  b. 1 centimeter $= x$ inches 0.4 in.

  c. 1 inch $= x$ centimeters 2.54 cm

  d. How many centimeters high is a doorway that measures 80 inches? 203 cm

| Step 6 | Using your ratio, set up a proportion and solve for the requested value. |

  a. y centimeters $= x$ inches. Solve for y. $y = x \cdot 0.39$

  b. c centimeters $= i$ inches. Solve for i. $i = c \cdot 2.54$

In the investigation you found a common ratio, or **conversion factor,** between inches and centimeters. Once you've determined the conversion factor, you can convert from one system to the other by solving a proportion. If your measurements in the investigation were very accurate, the mean and median of the ratios were very close to the conversion factor, 2.54 centimeters to 1 inch.

EXAMPLE A

Jonas drove his car from Montana to Canada on vacation. While there, he needed to buy gasoline and noticed that it was sold by the liter rather than by the gallon. Use the conversion factor 1 gallon $\approx$ 3.79 liters to determine how many liters will fill his 12.5-gallon gas tank.

▶ **Solution**

Using the conversion factor, you can write the proportion $\frac{3.79 \text{ liters}}{1 \text{ gallon}} = \frac{x \text{ liters}}{12.5 \text{ gallons}}$.

$$\frac{3.79}{1} = \frac{x}{12.5} \qquad \text{Original proportion.}$$

$$12.5 \cdot 3.79 = x \qquad \text{Undo the division.}$$

$$x = 47.375 \qquad \text{Multiply.}$$

Jonas' tank will hold about 47.4 liters of gasoline.

Some conversions require several steps. The next example offers a strategy called **dimensional analysis** for doing more complicated conversions.

EXAMPLE B

A radio-controlled car traveled 30 feet across the classroom in 1.6 seconds. How fast was it traveling in miles per hour?

▶ **Solution**

Using the given information, you can write the speed as the ratio $\frac{30 \text{ feet}}{1.6 \text{ seconds}}$. Multiplying by 1 doesn't change the value of a number, so you can use conversion factors that you know $\left(\text{like } \frac{60 \text{ minutes}}{1 \text{ hour}}\right)$ to create fractions with a value of 1. Then multiply your original ratio by those fractions to change the units.

Dimensional analysis requires deciding what conversion factors to multiply on the basis of how their units will divide out to leave the desired units. Students may need reminding of how to divide out common factors when multiplying fractions. Suggest that students write the conversion factors in a way that makes clear which units will divide out and check carefully for errors.

Some students will hesitate to insert units, either because they're not sure they have the freedom to do so or because they "don't want to make the problem harder." Show them how converting units in stages can help them keep track of the process.

Step 4 Some students will have trouble seeing a single number like 2.54 as a *ratio*. You'll need to remind them that the ratio is $\frac{2.54}{1}$. Because you're usually interested in knowing how many of one type of unit fit in 1 unit of a different type, most conversion factors have 1 in the denominator.

Step 5 Encourage students who can solve parts c and d without proportions, but challenge them to set up and solve proportions as a check.

Step 6 Be sure all students see that the ratio between the measurements applies even to inch-centimeter comparisons that they did not examine.

SHARING IDEAS

Students might report results of Steps 3, 5, and 6. As they do so, introduce the term *conversion factor.*

Point out that conversion factors can be used to convert within a measurement system as well as between systems. For example, to change yards to inches, you'd use the conversion factor 36 in./yd. **[Ask]** "In which measurement system—SI or English—is it easier to convert between units?" [In the SI system, conversion factors within the system are all powers of 10.]

Assessing Progress

Assess students' skill at setting up and solving proportions, entering calculator data, measuring carefully, and factoring.

▶ **EXAMPLE A**

This example gives students practice using a conversion factor.

▶ **EXAMPLE B**

This example develops the idea of dimensional analysis, which combines conversion factors into a product when no direct conversion factor is available.

Closing the Lesson

Conversion factors are ratios that allow the change from one unit to another. If a single conversion factor isn't available, you convert by multiplying conversion factors in **dimensional analysis.**

Mention again that each conversion factor used in dimensional analysis really has a value of 1. (For example, $\frac{60\,s}{min}$ means $\frac{60\,s}{1\,min}$ and both are equal to 1, so multiplying by the ratio doesn't change the value of an expression.)

MAKING THE CONNECTION

In their science classes, students may be learning that distance (or length), mass, time, and temperature are *fundamental quantities* and that, for example, volume (length³) and speed (distance/time) are *derived* quantities. You might use that terminology also.

Science
CONNECTION

Chemists often use dimensional analysis. For each chemical compound, 1 mole equals the compound's gram molecular weight. For water there are 18 grams per mole. If the density of water is 1 gram per milliliter, what is the volume of 1 mole of water in milliliters?

$$1\,mole \cdot \frac{18\,g}{1\,mole} \cdot \frac{1\,mL}{1\,g} = 18\,mL$$

$$\frac{30\,ft}{1.6\,s} \cdot \frac{60\,s}{1\,min} \cdot \frac{60\,min}{1\,h} \cdot \frac{1\,mi}{5,280\,ft} = \frac{108,000\,mi}{8,448\,h}$$

$$\approx \frac{12.8\,mi}{1\,h} \text{ or } 12.8 \text{ miles per hour}$$

Each of the fractions after the first one has a value of 1 because the numerator and denominator of each fraction are equivalent: 60 s = 1 min, 60 min = 1 h, and 1 mi = 5280 ft. The fractions equivalent to 1 are chosen so that when units cancel, the result is miles in the numerator and hours in the denominator.

The speed 12.8 miles per hour is a **rate** because it has a denominator of 1.

In Example B, you saw that 12.8 miles per hour is a rate. A rate of travel (or speed) is just one example of a rate. Your weekly allowance, the cost per pound of shipping a package, and the number of cookies per box are all rates. Rates make calculations easier in many real-life situations. For instance, grocery stores price fruits and vegetables by the pound. Rates make comparisons easier in other situations. For instance, a baseball player's batting average is a rate of hits per times at bat. What other rates have you seen in this book?

On average, the basketball player scores 19.1 points per game.

$$\frac{19.1\,\text{points}}{1\,\text{game}}$$

My brother drove at a speed of 65 mi/h.

$$\frac{65\,\text{miles}}{1\,\text{hour}}$$

These cookies have 35 grams of fat in one serving of 5 cookies.

$$\frac{35\,\text{grams}}{1\,\text{serving}} \text{ or}$$
$$\frac{35\,\text{grams}}{5\,\text{cookies}} = \frac{7\,\text{grams}}{1\,\text{cookie}}$$

EXERCISES

▶ Practice Your Skills

1. Find the value of x in each proportion.

a. $\dfrac{1 \text{ meter}}{3.25 \text{ feet}} = \dfrac{15.2 \text{ meters}}{x \text{ feet}}$ ⓐ $x = 49.4$

b. $\dfrac{1.6 \text{ kilometers}}{1 \text{ mile}} = \dfrac{x \text{ kilometers}}{25 \text{ miles}}$ $x = 40$

c. $\dfrac{0.926 \text{ meter}}{1 \text{ yard}} = \dfrac{200 \text{ meters}}{x \text{ yards}}$ $x \approx 216$

d. $\dfrac{1 \text{ kilometer}}{0.6 \text{ mile}} = \dfrac{x \text{ kilometers}}{350 \text{ miles}}$ $x = 583.\overline{3}$

2. In 2001, Alan Webb broke Jim Ryun's 36-year-old high school mile record by running 1 mile in 3 minutes 53.43 seconds. How fast was this in feet per second? ⓗ 22.62 ft/s

3. Use dimensional analysis to change

  a. 50 meters per second to kilometers per hour. ⓗ

  b. 0.025 day to seconds.

  c. 1200 ounces to tons (16 oz = 1 lb; 2000 lb = 1 ton).

4. Write a proportion and answer each question using the conversion factor 1 ounce = 28.4 grams.

227 g **a.** How many grams does an 8-ounce portion of prime rib weigh? ⓐ

  b. If an ice-cream cone weighs 50 grams, how many ounces does it weigh? ⓐ 1.76 oz

  c. If a typical house cat weighs 160 ounces, how many grams does it weigh? 4544 g

  d. How many ounces does a 100-gram package of cheese weigh? 3.52 oz

5. Write a proportion and answer each question using the conversion factor 1 inch = 2.54 centimeters.

  a. A teacher is 62.5 inches tall. How many centimeters tall is she? ⓐ 159 cm

  b. A common ceiling height is 96 inches (8 feet). About how high is this in centimeters? 244 cm

  c. The diameter of a CD is 12 centimeters. What is its diameter in inches? ⓐ 4.72 in.

  d. The radius of a typical soda can is 3.25 centimeters. What is its radius in inches? 1.28 in.

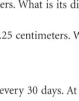

6. Tab and Crystal both own cats.

  a. Tab buys a 3-pound bag of cat food every 30 days. At what rate does his cat eat the food? ⓐ $\dfrac{3 \text{ lb}}{30 \text{ days}} = 0.1$ lb per day

  b. Crystal buys a 5-pound bag of cat food every 45 days. At what rate does her cat eat the food? $\dfrac{5 \text{ lb}}{45 \text{ days}} = 0.\overline{1}$ lb per day

  c. Whose cat, Tab's or Crystal's, eats more food per day? Crystal's cat

---

3a. $\dfrac{50 \text{ m}}{1 \text{ s}} \cdot \dfrac{1 \text{ km}}{1000 \text{ m}} \cdot \dfrac{60 \text{ s}}{1 \text{ min}} \cdot \dfrac{60 \text{ min}}{1 \text{ h}} = 180$ km/h

3b. $0.025 \text{ day} \cdot \dfrac{24 \text{ h}}{1 \text{ day}} \cdot \dfrac{60 \text{ min}}{1 \text{ h}} \cdot \dfrac{60 \text{ s}}{1 \text{ min}} = 2160$ s

3c. $1200 \text{ oz} \cdot \dfrac{1 \text{ lb}}{16 \text{ oz}} \cdot \dfrac{1 \text{ ton}}{2000 \text{ lb}} = 0.0375$ ton

ASSIGNING HOMEWORK

Essential	1–5, 8, 9
Performance assessment	6
Portfolio	8
Journal	9, 12
Group	4, 9
Review	12, 13

▶ Helping with the Exercises

Exercise 4 Students may be learning in their science classes that there is a fundamental difference between measures of weight (such as ounces, pounds, and tons) and measures of mass (such as grams). Weight depends on the pull of gravity, whereas mass does not. The conversion factor 1 oz ≈ 28.4 g is true only where the pull of gravity is approximately equivalent to Earth's.

7. A group of students measured several objects around their school in both yards and meters.

Measurement in Yards and Meters

Yards	7	3.5	7.5	4.25	6.25	11
Meters	6.3	3.2	6.8	3.8	5.6	9.9

a. Use their data, shown in the table, to find a conversion factor between yards and meters. $1 \text{ m} \approx 1.1 \text{ yd}$ or $1 \text{ yd} \approx 0.9 \text{ m}$

Use the conversion factor to answer these questions:

b. The length of a football field is 100 yards. How long is it in meters? ⓐ 90 m

c. If it is 200 meters to the next freeway exit, how far away is it in yards? 222 yd

d. How many yards long is a 100-meter dash? 111 yd

e. How many meters of fabric should you buy if you need 15 yards? 13.5 m

Exercises 8b and 10b These exercises lay the foundation for the concepts of linear growth and slope.

8. One yard is equal to three feet.

Measurement in Yards and Feet

Yards	1	2	3	4	5
Feet	3	6	9	12	15

a. Make a table like this showing the number of feet in lengths from 1 to 5 yards.

b. For each additional yard in your table, how many more feet are there? For each additional yard there are 3 more feet.

$\dfrac{f}{y} = \dfrac{3}{1}$ c. Write a proportion that you could use to convert the measurements between y yards and f feet.

d. Use the proportion you wrote to convert each measurement.

    i. 150 yards = f feet 450 ft   ii. 384 feet = y yards 128 yd

Exercise 9 Encourage multiple approaches. For example, students might multiply the conversion factor 1.6 km/mi by 1000 m/km to see that there are 1600 meters in a mile. **[Alert]** Students may reason that there are 1760 yards per mile and that meters are longer than yards, so there must be more than 1760 meters per mile. Suggest that they draw a diagram to see that there are fewer than 1760 meters per mile.

9. Which is longer: a 1-mile race or a 1500-meter race? Show your reasoning. $1500 \text{ m} \cdot \dfrac{1 \text{ km}}{1000 \text{ m}} \cdot \dfrac{1 \text{ mi}}{1.6 \text{ km}} = 0.9375$ mi; a 1 mi race is longer.

10. **APPLICATION** When mixed according to the directions, a 12-ounce can of lemonade concentrate becomes 64 ounces of lemonade.

a. How many 12-ounce cans of concentrate are needed to make 120 servings if each serving is 8 ounces? ⓐ fifteen 12 oz cans to make 960 oz

b. How many ounces of concentrate are needed to make 1 ounce of lemonade? $\dfrac{12}{64}$ or 0.1875 oz

c. Write a proportion that you can use to find the number of ounces of concentrate based on the number of ounces of lemonade wanted. ⓐ

d. Use the proportion you wrote to find the number of ounces of lemonade that can be made from a 16-ounce can of the same concentrate. $\dfrac{16 \text{ oz}}{L} = \dfrac{12}{64}$; $L \approx 85$ oz

11. **APPLICATION** Recipes in many international cookbooks use metric measurements. One cookie recipe calls for 120 milliliters of sugar. How much is this in our customary unit "cups"? (There are 1000 milliliters in a liter, 1.06 quarts in a liter, and 4 cups in a quart.)

$120 \text{ mL} \cdot \dfrac{1 \text{ L}}{1000 \text{ mL}} \cdot \dfrac{1.06 \text{ qt}}{1 \text{ L}} \cdot \dfrac{4 \text{ cups}}{1 \text{ qt}} = 0.5088$ cup or about $\dfrac{1}{2}$ cup

10c. $\dfrac{\textit{number of ounces of concentrate}}{\textit{number of ounces of lemonade}} = \dfrac{12}{64}$

Review

2.1 **12.** The students in the mathematics and chess clubs worked together to raise funds for their respective groups. Together the clubs raised $480. There are 12 members in the Mathematics Club and only 8 in the Chess Club. How should the funds be divided between the two clubs? Explain your answer. ⓐ *If the profits are divided in proportion to the number of students in the clubs, the Math Club would get $288, leaving $192 for the Chess Club.*

1.3 **13.** The box plot shows the length in centimeters of the members of the kingfisher family. The lengths of the five birds shown make up the five-number summary. Use the information below to match each kingfisher to its length.

Kingfisher length (cm)

Pygmy kingfisher
10 cm

Laughing kookaburra
46 cm

Green kingfisher
22 cm

Belted kingfisher
33 cm

Ringed kingfisher
41 cm

- These kingfishers range in size from the tiny pygmy kingfisher to the laughing kookaburra.

- The best known kingfisher, the belted kingfisher, breeds from Alaska to Florida. It is only 2.6 centimeters longer than the mean kingfisher length.

- The ringed kingfisher, a tropical bird, is much closer to the median length than the green kingfisher.

Exercise 12 This exercise has many possible answers. It can lead to a good group discussion.

IMPROVING YOUR VISUAL THINKING SKILLS

The seven pieces of the ancient Chinese puzzle called Tangram are defined using a square $ABCD$ and a set of midpoints. Points E, F, G, H, I, and J are the midpoints of segments AB, BC, AC, AG, GC, and EF, respectively. What is the ratio of the area of each of these Tangram pieces to the area of the whole square?

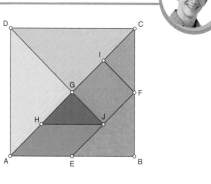

IMPROVING VISUAL THINKING SKILLS

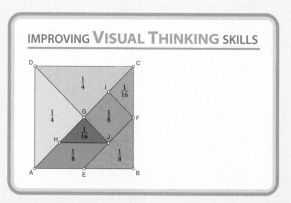

Direct Variation

In Lesson 2.3, you worked with conversion factors to change from one unit of measure to another. You also worked with rates, such as *miles per hour,* and saw that a rate has a 1 in the denominator. This makes rates convenient to calculate with. You'll see patterns arise when you use rates to make tables or graphs. In the investigation you'll use algebra to understand these patterns better.

PLANNING

LESSON OUTLINE

One day:

25 min	Investigation
10 min	Sharing
5 min	Example
5 min	Closing
5 min	Exercises

MATERIALS

- graph paper
- Ship Canals (T), *optional*
- Direct and Inverse Variation (T), *optional*
- Calculator Notes 1F, 1J, 1K, 2A
- Fathom demonstration Ship Canals, *optional*

TEACHING

The investigation in this lesson is the first step in finding a model to fit a scatter plot. Data points whose coordinates are directly proportional have a *direct variation* equation of the form $y = kx$, whose graph is a straight line through the origin.

 Guiding the Investigation

You can replace most of this investigation with the Fathom demonstration Ship Canals.

One Step

Prompt students to use a graph, a rate, an equation, and a calculator table to fill in the numbers missing from the Ship Canals table.

See page 722 for graphs for Steps 1, 2, and 3.

Investigation
Ship Canals

You will need
- graph paper

In this investigation you will use data about canals to draw a graph and write an equation that states the relationship between miles and kilometers. You'll see several ways of finding the information that is missing from this table.

Ship Canals

Canal	Length (miles)	Length (kilometers)
Albert (Belgium)	80	129
Alphonse XIII (Spain)	53	85
Houston (Texas)	50	81
Kiel (Germany)	62	99
Main-Danube (Germany)	106	171
Moscow-Volga (Russia)	80	129
Panama (Panama)	51	82
St. Lawrence Seaway (Canada/U.S.)	189	304
Suez (Egypt)	101	162
Trollhätte (Sweden)	54 or 55	87

(*The Top 10 of Everything 1998,* p. 57)

Step 1

Step 1 (189, 304), (106, 171), (80, 129), (80, 129), (62, 99), (53, 85), (51, 82), (50, 81)

Carefully draw and scale a pair of coordinate axes for the data in the table. Let *x* represent the length in miles and *y* represent the length in kilometers. Plot points for the first eight coordinate pairs.

Step 2

Step 2 A linear pattern or "rate"; find 101 mi on the *x*-axis and go up to the line; the *y*-value is the corresponding length in kilometers. Find 87 km on the *y*-axis and go to the line to approximate the length in miles of the Trollhätte Canal.

What pattern or shape do you see in your graph? Connect the points to illustrate this pattern. Explain how you could use your graph to approximate the length *in kilometers* of the Suez Canal and the length *in miles* of the Trollhätte Canal.

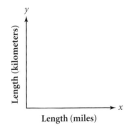

Step 3

On your calculator, make a plot of the same points and compare it to your hand-drawn plot. Use list L_1 for lengths in miles and list L_2 for lengths in kilometers. [▶ 🖳 See **Calculator Note 1F** to review this type of plot. ◀]

LESSON OBJECTIVES

- Learn the properties of a direct variation equation
- Graph a direct variation equation
- Read a direct variation graph to find missing values in the corresponding table
- Use a direct variation equation to extrapolate values from a given data set
- Develop an intuitive understanding of the concepts slope and linear equation

NCTM STANDARDS

CONTENT		PROCESS	
✔	Number	✔	Problem Solving
✔	Algebra	✔	Reasoning
	Geometry	✔	Communication
✔	Measurement	✔	Connections
✔	Data/Probability	✔	Representation

Step 4 Use list L3 to calculate the ratio $\frac{L2}{L1}$. [▶ 🖳 See **Calculator Note 1K** to review using lists to calculate this way. ◀] Explain what the values in list L3 represent. If you round each value in list L3 to the nearest tenth, what do you get? 1.6

Step 5 Use the rounded value you got in Step 4 to find the length in kilometers of the Suez Canal. Could you also use your result to find the length in miles of the Trollhätte Canal?

The number of kilometers is the same in every mile, so the value you found is called a **constant**.

Step 6 How can you change x miles to y kilometers? Using variables, write an equation to show how miles and kilometers are related. $y = 1.6x$

Step 7 Use the equation you wrote in Step 6 to find the length in kilometers of the Suez Canal and the length in miles of the Trollhätte Canal. How is using this equation like using a rate?

Step 8 Graph your equation on your calculator. [▶ 🖳 See **Calculator Note 1J** to review graphing equations. ◀] Compare this graph to your hand-drawn graph. Why does the graph go through the origin?

Step 9 Trace the graph of your equation. [▶ 🖳 See **Calculator Note 1J** to review tracing equations. ◀] Approximate the length in kilometers of the Suez Canal by finding when x is approximately 101 miles. Trace the graph to approximate the length in miles of the Trollhätte Canal. How do these answers compare to the ones you got from your hand-drawn graph?

Step 10 Use the calculator's table function to find the missing lengths for the Suez Canal and the Trollhätte Canal. [▶ 🖳 See **Calculator Note 2A** to learn about the table function. ◀]

Step 11 In this investigation you used several ways to find missing values—approximating with a graph, calculating with a rate, solving an equation, and searching a table. Write several sentences explaining which of these methods you prefer and why.

History CONNECTION

The Panama Canal allows ships to cross the strip of land between the Atlantic and Pacific Oceans. Before the canal was completed in 1913, ships had to sail thousands of miles around the dangerous Cape Horn, even though only 50 mi separate the two oceans. Learn more about famous canals at www.keymath.com/DA .

A ship passes through the Panama Canal.

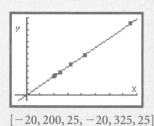

Ratios, rates, and conversion factors are closely related. In this investigation you saw how to change the ratio $\frac{129 \text{ km}}{80 \text{ mi}}$ to a rate of approximately 1.6 kilometers per mile. You can also use that rate as a conversion factor between kilometers and miles. The numbers in the ratio vary, but the resulting rate remains the same, or constant. Kilometers and miles are **directly proportional**—there will always be the same number of kilometers in every mile. When two quantities vary in this way, they have a relationship called **direct variation.**

Direct Variation

An equation in the form $y = kx$ is a **direct variation.** The quantities represented by x and y are **directly proportional,** and k is the **constant of variation.**

You can represent any ratio, rate, or conversion factor with a direct variation. Using a direct variation equation or graph is an alternative to solving proportions. A direct variation equation can also help you organize calculations with rates.

EXAMPLE

A grocery store advertises a sale on soda.

keymath.com/DA

a. Write a rate for the cost per six-pack.

b. Write an equation showing the relationship between the number of six-packs purchased and the cost.

c. How much will 15 six-packs cost?

d. Sol is stocking up for his restaurant. He bought $210 worth of soda. How many six-packs did he buy?

► Solution

a. The ratio given is $\frac{\$6.00}{4 \text{ six-packs}}$. This simplifies to a rate of $1.50 per six-pack.

b. Use x for the number of six-packs and y for the cost in dollars. Write a proportion.

$$\frac{y}{x} = \frac{1.50}{1}$$ y corresponds to 1.50 and x corresponds to 1.

$$y = \frac{1.50}{1} \cdot x$$ Multiply by x to undo the division.

$$y = 1.50x$$ Your result is a direct variation equation.

The constant, k, is the rate $1.50 per six-pack. Does every point on the graph of this equation make sense in this situation?

Would you get the same equation if you started with the proportion $\frac{y}{x} = \frac{6.00}{4}$? Do you see another way to find the equation once you know the rate?

Cost of Soda

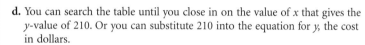

c. You can trace the graph to find the point where $x = 15$, or you can substitute 15 into the equation for x, the number of six-packs.

$$y = 1.50(15) = 22.50$$

Fifteen six-packs cost $22.50.

d. You can search the table until you close in on the value of x that gives the y-value of 210. Or you can substitute 210 into the equation for y, the cost in dollars.

$$210 = 1.50x \qquad \text{Substitute 210 for } y \text{ into the original equation.}$$

$$\frac{210}{1.50} = x \qquad \text{Divide by 1.50 to undo the multiplication.}$$

$$140 = x \qquad \text{Simplify.}$$

Sol purchased 140 six-packs for $210.

EXERCISES

You will need your graphing calculator for Exercises **1, 2, 3, 6,** and **9.**

▶ Practice Your Skills

Let x represent distance in miles and y represent distance in kilometers. Enter the equation $y = 1.6x$ into your calculator. Use it for Exercises 1–3.

1. Trace the graph of $y = 1.6x$ to find each missing quantity. Adjust the window settings as you proceed.

  a. 25 miles ≈ 40 kilometers @
                                  b. 120 kilometers ≈ 75 miles

2. Use the calculator table function to find the missing quantity.

  a. 55 miles ≈ 88 kilometers @
                                  b. 450 kilometers ≈ ☐ miles
                                                            281

3. Find the missing values in this table. Round each value to the nearest tenth.

Distance (mi)	Distance (km)
@ 2.8	4.5
7.8	12.5
650.0	1040.0
937.5	1500.0

substituted for k to arrive at an equation. Try to have students think about how the "per" (denominator) units of the rate will cancel with the units of x.

If students have graphed their equation and are trying to evaluate it at $x = 15$ by tracing, they might not find a point with x-coordinate exactly 15. They can get close by zooming in on the table, or their calculator may let them enter an exact value of x.

Closing the Lesson

As needed, remind students that a **direct variation** is an equation, often written $y = kx$, that relates two **directly proportional** variables x and y using a **constant of variation** k.

BUILDING UNDERSTANDING

As students work with direct variations and their graphs, continue to stress the importance of dimensional analysis.

ASSIGNING HOMEWORK

Essential	**1–4, 7**
Performance assessment	**11**
Portfolio	**6, 9**
Journal	**6d, 9**
Group	**5, 8, 9**
Review	**12–14**

▶ Helping with the Exercises

Exercises 1 and 2 Some students may prefer to use calculator tables. Others may prefer the graph.

Exercise 3 Students might recognize that the data tables they are developing are input-output tables. The widely differing values for x should help them connect the input-output process with the infinite length of the line that represents the relationship.

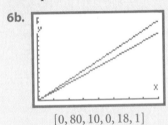
4. Describe how to solve each equation for x. Then solve.

    a. $14 = 3.5x$ ⓐ   **b.** $8x = 45(0.62)$ **c.** $\frac{x}{7} = 0.375$ **d.** $\frac{12}{x} = 0.8$

5. **APPLICATION** The equation $c = 1.25f$ shows the direct variation relationship between the length of fabric and its cost. The variable f represents the length of the fabric in yards, and c represents the cost in dollars. Use the equation to answer these questions.

$3.13   **a.** How much does $2\frac{1}{2}$ yards of fabric cost?

4 yd   **b.** How much fabric can you buy for $5?

    c. What is the cost of each additional yard of fabric? $1.25

Christo (b 1935, Bulgaria) and Jeanne-Claude (b 1935, Morocco) are environmental sculptors who wrap large objects and buildings in fabric. This is the German Reichstag in 1995.

▶ **Reason and Apply**

6. **APPLICATION** Market A sells 7 ears of corn for $1.25. Market B sells a baker's dozen (13 ears) for $2.75.

    a. Copy and complete the tables below showing the cost of corn at each market.

Market A

Ears	7	14	21	28	35	42
Cost	1.25	2.50	3.75	5.00	6.25	7.50

Market B

Ears	13	26	39	52	65	78
Cost	2.75	5.50	8.25	11.00	13.75	16.50

    b. Let x represent the number of ears of corn and y represent cost. Find equations to describe the cost of corn at each market. Use your calculator to plot the information for each market on the same set of coordinate axes. Round the constants of variation to three decimal places. ⓗ Market A: $y = 0.179x$; Market B: $y = 0.212x$

    c. If you wanted to buy only one ear of corn, how much would each market charge you? How do these prices relate to the equations you found in 6b?

    d. How can you tell from the graphs which market is the cheaper place to buy corn?

Why is 13 called a baker's dozen? In the 13th century, bakers began to form guilds to prevent dishonesty. To avoid the penalty for selling a loaf of bread that was too small, bakers began giving 13 whenever a customer asked for a dozen.

7. Bernard Lavery, a resident of the United Kingdom, has held several world records for growing giant vegetables. The graph shows the relationship between weight in kilograms and weight in pounds.

a. Use the information in the graph to complete the table.

Bernard Lavery's Vegetables

Vegetable	Weight (kg)	Weight (lb)
Cabbage	56	123
Summer squash	49	108
Zucchini	29	64
Kohlrabi	28	62
Celery	21	46
Radish	13	28
Cucumber	9	20
Brussels sprout	8	18
Carrot	5	11

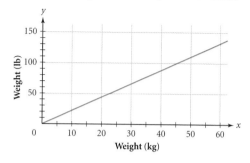

Relationship Between Kilograms and Pounds

(*The Top 10 of Everything 1998*, p. 98)

b. Calculate the rate of pounds per kilogram for each vegetable entry from the table. Use the rate you think best represents the data as the constant of variation. Write an equation to represent the relationship between pounds and kilograms. @ $y = 2.2x$

c. Use the equation you wrote in 7b to find the weight in kilograms for a pumpkin that weighs 6.5 pounds. @ 2.95 kg

d. Use the equation you wrote in 7b to find the weight in pounds for an elephant that weighs 3600 kilograms. @ 7920 lb

e. How many kilograms are in 100 pounds? How many pounds are in 100 kilograms? @ 100 lb = $45.\overline{45}$ kg; 100 kg = 220 lb

8. As part of their homework assignment, Thu and Sabrina each found equations from a table of data relating miles and kilometers. One entry in the table paired 150 kilometers and 93 miles. From this pair of data values, Thu and Sabrina wrote different equations.

a. Thu wrote the equation $y = 1.61x$. How did he get it? What does 1.61 represent? What do x and y represent? ⓗ

b. Sabrina wrote $y = 0.62x$ as her equation. How did she get it? What does 0.62 represent? What do x and y represent?

c. Whose equation would you use to convert miles to kilometers?

d. When would you use the other student's equation?
    Sabrina's equation may be more convenient when converting kilometers to miles.

Exercise 7a From the graph, students should be able to find the missing values to within 5 lb or 5 kg of the given answers.

Exercise 7b Students might check their conjectured equation by plotting it on a graph with the data points.

8a. Thu calculated the ratio $\frac{150}{93} \approx 1.61$; 1.61 is the rate of kilometers per mile; x represents miles, and y represents kilometers.

8b. Sabrina calculated the ratio $\frac{93}{150} = 0.62$; her constant is the rate of miles per kilometer; x represents kilometers, and y represents miles.

8c. Thu's equation may be more convenient because you can directly multiply the number of miles by 1.61.

Exercise 9 The *exchange rate* between two monetary systems is the conversion factor.

You may want to take some class time for students to come up with a common list of ten items.

9a. A sample answer is to use U.S. coins and denominations in dollars. {100, 50, 20, 10, 5, 1, 0.50, 0.25, 0.10, 0.05, 0.01}

9b. Multiply the list by the exchange rate. For example, to convert to Japanese yen, multiply the list by 104.160. {10416, 5208, 2083.2, 1041.6, 520.8, 104.16, 52.08, 26.04, 10.416, 5.208, 1.0416}

9c. Divide list L2 by the exchange rate to obtain the original values.

9d. Using dimensional analysis:

$$\frac{11.297 \text{ pesos}}{1 \text{ dollar}} \cdot \frac{1 \text{ dollar}}{0.772 \text{ euro}}$$

≈ 14.633 pesos per euro; multiply the number of euros by this exchange rate.

10d.

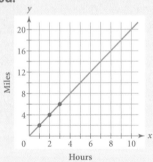

10e. 2 mi/h; this represents the constant walking speed.

Exercise 11 Suggest to students having difficulty that they draw a diagram, complete with the lengths of the sides of the room.

11e.

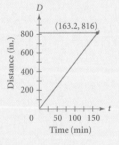

9. APPLICATION If you're planning to travel to another country, you will need to learn about its monetary system. This table gives some exchange rates that tell how many of each monetary unit are equivalent to one U.S. dollar.

International Monetary Units

Country	Monetary unit	Exchange rates (units per American dollar)
Brazil	real	2.686
Thailand	baht	38.600
Italy	euro	0.772
Japan	yen	104.160
Mexico	peso	11.297
India	rupee	43.650
United Kingdom	pound	0.536

(Federal Reserve Bank of New York for January 25, 2005)

a. Make a list of ten items and the price of each item in U.S. dollars. Enter these prices into list L1 on your calculator.

b. Choose one of the countries in the table and convert the U.S. dollar amounts in your list to that country's monetary unit. Use list L2 to calculate these new values from list L1.

c. Using list L3, convert the values in list L2 back to the values in list L1.

d. Describe how you would convert euros to pesos.

10. If you travel at a constant speed, the distance you travel is directly proportional to your travel time. Suppose you walk 3 mi in 1.5 h.

a. How far would you walk in 1 h? ⓗ 2 mi

b. How far would you walk in 2 h? 4 mi

c. How much time would it take you to walk 6 mi? 3 h

d. Represent this situation with a graph.

e. What is the constant of variation in this situation, and what does it represent? ⓐ

f. Define variables and write an equation that relates time to distance traveled. ⓐ $d = 2t$, where d is distance traveled in miles and t is travel time in hours.

11. A bug is crawling horizontally along the wall at a constant rate of 5 inches per minute. You first notice the bug when it is in the corner of the room, behind your music stand.

a. Define variables and write an equation that relates time (in minutes) to distance traveled (in inches). ⓐ $D = 5t$, where D is the distance traveled in inches and t is the time elapsed in minutes.

b. What is the constant of variation of this direct variation relationship, and what does it represent? The constant of variation is 5; this represents the constant rate of 5 inches every minute.

c. How far will the bug crawl in 1 h? 300 in.

d. How long would you have to practice playing your instrument before the bug completely "circled" the 14-ft-by-20-ft room? ⓐ 163.2 min, or 2.72 h

e. Draw a graph that represents this situation.

▶ Review

2.3 **12.** U.S. speed limits are posted in miles per hour (mi/h). Germany's Autobahn has stretches where speed limits are posted at 130 kilometers per hour (km/h).

 a. How many miles per hour is 130 km/h? @ 81.25 mi/h

 b. How many kilometers per hour is 25 mi/h? 40 km/h

 c. If the United States used the metric system, what speed limit do you think would be posted in place of 65 mi/h? 65 mi/h is 104 km/h. A speed limit sign might post 100 km/h.

2.3 **13.** APPLICATION Cecile started a business entertaining at children's birthday parties. As part of the package, Cecile arrives in costume and plays games with the children. She also makes balloon animals and paints each child's face. When she started the business, she charged $3.50 per child, but she is rethinking what her charges should be so that she will make a profit.

 a. The average children's party takes about 3 hours. Cecile wants to make at least $12 an hour. What is the minimum number of children she should arrange to entertain at a party at her current rate? 11 children

 b. The balloons and face paint cost Cecile about 60¢ per child. What percent is that of the fee per child? approximately 17%

 c. Cecile decided to raise her rates so that the cost of supplies for each child is only 10% of her fee. If the supplies for the party cost 60¢ per child, what should she charge per child? $6 per child

2.3 **14.** APPLICATION Marie and Tracy bought boxes of granola bars for their hiking trip. They noticed that the tags on the grocery-store shelf use rates.

 a. Each tag above uses two rates. Identify all four rates. @ $2.49 per box, 42¢ per bar, $2.99 per box, 25¢ per ounce

 b. A box of Crunchy Granola Bars contains 6 bars. Is the price per bar correct? yes

 c. A box of Chewy Granola Bars contains 8 bars. Use the information on the tag to find the number of ounces per bar. @ 1.495 oz per bar

 d. A box of Crunchy Granola Bars weighs 10 ounces. What is the price per ounce? about 25¢

 e. If Marie and Tracy like Crunchy Granola Bars as much as they like Chewy Granola Bars, which should they buy? Explain your answer.

Exercise 13 [Language] Most of the rates in the problem contain the word *per*. But $12 an hour is also a rate—$12 per hour.

Exercise 14 [Alert] Students may have difficulty with the dimensional analysis in 14c. Encourage them to try different units for ratios as they try to build ratios with units that will divide out, leaving *ounces* in the numerator and *bar* in the denominator.

14e. Possible answers: If comparing price per ounce, neither is a better value because both bars are 25¢ per ounce. If comparing price per bar, they should buy the Chewy Granola Bars because they are cheaper per bar (but the bars are smaller). If Marie and Tracy prefer fewer, larger bars, they should buy Crunchy Granola Bars. If they prefer more, smaller bars, they should buy Chewy Granola Bars.

The Scale Drawings Project

The Scale Drawings Project

Before students make their own scale drawing, you might want to have them practice reading information from an architectural drawing or blueprint. If your classroom is small, you can ask students to design the interior of a larger room or set of rooms in the school.

SCALE DRAWINGS

To design a building, an architect makes a scale drawing to show what the floor plan will look like. Maps of towns and cities are other common types of scale drawings. Interior decorators also use both floor plans and scale models of furniture to help them design a room.

If you could redecorate your mathematics classroom, what would you include? A pool table? A big-screen television? Couches? In this project you can let your imagination run wild and put whatever you want in the space inside your classroom. You will make a scale drawing of your room and decorate it in any way you wish. Your first step will be to measure your classroom. Then decide on an appropriate scale for your drawing. Next decide on the furnishings for your classroom. You may need to do some research to find reasonable dimensions for each item. If you are working on paper, it may be easiest to cut out pieces that are scaled representations of each furniture item and then physically move them around on your floor plan until you have the arrangement you like best. If you complete this project using The Geometer's Sketchpad or other geometry software, be sure that the figures representing each furniture item are draggable so that you can experiment with different furniture arrangements.

Your project should include

▸ A drawing or printout showing the outer classroom walls and any desks or other furniture.

▸ A key to show the scale factor you used.

▸ Sample calculations showing how you determined the dimensions on your drawing.

▸ The original measurements of walls and furniture.

Career
CONNECTION

There are several ways to do three-dimensional scale drawings. Some drawings show the object from the top, bottom, and each side. Others show the object with a perspective drawing. Architects use Computer Aided Design (CAD) software to help with these drawings.

Supporting the project

MOTIVATION

What might happen if an interior decorator bought all the furniture for a room without measuring or making a scale drawing?

OUTCOMES

▸ The shape of the classroom in the drawing is accurate.

▸ The dimensions of the drawn classroom are to scale.

▸ The objects drawn in the classroom are approximately to scale.

▸ The legend is clear and accurate.

▸ Sample calculations and original measurements are included.

LESSON

2.5

Inverse Variation

One person's constant is another person's variable.

SUSAN GERHART

In each relationship you have worked with in this chapter, if one quantity increased, so did the other. If one quantity decreased, so did the other. If the working hours increase, so does the pay. The shorter the trip, the less gas the car needs. These are direct relationships. Do all relationships between quantities work this way? Can two quantities be related so that increasing one causes the other to decrease?

Try opening your classroom door by pushing on it close to the hinge. Try it again farther from the hinge. Which way takes more force? As the distance from the hinge *increases,* the force needed to open the door *decreases.* This is an example of an *inverse* relationship.

Investigation

Speed versus Time

You will need

- one motion sensor

In this investigation you will explore the relationship between a walker's speed and the time it takes to cover a fixed-length course.

> **Procedure Note**
>
> 1. Download the INVERSE program to your graphing calculator. [▶ 🖳 See **Calculator Note 2B.**◀]
> 2. Run INVERSE, and follow the directions that appear on the calculator screen. To begin, the walker stands at the start line, and the CBR holder stands 1 m behind the start line, facing the walker.
> 3. The CBR holder presses the trigger of the CBR. The CBR will collect data for 10 s. Approximately 1 s after the CBR starts, the walker walks to the finish line and comes to a stop. The walker waits until the 10 s are complete.

Step 1 | Set up the course by marking a starting line and a finish line 2.00 m apart.

NCTM STANDARDS

CONTENT		PROCESS	
✔	Number	✔	Problem Solving
✔	Algebra	✔	Reasoning
	Geometry	✔	Communication
✔	Measurement		Connections
	Data/Probability	✔	Representation

LESSON OBJECTIVES

- Investigate inverse variation through real-world problems
- Learn the basic inverse variation equations
- Graph inverse variation functions

PLANNING

LESSON OUTLINE

One day:

5 min	Introduction
20 min	Investigation
10 min	Sharing
10 min	Examples
5 min	Closing

MATERIALS

- motion sensors (one per group)
- metersticks or tape measures
- masking tape (or other marker for start and finish lines)
- Lab Report (W), *optional*
- Seesaw Nickels (W), *optional*
- Direct and Inverse Variation (T), *optional*
- Calculator Notes 1B, 1F, 2B
- Fathom demonstration Inverse Variation, *optional*
- CBL 2 demonstration Light Intensity, *optional*

TEACHING

Like direct variation, inverse variation (aided by dimensional analysis) can provide a shortcut to setting up and solving proportions. In direct variation situations, the *ratios* of corresponding data values are constant; each equals a constant *multiplied by* the other. This lesson presents inverse variation situations, in which the constants are the *products* of corresponding data values; each data value equals the constant *divided by* the other data value.

If you don't have access to CBRs, use the alternate investigation Seesaw Nickels, found in the Teaching and Worksheet Masters. Answers are provided on page 126. You can replace Steps 6 and 7 with the Fathom demonstration Inverse Variation.

One Step

Distribute Calculator Note 2B and pose the problem: "Download and run the program INVERSE on a calculator connected to a motion sensor, using walks of different speeds. Graph an equation that relates the total times to the average speeds." As groups work, ask them to justify their equations using dimensional analysis and to write the equations as proportions. Introduce the terms *inverse proportion* and *indirect variation* during Sharing.

Step 1 Note that 2.00 m means 2 m accurate to the nearest hundredth meter, or cm.

Step 6 Refer students to Calculator Notes 1B and 1F as needed.

Step 6

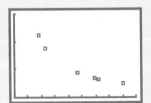

Step 7 If students can figure out this equation without much difficulty, you might skip Example A.

Step 8 Students may need to figure out the units on *a* before they can explain its significance.

Step 8 The value of *a* is the total distance walked; its units are meters.

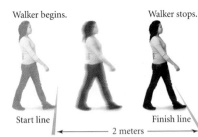

Walker begins.　Walker stops.

CBR holder　Start line　Finish line

← 2 meters →

Step 2　Perform the activity as described in the Procedure Note.

Step 3　On the calculator, press (ENTER) to download the data. Isolate the part of the graph that shows the walk by moving the cursor to the right to just where the walk began. (Remember, the graph shows speed versus time.) Press (ENTER). Move the cursor until it returns to the *x*-axis at the end of the walk. Press (ENTER) again. Now you should see just the walk data. If it is correct, press 1.

ISOLATE THE WALK
SPEED

Place the left bound here.

Place the right bound here.

TIME

Steps 4 and 5 sample data: Walk 1: 6.2 s, 0.322 m/s; Walk 2: 8 s, 0.25 m/s; Walk 3: 2.3 s, 0.870 m/s; Walk 4: 1.8 s, 1.111 m/s; Walk 5: 4.7 s, 0.426 m/s; Walk 6: 5.9 s, 0.339 m/s

Step 4　Your calculator will now display the walk number, the total time for the walk, and the average speed of the walker. Record these data.

Step 5　Press (ENTER), and trade jobs among the group members. Repeat Steps 1–4 five times, to collect data for six walks. Try to do two different slow walks, two different medium walks, and two different fast walks.

Step 6　When the program is complete, enter the six (*total time, average speed*) data points into lists in each group member's calculator. Create a graph that shows the data and both axes.

Step 7　Find an equation in the form $y = \frac{a}{x}$ that is a good model for the relationship between total time and average speed. Experiment with different values of *a* until you find a curve that looks like a good fit for the data. $y = \frac{2}{x}$

Step 8　What does the value of *a* found in Step 7 have to do with the experiment? What kind of units does it have?

In the investigation you dealt with the relationship between the time it takes a walker to cover a fixed distance and the speed at which the walker travels. You may have discovered that the product of the time and speed was constant. You could write the equation

first walk total time · first walk speed = second walk total time · second walk speed

SHARING IDEAS

During the group work, you might select groups to put their data and graphs from Step 6 onto transparencies for sharing. Have a student describe the numerical relationship from Step 7 and have other students describe any other relationships they found. As needed, bring out the constant product *xy*.

Help students rephrase their ideas more clearly by putting yourself in the place of someone ignorant of what's going on and asking for clarification. You might also try asking "Do you mean ..." and rephrasing what they're trying to say with clear terminology. You might have students write a lab report for this investigation.

You can also write this relationship as a proportion:

$$\frac{first\ walk\ total\ time}{second\ walk\ total\ time} = \frac{second\ walk\ speed}{first\ walk\ speed} \quad \text{or}$$

$$\frac{first\ walk\ total\ time}{second\ walk\ speed} = \frac{second\ walk\ total\ time}{first\ walk\ speed}$$

How can you show that all three of these equations are equivalent?

Look closely at the proportions above. How do they differ from the proportions you have written so far? When you wrote proportions for direct relationships, you had to make sure that the numerator and denominator of each ratio corresponded in the same way. In this inverse relationship, the proportion has ratios that correspond in the opposite (or inverse) way. The numerators and denominators seem to be flipped. These are called *inverse proportions*.

EXAMPLE A

Tyline measured the force needed as she opened a door by pushing at various distances from the hinge. She collected the data shown in the table. Find an equation for this relationship. (A newton, abbreviated N, is the metric unit of force.)

Distance (cm)	Force (N)
40.0	20.9
45.0	18.0
50.0	16.1
55.0	14.8
60.0	13.3
65.0	12.3
70.0	11.6
75.0	10.7

▶ **Solution**

Enter the data into two calculator lists and graph points. The graph shows a curved pattern that is different from the graph of a direct relationship. If you study the values in the table, you can see that as distance increases, force decreases. The data pairs of this relationship might have a constant product like your data in the investigation.

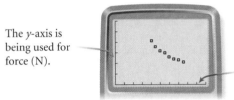

The *y*-axis is being used for force (N).

The *x*-axis is being used for distance from the hinge (cm).

[0, 100, 10, 0, 30, 5]

Calculate the products in another list. Their mean is approximately 810, so use that to represent the product. Let *x* represent distance and *y* represent force.

Distance (cm)	Force (N)	Force · Distance (N-cm)
40	20.9	836.0
45	18.0	810.0
50	16.1	805.0
55	14.8	814.0
60	13.3	798.0
65	12.3	799.5
70	11.6	812.0
75	10.7	802.5

Science

CONNECTION

Scientists use precise machines to measure the amount of force needed to pull or push. Manufacturers use these tools to test the strength of products like boxes. You can also measure force with simple tools like a spring scale. This box shows a certificate that gives the results from several force tests.

Assessing Progress

Watch for skill at careful measurement, following directions, isolating variables in experimentation, and recording data.

Another Example

If you have two days for this lesson, you might dramatize another inverse relationship with the help of a 60-watt bulb. Show students the light, and then ask them to close or cover their eyes as you move the lit bulb toward and away from them. **[Ask]** "What difference do you see in the light when it is close compared with what you see when it is far away?" [The distance away and the brightness are inversely related. Be careful not to say that they satisfy an inverse variation, though, because the brightness varies inversely as the *square* of the distance away.] You can also use the CBL 2 demonstration Light Intensity to explore this relationship.

▶ **EXAMPLE A**

This example is good for students who have not yet seen that the product of variables in an inverse variation is constant. **[Ask]** "How would you size the viewing window to get this graph?" Reemphasize looking for maximum and minimum values of the two variables.

Students have only been dealing with positive slope up to this point. Make sure that students do not confuse indirect variation with a decreasing linear relationship.

Students worked with dividing units in direct variation problems: 3 miles divided by 1.5 hours gives 2 miles per hour, or mi/h. Units can also be multiplied, as shown in the third column. Multiplying *distance* in centimeters times *force* in Newtons gives values in units of Newton-centimeters (N-cm).

► EXAMPLE B

[Language] Be sure students know what a seesaw, sometimes called a *teeter-totter,* is. You might demonstrate the girls' experiment with a ruler and nickels or with something larger. Full cans of tuna on a length of 1-by-4 in. lumber work well.

This example provides an application of an inverse relationship, discovered through the constant product property.

Prepare students for the exercises with a question. **[Ask]** "How can you tell whether the variables are in direct or inverse variation or neither?" [If all the quotients of pairs are the same, there's a direct variation. If all the products are the same, there's an inverse variation.] Also discuss how to draw a quick diagram of the balancing situation, to prepare for Exercise 8.

Answers for Seesaw Nickels Investigation Worksheet

Step 3 The one nickel should balance at 6 inches from the pencil.

Step 4 Distance from pencil: 6, 3, 2, 1.5, 1

Step 5 Possible answer: As the number of nickels increases, the distance from the pencil decreases. The number multiplied by the distance equals 6.

Step 6 The same relationship holds—as the number of nickels increases, the distance from the pencil decreases—but this time the product is 9.

Step 6

Left side		Right side	
No.	Distance	No.	Distance
1	can't be done	3	3
2	4.5	3	3
3	3	3	3
4	2 or 2.5 (2.25)	3	3
6	1.5	3	3

$$xy = 810$$ The product of distance and force is 810.

$$y = \frac{810}{x}$$ Divide by x to undo the multiplication.

Now you have the Y= form, so you can enter this equation into your calculator. Graph the equation. Does it go through all of the points? Why do you think the graph is not a perfect fit? It is a good practice to explore small changes to your equation's constant. A slightly different value might give an even better fit.

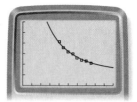

[0, 100, 10, 0, 30, 5]

The two variables in the inverse relationships you have seen have a constant product, so you can describe their relationship with an **inverse variation** equation. You can represent the constant product with k just like you use k to represent the constant ratio of a direct variation. The graph of an inverse variation is always curved and will never cross the x- or y-axis. Why couldn't x or y be zero?

Inverse Variation

An equation in the form $y = \frac{k}{x}$ is an **inverse variation.** Quantities represented by x and y are **inversely proportional,** and k is the **constant of variation.**

EXAMPLE B

Elaine, Ellen, and Eleanor, who are identical triplets, were playing together on a seesaw. When two of them sat on one side and one on the other, some careful positioning was needed to make the seesaw balance. After playing, they came indoors and did an experiment to understand this relationship. They placed a pencil under the center of a 12-in. ruler and gathered a pile of nickels. They placed 2 nickels 3 in. from the center on one side of the "seesaw." Then they placed different numbers of nickels on the other side and moved them until the balance point was found. Here is a data table of their results:

Nickels	1	2	3	4	5	6
Distance to center (in.)	6	3	2	1.5	1.2	1

a. If they placed 5 nickels 4 in. from the center, where would they have to place a pile of 8 nickels to balance the other side?

b. What can they learn from this experiment to help them in the playground?

Step 7 *(left nickels)* · *(left distance)*
= *(right nickels)* · *(right distance)*

$$\frac{left\ nickels}{right\ distance} = \frac{right\ nickels}{left\ distance}$$

Step 8 Possible answers: As one quantity increases, the other decreases. The "Right side" columns remained constant, and the product of the "Left side" values remained constant.

▶ **Solution**

Notice that the product of each data pair, *nickels · distance from center*, is a constant, 6. So this is an inverse relationship.

a. Using this relationship, 5 nickels at 4 in. must have the same product as 8 nickels at x in.

$$5 \cdot 4 = 8 \cdot x$$ Original equation.

$$\frac{5 \cdot 4}{8} = x$$ Undo the multiplication by 8.

$$2.5 = x$$ Multiply and divide.

So the pile of 8 nickels should be positioned 2.5 in. from the center.

b. The relationship between the number of triplets on a side of the seesaw and the distance they sit from the center is inverse. So, if one of the triplets sits 7 ft from the center, then the other two would have to sit so that the product of distance times weight is the same.

$$7 \cdot (1 \text{ triplet}) = x \cdot (2 \text{ triplets})$$ Original equation.

$$7 = 2x$$

$$3.5 = x$$ Undo the multiplication by 2.

So the other two triplets should sit together 3.5 ft from the center of the seesaw.

EXERCISES

You will need your graphing calculator for Exercises **3, 10,** and **11.**

▶ **Practice Your Skills**

1. Rewrite each equation in Y= form.
   a. $xy = 15$ ⓐ $y = \dfrac{15}{x}$
   b. $xy = 35$ $y = \dfrac{35}{x}$
   c. $xy = 3$ $y = \dfrac{3}{x}$

2. Two quantities, x and y, are inversely proportional. When $x = 3$, $y = 4$. Find the missing coordinates for the points below.
   a. $(4, y)$ ⓗ $(4, 3)$
   b. $(x, 2)$ $(6, 2)$
   c. $(1, y)$ $(1, 12)$
   d. $(x, 24)$ $(0.5, 24)$

3. Find five points that satisfy the inverse variation equation $y = \dfrac{20}{x}$. Graph the equation and the points to make sure the coordinates of your points are correct.
   Possible choices include $(4, 5), (2, 10), (5, 4), (10, 2),$ and $(2.5, 8)$.

4. Henry noticed that the more television he watched, the less time he spent doing homework. One night he spent 1.5 h watching TV and 1.5 h doing homework. Another night he spent 2 h watching TV and only 1 h doing homework. To try to catch up, the next night he spent only a half hour watching TV and 2.5 h doing homework. Is this an inverse variation? Explain why or why not.

Exercise 4 Students may be confused by the difference between an inverse relationship and inverse variation. This is an inverse relationship, but it's not an inverse variation because the products aren't all the same. In fact, the sums are the same, so the relationship is linear: $x + y = 3$.

4. This is not an inverse variation. The product of the quantities (*time spent watching TV, time spent doing homework*) is not constant. Instead, the sum is constant. This is a relationship of the form $x + y = k$, or $y = k - x$, not an inverse variation $xy = k$, or $y = \dfrac{k}{x}$.

Closing the Lesson

Remind the class that two positive data values have an inverse relationship when larger values of one correspond to smaller values of the other. In a special case, the variables satisfy an **inverse variation,** an equation of the form $y = \dfrac{k}{x}$, where k is the **constant of variation.** In this case, the product xy of the variables is constant.

Tell students that the next lesson will use multispeed bicycles. Ask for volunteers to bring in bicycles.

BUILDING UNDERSTANDING

Students practice working with inverse variations and their graphs. Continue to encourage the use of dimensional analysis. Allow students to use proportions, but encourage them to rewrite their equations as inverse variations.

ASSIGNING HOMEWORK

Essential	1–6, 8, 9
Performance assessment	7, 10
Portfolio	11, 12
Journal	4, 8
Group	11
Review	13–16

▶ **Helping with the Exercises**

Exercise 2 Two quantities x and y are *inversely proportional* if they satisfy an inverse variation—that is, if their product is constant.

Exercise 6 This is the type of problem students might see on a
standardized exam. As you may
have mentioned during Sharing,
students should check products
and quotients, looking for constants. **[Alert]** In 6b, students
may be confused and think that
because all other quotients are 12,
$\frac{0}{0} = 12$. Similarly, in 6c the 0's
might be confusing. All products
are 9 except those involving 0.

6a. inverse variation; $y = \frac{24}{x}$ or
$xy = 24$

6b. direct variation; $y = 12x$

6c. neither; neither x nor y can
be zero in an inverse variation,
and when $x = 0, y = 0$ in a
direct variation.

6d. inverse variation; $y = \frac{19.5}{x}$ or
$xy = 19.5$

7b. As you move closer to the
hinge, it takes more force to open
the door. Moving from 15 cm to
10 cm needs an increase of about
31.2 N. Moving 5 cm closer
requires an increase of 93.5 N.
As you move closer, the force
needed increases more rapidly.
When you get very close to the
hinge, the force needed becomes
extremely large.

8a. 104 lb

8b. $130 \cdot 4 = 104 \cdot D$; Emily
needs to sit approximately 5 ft
from the center. The seesaw is
only 4 ft long from the center
to the seat, so she can't balance
the two boys as long as they stay
on the seat. However, if the boys
move and Emily sits on the seat,
it can be done. $130 \cdot D = 104 \cdot 4$;
the boys must sit 3.2 ft from
the center.

5. APPLICATION The amount of time it takes to travel a given distance is inversely
proportional to how fast you travel.

a. How long would it take to travel 90 mi at 30 mi/h? @ 3 h

b. How long would it take to travel 90 mi at 45 mi/h? 2 h

c. How fast would you have to go to travel 90 mi in 1.5 h? 60 mi/h

▶ Reason and Apply

6. For each table of x- and y-values below, decide if the values show a direct variation,
an inverse variation, or neither. Explain how you made your decision. If the values
represent a direct or inverse variation, write an equation.

a.
@

x	y
2	12
8	3
4	6
3	8
6	4

b.

x	y
2	24
6	72
0	0
12	144
8	96

c.

x	y
4.5	2.0
0	9.0
3.0	3.0
9.0	0
6.0	1.5

d.

x	y
1.3	15.0
6.5	3.0
5.2	3.75
10.4	1.875
7.8	2.5

7. APPLICATION In Example A, you learned that the force in newtons needed to open
a door is inversely proportional to the distance in centimeters from the hinge. For
a heavy freezer door, the constant of variation is 935 N-cm.

a. Find the force needed to open the door by pushing at points 15 cm, 10 cm, and
5 cm from the hinge. @ 62.$\overline{3}$ N, 93.5 N, and 187 N

b. Describe what happens to the force needed to open the door as you push at
points closer and closer to the hinge. How does the change in force needed
compare as you go from 15 cm to 10 cm and from 10 cm to 5 cm?

c. How is your answer to 7b shown on the graph of
this equation? On the graph, the curve goes
up very steeply near the y-axis.

8. APPLICATION Emily and her little brother Sid
are playing on a seesaw. Sid weighs 65 lb.
The seesaw balances when Sid sits on the
seat 4 ft from the center and Emily
sits on the board $2\frac{1}{2}$ ft from the center.

a. About how much does Emily weigh? ⓗ

b. Sid's friend Seogwan sits with Sid
at the same end of the seesaw.
They weigh about the same. Can
Emily balance the seesaw with
both Sid and Seogwan on it? If so,
where should she sit? If not, explain
why not.

9. To use a double-pan balance, you put the object to be weighed on one side and then put known weights on the other side until the pans balance.

   a. Explain why it is useful to have the balance point halfway between the two pans.

   b. Suppose the balance point is off-center, 15 cm from one pan and 20 cm from the other. There is an object in the pan closest to the center. The pans balance when 7 kg is placed in the other pan. What is the weight of the unknown object? @ $15 \cdot M = 20 \cdot 7$; $M \approx 9.3$ kg

10. **APPLICATION** The student council wants to raise $10,000 to purchase computers. All students are encouraged to participate in a fund-raiser, but it is likely that some will not be able to.

   a. Pick at least four numbers to represent how many students might participate. Make a table showing how much each student will have to raise if each participant contributes the same amount. @   The table should include points such as (100, 100), (200, 50), (250, 40), (400, 25).

   b. Plot the points represented by your table on a calculator graph. Find an equation to fit the points. @ $y = \dfrac{10{,}000}{x}$

   c. Suppose there are only 500 students in the school. How would this number of students affect your graph? Sketch a graph to show this limitation. @ The graph should stop at $x = 500$ because there are only that many students.

11. A tuning fork vibrates at a particular frequency to make the sound of a note in a musical scale. If you strike a tuning fork and place it over a hollow tube, the vibrating tuning fork will cause the air inside the tube to vibrate, and the sound will get louder. Skye found that if you put one end of the tube in water and raise and lower it, the loudness will vary. She used a set of tuning forks and, for each one, recorded the tube length that made the loudest sound.

Tuning Fork Experiment

Note	Frequency (hertz)	Tube length (cm)
A_4	440.0	84.6
C_5	523.3	71.1
D_5	587.3	63.4
F_5	698.5	53.3
G_5	784.0	47.5

   a. Graph the data on your calculator and describe the relationship.   Answers will vary. On this graph, x represents frequency and y represents tube length.

   b. Find an equation to fit the data. Explain how you did this and what your variables and constants represent.

   c. The last tuning fork in Skye's set is A_5 with a frequency of 880.0 hertz. What tube length should produce the loudest sound? $y = \dfrac{37{,}227.1}{880.0}$; $y \approx 42.3$ cm

Exercise 9 Students might not have experience with a double-pan balance. You might borrow one from a science lab. Students will need to be familiar with pan balances for Chapter 3.

9a. If the balance point is at the center, then the weight of an unknown object will be exactly the same as the weight that balances it on the other side. If the balance point is off-center, you must know the two distances and do some calculation.

10b.

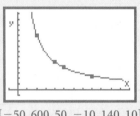

$[-50, 600, 50, -10, 140, 10]$

10c.

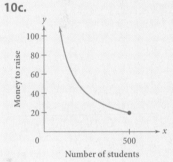

11a.

$[400, 1000, 100, 30, 90, 10]$

11b. Possible answer:
$y = \dfrac{37{,}227.1}{x}$;
the constant 37,227.1 is the mean of the products of the frequencies and tube lengths.

Exercise 12 1 atmosphere is the amount of air pressure at sea level, about 14.7 lb/in².

12d. Possible answer: You would have to increase the volume of the container. If you kept the same volume, you would have to suck some of the air out of the container.

12e.

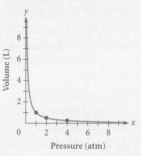

15a. 12 apartments

---

12. APPLICATION To squeeze a given amount of air into a smaller and smaller volume, you have to apply more and more pressure. Boyle's law describes the inverse variation between the volume of a gas and the pressure exerted on it. Suppose you start with a 1 L open container of air. If you put a plunger at the top of the container without applying any additional pressure, the pressure inside the container will be the same as the pressure outside the container, or 1 atmosphere (atm).

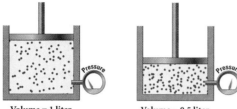

Volume = 1 liter   Volume = 0.5 liter

a. What will the pressure in atmospheres be if you push the plunger down until the volume of air is 0.5 L? @ 2 atm

b. What will the pressure in atmospheres be if you push the plunger down until the volume of air is 0.25 L? 4 atm

c. Suppose you exert enough pressure so that the pressure in the container is 10 atm. What will the volume of the air be? @ 0.1 L

d. What would you have to do to make the pressure inside the container less than 1 atm?

e. Graph this relationship, with pressure (in atmospheres) on the horizontal axis and volume (in liters) on the vertical axis.

▶ Review

2.4 **13.** APPLICATION A CD is on sale for 15% off its normal price of $13.95. What is its sale price? Write a direct variation equation to solve this problem. $s = 0.85p$; the sale price is $11.86.

2.1 **14.** Calcium and phosphorus play important roles in building human bones. A healthy ratio of calcium to phosphorus is 5 to 3.

   a. If Mario's body contains 2.5 pounds of calcium, how much phosphorus should his body contain? 1.5 lb

   b. About 2% of an average woman's weight is calcium. Kyla weighs 130 pounds. How many pounds of calcium and phosphorus should her body contain?
   2.6 lb of calcium and 1.56 lb of phosphorus

2.3 **15.** APPLICATION Two dozen units in an apartment complex need to be painted. It takes 3 gallons of paint to cover each apartment.

   a. How many apartments can be painted with 36 gallons?

   b. How many gallons will it take to paint all 24 apartments? 72 gal

2.1 **16.** Sulfuric acid, a highly corrosive substance, is used in the manufacture of dyes, fertilizer, and medicine. Sulfuric acid is also used by artists for metal etching and in aquatints. H_2SO_4 is the molecular formula for this substance. S stands for the sulfur atom. Use this information to answer each question.

  a. How many atoms of sulfur, hydrogen, and oxygen are in one sulfuric acid molecule?

  b. How many atoms of sulfur would it take to combine with 200 atoms of hydrogen? How many atoms of oxygen would it take to combine with 200 atoms of hydrogen?

  c. If 500 atoms of sulfur, 400 atoms of hydrogen, and 400 atoms of oxygen are combined, how many sulfuric acid molecules could be formed?

This untitled drypoint and aquatint is by the American artist Mary Cassatt (1844–1926).

16a. one sulfur atom, two hydrogen atoms, and four oxygen atoms

16b. 200 hydrogen atoms would combine with 100 sulfur atoms and 400 oxygen atoms.

16c. Use all 400 atoms of oxygen, 200 atoms of hydrogen, and 100 atoms of sulfur to make 100 molecules of sulfuric acid.

project

FAMILIES OF RECTANGLES

On each set of axes below, two rectangles are drawn with a common vertex at the origin. On the left, the rectangles are *similar,* meaning that the ratio $\frac{base}{height}$ is the same for each rectangle. On the right, the rectangles have the same area. If you draw more rectangles following the same patterns and then connect their upper-right vertices, what kinds of curves will you get? Write an equation for each pattern.

> **THE GEOMETER'S SKETCHPAD**
>
> With The Geometer's Sketchpad, you can construct families of rectangles and other polygons. Commands like Trace and Locus can help you dynamically create curves.

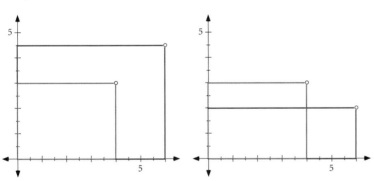

Explore at least four different families of rectangles or families of other shapes. Draw each family on its own set of axes and then describe the pattern in words. Connect corresponding vertices and see whether a curve is formed. (In mathematics, a straight line is actually considered a type of curve.) For each curve, write an equation or describe it in words. Summarize your findings in a paper or presentation.

Supporting the project

MOTIVATION

Are algebra and geometry unrelated fields of mathematics?

OUTCOMES

▶ Students can define simple families with patterns like "same area" or "same length."

▶ Students recognize the connected curves as direct variation and inverse variation.

▶ Students explore other families of rectangles or other polygons. These families may have other curves, such as horizontal or vertical lines or circles.

• Students write equations for the curves generated and recognize the connection to attributes of the polygons. (For example, when the area of rectangles is held constant, the equation is $xy = k$ or $lw = A$.)

• Students show that geometric figures can be described with algebra and that algebra can derive from geometry.

PLANNING

LESSON OUTLINE

One day:

5 min	Introduction
30 min	Activity
10 min	Sharing
5 min	Closing

MATERIALS

- metersticks or metric tape measures
- multispeed bicycles with 12, 18, or 24 speeds (one per group; each bike should have at least two sprockets in the front and several in the back)

TEACHING

Students who have ridden multispeed bicycles probably know which gear combinations are easier than others, but few of them have thought about how direct and inverse variations can represent the relative efficiency of the gears. If students bring in bicycles, warn administrators and security personnel.

Guiding the Activity

One Step

Pose this problem: "Experienced bicyclists often use terms such as *a 70 cm gear,* meaning a combination of sprockets for the chain that moves the bicycle 70 cm in one complete turn of the pedals. What centimeter gears are available on the bicycle you're working with today?" As you circulate, encourage systematic data collection, careful measurement, and use of direct and inverse variation equations to express relationships among number of teeth and either number of revolutions of the rear wheel or distance traveled.

Activity Day

Variation with a Bicycle

The Tour de France is a demanding bicycle race through France and several other countries. For 23 days, cyclists ride approximately 3500 kilometers on steep mountain roads before crossing the finish line in Paris. The cyclists rely on their knowledge of gear shifting and bicycle speeds.

Many bicycles have several speeds or gears. In a low gear, it's easier to pedal uphill. In a high gear, it's harder to pedal, but you can go faster on flat surfaces and down hills. When you change gears, the chain shifts from one sprocket to another. In this activity you will discover the relationships among the bicycle's gears, the teeth on the sprockets, how fast you pedal, and how fast the bike goes.

Activity

The Wheels Go Round and Round

You will need

- a meterstick or metric tape measure
- a multispeed bicycle

In Steps 1–5, you'll analyze the effect of the rear sprockets.

> **Procedure Note**
>
> **Changing Gears**
>
> You'll collect data with the bike upside down. You may be able to change gears in this position—rotate the pedals and crankshaft a few times. If you have to turn the bike right side up to change gears, then turn it upside down before you observe and record data.

Rear sprocket assemblies

Tooth

Crankshaft

Front sprocket assemblies

LESSON OBJECTIVE

- Investigate the direct and inverse variations between gear selection and wheel speeds on a multispeed bicycle

NCTM STANDARDS

CONTENT		PROCESS	
✔	Number		Problem Solving
✔	Algebra	✔	Reasoning
✔	Geometry		Communication
✔	Measurement	✔	Connections
✔	Data/Probability	✔	Representation

Step 1	Shift the bicycle into its lowest gear (using the smallest front sprocket and largest rear sprocket).
Step 2	Count the number of teeth on the front and rear sprockets in use. Record your numbers in a table like this one:

Number of teeth on front sprocket	Number of teeth on rear sprocket	Number of revolutions of rear wheel for one revolution of pedals

Step 3	Line up the air valve, or a chalk mark on the tire of the rear wheel, with part of the bicycle frame. This will be the "starting point." Rotate the pedal through one complete revolution and stop the wheel immediately. Estimate the number of wheel revolutions to the nearest tenth and enter it into the table.

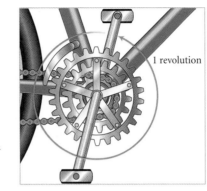

1 revolution

Step 4	Shift gears so that the chain moves onto the next rear sprocket. Do not change the front sprocket. Repeat Steps 2 and 3. Record your data in a new row of your table. Repeat this process for each rear sprocket.
Step 5	Describe how the number of teeth on the rear sprocket affects how the wheel turns. What kind of variation is this? Plotting the data on your calculator may help you to see this relationship. Define variables and write an equation that relates the number of wheel revolutions to the number of teeth on the rear sprocket. Explain the meaning of the constant in this equation.

In Steps 6–10, you'll analyze the effect of the front sprockets.

Step 6	Shift the bicycle into its lowest gear again.
Step 7	In a second table, record the number of teeth on the sprockets in use.
Step 8	As you did in Step 3, record the number of wheel revolutions for one revolution of the pedals.
Step 9	Keep the chain on the same rear sprocket and shift gears so that the chain is placed onto the next front sprocket. Repeat Steps 7 and 8. In the second table you should have one row of data for each front sprocket.
Step 10	Describe how the number of teeth on the front sprocket affects the turning of the wheel. What kind of variation models this relationship? Plot the data on your calculator to verify your answer. Define variables and write an equation that relates the number of teeth on the front sprocket to the number of wheel revolutions. What is the meaning of the constant in this equation?

Steps 2–4 sample table for a bike with six rear sprockets:

Front	Rear	Rev.
30	28	1.1
30	24	1.3
30	21	1.4
30	18	1.7
30	16	1.9
30	14	2.1

Steps 7–9 sample table for a bike with three front sprockets:

Front	Rear	Rev.
30	28	1.1
39	28	1.4
50	28	1.8

Step 1 Bicycles should be upside down. If needed, stabilize them with books or clothing. The lowest gear has the chain on the smallest front sprocket and the largest rear sprocket. You may need to point out the sprockets.

Step 2 Students may need to shift the chain off of these sprockets in order to see all the teeth.

Step 3 [Alert] Caution students to turn the pedal slowly in order to keep track of the revolutions. It will not be easy to count an exact number of revolutions of the rear wheel for one revolution of the pedals. Students will have to approximate this number as well as they can.

Step 5 The lower the number of teeth on the rear sprocket, the more the wheel turns in one pedal rotation. As the size of the rear sprocket increases, the number of wheel revolutions decreases. Indirect variation models this behavior. If w is the number of wheel revolutions, r is the number of teeth on the rear sprocket, and k is the proportionality constant, then the equation is $w = \frac{k}{r}$. The constant k represents the number of teeth on the front sprocket.

Step 8 Tell students to rotate the pair of pedals once.

Step 10 Encourage students to check their conjectured equation by graphing it on the calculator and comparing it to the scatter plot.

Step 10 The higher the number of teeth on the front sprocket, the more turns the wheel makes. Direct variation models this relationship. If f is the number of teeth on the front sprocket, w is the number of wheel revolutions, and k is the proportionality constant, then the equation is $f = kw$. The constant k represents the number of teeth on the rear sprocket.

Step 11 When looking for the mathematical relationship, students should concentrate on gear combinations where the number of teeth on the rear sprocket is a multiple of the number of teeth on the front sprocket. In these cases, the rear wheel should make a whole number of rotations for one revolution of the pedals.

Step 11 The proportion is

$$\frac{number\ of\ front\ teeth}{number\ of\ rear\ teeth}$$

$$= \frac{number\ of\ wheel\ revolutions}{1\ crankshaft\ revolution},$$

or $\frac{f}{r} = \frac{w}{1}$. For a gear combination with 45 front teeth and 15 rear teeth, the equation should predict 3 wheel revolutions.

Step 12 **[Alert]** Students may not realize that going faster means more revolutions of the rear wheel for one revolution of the pedals.

SHARING IDEAS

You might ask students to share their data and their results from Steps 5 and 10. Keep asking them to use the terms *direct variation* and *inverse variation*.

If you have time, extend the problem with a question. **[Ask]** "How many different pairs of front and back sprockets could be considered?" This question can lead to a discussion of multiplication in a "for each" situation. One way to answer it is to multiply the number of front sprockets by the number of back sprockets.

Assessing Progress
Watch for careful measurement and understanding of direct and inverse variation and rates.

Closing the Lesson

As needed, say that bicycle gears provide examples of both direct and inverse variations.

Now you'll see why gear shifting is such an important strategy in a bicycle race.

Step 11 Find a proportion relating the number of front teeth, rear teeth, wheel revolutions, and pedal revolutions. Use it to predict the number of wheel revolutions for a gear combination you have not tried yet. Test your prediction by doing the experiment with this gear combination.

Step 12 In a high gear, the rear wheel revolves more in one pedal rotation, making the bike travel farther in the same amount of time.

Step 13 A 70 cm diameter rim has a 220 cm circumference. This wheel makes 455 revolutions per kilometer.

Step 12 Explain why different gear ratios result in different numbers of rear wheel revolutions. Why is it possible to go faster in a high gear?

Step 13 Find the circumference of the rear wheel in centimeters. How far will the bicycle travel when the wheel makes one revolution? How many revolutions will it take to travel 1 kilometer without coasting?

Step 14 For the lowest and highest gear, how many times do you need to rotate the pedals for the bike to travel 1 kilometer? (*Hint:* Write a proportion or other equation involving the gear ratio and the number of revolutions of the pedals and the wheel.) A bicycle whose lowest front-to-back gear ratio is 30 : 28 has to be pedaled 425 times per kilometer. A bike with a high front-to-back gear ratio of 50 : 14 has to be pedaled 128 times per kilometer.

The wheels on Lance Armstrong's bicycle made roughly 1.6 million revolutions during the 2005 Tour de France. If he hadn't coasted or changed gears, he could have pedaled more than 1.5 million times.

In July 2005, Lance Armstrong became the first person to win the Tour de France seven times. He averaged 41.7 kilometers per hour and completed the race in 86 hours 15 minutes 2 seconds. Nine years before, he had been given a less than 50% chance of surviving cancer that had spread to his lungs and brain.

BUILDING UNDERSTANDING

Activity Days do not include homework exercises. You might want to assign exercises that you skipped from other lessons or a More Practice Your Skills worksheet. Other options are to give students time to work on a portfolio problem or a project or to have students revise a homework assignment that they had trouble with.

Evaluating Expressions

Melinda asked Tywan, "What's four plus six times three?" Do you think she meant $(4 + 6) \cdot 3$ or $4 + (6 \cdot 3)$? Is there a difference between these two expressions? What about $4 + 6 \cdot 3$? Is this the same as either one of the previous expressions? In order to avoid confusion there is a set of rules, called the **order of operations,** that is followed so that a written mathematical expression is read and evaluated the same by everyone.

Order of Operations

1. Evaluate expressions within parentheses or other grouping symbols.
2. Evaluate all powers.
3. Multiply and divide from left to right.
4. Add and subtract from left to right.

Using these rules, the expression $4 + 6 \cdot 3 = 4 + 18 = 22$ because multiplication and division (Rule 3) happen before addition and subtraction (Rule 4). If Melinda meant $(4 + 6) \cdot 3$, she could say "First add four and six, then multiply by three." In this lesson you will use the order of operations to write and evaluate expressions.

EXAMPLE A

Answer parts a–c using this statement:

Multiply 6 times a starting number, then add 15, divide this result by 3, and then subtract your answer from 80.

a. What is the result when you start with 5? With 14? With −3?

b. Write a mathematical expression that fits the statement, using x to represent the starting number.

c. Use your calculator to test your expression on the starting numbers in part a.

▶ **Solution**

Apply the operations in the order they are given in the statement.

a. Starting with 5   Starting with 14   Starting with −3

6*5		30
Ans+15		45
Ans/3		15
80−Ans		65

6*14		84
Ans+15		99
Ans/3		33
80−Ans		47

6*−3		−18
Ans+15		−3
Ans/3		−1
80−Ans		81

▶ **EXAMPLE A**

This example provides experience with writing algebraic expressions that include the variable x and with using the calculator to evaluate those expressions for different values of x. As needed, point out that multiplying a number times a variable, for example, multiplying 6 by x, is often represented by writing the number directly to the left of the variable, as in $6x$.

PLANNING

LESSON OUTLINE

One day:

5 min	Introduction
15 min	Example A, Investigation
10 min	Sharing
10 min	Examples B, C
5 min	Closing
5 min	Exercises

MATERIALS

• Order of Operations (T), *optional*

• Cross-number Puzzle (W), *optional*

• Calculator Notes 0A, 2C

TEACHING

This lesson develops the idea of undoing by having students figure out why some algebraic expressions have the same value at all numbers.

INTRODUCTION

[Language] If you use the term *convention,* be sure students know that here it means an agreed-upon rule or "tradition," not a large meeting.

If you skipped order of operations in Chapter 0, you may need to spend more time on it here.

[Link] If students aren't seeing the need for the conventional order of operations, mention another common convention that helps avoid confusion: reading and writing from left to right.

One Step

Ask each student to think of a number from 1 to 25. Have students take their number plus 9 times 3 minus 6 divided by 3 and then subtract the original number. You may need to review the order of operations and go through the process several times until all students get the answer 7. Or the class may decide to insert parentheses to change the result. After agreeing on an interpretation that gives a constant result, **[Ask]** "Will you always get the same result, even if the starting number is not between 1 and 25?" Suggest that students experiment with lists of numbers, including negatives and decimals, on their graphing calculators and represent the number trick with an algebraic expression. As you circulate, ask why the trick works, laying the groundwork for the idea of undoing. You might challenge groups that finish first to make up their own number trick.

b. You can organize your work in a table.

Description	Expression
Starting value.	x
Multiply by 6.	$6x$
Add 15.	$6x + 15$
Divide this result by 3.	$\dfrac{6x + 15}{3}$
Subtract your answer from 80.	$80 - \dfrac{6x + 15}{3}$

The fraction bar is a grouping symbol meaning that the entire numerator is divided by 3.

c. You can evaluate expressions on your calculator as shown here.

On the calculator you need the parentheses to indicate the grouping of the numerator.

In the example the letter x was used to represent the starting number. Because this number can *vary*, it is called a **variable.** In general the value of an expression depends on the number used in place of the variable. However, you can get surprising results, as you will see in the investigation.

Investigation
Number Tricks

Try this trick: Each member of your group should think of a different number from 1 to 25. Add 9 to it. Multiply the result by 3. Subtract 6 from the current answer. Divide this answer by 3. Now subtract your original number. Compare your results.

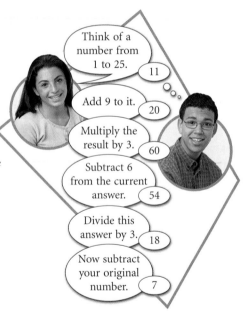

Think of a number from 1 to 25. 11

Add 9 to it. 20

Multiply the result by 3. 60

Subtract 6 from the current answer. 54

Divide this answer by 3. 18

Now subtract your original number. 7

LESSON OBJECTIVES

- Review or learn the rules governing order of operations
- Use calculator list operations to investigate the concepts *variables, terms,* and *expressions*
- Rewrite algebraic expressions that include multiplication and division, or addition and subtraction, by the same number

NCTM STANDARDS

CONTENT		PROCESS	
✔	Number	✔	Problem Solving
✔	Algebra	✔	Reasoning
	Geometry		Communication
	Measurement	✔	Connections
	Data/Probability	✔	Representation

Do you think the result will be the same regardless of the number you start with? Do you think it would still work even if you chose a decimal number, a fraction, or a negative number? One way to answer these questions is to use a list of numbers instead of just a single starting value.

Step 1 Encourage students to include decimals and negative numbers in their lists.

Step 1 Enter a list of at least four different numbers into the calculator home screen and store this list in list L1. In the example at right, the list is {20, 1.2, −5, 4}, but you should try different numbers. Perform the operations on your own starting numbers. The last operation is to subtract your original number.

```
{20, 1.2, -5, 4} → L1
                    {20 1.2 -5 4}
Ans + 9
                    {29 10.2 4 13}
Ans * 3
                    {87 30.6 12 39}
Ans - 6
                    {81 24.6 6 33}
Ans / 3
                    {27 8.2 2 11}
Ans - L1
                    {7 7 7 7}
```

Step 2 Explain how the last operation is different from the others. You are subtracting your original number instead of a constant value.

Step 3 Number tricks like this work because certain operations, such as multiplication and division, get "undone" in the course of the trick. Which step undoes Ans · 3? Ans/3

Step 4 One way to analyze what is happening in a number trick is to translate the steps of the trick into an algebraic expression. Return to the description at the beginning of this investigation and write an algebraic expression using x to represent your starting number. $\dfrac{3(x+9)-6}{3}-x$

Description	Expression
Starting value.	x
Add 9.	$x + 9$
$\vdots$	$\vdots$

Step 5 You can use the method below to help you figure out why any number trick works. The symbol +1 represents one positive unit. You can think of n as a variable or as a container for different unknown starting numbers. Complete the Description column by writing the steps in this new number trick.

Step 5 Be sure students understand that the table illustrates a new number trick, not the one they've been working with.

Stage	Picture	Description	Expression
1	n	Pick a number.	n
2	n +1 +1 +1	Add 3.	$n + 3$
3	n n +1 +1 +1 +1 +1 +1	Multiply by 2.	$2(n + 3)$
4	n n +1 +1	Subtract 4.	$2(n + 3) - 4$
5	n +1	Divide by 2.	$\dfrac{2(n + 3) - 4}{2}$
6	+1	Subtract the original number.	$\dfrac{2(n + 3) - 4}{2} - n$
7	+1 +1 +1	Add 2 or multiply by 3.	$\dfrac{2(n + 3) - 4}{2} - n + 2$ or $3 \cdot \left[\dfrac{2(n + 3) - 4}{2} - n \right]$

Step 7 The answer is always equal to 3. The steps given undo each other. The original number, *n*, is subtracted at Stage 6, leaving 1 at Stage 6, and 3 at Stage 7.

Step 8 Sample number trick: Pick a number. Double it. Add 6. Divide by 2. Subtract 7. Subtract your starting number. Groups may have difficulty coming up with a trick that gives predictable results each time. Focus them on the idea of undoing.

SHARING IDEAS

Have students share ideas about Steps 4 and 6 and perhaps 7. You might also have them challenge each other with their own number tricks, writing an algebraic expression for each trick. You can preview work in Lesson 2.8 by having them write algebraic expressions for which the answer depends on the starting number and then explain how to find the starting number from the result.

▶ EXAMPLE B

This example gives a number trick with nested parentheses. Point out why the group within a group requires two sets of parentheses: You want the calculator, following the order of operations, to evaluate the innermost parentheses first.

[Alert] Students may not understand that on a calculator a variable is the name of a storage location that holds a number. It might help if you ask them to type in *x* (ENTER) before and after storing their own value in *x*.

Note that an equation is a statement that two expressions are equal. You might point out that an *expression* is like a noun phrase and an *equation* is like an entire sentence that says something about two noun phrases. If one of the expressions involves a variable, a *solution* to the equation is a number that replaces that variable to make a true statement. *Equation* and *solution* are defined in Lesson 2.8.

Step 6 | Complete the Expression column by writing an algebraic expression for each step in the trick.

Step 7 | Evaluate the final expression in Step 6 using a list of starting numbers. What is the result? Explain why this happens.

Step 8 | Invent your own number trick that has at least five stages. Test it on your calculator with a list of at least four different numbers to make sure all the answers are the same. When you're convinced the number trick is working, try it on the other members of your group. Answers will vary.

Experimenting with number tricks and writing them in different forms can help you understand the role that variables and expressions play in algebra. A single expression can represent an entire number trick.

EXAMPLE B | Consider the expression

$$4\left(\frac{x+7}{4}+5\right) - x + 13$$

a. Write in words the number trick that the expression describes.

b. Test the number trick to be sure you get the same result no matter what number you choose.

c. Which operations that undo previous operations make this number trick work?

▶ Solution | **a.** Pick a number, *x*.
Add 7.
Divide the answer by 4.
Add 5 to this result.
Multiply the answer by 4.
Subtract your original number.
Then add 13.

b. One way to test the trick is to enter a list of numbers as list L1 and then enter the expression into your calculator using list L1 in place of the variable. Be sure to use parentheses to account for grouping symbols like the division bar: $4((L1 + 7)/4 + 5) - L1 + 13$.

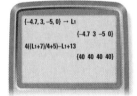

c. The multiplication by 4 undoes the division by 4. Because the original number, *x*, is subtracted away, it doesn't matter what number you start with.

An **algebraic expression** is an expression that can involve both numbers and variables. The number tricks you have seen in this lesson can be expressed as algebraic expressions, and their values are determined by correctly applying the order of operations. Understanding this order is essential for success in your continuing study of algebra.

EXAMPLE C | Al and Cal both evaluated the expression $7 - 4 + 2$. Al said, "The answer is one because you can add in any order so I did four plus two first." Cal said, "The answer is five because you have to go left to right." Who is right and why?

▶ **Solution** | Both Al and Cal have good ideas.

Al is correct that it doesn't matter what order you add numbers. However, he needs to remember that $7 - 4 + 2$ is the same as $7 + -4 + 2$, so if he wants to change the order he must add $-4 + 2$. Then he would get $7 + -2$, or 5, the same answer as Cal.

Cal is also correct in working from left to right. However, he may find it easier to evaluate some expressions if he thinks of subtraction as adding the opposite and then adds the numbers in the simplest combination, not necessarily always from left to right.

Thinking of subtraction as addition of negatives makes many calculations easier. Consider the number trick $\frac{5 - 3(x + 2)}{3} + x$. To describe the steps in a chart, it will be much easier to think of this as $\frac{5 + -3(x + 2)}{3} + x$ and then write

Pick a number.
Add 2.
Multiply by -3.
Add 5.
Divide by 3.
Add the original number.

Try to get in the practice of recognizing subtraction as just a form of addition. It is also often convenient to change division into multiplication by a fraction. (For example, dividing by 3 is the same as multiplying by $\frac{1}{3}$.) While these procedures do not change the problem or the answer, they do sometimes prevent you from making errors when evaluating more complex expressions.

EXERCISES

You will need your graphing calculator for Exercises **1** and **5**.

▶ **Practice Your Skills**

1. Use your calculator to evaluate each expression on the next page and enter the answer in the puzzle. Enter the entire expression into your calculator so that you get the correct answer without having to calculate part of the expression first. [▶🖵 See **Calculator Note 2C** to learn how to use the instant replay command.◀] For answers that can be expressed as either decimal numbers or fractions, you should use the answer form indicated in the puzzle. Each negative sign, fraction bar, or decimal point occupies one square in the puzzle. Commas, however, are not entered as part of the answer. For instance, an answer of 2,508.5 would require six squares. [▶🖵 See **Calculator Note 0A** for help converting answers from decimal numbers to fractions and vice versa.◀]

▶ **Helping with the Exercises**

Exercise 1 [ELL] Not all languages lend themselves to crossword puzzles. Be sure all students know how to use the puzzle clues. Numbered boxes start a number answer. When rows and columns intersect, the digit or symbol in that box works for the answers both across and down.

Encourage students to work in pairs. If students have weak arithmetic skills or are unfamiliar with crossword puzzles, you may want to make a

transparency of the Cross-number Puzzle worksheet from the Teaching and Worksheet Masters and model how to solve it. Point out the use of parentheses to denote multiplication of numbers. The multiplication symbol from arithmetic can be confusing in algebra because it looks like the variable x.

Another grouping symbol is a superscript exponent. By the order of operations, the expression 2^{3+5} means to calculate $3 + 5$, then raise 2 to the power of 8. On a calculator, parentheses must be used to show this grouping: $2\wedge(3 + 5)$.

▶ **EXAMPLE C**

This example is useful for challenging students who have learned the acronym PEMDAS for the order of operations and believe that addition comes before subtraction. **[Alert]** Students might not understand Al's reasoning about adding in either order because they don't see subtracting 4 as addition.

Closing the Lesson

Remind students of the main points of this lesson. An **algebraic expression** consisting of numbers and/or a variable can be evaluated by substituting a number for the variable and following the **order of operations** to arrive at a single number. A number trick in which all starting numbers end up with the same result can be represented by an algebraic expression in which multiplications are undone by appropriate divisions and additions are undone by appropriate subtractions.

BUILDING UNDERSTANDING

Students practice arithmetic operations and the distributive property.

ASSIGNING HOMEWORK

Essential	1, 4–6
Performance assessment	4, 6
Portfolio	10
Journal	8
Group	4, 6
Review	11–13

2. Seija; Peter incorrectly added before multiplying $\left(45 \text{ times } \frac{6}{2} \text{ is } 135\right)$.

3a. First multiply 16 by 4.5, then add 9.

3b. First divide 18 by 3, then add 15.

3c. First square 6, then add -5, then multiply by 4 and subtract the result, 124, from 3.

Exercises 4 and 6 Many students have a lot of fun with these essential exercises. Some, however, may find that keeping track of several columns is a challenge. Encourage them to work with other students.

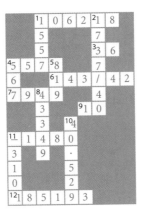

Across	Down
1. $\frac{2}{3}$ of 159,327	**1.** $9(-7 + 180)$
3. $\frac{-1 + 17^2}{4 + 2^2}$	**2.** $\left(\frac{9}{2}\right)\left(\frac{17}{5} + \frac{25}{4}\right)$ (fraction form)
4. $4835 - 541 + 1284$	**4.** $3 - 3(12 - 200)$
6. $\frac{3 + 140}{3 \cdot 14}$ (fraction form) @	**5.** $9 \cdot 10^2 - 9^2$
7. $8075 - 3(42)$	**8.** $15 + 47(922)$
9. $\sqrt{6^2 + 8^2}$	**10.** $25.9058 \cdot 20/4 - 89$ (decimal form) @
11. $\frac{740}{18.4 - 2.1 \cdot 9}$	**11.** $1284 - \frac{877}{0.2}$
12. 57^3	

Reason and Apply

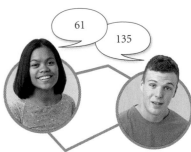

2. Peter and Seija evaluated the expression $37 + 8 \cdot \frac{6}{2}$. Peter said the answer was 135. Seija said it was 61. Who is correct? What error did the other person make?

3. In what order would you perform the operations to evaluate these expressions and get the correct answers?

a. $9 + 16 \cdot 4.5 = 81$ @

b. $18 \div 3 + 15 = 21$

c. $3 - 4(-5 + 6^2) = -121$

4. Daxun, Lacy, Claudia, and Al are working on a number trick. Here are the number sequences their number trick generates:

Description	Daxun's sequence	Lacy's sequence	Claudia's sequence	Al's sequence
Pick the starting number.	14	-5	-8.6	x
Add 5.	19	0	-3.6	$x + 5$
Multiply by 4.	76	0	-14.4	$4(x + 5)$
Subtract 12.	64	-12	-26.4	$4(x + 5) - 12$
Divide by 4.	16	-3	-6.6	$\frac{4(x + 5) - 12}{4}$
Subtract the original number.	2	2	2	$\frac{4(x + 5) - 12}{4} - x$

a. Describe the stages of this number trick in the first column.

b. Complete Claudia's sequence.

c. Write a sequence of expressions for Al in the last column.

5. In the scheme below, the symbol `+1` represents $+1$ and the symbol `-1` represents -1. The symbol `n` represents the original number.

Stage	Picture	Description
1	`n`	Pick a number.
2	`n` `-1` `-1` `-1`	Subtract 3.
3	`n` `n` `-1` `-1` `-1` `-1` `-1` `-1`	Multiply your result by 2.
4	`n` `n` `-1` `-1`	Add 4.
5	`n` `-1`	Divide by 2.
6	`-1`	Subtract the original number.
7	`+1` `+1` `+1`	Add 4 or multiply by -3.

a. Explain what is happening as you move from one stage to the next. The explanation for Stage 6 is provided. @

b. At which stage will everyone's result be the same? Explain. @ At Stages 6 and 7; the original number has been subtracted.

c. Verify that this trick works by using a calculator list and an answer routine.

d. Write an expression similar to the one shown in the solution to part b of Example A to represent this trick. @ $\dfrac{2(n-3)+4}{2} - n + 4$ or $-3\left[\dfrac{2(n-3)+4}{2} - n\right]$

6. Jo asked Jack and Nina to try two other number tricks that she had invented for homework. Their number sequences are shown in the tables. Use words to describe each stage of the number tricks.

a. Number Trick 1: @

Description	Jack's sequence	Nina's sequence
Pick the starting number.	5	3
Multiply by 2.	10	6
Multiply by 3.	30	18
Add 6.	36	24
Divide by 3.	12	8
Subtract your original number.	7	5
Subtract your original number again.	2	2

b. Number Trick 2:

Description	Jack's sequence	Nina's sequence
Pick the starting number.	-10	10
Add 2.	-8	12
Multiply by 3.	-24	36
Add 9.	-15	45
Subtract 15.	-30	30
Multiply by 2.	-60	60
Divide by 6 (you should have your original number).	-10	10

7. Insert operation signs, parentheses, or both into each string of numbers to create an expression equal to the answer given. Keep the numbers in the same order as they are written. Write an explanation of your answer, including information on the order in which you performed the operations.

   a. 3 2 5 7 = 18
   b. 8 5 6 7 = 13

8. Marcella wrote an expression for a number trick.

Marcella's Trick
$\dfrac{4(x - 5) + 8}{2} - x + 6$

   a. Describe Marcella's number trick in words.   Pick a number. Subtract 5. Multiply by 4. Add 8. Divide by 2. Subtract the original number. Add 6.

   b. Pick a number and use it to do the trick. What answer do you get? Pick another number and do the trick again. What is the "trick"?   Solutions will vary. The trick always produces the original number.

9. This problem is sometimes called Einstein's problem: "Use the digits 1, 2, 3, 4, 5, 6, 7, 8, 9 and any combination of the operation signs $(+, -, \cdot, /)$ to write an expression that equals 100. Keep the numbers in consecutive order and do not use parentheses."

Here is one solution:

   $123 - 4 - 5 - 6 - 7 + 8 - 9 = 100$

Your task is to find another one.

10. Write your own number trick with at least six stages.

   a. No matter what number you begin with, make the trick result in -4.

   b. Describe the process you used to create the trick.

   c. Write an expression for your trick. $\dfrac{2(x - 3) + 10}{2} - x - 6$

▶ **Review**

11. **APPLICATION** Portia drove her new car 308 miles on 10.8 gallons of gasoline.

   a. What is the car's rate of gasoline consumption in miles per gallon? about 28.5 mpg

   b. If this is the typical mileage for Portia's car, how much gas will it take for a 750-mile vacation trip? about 26.3 gal

   c. If gas costs $2.35 per gallon, how much will Portia spend on gas on her vacation? $61.81

   d. The manufacturer advertised that the car would get 30 to 35 miles per gallon. How does Portia's mileage compare to the advertised estimates?

   Portia's gas mileage is more than 19% or 6.5 mpg lower than the higher estimate. It is about 5% or 1.5 mpg lower than the lower estimate.

2.5 **12.** You are helping to design boxes for game balls that are 1 inch in diameter. Your supervisor wants the balls in one rectangular layer of rows and columns.

a. Use a table to show all the ways to package 24 balls in rows and columns.

b. Plot these points on a graph.

c. Do the possible box dimensions represent direct or inverse variation? Explain how you know.

d. Represent the situation with an equation. Does the equation have any limitations?

Learn about packaging science with the links at **www.keymath.com/DA** .

2.4 **13.** The table displays data for a bicyclist's distance from home during a four-hour bike ride.

a. Make a scatter plot of the data.

b. Find the bicyclist's average speed. 15 mi/h

c. Find an equation that models the data and graph it on the scatter plot. $y = 15x$

d. At what times might the bicyclist be riding downhill or pedaling uphill? Explain.

Time (h)	Distance (mi)
0	0
0.25	4
0.50	8
1.00	15
1.50	25
2.00	36
2.25	40
2.75	41
3.00	44
3.50	48
4.00	60

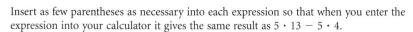

IMPROVING YOUR REASONING SKILLS

Insert as few parentheses as necessary into each expression so that when you enter the expression into your calculator it gives the same result as $5 \cdot 13 - 5 \cdot 4$.

a. $5 \cdot 13 - 4$ b. $5 \cdot 3\wedge2$ c. $5 \cdot 13 + 5 \cdot -4$ d. $100 + 35 / 1 + 2$

e. $6 + 3 \cdot 5$ f. $5 + 5 \cdot 8$ g. $5 \cdot 1 + 8$ h. $5 \cdot 3\wedge1 + 1$

i. $65 - 5 \cdot 3 + 1$ j. $87 - 6 \cdot 10 - 3$ k. $-3\wedge2 + 54$

IMPROVING REASONING SKILLS

Encourage students to check for unnecessary parentheses in their expressions. For example, $5 \cdot (3\wedge2)$ can be written as $5 \cdot 3\wedge2$.

a. $5 \cdot (13 - 4)$ b. $5 \cdot 3\wedge2$ c. $5 \cdot 13 + 5 \cdot -4$ d. $(100 + 35) / (1 + 2)$

e. $(6 + 3) \cdot 5$ f. $5 + 5 \cdot 8$ g. $5 \cdot (1 + 8)$ h. $5 \cdot 3\wedge(1 + 1)$

i. $65 - 5 \cdot (3 + 1)$ j. $87 - 6 \cdot (10 - 3)$ k. $-3\wedge2 + 54$

12a.

Length (in.)	Width (in.)
1	24
2	12
3	8
4	6
6	4
8	3
12	2
24	1

12b. Possible Boxes

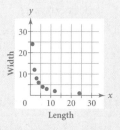

12c. Inverse variation; the product of the length and width is a constant.

12d. $l \cdot w = 24$ or $w = \frac{24}{l}$; yes, the situation requires the dimensions to be whole numbers of inches, so you can't have a box that is 16 in. by 1.5 in., even though it satisfies the equation.

13a. Distance Traveled

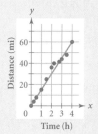

13d. downhill during the intervals of 1 to 2.25 h and 3.5 to 4 h (the bike's velocity is above average), and uphill during the interval of 2.25 to 3.5 h (the bike's speed is slower than average)

Undoing Operations

*All change is not growth; all
movement is not forward.*

ELLEN GLASGOW

After studying a lesson on number tricks, Virna came up with a new variation. She asked Killeen to pick a number and then do the following operations, in order: add 3, multiply by 7, subtract 4, divide by 2, and add 1. Killeen told her the final result was 13. Virna thought for a moment and then said, "Was your starting number 1?" It was, and Killeen was amazed! How did Virna figure that out? They tried the "trick" several more times, and each time Virna figured out Killeen's starting number.

In the investigation you will discover how Virna was using her understanding of the order of operations to solve an equation, and you'll see why it works.

Investigation
Just Undo It!

Step 1 Choose a secret number. Now choose four more nonzero numbers and in any random order add one of them, multiply by another, subtract another, and divide by the final number. Record in words what you did and your final result on a blank sheet of paper. (For example, "I took my secret number, divided by 4, added 7, multiplied by 2, and subtracted 8. The result was 28.") Do not record your secret number. Trade papers with another student.

Step 2 Use the description on the paper given to you to complete a table like this one:

Description	Sequence	Expression		
Picked a number.	?	x		
Divided by 4.	Ans / 4	$\dfrac{x}{4}$		
Added 7.	Ans + 7	$\dfrac{x}{4} + 7$		
Multiplied by 2.	Ans · 2	$2\left(\dfrac{x}{4} + 7\right)$		
Subtracted 8.	Ans − 8	$2\left(\dfrac{x}{4} + 7\right) - 8$		

Step 3 Now add another column listing the operations needed to undo each step.

Description	Sequence	Expression	Undo	
Picked a number.	?	x	/////	
Divided by 4.	Ans / 4	$\dfrac{x}{4}$	· (4)	
Added 7.	Ans + 7	$\dfrac{x}{4} + 7$	− (7)	
Multiplied by 2.	Ans · 2	$2\left(\dfrac{x}{4} + 7\right)$	/ (2)	
Subtracted 8.	Ans − 8	$2\left(\dfrac{x}{4} + 7\right) - 8$	+ (8)	

PLANNING

LESSON OUTLINE

One day:

5 min	Introduction
20 min	Investigation
5 min	Sharing
10 min	Examples
5 min	Closing
5 min	Exercises

MATERIALS

• Undoing Operations (W, T), *optional*

TEACHING

In this lesson students continue to look for patterns in sequences and work with the order of operations. They also write expressions for number tricks and evaluate these expressions. The undoing and working backward strategy is introduced as a way to find the starting number in a number trick.

INTRODUCTION

Do the number trick with the whole class and ask several students for their answers.

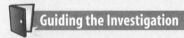

Guiding the Investigation

One Step

Tell students that an algebraic expression can represent a sequence of steps applied to a number even if the result isn't the same for every number. You might give as an example the algebraic expression for Virna's steps in the introduction to the lesson: $\dfrac{7(x + 3) - 4}{2} + 1$, resulting in 13. Ask groups to find the original number when another group challenges them with an expression and the

LESSON OBJECTIVES

• Build toward symbolic equation solving by working backward and undoing operations

• Translate situations into equations and solve by undoing

NCTM STANDARDS

CONTENT		PROCESS	
✓	Number	✓	Problem Solving
✓	Algebra	✓	Reasoning
	Geometry		Communication
	Measurement	✓	Connections
	Data/Probability	✓	Representation

| | | | Step 4 | Add a fifth column and put the final result in the bottom right cell. Then work up the table from the bottom, undoing each operation as shown, to discover the original number. Was this the secret number? (In this example the final result was 28 and the original secret number was 44.) |

Description	Sequence	Expression	Undo	Result
Picked a number.	?	x	////////	44
Divided by 4.	Ans / 4	$\dfrac{x}{4}$	$\cdot\,(4)$	11
Added 7.	Ans + 7	$\dfrac{x}{4} + 7$	$-\,(7)$	18
Multiplied by 2.	Ans $\cdot$ 2	$2\left(\dfrac{x}{4}+7\right)$	$/\,(2)$	36
Subtracted 8.	Ans $-$ 8	$2\left(\dfrac{x}{4}+7\right) - 8$	$+\,(8)$	28

Many equations can be solved using a table by undoing each operation, following these steps.

1. Complete the description column using the order of operations.

2. Complete the undo column.

3. Finally, work up from the bottom of the table to solve the equation.

You can check your solution to an equation by substituting the solution into the original equation and evaluating to check that you get a true statement.

Study this example. Next you will create your own table to solve an equation.

Equation: $\dfrac{3 + 2(x-4)}{5} + 6 = 11$		
Description	Undo	Result
Pick x.	////////	15
$-\,(4)$	$+\,(4)$	11
$\cdot\,(2)$	$/\,(2)$	22
$+\,(3)$	$-\,(3)$	25
$/\,(5)$	$\cdot\,(5)$	5
$+\,(6)$	$-\,(6)$	11

| | | Step 5 | Solve this equation using a table: $7 + \dfrac{x-3}{4} = 42$. Check your solution. |

| | | Step 6 | Write a few sentences explaining why this method works to solve an equation. |

resulting number. As you circulate, you can suggest that students use tables to organize their undoing process. You can also have students begin representing these challenges as *equations,* a term that you introduce during Sharing.

Steps 1–4 You might have groups rather than individuals make up the descriptions and try to solve the problems.

Step 3 Have students fill in the Undo column from the bottom to prepare them for Step 4.

Step 6 Explanations will vary. Students may say that every operation that is "done" to x is "undone" to solve for x.

SHARING IDEAS

Have at least one student share a table from Step 4 and another a table from Step 5. The class might have a discussion of why the method works.

Assessing Progress
Look for familiarity with arithmetic operations, with handling calculator lists, and with algebraic expressions. Students should be improving in their use of undoing.

Step 5

Equation: $7 + \dfrac{x-3}{4} = 42$		
Description	Undo	Result
Pick x.	////////	143
$-\,(3)$	$+\,(3)$	140
$/\,(4)$	$\cdot\,(4)$	35
$+\,(7)$	$-\,(7)$	42

$x = 143.$ Check: $7 + \dfrac{143 - 3}{4} = 7 + \dfrac{140}{4} = 7 + 35 = 42$

An **equation** is a statement that says the value of one expression is equal to the value of another expression. **Solving equations** is the process you use to determine the value of the unknown that "works" or makes the equation true. This value is called the **solution.** Once you can identify all of the steps that were done to the unknown number to come up with the result, you can simply **undo** them to find the solution. Remember, you have to undo the steps in reverse order of the way they were originally done. That means you need to pay close attention to the order of operations in the original equation.

▶ **EXAMPLE A**

In this example students see how to use an equation to represent the idea that a sequence of steps leads to a particular result. Be sure that in part c they don't begin by stating that a complicated expression equals 15 (which is what they are trying to verify) and conclude by stating that 15 equals 15 (which they know). Placing question marks over the equal signs is essential for the reasoning to be valid.

You might encourage students to adopt the undo strategy by presenting it in a real-world context: You buy a gift, put it in a box, wrap the box, put a bow on the box, and give it to your friend, who takes the bow off, unwraps the box, takes the gift out of the box, and returns it to the store.

EXAMPLE A

To some number, add 3, multiply by -2, add 18, and finally divide by 6.

a. Find the starting number if the final result is 15.

b. Convert the description into an expression, and write an equation that states that this expression is equal to 15.

c. Test your solution to part a using your equation from part b.

▶ **Solution**

a. You can find the starting number by working backward, undoing each operation described. Perform the undo operations in reverse order, starting with the number 15.

Operations on x	Undo operations	Results
		$x = -39$
$+ (3)$	$- (3)$	-36
$\cdot (-2)$	$/ (-2)$	72
$+ (18)$	$- (18)$	90
$/ (6)$	$\cdot (6)$	15

b. One way to write this equation is $\dfrac{18 + -2(x + 3)}{6} = 15$.

c. Substitute -39 for x, and determine whether the equation is true.

$$\frac{18 + -2(-39 + 3)}{6} \stackrel{?}{=} 15$$

$$\frac{18 + -2(-36)}{6} \stackrel{?}{=} 15$$

$$\frac{18 + 72}{6} \stackrel{?}{=} 15$$

$$\frac{90}{6} \stackrel{?}{=} 15$$

$$15 = 15$$

This is a true statement, so the solution is correct.

Much of algebra involves translating a real-world situation into an equation and finding the solution to the equation. Once you understand the situation, you can write the equation that represents it algebraically. Then you can *undo* the operations to solve the equation. The organization table that you used in the investigation may be helpful.

EXAMPLE B

An online ticket agency adds a charge of $2 to the price of each ticket. Kent bought four tickets and paid with his debit card. His account had a balance of $190 before he used it and $62 after he used it. What is the original cost of each ticket?

```
KL03521B    25        21    E      ADULT
EVENTCODE  SECTION/AISLE  ROW/BOX  SEAT    ADMISSION
$        X  LOWER OBSTRUCTED + $2.00
     2.00
SECTION/AISLE  FREAKRANGE PRODUCTIONS PRESENTS
     25
MC 68X          ANIMAL COLLECTIVE
ROW  SEAT      with DAS MONITR BATTS
21   E           NEW ZOO REVUE
ZUS4867
11NOV05      SAT DEC 17, 2005 8:00PM
```

▶ **Solution**

An algebraic expression for the cost of the four tickets is $4(x + 2)$. This cost was removed from Kent's original balance of $190, leaving a final balance of $62, so you can write the equation $190 - 4(x + 2) = 62$.

Equation: $190 + -4(x + 2) = 62$		
Description	**Undo**	**Result**
Pick x.		30
$+ (2)$	$- (2)$	32
$\cdot (-4)$	$/ (-4)$	-128
$+ (190)$	$- (190)$	62

Each ticket originally cost $30.

EXERCISES

You will need your graphing calculator for Exercise **1.**

▶ **Practice Your Skills**

1. Evaluate each expression without a calculator. Then check your result with your calculator.

a. $-4 + (-8)$ -12

b. $(-4)(-8)$ 32

c. $-2(3 + 9)$ -24

d. $5 + (-6)(-5)$ @ 35

e. $(-3)(-5) + (-2)$ 13

f. $\frac{-15}{3} + 8$ 3

g. $\frac{23 - 3(4 - 9)}{-2}$ @ -19

h. $\frac{-4[7 + (-8)]}{8} - 6.5$ -6

i. $\frac{6(2 \cdot 4 - 5) - 2}{-4}$ -4

2. The equation $\frac{5(F - 32)}{9} = C$ can be used to change temperatures in Fahrenheit to the Celsius scale.

a. What is the first step when converting a temperature in °F to °C? @ Subtract 32.

b. What is the last step when converting a temperature in °F to °C? Divide by 9.

c. What is the first step in undoing a temperature in °C to find the temp in °F? Multiply by 9.

d. What is the last step in undoing a temperature in °C to find the temp in °F? Add 32.

▶ **EXAMPLE B**

In this example students see how to undo an algebraic expression to solve an equation. If students suggest using balancing to find a solution, you can encourage them to try it, but challenge them to verify their solution by undoing and assure the class as a whole that they'll learn balancing later. **[Alert]** Students may think that the table should follow a chronological order of events, beginning with the original balance in Kent's account. Help them see that it should begin with the unknown number—in this case, the price of each ticket—so that undoing gets back to that number.

Closing the Lesson

As you summarize the main points of this lesson, try to stress the difference between an **equation** and an expression. An equation is a sentence claiming that two expressions are equal. A **solution** is a number that can be substituted for the variable to make the equation a true statement. If you substitute numbers for the variables in an expression, you get a number rather than an equation.

BUILDING UNDERSTANDING

Students practice simplifying algebraic expressions and solving linear equations. They revisit number tricks.

ASSIGNING HOMEWORK

Essential	**2–5, 10, 12**
Performance assessment	**10, 13**
Portfolio	**5, 13**
Journal	**5**
Group	**13**
Review	**14–16**

► Helping with the Exercises

Exercise 5 To encourage critical thinking, **[Ask]** "Will the steps given really convert miles per hour to feet per second?" Encourage the use of dimensional analysis to see why

$$\frac{\frac{mi}{h} \cdot \frac{ft}{mi}}{\frac{min}{h} \cdot \frac{s}{min}} = \frac{ft}{s}.$$

7b. Start with 3 and see if you get the answer 3.

7d. The final result is always the original number no matter what number you choose.

8d. $\dfrac{2(x + 10) - 12}{5}$

9a. 25; add 7, multiply by 5, divide by 3.

9b.

Equation: $\dfrac{5(x + 7)}{3} = -18$

Operations on x	Undo operations	Results
		$x = -17.8$
+ (7)	− (7)	−10.8
· (5)	/ (5)	−54
/ (3)	· (3)	−18

3. Evaluate each expression if $x = 6$.
   a. $2x + 3$ 15
   b. $2(x + 3)$ 18
   c. $5x - 13$ 17
   d. $\dfrac{x + 9}{3}$ 5

4. For each equation identify the order of operations. Then work backward through the order of operations to find x.
   a. $\dfrac{x - 3}{2} = 6$ 15
   b. $3x + 7 = 22$ @ 5
   c. $\dfrac{x}{6} - 20 = -19$ 6

5. To change from miles per hour to feet per second, you can multiply by 5280, divide by 60, then divide by 60 again. Use the idea of undoing to explain how to convert from feet per second into miles per hour.
   Multiply by 60, multiply by 60 again, and then divide by 5280.

6. Justine asked her group members to do this calculation: Pick a number, multiply by 5, and subtract 2. Quentin got 33 for an answer. Explain how Justine could determine what number Quentin picked. What number did Quentin pick?
   Work backward by adding 2 to 33 and then dividing by 5; 7.

► Reason and Apply

7. The final answer to the sequence of calculations shown at right is 3. Starting with the final number, work backward, from the bottom to the top, undoing the operation at each step.
   a. What is the original number? @ 3
   b. How can you check that your answer to 7a is correct? @
   c. What is the original number if the final result is 15? 15
   d. What makes this sequence of operations a number trick? @

x	____
Ans · 8	____
Ans + 9	____
Ans / 4	____
Ans + 5.75	14
Ans / 2	7
Ans − 4	3

8. The sequence of operations at right will always give you a different final answer depending on the number you start with.
   a. What is the final value if you start with 18? 8.8
   b. What number did you start with if the final answer is 7.6? 15
   c. Describe how you got your answer to 8a. Undo the operations shown in reverse order.
   d. Let x represent the number you start with. Write an algebraic expression to represent this sequence of operations.
   e. Set the expression you got in 8d equal to zero. Then solve the equation for x. Check that your solution is correct by using the value you got for x as the starting number. Do you get zero again? $x = -4$; yes; sequence: $-4, 6, 12, 0, 0$

Ans + 10	____
Ans · 2	____
Ans − 12	____
Ans / 5	____

9. Consider the expression
   $$\frac{5(x + 7)}{3}$$
   a. Find the value of the expression if $x = 8$. List the order in which you performed the operations.
   b. Solve the equation $\dfrac{5(x + 7)}{3} = -18$ by undoing the sequence of operations in 9a. $x = -17.8$

10. Solve each equation with an undo table.
    a. $3(x - 5) + 8 = -14.8$ @ -2.6
    b. $3.5\left(\dfrac{x - 8}{4}\right) = 2.8$ 11.2
    c. $\dfrac{4(x - 5) - 8}{-3} = 12$ -2
    d. $\dfrac{4 - 3(7 + 2x)}{5} + 18.5 = -74.9$ @ 75

11. Consider the expression

$$\frac{2.5(x - 4.2)}{5} - 4.3$$

  a. Find the value of the expression if $x = 8$. Start with 8 and use the order of operations. -2.4

  b. Solve the equation $\frac{2.5(x - 4.2)}{5} - 4.3 = 5.4$ by undoing the operations in 11a. $x = 23.6$

12. The equation $D = 6 + 0.4(t - 5)$ represents the depth of water, in inches, in a swimming pool after t minutes of filling.

  a. How deep is the water after 60 minutes? ⓗ 28 in.

  b. How long does it take until the water is 36 inches deep? 80 min

  c. Undo the sequence of operations on t to solve the original equation for t in terms of D. $t = \dfrac{D - 6}{0.4} + 5$

13. Find the errors in this undo table and correct them.

Equation: $\dfrac{3(2 - 4x)}{4} - 7 = 14$		
Description	**Undo**	**Result**
Pick x.	/////	~~52~~ − 6.5
$\cdot (-4)$	$/(-4)$ · ~~·(4)~~	~~13~~ 26
~~·(2)~~ + (2)	$-(2)$ ~~+(2)~~	~~27~~ 28
~~+(3)~~ · (3)	$/(3)$ ~~·(3)~~	~~81~~ 84
$/(4)$	· (4)	21
$-(7)$	+ (7)	14

▶ **Review**

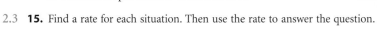

2.3 **14.** An electric slot car travels at a scale speed of 200 mi/h, meaning this would be its speed if it were full sized. If the car is $\frac{1}{87}$ of full size, find the car's actual speed in

  a. Feet per minute. about 202 ft/min

  b. Centimeters per second. about 103 cm/s

2.3 **15.** Find a rate for each situation. Then use the rate to answer the question.

  a. Kerstin drove 350 mi last week and used 12.5 gal of gas. How many gallons of gas will he use if he drives 520 mi this week? 18.7 gal (0.036 gal/mi)

  b. Angelo drove 225 mi last week and used 10.7 gal of gas. How far can he drive this week using 9 gal of gas? 189 mi (21 mi/gal)

Exercise 12 **[Alert]** Students may have difficulty understanding which variable has units of minutes and which has units of inches. Encourage them to read the problem aloud and discuss its meaning.

Exercise 13 As needed, encourage students to go through the process themselves on a different sheet of paper and then compare. **[Alert]** Students may agree with the undo table that multiplying by $+4$ undoes multiplying by -4.

Exercise 14 Encourage students to write units and use dimensional analysis.

Exercise 15 A reciprocal rate is needed for part a.

11b.

Equation: $\dfrac{2.5(x - 4.2)}{5} - 4.3 = 5.4$

Operations on x	Undo operations	Results
		$x = 23.6$
$-(4.2)$	$+(4.2)$	19.4
$\cdot(2.5)$	$/(2.5)$	48.5
$/(5)$	$\cdot(5)$	9.7
$-(4.3)$	$+(4.3)$	5.4

16. Natalie works in a shop that sells mixed nuts. Alice drops by and decides to buy a bag of mixed nuts with

$\frac{3}{4}$ cup of almonds

$\frac{2}{3}$ cup of cashews

$\frac{1}{2}$ cup of pecans

a. How many cups of mixed nuts will there be in the bag? @ $1\frac{11}{12}$ cups

b. Almonds cost \$6.98 a cup, cashews cost \$7.98 a cup, and pecans cost \$4.98 a cup. What is the cost of Alice's bag of nuts? @ \$13.05

IMPROVING YOUR REASONING SKILLS

Three children went camping with their parents, a dog, and a tin of cookies just for the children. They agreed to share the cookies equally.

The youngest child couldn't help thinking about the cookies, so alone she divided the cookies into three piles. There was one left over. She gave it to the dog, took her share, and left the rest of the cookies in the cookie tin.

A little later the middle child took the tin where he could be alone and divided the cookies into three piles. There was one left over. He gave it to the dog and took his share.

Not too long after that, the oldest child went alone to divide the cookies. When she made three piles, there was one left over, which the dog got. She took her share and put the rest back in the tin.

After dinner, the three children "officially" divided the contents of the cookie tin into three piles. There was one left over, which they gave to the dog.

What is the smallest number of cookies that the tin might have first contained?

IMPROVING REASONING SKILLS

This problem can be solved in several ways. Working backward is probably the method most students will use. As they work backward, students will realize that some numbers won't work. For example, for each child and the dog to get 1 cookie at the end, there must have been 7 cookies when the last child gives 1 to the dog and takes

one-third. But 7 is not two-thirds of any whole number, so each child must have gotten at least 2 in the end, and so on, up to 7, the smallest number that works.

Another approach is to create a function and put it into a graphing calculator. At the last split, the number of cookies each child

will receive can be given by the formula $y = \frac{1}{3}\left(\frac{2}{3}\left(\frac{2}{3}\left(\frac{2}{3}(x-1)-1\right)-1\right)-1\right)$. Looking at the table for this equation, you see that 79 is the first value of x that gives an integral value for y (when $x = 79$, $y = 7$).

CHAPTER 2 REVIEW

In this chapter you explored and analyzed relationships among **ratios, proportions,** and percents. You used a **variable** to represent an unknown number, defined a proportion using the variable, and then solved the proportion to determine the value of the variable. You learned that a ratio of two integers is a **rational number** and that decimal representations of rational numbers either **terminate** or have a **repeating** pattern.

You can also use ratios as **conversion factors** to change from one unit of measure to another. You used **dimensional analysis** to convert units such as miles per hour to meters per second. And you saw that a **rate** is a ratio with a denominator of 1.

You learned that quantities are **directly proportional** when an increase in one value leads to a proportional increase in another. These quantities form a **direct variation** when their *ratio* is constant. The constant ratio is called a **constant of variation.** When you graphed a direct relationship, you discovered a straight line that always passes through the origin.

For an **inverse variation,** the *product* of two quantities is constant. In this relationship, an increase in one variable causes a decrease in the other. The graph of the relationship is curved rather than straight, and the graph does not touch either axis.

You studied the **order of operations,** which is used to ensure that everyone evaluates expressions in the same way. You explored number tricks and learned how to use an **undoing** process to find the original number. You also practiced writing **equations** to represent real-world situations and learned how to use the undoing process to find **solutions** to these equations.

EXERCISES

You will need your graphing calculator for Exercises **8** and **10.**

@ Answers are provided for all exercises in this set.

1. Solve each proportion for the variable.

  a. $\dfrac{5}{12} = \dfrac{n}{21}$ **b.** $\dfrac{15}{47} = \dfrac{27}{w}$ **c.** $\dfrac{2.5}{3} = \dfrac{k}{6.2}$

2. Jeff can build 7 birdhouses in 5 hours. Write three different proportions that you could use to find out how long it would take him to build 30 birdhouses.

3. Plot the point (6, 3) on a graph.

  a. List four other points where the *y*-coordinate is 50% of the *x*-coordinate. Plot them on the same graph.

  b. Describe the pattern formed by the points.

1a. $n = 8.75$

1b. $w = 84.6$

1c. $k = 5\dfrac{1}{6}$, or $5.1\overline{6}$

2. possible answers:
$\dfrac{7\,\text{bh}}{5\,\text{h}} = \dfrac{30\,\text{bh}}{x\,\text{h}}, \dfrac{7\,\text{bh}}{30\,\text{bh}} = \dfrac{5\,\text{h}}{x\,\text{h}}, \dfrac{5\,\text{h}}{7\,\text{bh}} = \dfrac{x\,\text{h}}{30\,\text{bh}}$;
$\dfrac{30\,\text{bh}}{7\,\text{bh}} = \dfrac{x\,\text{h}}{5\,\text{h}}$

3a. Possible points include (2, 1), (3, 1.5), (4, 2), (5, 2.5), (6, 3), (7, 3.5), (8, 4).

3b. All points appear to lie on a line.

PLANNING

LESSON OUTLINE

One day:

 5 min Introduction

15 min Exercises and helping individuals

15 min Checking work and helping individuals

15 min Student self-assessment

REVIEWING

Pose this problem: "Your club has $900 to spend on a concert for its members to attend, so you're looking at ticket prices. If you spend *x* dollars per ticket, how many tickets can you buy?"

Encourage the use of dimensional analysis to set up the fraction $\dfrac{900}{x}$.

[Ask] "If 30 members want to go, how much can you spend per ticket?" You can review inverse variation and solving proportions.

[Ask] "If there's a $2 surcharge for each ticket, how much can the base price be?" This question can be solved simply, or you can set up and solve the equation
$\dfrac{900}{x + 2} = 30.$

Finally, **[Ask]** "In addition, if the members travel, on average, in groups of three and each group has to pay $4 for parking, how much can the base price of a ticket be?" Again encourage a variety of approaches, emphasizing dimensional analysis. One approach should be to set up and solve by undoing the equation
$\dfrac{900}{3(x + 2) + 4} = 10.$ (Start by inverting both sides of the proportion.)

4. In a fairy tale written by the Brothers Grimm, Rapunzel has hair that is about 20 ells in length (1 ell = 3.75 feet) by the time she is 12 years old. In the story, Rapunzel is held captive in a high tower with a locked door and only one window. From this window, she lets down her hair so that people can climb up.

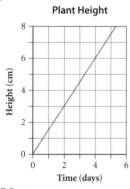

a. Approximately how long was Rapunzel's hair in feet when she was 12 years old? 75 ft

b. If Rapunzel's hair grew at a constant rate from birth, approximately how many feet did her hair grow per month? 0.52 ft/mo

5. **APPLICATION** A 13th-century Chinese manuscript (*Shu-shu chiu-chang*) contains this problem: You are sold 1,534 shih of rice but find that millet is mixed with the rice. In a sample of 254 grains, you find 28 grains of millet. About how many shih are actually rice? How many shih are millet? (Ulrich Libbrecht, *Chinese Mathematics in the Thirteenth Century*, 1973, p. 79) 1365 shih rice; 169 shih millet

6. On many packages the weight is given in both pounds and kilograms. The table shows the weights listed on a sample of items.

Kilograms	1.5	0.7	2.25	11.3	3.2	18.1	5.4
Pounds	3.3	1.5	5	25	7	40	12

a. Use the information in the table to find an equation that relates weights in pounds and kilograms. Explain what the variables represent in your equation.

b. Use your equation to calculate the number of kilograms in 30 pounds. about 13.6 kg

c. Calculate the number of pounds in 25 kilograms. 55 lb

> **6a.** If x represents the weight in kilograms and y represents weight in pounds, one equation is $y = 2.2x$ where 2.2 is the data set's mean ratio of pounds to kilograms.

7. Consider this graph of a sunflower's height above ground.

Plant Height

a. How tall was the sunflower after 5 days? about 7.5 cm

b. If the growth pattern continues, how many days will it take the plant to reach a height of 25 cm? approximately 17 days

c. Write an equation to represent the height of the plant after any number of days.
$H = 1.5 \cdot D$, where H represents height in centimeters and D represents time in days

8. Use the table of values to answer each question.

   a. Are the data in the table related by a direct variation or an inverse variation? Explain.

   b. Find an equation to fit the data. You may use your calculator graph to see how well the equation fits the data.

   c. Use your equation to predict the value of y when x is 32. $y = \frac{45.5}{32}, y \approx 1.4$

x	y
12	4
5	9
16	3
22	2
9	5
43	1

9. In the formula $d = vt$, d represents distance in miles, v represents rate in miles per hour (mi/h), and t represents time in hours. Use the word *directly* or *inversely* to complete each statement. Then write an equation for each.

   a. If you travel at a constant rate of 50 mi/h, the distance you travel is _____ proportional to the time you travel. directly; $d = 50t$

   b. The distance you travel in exactly 1 hour is _____ proportional to your rate. directly; $d = 1v$, or $d = v$

   c. The time it takes to travel 100 miles is _____ proportional to your rate.

10. **APPLICATION** Boyle's law describes the inverse variation between the volume of a gas and the pressure exerted on it. In the experiment shown, a balloon with a volume of 1.75 L is sealed in a bell jar with 1 atm of pressure. As air is pumped out of the jar, the pressure decreases, and the balloon expands to a larger volume.

   a. Find the volume under 0.8 atm of pressure. 2.1875 L

   b. Find the pressure when the volume is 0.75 L. $2.\overline{3}$ atm

   c. Write an equation that calculates the volume in liters from the pressure in atmospheres. $y = \frac{1.75}{x}$

   d. Graph this relationship on your calculator, then sketch it on your own paper. Show on your graph the solutions to 11a and b.

Pressure = 1 atm

Pressure = 0.8 atm

Air pumped out

11. The symbol +1 represents one positive unit and −1 represents one negative unit.

   You can think of x as a variable or as a container for different unknown starting values. Consider this sequence of expressions:

Stage	Picture
1	x
2	x x
3	x x −1
4	x x −1 x x −1 x x −1
5	x x −1 x x −1 x x

   a. Explain what is happening as you move from one stage to the next.

   b. Write an algebraic expression describing each stage. x; $2x$; $2x - 1$; $3(2x - 1)$; $3(2x - 1) + 1$

   c. If the starting value is 4.5, what is the result at each stage? 4.5, 9, 8, 24, 25

   d. If the result at the last stage is 22, then what is the starting value? The starting value is 4.

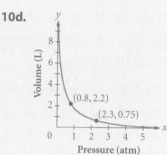

12. Start with 1. Add 4, to get 5. Multiply by -3, to get -15. Add 12, to get -3. Divide by 6, to get -0.5. Add 5, to get 4.5.

12. Describe a process to evaluate the expression $\frac{12 - 3(x + 4)}{6} + 5$ when $x = 1$.

13. Create an undo table and solve the equation given by undoing the order of operations.

Equation: $\frac{12 - 3(x + 4)}{6} + 5 = 4$		
Description	**Undo**	**Result**
Pick x.	///////	2
$+ (4)$	$- (4)$	6
$\cdot (-3)$	$/ (-3)$	-18
$+ (12)$	$- (12)$	-6
$/ (6)$	$\cdot (6)$	-1
$+ (5)$	$- (5)$	4

IMPROVING YOUR REASONING SKILLS

This problem is adapted from an ancient Chinese book, *The Nine Chapters of Mathematical Art.*

A city official was monitoring water use when he saw a woman washing dishes in the river. He asked, "Why are there so many dishes here?" She replied, "There was a dinner party in the house." His next question was "How many guests attended the party?" The woman did not know but replied, "Every two guests shared one dish for rice. Every three guests used one dish for broth. Every four guests used one dish for meat. And altogether there were sixty-five dishes used at the party." How many guests attended the party?

This is a detail from the 17th-century Chinese scroll painting *Landscapes of the Four Seasons* by Shen Shih-Ch'ing.

Reasoning Skills Answer

You could find the rate as about $1.083 \frac{\text{dishes}}{\text{guest}}$, which translates into $0.923 \frac{\text{guests}}{\text{dish}}$, and then multiply by 65 dishes. Or you can just use the ratio $\frac{13 \text{ dishes}}{12 \text{ guests}}$ and multiply the numerator and denominator by 5, to get $\frac{65 \text{ dishes}}{60 \text{ guests}}$. There were 60 guests.

IMPROVING REASONING SKILLS

Because you want the number of guests and you know the number of dishes, students might think that you can find the rate $\frac{\text{guests}}{\text{dish}}$ and multiply by the number of dishes. Encourage them to try, but point out that the given rates of $\frac{2 \text{ guests}}{1 \text{ rice dish}}$, $\frac{3 \text{ guests}}{1 \text{ broth dish}}$, and $\frac{4 \text{ guests}}{1 \text{ meat dish}}$ have different units

(kinds of dishes) in the denominators, so they can't be combined. The difference in units reflects the fact that the same guests will be sharing all three dishes. To get the same units in the denominator, use the reciprocals of the rates. The information translates into three ratios with the same units in the denominators:

$\frac{1 \text{ rice dish}}{2 \text{ guests}}$, $\frac{1 \text{ broth dish}}{3 \text{ guests}}$, and $\frac{1 \text{ meat dish}}{4 \text{ guests}}$

To find the total number of dishes, get a common denominator of 12 guests and add:

$\frac{6 + 4 + 3 \text{ dishes}}{12 \text{ guests}} = \frac{13 \text{ dishes}}{12 \text{ guests}}$

TAKE ANOTHER LOOK

The equation $y = kx$ is a *general equation* because it stands for a whole family of equations such as $y = 2x$, $y = \frac{1}{4}x$, even $y = \pi x$. (Does $C = \pi d$ look more familiar?)

What might k be in each line of these graphs? (If you're stumped, choose a point on the line, then divide its y-coordinate by its x-coordinate. Remember, $k = \frac{y}{x}$ is equivalent to $y = kx$.)

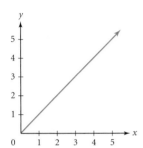 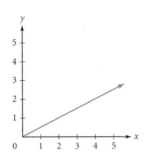 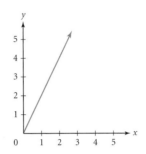

Most real-world quantities, like time and distance, are measured or counted in positive numbers. If two positive quantities vary directly, their graph $y = kx$ is in Quadrant I, where both x and y are positive. Because the quotient $\frac{y}{x}$ of two positive numbers x and y must be positive, the constant k is positive.

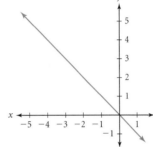

But the graph at right also shows a direct variation. What can you say about k for this graph?

What relationship do you see between the lines in each of the situations shown below? Between the k-values?

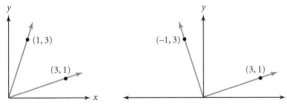

Finally, do you have a direct variation if $k = 0$? Why or why not?

▶ Take Another Look

Help students reflect on the idea that the equations $C = \pi d$, $D = rt$, and $P = 4s$ are direct variations. Even $A = lw$ is a direct variation if l is held constant.

This discussion moves students closer to the concept of slope and forms a good habit of putting the change in y over the change in x. In the first three graphs:

$$k = 1, k < 1\left(= \frac{1}{2}\right), \text{and } k > 1(= 2)$$

In the fourth graph, $k < 0(= -1)$ because the quotient $\frac{y}{x}$ is negative for every point on the graph.

In the last pair of graphs, the first set of lines is symmetric across $y = x$. Their k values $\left(3 \text{ and } \frac{1}{3}\right)$ are reciprocal. The second pair of lines is perpendicular. Their k values $\left(-3 \text{ and } \frac{1}{3}\right)$ are negative reciprocals. The geometric relationships can be confirmed with similar triangles.

Students may say that the equation $y = 0x$ is a direct variation because it fits the definition. Or they may say $y = 0$ is a constant function, not a direct variation, because there is no variation.

Use a test from Assessment Resources to assess how well students have learned the thought processes related to setting up and solving proportions, using equations and graphs to represent variation, correctly applying the order of operations to simplify expressions, and solving equations by undoing. Constructive Assessment items can be substituted for test questions or used as part of a group assessment.

Ideally, students have also become more accustomed to working collaboratively and have improved their facility with graphing calculators.

FACILITATING SELF-ASSESSMENT

This student self-assessment focuses on organizing notes. Students need to see a reason for doing this, such as keeping track of questions or finding portfolio items easily. If you allow students to use their notebooks during tests, you'll be giving them a powerful reason for knowing where to find things.

To help students complete the portfolio described in Assessing What You've Learned, suggest that they consider for evaluation their work on Lesson 2.1, Exercise 8; Lesson 2.2, Exercise 6; Lesson 2.3, Exercise 8; Lesson 2.4, Exercise 6 or 9; Lesson 2.5, Exercise 11 or 12; Lesson 2.7, Exercise 10; and Lesson 2.8, Exercise 5 or 13.

Assessing What You've Learned

ORGANIZE YOUR NOTEBOOK

You've been creating tables and answering questions as you do the investigations. You've been working the exercises and taking quizzes and tests. You've made notes on things that you want to remember from class discussions. Are those papers getting folded and stuffed into your book or mixed in with work from other classes? If so, it's not too late to get organized. Keeping a well-organized notebook is a habit that will improve your learning.

Your notebook should help you organize your work by lesson and chapter and give you room to summarize. Look through your work for a chapter and think about what you have learned. Write a short summary of the chapter. Include in the summary the new words you learned and things you learned about the graphing calculator. Write down questions you still have about the investigations, exercises, quizzes, or tests. Talk to classmates about your questions, or ask your teacher.

UPDATE YOUR PORTFOLIO Find the best work you have done in Chapter 2 to add to your portfolio. Choose at least one piece of work where you used proportions to solve a problem and at least one investigation or exercise that involves algebraic expressions or the undoing method. Choose one direct or inverse variation graph you made. You might decide to put the graph with the graphs you selected for your Chapter 1 portfolio.

WRITE IN YOUR JOURNAL Add to your journal by expanding on a question from one of the investigations or exercises. Or use one of these prompts:

▸ Does graphing relationships help you understand how the quantities vary? Do you understand variation between quantities better when you look at a graph or when you read an equation?

▸ Tables of values, graphs, equations, and word descriptions are four ways to tell about a variation. What other mathematical ideas can you show in more than one way?

▸ Describe the progress you are making toward the goals you have set for yourself in this class. What things did you do and learn in this chapter that are helping you achieve those goals? What changes might you need to make to help keep you on track?

3

Linear Equations

Overview

In Chapter 3, students use equations to model linear growth and graphs of straight lines and learn the balancing method for solving equations. This chapter builds toward the concept of *function*, which is formalized in Chapter 8.

Lesson 3.1 begins the development of linear growth with the study of recursive sequences. In **Lesson 3.2**, students encounter linear plots. These two ideas are combined through the notion of "walking instructions" to study motion in **Lesson 3.3**. The ideas of starting value and rate of change are formalized in **Lesson 3.4** with the intercept form of a line.

In **Lesson 3.5**, students study rates of change further, using input-output tables that foreshadow the study of functions. **Lesson 3.6** demonstrates the balancing technique for solving equations. In the Activity Day, **Lesson 3.7**, students model real-world data with their linear equations.

The Mathematics

Linearity

Having a *constant rate of change* is a primary characteristic of linearity. You start somewhere and advance by the same amount at each step. This kind of change is represented by a recursive sequence, easily generated on a calculator.

-15 (ENTER) Start with -15.

Ans $+10$ (ENTER) Add 10 to the answer.

(ENTER); (ENTER) Continue to add 10 to each answer.

A constant rate of change produces linear growth, though the values will be shrinking instead of growing if the rate of change is negative.

A second way to think about linearity is through equations that relate variables. Students begin to use, write, and make sense of the intercept form of the equation of a line, $y = a + bx$. Seeing and using multiple representations help students connect the recursive sequence start value with a and its constant rate of change with b. The calculator steps

for the recursive sequence above are equivalent to the equation $y = -15 + 10x$, when the initial x-value is 0.

The traditional *slope-intercept form*, $y = mx + b$, is mentioned in Lesson 4.2. In Lesson 4.3, students will see the *point-slope form*, $y = y_1 + b(x - x_1)$.

A third way to think about linearity is through *graphs*. Indeed, the term *linearity* comes from the fact that the associated graphs are (straight) lines. Students have seen linear graphs before—in data points, the graph of $y = x$ for comparing estimates with actual distances in Chapter 1, and direct variations $y = kx$ in Chapter 2.

The new forms of equations of a line indicate new ways of thinking of the graph. For example, the intercept form $y = a + bx$ allows students to graph by starting at point $(0, a)$ and moving vertically b units for each unit they move across from left to right. This process reflects the constant rate of change of linear growth and the recursive sequence. Later, in Chapter 8, students will discover that the point-slope equation $y = y_1 + b(x - x_1)$ represents a vertical shift of y_1 and a horizontal shift of x_1.

Most data sets from real-world situations with a linear trend aren't exactly linear. Lesson 3.7 provides an activity for finding an equation that models a set of data points that lie close to but not on a straight line. Students will learn more about lines of fit in Chapter 4.

Solving Equations

Many real-life situations call for predicting when linear growth will reach a certain value. Ways of making that prediction reflect the three ways of thinking about linearity—constant rate of change, equations that relate variables, and graphs.

From the *constant-rate-of-change* perspective, you can run the recursive routine until it reaches the desired output, counting input steps as you go. To mount a flagpole 75 ft up on a building, what floor would you go to if the building's basement floor is 15 ft below the ground and its floors are 10 ft apart?

Just run the sequence -15 (ENTER); Ans $+ 10$; (ENTER); (ENTER); ... until you get to 75 ft.

To undo those steps and get back to the number of floors, you can subtract -15 and divide by 10, the distance between floors.

This undoing process took place with equations in Chapter 2: If $10x - 15 = 75$, you can "get back to" x by adding 15 to 75 and then dividing by 10. The equation can also be solved using the metaphor of an equation as a pan balance. To keep it balanced, you do the same thing to both sides.

The third approach to linearity, *graphs*, also provides a means of solving equations. You can graph the data points or the equation on a graphing calculator and then use the trace feature to approximate the input value for the desired output value. Using the calculator's table features is another way to approximate a solution.

Using This Chapter

Lesson 3.1 is essential because recursive sequences will be used throughout the book. Solving by undoing is emphasized until the introduction of the balancing method in Lesson 3.6. If you must skip a lesson, you could skip the activity day, Lesson 3.7. No new material is presented, and the rope tying is done again in Lesson 5.2.

Resources

Discovering Algebra Resources

Teaching and Worksheet Masters
Lessons 3.2, 3.5, 3.6

Calculator Notes 0D, 1J, 2A, 2C, 3A, 3B, 3C, 3D

Sketchpad Demonstrations
Lessons 3.1, 3.5, 3.6

Fathom Demonstrations
Lessons 3.1, 3.2, 3.4, 3.7

CBL 2 Demonstration
Lesson 3.5

Dynamic Algebra Explorations online
Lessons 3.1, 3.2

Assessment Resources
Quiz 1 (Lessons 3.1–3.3)
Quiz 2 (Lessons 3.4–3.6)
Chapter 3 Test
Chapter 3 Constructive Assessment Options
Chapters 1 to 3 Exam

More Practice Your Skills for Chapter 3

Condensed Lessons for Chapter 3

Other Resources

Play It Again Sam: Recurrence Equations and Recursion in Mathematics and Computer Science by Rochelle Wilson Meyer and Walter Meyer.

For complete references to this and other resources see www.keypress.com/DA.

Pacing Guide

	day 1	day 2	day 3	day 4	day 5	day 6	day 7	day 8	day 9	day 10
standard	3.1	3.2	3.2	3.3	quiz, 3.4	3.5	3.6	3.7	review	assessment
enriched	3.1	3.2	3.2	3.3, project	quiz, 3.4	3.5	3.6	3.7	review, TAL	assessment
block	3.1, 3.2	3.2, 3.3, project	3.4, 3.5	3.6, quiz	3.7, review	assessment, mixed review	exam			

	day 11	day 12
standard	mixed review	exam
enriched	mixed review	exam

3

Linear Equations

- Investigate recursive (arithmetic) sequences using the calculator

- Graph scatter plots of recursive sequences

- Explore time-distance graphs

- Write a linear equation in intercept form given a recursion routine, a graph, or data

- Solve linear equations by undoing operations and by balancing

OBJECTIVES

In this chapter you will
- write recursive routines emphasizing start plus change
- study rate of change
- learn to write equations for lines using a starting value and a rate of change
- use equations and tables to graph lines
- solve linear equations

Weavers repeat steps when they make baskets and mats, creating patterns of repeating shapes. This process is not unlike recursion. In the top photo, a mat weaver in Myanmar creates a traditional design with palm fronds. The bottom photo shows bowls crafted by Native American artisans.

By keeping the amount of woven material constant, the weavers produce consistent patterns of lines and shapes. To make the mat in the chevron-like pattern, the weaver first lays the warp pieces lengthwise in a repeating pattern of two light and one dark. Then he weaves the woof (or weft) pieces horizontally with the same sequence of two light and one dark. Each woof piece alternately hops over three of the warp pieces and goes under three warp pieces.

Students can try this themselves with colored paper strips and write instructions for how to start the woof piece at the edge.

Coiled baskets begin with a spiral at the base, in contrast to baskets that begin with a wagon-wheel-like pattern at the base. As the basket diameter widens, the space widens between elements that cross the coil. Help students notice that some of the designs, when the baskets are viewed from top or

bottom, have reflective (mirror) symmetry, but others have radial symmetry.

Myanmar (Burma) is located between India and Thailand near the Bay of Bengal. The Native American baskets are a Pima coiled tray, an Apache coiled jar, two Yokuts coiled bowls, a Mono coiled bowl, a Maidu coiled bowl, a Washo coiled bowl, and a Pomo coiled gift basket.

PLANNING

LESSON OUTLINE

One day:

5 min	Introduction, Example A
20 min	Investigation
10 min	Sharing, Example B
5 min	Closing
10 min	Exercises

MATERIALS

- boxes of toothpicks (or have students draw line segments on paper)
- Calculator Note 0D
- Sketchpad demonstration Patterns and Recursion, *optional*
- Fathom demonstration Recursive Sequences, *optional*

TEACHING

In this lesson the idea of recursion, introduced in Chapter 0 with fractals and evaluation of expressions, is revisited with calculator home-screen iteration of recursive sequences.

INTRODUCTION

Students may say that they need only a proportion to determine the height of the 80th floor of the Empire State Building. However, they would be making some assumptions. Leave that question open until Exercise 5.

If you skipped Chapter 0, explain that while executing a *recursive procedure* you do the same thing repeatedly, at each step operating on the result of the previous step.

▶ EXAMPLE A

[ELL] *Floor*, or *story*, means the level of a building, usually beginning with 1. The *height of a floor* could mean the floor-to-ceiling distance of one floor, but here it

Recursive Sequences

A mathematician, like a painter or a poet, is a maker of patterns. If his patterns are more permanent than theirs, it is because they are made of ideas.

G. H. HARDY

The Empire State Building in New York City has 102 floors and is 1250 ft high. How high up are you when you reach the 80th floor? You can answer this question using a recursive sequence. In this lesson you will learn how to analyze geometric patterns, complete tables, and find missing values using numerical sequences.

A **recursive sequence** is an ordered list of numbers defined by a starting value and a rule. You generate the sequence by applying the rule to the starting value, then applying it to the resulting value, and repeating this process.

EXAMPLE A

The table shows heights above and below ground at different floor levels in a 25-story building. Write a **recursive routine** that provides the sequence of heights $-4, 9, 22, 35, \ldots, 217, \ldots$ that corresponds to the building floor numbers $0, 1, 2, \ldots$. Use this routine to find each missing value in the table.

Floor number	Basement (0)	1	2	3	4	...	10	...		...	25
Height (ft)	−4	9	22	35		...		...	217	...	

▶ Solution

The starting value is -4 because the basement is 4 ft below ground level. Each floor is 13 ft higher than the floor below it, so the rule for finding the next floor height is "add 13 to the current floor height."

The calculator screen shows how to enter this recursive routine into your calculator. Press -4 (ENTER) to start your number sequence. Press $+13$ (ENTER). The calculator automatically displays Ans $+13$ and computes the next value. Simply pressing (ENTER) again applies the rule for finding successive floor heights. [▶ ☐ See **Calculator Note 0D.** ◀] You can see that the 4th floor is at 48 ft.

How high up is the 10th floor? Count the number of times you press (ENTER) until you reach 10. Which floor is at a height of 217 ft? Keep counting until you see that value on your calculator screen. What's the height of the 25th floor? Keep applying the rule by pressing (ENTER) and record the values in your table.

The 10th floor is at 126 ft, the 17th floor is at 217 ft, and the 25th floor is at 321 ft.

LESSON OBJECTIVES

- Review or become familiar with the concept of recursion
- Investigate recursive (arithmetic) sequences using the calculator

NCTM STANDARDS

CONTENT		PROCESS	
✓	Number		Problem Solving
✓	Algebra	✓	Reasoning
✓	Geometry		Communication
	Measurement		Connections
	Data/Probability	✓	Representation

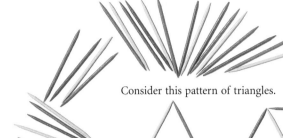

Investigation
Recursive Toothpick Patterns

In this investigation you will learn to create and apply recursive sequences by modeling them with puzzle pieces made from toothpicks.

You will need
- a box of toothpicks

Consider this pattern of triangles.

| Figure 1 | Figure 2 | Figure 3 |

keymath.com/DA

Step 1 Make Figures 1–3 of the pattern using as few toothpicks as possible. How many toothpicks does it take to reproduce each figure? How many toothpicks lie on the perimeter of each figure?

Step 2 Copy the table with enough rows for six figures of the pattern. Make Figures 4–6 from toothpicks by adding triangles in a row and complete the table.

Step 3 Toothpicks: Add 2 to the previous number. Perimeter: Add 1 to the previous perimeter. Press 3 (ENTER) and then Ans + 2 (ENTER) to find the successive numbers of toothpicks. For the perimeter, press 3 (ENTER) and then Ans + 1 (ENTER).

	Number of toothpicks	Perimeter
Figure 1		
Figure 2		

Step 3 What is the rule for finding the number of toothpicks in each figure? What is the rule for finding the perimeter? Use your calculator to create recursive routines for these rules. Check that these routines generate the numbers in your table.

Step 4 Now make Figure 10 from toothpicks. Count the number of toothpicks and find the perimeter. Does your calculator routine give the same answers? Find the number of toothpicks and the perimeter for Figure 25. Figure 10: 21 toothpicks with a perimeter of 12; Figure 25: 51 toothpicks with a perimeter of 27

Next you'll see what sequences you can generate with a new pattern.

Step 5 Design a pattern using a row of squares, instead of triangles, with your toothpicks. Repeat Steps 1–4 and answer all the questions with the new design.

Step 6 Choose a unit of measurement and explain how to calculate the area of a square made from toothpicks. How does your choice of unit affect calculations for the areas of each figure?

Step 3 As needed, ask what the starting values for the number of toothpicks and for the perimeter are. Then ask about the rules for finding the next numbers.

Step 5 Be sure the pattern of squares remains a row.

Step 2	
Toothpicks	Perimeter
3	3
5	4
7	5
9	6
11	7
13	8

Step 5	
Toothpicks	Perimeter
4	4
7	6
10	8
13	10
16	12
19	14

means the *height above ground level* of that floor. This example reminds students of how to use home-screen iteration. You may choose to do it as a class, especially if you skipped recursion in Chapter 0.

Students might wonder if −4 is the first term of the sequence. Point out that sequences can have "zeroth" terms to make the counting easier.

Guiding the Investigation

If you think your students will not handle toothpicks appropriately, you can have them draw line segments on paper.

One Step
Draw the three figures showing the growth of a triangle pattern or ask students to look at page 159. Point out how the perimeter is changing. Ask students to design their own toothpick pattern with a changing feature, such as perimeter, and to write a recursive routine to make their calculator generate the sequence of numbers. As you interact, be sure students see the idea of a common difference between consecutive terms.

Step 1 If students do not use just one toothpick per side, their answers will be multiples of 3.

Step 2 Be sure students extend their patterns of shapes horizontally. If they add shapes in several directions, their sequences will not be arithmetic.

The table is organized so that the calculated sequences are displayed vertically in columns. Calculators will also display the results of recursive routines vertically on the home screen.

Step 5 Toothpicks: Add 3 to the previous number. Perimeter: Add 2 to the previous perimeter. Press 4 (ENTER) and then Ans + 3 (ENTER) to find the number of toothpicks. To find the perimeter, press 4 (ENTER) and then Ans + 2 (ENTER). Figure 10: 31 toothpicks with 22 on the perimeter; Figure 25: 76 toothpicks with 52 on the perimeter.

Step 6 Students might measure a toothpick in centimeters, in inches, or as a unit 1 toothpick long. For a unit of 1 toothpick, the area is equal to the number of squares in the figure. Otherwise, the number of squares must be multiplied by the unit area of each square to calculate the area of the entire figure.

Step 7 Students might be reluctant to use figures whose areas are difficult to find in terms of the edges. Suggest that they can use the area of the first figure as 1 square unit even if their basic shape is not a square.

SHARING IDEAS

Ask several students to present their questions from Step 8. For one of them in which the perimeter increases by a different number from the number of toothpicks, ask why. Usually one or more toothpicks in the perimeter at the previous step are no longer in the perimeter.

You might begin to use the term *rate of change* to describe what's happening—for example, the amount being added to the perimeter is the rate of change of the perimeter, in toothpicks per stage.

If you ask some students to put up their sequences with terms missing and have the class guess the missing terms, you can anticipate Example B.

Now you'll create your own puzzle piece from toothpicks. Add identical pieces in one direction to make the succeeding figures of your design.

Step 7 Draw Figures 1–3 on your paper. Write recursive routines to generate number sequences for the number of toothpicks, perimeter, and area of each of six figures. Record these numbers in a table. Find the values for a figure made of ten puzzle pieces.

Step 8 Write three questions about your pattern that require recursive sequences to answer. For example: What is the perimeter if the area is 20? Test your questions on your classmates.

In the investigation you wrote number sequences in table columns. Remember that you can also display sequences as a list of numbers like this:

$$1, 3, 5, 7, \ldots$$

Each number in the sequence is called a **term.** The three periods indicate that the numbers continue.

EXAMPLE B   Find the missing values in each sequence.

a. 7, 12, 17, __ , 27, __ , __ , 42, __ , 52

b. 5, 1, −3, __ , −11, −15, __ , __ , −27, __

c. −7, __ , −29, __ , −51, −62, __ , −84, __

d. 2, −4, 8, −16, 32, __ , 128, −256, __ , __

How many hidden numbers can you find?

▶ **Solution**   For each sequence, identify the starting value and the operation that must be performed to get the next term.

a. The starting value is 7 and you add 5 each time to get the next number. The missing numbers are shown in red.

starting value

$+5$ $+5$ $+5$ $+5$ $+5$ $+5$ $+5$ $+5$ $+5$

7,   12,   17,   22,   27,   32,   37,   42,   47,   52

b. The starting value is 5 and you subtract 4 each time to get the next number. The missing numbers are shown in red.

starting value

-4 -4 -4 -4 -4 -4 -4 -4 -4

5,   1,   −3,   −7,   −11,   −15,   −19,   −23,   −27,   −31

Assessing Progress
Watch for systematic data collection, familiarity with geometric shapes and terms such as *perimeter* and *area,* and ability to contribute to group work.

▶ **EXAMPLE B**

This example is good for students who may not have grasped the nature of a sequence with common differences of consecutive terms. Many students enjoy creating and solving problems like this. Encourage differing approaches to part c. You can find the common difference by looking down the list to the first consecutive pair or by finding half the difference between the third term and the first term: $\frac{1}{2}[-29 - (-7)] = -11$. Hidden numbers in the illustration include 0, 1, 2, 3, 4, 7, 8, and 11.

---

c. The starting value is -7. The difference between the fifth and sixth terms shows that you subtract 11 each time.

starting value

$$\begin{array}{ccccccccc} & \overset{-11}{\searndown} & \overset{-11}{\searndown} & \overset{-11}{\searndown} & \overset{-11}{\searndown} & \overset{-11}{\searndown} & \overset{-11}{\searndown} & \overset{-11}{\searndown} & \overset{-11}{\searndown} \\ -7, & -18, & -29, & -40, & -51, & -62, & -73, & -84, & -95 \end{array}$$

d. Adding or subtracting numbers does not generate this sequence. Notice that the numbers double each time. Also, they switch between positive and negative signs. So the rule is to multiply by -2. Multiply 32 by -2 to get the first missing value of -64. The last missing values are 512 and -1024.

starting value

$$\begin{array}{ccccccccc} & \overset{\cdot(-2)}{\searndown} & \overset{\cdot(-2)}{\searndown} & \overset{\cdot(-2)}{\searndown} & \overset{\cdot(-2)}{\searndown} & \overset{\cdot(-2)}{\searndown} & \overset{\cdot(-2)}{\searndown} & \overset{\cdot(-2)}{\searndown} & \overset{\cdot(-2)}{\searndown} & \overset{\cdot(-2)}{\searndown} \\ 2, & -4, & 8, & -16, & 32, & -64, & 128, & -256, & 512, & -1024 \end{array}$$

EXERCISES

You will need your graphing calculator for Exercises **2, 5,** and **7.**

▶ Practice Your Skills

1. Evaluate each expression without using your calculator. Then check your result with your calculator.

a. $-2(5 - 9) + 7$ 15

b. $\dfrac{(-4)(-8)}{-5 + 3}$ -16

c. $\dfrac{5 + (-6)(-5)}{-7}$ -5

2. Consider the sequence of figures made from a row of pentagons.

  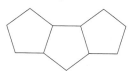

Figure 1   Figure 2   Figure 3

a. Copy and complete the table for five figures. @

b. Write a recursive routine to find the perimeter of each figure. Assume each side is 1 unit long.

c. Find the perimeter of Figure 10. @ 32

d. Which figure has a perimeter of 47?   Figure 15

Figure number	Perimeter
1	5
2	8
3	11
4	14
5	17

3. Find the first six values generated by the recursive routine

-14.2 (ENTER)

Ans $+ 3.7$ (ENTER), (ENTER), . . . @ $-14.2, -10.5, -6.8, -3.1, 0.6, 4.3$

4. Write a recursive routine to generate each sequence. Then use your routine to find the 10th term of the sequence.

a. $3, 9, 15, 21, \ldots$ @

b. $1.7, 1.2, 0.7, 0.2, \ldots$ @

c. $-3, 6, -12, 24, \ldots$

d. $384, 192, 96, 48, \ldots$

Closing the Lesson

You generate a **recursive sequence** on the calculator by entering a starting number and then designating how to operate on one number to get the next number in the sequence.

BUILDING UNDERSTANDING

Students practice writing recursive routines to generate sequences, most of which have a constant difference between consecutive terms.

ASSIGNING HOMEWORK

Essential	**1–4, 6**
Performance assessment	**5, 7, 8**
Portfolio	**6**
Journal	**10, 11**
Group	**6, 9, 11, 12**
Review	**13, 14**

▶ Helping with the Exercises

For more practice with recursive geometric sequences, you can use the Sketchpad demonstration Patterns and Recursion.

2b. 5 (ENTER), Ans $+ 3$ (ENTER), (ENTER), . . .

Exercise 4 In 4d, students see a recursive sequence defined by division for the first time. The Fathom demonstration Recursive Sequences can be used to replace this exercise.

4a. Start with 3, then apply the rule Ans $+ 6$; 10th term $= 57$.

4b. Start with 1.7, then apply the rule Ans $- 0.5$; 10th term $= -2.8$.

4c. Start with -3, then apply the rule Ans $\cdot -2$; 10th term $= 1536$.

4d. Start with 384, then apply the rule Ans/2 or Ans $\cdot 0.5$; 10th term $= 0.75$.

Exercise 5 Students may have difficulty calculating the heights of the floors. Encourage them to draw a picture to see that there are 16 floors, numbered 86 through 101, spanning a distance of 174 ft, and that the lower 85 floors cover a distance of 1050 ft. If students notice the height here of 1224 and the height in the introduction of 1250, say that the height 1224 is to the floor of the 102nd floor and 1250 includes the height of the antenna.

5a. The recursive routine is 0 (ENTER) and then Ans + 12.35 (ENTER). The starting value is 0, the height of ground level (the first floor). Add the average floor height for the next 85 floors: 12.35 ft.

5b. The recursive routine is 1050 (ENTER) and then Ans + 10.875 (ENTER). The starting value is the height of the 86th floor. Add 10.875, the average floor height of floors 86 through 101.

5c. When you are 531 ft high, you are 43 floors up and thus on the 44th floor.

6a. Possible explanation: The smallest square has an area of 1. The next larger white square has an area of 4, which is 3 more than the smallest square. The next larger gray square has an area of 9, which is 5 more than the 4-unit white square.

6b. The recursive routine is 1 (ENTER), Ans + 2 (ENTER), (ENTER), and so on.

6c. 17, the value of the 9th term in the sequence

> ## Reason and Apply

5. **APPLICATION** In the Empire State Building the longest elevator shaft reaches the 86th floor, 1050 ft above ground level. Another elevator takes visitors from the 86th floor to the observation area on the 102nd floor, 1224 ft above ground level. For more information about the Empire State Building, see **www.keymath.com/DA** .

   a. Write a recursive routine that gives the height above ground level for each of the first 86 floors. Tell what the starting value and the rule mean in terms of the building.

   b. Write a recursive routine that gives the heights of floors 86 through 102. Tell what the starting value and the rule mean in this routine.

   c. When you are 531 ft above ground level, what floor are you on?

   d. When you are on the 90th floor, how high up are you? When you are 1137 ft above ground level, what floor are you on?
   1093.5 ft; 94th floor

6. The diagram at right shows a sequence of gray and white squares each layered under the previous one.

   a. Explain how the sequence 1, 3, 5, 7, . . . is related to the areas of these squares.

   b. Write a recursive routine that gives the sequence 1, 3, 5, 7, ...

   c. Use your routine to predict the number of additional unit squares you would need to enlarge this diagram by one additional row and column. Explain how you found your answers.

   d. What is the 20th number in the sequence 1, 3, 5, 7, . . . ?   39

   e. The first term in the sequence is 1, and the second is 3. Which term is the number 95? Explain how you found your answer.
   The 48th term is 95; students might press (ENTER) 48 times or compute 2(48) − 1.

7. Imagine a tilted L-shaped puzzle piece made from 8 toothpicks. Its area is 3 square units. Add puzzle pieces in the corner of each "L" to form successive figures of the design. In a second figure, the two pieces "share" two toothpicks so that there are 14 toothpicks instead of 16.

   Figure 1   Figure 2   Figure 3

   a. As you did in the investigation, make a table with enough columns and rows for the number of toothpicks, perimeter, and area of each of six figures.

   b. Write a recursive routine that will produce the number sequence in each column of the table.

   c. Find the number of toothpicks, perimeter, and area of Figure 10.

   d. Find the perimeter and area of the figure made from 152 toothpicks.

7a. The table for six figures of the L-shaped puzzle pieces is

Figure	Toothpicks	Perimeter	Area
1	8	8	3
2	14	12	6
3	20	16	9
4	26	20	12
5	32	24	15
6	38	28	18

7b. To find the number of toothpicks, press 8 (ENTER) and then Ans + 6 (ENTER). To find the perimeter, press 8 (ENTER) and then Ans + 4 (ENTER). For the area, press 3 (ENTER) and then Ans + 3 (ENTER).

7c. Figure 10 has 62 toothpicks, a perimeter of 44, and an area of 30.

7d. Figure 25, made from 152 toothpicks, has a perimeter of 104 and an area of 75.

8. APPLICATION The table gives some floor heights in a building.

Floor	...	−1	0	1	2	...		...	25
Height (m)	...	−3	1	5	9	...	37	...	

   a. How many meters are between the floors in this building?   4 m

   b. Write a recursive routine that will give the sequence of floor heights if you start at the 25th floor and go to the basement (floor 0). Which term in your sequence represents the height of the 7th floor? What is the height?

   c. How many terms are in the sequence in 8b?   26 terms

   d. Floor "−1" corresponds to the first level of the parking substructure under the building. If there are five parking levels, how far underground is level 5?   19 m

9. Consider the sequence __ , −4, 8, __ , 32, ...

   a. Find two different recursive routines that could generate these numbers. ⓗ

   b. For each routine, what are the missing numbers? What are the next two numbers?

   c. If you want to generate this number sequence with exactly one routine, what more do you need?   More numbers are needed to uniquely determine a recursive routine.

10. Positive multiples of 7 are generally listed as 7, 14, 21, 28, ...

   a. If 7 is the 1st multiple of 7 and 14 is the 2nd multiple, then what is the 17th multiple? @ $17 \cdot 7$, or 119

   b. How many multiples of 7 are between 100 and 200? @   14

   c. Compare the number of multiples of 7 between 100 and 200 with the number between 200 and 300. Does the answer make sense? Do all intervals of 100 have this many multiples of 7? Explain. @

   d. Describe two different ways to generate a list containing multiples of 7. @

11. Some babies gain an average of 1.5 lb per month during the first 6 months after birth.

   a. Write a recursive routine that will generate a table of monthly weights for a baby weighing 6.8 lb at birth.   Press 6.8 (ENTER) and then Ans + 1.5 (ENTER), (ENTER) . . . .

   b. Write a recursive routine that will generate a table of monthly weights for a baby weighing 7.2 lb at birth.   Press 7.2 (ENTER), and then Ans + 1.5 (ENTER), (ENTER) . . . .

   c. How are the routines in 11a and 11b the same? How are they different?   The starting terms differ; the rule itself is the same.

   d. Copy and complete the table of data for this situation.

Age (mo)	0	1	2	3	4	5	6
Weight of Baby A (lb)	6.8	8.3	9.8	11.3	12.8	14.3	15.8
Weight of Baby B (lb)	7.2	8.7	10.2	11.7	13.2	14.7	16.2

   e. How are the table values for the two babies the same? How do they differ?   Each baby always increases by 1.5 lb, and the difference between the babies' weights is always 0.4 lb; the starting values are different.

Exercise 8b In other words, let the 25th floor height be the first term, the 24th floor height be the second term, and so on.

8b. Press 101 (ENTER) and then Ans − 4 (ENTER). The 19th term represents the height of the 7th floor. The height is 29 m.

9a. One routine is press −16 (ENTER) and then Ans + 12 (ENTER). Another is press 2 (ENTER) and then Ans · −2 (ENTER).

9b. Two possible sequences are {−16, −4, 8, 20, 32, 44, 56, . . .} and {2, −4, 8, −16, 32, −64, 128, . . .}.

Exercise 10 If appropriate, ask about multiples of 7 that aren't positive. Mention nonnegative multiples (which include 0) as well as negative multiples.

10c. Possible answer: There are 14 multiples between 100 and 200. There are also 14 multiples of 7 between 200 and 300, but there are 15 between 300 and 400.

10d. Possible answer: The 4th multiple of 7 is 4 · 7, or 28; the 5th multiple of 7 is 5 · 7, or 35; and so on. Recursively, you start with 7 and then continue adding 7.

12a. Press 1 (ENTER), Ans · 3
(ENTER), (ENTER) . . . ; the 9th term
is 6561.

12b. Press 5 (ENTER), Ans · (−1)
(ENTER), (ENTER) . . . ; the 123rd term
is 5.

12c. Press −16.2 (ENTER), Ans +
1.4 (ENTER), (ENTER) . . . ; the 13th
term is the first positive term.

Exercise 13 [ELL] *Precipitation* is
rain or snow.

13a. The top box plot is
Portland, the middle is San
Francisco, and the bottom
is Seattle.

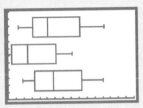

[0, 7, 0.5, 0, 12, 1]

San Francisco has the least
precipitation and is the only city
in which there is a month with
no precipitation. One indicator
that the weather is much drier in
San Francisco is that the month
with no precipitation is not an
outlier.

13b. You lose information
about what time of year is
wettest; a bar graph or scatter
plot would show trends over the
months of the year more clearly.

12. Write recursive routines to help you answer 12a–d.
  a. Find the 9th term of 1, 3, 9, 27, ... @
  b. Find the 123rd term of 5, −5, 5, −5, ... @
  c. Find the term number of the first positive term of the sequence −16.2, −14.8, −13.4, −12, ...
  d. Which term is the first to be either greater than 100 or less than −100 in the sequence −1, 2, −4, 8, −16, . . . ? Press −1 (ENTER), Ans · (−2) (ENTER), (ENTER) . . . ; the 8th term, 128, is the first to be greater than 100.

▶ Review

1.3 **13.** The table gives the normal monthly precipitation for three cities in the United States.
  a. Display the data in three box plots, one for each city, and use them to compare the precipitation for the three cities.
  b. What information do you lose by displaying the data in a box plot? What type of graph might be more helpful for displaying the data?

Precipitation for Three Cities

Month	Precipitation (in.)		
	Portland, Oregon	San Francisco, California	Seattle, Washington
January	5.4	4.1	5.4
February	3.9	3.0	4.0
March	3.6	3.1	3.8
April	2.4	1.3	2.5
May	2.1	0.3	1.8
June	1.5	0.2	1.6
July	0.7	0.0	0.9
August	1.1	0.1	1.2
September	1.8	0.3	1.9
October	2.7	1.3	3.3
November	5.3	3.2	5.7
December	6.1	3.1	6.0

(*The New York Times Almanac 2000*, pp. 480–481)

It's a rainy day in Portland, Oregon.

2.8 **14.** Create an undo table and solve the equation listed by undoing the order of operations. $x = -2.6$

Equation: $8 + 3(x - 5) = -14.8$		
Description	**Undo**	**Result**
Pick *x*.	⬚	− 2.6
− (5)	+ (5)	− 7.6
· (3)	/ (3)	− 22.8
+ (8)	− (8)	− 14.8

LESSON

3.2

LESSON 3.2

Linear Plots

In this lesson you will learn that the starting value and the rule of a recursive sequence take on special meaning in certain real-world situations. When you add or subtract the same number each time in a recursive routine, consecutive terms change by a constant amount. Using your calculator, you will see how the starting value and rule let you generate data for tables quickly. You will also plot these data sets and learn that the starting value and rule relate to characteristics of the graph.

In most sciences, one generation tears down what another has built, and what one has established, the next undoes. In mathematics alone, each generation builds a new story to the old structure.

HERMANN HANKEL

Many elevators use Braille symbols. This alphabet for the blind was developed by Louis Braille (1809–1852). For more information about Braille, see the links at **www.keymath.com/DA** .

EXAMPLE

You walk into an elevator in the basement of a building. Its control panel displays "0" for the floor number. As you go up, the numbers increase one by one on the display, and the elevator rises 13 ft for each floor. The table shows the floor numbers and their heights above ground level.

Floor number	Height (ft)
0 (basement)	−4
1	9
2	22
3	35
4	48
. . .	. . .

a. Write recursive routines for the two number sequences in the table. Enter both routines into calculator lists.

b. Define variables and plot the data in the table for the first few floors of the building. Does it make sense to connect the points on the graph?

c. What is the highest floor with a height less than 200 ft? Is there a floor that is exactly 200 ft high?

▶ Solution

The starting value for the floor numbers is 0, and the rule is to add 1. The starting value for the height is −4, and the rule is to add 13. You can generate both number sequences on the calculator using lists.

a. Press {0, −4} and press ENTER to input both starting values at the same time. To use the rules to get the next term in the sequence, press {Ans(1) + 1, Ans(2) + 13} ENTER .
[▶ 🖥 See **Calculator Note 3A.** ◀]

Starting values

Rule

```
{0, −4}
                        {0 −4}
{Ans (1) + 1, Ans (2) + 13}
                        {1 9}
                        {2 22}
                        {3 35}
```

These commands tell the calculator to add 1 to the first term in the list and to add 13 to the second number. Press ENTER again to compute the next floor number and its corresponding height as the elevator rises.

In this routine, the calculator displays a new list of numbers horizontally every time you press ENTER, but the terms for the sequences of floor numbers and heights appear vertically aligned on the screen.

Be sure students understand the important difference between the use of braces and parentheses on the calculator.

Emphasize the use of dimensions: $\frac{height}{floor}$. On the Elevator Table transparency, you might make marks between consecutive terms in the right column to show the common differences.

Ask why the term *linear relationship* was chosen for two quantities in which each unit increase in one results in a constant increase in the other. An answer to this question could wait until Sharing.

PLANNING

LESSON OUTLINE

First day:

5 min   Introduction, Example

45 min   Investigation

Second day:

15 min   Investigation

20 min   Sharing, Closing

15 min   Exercises

MATERIALS

- graph paper
- colored pencils
- Elevator Table (T), *optional*
- On the Road Again Grid (W)
- On the Road Again Table (W)
- On the Road Again Graph (T)
- Calculator Notes 0D, 2C, 3A
- Fathom demonstration On the Road Again, *optional*

TEACHING

This lesson describes quantities generated by a recursive additive sequence (that is, with a constant rate of change) as having a *linear relationship* because their graph is a set of points that lie on a straight line. If the amount being added (the rate of change per step) is positive, the line is rising (increasing) from left to right, with larger rates of change giving steeper lines. If the rate of change is negative, the line is falling (decreasing) from left to right.

EXAMPLE

This example shows how to enter a list of two starting values so you can keep track of the term number in a sequence. The output is a list of paired values.

[ELL] *Heads for Flint* means travels in the direction of Flint. *Heads south* means travels south.

It may help to have six students go to the front of the classroom with signs that say *green minivan*, *Mackinac Bridge*, and so on, and walk through the problem before students begin working on it.

You can modify the context of the investigation to suit your geographical area by choosing cities and highways with approximately these distances, and creating your own transparency and worksheet.

The Fathom demonstration On the Road Again can be used to replace this investigation.

One Step

Pose the investigation problem. Ask students to answer the questions in as many ways as possible. Encourage use of recursive calculator routines and graphs. Students may say that obviously the minivan arrives before the pickup because it's going faster over the same distance. It may not be as obvious that the minivan will arrive before the sports car because the sports car has less distance to travel, but it's moving more slowly. Others may point out that the pickup will pass the sports car in less than 2 h because the situation is equivalent to the sports car sitting still 35 mi up the road and the pickup traveling at 18 mi/h (66 − 48). Encourage this kind of variety in approach.

Step 1 Throughout the investigation, encourage the use of units and dimensional analysis.

b. Let x represent the floor number and y represent the floor's height in feet. Mark a scale from 0 to 5 on the x-axis and −10 to 50 on the y-axis. Plot the data from the table. The graph starts at $(0, -4)$ on the y-axis. The points appear to be in a line. It does not make sense to connect the points because it is not possible to have a decimal or fractional floor number.

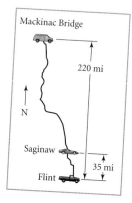

c. The recursive routine generates the points $(0, -4)$, $(1, 9)$, $(2, 22)$, . . . , $(15, 191)$, $(16, 204)$, ... The height of the 15th floor is 191 ft. The height of the 16th floor is 204 ft. So the 15th floor is the highest floor with a height less than 200 ft. No floor is exactly 200 ft high.

Notice that to get to the next point on the graph from any given point, move right 1 unit on the x-axis and up 13 units on the y-axis. The points you plotted in the example showed a **linear relationship** between floor numbers and their heights. In what other graphs have you seen linear relationships?

Investigation
On the Road Again

You will need

- the worksheet On the Road Again Grid

A green minivan starts at the Mackinac Bridge and heads south for Flint on Highway 75. At the same time, a red sports car leaves Saginaw and a blue pickup truck leaves Flint. The car and the pickup are heading for the bridge. The minivan travels 72 mi/h. The pickup travels 66 mi/h. The sports car travels 48 mi/h.

When and where will they pass each other on the highway? In this investigation you will learn how to use recursive sequences to answer questions like these.

Step 1 minivan: 1.2 mi/min; pickup: 1.1 mi/min; sports car: 0.8 mi/min

Step 1 Find each vehicle's average speed in miles per minute (mi/min).

Step 2 Write recursive routines to find each vehicle's distance from Flint at each minute. What are the real-world meanings of the starting value and the rule in each routine? Use calculator lists.

LESSON OBJECTIVES

- Graph scatter plots of recursive sequences
- Continue to explore the connection between graphs and tables and how they can be used to solve problems
- Build toward an introduction of the intercept form of a line

NCTM STANDARDS

CONTENT		PROCESS	
✓	Number	✓	Problem Solving
✓	Algebra		Reasoning
✓	Geometry	✓	Communication
✓	Measurement	✓	Connections
	Data/Probability	✓	Representation

Step 3 Make a table to record the highway distance from Flint for each vehicle. After you complete the first few rows of data, change your recursive routines to use 10 min intervals for up to 4 h.

Highway Distance from Flint

Time (min)	Minivan (mi)	Sports car (mi)	Pickup (mi)
0	220	35	0
1	218.8	35.8	1.1
2	217.6	36.6	2.2
5	214	39	5.5
10	208	43	11
20	196	51	22

Procedure Note

After you enter the recursive routine into the calculator, press **ENTER** five or six times. Copy the data displayed on your calculator screen onto your table. Repeat this process.

Step 4 Let *x* represent the time in minutes since the vehicles started their trips; let *y* represent the distance from Flint in highway miles.

Step 4 Define variables and plot the information from the table onto a graph. Mark and label each axis in 10-unit intervals, with time on the horizontal axis. Using a different color for each vehicle, plot its (*time, distance*) coordinates.

Step 5 On the graph, do the points for each vehicle seem to fall on a line? Does it make sense to connect each vehicle's points in a line? If so, draw the line. If not, explain why not. Yes; a line through the points for each vehicle represents every possible instant of time.

Step 6 On the *y*-axis representing each vehicle's initial distance from Flint; the rules affect the steepness and direction of each line.

Use your graph and table to find the answers for Steps 6–10.

Step 6 Where does the starting value for each routine appear on the graph? How does the recursive rule for each routine affect the points plotted?

Step 7 Which line represents the minivan? How can you tell?

Step 8 The minivan meets the sports car about 110 mi from Flint just after 90 min. The pickup is about 100 mi from Flint.

Step 8 Where are the vehicles when the minivan meets the first one headed north?

Step 9 The pickup is traveling faster because its line is steeper; it passes the sports car when their lines cross on the graph, after roughly 115 min.

Step 9 How can you tell by looking at the graph whether the pickup or the sports car is traveling faster? When and where does the pickup pass the sports car?

Step 10 The minivan arrives after approximately 185 min, the pickup 15 min later, and the sports car 45 min later.

Step 10 Which vehicle arrives at its destination first? How many minutes pass before the second and third vehicles arrive at their destinations? How can you tell by looking at the graph?

Step 11 What assumptions about the vehicles are you making when you answer the questions in the previous steps? The vehicles travel at a constant speed, never speeding up, slowing down, or stopping.

Step 7 Be sure students go beyond an answer like "It's colored green." **[Ask]** "How did you know which line to color green?"

Step 7 The line going down from left to right; it starts 220 units above the origin on the *y*-axis and gets closer to the *x*-axis as time passes and the minivan gets closer to Flint.

Steps 8 and 9 **[Alert]** Students may have difficulty keeping in mind both variables being graphed. Students may say, or at least believe, something like "They're at the same place but not at the same time."

You can find very good approximations for the answers to the questions using either the table or the graph. Ask students to save their results if you are going to assign Lesson 5.2, Exercise 11.

See page 723 for answers to Step 3.

Step 2 As needed, discuss how the different directions the vehicles are traveling affect whether you add or subtract in the recursive routine. Also discuss the difference between miles apart on the highway and miles apart in a straight line. The distances are all miles apart on the highway. Be ready to remind students how to enter recursive data into calculator lists. (See Calculator Note 0D.)

Step 2 To input the starting values in a calculator list for the times and the distances of the minivan, pickup, and sports car, respectively, press {0, 220, 0, 35}. To apply the rule, press {Ans (1) + 1, Ans(2) − 1.2, Ans(3) + 1.1, Ans(4) + 0.8}. The starting values represent the time in minutes and each vehicle's distance from Flint. The rule is to add or subtract the speed in miles per minute, depending on the vehicle's direction.

Step 3 Each student can choose a different car and generate the related sequence recursively. Remind students of the instant replay function (Calculator Note 2C). To modify the recursive routines to use 10 min intervals, you can recall the last entry and change it to read {Ans (1) + 10, Ans(2) − 12, Ans(3) + 11, Ans(4) + 8}.

Step 4 This is the most important phase of the investigation. Using different colors is important for differentiating the vehicles.

Step 5 The data will provide three linear patterns. Students should draw these three intersecting lines and justify connecting the points. This may be the first continuous graph students have constructed since Chapter 2. **[Alert]** Some students may interpret their coordinate graphs as the *paths* of the cars rather than as indicating the distance from a fixed point over time.

Consider how to model this situation more realistically. What if the vehicles are traveling at different speeds? What if one driver stops to get gas or a bite to eat? What if the vehicles' speeds are not constant? Discuss how these questions affect the recursive routines, tables of data, and their graphs. *If speeds are not constant, the points will not lie in a line and you would not be adding or subtracting the same number in the recursive routine. The lines would have horizontal pieces if drivers stop.*

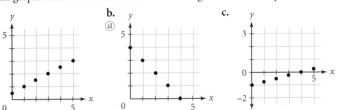

keymath.com/DA

[▶ You can use the **Dynamic Algebra Exploration** found at **www.keymath.com/DA** to further explore the situation described in the investigation. ◀]

EXERCISES

You will need your graphing calculator for Exercises **4–7** and **9**.

▶ **Practice Your Skills**

1. Decide whether each expression is positive or negative without using your calculator. Then check your answer with your calculator.

   a. $-35(44) + 23$ negative; -1517 **b.** $(-14)(-36) - 32$ positive; 472 **c.** $25 - \dfrac{152}{12}$ positive; $12.\overline{3}$

   d. $50 - 23(-12)$ positive; 326 **e.** $\dfrac{-12 - 38}{15}$ negative; $-3.\overline{3}$ **f.** $24(15 - 76)$ negative; -1464

2. List the terms of each number sequence of *y*-coordinates for the points shown on each graph. Then write a recursive routine to generate each sequence.

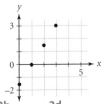

   a. **b.** **c.** **d.**

3. Make a table listing the coordinates of the points plotted in 2b and d.

4. Plot the first five points represented by each recursive routine in 4a and b on separate graphs. Then answer 4c and d.

   a. $\{0, 5\}$ (ENTER)

   $\{\text{Ans}(1) + 1, \text{Ans}(2) + 7\}$ (ENTER); (ENTER), . . .

   b. $\{0, -3\}$ (ENTER)

   $\{\text{Ans}(1) + 1, \text{Ans}(2) - 6\}$ (ENTER); (ENTER), . . .

2b.			2d.	
x	y		x	y
0	4		0	−1.5
1	3		1	0
2	2		2	1.5
3	1		3	3
4	0			

Assessing Progress

Your observations should help you assess students' skill at finding averages, writing recursive routines, plotting points, calculating rates of change, and interpreting graphs.

Closing the Lesson

Quantities generated by a recursive additive sequence (with a constant rate of change) have a **linear relationship** because their graphs lie on a straight line. If the amount being added at each step is positive, the line will rise from left to right, with larger rates of change giving steeper lines. If the amount being added is negative, the line will fall from left to right.

BUILDING UNDERSTANDING

Students move among recursive sequences, linear relationships, and their graphs.

ASSIGNING HOMEWORK

Essential	**2–4, 6, 7**
Performance assessment	**8, 10**
Portfolio	**6**
Journal	**7, 8**
Group	**6, 9**
Review	**1, 5, 11–14**

▶ Helping with the Exercises

2a. $\{0.5, 1, 1.5, 2, 2.5, 3\}$; 0.5, Ans + 0.5

2b. $\{4, 3, 2, 1, 0\}$; 4, Ans − 1

2c. $\{-1, -0.75, -0.5, -0.25, 0, 0.25\}$; −1, Ans + 0.25

2d. $\{-1.5, 0, 1.5, 3\}$; −1.5, Ans + 1.5

Exercise 4 Be sure students note the instructions for 4a and b at the beginning of the exercise.

See page 723 for answers to Exercises 4a and b.

SHARING IDEAS

If some students had the idea that the graphs showed the paths of the vehicles, ask the class to critique that notion. This is a good place to ask questions beginning with "Are you saying . . . ?" in order to clarify ideas without having to tell much.

Have students present Steps 9–12. **[Ask]** "Are you saying that the relationship is linear because the rate of change is constant?" Elicit the idea that the amount being added at each step of the recursive routine is the rate of change.

If you have time, **[Ask]** "How do linear relationships relate to directly proportional quantities and direct variation?" [Directly proportional quantities have a linear relationship, but the opposite is not necessarily true. The graph of a direct variation is a straight line through the origin. The graph of a linear relationship between variables is also a straight line, but not necessarily through the origin.]

As a synonym for *steepness,* you might use the word *slope,* though its formal definition will not come until Chapter 4.

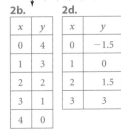

c. On which axis does each starting point lie? What is the *x*-coordinate of each starting point?   the *y*-axis; 0

d. As the *x*-value increases by 1, what happens to the *y*-coordinates of the points in each sequence in 4a and b? @   In 4a, the *y*-coordinates increase by 7. In 4b, the *y*-coordinates decrease by 6.

5. The direct variation $y = 2.54x$ describes the relationship between two standard units of measurement where *y* represents centimeters and *x* represents inches.

a. Write a recursive routine that would produce a table of values for any whole number of inches. Use a calculator list.

b. Use your routine to complete the missing values in this table.

Inches	Centimeters
0	0
1	2.54
2	5.08
14	35.56
17	43.18

Reason and Apply

6. APPLICATION A car is moving at a speed of 68 mi/h from Dallas toward San Antonio. Dallas is about 272 mi from San Antonio.

a. Write a recursive routine to create a table of values relating time to distance from San Antonio for 0 to 5 h in 1 h intervals.

b. Graph the information in your table.

c. What is the connection between your plot and the starting value in your recursive routine?

d. What is the connection between the coordinates of any two consecutive points in your plot and the rule of your recursive routine?

e. Draw a line through the points of your plot. What is the real-world meaning of this line? What does the line represent that the points alone do not?

f. When is the car within 100 mi of San Antonio? Explain how you got your answer.

g. How long does it take the car to reach San Antonio? Explain how you got your answer.

7. APPLICATION A long-distance telephone carrier charges $1.38 for international calls of 1 minute or less and $0.36 for each additional minute.

a. Write a recursive routine using calculator lists to find the cost of a 7-minute phone call. @

b. Without graphing the sequence, give a verbal description of the graph showing the costs for calls that last whole numbers of minutes. Include in your description all the important values you need in order to draw the graph.

5a. {0, 0} (ENTER), {Ans(1) + 1, Ans(2) + 2.54}

6a. {0, 272} (ENTER), {Ans(1) + 1, Ans(2) − 68} (ENTER), (ENTER), (ENTER), (ENTER), (ENTER)

6b and 6e.

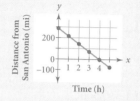

6c. The starting value is the point (0, 272) on the graph.

6d. On the graph, you move right 1 unit and down 68 units to get from one point to the next. In the recursive routine, you add 1 to the first number and subtract 68 from the second number.

6e. This is a linear graph relating a distance to any time between 0 and 5 h. The line represents the distances at all possible times; points represent distances only at certain times.

6f. The car is within 100 mi of San Antonio after 2.53 h have elapsed. Explanations will vary. Graphically, it is the time after which the line crosses the horizontal line $y = 100$.

6g. The car takes 4 h to reach San Antonio. Answers will vary. The answer is the fourth entry in the table. Graphically, it is where the line crosses the *x*-axis.

7a. Possible answer: {1, 1.38} (ENTER), {Ans(1) + 1, Ans(2) + 0.36} (ENTER), (ENTER), ... The recursive routine keeps track of time and cost for each minute. Apply the routine until you get {7, 3.54}. A 7 min call costs $3.54.

7b. Possible answer: The graph should consist of points that lie on a line. It should include the point (1, 1.38). Each subsequent point should be 1 unit to the right and $0.36 higher than the point before it.

Exercise 8 Discuss how measuring depth on the bow, bridge, or stern of a submarine as it is surfacing affects data.

8a.

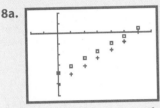

$$[-10, 35, 5, -60, 20, 10]$$

8b. The points for each submarine appear to lie on a line; the USS *Dallas* surfaces at a faster rate.

Exercise 9 Suggest that students calculate the perimeter by treating each edge as 1 unit long.

9b. Number of tiles: The starting value is 1; the rule is add 1.
Triangle: The starting value is 3; the rule is add 1.
Rhombus: The starting value is 4; the rule is add 2.
Pentagon: The starting value is 5; the rule is add 3.
Hexagon: The starting value is 6; the rule is add 4.
To generate the sequences for all tiles simultaneously, enter {1, 3, 4, 5, 6} and {Ans(1) + 1, Ans(2) + 1, Ans(3) + 2, Ans(4) + 3, Ans(5) + 4}.

9c. triangle: 52; rhombus: 102; pentagon: 152; hexagon: 202

9d.

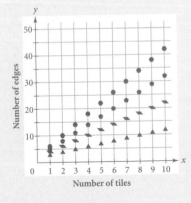

8. These tables show the changing depths of two submarines as they come to the surface.

USS *Alabama*

Time (s)	0	5	10	15	20	25	30
Depth (ft)	−38	−31	−24	−17	−10	−3	4

USS *Dallas*

Time (s)	0	5	10	15	20	25	30
Depth (ft)	−48	−40	−32	−24	−16	−8	0

a. Graph the data from both tables on the same set of coordinate axes.

b. Describe what you found by graphing the data. How are the graphs the same? How are they different?

c. Does it make sense to draw a line through each set of points? Explain what these lines mean. Yes; each line means that any time in this range corresponds to depth below the surface.

d. What is the real-world meaning of the point (30, 4) for the USS *Alabama*? The submarine's nose rises slightly above the water when surfacing.

9. Each geometric design is made from tiles arranged in a row.

Triangle   Rhombus   Pentagon   Hexagon

a. Make a table like the one shown. Find the number of tile edges on the perimeter of each design, and fill in ten rows of the table. Look for patterns as you add more tiles. ⓗ

Tile Edges on the Perimeter

Number of tiles	Triangle	Rhombus	Pentagon	Hexagon
1	3	4	5	6
2	4	6	8	10
3	5	8	11	14
4	6	10	14	18
⋯ 10	12	22	32	42

b. Write a recursive routine to generate the values in each table column.

c. Find the perimeter of a 50-tile design for each shape.

d. Draw four plots on the same coordinate axes using the information for designs of one to ten tiles of each shape. Use a different color for each shape. Put the number of tiles on the horizontal axis and the number of edges on the vertical axis. Label and scale each axis.

e. Compare the four scatter plots. How are they alike, and how are they different?

f. Would it make sense to draw a line through each set of points? Explain why or why not. ⓗ No; there must be a whole number of tiles and a whole number of edges.

9e. The points of each graph appear to lie on a line, and each graph starts at 1; the graphs increase in steepness from the triangle tile to the hexagon tile.

10. A bicyclist, 1 mi (5280 ft) away, pedals toward you at a rate of 600 ft/min for 3 min. The bicyclist then pedals at a rate of 1000 ft/min for the next 5 min.

   a. Describe what you think the plot of (*time, distance from you*) will look like. @

   b. Graph the data using 1 min intervals for your plot. @

   c. Invent a question about the situation, and use your graph to answer the question.

11b.

	Operations	Undo operations	Results
			$x = 3.4$
	$- (2.8)$	$+ (2.8)$	0.6
	$\cdot (3.2)$	$/ (3.2)$	1.92
	$+ (5.4)$	$- (5.4)$	7.32
	$/ (1.2)$	$\cdot (1.2)$	6.1
	$- (2.3)$	$+ (2.3)$	3.8

▶ **Review**

2.8 **11.** Consider the expression

$$\frac{5.4 + 3.2(x - 2.8)}{1.2} - 2.3$$

   a. Use the order of operations to find the value of the expression if $x = 7.2$. $13.9\overline{3}$

   b. Set the expression equal to 3.8. Solve for x by undoing the sequence of operations you listed in 11a. $x = 3.4$

2.8 **12.** Isaac learned a way to convert from degrees Celsius to Fahrenheit. He adds 40 to the Celsius temperature, multiplies by 9, divides by 5, and then subtracts 40.

   a. Write an expression for Isaac's conversion method. @ $\dfrac{9(C + 40)}{5} - 40$

   b. Write the steps to convert from Fahrenheit to Celsius by undoing Isaac's method. @

   c. Write an expression for the conversion in 12b. $\dfrac{5(F + 40)}{9} - 40$

2.3 **13.** **APPLICATION** Karen is a U.S. exchange student in Austria. She wants to make her favorite pizza recipe for her host family, but she needs to convert the quantities to the metric system. Instead of using cups for flour and sugar, her host family measures dry ingredients in grams and liquid ingredients in liters. Karen has read that 4 cups of flour weigh 1 pound.

In her dictionary, Karen looks up conversion factors and finds that 1 ounce ≈ 28.4 grams, 1 pound ≈ 454 grams, and 1 cup ≈ 0.236 liter.

   a. Karen's recipe calls for $\frac{1}{2}$ cup water and $1\frac{1}{2}$ cups flour. Convert these quantities to metric units.

   b. Karen's recipe says to bake the pizza at 425°. Convert this temperature to degrees Celsius. Use your work in Exercise 12 to help you. $218.\overline{3}$, or about 220°C

1.6 **14.** Draw and label a coordinate plane with each axis scaled from −10 to 10.

   a. Represent each point named with a dot, and label it using its letter name.

     $A(3, -2)$ $B(-8, 1.5)$ $C(9, 0)$ $D(-9.5, -3)$ $E(7, -4)$

     $F(1, -1)$ $G(0, -6.5)$ $H(2.5, 3)$ $I(-6, 7.5)$ $J(-5, -6)$

   b. List the points in Quadrant I, Quadrant II, Quadrant III, and Quadrant IV. Which points are on the x-axis? Which points are on the y-axis?

   c. Explain how to tell which quadrant a point will be in by looking at the coordinates. Explain how to tell if a point lies on one of the axes.

10a. Answers will vary. The graph starts at $(0, 5280)$. The points $(0, 5280)$, $(1, 4680)$, $(2, 4080)$, and $(3, 3480)$ will appear to lie on a line. From $(3, 3480)$ to $(8, -1520)$, the points will appear to lie on a steeper line. The bicyclist ends up 1520 ft past you.

10b.

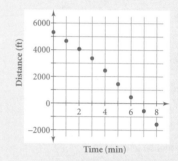

Bicyclist

10c. Sample answer: What place on the graph shows when the bicyclist passes you? The answer is on the x-axis between 6 and 7 min.

12b. Add 40, multiply by 5, divide by 9, then subtract 40.

13a. 0.118, about $\frac{1}{8}$ L water; 170.25, about 170 g flour

14a.

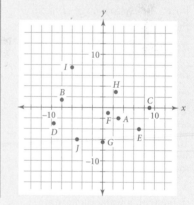

14b. Quad I: H; Quad II: B, I; Quad III: D, J; Quad IV: A, E, F; x-axis: C; y-axis: G

14c. Sample answer: If the coordinates are both 0, then the point is on the origin. If the x-coordinate is 0, then the point is on the y-axis. If the y-coordinate is 0, then the point is on the x-axis.

If the first coordinate is positive, then the point will be in Quadrant I or IV. To tell which quadrant, look at the y-coordinate. If the y-coordinate is positive, the point is in Quadrant I. If the y-coordinate is negative, the point is in Quadrant IV.

If the first coordinate is negative, then the point will be in Quadrant II or III. To tell which quadrant, look at the y-coordinate. If the y-coordinate is positive, the point is in Quadrant II. If the y-coordinate is negative, the point is in Quadrant III.

PLANNING

LESSON OUTLINE

One day:

30 min	Investigation
10 min	Example A
5 min	Example B
5 min	Exercises

MATERIALS

- 4 m measuring tapes, metersticks, or ropes
- motion sensors
- stopwatches or watches with second hands
- Calculator Note 3B

TEACHING

Becoming more familiar with time-distance graphs helps deepen students' understanding of graphs and rates of change.

One Step

Post a plot with a large circle in the first quadrant. **[Ask]** "How would a walker walk to produce this graph?" After some students respond that the walker should simply walk in a circle, label the axes with *time* and *distance*. Help students see that a single walker can't produce such a graph without being at two places at one time. Ask for other examples of plots that are impossible to make with a walker and motion sensor.

Guiding the Investigation

You might modify this investigation to use finger walking and rulers. Use the same numbers, but substitute inches for meters as the unit of measure.

LESSON 3.3

Time-Distance Relationships

Modeling time-distance relationships is one very useful application of algebra. You began working with this topic in Lesson 3.2. In this lesson you will explore time-distance relationships in more depth by considering various walking scenarios. You'll learn how the starting position, speed, direction, and final position of a walker influence a graph and an equation.

The (*time, distance*) graphs below provide a lot of information about the "walks" they picture. The fact that the lines are straight and increasing means that both walkers are moving away from the motion sensor at a steady rate. The first walker starts 0.5 meter from the sensor, whereas the second walker starts 1 meter from the sensor. The first graph pictures a walker moving $4.5 - 0.5 = 4$ meters in $4 - 0 = 4$ seconds, or 1 meter per second. The second walker covers $3 - 1 = 2$ meters in $4 - 0 = 4$ seconds, or 0.5 meter per second.

In this investigation you'll analyze time-distance graphs, and you'll use a motion sensor to create your own graphs.

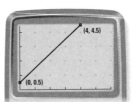

Investigation

Walk the Line

You will need

- a 4-meter measuring tape or four metersticks per group
- a motion sensor
- a stopwatch or watch that shows seconds

Imagine that you have a 4-meter measuring tape positioned on the floor. A motion sensor measures your distance from the tape's 0-mark as you walk, and it graphs the information. On the calculator graphs shown here, the horizontal axis shows time from 0 to 6 seconds and the vertical axis shows distance from 0 to 4 meters.

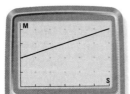

a.   b.   c.

LESSON OBJECTIVES

- Explore time-distance relationships
- Write walking instructions or act out walks for a given graph
- Sketch graphs based on given walking instructions or table data
- Use an electronic data collection device, motion sensor, and graphing calculator to collect and graph data

NCTM STANDARDS

CONTENT		PROCESS	
✔	Number	✔	Problem Solving
✔	Algebra	✔	Reasoning
	Geometry	✔	Communication
✔	Measurement	✔	Connections
	Data/Probability	✔	Representation

| Step 1 | Write a set of walking instructions for each graph. Tell where the walk begins, how fast the person walks, and whether the person walks toward or away from the motion sensor located at the 0-mark. |

| Step 2 | Graph a 6-second walk based on each set of walking instructions or data. |

a. Start at the 2.5-meter mark and stand still.

b. Start at the 3-meter mark and walk toward the sensor at a constant rate of 0.4 meter per second.

c.

Time (s)	0	1	2	3	4	5	6
Distance (m)	0.8	1.0	1.2	1.4	1.6	1.8	2.0

| Step 3 | Write a recursive routine for the table in Step 2c. The starting value is 0.8; the rule is add 0.2. |

Steps 4 and 5
Students should discuss the difficulty of walking at a constant speed and of changing speed or direction at a specific instant in time. The coach needs to give good directions.

For the next part of the investigation, you will need a graphing calculator and a motion sensor. Your group will need a space about 4 meters long and 1.5 meters wide (13 feet by 5 feet). Tape to the floor a 4-meter measuring tape or four metersticks end-to-end. Assign these tasks among your group members: walker, motion-sensor holder, coach, and timer.

| Step 4 | Your group will try to create the graph shown in Step 1, graph a. Remember that you wrote walking directions for this graph. Use your motion sensor to record the walker's motion. [▶ 💻 See **Calculator Note 3B** for help using the motion sensor.◀] After each walk, discuss what you could have done to better replicate the graph. Repeat the walk until you have a good match for graph a. |

| Step 5 | Rotate jobs, and repeat Step 4 to model graphs b and c from Step 1 and the three descriptions from Step 2. |

Using motion-sensor technology in the investigation, you were able to actually see how accurately you duplicated a given walk. The next examples will provide more practice with time-distance relationships.

EXAMPLE A

a. Graph a walk from the set of instructions "Start at the 0.5-meter mark and walk at a steady 0.25 meter per second for 6 seconds."

b. Write a set of walking instructions based on the table data, and then sketch a graph of the walk.

Time (s)	0	1	2	3	4	5	6
Distance (m)	4.0	3.6	3.2	2.8	2.4	2.0	1.6

tells the walker to start. The coach makes helpful comments to guide the walker.

Step 5 Groups should discuss what they could have done to match more accurately the given graph, table, or instructions.

EXAMPLE A

This example gives students more practice in graphing walking instructions, including some derived from a data table. As in the investigation, the rates are constant and the graphs are straight lines, slanting both upward and downward.

Step 1 If students need a hint, suggest that because the vertical axis measures distance, they can answer the question "How far does the walker start from the zero mark?" by considering the vertical axis. If students have trouble answering "How fast?" you can give a hint by pointing to graph a. **[Ask]** "How long did it take the walker to go 1 m from his or her starting point?" Some students may have trouble seeing that the walker ever walks toward the 0 mark because the graphs appear to proceed away from the start. Ask them to look at graph b and read off "meters" at the start and finish. Graph c can't be defined with just one rule.

Steps 4 and 5 Students will gain more if they are physically involved, even if minimally. If you have limited classroom space or equipment, you might have different groups demonstrate walks one at a time. You might select students to demonstrate two or three "walks" before the others start. However you do it, try to have each student take on each role—walker, holder, coach, and timer—for at least one walk. A group need not have a coach if there are too few students.

If you're not using motion sensors, the holder records in a table the walker's distance from the 0 m mark each second. The timer begins timing when the coach tells the walker to start and counts the seconds aloud.

If you are using motion sensors, the holder should hold the calculator and start collecting data on the coach's command. (See Calculator Note 3B.) The holder should hold the motion sensor chest high, keeping it level and aimed directly at the walker. Timing begins when the coach

See page 723 for answers to Steps 1 and 2.

EXAMPLE B

This example is for students who need further experience with writing walking instructions from a straight-line graph.

SHARING IDEAS

Have students present a variety of graphs and walking directions, including recursive routines. If a group has a graph that isn't a straight line, ask the group to present that graph as a springboard into a discussion of how speed affects a graph.

[Ask] "Can you tell from the graph whether the walker is moving toward or away from the motion sensor?" Elicit the idea that a horizontal line graph represents movement in neither direction and that a vertical line graph is impossible.

2.

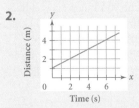

[Ask] "Is it clear how a recursive routine relates to the graph?" You need not mention the term *slope* or give a formal definition, but relate the additive constant to the speed of walking and the steepness of the line.

3. Start at the 0.8 m mark and walk away from the sensor at a constant rate of 0.2 m/s.

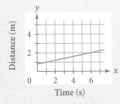

▸ **Solution**   Think about where the walker starts and how much distance he or she will cover in a given amount of time.

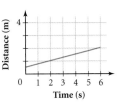

a. Walking at a steady rate of 0.25 meter per second for 6 seconds means the walker will move 0.25 m/s · 6 s = 1.5 m. The walker starts at 0.5 m and ends at 0.5 + 1.5 = 2 m.

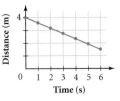

b. Walking instructions: "Start at the 4-meter mark and walk toward the sensor at 0.4 meter per second." You can graph this walk by plotting the data points given.

EXAMPLE B   Write a set of walking instructions for this graph:

▸ **Solution**   Start at the 0.5 m mark and walk away from the motion sensor at 1 m/s for 2 s. Then walk toward the sensor at $\frac{3}{4}$ m/s for 2 s. Then walk away from the sensor at 1 m/s for 2 s.

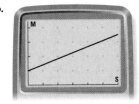

EXERCISES

▶ **Practice Your Skills**

1. Write a recursive routine for the table in Example A, part b. ⓐ
   {0, 4.0} and {Ans(1) + 1, Ans (2) − 0.4}

2. Sketch a graph of a walk starting at the 1-meter mark and walking away from the sensor at a constant rate of 0.5 meter per second.

3. Write a set of walking instructions and sketch a graph of the walk described by {0, 0.8} and {Ans(1) + 1, Ans(2) + 0.2}. ⓐ

4. Describe the walk shown in each graph. Include where it started and how quickly and in what direction the walker moved.

   a. ⓐ   **b.**

   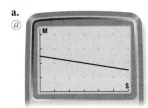   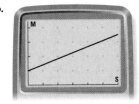

   The walker starts 2.5 m away from the motion sensor and walks toward it very slowly at a rate of 1 m in 6 s.

   The walker starts 1 m away from the motion sensor and walks away from it at a rate of 2.5 m in 6 s.

Closing the Lesson

The main point of this lesson is that motion at a constant speed is graphed with a straight line. If the walker is moving away from the motion sensor, so that distance is increasing, the line rises from left to right; if the walker is moving toward the sensor, so that distance is decreasing, the line falls from left to right; if the walker is motionless, the line is horizontal.

The speed of the walker is related to the steepness of the line and to the additive constant in a recursive routine. The higher the speed, the steeper the graph and the farther the additive constant is from 0.

5. Describe the walk represented by the data in each table.

a.

Time (s)	Distance (m)
0	6
1	5.8
2	5.6
3	5.4
4	5.2
5	5.0
6	4.8

The walker starts 6 m away from the motion sensor and walks toward it at a rate of 0.2 m/s for 6 s.

b.

Time (s)	Distance (m)
0	1
1	1.6
2	2.2
3	2.8
4	3.4
5	4.0
6	4.6

The walker starts 1 m away from the motion sensor and walks away from it at a rate of 0.6 m/s for 6 s.

▶ Reason and Apply

6. Which graph better represents a walk in which the walker starts 2 m from the motion sensor and walks away from it at a rate of 0.25 m/s for 6 s? Explain.

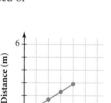

The first graph, which shows a line, because the walk is a continuous process; the walker is somewhere at every possible time in the 6 s.

7. At what rate in ft/s would you walk so that you were moving at a constant speed of 1 mi/h? ⓗ

8. The time-distance graph shows Carol walking at a steady rate. Her partner used a motion sensor to measure her distance from a given point.

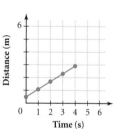

a. According to the graph, how much time did Carol spend walking? 4 s

b. Was Carol walking toward or away from the motion sensor? Explain your thinking. ⓐ Away; the distance is increasing.

c. Approximately how far away from the motion sensor was she when she started walking? approximately 0.5 m

d. If you know Carol is 2.9 m away from the motion sensor after 4 s, how fast was she walking? ⓗ $\frac{2.9 - 0.5}{4} = 0.6$ m/s

e. If the equipment will measure distances only up to 6 m, how many seconds of data can be collected if Carol continues walking at the same rate? ⓐ

f. Looking only at the graph, how do you know that Carol was neither speeding up nor slowing down during her walk? ⓐ The graph is a straight line.

9. Draw a scatter plot on your paper picturing (*time, distance*) at 1 s intervals if you start timing Carol's walk as she walks toward her partner starting at a distance of 5.9 m and moving at a constant speed of 0.6 m/s.

BUILDING UNDERSTANDING

In these exercises students describe walks using multiple representations, including graphs, tables, recursive rules, and walking instructions.

ASSIGNING HOMEWORK

Essential	1–5, 9
Performance assessment	6, 8, 10, 11, 13
Portfolio	10
Journal	6, 12
Group	12, 13
Review	7, 14–16

▶ Helping with the Exercises

Exercise 6 [Alert] Students may be confused by the dots. **[Ask]** "Where is the walker after 2.5 seconds? After 4.25 seconds?"

Exercise 7 If students are stuck, you might refer them to Lesson 2.8, Exercise 5.

7. Convert 1 mi/h to ft/s:
$$\frac{1\text{ mi}}{1\text{ h}} \cdot \frac{1\text{ h}}{60\text{ min}} \cdot \frac{1\text{ min}}{60\text{ s}} \cdot \frac{5280\text{ ft}}{1\text{ mi}}$$
$$= 1.4\overline{6}\text{ ft/s}$$

8e. $\frac{5.5\text{ m}}{0.6\text{ m/s}} = 9.1\overline{6}$ s, or approximately 9 s

Exercise 9 As needed, remind students that a scatter plot is simply a collection of dots.

9.

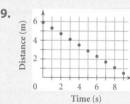

10. Describe how the rate affects the graph of each situation. The rate is negative, so the line

    a. The graph of a person walking toward a motion sensor. @ slopes down to the right.

    b. The graph of a person standing still. The rate is neither negative nor positive, it is zero, so the line is horizontal.

    c. The graph of a person walking slowly.
    The line is not very steep.

11. Match each calculator Answer routine to a graph.

ii **a.** 2.5 `ENTER`

      Ans + 0.5, `ENTER`, `ENTER`, . . . @

i.

iv **b.** 1.0 `ENTER`

      Ans + 1.0, `ENTER`, `ENTER`, . . .

ii.

iii **c.** 2.0 `ENTER`

      Ans + 1.0, `ENTER`, `ENTER`, . . .

iii.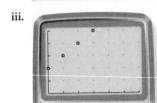

i **d.** 2.5 `ENTER`

      Ans − 0.5, `ENTER`, `ENTER`, . . .

iv.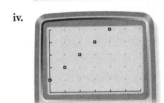

12. Describe how you would instruct someone to walk the line $y = x$, where x is measured in seconds and y is measured in feet. Describe how to walk the line $y = x$, where x is measured in seconds and y is measured in meters. Which line represents a faster rate? Explain.

13. For each situation, determine if it is possible to collect such walking data and either describe how to collect it or explain why it is not possible.

  a. 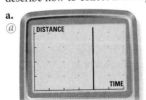 **b.**  **c.**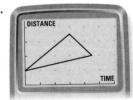

---

12. Start walking at the 0 mark when the sensor starts and walk 1 ft every second. Start walking at the 0 mark when the sensor starts and walk 1 m every second. 1 m/s is a faster rate, because more distance is covered per second.

13a. Not possible; the walker would have to be at more than one distance from the sensor at the 3 s mark.

13b. Possible; the walker simply stands still about 2.5 m from the sensor.

13c. Not possible; the walker can't be in two places at any given time.

▶ Review

2.1 **14.** Solve each proportion for x.

a. $\frac{x}{3} = \frac{7}{5}$ $x = \frac{21}{5}$, or 4.2   **b.** $\frac{2}{x} = \frac{9}{11}$ @ $x = \frac{22}{9}$, or $2.\overline{4}$ **c.** $\frac{x}{c} = \frac{d}{e}$ $x = \frac{cd}{e}$

2.3 **15.** On his Man in Motion World Tour in 1987, Canadian Rick Hansen wheeled himself 24,901.55 miles to support spinal cord injury research and rehabilitation, and wheelchair sport. He covered 4 continents and 34 countries in two years, two months, and two days. Learn more about Rick's journey with the link at **www.keymath.com/DA** .

a. Find Rick's average rate of travel in miles per day. (Assume there are 365 days in a year and 30.4 days in a month.) ⓗ

b. How much farther would Rick have traveled if he had continued his journey for another $1\frac{1}{2}$ years?

c. If Rick continued at this same rate, how many days would it take him to travel 60,000 miles? How many years is that?

Photo courtesy of The Rick Hansen Institute

China was one of the many countries through which Rick Hansen traveled during the Man in Motion World Tour.

2.3 **16.** **APPLICATION** Nicholai's car burns 13.5 gallons of gasoline every 175 miles.

a. What is the car's fuel consumption rate? ⓗ ~ 13 mi/gal or 0.077 gal/mi

b. At this rate, how far will the car go on 5 gallons of gas? 65 mi

c. How many gallons does Nicholai's car need to go 100 miles? 7.7 gal

project

PASCAL'S TRIANGLE

The first five rows of Pascal's triangle are shown.

```
            1
          1   1
        1   2   1
      1   3   3   1
    1   4   6   4   1
  1   5  10  10   5   1
```

The triangle can be generated recursively. The sides of the triangle are 1's, and each number inside the triangle is the sum of the two diagonally above it.

Complete the next five rows of Pascal's triangle. Research its history and practical application. What is the connection between Sierpiński's triangle and Pascal's triangle? Can you find the sequence of triangular numbers in Pascal's triangle? What is its connection to the Fibonacci number sequence? Present your findings in a paper or a poster.

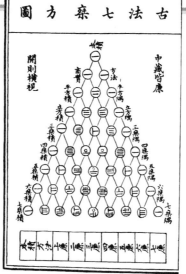

What became known as Pascal's triangle was first published in *Siyuan yujian xicao* by Zhu Shijie in 1303. This ancient version actually has one error. Can you find it?

The fourth number in row 8 should be 35.

Exercise 15 [Alert] Students may be misled by the extra information about continents and countries. The rate needed for 15c is the reciprocal of the rate needed for 15a and 15b.

15a. $\frac{24{,}901.55 \text{ mi}}{(2 \cdot 365 + 2 \cdot 30.4 + 2) \text{ days}}$

≈ 31.4 mi/day

15b. $\frac{31.4 \text{ mi}}{1 \text{ day}} \cdot \frac{(1.5 \cdot 365) \text{ days}}{1}$

$\approx 17{,}191.5$ mi

15c. $\frac{31.4 \text{ mi}}{1 \text{ day}} = \frac{60{,}000 \text{ mi}}{t}$;

$t \approx 1{,}911$ days, or more than 5 yr

Pascal's Triangle Project

The next four rows are:

1, 6, 15, 15, 6, 1

1, 7, 21, 35, 35, 21, 7, 1

1, 8, 28, 56, 70, 56, 28, 8, 1

1, 9, 36, 84, 126, 126, 84, 36, 9, 1

Fibonacci Numbers

```
      1  3  3  1       21
    1  4  6  4  1
  1  5 10 10  5  1
 1  6 15 20 15  6  1
1  7 21 35 35 21  7  1
```

Sierpiński's Triangle

▶ If the odd numbers in Pascal's triangle are colored in, the even numbers are left uncolored, and the triangle is extended infinitely, then it becomes a Sierpiński triangle.

Supporting the project

MOTIVATION

This pattern of numbers is named for a 17th-century mathematician. He used this pattern of numbers extensively in his study of probability. Was that the beginning of the history of this number pattern? (See above for the next four rows.)

OUTCOMES

▶ The recursive rule includes a starting 1 and this rule: If a number is at the end of a row, it's 1, and if it's not, then it's the sum of the two numbers diagonally above it.

▶ The report includes history going back to the ancient Chinese civilization.

▶ The triangular numbers (1, 3, 6, 10, 15, . . .) are in the third diagonal.

▶ The Fibonacci numbers (1, 1, 2, 3, 5, 8, . . .) are sums of the numbers on diagonals described by "start with a 1 on the left, go over one and a half numbers and up to the next row, follow that diagonal, adding the numbers." (For example, $1 + 3 + 1 = 5$; $1 + 4 + 3 = 8$; $1 + 5 + 6 + 1 = 13$.)

▶ Sierpiński's triangle (see above)

LESSON

3.4

Linear Equations and the Intercept Form

So far in this chapter you have used recursive routines, graphs, and tables to model linear relationships. In this lesson you will learn to write **linear equations** from recursive routines. You'll begin to see some common characteristics of linear equations and their graphs, starting with the relationship between exercise and calorie consumption.

Different physical activities cause people to burn calories at different rates depending on many factors such as body type, height, age, and metabolism. Coaches and trainers consider these factors when suggesting workouts for their athletes.

 ## Investigation
Working Out with Equations

Manisha starts her exercise routine by jogging to the gym. Her trainer says this activity burns 215 calories. Her workout at the gym is to pedal a stationary bike. This activity burns 3.8 calories per minute.

First you'll model this scenario with your calculator.

Step 1 Use calculator lists to write a recursive routine to find the total number of calories Manisha has burned after each minute she pedals the bike. Include the 215 calories she burned on her jog to the gym.

Step 1 {0, 215} (ENTER), {Ans(1) + 1, Ans(2) + 3.8} (ENTER), (ENTER) ...

Step 2 Copy and complete the table using your recursive routine.

Step 3 After 20 minutes of pedaling, how many calories has Manisha burned? How long did it take her to burn 443 total calories?

Step 3 291 calories; 60 min

Manisha's Workout

Pedaling time (min)	Total calories burned
x	y
0	215
1	218.8
2	222.6
20	291
30	329
45	386
60	443

LESSON OBJECTIVES

• Write a linear equation in intercept form given a recursion routine, a graph, or data

• Learn the meaning of y-intercept for a linear equation in intercept form

NCTM STANDARDS

CONTENT		PROCESS	
✔	Number	✔	Problem Solving
✔	Algebra	✔	Reasoning
	Geometry	✔	Communication
	Measurement	✔	Connections
	Data/Probability	✔	Representation

Next you'll learn to write an equation that gives the same values as the calculator routines.

Step 4 $215 + 3.8(20) = 291$

Step 4
Write an expression to find the total calories Manisha has burned after 20 minutes of pedaling. Check that your expression equals the value in the table.

Step 5 $215 + 3.8(38) = 359.4$ calories; you don't need to calculate the previous terms in the sequence or create a table to find the answer.

Step 5
Write and evaluate an expression to find the total calories Manisha has burned after pedaling 38 minutes. What are the advantages of this expression over a recursive routine?

Step 6
Let x represent the pedaling time in minutes, and let y represent the total number of calories Manisha burns. Write an equation relating time to total calories burned. $y = 215 + 3.8x$

Step 7 sample checks: $215 + 3.8(1) = 218.8$; $215 + 3.8(60) = 443$

Step 7
Check that your equation produces the corresponding values in the table.

Now you'll explore the connections between the linear equation and its graph.

Step 8 The x-axis represents every instant of time, and the y-axis represents every fraction of calories burned. This graph models a continuous linear relationship. See graph below.

Step 8
Plot the points from your table on your calculator. Then enter your equation into the Y= menu. Graph your equation to check that it passes through the points. Give two reasons why drawing a line through the points realistically models this situation. [▶ 🖥 See **Calculator Note 1J** to review how to plot points and graph an equation. ◀]

Step 9
Substitute 538 for y in your equation to find the elapsed time required for Manisha to burn a total of 538 calories. Explain your solution process. Check your result. $538 = 215 + 3.8x$; $x = 85$. Check: $215 + 3.8(85) = 538$.

Step 10
How do the starting value and the rule of your recursive routine show up in your equation? How do the starting value and the rule of your recursive routine show up in your graph? When is the starting value of the recursive routine also the value where the graph crosses the y-axis?

The equation for Manisha's workout shows a linear relationship between the total calories burned and the number of minutes pedaling on the bike. You probably wrote this linear equation as

$$y = 215 + 3.8x \qquad \text{or} \qquad y = 3.8x + 215$$

The form $y = a + bx$ is the **intercept form.** The value of a is the **y-intercept,** which is the value of y when x is zero. The intercept gives the location where the graph crosses the y-axis. The number multiplied by x is b, which is called the **coefficient** of x.

Step 8

Manisha's Workout

Step 10 In the equation $y = 215 + 3.8x$, the starting value is 215 and the rule to add shows up as the coefficient of x. The starting value is the y-intercept. The rule add 3.8 gives the steepness of the line. The starting value of the recursive routine is the y-intercept only when the starting value of x is zero.

use recursive routines, scatter plots, linear equations, graphs, and calculator tables to solve the problem. Be sure Sharing includes ideas about equations.

Step 1 [Language] If students ask, tell them that a *calorie* is the amount of heat energy needed to warm 1 g of water 1°C.

Step 4 As needed, suggest that students create an expression in words before they use symbols. Be sure they haven't forgotten to include the initial 215 calories.

Step 9 Allow any legitimate method for solving the equation, but insist on a good explanation. **[Alert]** Be especially wary of any student impulses to move numbers from one side of the equation to the other.

SHARING IDEAS

Ask several students to share their solution methods for Step 9.

At an appropriate time, introduce the term *intercept form* for the equation $y = a + bx$ and the related terms *y-intercept* and *coefficient of x.* **[Ask]** "Is the equation $y = bx + a$ equivalent to the intercept form?" [Yes] "Are equations $y = ax + b$ and $y = mx + b$ (often called the *slope-intercept form*) also equivalent?" [Yes] Substitute numbers for a, b, and m as needed. These questions may allow students to see that the letters a, b, and m represent constants in particular equations, whereas the letters x and y represent variables. **[Ask]** "Is the equation $y = a - bx$ equivalent to $y = bx - a$?" [No; $y = a - bx$ is equivalent to $y = -bx + a$. It is very important to keep the signs consistent.]

[Ask] "How are linear equations related to other equations you have seen in this course?" [The first, in Chapter 1, was $y = x$. It's a special case of a direct variation $y = kx$, with $k = 1$. And direct variations are special cases of the intercept form $a + bx$, with $a = 0$ and $b = k$.]

Elicit the fact that the coefficient of x, no matter what it's called, gives the rate of change as well as the common difference between consecutive terms in the recursive sequence.

[Ask] "Which variables might be called input and output variables for the investigation?" [The input variable is the number of minutes spent exercising. The output variable is the number of calories burned.] See Lesson 7.3 for a discussion of independent and dependent variables.

Assessing Progress
Your observations should allow you to assess students' abilities with recursive routines, calculator lists, scatter plots, graphing equations, and undoing operations.

► EXAMPLE A
Besides revisiting the ideas of the investigation, this example shows how the graph of the linear equation $y = a + bx$ is a shift of the graph of $y = bx$. Translation will come up in Chapter 8.

Be sure students understand that the second column in the given table refers only to the calories burned while swimming, whereas the third column refers to the total number of calories burned, including those Sam burned before he started swimming.

Some students may say one graph is a vertical shift of the other. Other students, considering the graphs over quadrants other than the first, may see it as a horizontal shift. Encourage both viewpoints. Explore why they are equivalent and how the constants affect the amount of shift.

In the equation $y = 215 + 3.8x$, 215 is the value of a. It represents the 215 calories Manisha burned while jogging before her workout. The value of b is 3.8. It represents the rate her body burned calories while she was pedaling. What would happen if Manisha chose a different physical activity before pedaling on the stationary bike?

You can also think of direct variations in the form $y = kx$ as equations in intercept form. For instance, Sam's trainer tells him that swimming will burn 7.8 calories per minute. When the time spent swimming is 0, the number of calories burned is 0, so a is 0 and drops out of the equation. The number of calories burned is proportional to the time spent swimming, so you can write the equation $y = 7.8x$.

The constant of variation k is 7.8, the rate at which Sam's body burns calories while he is swimming. It plays the same role as b in $y = a + bx$.

EXAMPLE A

Suppose Sam has already burned 325 calories before he begins to swim for his workout. His swim will burn 7.8 calories per minute.

a. Create a table of values for the calories Sam will burn by swimming 60 minutes and the total calories he will burn after each minute of swimming.

b. Define variables and write an equation in intercept form to describe this relationship.

c. On the same set of axes, graph the equation for total calories burned and the direct variation equation for calories burned by swimming.

d. How are the graphs similar? How are they different?

► Solution

a. The total numbers of calories burned appear in the third column of the table. Each entry is 325 plus the corresponding entry in the middle column.

Sam's Swim

Swimming time (min)	Calories burned by swimming	Total calories burned
0	0	325
1	7.8	332.8
2	15.6	340.6
20	156	481
30	234	559
45	351	676
60	468	793

b. Let y represent the total number of calories burned, and let x represent the number of minutes Sam spends swimming.

$$y = 325 + 7.8x$$

c. The direct variation equation is $y = 7.8x$. Enter it into Y1 on your calculator. Enter the equation $y = 325 + 7.8x$ into Y2. Check to see that these equations give the same values as the table by looking at the calculator table.

d. The lower line shows the calories burned by swimming and is a direct variation. The upper line shows the total calories burned. It is 325 units above the first line because, at any particular time, Sam has burned 325 more calories. Both graphs have the same value of b, which is 7.8 calories per minute. The graphs are similar because both are lines with the same steepness. They are different because they have different y-intercepts.

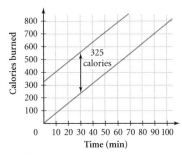

What will different values of a in the equation $y = a + bx$ do to the graph?

EXAMPLE B

A minivan is 220 mi from its destination, Flint. It begins traveling toward Flint at 72 mi/h.

a. Define variables and write an equation in intercept form for this relationship.

b. Use your equation to calculate the location of the minivan after 2.5 h.

c. Use your equation to calculate when the minivan will be 130 mi from Flint.

d. Graph the relationship and locate the points that are the solutions to parts b and c.

e. What is the real-world meaning of the rate of change in this relationship? What does the sign of the rate of change indicate?

▶ **Solution**

a. Let the independent variable, x, represent the time in hours since the beginning of the trip. Let y represent the distance in miles between the minivan and Flint. The equation for the relationship is $y = 220 - 72x$.

b. Substitute the time, 2.5 h, for x.

$$y = 220 - 72 \cdot 2.5 = 40$$

So the minivan is 40 mi from Flint.

c. Substitute 130 mi for y and solve the equation $220 - 72x = 130$.

$220 + -72x = 130$	Original equation. The subtraction of $72x$ is written as addition of $-72x$.
$-72x = -90$	Subtract 220 to undo the addition.
$x = 1.25$	Divide by -72 to undo the multiplication.

The minivan will be 130 mi from Flint after 1.25 h. You can change 0.25 h to minutes using dimensional analysis. $0.25 \text{ h} \cdot \frac{60 \text{ min}}{1 \text{ h}} = 15 \text{ min}$, so you can also write the answer as 1 h 15 min.

▶ **EXAMPLE B**

Use this example if your students are having difficulty connecting graphs to equations or relating the mathematical theory to the real world.

In part a, students might use variables such as t for time. Often the text mirrors graphing calculators in using x for the independent variable. Emphasize dimensional analysis in setting up the equation.

Students might trace the graph of part d to answer part c.

A linear equation in **intercept form,** $y = a + bx$, reflects the recursive routine used to generate a sequence of data values with a constant rate of change. Such a routine begins with a and adds b repeatedly. (The value of either a or b may be negative.)

BUILDING UNDERSTANDING

Students practice writing, graphing, and exploring linear equations, primarily in intercept form.

ASSIGNING HOMEWORK

Essential	1, 2 or 3, 6, 7, 10
Performance assessment	9, 10
Portfolio	6
Journal	5, 7, 8
Group	7
Review	4, 5, 11–15

▶ Helping with the Exercises

Exercise 1 If students have difficulty relating recursive routines to the explicit equations, suggest that they make tables of data.

Exercises 2 and 3 These are the first equations in a while that don't use just x and y for variable names. Encourage students to write the dimensions of each number and variable, especially the rate.

2c. 24 represents the initial number of miles the driver is from his or her destination.

2d. 45 means the driver is driving at a speed of 45 mi/h.

---

d. Set your calculator window to

[0, 3.5, 1, 0, 250, 50],

graph the equation, and press TRACE and the arrow keys to find the points where $x = 1.25$ and $x = 2.5$.

e. The rate of change indicates the speed of the car. If it is negative, the minivan is getting closer to Flint. That is, as time increases the distance decreases. A positive rate of change would mean that the vehicle was moving away from Flint.

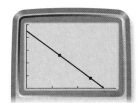

In linear equations it is sometimes helpful to say which variable is the input variable and which is the output variable. The horizontal axis represents the input variable, and the vertical axis represents the output variable. In Example B, the input variable, x, represents time so the x-axis is labeled time, and the output variable, y, represents distance so the y-axis is labeled distance. What are the input and output variables in the investigation and in Example A?
The input variable is time, and the output variable is calories burned.

EXERCISES

You will need your graphing calculator for Exercises **2, 3, 6,** and **9.**

▶ Practice Your Skills

1. Match the recursive routine in the first column with the equation in the second column.

ii **a.** 3 ⌷ENTER⌷

Ans + 4 ⌷ENTER⌷; ⌷ENTER⌷, ... @

i. $y = 4 - 3x$

iv **b.** 4 ⌷ENTER⌷

Ans + 3 ⌷ENTER⌷; ⌷ENTER⌷, ...

ii. $y = 3 + 4x$

iii **c.** −3 ⌷ENTER⌷

Ans − 4 ⌷ENTER⌷; ⌷ENTER⌷, ...

iii. $y = -3 - 4x$

i **d.** 4 ⌷ENTER⌷

Ans − 3 ⌷ENTER⌷; ⌷ENTER⌷, ...

iv. $y = 4 + 3x$

2. You can use the equation $d = 24 - 45t$ to model the distance from a destination for someone driving down the highway, where distance d is measured in miles and time t is measured in hours. Graph the equation and use the trace function to find the approximate time for each distance given in 2a and b.

a. $d = 16$ mi @ $t \approx 0.18$ h

b. $d = 3$ mi $t \approx 0.47$ h

c. What is the real-world meaning of 24? @

d. What is the real-world meaning of 45?

e. Solve the equation $24 - 45t = 16$. $t = \frac{8}{45}$, or $0.1\overline{7}$

Some rental cars have in-dash navigation systems.
© 2000 Hertz System, Inc. Hertz is a registered service mark and trademark of Hertz System, Inc.

3. You can use the equation $d = 4.7 + 2.8t$ to model a walk in which the distance from a motion sensor d is measured in feet and the time t is measured in seconds. Graph the equation and use the trace function to find the approximate distance from a motion sensor for each time value given in 3a and b.

a. $t = 12$ s $d \approx 38.3$ ft

b. $t = 7.4$ s $d \approx 25.42$ ft

c. What is the real-world meaning of 4.7?
The walker started 4.7 ft away from the motion sensor.

d. What is the real-world meaning of 2.8?
The walker was walking at a rate of 2.8 ft/s.

4. Undo the order of operations to find the x-value in each equation.

a. $3(x - 5.2) + 7.8 = 14$ @ $x \approx 7.267$

b. $3.5\left(\dfrac{x - 8}{4}\right) = 2.8$ $x = 11.2$

5. The equation $y = 35 + 0.8x$ gives the distance a sports car is from Flint after x minutes.

a. How far is the sports car from Flint after 25 minutes? $35 + 0.8(25) = 55$ mi

b. How long will it take until the sports car is 75 miles from Flint? Show how to find the solution using two different methods.   50 min; students might use a graph or the undo method.

▶ Reason and Apply

6. APPLICATION Louis is beginning a new exercise workout. His trainer shows him the calculator table with x-values showing his workout time in minutes. The Y_1-values are the total calories Louis burned while running, and the Y_2-values are the number of calories he wants to burn.

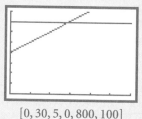

a. Find how many calories Louis has burned before beginning to run, how many he burns per minute running, and the total calories he wants to burn. ⓗ

b. Write a recursive routine that will generate the values listed in Y_1. @   400 (ENTER), Ans + 20.7 (ENTER)

c. Use your recursive routine to write a linear equation in intercept form. Check that your equation generates the table values listed in Y_1. $Y_1 = 400 + 20.7x$

d. Write a recursive routine that will generate the values listed in Y_2. @   700 (ENTER), Ans + 0 (ENTER)

e. Write an equation that generates the table values listed in Y_2. @ $Y_2 = 700 + 0x$ or $Y_2 = 700$

f. Graph the equations in Y_1 and Y_2 on your calculator. Your window should show a time of up to 30 minutes. What is the real-world meaning of the y-intercept in Y_1?

g. Use the trace function to find the approximate coordinates of the point where the lines meet. What is the real-world meaning of this point?

7. Jo mows lawns after school. She finds that she can use the equation $P = -300 + 15N$ to calculate her profit.

a. Give some possible real-world meanings for the numbers -300 and 15 and the variable N.

b. Invent two questions related to this situation and then answer them.

c. Solve the equation $P = -300 + 15N$ for the variable N. $N = \dfrac{(P + 300)}{15}$

d. What does the equation in 7c tell you?   It tells you the number of lawns you have to mow to make a certain amount of profit.

Exercise 6 In Example B, students moved the cursor to trace a graph and find specific points on the graph. In this exercise, they trace to find the intersection of a horizontal line $y = 700$ with the line $y = 400 + 20.7x$.

6a. Louis has burned 400 calories before beginning to run. His calorie-burning rate is 20.7 calories per minute, and he wants to burn 700 total calories.

6f. The y-intercept of Y_1, which is 400, is the number of calories burned after 0 min of running (before Louis begins to run).

$[0, 30, 5, 0, 800, 100]$

6g. The approximate coordinates of the point where the lines meet are (14.5, 700). This means that after 14.5 min of running, Louis will have burned off his desired total of 700 calories.

Exercise 7 Students may be confused by the variable names. Suggest that they write the appropriate dimensions.

7a. One possible scenario: Jo has an initial start-up cost of $300 for equipment and expenses. She makes $15 for every lawn she mows, N.

7b. Sample questions: How many lawns will Jo have to mow to break even? [Solve the equation $-300 + 15N = 0$; Jo must mow 20 lawns.] How much profit will Jo earn if she mows 40 lawns? [Substitute 40 for N; $300.]

Exercise 9 If students are having difficulty writing an equation, encourage them to generate the data with a recursive routine. As needed, point out that 12% is a rate.

9a. $y = 45 + 0.12x$, where x represents dollar amounts customers spend and y represents Manny's daily income in dollars

9b.

[0, 840, 120, 0, 180, 30]

Exercise 10 [Alert] In 10a–c, students might introduce several independent variables. For example, in 10a students might introduce b for minutes biked and s for minutes swum. They may or may not then replace all but one of these variables with the given constant(s)—in 10a, replacing b with 30. As needed, help students see that the question in 10d refers to each of the days described in 10a–c.

---

8. As part of a physics experiment, June threw an object off a cliff and measured how fast it was traveling downward. When the object left June's hand, it was traveling 5 m/s, and it sped up as it fell. The table shows a partial list of the data she collected as the object fell.

Time (s)	Speed (m/s)
0	5.0
0.5	9.9
1.0	14.8
1.5	19.7

a. Write an equation to represent the speed of the object. ⓐ $s = 5 + 9.8t$ or $s = 9.8t + 5$

b. What was the object's speed after 3 s? 34.4 m/s

c. If it were possible for the object to fall long enough, how many seconds would pass before it reached a speed of 83.4 m/s? ⓐ 8 s

d. What limitations do you think this equation has in modeling this situation? ⓐ It doesn't account for air resistance and terminal speed.

9. APPLICATION Manny has a part-time job as a waiter. He makes $45 per day plus tips. He has calculated that his average tip is 12% of the total amount his customers spend on food and beverages.

a. Define variables and write an equation in intercept form to represent Manny's daily income in terms of the amount his customers spend on food and beverages. ⓗ

b. Graph this relationship for food and beverage amounts between $0 and $900.

c. Write and evaluate an expression to find how much Manny makes in one day if his customers spend $312 on food and beverages. $45 + 0.12 \cdot 312 = \$82.44$

d. What amounts spent on food and beverages will give him a daily income between $105 and $120? between $500 and $625

10. APPLICATION Paula is cross-training for a triathlon in which she cycles, swims, and runs. Before designing an exercise program for Paula, her coach consults a table listing rates for calories burned in various activities.

Cross-training activity	Calories burned (per min)
Walking	3.2
Bicycling	3.8
Swimming	6.9
Jogging	7.3
Running	11.3

a. On Monday, Paula starts her workout by biking for 30 minutes and then swimming. Write an equation for the calories she burns on Monday in terms of the number of minutes she swims. $y = 114 + 6.9x$

b. On Wednesday, Paula starts her workout by swimming for 30 minutes and then jogging. Write an equation for the number of calories she burns on Wednesday in terms of the number of minutes she jogs. $y = 207 + 7.3x$

c. On Friday, Paula starts her workout by swimming 15 minutes, then biking for 15 minutes, then running. Write an equation for the number of calories she burns on Friday in terms of the number of minutes she spends running. $y = 160.5 + 11.3x$

d. How many total calories does Paula burn on each day described in 10a–c if she does a 60-minute workout? Monday: 321 calories; Wednesday: 426 calories; Friday: 499.5 calories

Review

2.2 **11.** At a family picnic, your cousin tells you that he always has a hard time remembering how to compute percents. Write him a note explaining what percent means. Use these problems as examples of how to solve the different types of percent problems, with an answer for each.

a. 8 is 15% of what number? @ $\frac{8}{n} = \frac{15}{100}$, $n \approx 53.3$ **b.** 15% of 18.95 is what number? $\frac{15}{100} = \frac{n}{18.95}$, $n \approx 2.8$

c. What percent of 64 is 326? $\frac{p}{100} = \frac{326}{64}$, $p \approx 509.4$ **d.** 10% of what number is 40? $\frac{10}{100} = \frac{40}{n}$, $n = 400$

2.3 **12.** **APPLICATION** Carl has been keeping a record of his gas purchases for his new car. Each time he buys gas, he fills the tank completely. Then he records the number of gallons he bought and the miles since the last fill-up. Here is his record:

Carl's Purchases

Miles traveled	Gallons	$\frac{miles}{gallon}$
363	16.2	22.4
342	15.1	22.6
285	12.9	22.1

a. Copy and complete the table by calculating the ratio of miles per gallon for each purchase.

b. What is the average rate of miles per gallon so far? 22.4 mi/gal

c. The car's tank holds 17.1 gallons. To the nearest mile, how far should Carl be able to go without running out of gas? 383 mi

d. Carl is planning a trip across the United States. He estimates that the trip will be 4230 miles. How many gallons of gas can Carl expect to buy?

approximately 189 gal

Consumer
● CONNECTION ●

Many factors influence the rate at which cars use gas, including size, age, and driving conditions. Advertisements for new cars often give the average mpg for city traffic (slow, congested) and highway traffic (fast, free flowing). These rates help consumers make an informed purchase. For more information about fuel economy, see the links at www.keymath.com/DA .

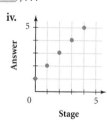

3.2 **13.** Match each recursive routine to a graph below. Explain how you made your decision and tell what assumptions you made.

ii **a.** 2.5 ⌈ENTER⌉
    Ans + 0.5 ⌈ENTER⌉ ; ⌈ENTER⌉ , . . .

iv **b.** 1.0 ⌈ENTER⌉
    Ans + 1.0 ⌈ENTER⌉ ; ⌈ENTER⌉ , . . .

iii **c.** 2.0 ⌈ENTER⌉
    Ans + 1.0 ⌈ENTER⌉ ; ⌈ENTER⌉ , . . .

i **d.** 2.5 ⌈ENTER⌉
    Ans − 0.5 ⌈ENTER⌉ ; ⌈ENTER⌉ , . . .

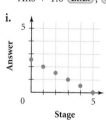
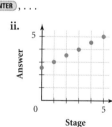
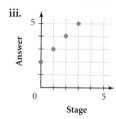

i. **ii.** **iii.** **iv.**

14c. {0,0} (ENTER) {Ans(1) + 1, Ans(2) + 14} (ENTER)

14d. The points lie on a line.

3.3 **14.** Bjarne is training for a bicycle race by riding on a stationary bicycle with a time-distance readout. He is riding at a constant speed. The graph shows his accumulated distance and time as he rides.

a. How fast is Bjarne bicycling? 14 m/s

b. Copy and complete the table. @

c. Write a recursive routine for Bjarne's ride.

d. Looking at the graph, how do you know that Bjarne is neither slowing down nor speeding up during his ride?

e. If Bjarne keeps up the same pace, how far will he ride in one hour? 50,400 m, or 50.4 km

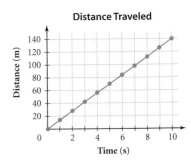

Distance Traveled

Bicyclists race through San Luis Obispo, California.

Time (s)	Distance (m)
1	14
2	28
3	42
4	56
5	70
6	84
7	98
8	112
9	126
10	140

15a. The expression equals −4.

Ans − 8	−3
Ans · 4	−12
Ans/3	−4

2.8 **15.** Consider the expression $\frac{4(y-8)}{3}$.

a. Find the value of the expression if $y = 5$. Make a table to show the order of operations. @

b. Solve the equation $\frac{4(y-8)}{3} = 8$ by undoing the sequence of operations. @ $y = 14$

IMPROVING YOUR REASONING SKILLS

You have two containers of the same size; one contains juice and the other contains water. Remove one tablespoon of juice and put it into the water and stir. Then remove one tablespoon of the water and juice mixture and put it into the juice. Is there more water in the juice or more juice in the water?

IMPROVING REASONING SKILLS

If students are having difficulty figuring out that the percentage of juice in the water is the same as the percentage of the water in the juice, you might suggest that they think about particular amounts of liquid, such as 10 oz of each with 1 oz being transferred. Or produce some decks of playing cards. Give each pair of students a pile of ten red cards and a pile of ten black cards. Have one student pull any number of red cards out and mix them among the black cards. The other student pulls out the same number of cards from the other pile and puts them into the red pile. Keeping track of how many of each color are moving and trying it with extreme cases might deepen students' understanding of the ratios involved.

LESSON 3.5

Linear Equations and Rate of Change

In this lesson you will continue to develop your skills with equations, graphs, and tables of data by exploring the role that the value of b plays in the equation

$$y = a + bx$$

You have already studied the intercept form of a linear equation in several real-world situations. You have used the intercept form to relate calories to minutes spent exercising, floor heights to floor numbers, and distances to time. So, defining variables is an important part of writing equations. Depending on the context of an equation, its numbers take on different real-world meanings. Can you recall how these equations modeled each scenario?

How can it be that mathematics, being after all a product of human thought independent of experience, is so admirably adopted to the objects of reality?

ALBERT EINSTEIN

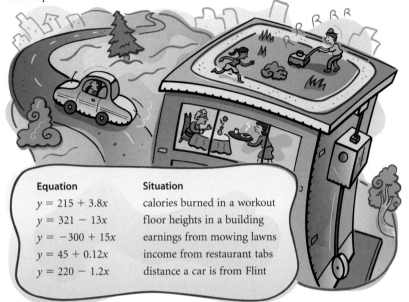

Equation	Situation
$y = 215 + 3.8x$	calories burned in a workout
$y = 321 - 13x$	floor heights in a building
$y = -300 + 15x$	earnings from mowing lawns
$y = 45 + 0.12x$	income from restaurant tabs
$y = 220 - 1.2x$	distance a car is from Flint

Winds of 40 mi/h blow on North Michigan Ave. in 1955 Chicago.

In most linear equations, there are different output values for different input values. This happens when the coefficient of x is not zero. You'll explore how this coefficient relates input and output values in the examples and the investigation.

In addition to giving the actual temperature, weather reports often indicate the temperature you *feel* as a result of the wind chill factor. The wind makes it feel colder than it actually is. In the next example you will use recursive routines to answer some questions about wind chill.

NCTM STANDARDS

CONTENT	PROCESS
✔ Number	Problem Solving
✔ Algebra	✔ Reasoning
✔ Geometry	✔ Communication
✔ Measurement	✔ Connections
Data/Probability	✔ Representation

LESSON OBJECTIVES

- Interpret equations in intercept form using input and output variables
- Explore the relationships among tables, scatter plots, recursive routines, and equations

► **EXAMPLE A**

This example introduces the notion of an input-output table and revisits the idea of rate of change. Students may be confused by the use of table entries as units rather than degrees. That is, the rate of change is 6.4° wind chill per table entry, or 1.28° wind chill per degree temperature.

Wind chill for other wind speeds is given in the investigation (20 mi/h), Exercise 2 (40 mi/h), and Exercise 6 (35 mi/h). The faster the wind, the greater the wind chill factor. Although wind chill appears to be linearly related to the wind speeds, it levels off at wind speeds greater than 45 mi/h.

 Guiding the Investigation

One Step

Show the Wind Chill transparency or refer to the table at the bottom of this page. **[Ask]** "What is the actual temperature if the weather report indicates a wind chill of 10.6° at this wind speed?" As students work, encourage them to use recursive routines, calculate rates of change, and use equations and graphs.

Step 1 In real life, it's not always clear which variable denotes input and which denotes output. The convention is to put input values in the left column and output values in the right column.

EXAMPLE A

The table relates the approximate wind chills for different actual temperatures when the wind speed is 15 mi/h. Assume the wind chill is a linear relationship for temperatures between −5° and 35°.

Temperature (°F)	−5	0	5	10	15	20	25	30	35
Wind chill (°F)	−25.8	−19.4	−13			6.2		19	25.4

a. What are the input and output variables?

b. What is the change in temperature from one table entry to the next? What is the corresponding change in the wind chill?

c. Use calculator lists to write a recursive routine that generates the table values. What are the missing entries?

► **Solution**

a. The input variable is the actual air temperature in °F. The output variable is the temperature you feel as a result of the wind chill factor.

b. For every 5° increase in temperature, the wind chill increases 6.4°.

c. The recursive routine to complete the missing table values is {−5, −25.8} (ENTER) and {Ans(1) + 5, Ans(2) + 6.4} (ENTER). The calculator screen displays the missing entries.

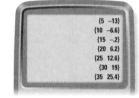

In Example A, the *rate* at which the wind chill drops can be calculated from the ratio $\frac{6.4}{5}$, or $\frac{1.28}{1}$. In other words, it feels 1.28° colder for every 1° drop in air temperature. This number is the rate of change for a wind speed of 15 mi/h. The **rate of change** is equal to the ratio of the change in output values divided by the corresponding change in input values.

Do you think the rate of change differs with various wind speeds?

 Investigation
Wind Chill

In this investigation you'll use the relationship between temperature and wind chill to explore the concept of rate of change and its connections to tables, scatter plots, recursive routines, equations, and graphs.

The data in the table represent the approximate wind chill temperatures in degrees Fahrenheit for a wind speed of 20 mi/h. Use this data set to complete each task.

Step 1 Define the input and output variables for this relationship.

Step 1 Let *x* be the input variable representing the temperature in °F, and let *y* be the output variable representing wind **Step 1** chill in °F.

Temperature (°F)	Wind chill (°F)
−5	−28.540
0	−21.980
1	−20.668
2	−19.356
5	−15.420
15	−2.300
35	23.940

[Data sets: **TMPWS, WNDCH**]

Step 2 | Plot the points and describe the viewing window you used.

Step 3 | Write a recursive routine that gives the pairs of values listed in the table.

Step 4 | Copy the table. Complete the third and fourth columns of the table by recording the changes between consecutive input and output values. Then find the rate of change.

Step 3 Starting value:
$\{-5, -28.54\}$ (ENTER)

Rule for 1° increment:
$\{\text{Ans}(1) + 1, \text{Ans}(2) + 1.312\}$

Input	Output	Change in input values	Change in output values	Rate of change	
−5	−28.540				
0	−21.980	5	6.56	$\frac{+6.56}{+5} =$	1.312
1	−20.668	1	1.312	$\frac{+1.312}{+1} =$	1.312
2	−19.356	1	1.312	$\frac{+1.312}{+1} =$	1.312
5	−15.420	3	3.936	$\frac{+3.936}{+3} =$	1.312
15	−2.300	10	13.12	$\frac{+13.12}{+10} =$	1.312
35	23.940	20	26.24	$\frac{+26.24}{+20} =$	1.312

High wind speeds in Saskatchewan, Canada, drop temperatures below freezing.

Step 5 $y = -21.980 + 1.312x$; the rule appears as the coefficient of x.

Step 5 | Use your routine to write a linear equation in intercept form that relates wind chill to temperature. Note that the starting value, −28.540, is not the y-intercept. How does the rule of the routine appear in your equation?

Step 6 | Graph the equation on the same set of axes as your scatter plot. Use the calculator table to check that your equation is correct. Does it make sense to draw a line through the points? Where does the y-intercept show up in your equation?

Step 7 | What do you notice about the values for rate of change listed in your table? How does the rate of change show up in your equation? In your graph?

Step 8 | Explain how to use the rate of change to find the actual temperature if the weather report indicates a wind chill of 9.5° with 20 mi/h winds.

Step 2

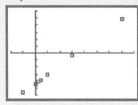

$[-10, 40, 5, -30, 30, 5]$

Step 5 If students are having difficulty, remind them that they can find the rate of change easily if they know output values for input values that are 1 unit apart. Also, elicit the idea that an input value of 0 gives the y-intercept as an output value.

Step 6 Yes, a line represents every possible temperature. The y-intercept shows up as the value of a in the equation. It is not the starting value of the routine.

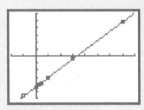

Step 7 The values for rate of change are all equivalent. The rate of change appears as b, the coefficient of x. In the graph, to go from one point to the next you move right 1 unit and up 1.312 units, which is the rate of change.

Step 8 Encourage a variety of approaches: tracing, calculator tables, or working backward to solve the equation $9.5 = -21.98 + 1.312x$.

Step 8 Explanations will vary. Students can add 1.312° nine times to −2.3 and add 9° to 15°. They can also subtract 1.312° eleven times from 23.940° and subtract 11° from 35°. The answer is 24°F.

SHARING IDEAS

Have students present several approaches to Step 8, describing their equations in the process. Mention that the constant rate of change is sometimes called the *wind chill factor* at this wind speed. Draw out the fact that a rate of change is a rate as defined in Chapter 2—that is, a ratio with denominator 1. The rate of change is the output change with each additional unit of input.

[Ask] "What do the equations have in common?" [Elicit the idea that the output variable is usually isolated on the left side, making it easy to enter functions in the calculator for graphing. The right side is like the recursive routine: A constant corresponds to the starting value, and the rate of change is multiplied by the input variable.]

▶ **EXAMPLE B**

EXAMPLE B

This table shows the temperature of the air outside an airplane at different altitudes.

Input	Output
Altitude (m)	Temperature (°C)
1000	7.7
1500	4.2
2200	−0.7
3000	−6.3
4700	−18.2
6000	−27.3

a. Add three columns to the table, and record the change in input values, the change in output values, and the corresponding rate of change.

b. Use the table and a recursive routine to write a linear equation in intercept form $y = a + bx$.

c. What are the real-world meanings of the values for a and b in your equation?

▶ **Solution**

a. Record the change in input values, change in output values, and rate of change in a table. Note the units of each value.

Input	Output			
Altitude (m)	Temperature (°C)	Change in input values (m)	Change in output values (°C)	Rate of change (°C/m)
1000	7.7			
1500	4.2	500	−3.5	$\frac{-3.5}{500} = -0.007$
2200	−0.7	700	−4.9	$\frac{-4.9}{700} = -0.007$
3000	−6.3	800	−5.6	$\frac{-5.6}{800} = -0.007$
4700	−18.2	1700	−11.9	$\frac{-11.9}{1700} = -0.007$
6000	−27.3	1300	−9.1	$\frac{-9.1}{1300} = -0.007$

b. Note that the rate of change, or slope, is always −0.007, or $\frac{-7}{1000}$. You can also write the rate of change as $\frac{-0.7}{100}$, so this recursive routine models the relationship:

{1000, 7.7} (ENTER)

{Ans(1) + 100, Ans(2) − 0.7} (ENTER)

Working this routine backward, {Ans(1) − 100, Ans(2) + 0.7}, will eventually give the result {0, 14.7}. So the intercept form of the equation is $y = 14.7 - 0.007x$, where x represents the altitude in meters and y represents the air temperature in °C.

[Ask] "How is the rate of change represented on the graph?" As needed, draw a picture showing that, as the line moves 1 unit from left to right, it rises by the amount of the rate of change, so the larger the rate of change, the steeper the line. You might use the word *slope* as a synonym for steepness of the line, representing the rate of change. The term *slope* will be defined in Lesson 4.1.

For more practice with linear equations, you might use the CBL 2 demonstration Heating Up, which has students model the relationship between Fahrenheit and Celsius.

Assessing Progress
Observe students' skills at making a scatter plot, choosing a viewing window, writing a recursive routine, writing a linear equation from a recursive routine, and graphing a line. Also assess their understanding of rate of change.

▶ **EXAMPLE B**
To encourage critical thinking, ask students if they believe the given data. They may speculate that the actual numbers depend on the time of year and the location. Part c gives you the chance to connect the mathematics to the real-world context.

Note that the starting value of the recursive routine is not the same as the value of the *y*-intercept in the equation.

c. The value of *a*, 14.7, is the temperature (in °C) of the air at sea level. The value of *b* indicates that the temperature drops 0.007°C for each meter that a plane climbs.

EXERCISES

You will need your graphing calculator for Exercises **4, 5,** and **10.**

▶ **Practice Your Skills**

1. Copy and complete the table of output values for each equation.

a. $y = 50 + 2.5x$
@

Input *x*	Output *y*
20	100
−30	−25
16	90
15	87.5
−12.5	18.75

b. $L_2 = -5.2 - 10 \cdot L_1$

L_1 *x*	L_2 *y*
0	−5.2
−8	74.8
24	−245.2
−35	344.8
−5.2	46.8

2. Use the equation $w = -29 + 1.4t$, where *t* is temperature and *w* is wind chill, both in °F, to approximate the wind chill temperatures for a wind speed of 40 mi/h.

a. Find *w* for *t* = 32°. *w* = 15.8°F

b. Find *t* for a wind chill of *w* = −8. @ *w* = 15°F

c. What is the real-world meaning of 1.4? @

d. What is the real-world meaning of −29?

3. Describe what the rate of change looks like in each graph.

a. the graph of a person walking at a steady rate toward a motion sensor @

b. the graph of a person standing still

c. the graph of a person walking at a steady rate away from a motion sensor

d. the graph of one person walking at a steady rate faster than another person

4. Use the "Easy" setting of the INOUT game on your calculator to produce four data tables. Copy each table and write the equation you used to match the data values in the table. [▶ 🖳 See **Calculator Note 3C** to learn how to run the program. ◀]

3c. The rate is positive, so the line goes from the lower left to the upper right.

3d. The rate for the speedier walker will be greater than the rate for the person walking more slowly, so the graph for the speedier walker will be steeper than the graph for the slower walker.

4. A sample:

```
IN OUT
    [[0  -5]
     [1  -3]
     [2  -1]
     [3   1 ]
     [4   3 ]
     [5   5 ]]
GUESS: -5+2L₁
```

Closing the Lesson

You can calculate the **rate of change** as a difference of output values divided by a difference of corresponding input values. The rate of change determines the steepness of the graph of the linear equation representing the data.

BUILDING UNDERSTANDING

Students work more with input and output variables, rates of change, and graphs of equations.

ASSIGNING HOMEWORK

Essential	1–3, 6–8
Performance assessment	5, 6, 7
Portfolio	10
Journal	2, 8
Group	4, 5, 7, 9
Review	11–14

▶ **Helping with the Exercises**

Exercise 2 If students are having difficulty, encourage them to measure or count how many units the line rises or falls as it moves 1 unit from left to right.

2c. The wind chill temperature changes by 1.4° for each 1° change in actual temperature.

2d. If the actual temperature is 0°F, the wind chill temperature is −29°F.

3a. The rate is negative, so the line goes from the upper left to the lower right.

3b. The rate is neither negative nor positive but zero. The line is a horizontal line.

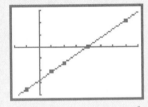
► Reason and Apply

5. Each table below shows a different input-output relationship.

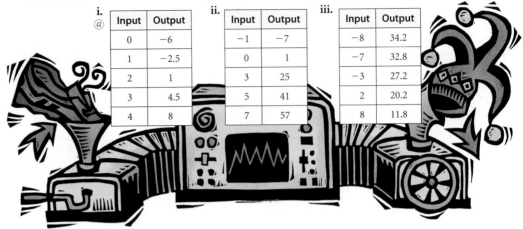

i.
Input	Output
0	−6
1	−2.5
2	1
3	4.5
4	8

ii.
Input	Output
−1	−7
0	1
3	25
5	41
7	57

iii.
Input	Output
−8	34.2
−7	32.8
−3	27.2
2	20.2
8	11.8

a. Find the rate of change in each table. Explain how you found this value. i. 3.5; ii. 8; iii. −1.4

b. For each table, find the output value that corresponds to an input value of 0. What is this value called? ⓗ i. −6; ii. 1; iii. 23; the y-intercept

c. Use your results from 5a and b to write an equation in intercept form for each table. i. $y = -6 + 3.5x$; ii. $y = 1 + 8x$; iii. $y = 23 - 1.4x$

d. Use a calculator list of input values to check that each equation actually produces the output values shown in the table.

6. The wind chill temperatures for a wind speed of 35 mi/h are given in the table.

Temperature (°F)	−5	5	10	20	35
Wind chill (°F)	−35	−21	−14	0	21

a. Define input and output variables. ⓐ

b. Find the rate of change. Explain how you got your answer. ⓐ

c. Write an equation in intercept form. ⓐ $y = -28 + 1.4x$

d. Plot the points and graph the equation on the same set of axes. How are the graphs for the points and the equation similar? How are they different?

7. Semantha's walk was recorded by a motion sensor. A graph of her walk and a few data points are shown here.

Time (s)	Distance (m)
0	3.5
2	3
6	2

a. Write an equation in the form *Distance from sensor* = *start distance* + *change* to model this walk. ⓗ

b. If she continues to walk at a constant rate, at what time would she pass the sensor?

8. You can use the equation $7.3x = 200$ to describe a rectangle with an area of 200 square units like the one shown. What are the real-world meanings of the numbers and the variable in the equation? Solve the equation for x and explain the meaning of your solution. Is the rectangle drawn to scale? How can you tell?

| 200 square units | 7.3 units |

x units

9. The total area of the figure at right is 1584 square units. You can use the equation $1584 - 33x = 594$ to represent an area of 1584 square units minus the area of $33x$ square units. The area remaining is 594 square units.

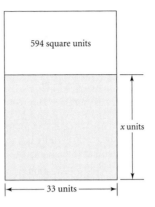

594 square units

x units

33 units

   a. What is the area of the shaded rectangle? @ 990 square units
   b. Write the equation you would use to find the height of the shaded rectangle. @ possible answers: $33x = 990$; $x = \frac{990}{33}$
   c. Solve the equation you wrote in 9b to find the height of the shaded rectangle. @ 30 units

10. Use the "Medium" setting of the INOUT game on your calculator to produce four data tables. Copy each table and write the equation you used to match the data values in the table. [▶ See **Calculator Note 3C.** ◀]

▶ Review

2.8 11. Show how you can solve these equations by using an undoing process. Check your results by substituting the solutions into the original equations.
   a. $-15 = -52 + 1.6x$ b. $7 - 3x = 52$

3.2 12. **APPLICATION** To plan a trip downtown, you compare the costs of three different parking lots. ABC Parking charges $5 for the first hour and $2 for each additional hour or fraction of an hour. Cozy Car charges $3 per hour or fraction of an hour, and The Corner Lot charges a $15 flat rate for a whole day.

   a. Make a table similar to the one shown. Write recursive routines to calculate the cost of parking up to 10 hours at each of the three lots.

Hours parked	ABC Parking	Cozy Car	The Corner Lot
1	5	3	15
2	7	6	15
3	9	9	15

   b. Make three different scatter plots on the same pair of axes showing the parking rates at the three different lots. Use a different color for each parking lot. Put the hours on the horizontal axis and the cost on the vertical axis.

   c. Compare the three scatter plots. Under what conditions is each parking lot the best deal for your trip? Use the graph to explain.

   d. Would it make sense to draw a line through each set of points? Explain why or why not. No; because you have to pay for a whole hour for any fraction of the hour, the price of parking does not increase continuously.

11a. -15
Ans + 52
Ans/1.6
$-52 + 1.6(23.125) = -15$

-15
37
23.125
Check.

11b. 52
Ans − 7
Ans/−3
$7 - 3(-15) = 52$

52
45
-15
Check.

12b.

Downtown Parking

◇ ABC Parking
□ Cozy Car
△ Corner Lot

Cost

Hours parked

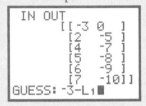

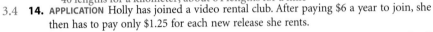

2.3 13. Today while Don was swimming, he started wondering how many lengths he would have to swim in order to swim different distances. At one end of the pool, he stopped, gasping for breath, and asked the lifeguard. She told him that 1 length of the pool is 25 yards and that 72 lengths is 1 mile. As he continued swimming, he wondered:

70.4 lengths **a.** Is 72 lengths really a mile? Exactly how many lengths would it take to swim a mile? ⓗ

b. If it took him a total of 40 minutes to swim a mile, what was his average speed in feet per second? 2.2 ft/s

c. How many lengths would it take to swim a kilometer? about 44 lengths

d. Last summer Don got to swim in a pool that was 25 meters long. How many lengths would it take to swim a kilometer there? How many for a mile?
40 lengths for a kilometer; about 64 lengths for a mile

3.4 14. APPLICATION Holly has joined a video rental club. After paying $6 a year to join, she then has to pay only $1.25 for each new release she rents.

a. Write an equation in intercept form to represent Holly's cost for movie rentals. ⓐ $y = 6 + 1.25x$

b. Graph this situation for up to 60 movie rentals.

c. Video Unlimited charges $60 for a year of unlimited movie rentals. How many movies would Holly have to rent for this to be a better deal? 44 movies

14b.
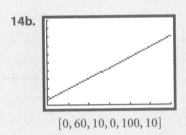
[0, 60, 10, 0, 100, 10]

project

LEGAL LIMITS

To make a highway accessible to more vehicles, engineers reduce its steepness, also called its **gradient** or grade. This highway was designed with switchbacks so the gradient would be small.

A gradient is the inclination of a roadway to the horizontal surface. Research the federal, state, and local standards for the allowable gradients of highways, streets, and railway routes.

Find out how gradients are expressed in engineering terms. Give the standards for roadway types designed for vehicles of various weights, speeds, and engine power in terms of rate of change. Describe the alternatives available to engineers to reduce the gradient of a route in hilly or mountainous terrain. What safety measures do they incorporate to minimize risk on steep grades? Bring pictures to illustrate a presentation about your research, showing how engineers have applied standards to roads and routes in your home area.

Supporting the project

MOTIVATION

Steep roads are harder to travel and harder to maintain. Engineers must consider steepness as they design roads. What guidelines and regulations do they follow?

OUTCOMES

► Gradient is defined. Stated as a percent, 20% means a rise of 20 ft every 100 ft. Stated as a ratio, 1 to 5 is the same as 20%.

► The report summarizes standards. A 20% gradient, an angle of 11.5°, is considered steep. A maximum of 15% sustained gradient is recommended. Where there is heavy snowfall, the maximum is 10%.

► The report includes techniques for reducing gradients and safety measures that can minimize risk on steep grades.

► The report includes relevant pictures of nearby roads.

• Gradients for roads are compared with gradients for railroads.

• The slope of a line is carefully defined.

Solving Equations Using the Balancing Method

In the previous two lessons, you learned about rate of change and the intercept form of a linear equation. In this lesson you'll learn symbolic methods to solve these equations. You've already seen the calculator methods of tracing on a graph and zooming in on a table. These methods usually give approximate solutions. Working backward to undo operations is a symbolic method that gives exact solutions. Another symbolic method that you can apply to solve equations is the **balancing method.** In this lesson you'll investigate how to use the balancing method to solve linear equations. You'll discover that it's closely related to the undoing method.

 ## Investigation
Balancing Pennies

You will need

- pennies
- three paper cups

Here is a visual model of the equation $2x + 3 = 7$. A cup represents the variable x and pennies represent numbers. Assume that each cup has the same number of pennies in it and that the containers themselves are weightless.

Step 1 2; sample explanation: Four pennies must be in the two cups, so there are two per cup.

Step 2 $2x = 4$

Step 1 | How many pennies must be in each cup if the left side of the scale balances with the right side? Explain how you got your answer.

Your answer to Step 1 is the solution to the equation $2x + 3 = 7$. It's the number that can replace x to make the statement true. In Steps 2 and 3, you'll use pictures and equations to show stages that lead to the solution.

Step 2 | Redraw the picture above, but with three pennies removed from each side of the scale. Write the equation that your picture represents.

NCTM STANDARDS

CONTENT		PROCESS	
✔	Number	✔	Problem Solving
✔	Algebra	✔	Reasoning
	Geometry	✔	Communication
✔	Measurement	✔	Connections
	Data/Probability	✔	Representation

LESSON OBJECTIVE

- Learn the balancing method to solve equations by doing the same thing to both sides

---

that an unbalanced scale doesn't tell as much as a balanced one. Remind students that to keep a balance they must do the same thing to both sides. If there's time, have each group set up an equation for other groups to solve.

Step 1 If students ask, point out that the balance pictured is a pan balance, with all masses on each side concentrated on one point, as opposed to the beam balance of Chapter 2, in which the distribution of masses was important.

Steps 7 and 8 Students may use undoing to solve the equation. Encourage them to see how working backward is used on one side of the balance to isolate the unknown.

SHARING IDEAS

At one station for groups to visit during Steps 4 through 8, you might place five pennies under each of two cups, lay out four pennies and seven washers on the same side, and put ten pennies and three washers on the other side. Explain to visiting students that each washer represents -1. Then, when the class is together, ask how they solved the equation $2x + 4 - 7 = 10 - 3$, or $2x - 3 = 7$. Elicit the idea that, just as they combined the four pennies with four washers and removed them, they could add three pennies to each side to "cancel out" the three washers remaining on the left. In other words, when you add a number to its opposite, you get 0, and you can remove 0's from anywhere on the balance without effect. (This wouldn't work on an actual pan balance, because the washers would have positive weights.)

If you don't have washers, ask during Sharing how you might model the equation $2x - 3 = 7$ on a pan balance. Students may suggest that you could add three

Step 3 $x = 2$

| Step 3 | Redraw the picture, this one showing half of what was on each side of the scale in Step 2. There should be just one cup on the left side of the scale and the correct number of pennies on the right side needed to balance it. Write the equation that this picture represents. This is the solution to the original equation. |

Now your group will create a pennies-and-cups equation for another group to solve.

Step 4	Divide the pennies into two equal piles. If you have one left over, put it aside. Draw a large equal sign (or form one with two pencils) and place the penny stacks on opposite sides of it.
Step 5	From the pile on one side of your equal sign, make three identical stacks, leaving at least a few pennies out of the stacks. Hide each stack under a paper cup. You should now have three cups and some pennies on one side of your equal sign.
Step 6	On the other side you should have a pile of pennies. On both sides of the equal sign you have the same number of pennies, but on one side some of the pennies are hidden under cups. You can think of the two sides of the equal sign as being the two sides of a balance scale. Write an equation for this setup, using x to represent the number of pennies hidden under one cup.
Step 7	Move to another group's setup. Look at their arrangement of pennies and cups, and write an equation for it. Solve the equation; that is, find how many pennies are under one cup without looking. When you're sure you know how many pennies are under each cup, you can look to check your answer.
Step 8	Write a brief description of how you solved the equation.

You can do problems like those in the investigation using a balance scale as long as the weight of the cup is very small. But an actual balance scale can only model equations in which all the numbers involved are positive. Still, the idea of balancing equations can apply to equations involving negative numbers. Just remember, when you add any number to its opposite, you get 0. For this reason, the opposite of a number is called the **additive inverse.** Think of negative and positive numbers as having opposite effects on a balance scale. You can remove 0 from either side of a balance-scale picture without affecting the balance. These three figures all represent 0:

$$1 + (-1) = 0$$

$$-3 + 3 = 0$$

$$2x + (-2x) = 0$$

pennies to the seven on the right. Point out that doing so models the equation $2x = 7 + 3$. **[Ask]** "Do the equations $2x - 3 = 7$ and $2x = 7 + 3$ have the same solution?" [yes]

For more practice with balancing, use the Sketchpad demonstration The Balancing Method.

EXAMPLE A | Draw a series of balance-scale pictures to solve the equation $6 = -2 + 4x$.

▶ **Solution** | The goal is to end up with a single x-cup on one side of the balance scale. One way to get rid of something on one side is to add its opposite to both sides.

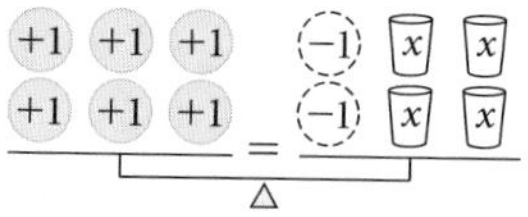

Here is the equation $6 = -2 + 4x$ solved by the balancing method:

Picture	Action taken	Equation
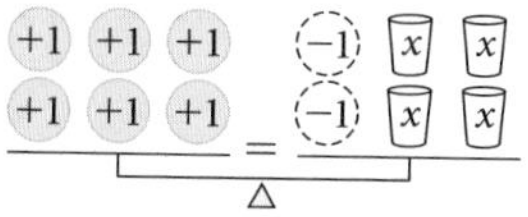	Original equation.	$6 = -2 + 4x$
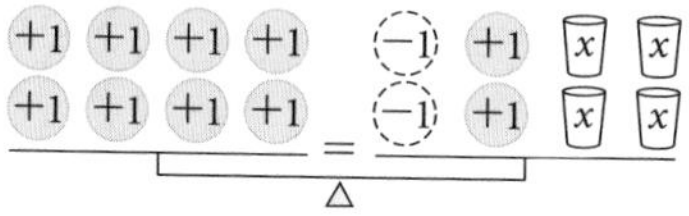	Add 2 to both sides.	$6 + 2 = -2 + 2 + 4x$
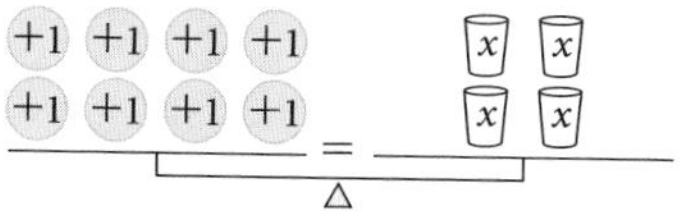	Remove the 0.	$8 = 4x$
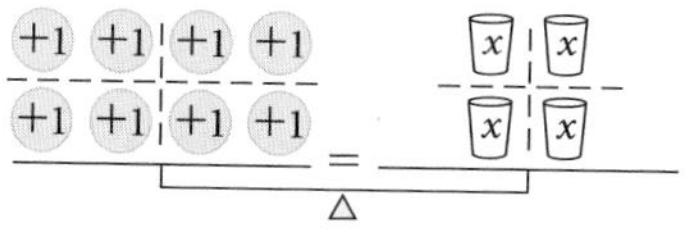	Divide both sides by 4.	$\frac{8}{4} = \frac{4x}{4}$
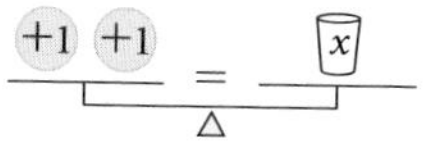	Reduce.	$2 = x$ or $x = 2$

In the second and third equations, you saw $6 + 2$ combine to 8, and $-2 + 2$ combine to 0. You can combine numbers because they are *like terms*. However, in the first equation you could not combine -2 and $4x$, because they are *not* like terms. **Like terms** are terms in which the variable component is the same, and they may differ only by a coefficient.

Assessing Progress

Observe how well students follow directions, work in groups, and understand the idea of balance.

▶ **EXAMPLE A**

This example continues the idea of working with negative numbers on a picture of a pan balance (not an actual balance). You might want to reinforce the new vocabulary *additive inverse* as you discuss this example. Exercise 6 defines *multiplicative inverse*.

If you decide to show students an example of an equation in which x has a negative coefficient, be aware of the pitfalls of the balancing model. You may use undoing and divide or multiply by the multiplicative inverse.

Another option is to move the term to the other side of the equation to give it a positive coefficient.

Balance-scale pictures can help you see what to do to solve an equation by the balancing method. But you won't need the pictures once you get the idea of doing the same thing to both sides of an equation. And pictures are less useful if the numbers in the equation aren't "nice."

► **EXAMPLE B**

This example illustrates how to solve a linear equation by four different methods. With an appropriate choice of window, the calculator methods can be made more exact, but in general finding that window is more difficult than using the other methods.

EXAMPLE B

Solve the equation $-31 = -50.25 + 1.55x$ using each method.

a. undoing operations

b. the balancing method

c. tracing on a calculator graph

d. zooming in on a calculator table

► **Solution**

Each of these methods will give the same answer, but notice the differences among the methods. When might you prefer to use a particular method?

a. undoing operations

Start with -31.

b. the balancing method

$-31 = -50.25 + 1.55x$	Original equation.
$-31 + 50.25 = -50.25 + 50.25 + 1.55x$	Add 50.25 to both sides.
$19.25 = 1.55x$	Combine like terms. (Evaluate and remove the 0.)
$\dfrac{19.25}{1.55} = \dfrac{1.55x}{1.55}$	Divide both sides by 1.55.
$12.42 \approx x$, or $x \approx 12.42$	Reduce.

This chart shows how balancing equations is related to the undoing method that you've been using. In the last column, as you work up from the bottom, you can see how the equation changes as you apply the "undo" operation to both sides of the equation.

Equation: $-31 = -50.25 + 1.55x$			
Description	**Undo**	**Result**	**Equation**
Pick x.	//////	≈ 12.42	$12.42 \approx x$
Multiply by 1.55.	$/ (1.55)$	19.25	$19.25 = 1.55x$
Subtract 50.25.	$+ (50.25)$	-31	$-31 = -50.25 + 1.55x$

In parts a and b, if you convert the answer to a fraction, you get an exact solution of $\frac{385}{31}$.

c. tracing on a calculator graph

Enter the equation into Y1. Adjust your window settings and graph. Press TRACE and use the arrow keys to find the x-value for a y-value of −31. (See Example B in Lesson 3.4 to review this procedure.) You can see that for a y-value of approximately −31.6 the x-value is 12.02.

$[-55, 35, 10, -120, 30, 10]$

d. zooming in on a calculator table

To find a starting value for the table, use guess-and-check or a calculator graph to find an approximate answer. Then use the calculator table to find the answer to the desired accuracy.

Once you have determined a reasonable starting value, zoom in on a calculator table to find the answer using smaller and smaller values for the table increment. [▶ 🖳 See **Calculator Note 2A** to review zooming in on a table. ◀]

You can also check your answer by using substitution.

The calculator result isn't exactly −31 because 12.42 is a rounded answer. If you substitute an exact solution such as $\frac{19.25}{1.55}$ or $\frac{385}{31}$, you'll get exactly −31.

From Example B, you can see that each method has its advantages. The methods of balancing and undoing use the same process of working backward to get an exact solution. The two calculator methods are easy to use but usually give approximate solutions to the equation. You may prefer one method over others, depending on the equation you need to solve. If you are able to solve an equation using two or more different methods, you can check to see that each method gives the same result. With practice, you may develop symbolic solving methods of your own. Knowing a variety of methods, such as the balancing and undoing methods, as well as the calculator methods, will improve your equation-solving skills, regardless of which method you prefer.

In Exercise 12, you'll see how to use the balancing method to solve an equation that has the variable on both sides.

Closing the Lesson

Of the two exact methods for solving linear equations, the **balancing method** is useful when the variable appears more than once in the equation. The undoing method helps students focus on the order of operations.

BUILDING UNDERSTANDING

Students practice solving equations by a variety of methods.

ASSIGNING HOMEWORK

Essential	1–6, 9, 12
Performance assessment	9
Portfolio	9
Journal	6
Group	8, 10–12
Review	13–15

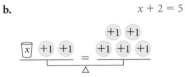

EXERCISES

You will need your graphing calculator for Exercises **8** and **14.**

▶ Practice Your Skills

1. Give the equation that each picture models.

a.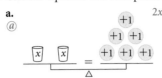
$2x = 6$

b.
$x + 2 = 5$

c.
$2x - 1 = 3$

d.
$2 = 2x - 3$

2. Copy and fill in the table to solve the equation as in Example A.

Picture	Action taken	Equation
	Original equation.	$2x - 2 = 4$
	Add 2 to both sides.	$2x - 2 + 2 = 4 + 2$
	Remove 0 from left side.	$2x = 6$
	Divide both sides by 2.	$\dfrac{2x}{2} = \dfrac{6}{2}$
	Reduce.	$x = 3$

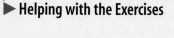
3. Give the next stages of the equation, matching the action taken, to reach the solution.

a. $0.1x + 12 = 2.2$ @   Original equation.

$0.1x + 12 - 12 = 2.2 - 12$ Subtract 12 from both sides.

$0.1x = -9.8$ Remove the 0 and subtract.

$x = -98$ Divide both sides by 0.1.

b. $\dfrac{12 + 3.12x}{3} = -100$ Original equation.

$12 + 3.12x = -300$ Multiply both sides by 3.

               Subtract 12 from both sides.

$12 - 12 + 3.12x = -300 - 12$

$3.12x = -312$ Remove the 0.

$x = -100$ Divide both sides by 3.12

4. Complete the tables to solve the equations.

a.

Equation: $\dfrac{3(x-8)}{5} + 7 = 34$			
Description	**Undo**	**Result**	**Equation**
Pick x.	▨	53	$x = 53$
Subtract 8.	$+ (8)$	45	$x - 8 = 45$
Multiply by 3.	$/ (3)$	135	$3(x - 8) = 135$
Divide by 5.	$\cdot (5)$	27	$\dfrac{3(x-8)}{5} = 27$
Add 7.	$- (7)$	34	$\dfrac{3(x-8)}{5} + 7 = 34$

b.

Equation: $7\left(\dfrac{2+x}{4}\right) - 5 = 16$			
Description	**Undo**	**Result**	**Equation**
Pick x.	▨	10	$x = 10$
Add 2.	$- (2)$	12	$2 + x = 12$
Divide by 4.	$\cdot (4)$	3	$\dfrac{2+x}{4} = 3$
Multiply by 7	$/ (7)$	21	$7\left(\dfrac{2+x}{4}\right) = 21$
Subtract 5.	$+ (5)$	16	$7\left(\dfrac{2+x}{4}\right) - 5 = 16$

5. Give the additive inverse of each number.

a. $\dfrac{1}{5}$ @ $-\dfrac{1}{5}$ **b.** 17 -17 **c.** -2.3 2.3 **d.** $-x$ x

---

▶ **Reason and Apply**

6. A **multiplicative inverse** is a number or expression that you can multiply by something to get a value of 1. The multiplicative inverse of 4 is $\frac{1}{4}$ because $4 \cdot \frac{1}{4} = 1$. Give the multiplicative inverse of each number.

a. 12 @ $\dfrac{1}{12}$ **b.** $\dfrac{1}{6}$ 6 **c.** 0.02 50 **d.** $-\dfrac{1}{2}$ -2

7. Solve these equations. Tell what action you take at each stage.

a. $144x = 12$ $x = \dfrac{1}{12}$ **b.** $\dfrac{1}{6}x + 2 = 8$ $x = 36$

8. *Mini-Investigation* A solution to the equation $-10 + 3x = 5$ is shown below.

$$-10 + 3x = 5$$
$$3x = 15$$
$$x = 5$$

a. Describe the steps that transform the original equation into the second equation and the second equation into the third (the solution).   Add 10 to both sides, divide both sides by 3.

b. Graph $Y_1 = -10 + 3x$ and $Y_2 = 5$, and trace to the lines' intersection. Write the coordinates of this point. $(5, 5)$

Exercise 7 Most students will divide both sides of 7a by 144. For 7b, students may multiply both sides by 6, then subtract 12 from both sides, or they may subtract 2 from both sides, then multiply both sides by 6.

8b.

$[-10, 10, 1, -5, 20, 1]$

8c.

Y1=3X

X=5.106383   Y=15.319149

8d.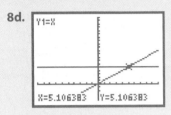

Y1=X

X=5.106383   Y=5.106383

8e. Even though the lines are different in each graph, in all three graphs the x-coordinate of the intersection is the same: $x = 5$. This illustrates that transforming the equation by doing the same thing to both sides does not change the solution.

Exercise 9 There are different ways to keep the equation balanced as it is solved. For example, the first step could be to multiply both sides by 10.

Exercise 11 As needed, remind students that lw means the product of l and w and that the answer gives the length of a rectangle in terms of its area and width. Although familiarity with the other formulas is not necessary in order to solve the equations, you might ask what the other formulas are used for. [a. circumference of a circle; b. area of a triangle; c. perimeter of a rectangle; d. perimeter of a square; e. distance traveled at a constant rate; f. area of a trapezoid] In 11f, students might have trouble isolating h. As a hint, you can suggest treating $(a + b)$ as a single number.

c. Graph $Y_1 = 3x$ and $Y_2 = 15$, and trace to the lines' intersection. Write the coordinates of this point. $(5, 15)$

d. Graph $Y_1 = x$ and $Y_2 = 5$, and trace to the lines' intersection. Write the coordinates of this point. $(5, 5)$

e. What do you notice about your answers to 8b–d? Explain what this illustrates.

9. Solve the equation $4 + 1.2x = 12.4$ by using each method.

  a. balancing   **b.** undoing   **c.** tracing on a graph   **d.** zooming in on a table

10. Solve each equation symbolically using the balancing method.

  a. $3 + 2x = 17$ @   **b.** $0.5x + 2.2 = 101.0$ **c.** $x + 307.2 = 2.1$

  d. $2(2x+2) = 7$ **e.** $\dfrac{4 + 0.01x}{6.2} - 6.2 = 0$ @

11. You can solve familiar formulas for a specific variable. For example, solving $A = lw$ for l you get

$$A = lw \qquad \text{Original equation.}$$
$$\frac{A}{w} = \frac{lw}{w} \qquad \text{Divide both sides by } w.$$
$$\frac{A}{w} = l \qquad \text{Reduce.}$$

You can also write $l = \frac{A}{w}$. Now try solving these formulas for the given variable.

  a. $C = 2\pi r$ for r @ $r = \dfrac{C}{2\pi}$ **b.** $A = \frac{1}{2}(hb)$ for h $h = \dfrac{2A}{b}$ **c.** $P = 2(l + w)$ for l @ $l = \dfrac{P}{2} - w$

  d. $P = 4s$ for s $s = \dfrac{P}{4}$ **e.** $d = rt$ for t $t = \dfrac{d}{r}$ **f.** $A = \frac{1}{2}h(a + b)$ for h $h = \dfrac{2A}{a + b}$

12. An equation can have the variable on both sides. In these cases you can maintain the balance by eliminating the x's from one of the sides before you begin undoing.

  a. Copy and complete this table to solve the equation. @

Picture	Action taken	Equation
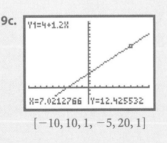	Original equation.	$2 + 4x = x + 8$
	Subtract $1x$ from both sides.	$2 + 3x = 8$
See picture at right.	Subtract 2 from both sides.	$3x = 6$
See picture at right.	Divide both sides by 3.	$x = 2$

Picture

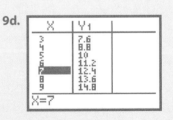

  b. Show the steps used to solve $5x - 4 = 2x + 5$ using the balancing method. Substitute your solution into the original equation to check your answer.

9a.

$4 + 1.2x = 12.4$	Original equation.
$4 - 4 + 1.2x = 12.4 - 4$	Subtract 4 from both sides.
$1.2x = 8.4$	Remove the 0 and subtract.
$\dfrac{1.2x}{1.2} = \dfrac{8.4}{1.2}$	Divide both sides by 1.2.
$x = 7$	Reduce.

9b. Start with 12.4.

  Ans $- 4$ 12.4

  Ans/1.2   8.4

                 7

9c.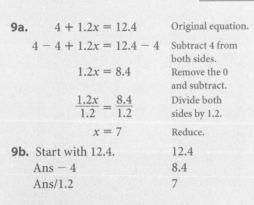

Y1=4+1.2X

X=7.0212766   Y=12.425532

$[-10, 10, 1, -5, 20, 1]$

9d.

X	Y1
3	7.6
4	8.8
5	10
6	11.2
7	12.4
8	13.6
9	14.8

X=7

▶ Review

2.1 **13.** APPLICATION Economy drapes for a certain size window cost \$90. They have shallow pleats, and the width of the fabric is $2\frac{1}{4}$ times the window width. Luxury drapes of the same fabric for the same size window have deeper pleats. The width of the fabric is 3 times the window width. What price should the store manager ask for the luxury drapes? ⓗ $\frac{\$90}{2.25} = \frac{x}{3}, x = \$120$

3.4 **14.** Run the easy level of the LINES program on your calculator. [▶ 🖥 See **Calculator Note 3D** to learn how to use the LINES program. ◀] Sketch a graph of the randomly generated line on your paper. Use the trace function to locate the *y*-intercept and to determine the rate of change. When the calculator says you have the correct equation, write it under the graph. Repeat this program until you get three correct equations in a row.

3.2 **15.** The local bagel store sells a baker's dozen of bagels for \$6.49, while the grocery store down the street sells a bag of 6 bagels for \$2.50.

a. Copy and complete the tables showing the cost of bagels at the two stores.

Bagel Store

Bagels	13	26	39	52	65	78
Cost	6.49	12.98	19.47	25.96	32.45	38.94

Grocery Store

Bagels	6	12	18	24	30	36	42	48	54	60
Cost	2.50	5.00	7.50	10.00	12.50	15.00	17.50	20.00	22.50	25.00

b. Graph the information for each market on the same coordinate axes. Put bagels on the horizontal axis and cost on the vertical axis.

c. Find equations to describe the cost of bagels at each store.

d. How much does one bagel cost at each store? How do these cost values relate to the equations you wrote in 15c?

e. Looking at the graphs, how can you tell which store is the cheaper place to buy bagels? the grocery store, because its line is lower

f. Bernie and Buffy decided to use a recursive routine to complete the tables. Bernie used this routine for the bagel store:

6.49 ⬚ENTER⬚

Ans · 2 ⬚ENTER⬚

Buffy says that this routine isn't correct, even though it gives the correct answer for 13 and 26 bagels. Explain to Bernie what is wrong with his recursive routine. What routine should he use? Bernie's routine calculates each price by doubling the last. It works the first time, because if you buy twice as many bagels, you pay twice as much. But using Bernie's routine, if you buy 36 bagels at the bagel store, you pay \$25.96 instead of \$19.47, which amounts to paying four times as much as a single dozen instead of three times the price of a dozen. The routine should be: 6.49 ⬚ENTER⬚, Ans + 6.49, ⬚ENTER⬚, ⬚ENTER⬚,....

15b.

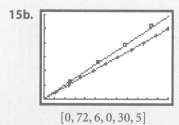

[0, 72, 6, 0, 30, 5]

The line with the square markers is the bagel store, and the line with the crosses is the grocery store.

15c. *y* represents cost; *x* represents number of bagels.

bagel store: $y = \frac{6.49}{13}x$ (or $y \approx 0.50x$)

grocery store: $y = \frac{2.50}{6}x$ (or $y \approx 0.42x$)

15d. Bagel store: about 50¢ per bagel; grocery store: about 42¢ per bagel; these are the coefficients of *x* or constants of variation in the equations.

10a. $3 + 2x = 17$

$3 - 3 + 2x = 17 - 3$

$2x = 14$

$\frac{2x}{2} = \frac{14}{2}$

$x = 7$

10b. $0.5x + 2.2 = 101.0$

$0.5x + 2.2 - 2.2 = 101.0 - 2.2$

$0.5x = 98.8$

$\frac{0.5x}{0.5} = \frac{98.8}{0.5}$

$x = 197.6$

10c. $x + 307.2 = 2.1$

$x + 307.2 - 307.2 = 2.1 - 307.2$

$x = -305.1$

10d. $2(2x + 2) = 7$

$\frac{2(2x + 2)}{2} = \frac{7}{2}$

$2x + 2 = 3.5$

$2x + 2 - 2 = 3.5 - 2$

$2x = 1.5$

$\frac{2x}{2} = \frac{1.5}{2}$

$x = 0.75$

10e. $\frac{4 + 0.01x}{6.2} - 6.2 = 0$

$\frac{4 + 0.01x}{6.2} - 6.2 + 6.2 = 0 + 6.2$

$\frac{4 + 0.01x}{6.2} = 6.2$

$\frac{4 + 0.01x}{6.2} \cdot 6.2 = 6.2 \cdot 6.2$

$4 + 0.01x = 38.44$

$4 - 4 + 0.01x = 38.44 - 4$

$0.01x = 34.44$

$\frac{0.01x}{0.01} = \frac{34.44}{0.01}$

$x = 3444$

12b. $5x - 4 = 2x + 5$

$5x - 2x - 4 = 2x - 2x + 5$

$3x - 4 = 5$

$3x - 4 + 4 = 5 + 4$

$3x = 9$

$x = 3$

Check: $5(3) - 4 \overset{?}{=} 2(3) + 5$

$15 - 4 \overset{?}{=} 6 + 5$

$11 = 11$

Exercise 15 As needed, remind students that a *baker's dozen* is 13.

LESSON

3.7

PLANNING

LESSON OUTLINE

One day:

30 min   Activity

20 min   Improving Reasoning Skills

MATERIALS

- pieces of rope of different lengths (around 1 m) and thickness (two per group)
- metersticks or tape measures (two per group)
- Fathom demonstration *Tying Knots, optional*

TEACHING

Students experiment with the slope and *y*-intercept of a line that fits real-world data.

Guiding the Activity

This activity works best with one pair of students working on each rope. The Fathom demonstration *Tying Knots* can be used for Steps 3–9 of the activity.

One Step

Pose this problem: "Tie up to six knots in each rope, and predict the length of 10 m of rope after making 17 knots in each."

Step 1 [ELL] The *length of the rope* after knots are tied means the distance from one end to the other when the rope is stretched tight. If students want to use a knot other than an overhand knot, encourage the creativity, but ask them to make all the knots the same and to be sure there's enough rope to tie at least six of those knots.

Step 3 Be sure students realize that the rate of change is negative.

Activity Day

Modeling Data

Whenever measuring is involved in collecting data, you can expect some variation in the pattern of data points. Usually, you can't construct a mathematical model that fits the data exactly. But in general, the better a model fits, the more useful it is for making predictions or drawing conclusions from the data.

Activity

Tying Knots

In this activity you'll explore the relationship between the number of knots in a rope and the length of the rope and write an equation to model the data.

You will need

- two pieces of rope of different lengths (around 1 m) and thickness
- a meterstick or a tape measure

Number of knots	Length of knotted rope (cm)
0	
1	
2	

Step 1 The length of rope should be reduced the same amount for each knot tied.

Step 2 The data should show a linear relationship.

Step 3 Answers will vary depending on the thickness of rope and type of knot. The rate of change represents the reduction of rope length for each knot tied. It is a negative number.

Step 1

Step 2

Step 3

Step 4

Choose one piece of rope and record its length in a table like the one shown. Tie 6 or 7 knots, remeasuring the rope after you tie each knot. As you measure, add data to complete a table like the one above.

Graph your data, plotting the number of knots on the *x*-axis and the length of the knotted rope on the *y*-axis. What pattern does the data seem to form?

What is the approximate rate of change for this data set? What is the real-world meaning of the rate of change? What factors have an effect on it?

What is the *y*-intercept for the line that best models the data? What is its real-world meaning? The *y*-intercept is the length of rope without any knots.

LESSON OBJECTIVES

- Find an equation that fits a set of real-world data
- Use a mathematical model to make predictions

NCTM STANDARDS

CONTENT		PROCESS	
✔	Number	✔	Problem Solving
✔	Algebra	✔	Reasoning
	Geometry		Communication
✔	Measurement	✔	Connections
	Data/Probability	✔	Representation

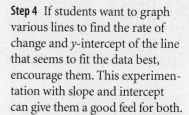

Step 5 | Write an equation in intercept form for the line that you think best models the data. Graph your equation to check that it's a good fit.   Graphs will vary. The line should go down from a positive y-intercept. It should pass through, or near, most of the points.

Now you'll make predictions and draw some conclusions from your data using the line model as a summary of the data.

Step 6 | Use your equation to predict the length of your rope with 7 knots. What is the difference between the actual measurement of your rope with 7 knots and the length you predicted using your equation?   Answers will vary.

Step 7 The equation says that you will eventually have a rope of length 0 if you tie enough knots.

Step 7 | Use your equation to predict the length of a rope with 17 knots. Explain the problems you might have in making or believing your prediction.

Step 8 | What is the maximum number of knots that you can tie with your piece of rope? Explain your answer.

Step 9 | Does your graph cross the x-axis? Explain the real-world meaning, if any, of the x-value of the intersection point.

Step 10 | Substitute a value for y into the equation. What question does the equation ask? What is the answer?   The question it asks is "How many knots are tied to produce a rope of length y?"

Step 11 | Repeat Steps 1–5 using a different piece of rope. Graph the data on the same pair of axes.

Step 12 | Compare the graphs of the lines of fit for both ropes. Give reasons for the differences in their y-intercepts, in their **x-intercepts,** and in their rates of change.

Step 12 Different lengths of ropes will account for different y-intercepts. Different thicknesses will account for different rates of change. Both affect the value of the x-intercepts.

IMPROVING YOUR **REASONING** SKILLS

There are 100 students and 100 lockers in a school hallway. All of the lockers are closed. The first student walks down the hallway and opens every locker. A second student closes every even-numbered locker. The third student goes to every third locker and opens it if it is closed or closes it if it is open. This pattern repeats so that the nth student leaves every nth locker the opposite of how it was before. After all 100 students have opened or closed the lockers, how many lockers are left open?

Step 4 If students want to graph various lines to find the rate of change and y-intercept of the line that seems to fit the data best, encourage them. This experimentation with slope and intercept can give them a good feel for both.

Step 5 As needed, explain that a line is a good fit to a data set if it goes pretty close to each data point and there are about as many points above the line as below the line. Students will see a more systematic way of finding lines of good fit in Lessons 4.6 and 4.7.

Step 8 Answers will vary. Students will get to a point where they're tying knots on top of knots.

Step 9 The equation will cross the x-axis, but the points will not. It is not possible to have zero rope length no matter how many knots are tied. Even the knot itself accounts for some length.

Step 12 [Ask] "Does the thickness of the rope itself have any bearing on the results? Does the type of knot affect the results?"

SHARING IDEAS

Pick out any unusual approaches for sharing.

Assessing Progress

Observe students' understanding of how y-intercept and rate of change affect the graph of a line.

IMPROVING **REASONING** SKILLS

After accumulating data, many students will see the pattern that the lockers left open at the end correspond to perfect squares—1, 4, 9, 16, 25, 36, 49, 64, 81, and 100. If needed, explain that *left open* means open after all 100 students pass. Be sure they actually answer the question of how many lockers are left open. [10] Ask students to explain.

[A locker changes once for each factor of its number. For example, locker number 24 is changed by students 1, 2, 3, 4, 6, 8, 12, and 24. So if a locker's number has an even number of factors, it is left closed. If a locker's number has an odd number of factors, it is left open. The numbers with an odd number of factors are the perfect squares.]

[Ask] "Why do perfect squares have an odd number of factors?" [Factors of numbers come in pairs: (1, 24), (2, 12), (3, 8), (4, 6). The square root of a perfect square is paired with itself; factors of 36: (1, 36), (2, 18), (3, 12), (4, 9), (6, 6). So the number of distinct factors is an odd number.]

• CHAPTER 3 REVIEW • CHAPTER 3 REVIEW • CHAPTER 3 REVIEW • CHAPTER 3 REVIEW • C

PLANNING

LESSON OUTLINE

One day:

5 min	Introduction
15 min	Exercises and helping individuals
15 min	Checking work and helping individuals
15 min	Student self-assessment

REVIEWING

Direct students' attention to the table of floor heights in Lesson 3.1, Example A. **[Ask]** "What linear equation describes the floor heights?" [$y = -4 + 13x$; this is intercept form.] Then **[Ask]** "What floor has height 282 ft?" To answer this, review how to set up the linear equation $-4 + 13x = 282$ and ask how to solve it. Bring out the ideas of generating the table recursively, undoing, and balancing. If needed, review rules for order of operations.

As students work individually on these exercises, you can work more with individual students who have been having difficulties. The Mixed Review contains problems from Chapters 1–3.

ASSIGNING HOMEWORK

Assigning either the evens or the odds will give students a good review. They could work on the other exercises in groups.

▶ **Helping with the Exercises**

Exercise 1 Reasons students give for each step will depend on their method of solving the equation.

You started this chapter by investigating **recursive sequences** by using their starting values and **rates of change** to write **recursive routines.** You saw how rates of change and starting values appear in plots.

In a walking investigation you observed, interpreted, and analyzed graphical representations of relationships between time and distance. What does the graph look like when you stand still? When you move away from or move toward the motion sensor? If you speed up or slow down? You identified real-world meanings of the **y-intercept** and the rate of change of a **linear relationship,** and used them to write a **linear equation** in the **intercept form,** $y = a + bx$. You learned the role of b, the coefficient of x. You explored relationships among verbal descriptions, tables, recursive rules, equations, and graphs.

Throughout the chapter you developed your equation-solving skills. You found solutions to equations by continuing to practice an undoing process and by using a **balancing** process. You found approximate solutions by tracing calculator graphs and by zooming in on calculator tables. Finally, you learned how to model data that don't lie exactly on a line, and you used your model to predict inputs and outputs.

EXERCISES

You will need your graphing calculator for Exercises **4, 6,** and **7.**

@ Answers are provided for all exercises in this set.

1. Solve these equations. Give reasons for each step.
   a. $-x = 7 \quad x = -7$
   b. $4.2 = -2x - 42.6 \quad x = -23.4$

2. These tables represent linear relationships. For each relationship, give the rate of change, the y-intercept, the recursive rule, and the equation in intercept form.

   a.

x	y
0	3
1	4
2	5

   1; 3; add 1; $y = 3 + x$

   b.

x	y
1	0.01
2	0.02
3	0.03

   0.01; 0; add 0.01; $y = 0.01x$

   c.

x	y
−2	1
0	5
3	11

   2; 5; add 2; $y = 5 + 2x$

   d.

x	y
−4	5
12	−3
2	2

   $-\frac{1}{2}$; 3; subtract $\frac{1}{2}$; $y = 3 - \frac{1}{2}x$

3. Match these walking instructions with their graph sketches.

i.   **ii.**   **iii.**

a. The walker stands still. iii

b. The walker takes a few steps toward the 0-mark, then walks away. i

c. The walker steps away from the 0-mark, stops, then continues more slowly in the same direction. ii

4. Graph each equation on your calculator, and trace to find the approximate y-value for the given x-value.

a. $y = 1.21 - x$ when $x = 70.2$ $y = -68.99$ **b.** $y = 6.02 + 44.3x$ when $x = 96.7$ $y = 4289.83$

c. $y = -0.06 + 0.313x$ when $x = 0.64$ $y = 0.14032$ **d.** $y = 1183 - 2140x$ when $x = -111$ $y = 238{,}723$

5. Write the equations for linear relationships that have these characteristics.

a. The output value is equal to the input value. $y = x$

b. The output value is 3 less than the input value. $y = -3 + x$

c. The rate of change is 2.3 and the y-intercept is -4.3. $y = -4.3 + 2.3x$

d. The graph contains the points (1, 1), (2, 1), and (3, 1). $y = 1$

6. The profit for a small company depends on the number of bookcases it sells. One way to determine the profit is to use a recursive routine such as

$\{0, -850\}$ (ENTER)

$\{\text{Ans}(1) + 1, \text{Ans}(2) + 70\}$ (ENTER); (ENTER), . . .

a. Explain what the numbers and expressions 0, -850, Ans(1), Ans(1) + 1, Ans(2), and Ans(2) + 70 represent.

b. Make a plot of this situation.

c. When will the company begin to make a profit? Explain.

d. Explain the relationship between the values -850 and 70 and your graph.

e. Does it make sense to connect the points in the graph with a line? Explain.
    No; partial bookcases cannot be sold.

7. A single section and a double section of a log fence are shown.

a. How many additional logs are required each time the fence is increased by a single section? 3

6a. 0 represents no bookcases sold; -850 represents fixed overhead, such as start-up costs; Ans(1) represents the previously calculated number of bookcases sold; Ans(1) + 1 represents the current number of bookcases sold, one more than the previous; Ans(2) represents the profit for the previous number of bookcases; Ans(2) + 70 represents the profit for the current number of bookcases—the company makes $70 more profit for each additional bookcase sold.

Exercise 6c Have the students create a table from their data. **[Ask]** "What is the value of x when $f(x) = 0$?" [$x \approx 12.1$] Relate this value (the zero of the function) to the answer found.

6c. Sample answer: The graph crosses the x-axis at approximately 12.1 and is positive after that; the company needs to make at least 13 bookcases to make a profit.

6d. -850, the profit if the company makes zero bookcases, is the y-intercept; 70, the amount of additional profit for each additional bookcase, is the rate of change; y goes up by $70 each time x goes up by one bookcase.

6b.

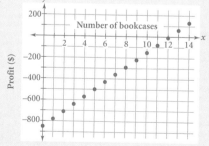

b. Copy and fill in the missing values in the table below.

Number of sections	1	2	3	4	...	30	...	50
Number of logs	4	7	10	13	...	91	...	151

c. Describe a recursive routine that relates the number of logs required to the number of sections. 4 (ENTER), Ans + 3 (ENTER), (ENTER), ...

d. If each section is 3 meters long, what is the longest fence you can build with 217 logs? 216 m

8a. Let *v* represent the value in dollars and *y* represent the number of years; $v = 5400 - 525y$.

8b. The rate of change is −525; in each additional year, the value of the computer system decreases by $525.

8c. The *y*-intercept is 5400; the original value of the computer system is $5,400.

Exercise 8d Have the students enter their equations into the graphing calculator and examine the table. **[Ask]** "What is the value of *x* when $f(x) = 0$?" [$x \approx$ 10.3] and "How does this value (the zero of the function) compare to the *x*-intercept of the graph?" [The value for which $f(x) = 0$ is the same as the point where the line crosses the *x*-axis.]

8d. The *x*-intercept is approximately 10.3; this means that the computer system no longer has value after approximately 10.3 yr.

9a. $50 = 7.7t$

$t = \dfrac{50}{7.7} \approx 6.5 \text{ s}$

9b. $50 = 5 + 6.5t$

$t = \dfrac{50 - 5}{6.5} \approx 6.9 \text{ s}$

9c. Andrei wins; when Andrei finishes, his younger brother is $50 - [5 + 6.5(6.5)] \approx 2.8 \text{ m}$ from the finish line.

Exercise 10 Students can also check their results by substituting them into the equation.

8. Suppose a new small-business computer system costs $5,400. Every year its value drops by $525.

a. Define variables and write an equation modeling the value of the computer in any given year.

b. What is the rate of change, and what does it mean in the context of the problem?

c. What is the *y*-intercept, and what does it mean in the context of the problem?

d. What is the *x*-intercept, and what does it mean in the context of the problem?

9. Andrei and his younger brother are having a race. Because the younger brother can't run as fast, Andrei lets him start out 5 m ahead. Andrei runs at a speed of 7.7 m/s. His younger brother runs at 6.5 m/s. The total length of the race is 50 m.

a. Write an equation to find how long it will take Andrei to finish the race. Solve the equation to find the time.

b. Write an equation to find how long it will take Andrei's younger brother to finish the race. Solve the equation to find the time.

c. Who wins the race? How far ahead was the winner at the time he crossed the finish line?

10. Solve each equation using the method of your choice. Then use a different method to verify your solution.

a. $14x = 63$ $x = 4.5$

b. $-4.5x = 18.6$ $x = -4.1\overline{3}$

c. $8 = 6 + 3x$ $x = 0.\overline{6}$

d. $5(x - 7) = 29$ $x = 12.8$

e. $3(x - 5) + 8 = 12$ $x = 6.\overline{3}$

11. For each table, write a formula for list L₂ in terms of list L₁.

a.

L₁	L₂
0	−5.7
1	−3.4
2	−1.1
3	1.2
4	3.5
5	5.8

L₂ = −5.7 + 2.3 · L₁

b.

L₁	L₂
−3	19
−1	3
0	−5
2	−21
5	−45
6	−53

L₂ = −5 − 8 · L₁

c.

L₁	L₂
3	13.5
−2	11
−9	7.5
0	12
6	15
−5	9.5

L₂ = 12 + 0.5 · L₁

12. You can represent linear relationships with a graph, a table of values, an equation, or a rule stated in words. Here are two linear relationships. Give all the other ways to show each relationship.

a.

b.

x	y
−2	2
−1.5	1.5
0	0
3	−3

MIXED REVIEW

13. APPLICATION Sonja bought a pair of 210 cm cross-country skis. Will they fit in her ski bag, which is $6\frac{1}{2}$ ft long? Why or why not? No, they won't fit; 210 cm is 6.89 ft.

2.3

1.4 **14.** Fifteen students counted the number of letters in their first and last names. Here is the data set [Data set: **NMLET**]:

6	15	8	12	8	17	9	7
13	15	14	9	16	15	10	

a. Make a histogram of the data with a bin width of 2.

b. What is the mean number of letters? 11.6 letters

2.7 **15.** Evaluate these expressions.

a. $-3 \cdot 8 - 5 \cdot 6$ −54 **b.** $[-2 - (-4)] \cdot 8 - 11$ 5

c. $7 \cdot 8 + 4 \cdot (-12)$ 8 **d.** $11 - 3 \cdot 9 - 2$ −18

3.2 **16.** On a recent trip to Detroit, Tom started from home, which is 12 miles from Traverse City. After 4 hours he had traveled 220 miles.

a. Write a recursive routine to model Tom's distance from Traverse City during this trip. State at least two assumptions you're making.

b. Use your recursive routine to determine his distance from Traverse City for each hour during the first 5 hours of the trip.

c. What is the rate of change, and what does it mean in the context of this situation?

16a. The starting value is 12; Ans + 55. Possible assumptions: Tom's home is 12 mi closer to Detroit than to Traverse City. He travels at a constant speed. We are measuring highway distance.

16b.

Hours	0	1	2	3	4	5
Distance (mi)	12	67	122	177	232	287

16c. Tom traveled 55 mi each additional hour. The rate of change is 55 mi/h.

12a. $y = 1 + \frac{1}{2}x$; the output value is half the input value plus 1.

x	y
0	1
1	1.5
2	2
3	2.5
4	3

12b. $y = -x$; the output value is the additive inverse (or opposite) of the input value, or the sum of the input value and the output value is 0.

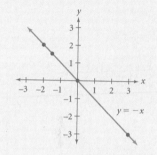

14a.

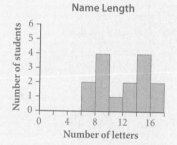

Name Length

Exercise 16a If students don't know what to assume about how Tom's home is related to Traverse City and Detroit, tell them to assume something they can explain in 15b.

17a. approximately 1061 thousand (or 1,0161,000) visitors

17b. 404, 482, 738, 1131, 3379

17c.

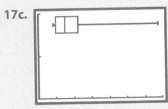

[0, 3500, 500, 0, 2, 1]

17d. Yosemite; the number of visitors exceeds 1131 by more than 1.5(1131 − 482).

1.3 **17.** California has many popular national parks. This table shows the number of visitors in thousands to national parks in 2003.

    a. Find the mean number of visitors.

    b. What is the five-number summary for the data?

    c. Create a box plot for the data.

    d. Identify any parks in California that are outliers in the numbers of visitors they had. Explain why they are outliers.

Park Attendance

National park	Visitors (thousands)
Channel Islands	586
Death Valley	890
Joshua Tree	1283
Kings Canyon	556
Lassen Volcanic	404
Redwood	408
Sequoia	979
Yosemite	3379

(*U.S. National Park Service*) [Data set: **CAPRK**]

Joshua Tree National Park, California

2.5 **18.** Ohm's law states that electrical current is inversely proportional to the resistance. A current of 18 amperes is flowing through a conductor whose resistance is 4 ohms.

Lassen Volcanic National Park, California

    a. What is the current that flows through the system if the resistance is 8 ohms? 9 amperes

    b. What is the resistance of the conductor if a current of 12 amperes is flowing? 6 ohms

Every knob or lever of this sound recording console regulates electric resistance in a current. The resistance varies directly with voltage and inversely with current.

2.8 **19.** Consider the equation $2(x - 6) = -5$.

    a. Solve the equation. Solution methods will vary; $x = 3.5$.

    b. Show how you can check your result by substituting it into the original equation.
    $2(3.5 - 6) = 2(-2.5) = -5$

2.3 **20.** **APPLICATION** Amber makes $6 an hour at a sandwich shop. She wants to know
how many hours she needs to work to save $500 in her bank account. On her first
paycheck, she notices that her net pay is about 75% of her gross pay.

    a. How many hours must she work to earn $500 in gross pay? $\dfrac{500}{6} \approx 83.3$ h

    b. How many hours must she work to earn $500 in net pay? $\dfrac{500}{0.75 \cdot 6} \approx 111.1$ h

TAKE ANOTHER LOOK

1. The picture at right is a **contour map.** This type of
map reveals the character of the terrain. All points
on an **isometric line** are the same height in feet
above sea level. The graph below shows how the
hiker's walking speed changes as she covers the
terrain on the dotted-line trail shown on the map.

    a. What quantities are changing in the
graph and in the map?

    b. How does each display reveal rate
of change?

    c. How could you measure distance on
each display?

    d. What would the graph sketch of this
hike look like if distance were plotted
on the vertical axis instead of speed?

    e. What do these two displays tell you
when you study them together?

Sediment layers form contour lines in the Grand Canyon.

2. You've learned that a rational number is a number that can be written as a ratio of
two integers. Every rational number can also be written in an equivalent decimal
form. In Lesson 2.1, you learned how to convert fractions into decimal form. In
some cases the result was a *terminating decimal,* and in other cases the result was a
repeating decimal, in which a digit or group of digits repeated.

1e. The graph and the contour map together show
that the speed of the hiker was decreasing at the
beginning because she was climbing a hill. As she
began to go down the hill, she kept moving faster
and faster until she was running. She stayed at a
constant run after she reached level ground.

Exercise 19 Students should solve
by undoing. The distributive
property will be introduced in
Lesson 4.4.

▶ Take Another Look

1a. The graph shows the change
in the hiker's speed over time. The
contour map shows the change in
the hiker's elevation as she follows
the dotted line. It also shows the
horizontal distance she has
traveled from her starting point.

1b. The graph shows rate of
change in speed as the steepness
(slope) of a line. At first the speed
is steadily decreasing, then it is
increasing, then it remains constant. The contour map shows rate
of change in elevation by the distance between the contour lines.
When the lines are very close
together, the elevation is changing
quickly.

1c. If a scale were provided, you
could infer distance from the
graph by estimating the average
speed up to a certain point and
multiplying that by the time at
that point. Students might refer to
the formula *distance* equals *rate*
(speed) times *time* ($d = rt$). You
could measure distance on the
contour map using the map scale.

1d. Student sketches of the graph
of (*distance, time*) should show
three sections. In each, the graph
is increasing. In the first section,
the graph is a curve that is concave down, showing a steadily
decreasing speed. The second
section of the graph is concave up
because the speed is increasing,
and the third section is a steep
straight line, showing a constant,
fast speed.

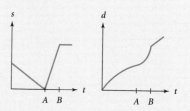

2a. $0.5, 0.4375, 0.088, 0.4\overline{6}, 0.4\overline{09},$
$0.3\overline{6}, 0.35$

2b. When the fraction is in lowest terms, if the denominator only has factors of 2 and/or 5, the fraction will terminate.

2c. $\dfrac{25}{100}$ or $\dfrac{1}{4}$, $\dfrac{8}{10}$ or $\dfrac{4}{5}$, $\dfrac{13}{100}$, $\dfrac{412}{1000}$ or $\dfrac{103}{250}$

2d. $\dfrac{18}{99}$; multiply by 100.

2e. i. $\dfrac{32}{99}$ **ii.** $\dfrac{325}{999}$ **iii.** $\dfrac{2323}{9990}$

a. Rewrite each of these fractions in decimal form. If the digits appear to repeat, indicate this by placing a bar over those digits that repeat.

$$\frac{1}{2}, \frac{7}{16}, \frac{11}{125}, \frac{7}{15}, \frac{9}{22}, \frac{11}{30}, \frac{7}{20}$$

b. Describe how you can predict whether a fraction will convert to a terminating decimal or a repeating decimal.

Reversing the process—converting decimals to fractions

c. Write the decimals 0.25, 0.8, 0.13, and 0.412 as fractions.

You can use what you've learned in this chapter about solving equations to help you write an infinite repeating decimal, like $0.\overline{1}$, as a fraction. For example, to find a fraction equal to $0.\overline{1}$, you are looking for a fraction F such that $F = 0.11111\ldots$. Follow the steps shown.

$$F = 0.11111\ldots$$
$$10F = 1.11111\ldots$$

So, $10F - F = 1.11111\ldots - 0.11111\ldots$

$$9F = 1$$
$$F = \frac{1}{9}$$

Here, the trick was to multiply by 10 so that $10F$ and F had the same decimal part. Then, when you subtract $10F - F$, the decimal portion is eliminated.

d. Write the repeating decimal $0.\overline{18}$ as a fraction. (*Hint:* What can you multiply $F = 0.\overline{18}$ by so that you can subtract off the same decimal part?)

e. Write these repeating decimals as fractions.

 i. $0.\overline{32}$　　　**ii.** $0.\overline{325}$　　　**iii.** $0.2\overline{325}$

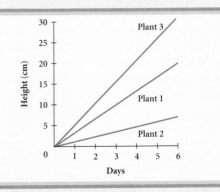

IMPROVING YOUR REASONING SKILLS

Did these plants grow at the same rate? If not, which plant was tallest on Day 4? Which plant took the most time to reach 8 cm? Redraw the graphs so that you can compare their growth rates more easily.

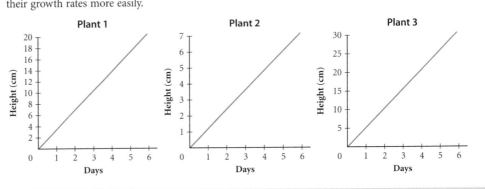

IMPROVING REASONING SKILLS

The differences in the vertical scale (height) indicate that the plants are growing at different rates. Plant 3 is the fastest growing; it is about 20 cm tall in 4 days. Plant 2 is slowest growing; it takes almost 6 days to reach 7 cm. This should suggest to students that the steepness of a line is relative to the scales on the axes. They have seen this many times on their calculators.

Assessing What You've Learned

GIVING A PRESENTATION

Making presentations is an important career skill. Most jobs require workers to share information, to help orient new coworkers, or to represent the employer to clients. Making a presentation to the class is a good way to develop your skill at organizing and delivering your ideas clearly and in an interesting way. Most teachers will tell you that they have learned more by trying to teach something than they did simply by studying it in school.

Here are some suggestions to make your presentation go well:

▶ Work with a group. Acting as a panel member might make you less nervous than giving a talk on your own. Be sure the role of each panel member is clear so that the work and the credit are equally shared.

▶ Choose the topic carefully. You can summarize the results of an investigation, do research for a project and present what you've learned and how it connects to the chapter, or give your own thinking on Take Another Look or Improving Your Reasoning Skills.

▶ Prepare thoroughly. Outline your presentation and think about what you have to say on each point. Decide how much detail to give, but don't try to memorize whole sentences. Illustrate your presentation with models, a poster, a handout, or overhead transparencies. Prepare these visual aids ahead of time and decide when to introduce them.

▶ Speak clearly. Practice talking loudly and clearly. Show your interest in the subject. Don't hide behind a poster or the projector. Look at the listeners when you talk.

Here are other ways to assess what you've learned:

 UPDATE YOUR PORTFOLIO Choose a piece of work you did in this chapter to add to your portfolio—your graph from the investigation On the Road Again (Lesson 3.2), the most complicated equation you've solved, or your research on a project.

 WRITE IN YOUR JOURNAL What method for solving equations do you like best? Do you always remember to define variables before you graph or write an equation? How are you doing in algebra generally? What things don't you understand?

 ORGANIZE YOUR NOTEBOOK You might need to update your notebook with examples of balancing to solve an equation, or with notes about how to trace a line or search a table to approximate the coordinates of the solution. Be sure you understand the meanings of important words like linear equation, rate of change, and intercept form.

CHAPTER 4

Fitting a Line to Data

Overview

Chapter 4 emphasizes slope in the context of finding lines of fit. **Lesson 4.1** presents a formula for determining slope using any two points on a line. Students learn about all four slope types: positive, negative, zero (horizontal), and undefined (vertical). In **Lesson 4.2,** students use their understanding of the intercept form to fit lines to data. **Lessons 4.3** and **4.4** introduce students to the point-slope form and its application. In **Lesson 4.5,** students apply their understanding of the point-slope form to fit lines to data. **Lessons 4.6** and **4.7** establish and develop the method for determining lines of fit based on quartiles of the two data sets; this standardized procedure allows everyone to get the same equation to model a given set of data. In **Lesson 4.7,** students compare and evaluate methods of fitting lines to data. **Lesson 4.8** is an activity day for reviewing lines of fit.

The Mathematics

Slope

Previous chapters related the constant rate of change of a data set or equation to the steepness of a line graphing the data or equation. Now we see a definition of the slope of a line through two points, as the ratio of the difference in y-coordinates to the difference in corresponding x-coordinates: $\frac{\text{change in } y}{\text{change in } x}$ or $\frac{y_2 - y_1}{x_2 - x_1}$.

This formula gives a static way to think about slope. A dynamic concept can also be useful. Imagine that you're moving from left to right along the line. Page 219 describes this dynamic concept of slope and gives ideas to help students understand dividing by zero.

Point-Slope Form

The point-slope form of an equation is often given as $\frac{y - y_1}{x - x_1} = m$, where m is the given slope and (x_1, y_1) is a point on the line. This form emphasizes that for "any point on the line" (x, y), the slope of the line segment between that point and the given point is the ratio $\frac{y - y_1}{x - x_1}$.

Using b instead of m to represent the slope, you can write the point-slope form as $y - y_1 = b(x - x_1)$, obtained from the previous form of the equation by multiplying both sides by the denominator. For graphing an equation on a graphing calculator, y must be expressed in terms of x. This motivates the form the student text uses, $y = y_1 + b(x - x_1)$.

You can see the equation $y = y_1 + b(x - x_1)$ as the result of translating the variation $y = bx$ to the right x_1 units and up y_1 units. When you slide up, you add to the y-value. But if you also slide the line to the right, the line now goes through the point (x_1, y_1), and the line will cross the y-axis below y_1.

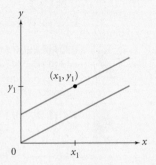

In practice, the point-slope form (in any version) is more useful than the intercept (or slope-intercept) form. Rarely do you know the y-intercept. If you need to find it, you can substitute 0 for x_1 in the point-slope form, so resist any impulses to change all linear equations into an intercept form.

Lines of Fit

A *line of fit* is intended to represent the points in a data set. You use it when you're trying to make a prediction based on a scatter plot that looks linear. You might use several methods of finding lines of fit. Very common is the *method of least squares,* in which the sum of squares of vertical distances between a line and the data points is minimized. This method is studied in statistics courses and advanced algebra.

In *Discovering Algebra,* students find the slope b of the line between two representative points, graph the variation $y = bx$, and then translate that line to an appropriate y-intercept so that it appears to

represent the data. This gives the intercept form, $y = a + bx$, of a line. Students also get the point-slope form by translating the line $y = bx$ to pass through one of the two points chosen to find the slope.

A third modeling method uses *Q-points*. For each of the four Q-points, the first coordinate is a first or third quartile of the *x*-coordinates of the data set, and the second coordinate is the first or third quartile of the *y*-coordinates: (x_{Q1}, y_{Q1}), (x_{Q3}, y_{Q1}), (x_{Q1}, y_{Q3}), and (x_{Q3}, y_{Q3}). These four points form a rectangle. The line of fit lies along one diagonal.

Another method of linear regression—the *median-median method*—is implemented on calculators and might be an appropriate extension for students in this course. In it, you divide each set of coordinates into thirds. You use the medians of the outer thirds to determine a line. Then you shift that line vertically $\frac{1}{3}$ of the way toward the point given by the medians of the middle thirds.

Using This Chapter

Lessons 4.6 and 4.7 provide valuable practice with linear equations and slope. Lesson 4.8 is a very popular activity and can be done even if you have skipped Lessons 4.6 and 4.7; it provides a good summary of Chapter 4. If your state standards require you to cover slopes of parallel and perpendicular lines, you may want to teach Lesson 11.1 directly after Lesson 4.4.

Resources

Discovering Algebra Resources

Teaching and Worksheet Masters
    Lessons 4.1, 4.4, 4.8

Calculator Notes 1D, 3D, 4A, 4B

Sketchpad Demonstrations
    Lessons 4.1, 4.3, 4.4

Fathom Demonstrations
    Lessons 4.2, 4.5, 4.6

CBR Demonstration
    Lesson 4.5

Dynamic Algebra Explorations online
    Lessons 4.1, 4.6

Assessment Resources
    Quiz 1 (Lessons 4.1, 4.2)
    Quiz 2 (Lessons 4.3, 4.4)
    Quiz 3 (Lessons 4.5–4.7)
    Chapter 4 Test
    Chapter 4 Constructive Assessment Options

More Practice Your Skills for Chapter 4

Condensed Lessons for Chapter 4

Other Resources

Data in Depth by Tim Erickson.

For complete references to this and other resources, see www.keypress.com/DA.

Materials

- graph paper
- rulers
- uncooked spaghetti
- several books
- 5 oz plastic cups
- string
- pennies (100 per group)
- empty boxes (one per group), *optional*
- sharp scissors or awls
- stopwatch
- bucket or other object to pass
- toy figures
- identical rubber bands (300)
- tape measures, metersticks, or yardsticks
- video camera, *optional*

Pacing Guide

	day 1	day 2	day 3	day 4	day 5	day 6	day 7	day 8	day 9	day 10
standard	4.1	4.2	4.2	4.3	4.4	4.4, quiz	4.5	4.6	4.6	4.7
enriched	4.1	project, 4.2	4.2	4.3	4.4	4.4, quiz	4.5	4.6	4.6, project	4.7
block	4.1, 4.2	4.2, 4.3	4.4	quiz, 4.5	4.6	project, 4.7	quiz, 4.8	review, assessment		

	day 11	day 12	day 13	day 14	day 15	day 16	day 17	day 18	day 19	day 20
standard	4.8, quiz	4.8	review	assessment						
enriched	4.8, quiz	4.8	review, TAL	assessment						

Fitting a Line to Data

- Learn how to calculate the slope of a line with slope triangles and the slope formula

- Learn about slopes of rising, falling, horizontal, and vertical lines

- Learn the point-slope form of an equation of a line

- Check the equivalence of linear equations by using algebraic properties

- Learn several approaches to finding a line that represents a set of real-world data points (eyeballing, representative points, Q-points)

- Evaluate the results of those approaches

Artists, like mathematicians, use lines to summarize their observations. An artist's data include contour, texture, color, shape, motion, and balance. The American artist Romaine Brooks (1874–1970) reduced her entire set of observations into the lines you see in this pencil sketch titled *Departure*.

OBJECTIVES

In this chapter you will

- define and calculate slope
- write an equation that fits a set of real-world data
- review the intercept form of a linear equation
- learn the point-slope form of a linear equation
- recognize equivalent equations written in different forms

You can ask the class to brainstorm other meanings of the word *line*. Some of these are boundary, course, limit, queue, series, and trend. Point out that, in colloquial use, a line is not always straight. In mathematics, *line* usually means a straight line or segment, whereas *curve* refers to a bending of a line.

In visual art, a line might be used in various ways. For example, an *outline* calls attention to the shape; this artist has emphasized the shape the human figure assumes in the position depicted. A *contour* gives the illusion of three-dimensionality; the continuation of

the line of the lower leg into the interior of the foot shape gives the clue that the toe is farther from us than the heel. A *gesture* line is executed quickly, recording the path of the eye and depicting motion.

A mathematical curve can be thought of geometrically, as a locus of points, or algebraically, as a set of points satisfying an equation. Curves that model numerical data are usually algebraic so that we can make predictions from the equation. Geometric curves can also be considered to be modeling data—data that are points rather than numbers.

A Formula for Slope

The nearest thing to nothing that anything can be and still be something is zero.

ANONYMOUS

You have seen that the steepness of a line can be a graphical representation of a real-world rate of change like a car's speed, the number of calories burned with exercise, or a constant relating two units of measure. Often you can estimate the rate of change of a linear relationship just by looking at a graph of the line. Can you tell which line in the graph matches which equation?

Slope is another word used to describe the steepness of a line or the rate of change of a linear relationship. In this investigation you will explore how to find the slope of a line using two points on the line.

Wayne Thiebaud's oil painting *Urban Downgrade, 20th and Noe* (1981) is an artistic representation of the steepness, or slope, of a street in San Francisco, California. Thiebaud is an American artist born in 1920.

Investigation
Points and Slope

You will need

- graph paper

Hector recently signed up with a limited-usage Internet provider. There is a flat monthly charge and an hourly rate for the number of hours he is connected during the month. The table shows the amount of time he spent using the Internet for the first three months and the total fee he was charged.

Step 1   Is there a linear relationship between the time in hours that Hector uses the Internet and his total fee in dollars? If so, why do you think such a relationship exists? yes

Step 2   Use the numbers in the table to find the hourly rate in dollars per hour. Explain how you calculated this rate. $0.29/h

Internet Use

Month	Time (h)	Total fee ($)
September	40	16.55
October	50	19.45
November	80	28.15

NCTM STANDARDS

CONTENT		PROCESS	
✓	Number	✓	Problem Solving
✓	Algebra	✓	Reasoning
	Geometry	✓	Communication
✓	Measurement		Connections
	Data/Probability	✓	Representation

LESSON OBJECTIVES

- Investigate and solve real-world problems that involve the slope of a line
- Learn how to calculate slopes with slope triangles and the slope formula
- Learn about slopes of rising, falling, horizontal, and vertical lines

PLANNING

LESSON OUTLINE

One day:

5 min	Introduction
20 min	Investigation
5 min	Sharing
10 min	Example and Visual Learning
5 min	Closing
5 min	Exercises

MATERIALS

- graph paper
- rulers
- The Four Slope Types (T), *optional*
- Coordinate Plane (T, from Chapter 1), *optional*
- Calculator Note 3D
- Sketchpad demonstration Slope, *optional*

TEACHING

The steepness of the graph of the line $y = a + bx$ is measured by the rate of change b, called the *slope* of the line.

INTRODUCTION

[ELL] A common meaning of *slope* is a piece of ground that isn't horizontal, such as a ski slope. In mathematics, slope is a number measuring steepness.

[Ask] "How are the lines on page 215 alike and how do they differ? How are these similarities and differences reflected in the equations?" [All the lines have a y-intercept of 1, but the slopes are different. The steepest line will match the equation with the largest rate of change. From bottom to top, the corresponding equations are Y_2, Y_3, Y_1, and Y_4.]

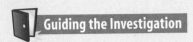
One Step

Point out Hector's bill and ask students to write careful instructions for finding the slope of a line between any two given points. As students work, suggest that they use slope triangles.

Step 1 Students can decide the relationship is linear either by graphing or by finding that the rate of change (in $/h) is constant.

Step 2 [Alert] Some students may not realize that there is a monthly charge. This relationship is not a direct variation, and the intercept will not be zero.

Step 2 From September to October, the hours increased by 10 and the cost increased by $2.90, so the increase is $0.29/h. From October to November, the hours increased by 30 and the cost increased by $8.70, also an increase of $0.29/h.

Step 3 Ask students to label their axes with their respective units of measure as well as to mark them numerically.

Step 3 The line should support the linear relationship students assumed in Step 1.

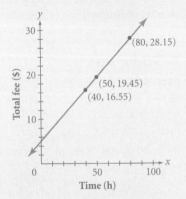

Step 4 [Alert] Students may not understand how to find the lengths of the arrows. Suggest that they draw horizontal and vertical lines to mark equal lengths on the axes. Use the Coordinate Plane transparency to demonstrate this process.

Step 3 Draw a pair of coordinate axes on graph paper. Use the *x*-axis for time in hours and the *y*-axis for total fee in dollars. Plot and label the three points the table of data represents. Draw a line through the three points. Does this line support your answer in Step 1?

Step 4 Choose two points on your graph. Use arrows to show how you could move from one point to the other using only one vertical move and one horizontal move. How long is each arrow? What are the units of these values?

Step 5 The arrows show the changes in total fee and time usage, which are divided to find the rate. The slope is $0.29/h, as in Step 2.

Step 5 How do the arrow lengths relate to the hourly rate that you found in Step 2? Use the arrow lengths to find the hourly rate of change, or slope, for this situation. What units should you apply to the number?

In Step 4, you used arrows to show the vertical change and the horizontal change when you moved from one point to another. The right triangle you created is called a **slope triangle.**

Step 6 Any pair of points will give the same slope.

Step 6 Choose a different pair of points on your graph. Create a slope triangle between them and use it to find the slope of the line. How does this slope compare to your answers in Step 2 and Step 5?

Step 7 Subtracting corresponding coordinates gives the arrows' lengths. Using (40, 16.55) and (80, 28.15), a numerical expression would be
$$\frac{28.15 - 16.55}{80 - 40}.$$

Step 7 Think about what you have done with your slope triangles. How could you use the coordinates of any two points to find the vertical change and the horizontal change of each arrow? Write a single numerical expression using the coordinates of two points to show how you can calculate slope.

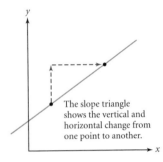

The slope triangle shows the vertical and horizontal change from one point to another.

Step 8
$$\frac{y_2 - y_1}{x_2 - x_1} \text{ or } \frac{y_1 - y_2}{x_1 - x_2}$$

Step 8 Write a symbolic algebraic rule for finding the slope between any two points (x_1, y_1) and (x_2, y_2). The subscripts mean that these are two distinct points of the form (x, y).

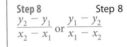

keymath.com/DA

[▶ Explore more about slope using the **Dynamic Algebra Exploration** at **www.keymath.com/DA** . ◀]

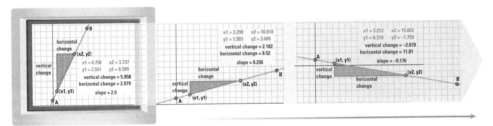

A slope triangle helps you visualize slope by showing you the vertical change and the horizontal change from one point to another. These changes are also called the "change in *y*" (vertical) and the "change in *x*" (horizontal). The example will help you see how to work with positive and negative numbers in slope calculations.

Students may draw the horizontal arrow before the vertical arrow, and the slope triangle may lie below the line.

Step 4 Arrows should form a right triangle. With the points (50, 19.45) and (80, 28.15) as an example, the horizontal arrow has length 30 h and the vertical arrow has length $8.70.

Step 5 [Alert] Some students may divide the horizontal change by the vertical change. As a guide, have them think about the units of the rate: $/h, not h/$.

Step 7 Students revisit what may have caused confusion in Step 4. When you think someone might not understand deeply enough, ask for explanations.

Step 8 This may be the first time students have seen subscripted variables. You might mention that x_1 is read "*x*-sub-one."

EXAMPLE

Consider the line through the points (1, 7) and (6, 4).

a. Find the slope of the line.

b. Without graphing, verify that the point (4, 5.2) is also on that line.

c. Find the coordinates of another point on the same line.

▶ **Solution**

Plot the given points and draw the line between them.

a. There are two different slope triangles you could draw using these points.

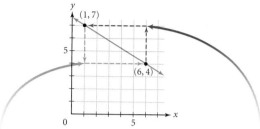

If you move from (1, 7) to (6, 4), the change in y is -3 (down 3) and the change in x is $+5$ (right 5). The slope is $\frac{-3}{+5}$.

If you move from (6, 4) to (1, 7), the change in y is $+3$ (up 3) and the change in x is -5 (left 5). The slope is $\frac{+3}{-5}$.

$\frac{-3}{+5}$ is equivalent to $\frac{+3}{-5}$. You get the same slope, $-\frac{3}{5}$ or -0.6, no matter which point you start from. The slope triangles help you see this relationship more clearly.

Move to (6, 4) from (1, 7).

$$\text{Slope} = \frac{4 - 7}{6 - 1} = \frac{-3}{5} = -\frac{3}{5} \quad \text{or}$$

Move to (1, 7) from (6, 4).

$$\text{Slope} = \frac{7 - 4}{1 - 6} = \frac{3}{-5} = -\frac{3}{5}$$

b. The slope between any two points on the line will be the same. (And, the slope between a point on the line and a point not on the line will be different.) So, if the slope between the point (4, 5.2) and either of the original two points is -0.6, then the point is on the line. The slope between (4, 5.2) and (1, 7) is

$$\frac{7 - 5.2}{1 - 4} = \frac{1.8}{-3} = -\frac{1.8}{3} = -0.6$$

So the point (4, 5.2) is on the line.

To find the slope when moving from (1, 7) to (6, 4), the coordinates of (1, 7) will come last in the slope formula. Saying to move to (6, 4) from (1, 7) mentions the points in the order they appear in the slope formula.

SHARING IDEAS

Request that students present Steps 5 and 8. Ask why the ratio of differences gives the slope. Keep asking "Are you saying . . . ?" to clarify thinking and help all students understand these important but difficult ideas.

[Ask] "Is a linear equation a good model?" [The relationship applies only to whole number values of x so the points on the line between the whole numbers have no meaning.]

Mention various descriptions of slope. For example, "rise over run," "vertical change over horizontal change," and "the change in y over the change in x." Draw out the formula (as written at the bottom of page 218), and write the slope using deltas: $\frac{\Delta y}{\Delta x}$. Delta is the Greek letter "D," standing here for "difference." **[Language]** A *delta* also is defined as a triangular deposit built up at the mouth of a river.

If students worked on the project Legal Limits from Lesson 3.5, point out that slope is the same as gradient. Slope is usually given as a fraction and gradient as a percent. A 9% gradient is a slope of $\frac{9}{100}$.

[Ask] "If unlimited service costs $21.95 per month, do you think Hector should change pricing plans or stay with limited usage?"

Assessing Progress

Note students' understanding of linear relationships and their ability to find rates and to graph points and to treat horizontal and vertical components separately.

EXAMPLE

This example provides a method for finding the slope of a line between two points. It also introduces the notion that a point C is on the same line as points A and B if and only if the slope of the segment AC is the same as the slope of the segment AB.

"If you know the equation for the line—say, $y = 7.6 - 0.6x$—how might you find another point on the line?" Encourage a variety of approaches: using the slope and $(0, 7.6)$, substituting a number for x and determining y, graphing, and so on. Have students work on the last two questions in part c for a few minutes to get $(1 - 5, 7 + 3) = (-4, 10)$ and either $(1 + 1, 7 - 0.6) = (2, 6.4)$ or $(6 + 1, 4 - 0.6) = (7, 3.4)$.

c. You can find the coordinates of another point by adding the change in x and the change in y from any slope triangle on the line to a known point.

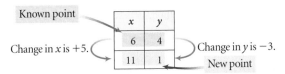

Starting with the point $(6, 4)$ and using

$$\frac{change\ in\ y}{change\ in\ x} = \frac{-3}{5}$$

gives the new point $(6 + 5, 4 + (-3)) = (11, 1)$.

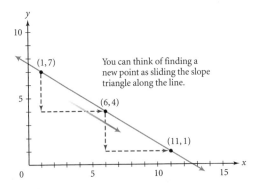

You can think of finding a new point as sliding the slope triangle along the line.

Try using the point $(1, 7)$ and using

$$\frac{change\ in\ y}{change\ in\ x} = \frac{3}{-5} \quad (-4, 10)$$

to find another point. Try using either original point and using

$$\frac{change\ in\ y}{change\ in\ x} = \frac{-0.6}{1} \quad (7, 3.4)\ \text{or}\ (2, 6.4)$$

to find another point.

Slope is an extremely important concept in mathematics and in applications like medicine and engineering that rely on mathematics. You may encounter different ways of describing slope—for example, "rise over run" or "vertical change over horizontal change." But you can always calculate the slope using this formula:

History
● **CONNECTION** ●

Slope is sometimes written $\frac{\Delta y}{\Delta x}$. The symbol Δ is the Greek capital letter delta. The use of Δ is linked to the history of calculus in the 18th century when it was used to mean "difference."

Slope Formula

The formula for the **slope** of the line passing through point 1 with coordinates (x_1, y_1) and point 2 with coordinates (x_2, y_2) is

$$slope = \frac{change\ in\ y}{change\ in\ x} = \frac{y_2 - y_1}{x_2 - x_1}$$

VISUAL LEARNING

As needed, review division with signed numbers. Students may forget, for example, that the quotient of two negative numbers is a positive number.

Emphasize that either point can be called (x_1, y_1), as long as subtraction between corresponding coordinates takes place in the same order in the numerator and the denominator.

Visual learners will also be helped by a graphic display such as this:

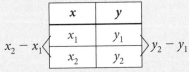

Be sure all students now recognize that a is the intercept and b is the slope in the equation $y = a + bx$.

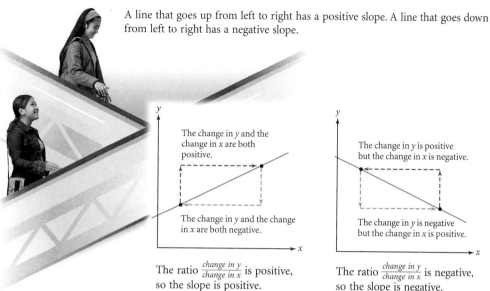

A line that goes up from left to right has a positive slope. A line that goes down from left to right has a negative slope.

The change in y and the change in x are both positive.

The change in y and the change in x are both negative.

The ratio $\frac{change\ in\ y}{change\ in\ x}$ is positive, so the slope is positive.

The change in y is positive but the change in x is negative.

The change in y is negative but the change in x is positive.

The ratio $\frac{change\ in\ y}{change\ in\ x}$ is negative, so the slope is negative.

Horizontal lines have a slope of zero because they have no change in y. Vertical lines have no change in x. To calculate the slope of a vertical line, you would have to divide by zero, which is impossible—we say that the slope of a vertical line is undefined.

The change in y is zero and the change in x is positive.

The change in y is zero and the change in x is negative.

The ratio becomes $\frac{0}{change\ in\ x}$, so the slope is zero.

The change in y is positive and the change in x is zero.

The change in y is negative and the change in x is zero.

The ratio becomes $\frac{change\ in\ y}{0}$, so the slope is undefined.

As you work on the exercises, keep in mind that the slope of a line is the same as the rate of change of its equation. When a linear equation is written in intercept form, $y = a + bx$, which letter represents the slope?

Dynamic Concept of Slope

Imagine that you're moving from left to right along the line. What happens to your y-coordinate? If your y-coordinate is increasing, the slope is positive. You're climbing up the line. The larger the slope, the harder you have to work to make that climb. If your y-coordinate is decreasing, you're going downhill. The more negative the rate of change, the steeper the hill.

The dynamic approach can help students understand slopes of horizontal and vertical lines, which can be especially confusing. If your y-coordinate doesn't change, you're moving "on the level," so the line is horizontal. Its slope is zero. If, on the other hand, your motion can't be from left to right at all because the line is vertical, it's impossibly steep. The slope is undefined. If you calculate the slope of a vertical line by the static model, you're dividing by zero, the difference in x-coordinates of two points on the line.

Dividing by Zero

If students ask why it is impossible to divide by 0, you might say, "If it were possible to divide 5 by 0, then the answer multiplied by 0 would equal 5." Or you might ask, "What number multiplied by 0 would equal 5?" [No such number exists, so $\frac{5}{0}$ is undefined.] If a student asks about the quotient $\frac{0}{0}$, say that $\frac{179}{541}$ (or any other number) multiplied by 0 equals 0. Any number could be the answer, so $\frac{0}{0}$ isn't defined.

Closing the Lesson

As needed, say that the **slope** of a line can be calculated by finding two points on the line and dividing the vertical change between those points by the corresponding horizontal change. You can use the Four Slope Types transparency.

You can use the Sketchpad demonstration Slope to further explore slope and to review the intercept form of linear equations.

EXERCISES

You will need your graphing calculator for Exercises **4** and **14**.

▶ Practice Your Skills

1. Find the slope of each line using a slope triangle or the slope formula.

a. 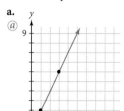 2

b. 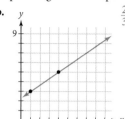 $\frac{2}{3}$

c. 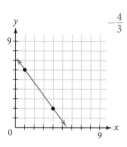 $-\frac{4}{3}$

2. Find the slope of the line through each pair of points. Then name another point on the same line.

a. (2, 4), (4, 7) @ **b.** (6, −1), (2, 5)

c.

x	y
−2	4
8	4

d.

x	y
1	−3
9	12

3. Given the slope of a line and one point on the line, name two other points on the same line. Then use the slope formula to check that the slope between each of the two new points and the given point is the same as the given slope.   Possible answers:

a. Slope $\frac{3}{1}$; point (0, 4) @   (1, 7), (−1, 1)   **b.** Slope −5; point (2, 8)   (3, 3), (1, 13)

c. Slope $-\frac{3}{4}$; point (8, 6)   (12, 3), (4, 9)   **d.** Slope 0.2; point (5, 7)   (6, 7.2), (4, 6.8)

4. Run the LINES program five times. Start by playing the easy level once or twice, then move on to the difficult level. On your paper, sketch a graph of each randomly generated line. Find the slope of the line by counting the change in y and the change in x on the grid, or trace the line for two points to use in the slope formula. Then find the y-intercept and write the equation of the line in intercept form.
[▶ 🖳 See **Calculator Note 3D** to learn how to use the LINES program. ◀]   Answers will vary.

▶ Reason and Apply

5. Each table gives the coordinates of four points on a different line.

i. @
x	y
4	−8
4	0
4	3
4	20

ii.
x	y
0	5
1	3
3	−1
4	−3

iii.
x	y
−4	−5
−3	−5
1	−5
4	−5

iv.
x	y
−4	−5
−2	−3.5
0	−2
4	1

a. Without calculating, can you tell whether the slope of the line through each set of points is positive, negative, zero, or undefined? If so, explain how you can tell.

b. Choose two points from each table and calculate the slope. Check that your answer is correct by calculating the slope with a different pair of points.

c. Write an equation for each table of values.

6. Consider lines a and b shown in the graph at right.

a. How are the lines in the graph alike? How are they different?

b. Which line matches the equation $y = -3 + \frac{2}{5}x$? line b

c. What is the equation of the other line? $y = 1 + \frac{2}{5}x$

d. How are the equations alike? How are they different?

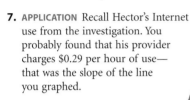

7. **APPLICATION** Recall Hector's Internet use from the investigation. You probably found that his provider charges $0.29 per hour of use— that was the slope of the line you graphed.

Internet Use

Month	Time (h)	Total fee ($)
September	40	16.55
October	50	19.45
November	80	28.15

a. Use the rate of change and the data in the table to find out how much the total fee is for 30 h of use. How much is the total fee for 20 h? @

b. Repeat the process in 7a to find out how much the total fee is for 0 h of use. What is the real-world meaning of this number in this situation? (Look back at the investigation for help.) @

c. A mathematical model can be an equation, a graph, or a drawing that helps you better understand a real-world situation. Write a linear equation in intercept form that you can use to model this situation.

d. Use your linear equation to find out how much the total fee is for 280 h of use.
Substitute 280 for x and solve for y: $y = 4.95 + 0.29(280) = 86.15$, or $86.15 for 280 h.

8. If a and c are the lengths of the vertical and horizontal segments and $(0, e)$ is the y-intercept, what is the equation of the line? ⓗ $y = e - \frac{a}{c}x$

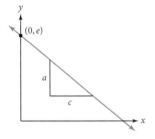

5a. iii. The y-values don't change, so the slope is zero.

5a. iv. The y-values increase as the x-values increase, so the slope is positive.

5b. i. Using the points $(4, 0)$ and $(4, 3)$, the slope is $\frac{3 - 0}{4 - 4} = \frac{3}{0}$. You can't divide by 0, so the slope is undefined.

5b. ii. Using the points $(1, 3)$ and $(4, -3)$, the slope is $\frac{-3 - 3}{4 - 1} = -2$.

5b. iii. Using the points $(-4, -5)$ and $(-3, -5)$, the slope is $\frac{-5 - (-5)}{-3 - (-4)} = 0$.

5b. iv. Using the points $(0, -2)$ and $(4, 1)$, the slope is $\frac{1 - (-2)}{4 - 0} = \frac{3}{4}$.

5c. i. $x = 4$; **ii.** $y = 5 - 2x$; **iii.** $y = -5$; **iv.** $y = -2 + \frac{3}{4}x$

Exercise 6 Students will often use the fact that lines are parallel when they have the same slope.

6a. The lines are parallel, so they have the same slope; the y-intercepts are different.

6d. The slope, $\frac{2}{5}$, is the same in each equation; the y-intercepts, -3 and 1, are different.

7a. Use the slope to move backward from $(40, 16.55)$: $(40 - 10, 16.55 - 0.29 \cdot 10) = (30, 13.65)$, or $13.65 for 30 h; $(30 - 10, 13.75 - 0.29 \cdot 10) = (20, 10.75)$, or $10.75 for 20 h.

Exercise 7b This approach to finding the y-intercept by working backward is referred to in Lesson 4.3.

7b. Continuing the process in 7a leads to $(0, 4.95)$, or $4.95 for 0 h. This is the flat monthly rate for Hector's Internet service.

Exercise 7c Mathematical models have limitations. For example, the line contains points with negative x-values, but they don't make sense in the situation being modeled.

7c. $y = 4.95 + 0.29x$, where x is time in hours and y is total fee in dollars

Exercise 8 Some students may try measuring to find a numerical answer. Point out that when distances are represented by letters, students should express their answer in terms of those letters. **[ELL]** *In terms of* means *using*.

The slope can't be written using only those letters, however. A minus sign is needed because the slope is negative. Stress again that a negative slope means the line is falling *from left to right*. Any of the expressions $y = e - \frac{a}{c}x$, $y = e + \frac{-a}{c}x$, or $y = e + \frac{a}{-c}x$ are okay.

9a. The change in y and the change in x are the same for any slope triangle on the line.

9b. A steeper line would have a greater change in y than its change in x. Numerically, the slope would be greater than 1.

9c. A less steep line would have a greater change in x than its change in y. Numerically, the slope would be between 0 and 1.

9d. The line would go down from left to right, because the slope is negative; the line would be very steep, because 15 is significantly greater than 1.

Exercise 10 Some students may be confused about how the height of the balloon can already be 14 m at time 0 min. If possible, ask the class to explain it. There can be several reasons. The timing need not start when the balloon starts rising. Or the measurement might be to the top of the balloon, which might very well be 14 m high when the basket is still on the ground. In case the balloon has not started rising, the time-distance relationship would not be perfectly linear. To explain, you might note that when you start walking, you have some acceleration before you obtain any speed. Hence, the beginning of the graph would be slightly curved.

[Ask] "How can you tell whether the data are linear?" [Slope between pairs of points is constant.]

10b. m/min; the hot-air balloon rises at a rate of 30 m/min.

10c. $y = 14 + 30x$

Exercise 11 This is a good exercise for leading up to Lesson 4.2.

---

9. This line has a slope of 1. Graph it on your own paper.

a. Draw a slope triangle on your line. How do the change in y and the change in x compare?

b. Draw a line that is steeper than the given line. How do the change in y and the change in x compare? How does the numerical slope compare to that of the original line?

c. Draw a line that is less steep than the given line, but still increasing. How do the change in y and the change in x compare? How does the numerical slope compare to that of the given line?

d. How would a line with a slope of -15 compare to your other lines? Explain your reasoning.

10. APPLICATION A hot-air balloonist gathered the data in this table.

a. What is the slope of the line through these points? 30 m/min

b. What are the units of the slope? What is the real-world meaning of the slope? @

c. Write a linear equation in intercept form to model this situation.

d. What is the height of the balloon after 8 min? @ 254 m

e. During what time interval is the height less than or equal to 500 m? between 0 and 16.2 min

Hot-Air Balloon Height

Time (min)	Height (m)
0	14
2.2	80
3.4	116
4	134
4.6	152

11. When you make a scatter plot of real-world data, you may see a linear pattern.

a. Which line do you think "fits" each scatter plot? Think about slope and how the points are scattered. Explain how you chose your lines.

i.
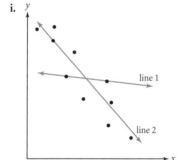

ii.
@

Line 2 is a better choice. A majority of points are closer to line 2 than to line 1.

Line 4 is a better choice. Line 3 passes through or is close to a good number of points, but too many points are above this line and too few are below it. Even though line 4 does not intercept any points, it is the better choice because about the same number of points are above the line as below it.

b. Trace each scatter plot onto your own paper. Then draw a line that you think fits the data.

i.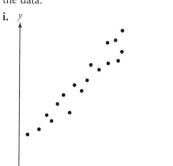

ii.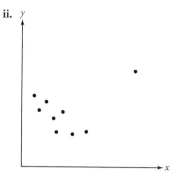

c. List two features that you think are important for a line that fits data.

▶ Review

1.7 **12.** The base of a triangle was recorded as 18.3 ± 0.1 cm and the height was recorded as 7.4 ± 0.1 cm. These measurements indicate the measured value and an accuracy component.

    a. Use the formula $A = 0.5bh$ and the measured values for base and height to calculate the area of the triangle. $0.5(18.3)(7.4) = 67.7$ cm^2

    b. Use the smallest possible lengths for base and height to calculate an area. ⓐ $0.5(18.2)(7.3) = 66.4$ cm^2

    c. Use the largest possible lengths for base and height to calculate an area. $0.5(18.4)(7.5) = 69.0$ cm^2

    d. Use your answers to 12a–c to express the range of possible area values as a number $\pm$ an accuracy component. ⓗ 67.7 ± 1.3 cm^2

1.2 **13.** Calista has five brothers. The mean of her brothers' ages is 10 years, and the median is 6 years. Create a data set that could represent the brothers' ages. Is this the only possible answer? $\{3, 3, 6, 16, 22\}$; no

2.8 **14.** Enter $\{-3, -1, 2, 8, 10\}$ into list L1 on your calculator.

    a. Write a rule for list L2 that adds 14 to each value in list L1 and then multiplies the results by 2.5. What are the values in list L2? ⓐ

    b. Write a rule for list L3 that works backward and undoes the operations in list L2 to produce the values in list L1. ⓐ $L_3 = \dfrac{(L_2 - 35)}{2.5}$, or $L_3 = \dfrac{L_2}{2.5} - 14$

2.2 **15.** Convert each decimal number to a percent.

    a. 0.85 85%   **b.** 1.50 150%   **c.** 0.065 6.5%   **d.** 1.07 107%

11b. i.

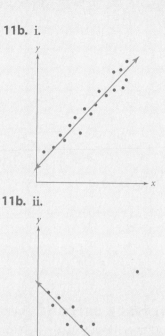

11b. ii.

11c. Answers will vary. The line should reflect the direction of the data, and about the same number of points should be above the line as below it.

Exercise 12 [Alert] Students may calculate to two decimal places, finding that the minimum is $67.71 - 1.28$ and the maximum is $67.71 + 1.29$. The initial measurements were to one decimal place, so these numbers must also be to one decimal place.

14a. $L_2 = 2.5(L_1 + 14)$; $\{27.5, 32.5, 40, 55, 60\}$

3.6 **16.** The equation $7x - 10 = 2x + 3$ is solved by balancing. Explain what happens in Stages 3, 4, and 6 of the balancing process.

$2x - 10 = 7x + 3$	1. Original equation.
$2x - 2x - 10 = 7x - 2x + 3$	2. Subtract $2x$ from both sides.
$-10 = 5x + 3$	3. <u>Combine like</u> terms.
$-10 - 3 = 5x + 3 - 3$	4. <u>Subtract 3 from</u> both sides.
$-13 = 5x$	5. Combine like terms.
$\dfrac{-13}{5} = \dfrac{5x}{5}$	6. <u>Divide both</u> sides by 5.
$x = -2.6$	7. Reduce.
$2(-2.6) - 10 \overset{?}{=} 7(-2.6) + 3$	
$-5.2 - 10 \overset{?}{=} -18.2 + 3$	
$-15.2 = -15.2$	Solution checks.

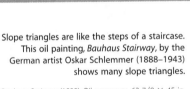

project

STEP RIGHT UP

How would it feel to climb a flight of stairs if every step were a little taller or shorter, or wider or narrower, than the previous one? The constant measure for treads and risers on most stairs keeps you from tripping. Have you noticed that the stairs outside some public buildings slow you down to a "ceremonial" pace? Or that little-used stairs to a cellar seem dangerously steep? Investigate the standards for stairs in various architectural settings and learn the reasons for their various slopes.

Your project should include

▶ Tread-and-riser data and slope calculations for several different stairways.

▶ The building codes or recommended standards in your area for home stairways. Is a range of slopes permitted? When are landings or railings required?

▶ Scale drawings for at least three different stairways.

After you've done your research, consider this question: Does a spiral staircase have a constant slope?

Slope triangles are like the steps of a staircase. This oil painting, *Bauhaus Stairway*, by the German artist Oskar Schlemmer (1888–1943) shows many slope triangles.

Bauhaus Stairway (1932). Oil on canvas, 63-7/8 × 45 in. The Museum of Modern Art, New York. Gift of Philip Johnson. Photograph © 2000 The Museum of Modern Art, New York

Supporting the project

MOTIVATION

If you were going to design a stairway for a child's play structure, would you use the same standards as for an adult house? If not, what would be the difference and why?

OUTCOMES

▶ The report is accurate on all required elements.

▶ The report on building codes cites sources.

▶ The report includes spiral staircases. To determine their slope, take measurements at the same distance from the center of the circle the staircase is based on.

▶ The scale for scale drawings of different stairways is marked.

• The report discusses safety.

• The paper lists reasonable factors for determining the slope within the allowable range, such as frequency of use or user age and agility.

Writing a Linear Equation to Fit Data

When you plot real-world data, you will often see a linear pattern. If you can find a line or an equation to model linear data, you can make predictions about unknown data values. However, data points rarely fall exactly on a line. How can you tell if a particular line is a good model for the data? One of the simplest ways is to ask yourself if the line shows the general direction of the data and if there are about the same number of points above the line as below the line. If so, then the line will appear to "fit" the data, and we call it a **line of fit.**

Can you visualize two lines that model this arrangement of geese?

Sometimes one line will be a better model for your data than another. Each of these graphs shows a scatter plot of data points and possible lines of fit.

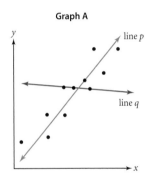
Graph A

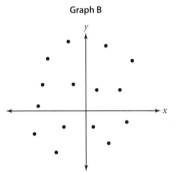
Graph B

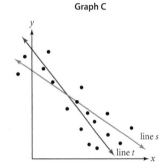
Graph C

In Graph A, line *p* fits better because it shows the general direction of the data and there are the same number of points above the line as below the line. Although line *q* goes through several points, it does not show the direction of the data.

In Graph B, the data don't seem to have a pattern. No lines of fit are shown because you can't say that one line would fit the data better than another line would.

In Graph C, both lines show the general direction of the data and both lines have the same number of points above and below them. You could consider either line a line of fit. When making predictions, how would your calculations using the equation for line *s* differ from those using the equation for line *t*?

In the next investigation you will learn one method to find a possible line of fit.

PLANNING

LESSON OUTLINE

First day:

15 min   Introduction

35 min   Investigation (Steps 1–8)

Second day:

10 min   Investigation (Steps 9–12)

10 min   Sharing

20 min   Example

5 min   Closing

5 min   Exercises

MATERIALS

- graph paper (several sheets per group)
- box of (uncooked) spaghetti, 10 in. long
- several books for each group
- 5 oz plastic cups (one per group)
- string
- pennies (100 per group)
- empty boxes (one per group), *optional*
- sharp scissors or awls (to punch cups for string)
- Fathom demonstration Fast Food, *optional*

TEACHING

A *line of fit* models a data set to allow predictions. In this lesson students work with slopes and intercepts to gain an intuitive feeling for finding lines of fit, otherwise known as *trend lines*.

NCTM STANDARDS

CONTENT		PROCESS	
✔	Number	✔	Problem Solving
✔	Algebra	✔	Reasoning
	Geometry	✔	Communication
	Measurement	✔	Connections
✔	Data/Probability	✔	Representation

LESSON OBJECTIVES

- Draw a line that fits or models a set of points
- Write an intercept equation that fits a set of real-world data

Procedure Note You might use angel hair pasta so that fewer pennies are needed to break a beam. Using similar books allows students to make stacks of the same height. Facilitate cleanup by putting a box under each experiment to catch the broken spaghetti. To save time, you can divide the Step 3 tasks between groups, and create one data set for the class.

One Step

Ask students to experiment with 1 to 6 strands of spaghetti and predict how many pennies 17 strands of spaghetti will support and how many spaghetti strands will be needed to support $5 worth of pennies. As you circulate, suggest that students lay out spaghetti strands on the graphs they create to help them visualize lines of fit.

Step 1 The string should be tied short to keep the cup off the base.

Step 2 [Language] The *maximum load* is the number of pennies in the cup *before* the one is added that breaks the beam.

As students devise their own tables for recording data, suggest that they think about the input and output variables in deciding how to title the columns.

Step 3 You may want to ask, "Would your results be the same if you moved the books closer or farther apart?" "Are your results with spread-out spaghetti strands different from those with bunched-up strands?"

Steps 4–7 These steps are to be worked on individually. Results will be shared with the group in Step 8.

Students might also make an accurate sketch on graph paper and then use a strand of spaghetti to visualize the line of fit. To get to an equation in intercept form, they might draw a slope triangle for the spaghetti and approximate where the spaghetti crosses the *y*-axis.

 ## Investigation
Beam Strength

How strong do the beams in a ceiling have to be? How do bridge engineers select beams to support traffic? In this investigation you will collect data and find a linear model to determine the strength of various "beams" made of spaghetti.

Steps 1–7 Answers will vary.

Step 1 Make two stacks of books of equal height. Punch holes on opposite sides of the cup and tie the string through the holes.

Step 2 Follow the Procedure Note for a beam made from one strand of spaghetti. Record the maximum load (the number of pennies) that this beam will support.

Step 3 Repeat Step 2 for beams made from two, three, four, five, and six strands of spaghetti.

Procedure Note

1. Hang your cup at the center of your spaghetti beam.
2. Support the beam between the stacks of books so that it overlaps each stack by about 1 inch. Put another book on each stack to hold the beam in place.
3. Put pennies in the cup, one at a time, until the beam breaks.

Step 4 Plot your data on your calculator. Let *x* represent the number of strands of spaghetti, and let *y* represent the maximum load. Sketch the plot on paper too.

Step 5 Use a strand of spaghetti to visualize a line that you think fits the data on your sketch. Choose two points on the line. Note the coordinates of these points. Calculate the slope of the line between the two points.

Step 6 Use the slope, *b*, that you found in Step 5 to graph the equation $y = bx$ on your calculator. Why is this line parallel to the direction the points indicate? Is the line too low or too high to fit the data?

Step 7 Using the spaghetti strand on your sketch, estimate a good *y*-intercept, *a*, so that the equation $y = a + bx$ better fits your data. On your calculator, graph the equation $y = a + bx$ in place of $y = bx$. Adjust your estimate for *a* until you have a line of fit.

Step 8 Students should see that everyone could come up with a different line of fit. Some lines may pass through data points, but it is not a requirement.

Step 8 In Step 5, everyone started with a visual model that went through two points. In your group, compare all final lines. Did everyone end up with the same line? Do you think a line of fit must go through at least two data points? Is any one line better than the others?

Step 4 In making a scatter plot on a calculator, using a box or a plus mark makes it easier to see a line of fit than using a dot mark. You might encourage students to use list L1 for input data and list L2 for output data whenever possible, to avoid having to specify lists each time they make a plot.

Step 7 You may want to write the equation $y = bx$ as $y = 0 + bx$ to help students see the connection to $y = a + bx$ and the *y*-intercept of zero. As needed, remind them of the meaning of *y-intercept*.

Your line is a model for the relationship between the number of strands of spaghetti in the beam and the load in pennies that the beam can support.

Step 9 the additional number of pennies each additional strand of spaghetti can hold

Step 9 Explain the real-world meaning of the slope of your line.

Step 10 Use your linear model to predict the number of spaghetti strands needed to support $5 worth of pennies.

Step 11 Use your model to predict the maximum loads for beams made of 10 and 17 strands of spaghetti.

Step 12 errors in data collection or a poor line of fit

Step 12 Some of your data points may be very close to your line, while others could be described as outliers. What could have caused these outliers?

Engineers conduct tests using procedures similar to the one you used in your investigation. The test results help them select the best materials and sizes for beams in buildings, bridges, and other forms of architecture.

Despite engineering tests, buildings can suffer damage during stress. This building in San Francisco, California, collapsed during an earthquake in October 1989.

EXAMPLE

This table shows how many fat grams there are in some hamburgers sold by national chain restaurants.

Nutrition Facts

Burger	Saturated fat (g)	Total fat (g)
Burger King Bacon Double Cheeseburger	17	34
Burger King Original WHOPPER® Sandwich with Cheese	18	49
Hardee's 2/3 lb Double Thickburger	38	90
Hardee's 2/3 lb Bacon Cheese Thickburger	40	96
Jack in the Box Bacon Ultimate Cheeseburger	29	70.5
Jack in the Box Jumbo Jack with Cheese	16	41.5
McDonald's Big Mac	11	33
McDonald's Quarter Pounder	8	21
Wendy's Jr. Hamburger	3.5	9
Wendy's Classic Single with Everything	7	19

(*www.burgerking.com, www.hardeesrestaurants.com, www.jackinthebox.com, www.mcdonalds.com, www.wendys.com*)

a. Find a linear equation to model the data (*saturated fat, total fat*).

b. Tell the real-world meanings of the slope and intercept of your line.

c. Predict the total fat in a burger with 20 g of saturated fat.

d. Predict the saturated fat in a burger with 50 g of total fat.

This is a ceramic sculpture of a hamburger. Imagine how much total fat this burger would have if it were real!

Hamburger (1983) by David Gilhooly, Collection of Harry W. and Mary Margaret Anderson, Photo by M. Lee Fatheree

SHARING IDEAS

[Language] You may want to introduce the term *extrapolate,* meaning to estimate outside the observed range.

Pick students who will present a variety of answers to Steps 10 and 11. (If students are putting their scatter plots on a calculator with an overhead projection panel, placing a spaghetti strand on the panel is good for showing a line of fit.) Point out that lines of fit that are only slightly different on a graph can produce drastically different results when extended very far.

Ask the class to decide which results they find most believable and why. Motivate the need for an objective, standard way to find a line of best fit, foreshadowing Lesson 4.6.

If the opportunity arises, you might ask how to get the equation by shifting the line through the origin, not just up but also to the right, to go through one of the two points chosen. This could motivate Lesson 4.3.

You might say that a mathematical model or a line of fit is an idealization. Rarely will the data fit the model exactly. In fact, in the case of beams, the strength is proportional to the cross-sectional area (and thus to the square of the number of spaghetti strands) and inversely proportional to the length of the beam between supports. So a linear model isn't a very good predictor beyond a few strands.

Assessing Progress

Watch for students' understanding of input-output tables and their skill at making scatter plots, collecting data systematically, working with a group, finding the slope and *y*-intercept of a line, writing the intercept form of the equation of a line, evaluating an equation at a point, and solving a linear equation.

EXAMPLE

This example is for students who had difficulty with the investigation. You can use the Fathom demonstration Fast Food to replace this example.

In the solution to part a, students may ask how to determine how far the line should be raised. Point out that they can use the graph to guess at the y-intercept. The line $y = 2.6 + 2.3x$ goes through the points used to find the slope, but that line has more data points above the line than below.

MAKING THE CONNECTION

Saturated and trans fats increase the amount of cholesterol in the blood, leading to increased risk of heart disease and hardening of the arteries. Unsaturated fat doesn't increase cholesterol.

Health
CONNECTION

Saturated and trans fats increase cholesterol and your risk of coronary heart disease. Trans fats, a result of hydrogenating or solidifying oil, have become increasingly common in processed foods—the U.S. Food and Drug Administration (FDA) required all foods to begin listing trans fat content beginning in January 2006. To learn more about trans fats, see **www.keymath.com/DA** .

▶ **Solution**

Draw a scatter plot of the data. Let x be the number of grams of saturated fat, and let y be the total number of grams of fat.

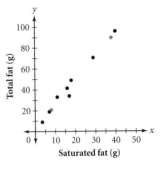

a. The scatter plot shows a linear pattern in the data. A line through the points (8, 21) and (38, 90) seems to show the direction of the data. Calculate the slope b of the line between these two points.

$$b = \frac{y_2 - y_1}{x_2 - x_1} = \frac{90 - 21}{38 - 8} = \frac{69}{30} = 2.3$$

Substitute 2.3 for b in $y = bx$ to get

$$y = 2.3x$$

The equation $y = 2.3x$ shows the direction of the line, but has only one point below the line and the other nine above.

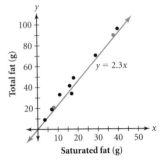

Adjust the y-intercept by tenths until you find a line that appears to be a good fit for the data. You may find that the equation

$$y = 3.5 + 2.3x$$

is a good model. Notice that the line of fit doesn't have to go through any data points.

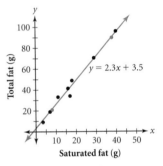

b. The y-intercept, 3.5, means that even without any saturated fat, a burger has about 3.5 grams of total fat. The slope, 2.3, means that for each additional gram of saturated fat there are an additional 2.3 grams of total fat.

c. Substitute 20 g of saturated fat for x in the equation.

$y = 3.5 + 2.3x$	Original equation.
$y = 3.5 + 2.3(20)$	Substitute 20 for x.
$y = 49.5$	Multiply and add.

The model predicts that there would be 49.5 g of total fat in a burger with 20 g of saturated fat.

d. Substitute 50 g of total fat for y in the equation.

$y = 3.5 + 2.3x$	Original equation.
$50 = 3.5 + 2.3x$	Substitute 50 for y.
$50 - 3.5 = 3.5 + 2.3x - 3.5$	Subtract 3.5 from both sides.
$46.5 = 2.3x$	Subtract.
$\dfrac{46.5}{2.3} = \dfrac{2.3x}{2.3}$	Divide both sides by 2.3.
$20.2 \approx x$	Reduce.

The model predicts that there would be about 20 g of saturated fat in a burger with 50 g of total fat.

Notice that you find the slope before the y-intercept when finding a line of fit. Because of the importance of slope, some mathematicians show it first. They use the **slope-intercept form** of a linear equation, often calling the slope m and the y-intercept b. This gives $y = mx + b$. Why is this equation equivalent to the intercept form that you have learned?

EXERCISES

You will need your graphing calculator for Exercise **4.**

Practice Your Skills

1. For each graph below, tell whether or not you think the line drawn is a good representation of the data. Explain your reasoning.

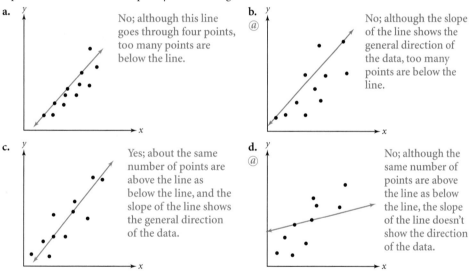

a. No; although this line goes through four points, too many points are below the line.

b. No; although the slope of the line shows the general direction of the data, too many points are below the line.

c. Yes; about the same number of points are above the line as below the line, and the slope of the line shows the general direction of the data.

d. No; although the same number of points are above the line as below the line, the slope of the line doesn't show the direction of the data.

2. The line through the points (0, 5) and (4, 5) is horizontal. The equation of this line is $y = 5$ because the y-value of every point on it is 5. If a line goes through the points (2, −6) and (2, 8), what kind of line is it? What is its equation? vertical; $x = 2$

4a. There is a linear pattern.

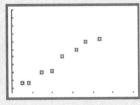

[0, 36, 6, 200, 1200, 100]

4b. Answers will vary. Using the points (8, 376) and (19, 684), the slope is 28.

4c. The slope represents the number of quarters Penny collects per month.

4d. $y = 28x$; the line needs to move up (the y-intercept needs to increase).

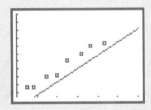

4e. A possible equation is $y = 152 + 28x$.

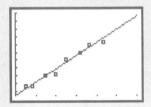

4f. The y-intercept represents the number of quarters Penny's grandmother gave her.

4g. Possible answer: 1160 quarters. The prediction may not be reliable because it extrapolates 10 months beyond the data.

---

3. Write the equation of the line in each graph.

a.
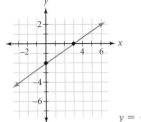
$y = -2 + \frac{2}{3}x$

b.
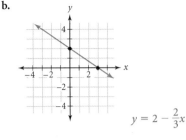
$y = 2 - \frac{2}{3}x$

c.
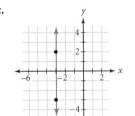
$x = -3$

d.
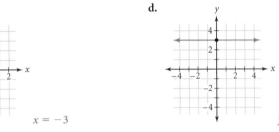
$y = 3$

4. On Penny's 15th birthday, her grandmother gave her a large jar of quarters. Penny decided to continue to save quarters in the jar. Every few months she counts her quarters and records the number in a table like this one. Predict how many quarters she'll have on her 18th birthday.

Penny's Savings

Number of months x	3	5	8	12	15	19	22	26
Number of quarters y	270	275	376	420	602	684	800	830

[Data sets: **SAVMO, SAVQU**]

a. Make a scatter plot of the data on your calculator. Is there a pattern?

b. Select two points through which a line of fit would pass. Find the slope of the line between these points.

c. What is the real-world meaning of the slope?

d. Use the slope you found in 4b to write an equation of the form $y = bx$. Graph this line on the scatter plot. What do you need to do to this line to better fit the data?

e. Estimate the y-intercept and write an equation in the form $y = a + bx$. Graph this new line. @

f. What is the real-world meaning of the y-intercept? @

g. Use your equation to predict how many quarters Penny will have on her 18th birthday.

Reason and Apply

5. **APPLICATION** A U.S. Census is conducted every ten years. One of the purposes of the Census is to measure each state's population in order to determine how many members each state will have in the House of Representatives for the next decade. Use the table to look for a relationship between a state's population and the number of members from that state in the House of Representatives.

Statistics for Some States

State	Estimated population, 2000 (millions)	Number of members in House of Representatives, 2001–2010	Number of members in Senate, 2001–2010
Alabama	4.4	7	2
Indiana	6.1	9	2
Michigan	9.9	15	2
Mississippi	2.8	4	2
North Carolina	8.0	13	2
Oklahoma	3.5	5	2
Oregon	3.4	5	2
Tennessee	5.7	9	2
Utah	2.2	3	2
West Virginia	1.8	3	2

(U.S. Bureau of the Census, in *Time Almanac 2004*, pp. 101–103, 177)
[Data sets: **STPOP, HREPS**]

a. Which statement makes more sense: The population depends on the number of members in the House of Representatives, or the number of members in the House of Representatives depends on the population? ⓐ

b. Based on your answer to 5a, define variables and make a scatter plot of the data. ⓐ

c. Find the equation of a line of fit. What is the real-world meaning of the slope? What is the real-world meaning of the *y*-intercept? ⓐ

d. The 2000 Census estimated California's population at 33.9 million. Use your equation to estimate the number of members California has in the House of Representatives.

e. Minnesota has eight members in the House of Representatives. Use your equation to estimate the population of Minnesota.

f. You might find that a direct variation equation in the form $y = bx$ fits your data. Is this a reasonable model for the data? Explain why or why not. The relationship should be a direct variation because it should go through the point $(0, 0)$. A state with no population would have no representatives.

The United States Constitution gives each state representation in the House of Representatives based on its population. To learn about historical methods of calculating representation, see **www.keymath.com/DA** . In the Senate, each state has equal representation regardless of size. This photo shows a joint session of both the House and the Senate.

Exercise 5 You might encourage students to research the laws dictating the number of members in the House of Representatives. The actual formula for determining representation is not linear, but a linear model fits fairly well. See www.keymath.com for links to sources. The first question gives an opportunity for more thinking about input and output variables.

5a. The number of representatives depends on the population.

5b. Let *x* represent population in millions, and let *y* represent the number of representatives.

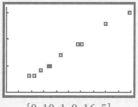

[0, 10, 1, 0, 16, 5]

5c. Answers will vary. Two possible points are (2.8, 4) and (6.1, 9). The slope between these points is approximately 1.5. The equation $y = 1.5x$ appears to fit the data with a *y*-intercept of 0. The slope represents the number of representatives per 1 million people. The *y*-intercept means that a state with no population would have no representatives.

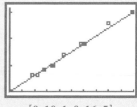

[0, 10, 1, 0, 16, 5]

5d. The equation $y = 1.5x$ gives $y = 1.5(33.9) = 50.85$, or 51 representatives. (For 2001–2010, California actually has 53 representatives.)

5e. The equation $y = 1.5x$ gives $8 = 1.5x; x = \frac{8}{1.5} = 5.\overline{3}$; 5.3 million. (The estimated population of Minnesota in the 2000 census was 4.9 million.)

6b. $y = 2$, where x represents population in millions and y represents the number of senators

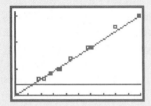

Exercise 7 If the person walks at a truly constant rate, the data fit a line exactly. The slope and y-intercept of the line describe the data exactly.

8a. The slope is negative because the distance decreases as the time increases.

8b. The y-intercept represents the start distance for the walk; the x-intercept represents the time elapsed when the walker reaches the detector.

8c. Answers will vary. Quadrant II could indicate walking before you started timing. Quadrant IV could indicate that the walker walks past you; the distances behind you are considered negative.

Exercise 9 Be sure students realize that no single line satisfies all four conditions. Students can slide a slope triangle to work backward and find the y-intercept. This technique foreshadows the beginning of Lesson 4.3.

Exercise 10 You may need to say that a "family of lines" is a collection of lines that share some property. If students haven't worked on Exercise 2, they may need help with the equation of a vertical line in 10d. They may not recognize that c is a constant. Or they may not understand very deeply that the equation of a line gives a statement about both the x- and y-coordinates for points on that line. Pick a particular value for c and suggest that students name some points that satisfy that equation and draw the line connecting them. Then try it with one or two other values.

6. Use the table in Exercise 5 to answer these questions.

    a. Does the population of a state affect its number of members in the Senate?   No; each state has two senators regardless of its population.

    b. Write an equation that models the number of senators from each state. Graph this equation on the same coordinate axes as 5c.

    c. Describe the graph and explain why it looks this way.   The graph is a horizontal line because there's no change in y, the number of senators.

7. Your friend walks steadily away from you at a constant rate such that her distance at 2 s is 3.4 m and her distance at 4.5 s is 4.4 m. Let x represent time in seconds, and let y represent distance in meters.

$$\frac{y_2 - y_1}{x_2 - x_1} = \frac{4.4 - 3.4}{4.5 - 2}; \text{ the slope is 0.4 m/s.}$$

    a. What is the slope of the line that models this situation? ⓗ

    b. What is the y-intercept of this line? Explain how you found it.   The y-intercept is 2.6 m; students can find this by working backward with the slope or by estimating from a graph.

    c. Write a linear equation in intercept form that models your friend's walk. $y = 2.6 + 0.4x$

8. Suppose this line represents a walking situation in which you're using a motion sensor to measure distance. The x-axis shows time and the y-axis shows distance from the sensor.

    a. Is the slope positive, negative, zero, or undefined? Explain. ⓐ

    b. What is the real-world meaning of the x- and y-intercepts? ⓐ

    c. If the line extended into Quadrant II, what could that mean? If the line extended into Quadrant IV? ⓐ

9. Find the equation of a line that

    a. Has a positive slope and a negative y-intercept.   Answers will vary. $y = -8 + 4x$ is one possibility.

    b. Has a negative slope and a y-intercept of 0.   Answers will vary. $y = -2x$ is one possibility.

    c. Passes through the points $(1, 7)$ and $(4, 10)$. $y = 6 + x$

    d. Passes through the points $(-2, 10)$ and $(4, 10)$. $y = 10$

10. Each equation below represents a family of lines. Describe what the lines in each form have in common.

    a. $y = a + 3x$ ⓐ   **b.** $y = 5 + bx$ **c.** $y = a$ **d.** $x = c$

10a. All lines have a slope of 3; they are all parallel.

10b. All lines cross the y-axis at 5; they radiate around the point $(0, 5)$.

10c. All lines are parallel to the x-axis, or horizontal.

10d. All lines are parallel to the y-axis, or vertical.

▶ Review

2.5 **11.** For each of these tables of *x*- and *y*-values, decide if the values indicate a direct variation, an inverse variation, or neither. Explain how you made your decision. If the values represent a direct or inverse variation, write an equation.

a.
@

x	y
−3	9
−1	1
−0.5	0.25
0.25	0.0625
7	49

b.
@

x	y
−20	−5
−8	−12.5
2	50
10	10
25	4

c.

x	y
0	0
−6	15
8	−20
−12	30
4	−10

d.

x	y
78	6
31.2	2.4
−145.6	−11.2
14.3	1.1
−44.2	−3.4

3.6 **12.** Show the steps to solve each equation. Then use your calculator to verify your solution.

a. $8 - 12m = 17$

$$8 - 12m = 17$$
$$-12m = 9$$
$$m = -0.75$$

b. $2r + 7 = -24$

$$2r + 7 = -24$$
$$2r = -31$$
$$r = -15.5$$

c. $-6 - 3w = 42$

$$-6 - 3w = 42$$
$$-3w = 48$$
$$w = -16$$

1.2 **13.** Give the mean and median for each data set.

a. {1, 2, 4, 7, 18, 20, 21, 21, 26, 31, 37, 45, 45, 47, 48} mean: 24.8$\overline{6}$; median: 21

b. {30, 32, 33, 35, 39, 41, 42, 47, 72, 74} mean: 44.5; median: 40

c. {107, 116, 120, 120, 138, 140, 145, 146, 147, 152, 155, 156, 179} mean: approximately 140.1; median: 145

d. {85, 91, 79, 86, 94, 90, 74, 87} mean: 85.75; median: 86.5

11a. neither

11b. inverse variation; $y = \frac{100}{x}$

11c. direct variation; $y = -2.5x$

11d. direct variation; $y = \frac{1}{13}x$

Exercise 12 Students might use either the undoing or the balancing method.

IMPROVING YOUR **VISUAL THINKING** SKILLS

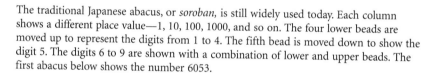

The traditional Japanese abacus, or *soroban,* is still widely used today. Each column shows a different place value—1, 10, 100, 1000, and so on. The four lower beads are moved up to represent the digits from 1 to 4. The fifth bead is moved down to show the digit 5. The digits 6 to 9 are shown with a combination of lower and upper beads. The first abacus below shows the number 6053.

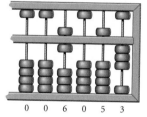 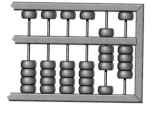 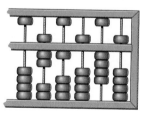

0 0 6 0 5 3

What numbers do the second and third abacuses show?

Sketch an abacus to show the number 27,059.

You can learn more about the abacus at **www.keymath.com/DA** .

IMPROVING **VISUAL THINKING** SKILLS

The second and third abacuses show 84 and 71,545, respectively; 27,059 would look like this:

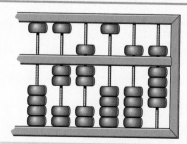

Point-Slope Form of a Linear Equation

Success breeds confidence.

BERYL MARKHAM

So far you have worked with linear equations in intercept form, $y = a + bx$. When you know a line's slope and *y*-intercept, you can write its equation directly in intercept form. But what if you don't know the *y*-intercept? One method that you might remember from your homework is to work backward with the slope until you find the *y*-intercept. But you can also use the slope formula to find the equation of a line when you know the slope of the line and the coordinates of only one point on the line.

EXAMPLE

Since the time Beth was born, the population of her town has increased at a rate of approximately 850 people per year. On Beth's 9th birthday the total population was nearly 307,650. If this rate of growth continues, what will be the population on Beth's 16th birthday?

▶ **Solution**

Because the rate of change is approximately constant, a linear equation should model this population growth. Let *x* represent time in years since Beth's birth, and let *y* represent the population.

In the problem, you are given one point, (9, 307650). Any other point on the line will be in the form (*x*, *y*). So let (*x*, *y*) represent a second point on the line. You also know that the slope is 850. Now use the slope formula to find a linear equation.

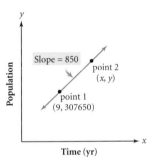

$$\frac{y_2 - y_1}{x_2 - x_1} = b \qquad \text{Slope formula.}$$

$$\frac{y - 307{,}650}{x - 9} = 850 \qquad \text{Substitute the coordinates of the point (9, 307650)}$$
$$\text{for } (x_1, y_1), \text{ and the slope 850 for } b.$$

Because we know only one point, we use (*x*, *y*) to represent any other point.

LESSON OBJECTIVES

• Learn the point-slope form of an equation of a line

• Write equations in point-slope form that model real-world data

NCTM STANDARDS

CONTENT		PROCESS
✓	Number	Problem Solving
✓	Algebra	✓ Reasoning
	Geometry	Communication
✓	Measurement	Connections
	Data/Probability	✓ Representation

Now solve the equation for y by undoing the subtraction and division.

$$y - 307{,}650 = 850(x - 9)$$

Multiply by $(x - 9)$ to undo the division.

$$y = 307{,}650 + 850(x - 9)$$

Add 307,650 to undo the subtraction.

The equation $y = 307{,}650 + 850(x - 9)$ is a linear equation that models the population growth. To find the population on Beth's 16th birthday, substitute 16 for x.

$$y = 307{,}650 + 850(x - 9)$$ Original equation.

$$y = 307{,}650 + 850(16 - 9)$$ Substitute 16 for x.

$$y = 313{,}600$$ Use order of operations.

The model equation predicts that the population on Beth's 16th birthday will be 313,600.

The equation $y = 307{,}650 + 850(x - 9)$ is a linear equation, but it is not in intercept form. This equation has its advantages too because you can clearly identify the slope and one point on the line. Do you see the slope of 850 and the point (9, 307650) within the equation? This form of a linear equation is appropriately called the **point-slope form.**

Point-Slope Form

If a line passes through the point (x_1, y_1) and has slope b, the **point-slope form** of the equation is

$$y = y_1 + b(x - x_1)$$

Investigation
The Point-Slope Form for Linear Equations

Silo and Jenny conducted an experiment in which Jenny walked at a constant rate. Unfortunately, Silo recorded only the data shown in this table.

Elapsed time (s) x	Distance to walker (m) y
3	4.6
6	2.8

Step 1   Find the slope of the line that represents this situation. -0.6 m/s

Step 2   Write a linear equation in point-slope form using the point (3, 4.6) and the slope you found in Step 1. $y = 4.6 - 0.6(x - 3)$

Step 3   Write another linear equation in point-slope form using the point (6, 2.8) and the slope you found in Step 1. $y = 2.8 - 0.6(x - 6)$

[Alert] Some students may be confused about choosing (x, y) to represent any point on the line. They may not yet grasp the idea that the equation relates coordinates of exactly those points lying on the line. Help them keep in mind the goal of coming up with such an equation.

[Alert] A few students may be confused about multiplying by $(x - 9)$. Remind them that they can consider $(x - 9)$ as a single number.

Resist simplifying $y = 307{,}650 + 850(x - 9)$ to $y = 300{,}000 + 850x$. Although the equations are equivalent, the latter is not in point-slope form. Students will learn the distributive property in Lesson 4.4.

You might ask students to go through the derivation again, using x_1, y_1, and b instead of the numbers.

Emphasize that x_1, y_1, and b represent constants, whereas x and y represent variables. Also note that the coordinate x_1 is being subtracted from x.

 Guiding the Investigation

One Step

Direct students' attention to the Water Temperature table on page 236 and ask them to find a line of fit without finding the y-intercept.

Step 4 There appears to be only one line, which implies that the equations are equivalent.

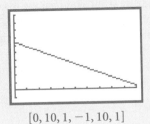

$[0, 10, 1, -1, 10, 1]$

Step 5 The Y₁- and Y₂-values are equivalent; again, this implies that the two seemingly different equations are equivalent.

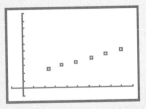

Step 6 Let x represent time in seconds, and let y represent temperature in degrees Celsius. The data set appears to have a linear pattern.

$[-10, 100, 10, -10, 100, 10]$

Steps 7 and 8 Each member of the group should be encouraged to select a different pair of points. Suggest that each group graph all of their lines on one calculator for easy comparison.

Step 8 Using the slope from Step 7, one possibility is $y = 35 + 0.38(x - 49)$.

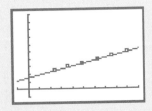

Step 4 Enter the equation from Step 2 into Y₁ and the equation from Step 3 into Y₂ on your calculator, and graph both equations. What do you notice?

Step 5 Look at a table of Y₁- and Y₂-values. What do you notice? What do you think the results mean?

Now that you have some practice at writing point-slope equations, try using a point-slope equation to fit data.

The table shows how the temperature of a pot of water changed over time as it was heated.

Step 6 Define variables and plot the data on your calculator. Describe any patterns you notice.

Step 7 Choose a pair of points from the data. Find the slope of the line between your two points.

Step 7 Answers will vary. Using $(49, 35)$ and $(62, 40)$, the slope is $\frac{5}{13}$.

Step 8 Write an equation in point-slope form for a line that passes through your two points. Graph the line. Does your equation fit the data?

Water Temperature

Time (s) x	Temperature (°C) y
24	25
36	30
49	35
62	40
76	45
89	50

Step 9 Compare your graph to those of other members of your group. Does one graph show a line that is a better fit than the others? Explain. Answers will vary. Because the data are in such a tight linear pattern, there may not appear to be one better line of fit—they will all be pretty good.

If you look back at the investigation, you will notice that you found the point-slope form of a line even though you had only points (but not a slope) to start with. This is possible because you can still use the point-slope form when you know two points on the line; there's just one additional step. What is it? You must calculate the slope using the two points.

EXERCISES

You will need your graphing calculator for Exercises **3, 4, 5, 9**, and **10**.

Practice Your Skills

1. Name the slope and one point on the line that each point-slope equation represents.
   a. $y = 3 + 4(x - 5)$ @ $4; (5, 3)$
   b. $y = 1.9 + 2(x + 3.1)$ $2; (-3.1, 1.9)$
   c. $y = -3.47(x - 7) - 2$ @ $-3.47; (7, -2)$
   d. $y = 5 - 1.38(x - 2.5)$ $-1.38; (2.5, 5)$

2. Write an equation in point-slope form for a line, given its slope and one point that it passes through.
   a. Slope 3; point $(2, 5)$ $y = 5 + 3(x - 2)$
   b. Slope -5; point $(1, -4)$ $y = -4 - 5(x - 1)$

Step 9 **[Ask]** "How could you have wisely selected points in order to find the line of best fit to begin with?" [Choose points neither close together nor too far apart that appear to lie on a line that passes near most of the data.]

SHARING IDEAS

Choose students to present several different equations that have the same graphs. **[Ask]** "Is there a way to tell that the equations have the same graphs

without actually graphing them?" Encourage all ideas. You don't need to answer this question. Students will get more experience identifying equivalent equations in Lesson 4.4.

Assessing Progress

You can assess students' understanding of input and output variables and their ability to find the slope of a line through two points and to graph data points and lines on a graphing calculator.

3. A line passes through the points $(-2, -1)$ and $(5, 13)$.

   a. Find the slope of this line. ⓐ   2

   b. Write an equation in point-slope form using the slope you found in 3a and the point $(-2, -1)$. ⓐ $y = -1 + 2(x + 2)$

   c. Write an equation in point-slope form using the slope you found in 3a and the point $(5, 13)$. $y = 13 + 2(x - 5)$

   d. Verify that the equations in 3b and c represent the same line. Enter the equations into Y_1 and Y_2 on your calculator, and compare their graphs and tables.
The graphs coincide, and the tables are identical.

4. APPLICATION This table shows a linear relationship between actual temperature and approximate wind chill temperature when the wind speed is 20 mi/h.

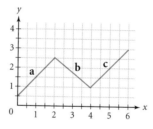

Wind Chill with Wind Speed of 20 mi/h

Temperature (°F) x	5	10	15	20	25
Wind chill (°F) y	−15	−8.5	−2	4.5	11

   a. Find the rate of change of the data (the slope of the line).

   b. Choose one point and write an equation in point-slope form to model the data.

   c. Choose another point and write another equation in point-slope form to model the data.

   d. Verify that the two equations in 4b and c represent the same line. Enter the equations into Y_1 and Y_2 on your calculator, and compare their graphs and tables.

   e. What is the wind chill temperature when the actual temperature is 0°F? What does this represent in the graph?   −21.5°F; this is the graph's y-intercept.

5. Play the BOWLING program at least four times. [▶🖩 See **Calculator Note 4A** for instructions on how to play the game. ◀] Each time you play, write down any equations you try and how many points you score.

▶ Reason and Apply

6. The graph at right is made up of linear segments **a, b,** and **c.** Write an equation in point-slope form for the line that contains each segment. ⓗ

7. A **quadrilateral** is a polygon with four sides. Quadrilateral $ABCD$ is graphed at right.

   a. Write an equation in point-slope form for the line containing each segment in this quadrilateral. Check your equations by graphing them on your calculator.

   b. What is the same in the equations for the line through points A and D and the line through points B and C? What is different in these equations? ⓐ

   c. What kind of figure does $ABCD$ appear to be? Do the results from 7b have anything to do with this? ⓐ
$ABCD$ appears to be a parallelogram because each pair of opposite sides is parallel; the equal slopes in 7b mean that $\overline{AD}$ and $\overline{BC}$ are parallel. $\overline{AB}$ and $\overline{DC}$ are parallel because they both have slope 2.

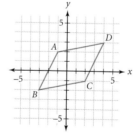

6a. $y = 0.5 + 1(x - 0)$ or $y = 2.5 + 1(x - 2)$
6b. $y = 2.5 - 0.75(x - 2)$ or $y = 1 - 0.75(x - 4)$
6c. $y = 1 + 1(x - 4)$ or $y = 3 + 1(x - 6)$

7a. AD: $y = 2 + 0.2(x + 1)$ or $y = 3 + 0.2(x - 4)$
BC: $y = -2 + 0.2(x + 3)$ or $y = -1 + 0.2(x - 2)$
AB: $y = 2 + 2(x + 1)$ or $y = -2 + 2(x + 3)$
DC: $y = 3 + 2(x - 4)$ or $y = -1 + 2(x - 2)$

7b. The slopes are the same; the coordinates of the points are different.

Exercise 8 Letters or packages
weighing more than 13 oz are subject to a different rate schedule.
Therefore, the possible *x*-values
for these data are restricted to
whole numbers from 1 to 13.
Research current postal rates
through www.keymath.com/DA.

Bring up the idea of step functions.
[Ask] "How could you graph this
relationship accurately?"

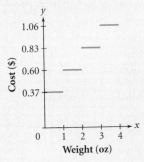

8a. The data appear linear.

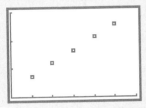

$[0, 6, 1, 0, 1.5, 0.5]$

8b. $0.23/oz; this is the cost per
additional ounce after the first.

8c. Answers will vary. Using the
point $(1, 0.37)$, the equation is
$y = 0.37 + 0.23(x - 1)$.

8e. The rates are given for
weights not exceeding the given
weights, so a letter weighing
3.5 oz would cost the same as
a 4 oz letter, or $1.06; a letter
weighing 9.1 oz would cost the
same as a 10 oz letter, or $2.44.

8f. Answers will vary. A continuous line includes points whose
x-values are not whole numbers
and whose *y*-values are not
possible rates.

9a. The data are approximately
linear.

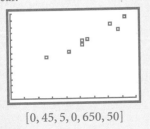

$[0, 45, 5, 0, 650, 50]$

8. APPLICATION The table shows postal rates for first-class U.S. mail in the year 2004.

a. Make a scatter plot of the data. Describe any patterns you notice.

b. Find the slope of the line between any two points in the data.
What is the real-world meaning of this slope? @

c. Write a linear equation in point-slope form that
models the data. Graph the equation to check
that it fits your data points.

d. Use the equation you wrote in 8c to find the
cost of mailing a 10 oz letter. $2.44

e. What would be the cost of mailing a 3.5 oz
letter? A 9.1 oz letter?

f. The equation you found in 8c is useful for
modeling this situation. Is the graph of this
equation, a continuous line, a correct model
for the situation? Explain why or why not. @

9. APPLICATION The table below shows fat grams and
calories for some breakfast sandwiches.

Postal Rates

Weight not exceeding (oz) x	Cost ($) y
1	0.37
2	0.60
3	0.83
4	1.06
5	1.29

(U.S. Postal Service, www.usps.com)

Nutrition Facts

Breakfast sandwich	Total fat (g) x	Calories y
Arby's Bacon 'n Egg Croissant	26	410
Burger King Croissanwich with Sausage, Egg & Cheese	39	520
Carl's Jr. Sunrise Sandwich	21	356
Hardee's Country Steak Biscuit	41	620
Jack in the Box Sourdough Breakfast Sandwich	26	445
McDonald's Sausage McMuffin with Egg	28	450
Sonic Sausage, Egg & Cheese Toaster	36	570
Subway Ham & Egg Breakfast Deli Sandwich	13	310

(www.arbys.com, www.burgerking.com, www.carlsjr.com,
www.hardeesrestaurants.com, www.jackinthebox.com, www.mcdonalds.com,
www.sonicdrivein.com, www.subway.com) [Data sets: **FFFAT, FFCAL**]

a. Make a scatter plot of the data. Describe any patterns you notice.

b. Select two points and find the equation of the line that passes through these two
points in point-slope form. Graph the equation on the scatter plot.

c. According to your model, how many calories would you expect in a Hardee's
Country Steak Biscuit with 41 grams of fat? $y = 310 + 9.3(41 - 13) = 570.4$; approximately
570 calories

d. Does the actual data point representing the Hardee's Country Steak Biscuit lie
above, on, or below the line you graphed in 9b? Explain what the point's
location means. The actual data point lies above the graph of $y = 310 + 9.3(x - 13)$; if a point lies
above the line, the sandwich has more calories than the model predicts.

9b. Answers will vary. Using the points $(28, 450)$ and
$(13, 310)$, the equation is $y = 310 + 9.3(x - 13)$.

Exercise 9g Some students may misinterpret this to
mean that all fat-free foods have 189 calories. Warn
them that many factors influence calories.

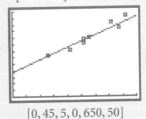

$[0, 45, 5, 0, 650, 50]$

e. Check each breakfast sandwich to find if its data point falls above, on, or below your line. Answers will vary. Using $y = 310 + 9.3(x - 13)$ as a model, three points are above the line, two points are on the line, and three points are below the line.

f. Based on your results for 9d and e, how well does your line fit the data?

g. If a sandwich has 0 grams of fat, how many calories does your equation predict? Does this answer make sense? Why or why not? Answers will vary. Using $y = 310 + 9.3(x - 13)$, approximately 189 calories; this makes sense, because not all calories in food come from fat.

10. APPLICATION This table shows the amount of trash produced in the United States in 1990 and 1995.

a. Let x represent the year, and let y represent the amount of trash in millions of tons for that year. Write an equation in point-slope form for the line passing through these two points. ⓐ

b. Plot the two data points and graph the equation you found in 10a. ⓐ

c. In 2000, 232 million tons of trash were produced in the United States. Plot this data point on the same graph you made in 10b. Do you think the linear equation you found in 10a is a good model for these data? Explain why or why not. ⓐ

U.S. Trash Production

Year	Amount of trash (million tons)
1990	205
1995	214

(Environmental Protection Agency, www.epa.gov)

This table shows more data about the amount of trash produced in the United States.

d. Add these data points to your graph. Adjust the window as necessary.

e. Do you think the linear equation found in 10a is a good model for this larger data set? Explain why or why not.

f. Find the equation of a better-fitting line. ⓗ

g. Use your new equation from 10f to predict the amount of trash produced in 2010.

Answers will vary. Using $y = 200 + 3.7(x - 1990)$, 274 million tons.

U.S. Trash Production

Year	Amount of trash (million tons)
1960	88
1965	103
1970	121
1975	128
1980	152
1985	164

(Environmental Protection Agency, www.epa.gov) [Data sets: **TRYR, TRAMT**]

▶ **Review**

2.4 **11. APPLICATION** The volume of a gas is 3.50 L at 280 K. The volume of any gas is directly proportional to its temperature on the Kelvin scale (K).

a. Find the volume of this gas when the temperature is 330 K. 4.125 L

b. Find the temperature when the volume is 2.25 L. 180 K

4.1 **12.** Find the slope of the line through the first two points given. Assume the third point is also on the line and find the missing coordinate.

a. $(-1, 5)$ and $(3, 1)$; $(5, \boxed{-1})$ -1 **b.** $(2, -5)$ and $(2, -2)$; $(\boxed{2}, 3)$ undefined

c. $(-10, 22)$ and $(-2, 2)$; $(\boxed{0}, -3)$ $-\dfrac{5}{2}$

3.6 **13.** Write the equation represented by this balance. Then solve the equation for x using the balancing method. ⓐ

Exercise 11 Remind students of direct variations $y = kx$. You might say that Kelvin units are the same size as Celsius degrees but that 0 K is at about $-273°$C. It's called *absolute zero* because electrons at that temperature can't move. The word *degrees* is not used with the Kelvin scale.

Exercise 12 Encourage a variety of approaches. Students might graph, step over 1 unit at a time, draw slope triangles, or make calculator tables.

Exercise 13 Encourage students who are struggling to model the process using the balance. They may need to draw the steps. Don't rush students into solving equations with x's on both sides. They will see many of this type of problem in Chapter 5 in the context of solving systems of equations.

9f. Answers will vary. The line $y = 310 + 9.3(x - 13)$ appears to be a good fit.

Exercise 10 In 10e, a "good model" is one that allows accurate predictions. Part of the goal of 10g is to show that basing a model on a small set of data can lead to wild predictions. **[Ask]** "In what year does your equation predict that there were zero million tons of trash?" [Using $y = 214 + 1.8(x - 1995)$, the year would be 1876.] "Is this possible?"

10a. $y = 205 + 1.8(x - 1990)$ or $y = 214 + 1.8(x - 1995)$

10b and 10c.

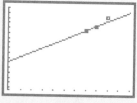

[1955, 2010, 5, 85, 250, 10]

The point (2000, 223) is somewhat close to the line, but the predicted value is too low.

10d.

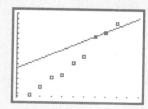

[1955, 2010, 5, 85, 250, 10]

10e. The data are generally linear, but the line doesn't fit them very well; a line with a steeper slope would be a better fit.

10f. Answers will vary. $y = 200 + 3.7(x - 1990)$ gives a reasonable fit.

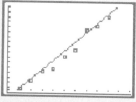

[1955, 2010, 5, 85, 250, 10]

See page 723 for the answer to Exercise 13.

Equivalent Algebraic Equations

In Lesson 4.3, you learned how to find an equation of a line through a given point. But a line goes through many points, so if you choose a different point, you'll get a different equation! In this lesson, you'll learn how to identify different equations that describe the same line.

These self-portraits of the American pop artist Andy Warhol (1928–1987) are like equivalent equations. Each screen-printed image is the same as the next, but Warhol's choice of colorization makes each look different.

For example, the line with slope 2 that passes through the point $(-4, 3)$ can be described by the equation $y = 3 + 2(x + 4)$. This line also passes through $(1, 13)$, so it can also be described by the equation $y = 13 + 2(x - 1)$. You can test that these equations are equivalent by graphing $Y_1 = 3 + 2(x + 4)$ and $Y_2 = 13 + 2(x - 1)$. The two equations graph the same line and give the same table values.

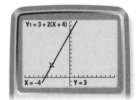

There are many different **equivalent equations** that can be used to describe any given line. In fact, both of the equations above can also be described in intercept form, $y = a + bx$. In this lesson you'll learn how to change equations to equivalent equations in intercept form by using mathematical properties and the rules for order of operations.

LESSON OBJECTIVES

- Learn and use the distributive property
- Rewrite equations to determine whether they are equivalent
- Formalize algebraic properties
- Identify properties as they are used in solving equations
- Introduce factoring as the reverse of the distributive property

NCTM STANDARDS

CONTENT		PROCESS
✔	Number	Problem Solving
✔	Algebra	✔ Reasoning
✔	Geometry	Communication
	Measurement	✔ Connections
	Data/Probability	✔ Representation

The **distributive property** allows you to rewrite some expressions that contain parentheses. For an expression like $2(4 + 3)$, you can use the order of operations and add 4 and 3, then multiply this value by 2, to get 14. Or you can "distribute" the number outside the parentheses to all the numbers inside: $2(4 + 3) = 2 \cdot 4 + 2 \cdot 3$. This figure shows a model of the expression $2(4 + 3)$. You can think of the large rectangle either as a 2×7 rectangle or as a 2×4 rectangle and a 2×3 rectangle. The area is 14 no matter which way you compute it.

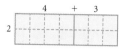

EXAMPLE A | Use the distributive property to write $y = 3 + 2(x + 4)$ without parentheses.

▶ **Solution** | Before adding 3, distribute the 2 through the sum of x and 4.

$y = 3 + 2(x + 4)$ Point-slope equation.

$y = 3 + 2 \cdot x + 2 \cdot 4$ Use the distributive property: Distribute 2 through $x + 4$.

$y = 3 + 2x + 8$ Multiply $2 \cdot 4$.

$y = 11 + 2x$ Combine like terms (add $3 + 8$).

So, $y = 3 + 2(x + 4)$ is equivalent to $y = 11 + 2x$. These are a point-slope equation and an intercept equation for the same line. What does each of the forms tell you about the line it describes?

The distributive property can be generalized like this:

Distributive Property

For any values of a, b, and c, this equation is true:

$$a(b + c) = a \cdot b + a \cdot c$$

In the investigation you'll further explore how to identify equivalent equations.

Investigation
Equivalent Equations

Here are six different-looking equations in point-slope form.

a. $y = 3 - 2(x - 1)$ **b.** $y = -5 - 2(x - 5)$ **c.** $y = 9 - 2(x + 2)$

d. $y = 0 - 2(x - 2.5)$ **e.** $y = 7 - 2(x + 1)$ **f.** $y = -9 - 2(x - 7)$

Step 1 Answers will vary. Some students might say that they cannot tell whether the equations are the same or different. Others may try graphing them and see that they are equivalent.

keymath.com/DA

Step 1 | Do the six equations represent the same line or different lines? Explain.

Step 2 | Divide these equations among the members of your group. Use the distributive property to rewrite the right side of each equation. When you combine like terms, you should get an equation in intercept form.   All equations become $y = 5 - 2x$.

Step 3 | Enter your point-slope equation into Y₁, and enter your intercept equation into Y₂. Check that the two equations have the same calculator graph or table. How does this show that the equations are equivalent?

Step 2 Depending on the size of the group, each student may need to work with more than one equation.

Step 3 For all equations, the point-slope equation and the intercept equation should show identical graphs and tables, which means the same values satisfy both equations.

Distributive Property
Consider using algebra tiles to show several examples of the distributive property. The Sketchpad demonstration Distributive Property uses an algebra tile environment to explore the distributive property and factoring, which is introduced in Exercise 7.

EXAMPLE A

The equation $y = 3 + 2(x + 4)$ describes a line with slope 2 that passes through the point $(-4, 3)$, while the equation $y = 11 + 2x$ describes a line with slope 2 and y-intercept 11.

Guiding the Investigation

One Step
Point out the 15 equations listed on page 242 after Step 5 and ask students to categorize the lines by their equations. Encourage a variety of ways of checking for equivalence, focusing on graphing. Ask students how they could determine equivalence by looking at the expressions, and bring out the idea of the distributive property. Ask what other properties they know of that apply to operations on numbers, and list the properties of commutativity, associativity, and equality.

Step 1 [Alert] Watch for the claim that the lines are the same because their slopes are the same. Remind students that many parallel yet different lines can have the same slope. Students can compare the lines by graphing, by looking at tables, or by distributing and simplifying.

Step 6 Students might make four columns and place each equation in a column with equivalent equations. **[Alert]** Students may be confused by parts h and j. **[Ask]** "What's needed to get the equation in h or j into the same form as the others?" [For h, subtract $6x$ from both sides; for j, subtract $12x$ and divide by 2.] Students may forget to distribute the negative sign through part l and therefore may not be able to find an equivalent equation.

SHARING IDEAS

Ask for reports on Steps 5 and 6. If anyone disagrees about the report on Step 6, encourage discussion of the arguments rather than taking sides. If you announce a right answer, thinking about the problem might cease.

Introduce the term *standard form* to describe the equations in parts h and j. **[Ask]** "How would you generalize the standard form?" [The idea of generalizing may take some explaining. You might give the example of $y = a + bx$ as the generalized intercept form and elicit the idea that the standard form could be expressed as $ax + by = c$. Encourage representations that use other letters for the coefficients to communicate that the choice of letters is irrelevant.]

[Ask] "How many different equations in point-slope form might a line have?" [There are infinitely many, because a line contains infinitely many points.]

Ask what steps students took in transforming equations. Solicit a generalization of each and write down the property names from page 243, or use the two transparencies to point out the properties.

Step 4 Now, as a group, compare your intercept equations. What do the results show about the six equations? All six point-slope equations can be transformed into $y = 5 - 2x$.

Step 5 As a group, explain how you can tell that an equation in point-slope form is equivalent to one in intercept form. Think about how you can do this graphically and symbolically.

Step 5 Answers will vary. You could graph the equations to see if they are the same line, or you could symbolically manipulate the point-slope form into intercept form.

Here are fifteen equations. They represent only four different lines.

a. $y = 2(x - 2.5)$

b. $y = 18 + 2(x - 8)$

c. $y = 52 - 6(x + 8)$

d. $y = -6 + 2(x + 4)$

e. $y = 21 - 6(x + 4)$

f. $y = -14 - 6(x - 3)$

g. $y = -10 + 2(x + 6)$

h. $6x + y = 4$

i. $y = 11 + 2(x - 8)$

j. $12x + 2y = -6$

k. $y = 2(x - 4) + 10$

l. $y = 15 - 2(10 - x)$

m. $y = 7 + 2(x - 6)$

n. $y = -6(x + 0.5)$

o. $y = -6(x + 2) + 16$

Step 6 The intercept form for the equation of each line is given along with the letters of the equivalent equations.
$y = -5 + 2x$: a, i, l, m
$y = 2 + 2x$: b, d, g, k
$y = -3 - 6x$: e, j, n
$y = 4 - 6x$: c, f, h, o

Step 6 Test your answer to Step 5 by finding the intercept form of each equation and then grouping equivalent equations.

Step 7 As a group, explain how you can tell that two equations in point-slope form are equivalent. Students should recognize that intercept form is consistent, and therefore they should transform each point-slope form to intercept form.

You have learned how to write linear equations in two different forms:

Intercept form $y = a + bx$

Point-slope form $y = y_1 + b(x - x_1)$

In the second part of the investigation, some of the equations had x and y on the same side, as in $12x + 2y = -6$. Equations in the form $ax + by = c$ are in **standard form.** What other equation in the investigation is in standard form?

No matter what form you start with, you can always rewrite any linear equation in intercept form. Then it's easy to recognize equivalent equations. Let's review properties that help you change the form of an equation.

For any values of a, b, and c, these properties are true:

Distributive Property

$a(b + c) = a(b) + a(c)$ Example: $6(-2 + 3) = 6(-2) + 6(3)$

Commutative Property of Addition

$a + b = b + a$ Example: $3 + 4 = 4 + 3$

Commutative Property of Multiplication

$ab = ba$ Example: $\frac{1}{2} \cdot \frac{3}{4} = \frac{3}{4} \cdot \frac{1}{2}$

Associative Property of Addition

$a + (b + c) = (a + b) + c$ Example: $2 + (1.5 + 3) = (2 + 1.5) + 3$

Associative Property of Multiplication

$a(bc) = (ab)c$ Example: $4\left(\frac{1}{3} \cdot 6.3\right) = \left(4 \cdot \frac{1}{3}\right) 6.3$

There are also the properties that you have used to solve equations by balancing.

Properties of Equality

Given $a = b$, for any number c,

$a + c = b + c$	addition property of equality
$a - c = b - c$	subtraction property of equality
$ac = bc$	multiplication property of equality
$\frac{a}{c} = \frac{b}{c}\ (c \neq 0)$	division property of equality

EXAMPLE B Is the equation $y = 2 + 3(x - 1)$ equivalent to $6x - 2y = 2$?

▶ Solution Use the properties to rewrite each equation in intercept form.

$y = 2 + 3(x - 1)$	Original equation.
$y = 2 + 3x - 3$	Distributive property (distribute 3 over $x - 1$).
$y = -1 + 3x$	Combine like terms.

So the intercept form of the first equation is $y = -1 + 3x$.

$6x - 2y = 2$	Original equation.
$-2y = 2 - 6x$	Subtraction property (subtract $6x$ from both sides).
$y = \frac{2 - 6x}{-2}$	Division property (divide both sides by -2).
$y = -1 + 3x$	Distributive property (divide each term by -2).

Assessing Progress

In their work on the investigation and in their presentations, students will demonstrate their ability to use the various properties of algebra, even if they don't yet know names for them.

The commutative and associative properties have been used informally up to this point. Students who have an intuitive sense of the properties may find it frustrating to have to justify each step. Encourage students to show their work clearly, but do not penalize students for doing easier steps in their head.

EXAMPLE B

This example repeats the ideas of the investigation and cites the relevant properties.

[Alert] Students may not understand how the distributive property applies to the fraction, which doesn't look like multiplication. You might review the term *multiplicative inverse* and use the multiplication property to write the equation as $y = -\frac{1}{2}(2 - 6x)$.

EXAMPLE C

Depending on students' comfort level with solving equations, you may want to show more detail than in this solution. For example, between the first two steps show $\frac{3x + 4}{6} - 5 + 5 = 7 + 5$. **[Ask]** "Can the equation be solved a different way?" ["First multiply both sides by 6" is one possibility.]

Closing the Lesson

As needed, remind students that another form of a linear equation is the **standard form.** Linear equations are **equivalent** if their graphs are the same or if symbolic manipulation of one can give the other.

BUILDING UNDERSTANDING

Students practice using algebraic and equality properties to determine whether algebraic expressions are equivalent. They also encounter some simple factoring.

ASSIGNING HOMEWORK

Essential	1–4, 7–10
Performance assessment	6, 12
Portfolio	12, 13
Journal	11
Group	3, 5
Review	14–16

▶ Helping with the Exercises

Exercise 1 This exercise gives yet another way to check equivalence of linear equations, besides graphing, algebraic manipulation, and calculator tables. For linear equations, if two points match exactly, then the equations are equivalent.

The intercept form of the second equation is also $y = -1 + 3x$. So they are equivalent. You can also check that the intercept form and the point-slope form of the equation are equivalent by verifying that they produce the same line graph and have the same table of values. Unfortunately, you cannot enter the standard form into your calculator.

One of the authors, Jerald Murdock, works with two students.

$$[-5, 5, 1, -4, 4, 1]$$

EXAMPLE C | Solve the equation $\frac{3x + 4}{6} - 5 = 7$. Identify the property of equality used in each step.

▶ **Solution**

$\dfrac{3x + 4}{6} - 5 = 7$	Original equation.
$\dfrac{3x + 4}{6} = 12$	Addition property (add 5 to both sides).
$3x + 4 = 72$	Multiplication property (multiply both sides by 6).
$3x = 68$	Subtraction property (subtract 4 from both sides).
$x = 22\dfrac{2}{3}$	Division property (divide both sides by 3).

EXERCISES

You will need your graphing calculator for Exercises **1, 2,** and **10.**

▶ Practice Your Skills

1. Is each pair of expressions equivalent? If they are not, change the second expression so that they are equivalent. Check your work on your calculator by comparing table values when you enter the equivalent expressions into Y_1 and Y_2.

   a. $3 - 3(x + 4)$ $3x - 9$ @   not equivalent; $-3x - 9$

   b. $5 + 2(x - 2)$ $2x + 1$ equivalent

   c. $5x - 3$ $2 + 5(x - 1)$ equivalent

   d. $-2x - 8$ $-2(x - 4)$ not equivalent; $-2(x + 4)$ or $2(-x - 4)$

2. Rewrite each equation in intercept form. Show your steps. Check your answer by using a calculator graph or table.

a. $y = 14 + 3(x - 5)$
  $y = -1 + 3x$

b. $y = -5 - 2(x + 5)$ ⓐ
  $y = -15 - 2x$

c. $6x + 2y = 24$
  $y = 12 - 3x$

3. Solve each equation by balancing and tell which property you used in each step.

a. $3x = 12$ $x = 4$; division property

b. $-x - 45 = 47$ ⓐ $-x = 92$; addition property
  $x = -92$; multiplication property

c. $x + 15 = 8$ $x = -7$; subtraction property

d. $\dfrac{x}{4} = 28$
  $x = 112$; multiplication property

4. Use the distributive property to rewrite each expression without parentheses.

a. $3(x - 2)$ $3x - 6$

b. $-4(x - 5)$ $-4x + 20$

c. $-2(x + 8)$ $-2x - 16$

5. An equation of a line is $y = 25 - 2(x + 5)$.

a. Name the point used to write the point-slope equation. ⓗ $(-5, 25)$

b. Find x when y is 15. $x = 0$

▶ Reason and Apply

6. Solve each equation for the indicated variable.

a. $y = 3(x + 8)$ solve for x $x = \dfrac{y}{3} - 8$

b. $\dfrac{y - 3}{x - 4} = 10$ solve for y $y = 3 + 10(x - 4)$

c. $4(2y - 5) - 12 = x$ solve for y

7. In the expression $3x + 15$, the greatest common factor (GCF) of both $3x$ and 15 is 3. You can write the expression $3x + 15$ as $3(x + 5)$. This process, called **factoring,** is the reverse of distributing. Rewrite each expression by factoring out the GCF that will leave 1 as the coefficient of x. Use the distributive property to check your work.

a. $3x - 12$ ⓐ $3(x - 4)$ **b.** $-5x + 20$ ⓐ   **c.** $32 + 4x$ $4(8 + x)$ **d.** $-7x - 28$ $-7(x + 4)$
      $-5(x - 4)$

8. *Mini-Investigation* Consider the equation $y = 10 + 5x$ in intercept form.

a. Factor the right side of the equation. $y = 5(2 + x)$

b. Use the commutative property of addition to swap the terms inside the parentheses. $y = 5(x + 2)$

c. Your result should look similar to the point-slope form of the equation. What's missing? What is the value of this missing piece? ⓐ The y_1-value is missing, which means it is zero; $y = 0 + 5(x + 2)$.

d. What point could you use to write the point-slope equation in 8c? What is special about this point? ⓐ $(-2, 0)$; this is the x-intercept.

9. In each set of three equations, two equations are equivalent. Find them and explain how you know they are equivalent.

a. **i.** $y = 14 - 2(x - 5)$ Equations i and ii are equivalent.
  ⓐ **ii.** $y = 30 - 2(x + 3)$
  iii. $y = -12 + 2(x - 5)$

b. **i.** $y = -13 + 4(x + 2)$ Equations i and iii are equivalent.
  ii. $y = 10 + 3(x - 5)$
  iii. $y = -25 + 4(x + 5)$

c. **i.** $y = 5 + 5(x - 8)$ Equations ii and iii are equivalent.
  ii. $y = 9 + 5(x + 8)$
  iii. $y = 94 + 5(x - 9)$

d. **i.** $y = -16 + 6(x + 5)$ Equations i and iii are equivalent.
  ii. $y = 8 + 6(x - 5)$
  iii. $y = 44 + 6(x - 5)$

Exercise 2 Also encourage checks by substitution.

Exercise 3 Encourage variety. Students may solve 3a by dividing by 3 or multiplying by $\frac{1}{3}$. Similarly, 3b could involve division by -1 or multiplication by -1, and 3c could be solved by adding -15 or subtracting 15.

Exercise 6 If students are having trouble, suggest that they solve by undoing.

6c. $y = \dfrac{\dfrac{x + 12}{4} + 5}{2}$, or

$y = \dfrac{1}{8}x + 4$

Exercise 7 Make sure you assign this problem. **[Alert]** If students don't remember how to find the GCF, remind them that a number m is a *factor* of a number n if n is the product of m and some number. For example, 3 is a factor of 15 because 15 is the product of 3 and 5, and 3 is a factor of $3x$ because $3x$ is the product of 3 and x. So 3 is a common factor of 15 and $3x$. Factoring is mentioned again in the Chapter Review, Exercise 5.

10c.

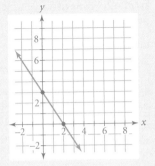

10e.

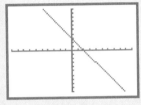

$[-10, 10, 1, -10, 10, 1]$

The two lines are the same; hence the equations are equivalent.

10f. See below.

11e. Answers will vary. You could rewrite each point-slope equation in slope-intercept form.

11f. $(4, -12)$ is not on the line; $(-3, 16.6)$ is on the line. Possible answer: Substitute the x- and y-values into the equation and check whether you get a true statement when you evaluate the equation. Or substitute the given x-value into the equation, evaluate, and see if it is equivalent to the given y-value.

12c. The equation is used to model the bill only when Dorine is logged on for more than 15 h. Substituting 15 for x gives the flat rate of $10.95 for all amounts of time less than or equal to 15 h.

---

10. The equation $3x + 2y = 6$ is in standard form.

   a. Find x when y is zero. Write your answer in the form (x, y). What is the significance of this point? @ $x = 2$; the point $(2, 0)$ is the x-intercept.

   b. Find y when x is zero. Write your answer in the form (x, y). What is the significance of this point? @ $y = 3$; the point $(0, 3)$ is the y-intercept.

   c. On graph paper, plot the points you found in 10a and b and draw the line through these points. @

   d. Find the slope of the line you drew in 10c and write a linear equation in intercept form.   The slope is $-\frac{3}{2}$; $y = 3 - \frac{3}{2}x$.

   e. On your calculator, graph the equation you wrote in 10d. Compare this graph to the one you drew on paper. Is the intercept equation equivalent to the standard-form equation? Explain why or why not.

   f. Symbolically show that the equation $3x + 2y = 6$ is equivalent to your equation from 10d.

11. A line has the equation $y = 4 - 4.2x$.

   a. Find the y-coordinate of the point on this line whose x-coordinate is 2. $y = -4.4$

   b. Use the point you found in 11a to write an equation in point-slope form. $y = -4.4 - 4.2(x - 2)$

   c. Find the x-coordinate of the point whose y-coordinate is 6.1. $x = -0.5$

   d. Use the point you found in 11c to write a different point-slope equation. $y = 6.1 - 4.2(x + 0.5)$

   e. Show that the point-slope equations you wrote in 11b and d are equivalent to the original equation in intercept form. Explain your procedure.

   f. Is the point $(4, -12)$ on the line? How about $(-3, 16.6)$? Explain how you can determine whether a given point is on a line.

12. APPLICATION Dorine subscribes to an Internet service with a flat rate per month for up to 15 h of use. For each hour over this limit, there is an additional per-hour fee. The table shows data about Dorine's first two bills.

Internet Use

Month	Logged on (h)	Monthly fee ($)
January	20	15.20
February	23	17.75

   a. Define your variables and use the data in the table to write an equation in point-slope form that models Dorine's total fee. @ $y = 15.20 + 0.85(x - 20)$

   b. During March, Dorine was incorrectly charged $20 for being logged on for 25 h. What is her correct total fee? $19.45

   c. In April, Dorine was logged on for 14 h. What was her total fee that month? Explain why you can't use your equation to answer this question. (*Hint:* Reread the problem carefully.)

   d. How many hours was Dorine logged on during a month when her fee was $23.70?   30 h

10f. $3x + 2y = 6$ Original equation.

            $2y = 6 - 3x$ Subtract $3x$ from both sides.

            $y = 3 - \frac{3}{2}x$ Divide both sides by 2.

13. On Saturday morning, Avery took a hike in the hills near her house. The table shows the cumulative number of calories she burned from the time she went to sleep Friday night until she finished her hike.

a. Write a point-slope equation of a line that fits the data. @

b. Rewrite your equation from 13a in intercept form.
$y = 545 + 4.6x$

c. What are the real-world meanings of the slope and the y-intercept in this situation? ⓗ

d. Could you use the point-slope equation $y = 821 + 4.6(x - 60)$ to model this situation? Explain why or why not.

e. What is the real-world meaning of the point used to write the equation in 13d?

Avery's Hike

Time spent hiking (min)	Cumulative number of calories burned
5	568
10	591
15	614
20	637

▶ Review

3.4 **14.** Moe Beel has a new cell phone service that is billed at a base fee of $15 per month, plus 45¢ for each minute the phone is used. Consider the relationship between the time the phone is used and the total monthly cost. Let x represent time, in minutes, and let y represent cost, in dollars.

a. Give one point on the line, and state the slope of the line in dollars per minute. @ possible answer: (0, 15); $0.45/min

b. Write the equation of the line. Sketch its graph for the first 30 minutes.

c. How will the graph change if Moe adds Call Forwarding, changing the base fee to $20? The line will be parallel to the original line, but 5 units higher.

d. How will the graph change if Moe drops Caller ID and Voice Mail so that there is no monthly base fee? The line will be parallel to the original line, but 15 units lower (passing through the origin).

e. How will the graph change if instead Moe adds the Text Messaging option, increasing his rate to 55¢ per minute? The line will be steeper but will have the same y-intercept.

4.1 **15.** Plot the points (4, 2), (1, 3.5), and (10, −1) on graph paper. These points are on the same line, or *collinear,* so you can draw a line through them.

a. Draw a slope triangle between (4, 2) and (1, 3.5), and calculate the slope from the change in y and the change in x.

b. Draw another slope triangle between (10, −1) and (4, 2), and calculate the slope from the change in y and the change in x.

c. Compare the slope triangles and the slopes you calculated. What do you notice?

d. What would happen if you made a slope triangle between (10, −1) and (1, 3.5)?

2.8 **16.** Show how to solve the equation $3.8 = 0.2(z + 6.2) - 5.4$ by using an undoing process to write an expression for z. Check your answer by substituting it into the original equation. $z = \dfrac{3.8 + 5.4}{0.2} - 6.2; z = 39.8$

13a. The possible answers are
$y = 568 + 4.6(x - 5)$;
$y = 591 + 4.6(x - 10)$;
$y = 614 + 4.6(x - 15)$;
$y = 637 + 4.6(x - 20)$.

13c. The slope represents the number of calories burned per minute; the y-intercept represents the number of calories Avery burned from the time she went to sleep Friday night until she started hiking.

13d. Yes; it is equivalent to the slope-intercept equation $y = 545 + 4.6x$.

13e. The point (60, 821) tells you that if Avery hikes for 60 min, she will have burned a cumulative total of 821 calories since she went to sleep Friday night.

14b. $y = 15 + 0.45x$

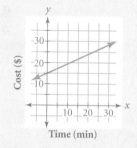

Exercise 15 [Language] Emphasize that *collinear* means lying on the same line. Students will learn the definition of similar triangles in Chapter 11. Help them use terms such as *equal ratios* and *proportional* from Chapter 2 to describe the lengths of the sides of the slope triangles for 15c and d.

15a. $\dfrac{change\ in\ y}{change\ in\ x} = -\dfrac{1.5}{3} = -0.5$

15b. $\dfrac{change\ in\ y}{change\ in\ x} = -\dfrac{3}{6} = -0.5$

15c. Possible answers: The slope triangle side lengths for 15b are twice as long, but the slopes are equal.

15d. Possible answer: You would get a larger triangle, but the ratio of the side lengths would equal −0.5, giving a slope of −0.5.

LESSON

4.5

Writing Point-Slope Equations to Fit Data

To give an accurate description of what has never occurred is the proper occupation of the historian.

OSCAR WILDE

In this lesson you'll practice modeling data that have a linear pattern with the point-slope form of a linear equation. You may find that using the point-slope form is more efficient than using the intercept form because you don't have to first write a direct variation equation and then adjust it for the intercept.

The development and improvement of vaccinations is one factor that has increased life expectancy over the decades.

 Investigation
Life Expectancy

You will need
- graph paper

This table shows the relationship between the number of years a person might be expected to live and the year he or she was born. Life expectancy is a prediction that is very useful in professions like medicine and insurance.

Step 1 | Choose one column of life expectancy data—female, male, or combined. Let x represent birth year, and let y represent life expectancy in years. Graph the data points.

Step 2 | Choose two points on your graph so that a line through them closely reflects the pattern of all the points on the graph. Use the two points to write the equation of this line in point-slope form.

Step 3 | Graph the line with your data points. Does it fit the data?

Step 4 | Use your equation to predict the life expectancy of a person who will be born in 2022.

U.S. Life Expectancy at Birth

Birth year	Female	Male	Combined
1940	65.2	60.8	62.9
1950	71.1	65.6	68.2
1960	73.1	66.6	69.7
1970	74.7	67.1	70.8
1975	76.6	68.8	72.6
1980	77.5	70.0	73.7
1985	78.2	71.2	74.7
1990	78.8	71.8	75.4
1995	78.9	72.5	75.8
2000	79.5	74.1	76.9

(National Center for Health Statistics, in *The World Almanac and Book of Facts 2004*, p. 76) [Data sets: **LEYR, LEFEM, LEMAL, LECOM**]

Step 5 | Compare your prediction from Step 4 to the prediction that another group made analyzing the same data. Are your predictions the same? Are they close? Explain why it's possible to make different predictions from the same data.

PLANNING

LESSON OUTLINE

One day:

25 min	Investigation
5 min	Sharing
5 min	Closing
15 min	Exercises

MATERIALS

- graph paper
- uncooked spaghetti, *optional*
- Fathom demonstration Life Expectancy, *optional*
- CBR demonstration Roll with It, *optional*

TEACHING

A linear equation in point-slope form, with the slope based on two points in a scatter plot, can help you make predictions.

 Guiding the Investigation

The Fathom demonstration Life Expectancy can be used to replace this investigation.

One Step

Direct students' attention to the U.S. Life Expectancy at Birth table and ask students to predict the life expectancy of a person who will be born in 2022. Encourage a variety of approaches to finding lines of fit, but suggest choosing two data points that are not too close or too far apart. Urge students to express linear equations in point-slope form.

Step 1 Some students might call these "death predictions." Point out that life expectancy calculations don't predict when any particular person will die.

Step 2 answers using the 1970 and 1990 data:
Female:
$y = 74.7 + 0.205(x - 1970)$
Male:
$y = 67.1 + 0.235(x - 1970)$
Combined:
$y = 70.8 + 0.23(x - 1970)$

Step 4 answer using the equations from Step 2: Female: 85.36 Male: 79.32 Combined: 82.76

Step 5 Predictions made from equations created with different points will vary, despite being from the same data set.

To help students make sense of the table, **[Ask]** "Why are the numbers increasing?" [Each year has brought better average living and working conditions and better food and medicine.]

Students can carry out this investigation on a calculator without graph paper. Be sure some groups work with the combined data.

Step 1

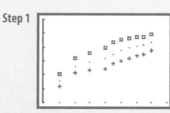

□ female
\+ male
• combined

[1930, 2010, 10, 55, 85, 5]

Step 2 Suggest that students not choose points that are adjacent or at extremes of the data. Have some spaghetti ready for students who'd like to use it to indicate an easily adjustable line of fit.

Step 6 Slopes are around 0.2. This means that life expectancy increases by 0.2 yr each year, regardless of gender. Some students may notice that the slope of the data for males is slightly greater, which means that male life expectancy may eventually catch up with female life expectancy.

Step 6 Compare the slope of your line of fit to the slopes that other groups found working with different data sets. What does the slope for each data set tell you?

Step 7 As a class, select one line of fit that you think is the best model for each column of data—female, male, and combined. Graph all three lines on the same set of axes. Is it reasonable for the line representing the combined data to lie between the other two lines? Explain why or why not.

Step 8 How does the point-slope method of finding a line compare to the intercept-form method you learned about in Lesson 4.2? What are the strengths and weaknesses of each method?

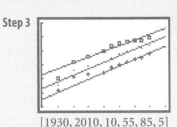

Step 3

[1930, 2010, 10, 55, 85, 5]

The graph fits the data reasonably well.

Step 7 Use a calculator projection panel if you have one. Point out that the chart shows the combined life expectancy. **[Ask]** "Is the combined data simply an average of the male and female numbers?" [no] "Why not?" [Averaging averages doesn't work when the sizes of data sets are different. The number of men and the number of women are not exactly the same.]

Each student will have a different impression of the artwork in this museum. Similarly, different people can have different impressions of a set of data; this can result in different mathematical models.

You can summarize the point-slope method of fitting a line to the data like this: First, graph the data. Next, choose two points on a line that appears to show the direction of the data. Then, write the equation of the line.

Finally, you will need to graph the equation with the data and decide if the model is a good fit. With a wide scattering of points, there may be no pair of points from the existing data set that make a good model for the data. So you may need to adjust one or more of the three values in your equation $(x_1, y_1,$ or $b)$ to improve the model. Exercise 8 will give you a chance to experiment with these changes.

SHARING IDEAS

Ask students how accurate they think their prediction is. Have them discuss the number of years they think their linear model will give a reliable prediction.

Point out the quotation from Oscar Wilde at the beginning of the lesson. Ask the class to brainstorm methods that mathematicians use to "give an accurate description of what has never occurred." Besides using lines of fit to make predictions, students might raise ideas such as that the "perfect" geometric figures of mathematics never occur and that perfectly accurate measurements (except when counting discrete objects) are impossible.

You can use the CBR demonstration Roll with It to give students more practice modeling data with point-slope equations.

EXERCISES

You will need your graphing calculator for Exercises **3, 4, 5, 6, 8,** and **9.**

▶ **Practice Your Skills**

1. Write the point-slope form of the equation for each line graphed below.

a.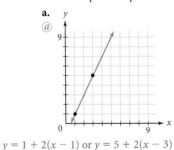

$y = 1 + 2(x - 1)$ or $y = 5 + 2(x - 3)$

b.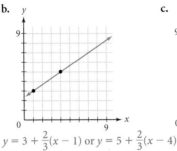

$y = 3 + \frac{2}{3}(x - 1)$ or $y = 5 + \frac{2}{3}(x - 4)$

c.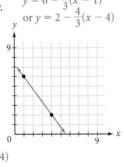

$y = 6 - \frac{4}{3}(x - 1)$ or $y = 2 - \frac{4}{3}(x - 4)$

2. Look at each graph in Exercise 1 and estimate the y-intercept. Then convert your point-slope equations to intercept form. How well did you estimate? Ⓗ

$y = -1 + 2x$ $y = \frac{7}{3} + \frac{2}{3}x$ or $y = 2.\overline{3} + 0.\overline{6}x$ $y = \frac{22}{3} - \frac{4}{3}x$ or $y = 7.\overline{3} - 1.\overline{3}x$

See page 723 for answers to Steps 7 and 8.

NCTM STANDARDS

CONTENT		PROCESS	
✔	Number	✔	Problem Solving
✔	Algebra	✔	Reasoning
	Geometry	✔	Communication
	Measurement	✔	Connections
✔	Data/Probability	✔	Representation

LESSON OBJECTIVES

- Write linear equations in point-slope form that model real-world data
- Discover strengths of the point-slope form for linear equations
- Learn to deal with variation in linear data

Assessing Progress

Look for students' abilities at making scatter plots, finding the slope of a line through two points, and evaluating an equation at a point. Also check their understanding of the intercept form and their skill at comparing and contrasting different approaches.

Say that you can use two points in a data set to find the point-slope form of a linear equation and then use it to make predictions.

BUILDING UNDERSTANDING

The exercises involve using the point-slope form of linear equations to fit data and make predictions.

ASSIGNING HOMEWORK

Essential	1–5, 8
Performance assessment	7, 8
Portfolio	8
Journal	3, 5
Group	4–6
Review	9–11

▶ Helping with the Exercises

Exercise 3 Remind students that the *x-intercept* is the point where the line crosses the *x*-axis. This exercise previews the factored form of polynomials that will be introduced in Lesson 9.4.

Exercise 4 Students might choose to use as input values the number of years since 1900 or 1950 or 1976. Discuss 4d with students. They should be aware that mathematical models like this one, based on a short time period of about 30 yr, cannot necessarily be used to make conclusions about the distant past or future.

4a. Answers will vary. Using the points (1982, 341) and (1996, 363) gives the equation $y = 341 + 1.6(x - 1982)$, where x is the year and y is the concentration of CO_2 in parts per million.

3. Graph each linear equation on your calculator and name the *x*-intercept. Make a conjecture about the *x*-intercept of any equation in the form $y = b(x - x_1)$.

a. $y = 2(x - 3)$ @ 3
b. $y = \frac{1}{3}(x + 4)$ −4
c. $y = -1.5(x - 6)$ 6

The *x*-intercept of $y = b(x - x_1)$ is at $x = x_1$.

4. **APPLICATION** Carbon dioxide is one of several greenhouse gases that is emitted into the atmosphere from a variety of sources, including automobiles. The table shows the concentration of carbon dioxide (CO_2) in the atmosphere measured from the top of Mauna Loa volcano in Hawaii each January. The concentration of CO_2 is measured in parts per million (ppm).

a. Define variables and write an equation in point-slope form that models the data.

b. Graph your equation to confirm that the line fits the data.

c. Use your equation to predict what the concentration of CO_2 will be in 2020.

d. What would be the *x*-intercept for your equation? Does its real-world meaning make sense? Explain why or why not.

e. According to your equation, what is the typical change in CO_2 concentration per year? about 1.6 ppm/yr

CO_2 Concentration

Year	CO_2 (ppm)
1976	332
1978	336
1980	339
1982	341
1984	344
1986	347
1988	351
1990	354
1992	356
1994	359
1996	363
1998	367
2000	369
2002	373

(Carbon Dioxide Information Analysis Center, *cdiac.esd.ornl.gov*) [Data sets: **CO2YR, CO2CN**]

Mauna Loa is the largest and most active volcano on Earth. Research on Mauna Loa has revealed a great deal about global changes in the atmosphere. For more information about the causes and effects of the increase in atmospheric CO_2, see www.keymath.com/DA .

▶ Reason and Apply

5. **APPLICATION** Alex collected this table of data by using two thermometers simultaneously. Alex suspects that one or both of the thermometers are somewhat faulty.

a. Graph the data. @

b. Write an equation in point-slope form that models Alex's data. @

c. Graph your equation to confirm that the line fits the data.

d. The freezing point of water is 0°C, which is equivalent to 32°F. The boiling point of water is 100°C, which is equivalent to 212°F. Use this information to write another equation in point-slope form that models the true relationship between the Celsius and Fahrenheit temperature scales. @

e. Write the equations from 5b and d in intercept form. Are they equivalent? @

f. Do you think that Alex's thermometers are faulty? Explain why or why not.
The difference could be a result of measurement error or faulty procedures.

Temperature Readings

Celsius (°C) x	Fahrenheit (°F) y
14.5	55.0
20.0	67.0
28.4	86.7
39.5	105.6
32.3	87.1
29.0	81.6
26.2	82.3
25.7	75.2
31.2	88.6

[Data sets: **TEMPC, TEMPF**]

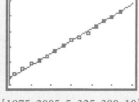

4b. All graphs should look approximately like this

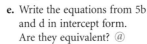

[1975, 2005, 5, 325, 380, 10]

4c. The equation $y = 341 + 1.6(x - 1982)$ gives 402 ppm.

4d. Using the equation in 4c, the *x*-intercept is about 1769. It represents the year when the concentration of CO_2 would have been zero. This is not reasonable, because plants depend on CO_2 and there would have been some concentration of CO_2 for as long as there have been plants. The model is limited; it cannot be extended much before or after the time period of the data.

Exercise 5 If you did the CBL 2 demonstration Heating Up with your class, this exercise would make an interesting follow-up.

6. APPLICATION The table lists the concentration of dissolved oxygen (DO) in parts per million at various temperatures in degrees Celsius from a sample of lake water.

a. Graph the data.

b. Write an equation in point-slope form that models the data.

c. Graph your equation to confirm that the line fits the data.

d. Use your equation to predict the concentration of dissolved oxygen in parts per million when the water temperature is 2°C.

e. Use your equation to predict the water temperature in degrees Celsius when the concentration of dissolved oxygen is 12 ppm.
Using $y = 11 - 0.6(x - 13)$, the temperature is about 11.3°C.

7. Use the data and the equation you found in Exercise 6.

a. Write an equation with the same slope that passes through the point farthest above the line. Using the slope -0.6,
$y = 14 - 0.6(x - 11)$.
b. Write an equation with the same slope that passes through the point farthest below the line. $y = 13 - 0.6(x - 7)$

c. Rewrite all three equations in intercept form.

d. Based on your answer to 7c, how accurate are predictions made using your equation from Exercise 6 likely to be? ⓗ
The equation has prediction accuracy within 1.8 ppm.

8. *Mini-Investigation* Scoop has a rolling ice cream cart. He recorded his daily sales for the last seven days and the mean daytime temperature for each day.

Ice Cream Sales

Day	1	2	3	4	5	6	7
Temperature (°F)	83	79	75	70	71	67	62
Sales (cones)	66	47	51	23	33	30	21

[Data sets: ICTMP, ICSAL]

a. Find the equation of the line that passes through the points (79, 47) and (67, 30). (Use the second point as the point in the point-slope form.) ⓐ $y = 30 + 1.4(x - 67)$

b. Graph the data and your line from 8a on your calculator. Sketch the result.

You should have noticed in 8b that the line does not fit the data well. In fact, no two points from this data set make a good model. In 8c–e you'll adjust the values of y_1 and b in $y = y_1 + b(x - x_1)$ to find a better model.

c. Copy the table shown, and begin by changing the value of y_1. Write two new equations, one with a larger value for y_1 and one with a smaller value for y_1. Graph each equation, and describe how the graphs compare to your original equation. ⓐ

Value	Increase	Decrease
y_1		
b		

d. Now write two new equations that have the same values of x_1 and y_1 as the original, but larger and smaller values of b. Graph each equation, and describe how the graphs compare to your original equation.

e. Continue to adjust your values for y_1 and b until you find a line that fits the data well. Record your final equation. Graph your equation with the data and sketch the result.

Dissolved Oxygen

Temperature (°C) x	DO (ppm) y
17	8
15	9
13	11
16	10
11	14
13	11
10	14
8	14
6	16
7	13
8	14
4	17
5	15
9	13
6	16

[Data sets: DOTMP, DOPPM]

Exercise 6 [Ask] "Why does the graph of the data show only 12 points?" [Three are double points: (6, 16), (8, 14), (13, 11).]

6a.

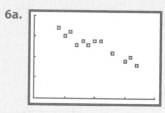

$[0, 20, 5, 0, 20, 5]$

6b. Using (13, 11) and (8, 14), the equation is
$y = 11 - 0.6(x - 13)$ or
$y = 14 - 0.6(x - 8)$.

6c. one possible answer:

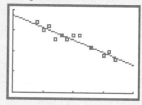

6d. Using $y = 11 - 0.6(x - 13)$, the concentration of dissolved oxygen is 17.6 ppm.

7c. $y = 18.8 - 0.6x$;
$y = 20.6 - 0.6x$;
$y = 17.2 - 0.6x$

Exercise 7d [Alert] Students may claim that the line can predict within 1.6 ppm because the lower line is within 1.6 ppm of the modeling line. Bring out the fact that the line is not within 1.6 ppm of all the data points, but it is within 1.8 ppm.

Exercise 8 This would be a good exercise for movable lines in Fathom.

8b.

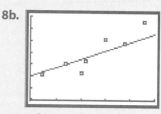

$[60, 85, 5, 0, 70, 10]$

8c. Equations will vary. The graph with a larger y_1-value is parallel but higher, and the graph with a smaller y_1-value is parallel but lower.

5a.

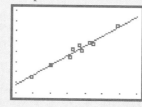

$[10, 45, 5, 40, 120, 20]$

5b. Using the points (20, 67) and (31.2, 88.6), the slope is approximately 1.9 and a possible equation is $y = 67 + 1.9(x - 20)$.

5c. one possible answer:

$$ $$

5d. $y = 32 + 1.8(x - 0)$ or $y = 212 + 1.8(x - 100)$

5e. The sample equation in 5b gives $y = 29 + 1.9x$; the equations in 5d both give $y = 32 + 1.8x$.

See page 252 for answers to Exercises 8d and 8e.

8d. Equations will vary. The graphs pass through the point (67, 30), but the one with a larger value of b is steeper and the one with a smaller value of b is less steep.

8e. possible equation:
$y = 26 + 2(x - 67)$

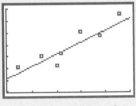

$[60, 85, 5, 0, 70, 10]$

9c. After 45 full days, there will be only one biscuit left, so the box will be empty at some time on the 46th day.

9d. When the box was new, before Anchor had any biscuits, there were 136 biscuits.

▶ Review

4.3 **9.** APPLICATION Bryan has bought a box of biscuits for his dog, Anchor. Anchor always gets three biscuits a day. At the start of the 10th day after opening the box, Bryan counts 106 biscuits left. Let x represent the number of days after opening the box, and let y represent the number of biscuits left.

   a. In a graph of this situation, what is the slope? ⓗ -3

   b. Write a point-slope equation that models the situation. $y = 106 - 3(x - 10)$

   c. When will the box be empty?

   d. What is the real-world meaning of the y-intercept?

2.8 **10.** Solve the equation $2x - 3(y + 1) = 12$ for y by copying and filling in this table. ⓐ

Description	Undo	Equation
Pick y.	▨▨▨	$y =$
$+ 1$	-1	
$\cdot (-3)$	$/ (-3)$	
$+ 2x$	$- 2x$	

$y = \dfrac{12 - 2x}{-3} - 1$, or $y = -5 + \dfrac{2x}{3}$

$y + 1 = \dfrac{12 - 2x}{-3}$, or $y + 1 = -4 + \dfrac{2x}{3}$

$-3(y + 1) = 12 - 2x$

$2x - 3(y + 1) = 12$

11. You've worked with various types of problems involving rates. A new kind of problem that uses rates is called a **work problem.** In a work problem, you usually know how long it would take someone or something to complete an entire job. You use the reciprocal of the complete time to find a rate of work. For example, if Mavis paints 1 entire room in 10 hours, she paints $\frac{1}{10}$ of the room each hour. These problems rely on the formula *rate of work · time = part of work*. These problems also assume that a complete job is equivalent to 1.

Mavis and Claire work for a house painter. Mavis can paint a room in 10 hours, and Claire can paint a room in 8 hours. How long will it take them to paint a room if they work together?

Let t represent the number of hours that Mavis and Claire paint. Mavis paints $\frac{1}{10}$ of a room each hour, and Claire paints $\frac{1}{8}$ of a room each hour. So you can write the equation $\frac{1}{10}t + \frac{1}{8}t = 1$.

   a. Solve this equation, check your answer, and state the solution. $4.\overline{4}$ h, or about 4 h 27 min

   b. Solve this problem using a similar procedure: When fully turned on, the faucet of a bathtub fills a tub in 30 minutes. When the tub is full of water and the drain is opened, the tub empties in 45 minutes. If the faucet is fully turned on *and* the drain is open at the same time, how much time does it take to fill the tub? 90 min

More on Modeling

Several times in this chapter you have found the equation of a representative line to fit data. Making, analyzing, and using predictions based on equation models is important in the real world. For this reason it is often helpful and even important that different people arrive at the same model for a given set of data. For this to happen, each person must get the same slope and *y*-intercept. To do that, they have to follow the same systematic method.

Statisticians have developed many methods of finding a line or curve that fits a set of data well. In this lesson you'll learn a method that uses the quartiles you learned about in Chapter 1.

When you can measure what you are talking about and express it in numbers, you know something about it.
LORD KELVIN

Investigation
Bucket Brigade

In this investigation you will use a systematic method for finding a particular line of fit for data.

You will need
- a stopwatch
- a bucket
- graph paper

Procedure Note

Select a class member as timer. Everyone should line up single file. Your line might wrap around the room. Spread out so that there is an arm's length between two people.

Step 1	Line up in a bucket brigade. (See the Procedure Note.) Record the number of people in the line. Starting at one end of the line, pass the bucket as quickly as you can to the other end. Record the total passing time from picking up the bucket to setting it down at the very end.
Step 2	Now have one or two people sit down and close up the gaps in the line. Repeat the bucket passing. Record the new number of people and the new passing time.
Step 3	Continue the bucket brigade until you have collected 10 data points in the form (*number of people, passing time in seconds*).

PLANNING

LESSON OUTLINE

First day:

50 min   Investigation (Steps 1–12)

Second day:

10 min   Investigation (Step 13)

10 min   Sharing

10 min   Example

5 min   Closing

15 min   Exercises

MATERIALS

- stopwatch or watch with second hand
- bucket or other object to pass
- graph paper
- Calculator Notes 1D, 4B
- Fathom demonstration More on Modeling, *optional*

TEACHING

This lesson builds on the five-number summaries introduced in Lesson 1.3. If you didn't cover Lesson 1.3, you can still cover Lessons 4.6–4.8, but you'll need to introduce five-number summaries first. One way to standardize the choice of two points through which a line of fit passes is to use the first and third quartiles of each data variable.

Guiding the Investigation

One Step

Using some data (perhaps from a bucket brigade such as in the first part of the investigation or from the example), point out that so far students have come up with different valid modeling lines. Challenge groups to develop systematic methods, based on statistics of the two data sets, for

producing these lines. As you circulate, remind students that the mean is overly sensitive to outliers. Some groups might develop something like the median-median line, but encourage groups that are stuck to produce two points through which the line will pass. The "middle of each half" is a natural idea that leads to Q-points.

Step 1 **[ELL]** A *bucket brigade* is a line of people passing a bucket, usually full of water to help put out a fire.

In place of a bucket, students can use any object they can pass. They might run each brigade several times and average the times. In this unusual situation, time is the output rather than the input variable. **[Ask]** "Which variable depends on which other variable?" [The time depends on how far the bucket needs to be passed.]

Step 2 Students who have just sat down might do the timing, record the data, or begin to make scatter plots. You can also vary the size of groups that sit down.

Step 5 Refer students to Lesson 1.3 or Calculator Note 1D to review five-number summaries.

Step 7 If students have difficulty making a vertical box plot, encourage them to make a horizontal one and then rotate it.

Step 11 The slope represents how long it takes one person to pass the bucket. The y-intercept is the time it takes for no people to pass the bucket (0), or it might represent the time to begin and end the experiment (to lift the bucket and set it down at the end).

Step 12 Answers will vary. The advantage of having a systematic procedure is that everyone will arrive at the same model. Students may feel that the line through the Q-points does not capture the data as well as a line through two representative points.

SHARING IDEAS

Ask what Q-points and equations different groups found. Be sure students see that this method always yields the same lines.

Have groups share their ideas about the questions in Steps 11 and 12. Step 12 foreshadows Lesson 4.7. **[Ask]** "Why are the Q-points better than extreme points?" [Points at the extremes of data tend to be less reliable because measurements and instruments are often least accurate there. Also, in the real world, some relationships have non-linear end-behavior, such as a rubber band stretched to its breaking point.]

Ask when Q-points will be actual data points. Even if the quartiles are points in the one-variable data, the pairs of quartiles might not be points in the two-variable data.

Step 8 Q-points may not be data points. Many factors influence this, including the number of data points and the strength of the linear relationship (how close the points are to a line). However, everyone should get the same Q-points.

Step 4 Let x represent the number of people, and let y represent time in seconds. Plot your data on graph paper.

Step 5 List the five-number summary for the x-values and the five-number summary for the y-values.

Step 6 What are the first-quartile (Q1) and third-quartile (Q3) values for the x-values in your data set? What are the Q1- and Q3-values for the y-values in your data set?

Step 7 On your graph, draw a horizontal box plot just below the x-axis using the five-number summary for the x-values. Draw a vertical box plot next to the y-axis using the five-number summary for the y-values. A sample graph is shown. Your data and graph will look different based on the data that you collect.

Step 8 Draw vertical lines from the Q1- and Q3-values on the x-axis box plot into the graph. Draw horizontal lines from the Q1- and Q3-values on the y-axis box plot into the graph. These lines should form a rectangle in the plot. The vertices of this rectangle are called **Q-points.** Do the Q-points have to be actual data points? Why or why not? Will everyone get the same Q-points?

Step 9 Draw the diagonal of this rectangle that shows the direction of the data. Extend this diagonal through the plot. Is the line a good fit for the data? Are any of the original data points on your line? If so, which ones?

Step 10 Find the coordinates of the two Q-points the line goes through and write a point-slope equation for the line.

Step 11 What are the real-world meanings of the slope and y-intercept of this model?

Step 12 What are the advantages and disadvantages of having a systematic procedure for finding a model for data?

Step 13 Use your calculator to plot the data points, draw the vertical and horizontal lines, and plot a line of fit found by this method. [▶ 🖳 See **Calculator Note 4B** for help on using the draw menu.◀]

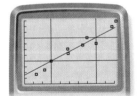

LESSON OBJECTIVES

- Use quartiles to find an equation to fit a set of data
- Develop a strategy for agreeing on one equation for a set of data
- Review five-number summaries and box plots

NCTM STANDARDS

CONTENT		PROCESS	
✔	Number	✔	Problem Solving
✔	Algebra	✔	Reasoning
	Geometry	✔	Communication
	Measurement	✔	Connections
✔	Data/Probability	✔	Representation

The method of finding a line of fit based on Q-points is more direct than the methods you used in Lessons 4.2 and 4.5. It is more systematic, too, because everyone will get the same points and the points themselves relate to measures of center in the upper and lower halves of the data set.

keymath.com/DA

[▶ For a **Dynamic Algebra Exploration** that investigates how moving one data point affects box plots and Q-points, see www.keymath.com/DA . ◄]

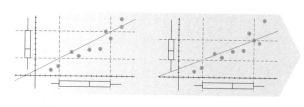

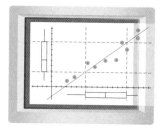

These students are collecting water samples. Their samples can be analyzed for many things, including dissolved oxygen.

EXAMPLE

The table lists the concentration of dissolved oxygen (DO) in parts per million at various temperatures in degrees Celsius from a sample of lake water. Find a line of fit based on Q-points for the data, and use it to predict the temperature for water with only 4 ppm dissolved oxygen.

Dissolved Oxygen

Temperature (°C) x	DO (ppm) y	Temperature (°C) x	DO (ppm) y
17	8	8	14
16	10	8	14
15	9	7	13
13	11	6	16
13	11	6	16
11	14	5	15
10	14	4	17
9	13		

Assessing Progress
From students' work on the investigation and their contributions to Sharing, you can assess their skill at recording data systematically, plotting points, finding five-number summaries, drawing box plots, and writing linear equations in point-slope form.

EXAMPLE

This example is good for students who didn't understand the investigation very well. In Lesson 4.5, Exercise 6, students found the equation of a line of fit for these data by guessing and adjusting. Now they will use the standardized method to find the equation of the line of fit based on Q-points. **[Ask]** "Why is the slope negative?" [As a point moves along the line from left to right, its y-value decreases while its x-value increases. Hence either the numerator or the denominator of the slope will be negative.]

The Fathom demonstration More on Modeling can be used to replace this example.

Closing the Lesson

As needed, say that one way to standardize the choice of two points through which a line of fit passes is to use the first and third quartiles for each data variable.

▶ *Solution*

The five-number summaries are

For temperature (*x*-values): 4, 6, 9, 13, 17

For dissolved oxygen (*y*-values): 8, 11, 14, 15, 17

The first-quartile and third-quartile values are

For the *x*-values: Q1 = 6, Q3 = 13

For the *y*-values: Q1 = 11, Q3 = 15

A sketch of the scatter plot shows that the appropriate Q-points are (6, 15) and (13, 11). Why are these the correct points, rather than (6, 11) and (13, 15)? Note that (6, 15) is not actually one of the data points but (13, 11) is.

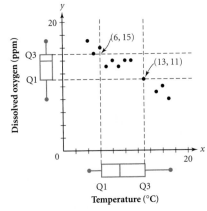

Calculating the slope between these two points, you get

$$b = \frac{y_2 - y_1}{x_2 - x_1} = \frac{(11 - 15)}{(13 - 6)} = \frac{-4}{7} \approx -0.57$$

This means that if the temperature *rises* 1°C, the dissolved oxygen concentration *decreases* by 0.57 ppm. It also means that if the temperature *drops* 1°C, the dissolved oxygen concentration *increases* by 0.57 ppm.

Using the slope −0.57 and the coordinates of the point (6, 15) in the point-slope form, $y = y_1 + b(x - x_1)$, gives

$$y = 15 - 0.57(x - 6)$$

To find the temperature when the concentration of dissolved oxygen is 4 ppm, substitute 4 for *y* in the equation and solve for *x*.

$y = 15 - 0.57(x - 6)$	Original equation.
$4 = 15 - 0.57(x - 6)$	Substitute 4 for *y*.
$-11 = -0.57(x - 6)$	Subtraction property (subtract 15 from both sides).
$19.3 \approx x - 6$	Division property (divide both sides by −0.57).
$25.3 \approx x$	Addition property (add 6 to both sides).

At about 25°C, the water will have about 4 ppm dissolved oxygen.

EXERCISES

▶ Practice Your Skills

1. **APPLICATION** This table shows that the traveling distances between some cities depend on how you travel.

Traveling Distances

From	To	Flying distance (mi)	Driving distance (mi)
Detroit, MI	Memphis, TN	623	756
St. Louis, MO	Minneapolis, MN	466	559
Dallas, TX	San Francisco, CA	1483	1765
Seattle, WA	Los Angeles, CA	959	1150
Washington, DC	Pittsburgh, PA	192	241
Philadelphia, PA	Indianapolis, IN	585	647
New Orleans, LA	Chicago, IL	833	947
Cleveland, OH	New York, NY	405	514
Birmingham, AL	Boston, MA	1052	1194
Denver, CO	Buffalo, NY	1370	1991
Kansas City, MO	Omaha, NE	166	204

[Data sets: **FLYDS, DRVDS**]

a. What are the five-number summary values of the flying distances? @ 166, 405, 623, 1052, 1483

b. What are the five-number summary values of the driving distances? @ 204, 514, 756, 1194, 1991

c. Plot the data points. Let x represent flying distance in miles, and let y represent driving distance in miles. @

d. Will the slope of the line through these points be positive or negative? Explain your reasoning. @ The slope will be positive because as the flying distance increases so does the driving distance.

e. Use the five-number summary values to draw a rectangle on the graph of the data. Name the two Q-points you should use for your line of fit. @

f. Find the equation of the line and graph the line with your data points.

g. The flying distance from Louisville, Kentucky, to Miami, Florida, is 919 miles. Predict the driving distance from Louisville to Miami. @ approximately 1054 mi

h. The driving distance from Phoenix, Arizona, to Salt Lake City, Utah, is 651 miles. Predict the flying distance from Phoenix to Salt Lake City. approximately 535 or 536 mi

BUILDING UNDERSTANDING

Students get practice in using Q-points to develop lines of fit.

ASSIGNING HOMEWORK

Essential	**1–4, 7 or 8**
Performance assessment	**7, 8**
Portfolio	**4**
Journal	**3, 6, 12**
Group	**5, 9**
Review	**10–12**

▶ Helping with the Exercises

Exercise 1 Either column of data may be considered input or output. Choosing the driving distance as input would give different equations. Different procedures for rounding will also lead to a variety of answers.

1c.

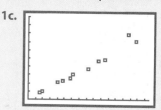

[0, 1650, 100, 0, 2500, 250]

1e.

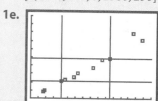

Q-points: (405, 514), (1052, 1194)

1f.

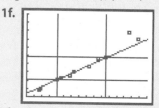

The slope is approximately 1.05; $y = 1194 + 1.05(x - 1052)$ or $y = 514 + 1.05(x - 405)$.

2. APPLICATION Let x represent total fat in grams, and let y represent saturated fat in grams. Use the model $y = 10 + 0.5(x - 28)$ to predict

    a. The number of saturated fat grams for a hamburger with a total of 32 grams of fat. 12 g saturated fat

    b. The total number of fat grams for a hamburger with 15 grams of saturated fat. 38 g total fat

3. Give the coordinates of the Q-points for each data set.

a. 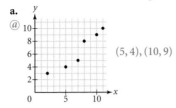 $(5, 4), (10, 9)$

b. 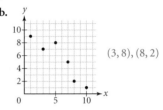 $(3, 8), (8, 2)$

▶ Reason and Apply

4. The table gives the winning times for the Olympic men's 10,000-meter run.

    a. Define variables and find the line of fit based on Q-points for the data.

    b. Plot the data points and graph the equation of the model to verify that it is a good fit. @

    c. What is the real-world meaning of the slope?

    d. Kenenisa Bekele of Ethiopia won the 10,000-meter race in the 2004 Olympic Games. Compare his actual winning time of 27.08 minutes with the winning time predicted by your model.

    e. Could you use this model to predict the winning time 100 years from now? Explain why or why not.

5. Create a data set that has Q-points at $(4, 28)$ and $(12, 47)$ so that only one of those two points is actually part of the data set. ⓗ

6. Which linear equation below best fits the data at right? Explain your reasoning.

    i. $y = 1.3 + 0.18(x - 6)$

    ii. $y = 2.2 + 0.18(x - 6)$

    iii. $y = 1.3 - 0.18(x - 6)$

    iv. $y = 2.2 - 0.18(x - 6)$

Men's 10,000-meter Run

Year	Champion	Time (min)
1952	Emil Zatopek, Czechoslovakia	29.28
1956	Vladimir Kuts, USSR	28.76
1960	Pyotr Bolotnikov, USSR	28.54
1964	Billy Mills, United States	28.41
1968	Naftali Temu, Kenya	29.46
1972	Lasse Viren, Finland	27.64
1976	Lasse Viren, Finland	27.67
1980	Miruts Yifter, Ethiopia	27.71
1984	Alberto Cova, Italy	27.79
1988	Brahim Boutaib, Morocco	27.36
1992	Khalid Skah, Morocco	27.78
1996	Haile Gebrselassie, Ethiopia	27.12
2000	Haile Gebrselassie, Ethiopia	27.30

(International Olympic Committee, in *The World Almanac and Book of Facts 2004*, p. 866) [Data sets: **RUNYR, RUNTM**]

Time (s) x	Distance from motion sensor (m) y
2	2.8
6	2.2
8	1.7
9	1.5
11	1.3
14	0.9

4a. Let x represent years, and let y represent winning time in minutes. The five-number summary for x is 1952, 1962, 1976, 1990, 2000. The five-number summary for y is 27.12, 27.5, 27.78, 28.65, 29.46. The Q-points are (1962, 28.65) and (1990, 27.5). The slope of the line through these two points is about -0.0411, so the possible equations are $y = 28.65 - 0.0411(x - 1962)$ and $y = 27.5 - 0.0411(x - 1990)$.

4b.

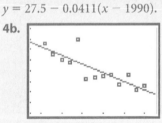

[1945, 2005, 10, 26, 30, 0.5]

4c. The slope, -0.0411, means that the winning time decreases by an average of 0.0411 min (2.47 s) each year.

4d. The prediction is 26.92 min, which is 0.16 min (9.6 s) less than the actual winning time.

Exercise 4e This question shows the limitations of the model for making long-range predictions.

4e. Answers will vary. However, there is a physical limit to how fast a runner can run. Eventually, the times will have to level off.

5. Answers will vary. One example is $\{(2, 22), (4, 30), (6, 28), (8, 35), (10, 42), (12, 47), (14, 53)\}$.

Exercise 6 Encourage lots of approaches here. Some students may find the Q-points and see which line goes through them. Others may count the number of data points on each side of a line or measure the vertical distance from data points to the line.

6. Reasons will vary. The data pattern has a negative slope, and the Q-points that lie on the line are $(11, 1.3)$ and $(6, 2.2)$. The point $(6, 1.3)$ is not one of the Q-points used to draw the line, so equation iv is the correct equation.

7. At 2:00 P.M., elevator A passes the second floor of the Empire State Building going up. The table shows the floors and the times in seconds after 2:00.

Floor x	2	4	6	8	10	12	14
Time after 2:00 (s) y	0	1.3	2.5	3.8	5	6.3	7.5

  a. What is the line of fit based on Q-points for the data? @

  b. Give a real-world meaning for the slope. @   The elevator is rising at a rate of 0.625 s per floor.

  c. About what time will this elevator pass the 60th floor if it makes no stops? @

  d. Where will this elevator be at 2:00:45 if it makes no stops? @

    almost at the 74th floor

8. At 2:00 P.M., elevator B passes the 94th floor of the same building going down. The table shows the floors and the times in seconds after 2:00.

Floor x	94	92	90	88	86	84	80
Time after 2:00 (s) y	0	1.3	2.5	3.8	5	6.3	8.6

  a. What is the line of fit based on Q-points for the data?

  b. Give a real-world meaning of the slope.   The elevator is moving down at 0.625 s per floor.

  c. About what time will this elevator pass the 10th floor if it makes no stops?

  d. Where will this elevator be at 2:00:34 if it makes no stops?   between the 39th and 40th floors

9. Think about the elevators in Exercises 7 and 8.

  a. Estimate when elevator A will pass elevator B if neither makes any stops.   Estimates will vary.

  b. Calculate the actual time.   At 28.8 s, or at about 2:00:29, the elevators will pass at the 48th floor.

▶ Review

3.2   **10.** A car is traveling from Sioux Falls, South Dakota, to Mt. Rushmore, which is near Rapid City, South Dakota. The car is traveling about 54 mi/h, and it is about 370 mi from Sioux Falls to Mt. Rushmore.

  a. Write a recursive routine to create a table of values in the form (*time, distance from Mt. Rushmore*) for the relationship from 0 to 6 h. @

  b. Graph a scatter plot using 1 h time intervals.

  c. Draw a line through the points of your scatter plot. What is the real-world meaning of this line? What does the line represent that the points alone do not?

Wall Drug is a landmark in South Dakota. The store's fame began during the Great Depression, when it offered free ice water to travelers.

  d. What is the slope of the line? What is the real-world meaning of the slope?

  e. When will the car be at the Wall Drug Store, which is 80 mi from Mt. Rushmore? Explain how you know.

  f. When will the car arrive at Mt. Rushmore? Explain how you know.

10e. Answers will vary. The car will reach the Wall Drug Store in the first half hour of the fifth hour of the trip. You can see this on the graph if you look at the line where it has a *y*-value of about 80.

10f. The car will reach Mt. Rushmore after almost 7 h of travel. You can see this on the graph or in the table, because after 7 h, the car would have gone 8 mi too far.

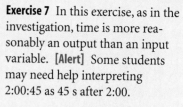

Exercise 7 In this exercise, as in the investigation, time is more reasonably an output than an input variable. **[Alert]** Some students may need help interpreting 2:00:45 as 45 s after 2:00.

7a. $y = 1.3 + 0.625(x - 4)$ or $y = 6.3 + 0.625(x - 12)$

7c. 36.3 s after 2:00, or at approximately 2:00:36

8a. $y = 1.3 - 0.625(x - 92)$ or $y = 6.3 - 0.625(x - 84)$

8c. after 52.55 s, or at approximately 2:00:53

10a. Start with 370, then use the rule Ans − 54.

Time (h)	Distance from Mt. Rushmore (mi)
0	370
1	316
2	262
3	208
4	154
5	100
6	46

10b.

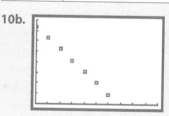

[0, 10, 1, 0, 400, 50]

10c.

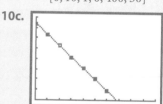

The line represents the distance remaining at any time during the trip. With the line, you can see how far away from Mt. Rushmore you are at any time, instead of just at the top of each hour.

10d. −54; the real-world meaning of the slope is that your distance from Mt. Rushmore decreases by 54 mi each hour.

11. The size and cost are almost directly proportional; the 4 oz bottle costs $0.22/oz, the 7.5 oz bottle costs $0.22/oz, and the 18 oz bottle costs $0.2217/oz. If you change the price of the 18 oz bottle to $3.96, then it also will cost exactly $0.22/oz.

Exercise 12 Have students read and critique each other's e-mails. A good technique is to choose a few papers, delete the students' names, make overheads, and have each class critique the explanations from another class.

2.4 **11.** A 4 oz bottle of mustard costs $0.88, a 7.5 oz bottle costs $1.65, and an 18 oz bottle costs $3.99. Is the size of the mustard bottle directly proportional to the price? If so, show how you know. If not, suggest the change of one or two prices so that they will be directly proportional. *(h)*

4.4 **12.** Imagine that a classmate has been out of school for the past few days with the flu. Write him or her an e-mail describing how to convert an equation such as $y = 4 + 2(x - 3)$ from point-slope form to slope-intercept form. Be sure to include examples and explanations. End your note by telling your classmate how to find out if the two equations are equivalent. Answers will vary.

project

STATE OF THE STATES

Fathom

Fathom comes with many data sets that contain information about the states, and you can easily download more information from websites.

Plot quartiles and use Fathom's movable line to find the slope.

Many characteristics of a state vary with the size of the state's population. Some of these relationships are linear. The more people who live in a state, the more houses, cars, schools, and prisoners there are. A lot of data about the states is available on the Internet. You can link to a useful site through **www.keymath.com/DA** .

Here are two scatter plots that show a comparison of the population of a state to two different characteristics of the state—number of prisoners and median household income. Which scatter plot shows a linear pattern?

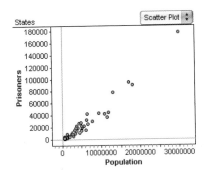
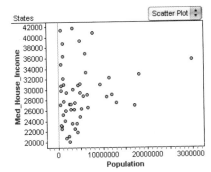

Investigate various pairs of states' characteristics that you think might be related.

Your project should include

▸ Several scatter plots, investigating relationships between various pairs of characteristics for states.

▸ Lines of fit for your plotted data, their slopes and intercepts along with their real-world meanings (that is, if there appears to be a linear relationship).

▸ Explanations of why some relationships do not appear linear.

Supporting the project

MOTIVATION

The project gives students a chance to study data sets and decide how close to linear they are. **[Ask]** "What characteristics of a state are related to the population?" [One answer: The number of prisoners has a linear relationship to the population.]

OUTCOMES

▸ The report includes several scatter plots of data.

▸ Lines of fit are graphed on the scatter plots.

▸ Slopes and intercepts of the lines of fit are included.

▸ There's a discussion of why the data are linear or nonlinear.

• The student explains how the lines of fit were determined.

• The student assesses the goodness of the fit.

• Predictions are made on the basis of the lines of fit.

Applications of Modeling

In Lesson 4.6, you learned a systematic method, using quartile values, to find a line of fit for data points that appear to have a linear pattern. In this lesson, you'll contrast that method with ways you've used before and evaluate your results.

Investigation
What's My Line?

You will need

- graph paper
- a strand of spaghetti

This table shows data that Edwin Hubble used in 1929 to formulate Hubble's Law. The table includes the distance from Earth to known nebulae (clouds of gas or dust) measured in megaparsecs (Mpc, about 3.258×10^6 light-years), and the speed at which each nebula is moving away from or toward Earth. In this investigation, you'll create three linear models, you'll analyze your models, and you'll use them to make a prediction.

Science
● ● ● CONNECTION ● ● ●

In 1929, American astronomer Edwin Hubble (1889–1953) formulated Hubble's Law, which describes the rate at which galaxies move away from each other. This law led to the concept of an expanding universe, and, working back in time, it also provides a basis for the big bang theory. For more information on Hubble's Law and the big bang theory, see **www.keymath.com/DA** .

Distance and Speed of Nebulae

Distance (Mpc)	Speed (km/s)	Distance (Mpc)	Speed (km/s)
0.032	170	0.9	650
0.034	290	0.9	150
0.214	−130	0.9	500
0.263	−70	1.0	920
0.275	−185	1.1	450
0.275	−220	1.1	500
0.45	200	1.4	500
0.5	290	1.7	960
0.5	270	2.0	500
0.63	200	2.0	850
0.8	300	2.0	800
0.9	−30	2.0	1090

(Edwin Hubble, in *Proceedings of the National Academy of Sciences*, Volume 15, Number 3)
[Data sets: **GXYDS, GXYSP**]

The expanding-universe theory can be illustrated by placing dots on a balloon and inflating it. The dots represent galaxies. If you imagine standing in one galaxy, you'll see that galaxies farther from you move away at a faster rate than galaxies that are closer.

First, you'll find a line of fit using an "eyeballing" method. Remember that the object of a linear model is to summarize or generalize the data.

Step 2 Answers will vary. Students will need to use the *y*-intercept and the second point to find the slope— remind them that the *x*-coordinate for the *y*-intercept is 0.

Step 1 Plot the data on graph paper. Lay a piece of spaghetti on the plot so that it crosses the *y*-axis and follows the direction of the data. Try to focus not on the points themselves, but on the general direction of the "cloud" of points.

Step 2 Estimate the *y*-intercept. Locate a point with convenient coordinates along the strand. Use this information to write the equation of the line.

NCTM STANDARDS

CONTENT		PROCESS	
✔	Number	✔	Problem Solving
✔	Algebra	✔	Reasoning
	Geometry	✔	Communication
	Measurement	✔	Connections
✔	Data/Probability	✔	Representation

LESSON OBJECTIVES

- Review various approaches to finding lines to fit sets of data
- Evaluate the results of those approaches

PLANNING

LESSON OUTLINE

One day:

30 min   Investigation
5 min   Sharing
5 min   Closing
10 min   Exercises

MATERIALS

- graph paper
- uncooked spaghetti

TEACHING

In this lesson students practice their skills of finding and evaluating lines of fit. They compare the results of the different methods when applied to the same data set.

Guiding the Investigation

One Step
Ask students to find lines of fit for the data in the table in as many ways as possible and to decide which line fits best. Encourage a variety of approaches, at least reviewing all methods seen so far.

You might want to use Fathom for this investigation if it's available. Students will need the Fathom skills shown in the Fathom demonstrations for Lessons 4.5 and 4.6.

Step 1 How to assign input and output variables may not be clear to students. Neither variable is obviously the independent variable. In this case most mathematicians would use the horizontal axis for the first variable listed, *distance*.

See page 262 for answers to Step 1.

Step 1

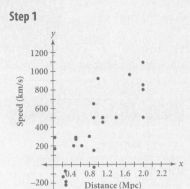

Step 2 Because students have found the y-intercept, they will probably want to use the intercept form for the equation. Try to be sure all students know how to do that.

Step 5 As needed, suggest that students draw horizontal and vertical lines to help find the Q-points.

Step 6 Although no particular form of the equation is requested, students will find it easiest to follow the precedent of Step 4 and find the point-slope form.

Step 8 Answers will vary. Using the equation from Step 6, the y-intercept is the speed at which a galaxy would be moving away from Earth if the galaxy were located at the same place as Earth.

Step 10 As you change the y-intercept, the y-coordinate of every point on the line increases by the same amount. For example, if the y-intercept changes from -10 to 0, the point $(1, 458)$ moves to $(1, 468)$.

Step 11 A distance "far from most of the given points" might be 3.

Next, you'll find a line of fit by choosing "representative" data points.

Steps 3 and 4 Answers will vary.

| Step 3 | Make a scatter plot of the data on your calculator. Choose two data points that you think show the direction of the data. |
| Step 4 | Use the two points to write a linear equation in point-slope form. |

Next, you'll find a line of fit using Q-points.

Step 5 Use your calculator to get the five-number summaries for the x- and y-values. Draw a rectangle using the first- and third-quartile values for the x-values and the first- and third-quartile values for the y-values. Name the Q-points you should use for the data. x-values: 0.032, 0.3625, 0.9, 1.25, 2.0; y-values: -220, 160, 295, 575, 1090; Q-points: (0.3625, 160), (1.25, 575)

Step 6 Write the equation of the line of fit you can draw through your selected Q-points. Graph the equation to verify that it is the diagonal of the rectangle you drew on the plot. $y = 160 + 468(x - 0.3625)$ or $y = 575 + 468(x - 1.25)$

Finally, you'll compare the lines and their characteristics and decide which method has given you the best-fitting line.

Step 7 Answers will vary. The slopes all represent the rate at which speed (in km/s) increases for each increase of one megaparsec.

Step 7 Compare the slopes of all three lines for each table. Do all these numbers have the same real-world meaning? If so, what is it?

Step 8 Compare the y-intercepts of all three lines for each table. Do they all have the same real-world meaning? If so, what is it?

Step 11 A small change in the slope will have a magnifying change for points far out on the line. For example, if the equation $y = 1x$ is changed to $y = 5x$, the point $(0.1, 0.1)$ only changes to $(0.1, 0.5)$, but the point $(100, 100)$ changes to $(100, 500)$.

Step 9 What distance would you expect for a galaxy that is moving away from Earth at a rate of 750 km/s? Show how to find this value symbolically. 1.6 Mpc

Step 10 What is the effect of a small change in the y-intercept when you use the model to predict a value in the middle of the data set?

Step 11 What is the effect of a small change in the slope when you try to predict a y-value far from most of the given points?

Step 12 Discuss the pros and cons of each procedure you used to find a line of fit. Which method do you like best and why? Answers will vary.

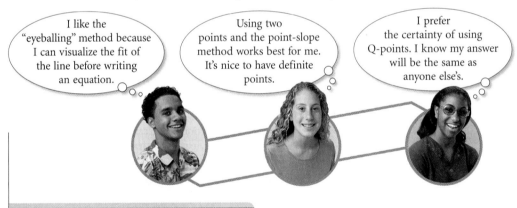

SHARING IDEAS

After Step 6, have several groups graph their lines, using a single overhead transparency for each table of data and a different color for each group. You might lead a full-class discussion of Steps 7–12, or ask students to return to their groups. In a class discussion, be especially careful to treat all answers to questions equally, asking the class to critique them, whether or not you agree with them. (If some students seem uncomfortable participating in the class discussion, adjust your plans and return to groups.)

Ask if a line can be a reliable predictor if it's not the best fit. Elicit the idea that the quality of fit is determined by the accuracy of the prediction, so it depends on the situation.

If your class is ready, you might introduce the median-median method for finding a line of fit. (See page 214B.) Students can check hand calculations with a calculator. Ask if this line is a better model of the data.

As you study more about finding models for data, you will also learn more about methods you can use to tell how well a model fits data. In this course the emphasis will be on finding a reasonable model—even though it may not be the best-fitting model—so that you can use it to make reliable predictions.

EXERCISES

You will need your graphing calculator for Exercise **6.**

► Practice Your Skills

1. The equation of a line in point-slope form is $y = 6 - 3(x - 6)$.
   a. Name the point on this line that was used to write the equation. $(6, 6)$
   b. Name the point on this line with an x-coordinate of 5. $(5, 9)$
   c. Using the point you named in 1b, write another equation of the line in point-slope form. $y = 9 - 3(x - 5)$
   d. Write the equation of the line in intercept form. $y = 24 - 3x$
   e. Find the coordinates of the x-intercept. $(8, 0)$

2. Solve each equation symbolically for x. Use another method to verify your solution.
   a. $3(x - 5) + 14 = 29$ @ $x = 10$ b. $\dfrac{8 - 13}{x + 5} = 2$ $x = -7.5$
   c. $\dfrac{2(3 - x)}{4} - 8 = -7.75$ $x = 2.5$ d. $11 + \dfrac{6(x + 5)}{9} = 42$ $x = 41.5$

3. Solve each equation for y.
   a. $2x + 5y = 18$ @
   $y = \dfrac{18 - 2x}{5}$, or $y = 3.6 - 0.4x$
   b. $5x - 2y = -12$
   $y = \dfrac{-12 - 5x}{-2}$, or $y = 6 + 2.5x$

Men's Discus

► Reason and Apply

4. **APPLICATION** This table shows winning distances for the Olympic men's discus throw.
   a. Define variables and find the line of fit based on Q-points for this data set. Give the real-world meanings of the slope and the y-intercept. @
   b. In 1912, Armas Taipale of Finland threw the discus 45.21 m. What value does your model predict for that year? What is the difference in the two values?
   c. According to your model, what year might you expect the winning distance to pass 80 m? Show how to find this value symbolically.

Year	Champion	Distance (m)
1952	Sim Iness, United States	55.03
1956	Al Oerter, United States	56.36
1960	Al Oerter, United States	59.18
1964	Al Oerter, United States	61.00
1968	Al Oerter, United States	64.78
1972	Ludvik Danek, Czechoslovakia	64.40
1976	Mac Wilkins, United States	67.50
1980	Viktor Rashchupkin, USSR	66.64
1984	Rolf Danneberg, West Germany	66.60
1988	Jürgen Schult, East Germany	68.82
1992	Romas Ubartas, Lithuania	65.12
1996	Lars Riedel, Germany	69.40
2000	Virgilijus Alekna, Lithuania	69.30
2004	Virgilijus Alekna, Lithuania	69.89

(International Olympic Committee, in *The World Almanac and Book of Facts 2004*, p. 867)

4a. Let x represent years, and let y represent distance in meters. The Q-points are $(1964, 61.00)$ and $(1992, 68.82)$. The slope of the line through these points is about 0.28, so the equation is $y = 61.00 + 0.28(x - 1964)$ or $y = 68.82 + 0.28(x - 1992)$. The slope, 0.28, means that the winning distance increases an average of 0.28 m, or 28 cm, each year. The y-intercept, -489 m, is meaningless in this situation because it would indicate that a negative distance was the winning distance in year 0. The model cannot predict that far out from the data range.

4b. 46.44 m using $y = 61.00 + 0.28(x - 1964)$; the predicted distance is 1.23 m more than the actual distance.

4c. 2032 using $80 = 61.00 + 0.28(x - 1964)$

Assessing Progress
Watch for students' ability to plot points, find slopes and y-intercepts, write equations of lines given the y-intercept and a slope, write equations given points and slopes, find lines of fit using Q-points, figure out the real-world meaning of a slope or y-intercept, and find the value of an expression at a point.

Closing the Lesson
A variety of approaches yield lines to model a set of data. The best of these will be a good predictor of data points not already found.

BUILDING UNDERSTANDING
Students practice making predictions from lines of fit found using Q-points.

ASSIGNING HOMEWORK

Essential	**1, 4**
Performance assessment	**5**
Portfolio	**4**
Journal	**8**
Group	**2**
Review	**1–3, 6–8**

▶ Helping with the Exercises

Exercise 5 [Alert] Some students may not realize that columns 1 and 3 are extraneous. Either column 2 or 4 can be used for input data and the other for output.

5a. Let x represent distance from Los Angeles in miles, and let y represent elapsed time from Seattle in minutes; $y = 1439 - 1.51(x - 411.5)$ or $y = 273 - 1.51(x - 1181.5)$; the slope means the distance from Los Angeles decreases by 1 mi each 1.51 min.

5b. approximately 1758, or 29 h 18 min, by the first equation or approximately 1755 min, or 29 h 15 min, by the second equation

5c. approximately 967 mi by the first equation or 965 mi by the second equation

5. APPLICATION The table shows the timetable for the Coast Starlight train from Seattle to Los Angeles.

Coast Starlight

Location	Distance from Los Angeles (mi)	Arrival time	Elapsed time from Seattle (min)
Kelso, WA	1252	12:48	168
Vancouver, WA	1213	13:29	209
Salem, OR	1150	15:37	337
Eugene, OR	1079	17:10	430
Sacramento, CA	552	6:35	1205
Emeryville, CA	468	8:10	1330
Salinas, CA	355	11:48	1548
Santa Barbara, CA	103	18:17	1937

a. Define variables and give the line of fit based on Q-points for this data set. Give the real-world meaning of the slope.

b. While riding the train, you pass a sign that says you are 200 mi from Los Angeles. What length of time does your model predict you have traveled?

c. The train comes to a stop after 10 h (600 min). According to your model, how far are you from Los Angeles? Show how to find this value symbolically.

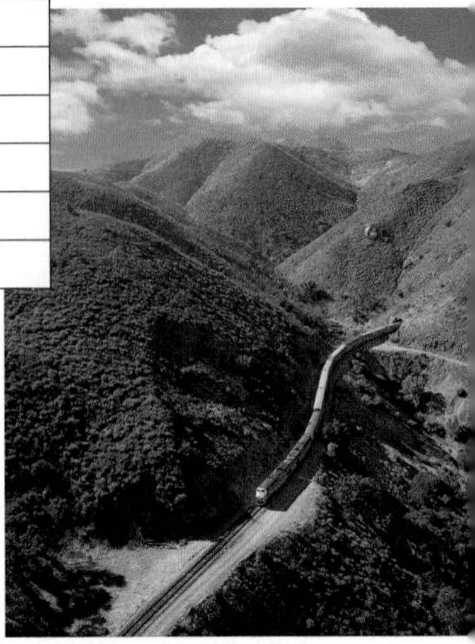

Before 1971, when Amtrak created the Coast Starlight, passengers had to ride three different trains to go from Seattle to Los Angeles.

▶ Review

6. In Chapter 3 you worked with problems involving rate, often involving the equation $d = rt$. Here is another kind of **rate problem.**

Ellen and Eric meet on Saturday to train for a marathon. They live 7 miles apart and meet at the high-school track that is between their two homes. Ellen leaves at 8:00 A.M. and jogs south toward the school at 4 mi/h. Eric waits until 8:30 A.M. and jogs north toward the school at 6 mi/h. The two friends arrive at the school at exactly the same time. How much time did each person jog?

To solve this problem, let t represent Ellen's time in hours. Because Eric left a half hour after Ellen, but arrived at the same time, he jogged for a half hour less. So let $t - \frac{1}{2}$ represent Eric's time in hours. You might now fill out a table like this to get expressions for distance. (Remember that *distance* = *rate* · *time*.)

	rate (mi/h)	*time* (h)	*distance* (mi)
Ellen	4	t	$4 \cdot t$
Eric	6	$t - \frac{1}{2}$	$6 \cdot \left(t - \frac{1}{2}\right)$
Combined			7

a. Write an equation that states that Ellen's distance and Eric's distance combine to 7 miles. $4t + 6\left(t - \frac{1}{2}\right) = 7$

b. Solve the equation from 6a, check your answer, and state the solution.

c. Solve this problem using a similar procedure: A propeller airplane and a jet airplane leave the same airport at the same time, and both go in the same direction. The jet airplane's velocity is five times the propeller airplane's velocity. After 2.25 h, the jet airplane is 1170 km ahead of the propeller plane. What is the velocity of each plane in kilometers per hour?   propeller airplane: 130 km/h; jet airplane: 650 km/h

2.3 **7.** A sample labeled "50 grains" weighs 3.24 grams on a balance. What is the conversion factor for grams to grains?   15.4321 grains per gram

3.6 **8.** Write the equation represented by this balance. Then solve the equation for x using the balancing method.

$4x + 2 = x + 7$	Original equation.
$4x - x + 2 = x - x + 7$	Subtract x from both sides.
$3x + 2 = 7$	Combine like terms.
$3x + 2 - 2 = 7 - 2$	Subtract 2 from both sides.
$3x = 5$	Combine like terms.
$\dfrac{3x}{3} = \dfrac{5}{3}$	Divide both sides by 3.
$x = \dfrac{5}{3}$, or $1.\overline{6}$	Reduce.

6b. $t = 1$; Ellen jogged for 1 hour and Eric jogged for $\frac{1}{2}$ hour.

IMPROVING YOUR REASONING SKILLS

Not all data sets form a linear pattern. Here is a set that doesn't. It relates speed and time for the same car trip made by several drivers. Plot the data and see if you recognize the shape. Once you do, write an equation whose graph shows this shape. Then adjust it, if necessary, to better show the shape of the data. Use your equation to predict how much time a driver who averages 45 mi/h would need for the trip and the average speed that would give a time of 70 min.

Average Speed and Time for the Same Trip

Average Speed (mi/h) x	Time (min) y	Average Speed (mi/h) x	Time (min) y
25	144	45	
26	137.6	50	72
30	120		70
34	106.1	55	65.5
36	99.7	56.5	63.7
37.4	96.4	60	59.8
40.5	89.3	62	58
42.2	85.4	65	55.5

IMPROVING REASONING SKILLS

This relationship is an inverse variation. Students can find the product xy for each speed and average them to get the constant of variation, approximately 3600. Using this approach, the curve of fit is $y = \frac{3600}{x}$.

According to this model, at an average speed of 45 mi/h, the trip would take approximately 80 min. To take 70 min, the average speed would have to be approximately 51.4 mi/h.

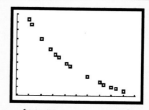

$[20, 70, 5, 50, 150, 10]$

LESSON

4.8

Activity Day

Data Collection and Modeling

Here's your chance to take part in an extreme sport without the risk! In this activity you'll set up a bungee jump and collect data relating the distance a "jumper" falls and the number of rubber bands in the bungee cord. Then you'll model the data with an equation. Next you'll use your model to find the number of rubber bands you'd need in the cord for a near miss from a specific height.

Activity

The Toyland Bungee Jump

You will need

- a toy to serve as "jumper"
- a supply of equal-sized rubber bands
- a tape measure

| Step 1 | Make a bungee cord by attaching two rubber bands to your "jumper." (You may first need to make a harness by twisting a rubber band around the toy.) |
| Step 2 | Place your jumper on the edge of a table or another surface while holding the end of the bungee cord. Then let your jumper fall from the table. Use your tape measure to measure the maximum distance the jumper falls on the first plunge. |

PLANNING

LESSON OUTLINE

First day:

5 min	Introduction
35 min	Activity (Steps 1–7)
10 min	Quiz or Review exercises

Second day:

25 min	Activity (Steps 8 and 9)
15 min	Sharing
10 min	Review exercises

MATERIALS

- toy figures
- identical rubber bands (about 300)
- tape measures, metersticks, or yardsticks
- video camera, *optional*
- Lab Report (W from Chapter 1), *optional*

TEACHING

Besides predicting the output value of a linear equation for a given input value, you often need to determine the input value for a given output value. Students do that in this activity.

G uiding the Activity

A compact toy like a 10 in. action figure, stuffed animal, or beanbag works best. You can also use a small water balloon or a plastic water bottle with a little water in it. Size 32 rubber bands work well.

LESSON OBJECTIVES

- Review the process of finding equations to model data
- Learn about writing lab reports
- Learn about careful data collection and attention to procedure

NCTM STANDARDS

CONTENT		PROCESS	
	Number	✔	Problem Solving
✔	Algebra	✔	Reasoning
	Geometry	✔	Communication
✔	Measurement	✔	Connections
✔	Data/Probability	✔	Representation

| Step 3 | Repeat this jump several times and find a mean value for the distance. Record the number of rubber bands (2) and the mean distance the jumper falls in a table like this one. |

Number of rubber bands	2	4	5	6
Distance fallen				

Step 4	Add one or two rubber bands to the bungee cord and repeat the experiment. Record this new information.
Step 5	Continue to make bungee cords of different lengths, and measure the distance your jumper falls until you have at least seven pairs of data. When using long cords, you may need to move to a higher place to measure the falls.
Step 6	Define variables and make a scatter plot of the information from your table.
Step 7	Find the equation of a line of fit for your data. You may use any procedure, but be able to justify why your equation is a reasonable fit.

Step 8	The test! Decide on a good location for all the groups to conduct final bungee jumps from a particular height. Use your equation to determine the number of rubber bands you need in the cord to give your jumper the greatest thrill— falling as close as possible to the ground without touching. When you have determined the number of rubber bands, make the bungee cord and wait your turn to test your prediction.

Step 9	Write a group report for this activity. Follow this outline to produce a neat, organized, thorough, and accurate report. Any reader of your report should not need to have watched the activity to know what is going on.

Report Outline

A. Overview	Tell what the investigation was about, its purpose or objective.
B. Data collection	Describe the data you collected and how you collected it.
C. Data table	Use labels and units.
D. Graph	Show all data points. Use labels and units. Show the line of fit.
E. Model	Define your variables and give the equation. Tell how you found this equation and why you used this method.
F. Calculations	Show how you decided how many rubber bands to use in the final jump.
G. Results	Describe what happened on the final jump.
H. Conclusion	What problems did you have? What worked really well? If you could repeat the whole experiment, what would you do to improve it?

Step 3 Students may want to proceed after one measurement. Ask them why they should take the mean of several measurements.

Step 8 Students can solve the equation by undoing or balancing. You'll want to guide them in selecting a location. Bleachers, a balcony, a stairwell, or a second-story window work well. You might advise students that they will have one opportunity to conduct their final jump. They should have their rubber bands in place before going to the test location.

If possible, set up a video camera to film the final drops. Focus on the area near the floor or ground. Then view the videotape in slow motion, one frame at a time, to see just how close to the ground the object comes. You can actually measure a distance on the television screen and then compare the various distances to determine the best bungee jump. Or, a student can hold a meterstick behind the drop location to be captured on the tape.

You might hand out the Lab Report Worksheet from Chapter 1 if you haven't had students write a lab report before.

SHARING IDEAS

You might ask the groups that made the best predictions to share with the class parts D–F of their report.

Assessing Progress

Assess students' ability to work together, make careful measurements, gather data systematically, find the mean of a data set, make scatter plots, find equations of lines of fit, and solve linear equations.

Closing the Lesson

As needed, point out that after finding the best line of fit, students had to solve a linear equation to predict the number of rubber bands for a given distance.

CHAPTER

4

REVIEW

PLANNING

LESSON OUTLINE

One day:

10 min   Introduction

25 min   Exercises

15 min   Student self-assessment

REVIEWING

Direct attention to the Nutrition Facts data from the example in Lesson 4.2. Ask the class how to predict the saturated fat in a burger with 50 g total fat. Be sure students describe a variety of ways of finding a line of fit— eyeballing, finding a line through representative points, using Q-points. Don't be satisfied with a list. Ask for demonstrations of techniques, emphasizing how to find the slope of a line with slope triangles and how to find the point-slope form of an equation. Show how different equations might arise from different choices of points, and review the algebraic properties used to check the equivalence of the equations and to solve equations.

ASSIGNING HOMEWORK

If students complete the odd-numbered exercises on their own, they could do the even-numbered ones in groups.

▶ **Helping with the Exercises**

1. $x_2 = 4$

3. Line a has slope -1, y-intercept 1, and equation $y = 1 - x$. Line b has slope 2, y-intercept -2, and equation $y = -2 + 2x$.

In Chapter 3, you learned how to write equations in intercept form, $y = a + bx$. In this chapter, you learned how to calculate **slope** using the slope formula, $b = \frac{y_2 - y_1}{x_2 - x_1}$. You also used the slope formula to derive another form for a linear equation—the **point-slope form.** The point-slope form, $y = y_1 + b(x - x_1)$, is the equation of a line through point (x_1, y_1) with slope b. You learned that this form is very useful in real-world situations when the starting value is not on the y-axis.

You investigated equivalent forms of expressions and equations using tables and graphs. You used the **distributive property** of multiplication over addition and the **commutative** and **associative** properties of addition and multiplication to write point-slope equations in intercept form.

You investigated several methods of finding a **line of fit,** and you discovered how to use the first and third quartiles from the five-number summaries of x- and y-values in a data set to write a linear model for data based on **Q-points.**

EXERCISES

You will need your graphing calculator for Exercises **3, 4,** and **9.**

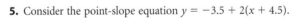

@ Answers are provided for all exercises in this set.

1. The slope of the line between $(2, 10)$ and $(x_2, 4)$ is -3. Find the value of x_2.

2. Give the slope and the y-intercept for each equation.

a. $y = -4 - 3x$
slope: -3; y-intercept: -4

b. $2x + 7 = y$
slope: 2; y-intercept: 7

c. $38x - 10y = 24$
slope: 3.8; y-intercept: -2.4

3. Line a and line b are shown on the graph at right. Name the slope and the y-intercept, and write the equation of each line. Check your equations by graphing on your calculator.

4. Write each equation in the form requested. Check your answers by graphing on your calculator.
$y = 13.6x - 25{,}709$

a. Write $y = 13.6(x - 1902) + 158.2$ in intercept form.

b. Write $y = -5.2x + 15$ in point-slope form using $x = 10$ as the first coordinate of the point. $y = -37 - 5.2(x - 10)$

5. Consider the point-slope equation $y = -3.5 + 2(x + 4.5)$.

a. Name the point used to write this equation. $(-4.5, -3.5)$

b. Write an equivalent equation in intercept form. $y = 2x + 5.5$

c. Factor your answer to 5b and name the x-intercept. $y = 2(x + 2.75)$; the x-intercept is -2.75.

d. A point on the line has a y-coordinate of 16.5. Find the x-coordinate of this point and use this point to write an equivalent equation in point-slope form.

e. Explain how you can verify that all four equations are equivalent.   Answers will vary. Possible methods are graphing, using a calculator table, and putting all equations in intercept form.

Exercise 5   Some students may have missed the idea of factoring from Lesson 4.4, Exercise 7. Realizing that the x-intercept is the number subtracted from x might also be a challenge. **[Ask]** "What value of x makes y equal zero?"

5d. The x-coordinate is 5.5; $y = 16.5 + 2(x - 5.5)$.

6. Show all steps for a symbolic solution to each problem.

a. $4 + 2.8x = 51$

b. $38 - 0.35x = 27$

c. $11 + 3(x - 8) = 41$

d. $220 - 12.5(x - 6) = 470$

7. **APPLICATION** Suppose Karl bought a used car for $12,600. Each year its value is expected to decrease by $1,350.

a. Write an equation modeling the value of the car over time. Let x represent the number of years Karl owns the car, and let y represent the value of the car in dollars. $y = 12,600 - 1,350x$

b. What is the slope, and what does it mean in the context of the problem?

c. What is the y-intercept, and what does it mean in the context of the problem?

d. What is the x-intercept, and what does it mean in the context of the problem?

8. Recall the data about heating a pot of water from the investigation in Lesson 4.3. A possible linear model relating the time in seconds, x, to the temperature in °C, y, is $y = 30 + 0.375(x - 36)$.

a. What equation could you solve to find how long it would take before the pot of water reaches 43°C? $43 = 30 + 0.375(x - 36)$

b. Find the approximate time indicated in 8a using a table or graph. $x \approx 71$ s

c. Show a symbolic solution for your equation in 8a. $x = \dfrac{43 - 30}{0.375} + 36 = 70.\overline{6}$

9. **APPLICATION** The table gives the winning heights for the Olympic women's high jump.

a. Find the five-number summaries for the year and height data.

Yelena Yelesina was the first Russian woman to win the Olympic high jump title.

Women's High Jump

Year	Champion	Height (m)
1956	Mildred McDaniel, United States	1.76
1960	Iolanda Balas, Romania	1.85
1964	Iolanda Balas, Romania	1.90
1968	Miloslava Rezková, Czechoslovakia	1.82
1972	Ulrike Meyfarth, West Germany	1.92
1976	Rosemarie Ackerman, East Germany	1.93
1980	Sara Simeoni, Italy	1.97
1984	Ulrike Meyfarth, West Germany	2.02
1988	Louise Ritter, United States	2.03
1992	Heike Henkel, Germany	2.02
1996	Stefka Kostadinova, Bulgaria	2.05
2000	Yelena Yelesina, Russia	2.01
2004	Yelena Yelesina, Russia	2.06

(International Olympic Committee, in *The World Almanac and Book of Facts 2004*, p. 869) [Data sets: **JMPYR, JMPHT**]

Exercise 6 You might ask students to give the reason for each step as a review of the algebraic properties.

7b. $-1,350$; the car's value decreases by $1,350 each year.

7c. 12,600; Karl paid $12,600 for the car.

7d. $9\frac{1}{3}$; in $9\frac{1}{3}$ years the car will have no monetary value.

8b.

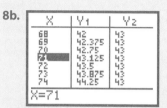

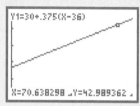

[0, 80, 10, 0, 50, 10]

Exercise 9 Rounding the numerical value of the slope will affect the answer to 9e.

9a. 1956, 1966, 1980, 1994, 2004; 1.76, 1.875, 1.97, 2.025, 2.06

6a. $4 + 2.8 = 51$

$2.8x = 51 - 4 = 47$

$x = \dfrac{47}{2.8} \approx 16.8$

6b. $38 - 0.35x = 27$

$-0.35x = 27 - 38 = -11$

$x = \dfrac{-11}{-0.35} \approx 31.4$

6c. $11 + 3(x - 8) = 41$

$3(x - 8) = 41 - 11 = 30$

$x - 8 = \dfrac{30}{3} = 10$

$x = 10 + 8 = 18$

6d. $220 - 12.5(x - 6) = 470$

$-12.5(x - 6) = 470 - 220 = 250$

$x - 6 = \dfrac{250}{-12.5} = -20$

$x = -20 + 6 = -14$

9b. The Q-points are (1966, 1.875) and (1994, 2.025).

9d. Answers will vary. There are more points above the line than below the line.

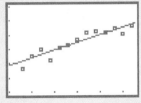

[1950, 2005, 10, 1.6, 2.2, 0.1]

Exercise 10 [Link] You may want to have students do research on minimum wage. Some questions to research are these: Why was a minimum-wage law enacted? Why doesn't the minimum wage change every year? Does the minimum-wage law apply to all professions?

10a. $y = 2.25 + 0.13(x - 1976.5)$ or $y = 4.025 + 0.13(x - 1990.5)$

10b. The slope means the minimum hourly wage increased approximately $0.13 per year.

10c. Using the equation $y = 2.25 + 0.13(x - 1976.5)$, the prediction is $6.61; if the other equation is used, the prediction is $6.56.

10d. Using either equation from 10a, the prediction is 1967.

11. Answers will vary. Possible answers:

11a. In an equation written as $y = a + bx$, b is the slope and a is the y-intercept.

11b. If the points are (x_1, y_1) and (x_2, y_2), then the slope of the line is given by the equation $\frac{y_2 - y_1}{x_2 - x_1} = b$. The equation of the line is $y = y_1 + b(x - x_1)$.

---

b. Name the Q-points for this data set.

c. Write an equation for the line through the Q-points. $y = 1.875 + 0.00536(x - 1966)$ or $y = 2.025 + 0.00536(x - 1994)$

d. Graph the line and the data, and explain whether or not you think this line is a good model for the data pattern.

e. Predict the winning height for the year 2012. Using $y = 1.875 + 0.00536(x - 1966)$, the prediction is 2.12 m.

10. APPLICATION This table shows the federal minimum hourly wage for 1974–1997.

a. Find the line of fit based on Q-points.

b. Give the real-world meaning of the slope.

c. Use your model to predict the minimum hourly wage for 2010.

d. Estimate when the minimum hourly wage was $1.00.

11. Explain how to find the equation of a line when you know

a. The slope and the y-intercept.

b. Two points on that line.

United States Minimum Wage

Year x	Hourly minimum y	Year x	Hourly minimum y
1974	$1.90	1980	$3.10
1975	$2.00	1981	$3.35
1976	$2.20	1990	$3.80
1977	$2.30	1991	$4.25
1978	$2.65	1996	$4.75
1979	$2.90	1997	$5.15

(Bureau of Labor Statistics, *www.bls.gov*)

TAKE ANOTHER LOOK

Is rate of change the same as slope? For linear equations, you've seen that it is. But what about curves? You've studied inverse variations, whose equations have the form $y = \frac{k}{x}$. Let's look at the equation $y = \frac{12}{x}$ and its graph.

(3, 4) is a point on the curve. Let's choose another nearby point. Substituting 3.5 for x in the equation, you get $y \approx 3.4$. Using the points (3, 4) and (3.5, 3.4) in the formula for slope, you get

$$b = \frac{y_2 - y_1}{x_2 - x_1} = \frac{3.4 - 4}{3.5 - 3} = \frac{-0.6}{0.5} = -1.2$$

We can say that the *average* rate of change for $y = \frac{12}{x}$ on the interval $x = 3$ to $x = 3.5$ is -1.2. But -1.2 is not the "slope" of $y = \frac{12}{x}$. Instead, it is the slope of the *straight* line through the two points (3, 4) and (3.5, 3.4). Is the average rate of change on the x-interval from 3 to 3.25 the same as from 3.25 to 3.5?

Try points on the "wings" of the curve. For instance, (8, 1.5) is on the curve and so is (8.5, 1.4). Again, the y-coordinate is approximate. What is the average rate of change between these points? The x-interval is the same as for the points (3, 4) and (3.5, 3.4), but is the rate of change the same? What does this tell you? What *straight* line through (8, 1.5) has slope equal to the average rate of change on the interval $x = 8$ to $x = 8.5$?

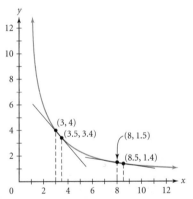

▶ **Take Another Look**

The rate of change of a curve (other than a straight line) is not constant. In general, you can't find the slope of a curve at a point by finding the slope of a line between two points on the curve, no matter how close together those points are. The average rate of change over the x-interval from 3 to 3.25 will not be the same as over the interval from 3.25 to 3.5.

The rate of change between the points (3, 4) and (3.5, 3.4) is -1.2 and between (8, 1.5) and (8.5, 1.4) is -0.2. This tells us that the rate of change of the y-values is slower on the wings than at the portion of the graph nearest the origin. The equation of the line through the points (8, 1.5) and (8.5, 1.4) is $y = 1.5 - 0.2(x - 8)$.

Assessing What You've Learned

PERFORMANCE ASSESSMENT

This chapter has been about writing equations for lines, recognizing equivalent equations written in different forms, and fitting lines to data. So, assessing what you've learned really means checking to see if you can write the equation for a given line in one or more forms, if you can find an equivalent equation for the one you've already written, and if you can write an equation for a line that looks like a good fit for a given set of data. Can you do one of the investigations in this chapter on your own? Can you verify whether two equations are equivalent? Showing that you can do tasks like these is sometimes called "performance assessment."

Review the Investigations Equivalent Equations in Lesson 4.4 and Life Expectancy in Lesson 4.5. Identify the equivalent equations in Step 6 of Investigation 4.4, and reconstruct your work in Steps 1–4 of Investigation 4.5. See if the skills you learned in these investigations have become easier for you. Get help with any part of the processes you're not sure of.

As a classmate, parent, or your teacher watches, convert an equation in point-slope form to intercept form. Explain each step, and show how you might verify that the two equations are equivalent using a graph or table. Then, find an equation that is a good fit for a set of data, using any method you like. Show that your equation is a good fit, and use your equation to make a prediction.

 UPDATE YOUR PORTFOLIO Choose a piece of work from this chapter to add to your portfolio. Describe the work in a cover sheet, giving the objective, the result, and what you might have done differently.

 WRITE IN YOUR JOURNAL What have you enjoyed more in studying algebra—the numbers, symbols, graphs, and other abstract ways of describing relationships, or the concrete applications and examples that show how people use these ideas in the real world?

Do you find it interesting that a single linear relationship can be described in so many ways, or does that add confusion for you?

 GIVE A PRESENTATION Research a topic of interest to you that involves two kinds of numerical data. Present the data in a table, make a scatter plot, and describe the pattern of the points. If the data points show a linear pattern, tell how to find a line of fit for the data set and why that line is useful.

ASSESSING

Choose three or four constructive assessment items from the Assessment Resources. Use one of the chapter tests, or create your own test.

FACILITATING SELF-ASSESSMENT

To help students complete the portfolio described in Assessing What You've Learned, suggest that they consider for evaluation their work on Lesson 4.1, Exercise 7; Lesson 4.2, Exercises 5 and 7; Lesson 4.3, Exercise 10; Lesson 4.4, Exercises 12 and 13; Lesson 4.5, Exercise 8; Lesson 4.6, Exercise 4; and Lesson 4.7, Exercise 4.

5

Systems of Equations and Inequalities

Overview

In Chapter 5, students look at systems of linear equations and consider linear inequalities. Then they put these two ideas together to think about systems of linear inequalities. In **Lessons 5.1** through **5.4,** students learn five ways to solve a system of equations: tables, graphs, the substitution method, the elimination method, and row operations on matrices. Inequalities in one variable are introduced in **Lesson 5.5;** students perform operations on inequalities and learn why multiplying an inequality by a negative number reverses the direction of the inequality. In **Lesson 5.6,** students learn how to graph inequalities in two variables and how to check whether given points are solutions. In **Lesson 5.7,** students graph and solve systems of inequalities.

The Mathematics

Systems of Linear Equations

A linear equation in two variables has infinitely many solutions. Each solution is an ordered pair of numbers. If you substitute those numbers for the two variables, the equation becomes a true statement. A *solution* to a **system** of two such equations is an ordered pair that is a solution to each equation.

A system may have zero solutions, one solution, or infinitely many solutions. In the first case, the equations are called *inconsistent*. In the last, they're called *redundant*.

A system of two linear equations in two variables can be solved using many methods.

Graphing. If you graph the line represented by each equation, the point of intersection will have coordinates that give a solution to (that is, *satisfy*) both equations. If the lines are parallel, there is no solution. If the lines coincide, the system has infinitely many solutions.

Tables. To find a solution, if there is one, look for a pair of numbers that appears in the table of solution values for each equation.

Method of substitution. For an exact solution to a system, solve one equation for one of the variables in terms of the other variable, substitute the resulting expression for that variable in the other equation, solve that linear equation in the one remaining variable, substitute the solution into either original equation, and solve for the other variable.

Method of elimination. If the coefficients make it difficult to solve either equation for a variable, multiply one or both equations by a constant to get the opposite coefficients for the same variable in the two equations. Then add the equations to eliminate that variable, leaving a single linear equation in the other variable. Substitute the solution to that equation into either original equation, which can then be solved for the other variable.

Row reduction of a matrix. Put the coefficients of the two equations into a matrix and then perform row operations that mimic the steps in the method of elimination. A procedure that systematically obtains a diagonal matrix from which the solution can be easily read is called *Gaussian elimination*. Calculators and computers solve systems of equations by using variations on this method.

Linear Inequalities

An inequality is like an equation except that the equal sign is replaced by < (less than), > (greater than), ≤ (less than or equal to), or ≥ (greater than or equal to). Statements using < or > are called *strict inequalities*.

You can solve linear inequalities in one variable as you would solve linear equations by balancing, with the exception that if you multiply or divide by a negative number, you must switch the direction of the inequality. The solution can be graphed as

a ray on a number line. The endpoint of the ray is either an open circle (for strict inequalities) or a solid circle.

Solutions to an inequality in two variables can be graphed on a plane. First you write an equation by replacing the inequality symbol with an equal sign. Graph that equation. If the inequality is strict, draw a dashed line; otherwise, draw a solid line. The solutions to the inequality form a half-plane on one side of that line. Shade in the solution region.

The solutions to a system of inequalities in two variables are graphed as the intersection of the half-planes representing the solutions of the individual inequalities in the system. Such a graph provides a way of solving simple problems in the area of mathematics called *linear programming.* In that field, the inequalities are called *constraints,* and the solution set is called a *feasible region.* An example of a linear programming problem appears in Take Another Look on page 330. Linear programming is discussed more extensively in *Discovering Advanced Algebra*.

Using This Chapter

If you prefer not to introduce all five methods for solving systems of equations, the most important methods are in the first two lessons. Lesson 5.4 assumes students have used matrices before.

Resources

Discovering Algebra Resources

Teaching and Worksheet Masters
  Lessons 5.2, 5.4–5.7

Calculator Notes 1B, 3B, 4B, 5A, 5B, 5C, 7D

Sketchpad Demonstrations
  Lessons 5.1, 5.6, 5.7

Fathom Demonstration
  Lesson 5.2

CBL 2 Demonstration
  Lesson 5.1

Dynamic Algebra Explorations online
  Lessons 5.3, 5.5, 5.8

Assessment Resources
  Quiz 1 (Lessons 5.1–5.4)
  Quiz 2 (Lessons 5.5–5.7)
  Chapter 5 Test
  Chapter 5 Constructive Assessment Options

More Practice Your Skills for Chapter 5

Condensed Lessons for Chapter 5

Other Resources

Chinese Mathematics: A Concise History by Lǐ Yǎn and Dù Shírán.

Jinkōki by the Waasen Institute.

For complete references to these and other resources, see www.keypress.com/DA.

Materials

- watches with second hands
- masking tape, 6 m ropes, or chalk
- motion sensors, *optional*
- ropes of different thickness, each 1 m long (two per group)
- meterstick or tape measure
- 9 m thin rope, *optional*
- 10 m thick rope, *optional*
- 30 paper clips, all the same size
- pennies (120)
- 8.5-by-11 in. sheets of paper
- 20–40 ft rope marked with whole numbers from −10 to 10, or paper or chalk number line with two markers, *optional*

Pacing Guide

	day 1	day 2	day 3	day 4	day 5	day 6	day 7	day 8	day 9	day 10
standard	5.1	5.2	5.2	5.3	5.3	5.4	5.4	quiz, 5.5	5.6	5.7
enriched	5.1	5.2	5.2	5.3	5.3	5.4	5.4	quiz, 5.5	5.6, project	5.7
block	5.1	5.2	5.3	5.4, quiz	5.5, 5.6	5.7, review	assessment			

	day 11	day 12	day 13	day 14	day 15	day 16	day 17	day 18	day 19	day 20
standard	quiz, review	assessment								
enriched	review, TAL	assessment								

5

Systems of Equations and Inequalities

CHAPTER 5 OBJECTIVES

- Model real-world situations with systems of two linear equations in two variables

- Approximate solutions to systems of two linear equations using tables and graphs, understanding how the relative position of the lines indicates the number of solutions to the system

- Solve systems of linear equations using substitution, elimination, and row operations on a matrix (Gaussian elimination)

- Model real-world situations with one-variable inequalities

- Solve one-variable inequalities, including use of the sign-change rule when multiplying or dividing both sides by a negative number

- Graph solutions to one-variable inequalities on a number line, showing whether they are strict inequalities

- Model real-world problems with two-variable inequalities and show their solutions as half-planes on the coordinate plane

- Model real-world problems with systems of two-variable inequalities and show the solutions as the intersection of two or more half-planes

Freshly painted umbrellas dry in the sun outside the Nagatsu factory in Kyushu, Japan. The sticks in their frames form intersecting lines like the graphs of linear equations. Where do you see only two lines intersecting at a point? Where do several lines intersect?

OBJECTIVES

In this chapter you will
- learn to solve systems of linear equations
- solve systems using the substitution method
- solve systems using the elimination method
- solve systems using matrices
- graph inequalities in one and two variables
- solve systems of linear inequalities

This photo suggests many lines graphed on a plane, and the points of their intersection suggest solutions to systems of equations. As you look at this image with your students, you can look at it as a two-dimensional image or imagine the three-dimensional space in which the umbrellas exist. Looked at as a two-dimensional picture, the lines formed by the mechanism that opens and supports the umbrella cross the lines of the umbrella structure. What other lines intersect? What lines intersect in the three-dimensional space? At which points do several lines intersect?

Solving Systems of Equations

In previous chapters you studied linear relationships in the contexts of elevators, wind chill, rope length, and walks. In this chapter you'll consider two or more linear equations together. A **system of equations** is a set of two or more equations that have variables in common. The common variables relate similar quantities. You can think of an equation as a condition imposed on one or more variables, and a system as several conditions imposed simultaneously.

When solving a system of equations, you look for a solution that makes each equation true. There are several strategies you can use. In this lesson you will solve systems using tables and graphs.

Investigation
Where Will They Meet?

In this investigation you'll solve a system of simultaneous equations to find the time and distance at which two walkers meet.

Suppose that two people begin walking in the same direction at different average speeds. The faster walker starts behind the slower walker. When and where will the faster walker overtake the slower walker?

You will need

- one motion sensor
- a tape measure or chalk to make a 6-meter line segment

Step 1 | Sketch a graph showing both walks. Which line represents the faster walker?

Now act out the walk.

Step 2 | Mark a 6 m segment at 1 m intervals. In your group, designate Walkers A and B, a timekeeper, and a recorder.

Step 3 | Practice these walks: Walker A starts at the 0.5 m mark and walks toward the 6 m mark at a speed of 1 m/s. Walker B starts at the 2 m mark and walks toward the 6 m mark at 0.5 m/s.

> **Procedure Note**
>
> The timekeeper counts each second out loud. The walkers walk at the given speeds by noting their positions on the marked segment. The recorder uses a motion sensor to measure the time and position of each walker.

NCTM STANDARDS

CONTENT	PROCESS
Number	Problem Solving
✓ Algebra	✓ Reasoning
Geometry	Communication
✓ Measurement	✓ Connections
Data/Probability	✓ Representation

LESSON OBJECTIVES

- Model real-world situations with systems of two equations
- Solve systems of two linear equations using tables and graphs
- Understand that the intersection of the two lines provides a solution to the system and thus to the real-world problem

PLANNING

LESSON OUTLINE

One day:

20 min	Investigation
10 min	Example
10 min	Sharing
5 min	Closing
5 min	Exercises

MATERIALS

- watch with second hand (one per group)
- 6 m or 6 yd path with 1 m or 1 yd marks on the floor or ground (masking tape or 6 m ropes with 1 m marks are good inside; use chalk or the yard markers on a football field outside)
- motion sensors (one per group), *optional*
- Calculator Notes 1B, 3B, 7D
- Sketchpad demonstration Solving Systems of Equations, *optional*
- CBL 2 demonstration Hot and Cold, *optional*

TEACHING

A system of two linear equations can model some real-world problems. These systems can be solved using graphs or tables.

Guiding the Investigation

In the step-by-step investigation, both walkers travel in the same direction, so their slopes have the same sign. The example describes a situation in which two people walk in opposite directions, so the two slopes have opposite signs.

See page 274 for the answer to Step 1.

One Step

Ask that one student in each group walk toward a point (the motion sensor, if you are using one) from 6 m away at a rate of 1 m/s, while another student walks away from that point, beginning 2 m away, at 0.5 m/s. The group is to represent the situation, and the meeting point, in as many ways as it can. Encourage students to use graphs and pairs of equations and to think about rates at which the two walkers are closing the distance between them. As groups accomplish this task, ask them to repeat the process, but this time with the first person beginning 0.5 m away from the given point and walking *away* from it at 1 m/s.

Step 1 As needed, remind students that a graph sketch needs to have labels on the axes. Students may need clarification that the time is the number of seconds elapsed since the walkers started and the distance is the number of meters the walkers are from one end of the path.

Step 1

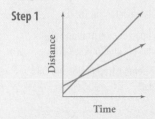

The steeper line represents the faster walker.

Step 2 In a group of three, one person will need to be both a walker and the timekeeper.

Steps 3 and 4 Before students start recording data, they should practice the walks until they know how fast to move. Even with experience, they might want to do each walk three times and average the results.

The recorder should stand at the 0 m mark and hold the sensor to collect the data on each walker separately. See Calculator Note 3B to learn how to collect the data.

Step 5 Answers will vary, but equations should be approximately $y = 0.5 + x$ for Walker A and $y = 2 + 0.5x$ for Walker B, where x represents time in seconds and y represents the position on the marked line in meters.

Step 7 After 3 s, both walkers are at the 3.5 m mark.

Step 8 Substitute $x = 3$ and $y = 3.5$ into both equations:

Walker A   Walker B
$3.5 = 0.5 + 3$ $3.5 = 2 + 0.5(3)$

Step 9 The line for Walker A will be steeper, and the solution point will move toward the y-axis.

Step 10 This graph shows two parallel lines. There is no solution point because the lines never meet.

Step 4 When the walkers can follow the walk instructions accurately, record and download the motion of each walker as a separate event. First record Walker A's motion with the motion sensor. Download Walker A's data to a graphing calculator and move it to other lists. [▶ ▭ See **Calculator Notes 3B** and **1B.**◀] Then record Walker B's motion, and download these data to the same graphing calculator.   Answers will vary.

Next you'll model the walks with a system of equations.

Step 5   Find an equation to model the data for each of the two walkers.

Step 6   Graph the two equations on the same set of axes with both sets of data. Find the approximate point where the lines intersect.

Step 7   Explain the real-world meaning of the intersection point in Step 6.

Step 8   Check that the coordinates of the point of intersection satisfy both of your equations.

Next you'll consider what happens under different conditions.

Step 9   Suppose that Walker A walks faster than 1 m/s. How is the graph different? What happens to the point of intersection?

Step 10   Suppose that two people walk at the same speed and direction from different starting marks. What does this graph look like? What happens to the solution point?

Step 11   Suppose that two people walk at the same speed in the same direction from the same starting mark. What does this graph look like? How many points satisfy this system of equations?   The two lines overlap on the graph. Every point on the line is a solution to the system of equations.

In the investigation you were asked to find the point of intersection of two lines. In this example you'll see how you can find or confirm a point of intersection using a graph, a table of values, and some calculations.

EXAMPLE

Edna leaves the trailhead at dawn to hike 12 mi toward the lake, where her friend Maria is camping. At the same time, Maria starts her hike toward the trailhead. Edna is walking uphill so she averages only 1.5 mi/h, while Maria averages 2.5 mi/h walking downhill. When and where will they meet?

a. Define variables for time and for distance from the trailhead.

b. Write a system of two equations to model this situation.

c. Solve this system by creating a table and finding the values for the variables that make both equations true. Then locate this solution on a graph.

d. Check your solution and explain its real-world meaning.

Step 6 Graphs will vary. The point of intersection should be approximately (3, 3.5).

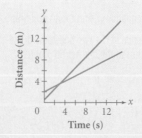

Step 10 Encourage a variety of starting points.

Step 11 You might also ask students to consider a scenario in which two people walk in opposite directions.

▶ **Solution**

Both women hike the same amount of time. When Edna and Maria meet they will both be the same distance from the trailhead, although they will have hiked different distances.

a. Let x represent the time in hours. Let y represent the distance in miles from the trailhead.

b. The system of equations that models this situation is grouped in a brace:

$$\begin{cases} y = 1.5x & \text{Edna's hike.} \\ y = 12 - 2.5x & \text{Maria's hike.} \end{cases}$$

Edna starts at the trailhead so she increases her distance from it as she hikes 1.5 mi/h for x hours. Maria starts 12 mi from the trailhead and reduces her distance from it as she hikes 2.5 mi/h for x hours.

c. Create a table from the equations. Fill in the times and calculate each distance. The table shows the x-value that gives equal y-values for both equations. When $x = 3$, both y-values are 4.5. So the solution is the ordered pair $(3, 4.5)$. We say that these values "satisfy" both equations.

Hiking Times and Distances

x	$y = 1.5x$	$y = 12 - 2.5x$
0	0	12
1	1.5	9.5
2	3	7
3	4.5	4.5
4	6	2
5	7.5	−0.5

SHARING IDEAS

Have students present different responses to Steps 7, 9, 10, and 11. Ask why there is variety. They might mention the need to accelerate from standing still and the difficulty of maintaining a constant speed.

Talk through the logic of verifying answers, as in Step 8. Be sure students do not get the notion that they can just substitute and then manipulate the equation to get one that is true. Instead, help students see the validity of evaluating the expressions on each side of the equal sign and showing that they are equal.

[Ask] "What are the disadvantages of the graphical method of solving a system of equations?" To motivate the rest of the chapter, elicit the ideas that the result might be only approximate and that the problem solver needs to construct graphs rather than just work with the equations.

EXAMPLE

This example shows students how to solve a system of linear equations using a calculator graph or table.

You might draw a diagram or ask two students to act out the situation to help students envision what's happening. **[Ask]** "Does Edna's graph slope upward because she's hiking uphill?" [No; stress that the graph rises because her distance from the trailhead increases with time.]

In part b of the solution, Maria's equation is written in intercept form. Edna's equation is a direct variation (also in intercept form with a y-intercept of 0).

Encourage thinking about different ways to approach a problem. If a student asks, "Why not just divide the 12 mi by the speed of 4 mi/h at which the two hikers are approaching each other?" point out that if the problem can be solved that way,

the result is the same as if Maria didn't hike and Edna walked (or jogged) at 4 mi/h. **[Ask]** "Are the situations the same?" [This would give the time they meet, but not the place.]

In part c of the solution, you may need to point out that the pair (x, y) is the solution. Also note the use of the word *satisfy*. It's used later, too.

For another example, you could use the CBL 2 demonstration Hot and Cold, in which data gathered from temperature probes are graphed to create a roughly linear system of equations.

Verifying Solutions

Each solution to a system should be checked in both of the original equations, and the check must be logically correct. A solution can be checked by evaluating both sides of the equation and showing that they are equal.

One common faulty method involves substituting into only one of the equations and not discovering that the solution does not satisfy the other equation. Another common mistake is making an error in solving for a variable and then checking in the incorrect form of the equation. Make sure that students check their solution in the two original equations to avoid these pitfalls.

Assessing Progress

You can assess understanding of time-distance relationships and graphs and of how slopes of lines represent rates of change. You can also observe skill at plotting points, writing equations to represent motion with constant speed, and graphing linear equations.

On the graph this solution is the point where the two lines intersect. You can use the trace function on your calculator to approximate the coordinates of the solution point, though sometimes you'll get an exact answer.

d. The coordinates (3, 4.5) must satisfy both equations.

$Y_1 = 1.5x$

X = 3.0212766   Y = 4.5319149

$[-1, 8, 1, -2, 14, 1]$

Edna	Maria	
$y = 1.5x$	$y = 12 - 2.5x$	Original equations.
$4.5 \overset{?}{=} 1.5(3)$	$4.5 \overset{?}{=} 12 - 2.5(3)$	Substitute 3 for the time x and 4.5 for the distance y into both equations.
$4.5 = 4.5$	$4.5 = 4.5$	These are true statements, so (3, 4.5) is a solution for both equations.

So, after hiking for 3 h, Edna and Maria meet on the trail 4.5 mi from the trailhead.

Is it possible to draw two lines that intersect in two points? How many possible solutions do you think a linear system of two equations in two variables can have?

When you solve a system of two equations, you're finding a solution in the form (x, y) that makes both equations true. When you have a graph of two distinct linear equations, the solution of the system is the point where the two lines intersect, if they cross at all. You can estimate these coordinates by tracing on the graph. To find the solution more precisely, zoom in on a table. In the next lesson you'll learn how to find the *exact* coordinates of the solution by working with the equations.

Dancers step between the parallel and intersecting sticks of a bamboo dance in Thailand.

EXERCISES

You will need your graphing calculator for Exercises **3, 4, 6, 7,** and **10.**

▶ Practice Your Skills

1. Verify whether the given ordered pair is a solution to the system. If it is not a solution, explain why not.

a. $(-15.6, 0.2)$
$$\begin{cases} y = 47 + 3x \\ y = 8 + 0.5x \end{cases}$$

b. $(-4, 23)$
$$\begin{cases} y = 15 - 2x \\ y = 12 + x \end{cases}$$

c. $(2, 12.3)$
$$\begin{cases} y = 4.5 + 5x \\ y = 2.3 + 5x \end{cases}$$ ⓐ

Closing the Lesson

As needed, explain that some problem situations are modeled with a **system of equations.** Solutions to systems of two linear equations can be approximated by seeing where the equations' graphs intersect or by making tables.

1a. yes, because $47 + 3(-15.6) = 0.2$ and $8 + 0.5(-15.6) = 0.2$

1b. No, because $23 \neq 12 + (-4)$; the point satisfies only one of the equations.

1c. No, because $12.3 \neq 4.5 + 5(2)$; furthermore, the lines are parallel, so the system has no solution.

2. Match each graph of a system of equations with its corresponding table values. The tick marks on each graph are one unit apart.

Graph of system   **Table values of system**

table iv **a.**    **i.**

table iii **b.**    **ii.**

table i **c.**    **iii.**

table ii **d.**    **iv.**

3. Graph each system on your calculator using the window given. Use the trace function to find the point of intersection. Is the calculator giving you approximate or exact solutions?

  a. $[-18.8, 18.8, 5, -12.4, 12.4, 5]$
  $$\begin{cases} y = 3 + 0.5x \\ y = -9 + 2x \end{cases} \text{@}$$

  b. $[-4.7, 4.7, 1, -3.1, 3.1, 1]$
  $$\begin{cases} y = 4x - 5.5 \\ y = -3x + 5 \end{cases}$$

4. Use the calculator table function to find the solution to each system of equations. (In 4b, you'll need to solve the equations for y first.)

  a. $y = 7 + 2.5x$
  $\quad y = 35.9 - 6x$

  b. $2x + y = 9$
  $\quad 3x + y = 16.3$

5. Solve the equations for y, then find the value of y when $x = 1$. Substitute these values for x and y into their original equations. What does this tell you?

  a. $4x + 2y = 6$

  b. $2x - 5y = 20$ @

▶ **Helping with the Exercises**

Exercise 1c The lines graphing the system are parallel, so the system has no solution. The given point does lie on one of the lines, though, so accept an answer that says the point isn't a solution because it doesn't lie on the other line.

Exercise 3 Be prepared to explain the list of numbers in the window settings. Visual learners might be helped with a display that shows [Xmin, Xmax, Xscl, Ymin, Ymax, Yscl]. These settings enable the calculator to provide exact solutions for these problems. Students will get approximate solutions if they graph in the standard viewing window (ZOOM 6: ZStandard). Friendly windows are introduced in Chapter 7. (See Calculator Note 7D.)

3a. $(8, 7)$

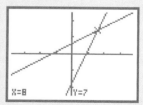

3b. $(1.5, 0.5)$

In this case, the calculator gives exact solutions that satisfy each system.

4a. $(3.4, 15.5)$ **4b.** $(7.3, -5.6)$

5a. $y = 3 - 2x$; $(1, 1)$: $4(1) + 2(1) = 6$

5b. $y = -4 + 0.4x$; $(1, -3.6)$: $2(1) - 5(-3.6) = 20$

The point satisfies both forms of the linear equation.

Exercise 6 [Language] The *start-up costs* for a business are the amount of money that must be spent to begin the business. The *k* in *.kom* is a deliberate misspelling to avoid confusion with actual "dot com" companies. You may need to explain that profit is the difference between revenue ($2.50 multiplied by the number of hits) and cost (the start-up cost). **[Alert]** Some students may be uncomfortable with the use of variables other than *x* and *y*, especially for graphing. Help them convert to *x* and *y*. Some students also may need help in setting an appropriate viewing window for large numbers.

6a. Let *P* represent profit in dollars and *N* represent the number of hits; $P = -12{,}000 + 2.5N$.

6b. *P* represents profit, *N* represents hits. Widget.kom's start-up costs are $5,000, and its advertisers pay $1.60 per hit. Because Widget.kom spent less in start-up costs, its website might be less attractive to advertisers, hence the lower rate.

6c. When $N \approx 7778$, $P \approx 7445$ in both equations.

6e. Use the table to find $(7778, 7445)$. Tracing on this graph is not precise.

6f. This intersection point indicates that for 7778 hits to their websites, the two companies make a profit of about $7,445.

Exercise 7 [Alert] If students didn't hear the term *start-up costs* in connection with Exercise 6, they may not know what it means.

7c. Sally will always profit more than Gizmo.kom for the same number of website hits. Because their lines never intersect, there is no solution to the system of equations, and their profits will never be equal.

7d. 2000 hits; after 2000 hits, Sally will have earned back her start-up costs.

See page 723 for answers to Exercises 6d and 7b.

▶ Reason and Apply

6. **APPLICATION** Two friends start rival Internet companies in their homes. It costs Gizmo.kom $12,000 to set up the computers and buy the necessary office supplies. Advertisers pay Gizmo.kom $2.50 for each hit (each visit to the website).

   a. Define variables and write an equation to describe the profits for Gizmo.kom. @

   b. The profit equation for the rival company, Widget.kom, is $P = -5000 + 1.6N$. Explain possible real-world meanings of the numbers and variables in this equation, and tell why they're different from those in 6a. @

   c. Use a calculator table to find the *N*-value that gives approximately equal *P*-values for both equations. @

   d. Use your answer to 6c to select a viewing window, and graph both equations to display their intersection and all *x*- and *y*-intercepts.

   e. What are the coordinates of the intersection point of the two graphs? Explain how you found this point and how accurate you think it is.

   f. What is the real-world meaning of these coordinates?

7. **APPLICATION** After seeing her friends profit from their websites in Exercise 6, Sally wants to start a third company, Gadget.kom, with the start-up costs of Widget.kom and the advertising rate of Gizmo.kom.

   a. What is Sally's profit equation? $P = -5000 + 2.5N$

   b. Graph the profit equations for Gadget.kom and Gizmo.kom.

   c. What does the graph tell you about Sally's profits compared to Gizmo.kom's? ⓗ

   d. What is the *x*-intercept for Sally's equation? What is its real-world meaning?

8. **APPLICATION** The total tuition for students at University College and State College consists of student fees plus costs per credit. Some classes have different credit values. The table shows the total tuition for programs with different numbers of credits at each college.

   a. Write a system of equations that represents the relationship between credit hours and total tuition for each college. @

   b. Find the solution to this system of equations and check it. @

   c. Which method did you use to solve this system? Why?

   d. What is the real-world meaning of the solution? @

   e. When is it cheaper to attend University College? State College?

Total Tuition

Credits	University College ($)	State College ($)
1	55	47
3	115	111
6	205	207
9	295	303
10	325	335
12	385	399

Exercise 8 Some students may find it easier to find the *y*-intercept if they insert a row for 0 credits into the table. You can use the Sketchpad demonstration Solving Systems of Equations to replace this exercise.

8a. $y = 25 + 30x$, where *y* is tuition for *x* credits at University College; $y = 15 + 32x$, where *y* is tuition for *x* credits at State College

8b. $(5, 175)$; check: $175 = 25 + 30(5)$, $175 = 15 + 32(5)$

8c. Answers will vary. The table is more accurate than tracing on the calculator graph.

8d. When a student takes 5 credit hours, the tuition at either college is $175.

8e. It is cheaper to attend University if taking more than 5 credits; for fewer than 5 credits, it is cheaper to attend State. For 5 credits, they cost the same.

9. The high school band and drill team both practice on the football field. During one part of the routine, a drill team member marches from the 9 yd mark on the sideline at 1 yd/s toward the 0-yard mark. At the same time, the tuba player marches from the 3 yd mark at 0.5 yd/s in the opposite direction.

a. Write a system of equations to describe this situation.

b. Find the solution to this system and explain its meaning.
(4, 5); after 4 s, the tuba player bumps into the drill team member at the 5 yd mark.

The marching band performs at halftime during a football game at West Point.

10. The equations $y = 28.65 - 0.0411(x - 1962)$ and $y = 27.5 - 0.0411(x - 1990)$ both model the data for the winning times for the Olympic men's 10,000-meter race. The variable x represents the year, and y represents the winning time, in minutes.

a. Find the approximate winning time for the year 1972 given by each equation. What is the difference between the values?

b. Find the approximate winning time for the year 2008 given by each equation. What is the difference between the values?

c. Select an appropriate window and graph the two equations.

d. Do you think these equations represent the same line? Explain your reasoning. @

11. *Mini-Investigation* Consider the system of equations
$$\begin{cases} y = a + bx \\ y = 2 - 5x \end{cases}$$
Explain what values of a and b give this system

a. exactly 1 solution   **b.** no solutions   **c.** infinitely many solutions @

▶ **Review**

2.3   **12. APPLICATION** Hydroplanes are boats that move so fast they skim the top of the water. The hydroplane *Spirit of the Tri-Cities* qualified for the 2004 Columbia Cup race with a speed of 145.000 mi/h. The hydroplane *Miss B* qualified with a speed of 163.162 mi/h. (Northwest Hydro Racing, *www.hydroracing.com*)

a. How long will each hydroplane take to run a 5-lap race if one lap is 2.5 miles?
Spirit of the Tri-Cities: 5.172 min; *Miss B:* 4.597 min

9a. $d = 9 - t$, where d is the drill team member's distance from the end zone; $d = 3 + 0.5t$, where d is the tuba player's distance from the end zone

10a. The equations give winning times of 28.239 min and 28.2398 min; the difference is 0.0008.

10b. The equations give winning times of 26.7594 min and 26.7602 min; the difference is 0.0008.

10c.

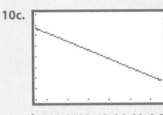

[1945, 2005, 10, 26, 30, 0.5]

10d. $\begin{cases} y = 109.2882 - 0.0411x \\ y = 109.289 - 0.0411x \end{cases}$

The graph in 10c appears to show one line; however, the y-values are 0.0008 unit apart. While the two lines are not identical, they are well within the accuracy of the model, so you could say they are the same model.

11a. Because lines with different slopes always intersect, the y-intercept a can equal any number, and b can be any number except -5.

11b. $a \neq 2$ and $b = -5$; same slope, different y-intercept, lines do not intersect

11c. $a = 2$ and $b = -5$; same slope and y-intercept, lines overlap

---

Exercise 12 Assume that the boats maintain their qualifying speeds throughout the race. This exercise provides an excellent review of the concepts presented in Lesson 2.3 and shows the usefulness of dimensional analysis, but it is complex. If students have difficulty, encourage them to slowly build up the problem to the result in gallons.

$$\dfrac{\dfrac{4.3 \text{ gal}}{\text{min}} \cdot \dfrac{60 \text{ min}}{\text{h}} \cdot \dfrac{2.5 \text{ mi}}{\text{lap}} \cdot 5 \text{ laps}}{\dfrac{163.162 \text{ mi}}{\text{h}}}$$

$$\text{gal} = \dfrac{\text{gal}}{\text{min}}(\text{min})$$

$$= \dfrac{\text{gal}}{\text{min}} \cdot \dfrac{\text{min}}{\text{h}}(\text{h})$$

$$= \dfrac{\dfrac{\text{gal}}{\text{min}} \cdot \dfrac{\text{min}}{\text{h}}(\text{mi})}{\dfrac{\text{mi}}{\text{h}}}$$

$$= \dfrac{\dfrac{\text{gal}}{\text{min}} \cdot \dfrac{\text{min}}{\text{h}} \cdot \dfrac{\text{mi}}{\text{lap}} \cdot \text{laps}}{\dfrac{\text{mi}}{\text{h}}}$$

12b. *Spirit of the Tri-Cities:*
22.241 gal; *Miss B:* 19.766 gal

12c. *Spirit of the Tri-Cities:*
24.167 mi; *Miss B:* 27.194 mi

12d. *Spirit of the Tri-Cities:*
0.562 mpg; *Miss B:* 0.632 mpg

Exercise 13 Be sure the logic of the check by substitution is correct.

Exercise 15 This review of matrices helps prepare for solving systems of equations with matrices in Lesson 5.4. Assign it only if you did Lesson 1.8.

b. Some boats limit the amount of fuel the motor burns to 4.3 gallons per minute. How much fuel will each boat use to run a 5-lap race?

c. Hydroplanes have a 50-gallon tank though generally only about 43 gallons are put in. The rest of the tank is filled with foam to prevent sloshing. How many miles can each hydroplane go on one 43-gallon tank of fuel?

d. Find each boat's fuel efficiency rate in miles per gallon.

3.6 **13.** Solve each equation using the method you like best. Then substitute your value for x back into the equation to check your solution.

a. $0.75x = 63.75$ $x = 85$

b. $18.86 = -2.3x$ $x = -8.2$

c. $6 = 12 - 2x$ $x = 3$

d. $9 = 6(x - 2)$ $x = 3.5$

e. $4(x + 5) - 8 = 18$ $x = 1.5$

3.6 **14.** Write the equation represented by this balance. Then solve the equation for x using the balancing method. @

1.8 **15.** Find each matrix sum and difference.

a. $\begin{bmatrix} 3 & -3 \\ -9 & 1 \end{bmatrix} + \begin{bmatrix} -2 & -8 \\ 3 & 7 \end{bmatrix}$ $\begin{bmatrix} 1 & -11 \\ -6 & 8 \end{bmatrix}$

b. $\begin{bmatrix} 5 & 0 \\ 2 & 7 \end{bmatrix} - \begin{bmatrix} -8 & 1 \\ -5 & -1 \end{bmatrix}$ $\begin{bmatrix} 13 & -1 \\ 7 & 8 \end{bmatrix}$

4.3 **16.** Solve each equation for y.

a. $y + 2 = 5x$ $y = 5x - 2$ **b.** $5y = 4 - 7x$ $y = 0.8 - 1.4x$ **c.** $2y - 6x = 3$ $y = 1.5 + 3x$

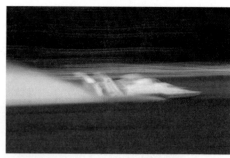

This hydroplane travels so fast that its image is blurred in the photo. Learn about hydroplane racing at **www.keymath.com/DA** .

14.

$2x + 9 = 6x + 1$	Original equation.
$2x - 2x + 9 = 6x - 2x + 1$	Subtract $2x$ from both sides.
$9 = 4x + 1$	Combine like terms.
$9 - 1 = 4x + 1 - 1$	Subtract 1 from both sides.
$8 = 4x$	Combine like terms.
$\dfrac{8}{4} = \dfrac{4x}{4}$	Divide both sides by 4.
$x = 2$	Reduce.

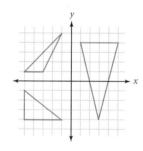

IMPROVING YOUR GEOMETRY SKILLS

Draw a triangle that satisfies each of these sets of conditions. If it's not possible, tell why not.

1. a triangle with all three sides having positive slope

2. an equilateral triangle (three equal sides) with one side having slope 0

3. an isosceles triangle (two equal sides) with all three sides having positive slope

4. a right triangle with one side having undefined slope, one side having slope 0, and one side having slope 1

5. a triangle with two sides having the same slope

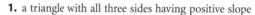

IMPROVING GEOMETRY SKILLS

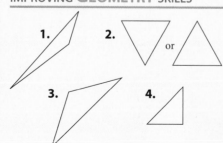

1.

2. or

3.

4.

5. This is not possible because two lines with the same slope are parallel and never meet, but each pair of a triangle's edges must meet at a vertex.

Solving Systems of Equations Using Substitution

Graphing systems and comparing their table values are good ways to see solutions. However, it's not always easy to find a good graphing window or the right settings for a table. Also, the solutions you find are often only approximations. To find exact solutions, you'll need to work algebraically with the equations themselves. One way is called the **substitution method.**

EXAMPLE A

On a rural highway a police officer sees a motorist run a red light at 50 mi/h and begins pursuit. At the instant the police officer passes through the intersection at 60 mi/h, the motorist is 0.2 mi down the road. When and where will the officer catch up to the motorist?

a. Write a system of equations in two variables to model this situation.

b. Solve this system by the substitution method, and check the solution.

c. Explain the real-world meaning of the solution.

▶ **Solution**

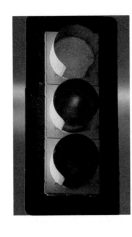

Let t represent the time in hours, with $t = 0$ being the instant the officer passes through the intersection. Let d represent the distance in miles from the intersection.

a. The system of equations is

$$\begin{cases} d = 0.2 + 50t \\ d = 60t \end{cases}$$

The first equation represents the motorist, who is already 0.2 mi away when the timing begins. The second equation represents the officer.

b. When the officer catches up to the motorist, they will both be the same distance from the intersection. At this time, both equations will have the same d-value. So you can replace d in one equation with an equivalent expression for d that you find from the other equation. Substituting $60t$ for d into $d = 0.2 + 50t$ gives the new equation:

$$\begin{cases} d = 0.2 + 50t \\ d = 60t \end{cases} \longrightarrow 60t = 0.2 + 50t$$

There is now one equation to solve. Notice that the variable t occurs on both sides of the equal sign and that d has dropped out. Now you use the balancing method to find the solution.

$60t = 0.2 + 50t$	New equation.
$60t - 50t = 0.2 + 50t - 50t$	Subtract 50t from both sides of the equation.
$10t = 0.2$	Combine like terms.
$t = 0.02$	Divide both sides of the equation by 10 and reduce.

NCTM STANDARDS

CONTENT		PROCESS	
	Number	✓	Problem Solving
✓	Algebra	✓	Reasoning
✓	Geometry	✓	Communication
✓	Measurement	✓	Connections
✓	Data/Probability	✓	Representation

LESSON OBJECTIVES

• Understand the limitations of solving systems graphically

• Solve systems of linear equations using substitution

point out that the time required will be $\frac{0.2}{10}$, or 0.02 h.

[Alert] If students suggest substituting into the same equation, try it to show that all variables will drop out. They must use the other equation.

Some spatially challenged students may understand the substitution better if the two equations are written side by side rather than one under the other.

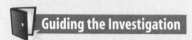

Guiding the Investigation

One Step

Ask students to tie knots in the ropes and collect data as in Lesson 3.7. Then ask them to find the number of knots that make the thick and thin ropes the same length without using graphs or tables. As you observe, encourage them to write the equations next to each other to see how to substitute.

Steps 1–4 As an alternative to students' collecting data in Steps 1 and 3, you might pass out sample data. Assign each group the data from any one of these rope pairs: 1 and 4; 1 and 5; 2 and 4; 2 and 5; 3 and 4; 3 and 5. To move directly to Step 2, you can give them these equations, based on the sample data:

Type 1 rope: $y = 89.9 - 4.2x$

Type 2 rope: $y = 93.9 - 4.2x$

Type 3 rope: $y = 100 - 6x$

Type 4 rope: $y = 100 - 10.3x$

Type 5 rope: $y = 97.8 - 13.6x$

The units are centimeters.

Step 1 Data will vary; a sample for the thin rope (Type 3):

Number of knots	Length (cm)
0	100
1	94
2	88
3	81.3
4	75.7
5	69.9
6	63.5

Step 2 If x represents the number of knots and y represents the sample-rope length in centimeters, then the equation is $y = 100 - 6x$. The y-intercept, 100, is the length of rope in centimeters without knots, and the slope, -6, is the amount of thin rope in centimeters that each knot takes.

Step 3 Data will vary; a sample for Type 4:

Number of knots	Length (cm)
0	100
1	89.7
2	78.7
3	68.6
4	57.4
5	47.8
6	38.1

To find the d-value of the solution, substitute 0.02 for t into one of the original equations.

$$t = (0.02)$$

$$d = 0.2 + 50t \qquad \text{and} \qquad d = 60t$$
$$d = 0.2 + 50(0.02) \qquad\qquad d = 60(0.02)$$
$$d = 1.2 \qquad\qquad\qquad\qquad d = 1.2$$

If both equations give the same d-value, 1.2 in this case, then you have the correct solution.

c. The solution is the only ordered pair of values, (0.02, 1.2), that works in both equations. The police officer will catch up to the motorist 1.2 mi from the intersection in 0.02 h, which is 1 min 12 s after passing through the intersection.

The calculator screen shows the system of equations from the example in the window [0, 0.04, 0.01, 0, 4, 1]. It is difficult to guess the solution at these window settings because the two lines have very similar slopes and close y-intercepts. But the substitution method helps you find the exact solution no matter how difficult it is to set windows or tables. Once you have the exact solution, it is much easier to find a good window to display it.

Investigation
All Tied Up

In this investigation you'll work with rope lengths and predict how many knots it would take in each rope to make a thicker rope the same length as a thinner one.

You will need

- two ropes of different thickness, both about 1 meter long
- a meterstick or tape measure
- a 9-meter-long thin rope (optional)
- a 10-meter-long thick rope (optional)

First you'll collect data and write equations.

Step 1 Measure the length of the thinner rope without any knots. Then tie a knot and measure the length of the rope again. Continue tying knots until no more can be tied. Knots should be of the same kind, size, and tightness. Record the data for number of knots and length of rope in a table.

Step 2 Define variables and write an equation in intercept form to model the data you collected in Step 1. What are the slope and y-intercept, and how do they relate to the rope?

Step 3 Repeat Steps 1 and 2 for the thicker rope.

Step 4 Suppose you have a 9-meter-long thin rope and a 10-meter-long thick rope. Write a system of equations that gives the length of each rope depending on the number of knots tied. A sample system is
$$\begin{cases} y = 900 - 6x \\ y = 1000 - 10.3x \end{cases}.$$

If x represents the number of knots and y represents the sample-rope length in centimeters, then the equation is $y = 100 - 10.3x$. The y-intercept, 100, is the length of rope in centimeters without knots, and the slope, -10.3, is the amount of thick rope in centimeters that each knot takes.

Step 4 Equations will vary because they use student-collected data.

Step 6 Possible
window is   **Step 5**
[0, 40, 5, 0, 1100, 100];
estimated coor-   **Step 6**
dinates from
sample: (23, 760).

Step 7 At 23 knots, **Step 7**
both ropes have
nearly equal   **Step 8**
lengths of 760 cm.

Next you'll analyze the system to find a meaningful solution.

Solve this system of equations using the substitution method.

Select an appropriate window setting and graph this system of equations.
Estimate coordinates for the point of intersection to check your solution.
Compare this solution with the one from Step 5.

Explain the real-world meaning of the solution to the system of equations.

What happens to the graph of the system if the two ropes have the same
thickness? The same length?   If two ropes have the same thickness, the slopes
will be equal; if they have the same length, the y-intercepts are the same.

So far in this chapter, you've seen equations only in intercept form. In other words,
they are already solved for the output variable, y. This form makes it easy to use the
substitution method: You can simply set the two expressions in x equal to each
other because they are both equal to y. Sometimes you have to put the equations
into intercept form before substituting. In the next example, you'll have to change
an equation in standard form to intercept form.

EXAMPLE B

A pharmacist has 5% saline (salt) solution
and 20% saline solution. How much of
each solution should be combined to
create a bottle of 90 mL of 10% saline
solution?

a. Write a system of equations that models
this situation.

b. Solve one equation for x or y and
substitute into the other equation
to find a solution.

c. Check your solution.

▶ **Solution**

First decide what your variables are. You are trying to find how much of 5%
and how much of 20% saline solution to use. So let x = amount of 5% saline
solution, and let y = amount of 20% saline solution, in mL.

a. The total amount of saline solution needed is 90 mL, so write the equation

$$x + y = 90$$

The amount of salt in x mL of 5% saline solution is $0.05x$, and the amount
of salt in y mL of 20% saline solution is $0.2y$. The total combined salt must
be 10% of 90 mL, or $0.1(90)$. So write the equation

$$0.05x + 0.2y = 0.1(90)$$

So the system of equations that models this situation is

$$\begin{cases} x + y = 90 \\ 0.05x + 0.2y = 9 \end{cases}$$

Step 5 From sample:
$900 - 6x = 1000 - 10.3x$,
$4.3x = 100$, $x = 23\frac{11}{43}$; round
to 23 knots; $y = 760\frac{20}{43}$; round to
760 cm.

Step 6
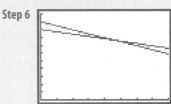

Step 7 In the solution, x will be
the number of knots needed in
each rope for the two ropes to be
the same length, and y will be that
length. Note that the number of
knots must be an integer value.
Students will need to round off
their actual answers to get
realistic values.

You may want to check the students' solutions as a class by having each half of the class tie knots
in the optional longer ropes and
then comparing the ropes. The
longer ropes must have the same
thickness as the shorter ropes.

You might have students write a
lab report for this investigation.

SHARING IDEAS

Have students present several different systems for Steps 4 and 5.
Ask students why the results differ. Then lead a discussion of
ideas about Step 8. **[Ask]** "Solve
the system $3x - 4y = 11$ and
$3x + 2y = -1$ in as many ways
as you can." Not only does this get
students thinking about solving
equations in standard form, but it
also motivates solving by elimination, the topic of Lesson 5.3.

Assessing Progress
Watch for the ability to collect
data systematically into tables,
write linear equations in intercept form, find the slope and
y-intercept, and decide the conditions under which a system has
zero solutions, one solution, or
infinitely many solutions.

Ask students to predict the answer before solving the equations. They can better judge the correctness of their results if they first decide on a reasonable estimate. Students may reason that 10% is closer to 5% than 20% is, so they will need more of the 5% solution. Make sure that students understand that the first equation, $x + y = 90$, represents the total amount of saline solution, while the second equation, $0.05x + 0.2y = 0.1(90)$, represents the amount of salt in the solution. Exercises 13 and 14 are mixture problems.

The More Practice Your Skills worksheet for Lesson 5.7 gives more practice with rate, work, and mixture problems.

Closing the Lesson

The **substitution method** allows you to solve a system of linear equations exactly and without graphing or constructing a table. Following are the stages of this method:

1. Solve both equations for one variable and set the two equations equal. Or solve one equation for one variable and substitute that value into the other equation.

2. Solve the resulting equation for the other variable.

3. Substitute that solution for that variable into the first equation.

4. Solve for the second variable.

b. To use the substitution method, one of the equations must be solved for the variable. It'll be easiest to solve the first equation for one of the variables. You can solve for either x or y, using the balancing method.

$x + y = 90$	Original equation.
$x + y - y = 90 - y$	Subtract y from both sides.
$x = 90 - y$	Combine like terms.

Substitute $90 - y$ for x into the second equation, and solve for y.

$0.05x + 0.2y = 9$	Original equation.
$0.05(90 - y) + 0.2y = 9$	Substitute $90 - y$ for x.
$4.5 - 0.05y + 0.2y = 9$	Distribute the 0.05 through the parentheses.
$4.5 + 0.15y = 9$	Combine like terms.
$0.15y = 4.5$	Subtract 4.5 from both sides.
$y = 30$	Divide both sides by 0.15 and reduce.

To find the corresponding x-value, substitute 30 for y into one of the equations.

$x = 90 - y$	The first equation, in intercept form.
$x = 90 - 30 = 60$	Substitute 30 for y and evaluate.

c. To check your solution, substitute 60 for x and 30 for y into the original equations.

$x + y = 90$	$0.05x + 0.2y = 9$
$30 + 60 \overset{?}{=} 90$	$0.05(60) + 0.2(30) \overset{?}{=} 9$
$90 = 90$	$3 + 6 \overset{?}{=} 9$
	$9 = 9$

Both equations result in true statements, so the solution is correct. So the pharmacist must combine 60 mL of 5% saline solution and 30 mL of 20% saline solution.

Problems like those in Example B are called **mixture problems.** This type of problem often involves a system of equations.

There are many ways to solve systems by using the substitution method. You can set expressions equal to one another, or solve for one of the variables and substitute the expression you get into the other equation. Both ways are examples of **symbolic manipulation,** which simply means that you are working with the properties you have used in the balancing method and "undoing" to keep sides of the equation equal. It does not matter which equation or variable you work with first, but you must always substitute the resulting expression into the *other* equation to find a solution. When you solve a system of equations using the substitution method, you can always find an exact solution, not just its approximate coordinates.

You will need your graphing calculator for Exercises **12** and **15**.

▶ Practice Your Skills

1. The system of equations
$$\begin{cases} d = 1.5t \\ d = 12 - 2.5t \end{cases}$$
describes the distance of two hikers, Edna and Maria, from the example in Lesson 5.1. By setting the expressions of the right sides of the equations equal to each other, you can find the time when Edna and Maria meet. Explain what happens in Stages 3 and 5 of the substitution process.

$d = 12 - 2.5t$	1. Original equation.
$1.5t = 12 - 2.5t$	2. Substitute $1.5t$ for d.
$1.5t + 2.5t = 12 - 2.5t + 2.5t$	3. Add $2.5t$ to both sides.
$4t = 12$	4. Combine like terms.
$\dfrac{4t}{4} = \dfrac{12}{4}$	5. Divide both sides by 4.
$t = 3$	6. Reduce.

2. Check that each ordered pair is a solution to each system. If the pair is not a solution point, explain why not. Ⓗ

   a. $(-2, 34)$
   $$\begin{cases} y = 38 + 2x \\ y = -21 - 0.5x \end{cases}$$

   b. $(4.25, 19.25)$
   $$\begin{cases} y = 32 - 3x \\ y = 15 + x \end{cases}$$

   c. $(2, 12.3)$
   $$\begin{cases} y = 2.3 + 3.2x \\ y = 5.9 + 3.2x \end{cases}$$

3. Solve each equation by symbolic manipulation.

   a. $14 + 2x = 4 - 3x$ Ⓐ

   b. $7 - 2y = -3 - y$ Ⓐ

   c. $5d = 9 + 2d$

   d. $12 + t = 4t$

4. Solve the system of equations using the substitution method, and check your solution. Ⓗ
$$\begin{cases} y = 25 + 30x \\ y = 15 + 32x \end{cases}$$
$(5, 175)$; check: $175 = 25 + 30(5)$ and $175 = 15 + 32(5)$

5. Substitute $4 - 3x$ for y. Then rewrite each expression in terms of one variable.

   a. $5x + 2y$ $\quad 5x + 2(4 - 3x) = 5x + 8 - 6x$
   $= -x + 8$

   b. $7x - 2y$ Ⓐ $\quad 7x - 2(4 - 3x) = 7x - 8 + 6x$
   $= 13x - 8$

6. Solve each system of equations by substitution, and check your solution.

   a. $\begin{cases} y = 4 - 3x \\ y = 2x - 1 \end{cases}$ $(1, 1)$; check: $1 = 4 - 3(1)$ and $1 = 2(1) - 1$

   b. $\begin{cases} 2x - 2y = 4 \\ x + 3y = 1 \end{cases}$ $\left(\dfrac{7}{4}, -\dfrac{1}{4}\right)$ or $(1.75, -0.25)$; check: $2(1.75) - 2(-0.25) = 4$ and $1.75 + 3(-0.25) = 1$

Students practice solving systems of equations by substitution.

ASSIGNING HOMEWORK

Essential	**1–4, 6, 7, 10**
Performance assessment	**8, 9, 12**
Portfolio	**12**
Journal	**8, 10**
Group	**5, 11, 13, 14**
Review	**15–18**

▶ Helping with the Exercises

Exercise 2 Be sure students use good logic as they verify solutions by evaluating both sides and comparing them. Even without substituting the value into either equation, students may recognize that both equations in 2c have the same slope, which means the lines are parallel and therefore cannot intersect.

2a. no, because the point satisfies only the first equation

2b. yes, because $19.25 = 32 - 3(4.25)$ and $19.25 = 15 + 4.25$

2c. No, because the point satisfies only the second equation; furthermore, the lines have the same slope, so they are parallel and there is no solution.

3a. $2x + 3x = 4 - 14$
$5x = -10$
$x = -2$

3b. $-2y + y = -3 - 7$
$-y = -10$
$y = 10$

3c. $5d - 2d = 9$
$3d = 9$
$d = 3$

3d. $t - 4t = -12$
$-3t = -12$
$t = 4$

▶ Reason and Apply

7. APPLICATION This system of equations models the profits of two home-based Internet companies.

$$\begin{cases} P = -12000 + 2.5N \\ P = -5000 + 1.6N \end{cases}$$

The variable P represents profit in dollars, and N represents hits to the company's website.

a. Use the substitution method to find an exact solution. @   See below.

b. Is an approximate or exact solution more meaningful in this model? @   The approximate solution, $N \approx 7778$ and $P \approx 7444$, is more meaningful because there cannot be a fractional number of website hits.

8. The costs for two families to attend Friday night's basketball game are given by $2x + 3y = 13.50$ and $3x + 2y = 16.50$, where x is the cost of an adult ticket and y is the cost of a student ticket, in dollars.

a. What is the real-world meaning of the first equation?

b. Solve this system of equations using the substitution method.

c. What are the prices of adult and student tickets?

9. APPLICATION The manager of a movie theater wants to know the number of adults and children who go to the movies. The theater charges $8 for each adult ticket and $4 for each child ticket. At a showing where 200 tickets were sold, the theater collected $1304.

a. Let the variable A represent the number of adult tickets and C represent the number of child tickets. Write an equation for the total number of tickets sold. @

b. Write an equation showing the total cost of the tickets. @

c. Use your equations from 9a and b to write a system whose solution represents the number of adult and child tickets sold. Solve this system by symbolic manipulation.

10. Students in an algebra class did an experiment similar to the Investigation Where Will They Meet? from Lesson 5.1. They wrote the system

$$\begin{cases} d = 0.5 + 0.75t \\ d = 2.5 + 0.75t \end{cases}$$

The first walker starts at the 0.5 m mark and walks away at 0.75 m/s. The second walker starts at the 2.5 m mark and walks away at 0.75 m/s.

a. What real-world information does the system tell you?

b. Use the substitution method to solve this system.   no solution

c. What is the real-world meaning of the solution you found in 10b?   The walkers will never meet.

8a. The total admission price for two adults and three students is $13.50.

8b. $x = 4.5$ and $y = 1.5$

8c. An adult ticket costs $4.50, and a student ticket costs $1.50.

Exercise 9 This problem is a variation on an old puzzle, so a student might point out that it can be solved without using a system of equations. Each of the 200 tickets brought in $4, making $800. The remainder of the ticket sales, $504, came from the adults, each of whom paid an additional $4. So there were $\frac{504}{4}$, or 126, adults. Encourage good thinking like this. Challenge these students to represent each step of their reasoning in a system of equations. Their method will motivate solving systems by elimination in Lesson 5.3.

9a. $A + C = 200$

9b. $8A + 4C = 1304$

9c. $A = 126$ and $C = 74$, so the theater sold 126 adult tickets and 74 child tickets.

7a. Answers will vary. A sample solution:

$-12{,}000 + 2.5N = -5{,}000 + 1.6N$ Set equations equal to each other.

$-12{,}000 + 0.9N = -5{,}000$ Subtract 1.6N from both sides.

$0.9N = 7{,}000$ Add 12,000 to both sides.

$N = \dfrac{70{,}000}{9} = 7{,}777\dfrac{7}{9}$ Divide both sides by 0.9.

$P = -12{,}000 + 2.5\left(\dfrac{70{,}000}{9}\right) = 7{,}444\dfrac{4}{9}$

11. The table at right gives the equations that model the three vehicles' distances in the Investigation On the Road Again from Lesson 3.2. The variable d represents the distance in miles from Flint and t represents time in minutes, with $t = 0$ being the instant all three vehicles start traveling.

For each event described in 11a–c, write a system of equations, solve using the substitution method, and explain the real-world meaning of your solution.

a. The pickup truck passes the sports car. @

b. The minivan meets the pickup truck.

c. The minivan meets the sports car.

d. Write and solve an equation to find when the minivan is twice as far from Flint as the sports car. (h) $220 - 1.2t = 2(35 + 0.8t)$, $t \approx 53.6$ min; minivan is about 156 mi, sports car is about 78 mi.

Distance from Flint

Equation	Vehicle
$d = 220 - 1.2t$	minivan
$d = 35 + 0.8t$	sports car
$d = 1.1t$	pickup truck

12. **APPLICATION** This table shows the winning times for the Olympic women's and men's 100-meter breaststroke. The times are given in minutes and seconds. For example, 1:15.80 means 1 min 15.80 s.

Women's and Men's 100-meter Breaststroke

Year	Women's champion and country	Time	Men's champion and country	Time
1968	Djurdjica Bjedov, Yugoslavia	1:15.80	Donald McKenzie, United States	1:07.70
1972	Catherine Carr, United States	1:13.58	Nobutaka Taguchi, Japan	1:04.94
1976	Hannelore Anke, East Germany	1:11.16	John Hencken, United States	1:03.11
1980	Ute Geweniger, East Germany	1:10.22	Duncan Goodhew, Great Britain	1:03.44
1984	Petra Van Staveren, Netherlands	1:09.88	Steve Lundquist, United States	1:01.65
1988	Tanya Dangalakova, Bulgaria	1:07.95	Adrian Moorhouse, Great Britain	1:02.04
1992	Elena Roudkovskaia, Unified Team	1:08.00	Nelson Diebel, United States	1:01.50
1996	Penny Heyns, South Africa	1:07.73	Frédéric Deburghgraeve, Belgium	1:00.60
2000	Megan Quann, United States	1:07.05	Domenico Fioravanti, Italy	1:00.46
2004	Xuejuan Luo, China	1:06.64	Kosuke Kitajima, Japan	1:00.08

(International Olympics Committee, in *The World Almanac and Book of Facts 2004*, pp. 870, 872) [Data sets: **SWMYR, SWMWM, SWMMN**]

a. Find a line of fit based on Q-points for the women's and the men's data sets. (*Hint:* You'll probably want to change the times to seconds. For example, 1:15.80 is 75.80 s.) @

b. Solve a system of equations whose solution tells you when the men and women will have equal winning times for this Olympic event. @ $x \approx 2238, y \approx 26.23$

c. Select an appropriate window to graph this system and its solution.

d. Discuss the reasonableness of this model and the solution. @

Japan's Kosuke Kitajima swims to win the men's 100-meter breaststroke final at the Athens 2004 Olympic Games.

Exercise 11d Students may be confused by the phrase "twice as far." Ask them how far the sports car is from Flint at any time, and then ask what twice that distance would be.

Exercise 12 The Fathom demonstration Olympic Times can replace this exercise.

12a. women: $y = 71.16 - 0.1715(x - 1976)$ or $y = 67.73 - 0.1715(x - 1996)$; men: $y = 63.44 - 0.142(x - 1976)$ or $y = 60.60 - 0.142(x - 1996)$

12c. Answers will vary. The window shown is $[1950, 2300, 100, 0, 80, 10]$.

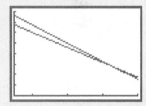

12d. The solution means that in the year 2238 (a little more than 230 years from now), both men and women will swim this race in 26.23 s. This is not likely. The model may be a good fit for the data, but extrapolating that far into the future produces unlikely predictions.

11a. $\begin{cases} d = 35 + 0.8t \\ d = 1.1t \end{cases}$

$1.1t = 35 + 0.8t$; $\left(116\frac{2}{3}, 128\frac{1}{3}\right)$

The pickup passes the sports car roughly 128 mi from Flint after approximately 117 min.

11b. $\begin{cases} d = 220 - 1.2t \\ d = 1.1t \end{cases}$

$220 - 1.2t = 1.1t$, $\left(\dfrac{2200}{23}, \dfrac{2420}{23}\right) \approx (95.7, 105.2)$

The minivan meets the pickup truck about 105 mi from Flint after approximately 96 min.

11c. $\begin{cases} d = 220 - 1.2t \\ d = 35 + 0.8t \end{cases}$

$35 + 0.8t = 220 - 1.2t$; $(92.5, 109)$

The minivan meets the sports car 109 mi from Flint after 92.5 min.

Exercise 13 Exercise 13 is a mixture problem, but students may not see the similarity to Example B. The equations for Example B modeled the total amount of solution and the total amount of salt. In this exercise, students should consider the total amount of candy and the total cost of the candy.

16c. $y = 100 + 12.1x$, where x represents the time in seconds and y represents her height above ground level. To find out how long her ride to the observation deck is, solve the equation $520 = 100 + 12.1x$.

Exercise 18 The return to matrices helps prepare for Lesson 5.4. Assign this problem only if you did Lesson 1.8 and plan to do Lesson 5.4.

13. A candy store manager is making a sour candy mix by combining sour cherry worms, which cost her $2.50 per pound, and sour lime bugs, which cost her $3.50 per pound. How much of each candy should she include if she wants 20 pounds of a mix that costs her a total of $65? @ 5 lb of sour cherry worms and 15 lb of sour lime bugs

14. Mrs. Abdul mixes bottled fruit juice with natural orange soda to make fruit punch for a party. The bottled fruit juice is 65% real juice and the natural orange soda is 5% real juice. How many liters of each are combined to make 10 liters of punch that is 33% real juice? $4\frac{2}{3}$ L of bottled fruit juice and $5\frac{1}{3}$ L of natural orange soda

▶ Review

4.2 **15.** A system of two linear equations has the solution $(3, -4.5)$. Write the equations of
 a. A horizontal line through the solution point. $y = -4.5$
 b. A vertical line through the solution point. $x = 3$

4.2 **16.** You and your family are visiting Seattle and take the elevator to the observation deck of the Space Needle. The observation deck is 520 ft high while the needle itself is 605 ft high. The elevator travels at a constant speed, and it takes 43 s to travel from the base at 0 ft to the observation deck.
 a. What is the slope of the graph of this situation? @ 12.1 ft/s
 b. If the elevator could go all the way to the top, how long would it take to get there? @ 50 s
 c. If a rider got on the elevator at the restaurant at the 100 ft level, what equation models her ride to the observation deck? @

The Space Needle, shown here in the city skyline, was built for the 1962 Seattle World's Fair. For interesting information about the Space Needle, see the links at **www.keymath.com/DA** .

0.1 **17.** Do each calculation by hand, and then check your results with a calculator. Express your answers as fractions.
 a. $3 - \frac{5}{6}$ $2\frac{1}{6}$
 b. $\frac{1}{4} + \frac{5}{12}$ $\frac{2}{3}$
 c. $\frac{3}{4} \cdot \frac{2}{9}$ $\frac{1}{6}$
 d. $\frac{1}{5} + \frac{2}{3} + \frac{3}{4}$ $\frac{97}{60}$, or $1\frac{37}{60}$

1.8 **18.** Match each matrix multiplication with its answer.

i a. $\begin{bmatrix} 8 & -2 \\ 1 & 9 \end{bmatrix} \times \begin{bmatrix} 3 & 8 \\ -1 & -4 \end{bmatrix}$ i. $\begin{bmatrix} 26 & 72 \\ -6 & -28 \end{bmatrix}$

iii b. $\begin{bmatrix} 24 & -16 \\ -1 & -36 \end{bmatrix} \times \begin{bmatrix} 1 & 0 \\ 0 & 1 \end{bmatrix}$ ii. $\begin{bmatrix} 36 \\ -17 \end{bmatrix}$

ii c. $\begin{bmatrix} 6 & 8 \\ -7 & -1 \end{bmatrix} \times \begin{bmatrix} 2 \\ 3 \end{bmatrix}$ iii. $\begin{bmatrix} 24 & -16 \\ -1 & -36 \end{bmatrix}$

Solving Systems of Equations Using Elimination

I happen to feel that the degree of a person's intelligence is directly reflected by the number of conflicting attitudes she can bring to bear on the same topic.

LISA ALTHER

You have seen how to approximate the solution to a system of equations using a table or graph, and you've seen how to calculate the exact answer to a system of equations using the substitution method. In this lesson you'll learn another method for finding an exact solution, which will have advantages for certain systems.

You know that when you add equal quantities to each side of an equation, the resulting equation is equivalent and has the same solution as the original.

$$
\begin{array}{ll}
y - 7 = 12 & \text{Original equations.} \\
+\quad 7 = 7 & \text{Add equal quantities to both sides.} \\
\hline
y \quad = 19 & \text{The resulting equations are true and have} \\
& \text{the same solutions as the originals.}
\end{array}
$$

$$
\begin{array}{l}
3x - 5y = 9 \\
+\quad 5y = 5y \\
\hline
3x \quad = 9 + 5y
\end{array}
$$

In the same way, when you add two quantities that are equal, c and d, to two other quantities that are equal, a and b, the resulting expressions are equal.

$$
\begin{array}{ll}
a = b & \text{Original equation.} \\
+\ c = d & \text{Add equal quantities.} \\
\hline
a + c = b + d & \text{The resulting equation is true and has} \\
& \text{the same solutions as the originals.}
\end{array}
$$

The **elimination method** makes use of this fact to solve systems of linear equations.

EXAMPLE A

J. P. is thinking of two numbers, but he won't say what they are. He tells you that the sum of the two numbers is 163 and that their difference is 33. Find the two numbers.

Sum = 163
Difference = 33

a. Write a system of equations for the sum and difference of these numbers.

b. Use the elimination method to solve this system.

▶ **Solution**

a. Let f and s represent the first and second numbers, respectively. Then the system is

$$
\begin{cases} f + s = 163 \\ f - s = 33 \end{cases}
$$

The first equation describes the sum, and the second describes the difference.

b. Note that adding the equations eliminates the variable s. Then solve for f.

$$
\begin{array}{ll}
f + s = 163 & \\
+\ f - s = 33 & \text{Original equations.} \\
\hline
2f = 196 & \text{Add.} \\
f = 98 & \text{Divide both sides by 2.}
\end{array}
$$

So the first number is 98. Now you need to find the second number.

NCTM STANDARDS

CONTENT	PROCESS
Number	✔ Problem Solving
✔ Algebra	✔ Reasoning
Geometry	✔ Communication
✔ Measurement	Connections
Data/Probability	✔ Representation

LESSON OBJECTIVES

- Solve systems of linear equations in two variables by eliminating one variable
- See more examples in which two linear equations can model real-world situations

substitution isn't being used here because different steps began the process of elimination. The solution to the system would be expressed algebraically as $(f, s) = (98, 65)$.

Be careful to write the check of the solutions in a logically correct way.

 Guiding the Investigation

One Step

Ask students to line up four paper clips along the long edge of a piece of paper and to fill in the rest of the length with pennies. Then have them do the same with two paper clips along the short edge and write and solve a system of equations representing the situation. As you circulate, suggest that they double the second equation and combine it somehow with the first to eliminate a variable. Then have them use three instead of four paper clips along the long edge and try to solve the resulting equations by elimination.

Step 1 All groups should use the same size paper clips.

Step 3 Students may need to use clips and pennies that were used along the long edge.

Step 5 [Ask] "Why was C eliminated and not P?" [It's easier to eliminate C, but encourage a variety of approaches: multiplying one equation by -2 or dividing the other by -2, for example.]

Step 10 Answers will vary. Regular: $(0.75, 1.25)$; jumbo: $(0.75, 2)$. The diameter of the penny is 0.75 in. The regular paper clip is 1.25 in. long, and the jumbo clip is 2 in. long. Linear systems in experiments like this one can measure walking and running strides, percent mixture in solutions, and city and highway fuel mileage.

To find s, substitute 98 for f into one of the original equations:

$$98 + s = 163 \qquad \text{or} \qquad 98 - s = 33$$

Either way, the second number is 65. Check that your solutions are correct.

$$\begin{array}{cc} f + s = 163 & f - s = 33 \\ 98 + 65 \overset{?}{=} 163 & 98 - 65 \overset{?}{=} 33 \\ 163 = 163 & 33 = 33 \end{array}$$

Adding the two equations quickly leads to a solution because the resulting equation has only one variable. The other variable was eliminated! However, you won't always have coefficients that add to 0. In these cases, you'll need another strategy for the elimination method to work.

 Investigation
Paper Clips and Pennies

In this investigation you'll create a system of equations by using paper clips and pennies as variables.

You will need

- three paper clips
- several pennies
- an 8.5-by-11-inch sheet of paper

Step 1 Lay one paper clip along the long side of the paper. Then add enough pennies to complete the 11-inch length.

Step 2 Use C for the length of one paper clip and P for the diameter of one penny. Write an equation in standard form showing your results.

Step 3 Now you'll write the other equation for the system. Lay two paper clips along the shorter edge of your paper, and then add pennies to complete the 8.5-inch length.

Step 4 Using the same variables as in Step 2, write an equation to record your results for the shorter side.

Step 5 In this system the equations from Steps 2 and 4 have different coefficients for each variable. What can you do to one equation so that the variable C is eliminated when you add both equations?

Step 6 Use your answer to Step 5 to set up the addition of two equations. Once you eliminate the variable C, use the balancing method to solve for P.

Step 7 Substitute the value for P into one of the original equations to find C.

Step 8 Check that your solution satisfies both equations.

Step 9 Describe at least one other way to solve this system by elimination.

Step 10 Explain the real-world meaning of the solution. Describe other experiments in measuring that you can solve using a system of equations.

Steps 1 and 2 sample answers: for a regular paper clip, $C + 13P = 11$; for a jumbo paper clip, $C + 12P = 11$

Steps 3 and 4 sample answers: for a regular paper clip, $2C + 8P = 8.5$; for a jumbo paper clip, $2C + 6P = 8.5$

Step 6 The same equation results from either sample system: $-18P = -13.5$; $P = 0.75$. This makes sense because the penny's diameter is constant.

Step 9 Descriptions will vary. For example, you can eliminate P first and then substitute to find C. Or, instead of substituting to find the second value, you can start again and eliminate the other variable in the system.

Step 5 In both samples you need to multiply the top equation by (-2).

regular: $\begin{cases} C + 13P = 11 \\ 2C + 8P = 8.5 \end{cases} \rightarrow \begin{cases} -2C - 26P = -22 \\ 2C + 8P = 8.5 \end{cases}$

jumbo: $\begin{cases} C + 12P = 11 \\ 2C + 6P = 8.5 \end{cases} \rightarrow \begin{cases} -2C - 24P = -22 \\ 2C + 6P = 8.5 \end{cases}$

Step 7 regular: $C = 1.25$; jumbo: $C = 2$

Step 8 regular: $\begin{cases} 1.25 + 13(0.75) = 11 \\ 2(1.25) + 8(0.75) = 8.5 \end{cases}$

jumbo: $\begin{cases} 2 + 12(0.75) = 11 \\ 2(2) + 6(0.75) = 8.5 \end{cases}$

The goal of the elimination method is to get one of the variables to have a coefficient of 0 when you add the two equations. If you start with additive inverses, such as s and $-s$ in Example A, then you can simply add the equations. But often you must first multiply one or both of the equations by some convenient number before you combine them.

EXAMPLE B

A molecule of hexane, C_6H_{14}, has six carbon atoms and fourteen hydrogen atoms. Its molecular weight in grams per mole, the sum of the atomic weights of carbon and hydrogen, is 86.178. The molecular weight of octane, C_8H_{18}, is 114.232 grams per mole. Octane has eight carbon atoms and eighteen hydrogen atoms per molecule. Find the atomic weights of carbon and hydrogen.

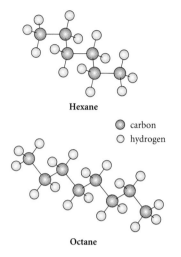

Hexane

○ carbon
○ hydrogen

Octane

a. Define variables and write a system of linear equations in the standard form $ax + by = c$ for these molecular weights.

b. Use elimination to solve this system.

c. Check your solution in the original equations.

▶ **Solution**

a. Let c represent the atomic weight of carbon in grams per mole. Let h represent the atomic weight of hydrogen in grams per mole. Because the molecular weight of the compounds is the sum of the atomic weights of carbon and hydrogen, you can write the system

$$\begin{cases} 6c + 14h = 86.178 & \text{hexane's molecular weight} \\ 8c + 18h = 114.232 & \text{octane's molecular weight} \end{cases}$$

b. To eliminate c when you add the equations, you must make its coefficients additive inverses, that is, numbers with opposite signs. If you multiply the hexane equation by 4 and the octane equation by -3, then you get two new equations set up for elimination.

$4(6c + 14h) = 4(86.178) \rightarrow 24c + 56h = 344.712$ Multiply both sides by 4.

$-3(8c + 18h) = 3(114.232) \rightarrow \underline{-24c - 54h = -342.696}$ Multiply both sides by -2.

$2h = 2.016$ Add the equations.

$h = 1.008$ Divide both sides by 2 and reduce.

To find the value of c, you could substitute 1.008 for h in one of your original equations and solve for c, as you did in the previous lesson. Or you could go back to the original equations and use elimination on h. If you multiply the hexane equation by -9 and the octane equation by 7, then you get two equations set up to eliminate h.

SHARING IDEAS

Have groups share different methods for eliminating C in Step 5, and present their ideas for Step 9.

Ask if there's another way to check the solutions. Students might suggest using a ruler to measure the paper clips and pennies.

Assessing Progress

Watch for the ability to follow directions, make careful measurements, and set up a system of two linear equations.

EXAMPLE B

This example shows how to eliminate a variable in a system of equations by multiplying the equations by different numbers.

You may want to review the chemical terms *mole* and *molecular weight*. 1 mole of a substance means 6.02×10^{23} molecules of that substance (just as 1 dozen eggs means 12 eggs). The molecular weight of a substance is the weight in grams of 1 mole of that substance.

[Ask] "How do you choose the numbers by which to multiply both sides of the equation?" [Students might use the coefficients themselves, the opposites of coefficients, or the products or least common multiples of coefficients.]

Part b of the solution illustrates how an arrow can mean *implies*. Remind students that the implies arrow is more than a vague link between steps in a process. If required, again stress the need for logical correctness in checking a solution.

You might ask students to solve the same system by substitution and think about when one method is preferable to the other. A few more examples might help them see that substitution is preferable if the coefficient of one variable in one equation is 1.

Closing the Lesson

As needed, point out that the **elimination method** is a fourth method of solving a system of equations, along with substitution, graphing, and tables. The last two often give only approximations, but elimination and substitution give exact solutions.

BUILDING UNDERSTANDING

Students practice the elimination method for solving systems of equations and deepen their understanding of the graphical meaning of a solution to a system.

ASSIGNING HOMEWORK

Essential	1–4, 7, 9
Performance assessment	4, 11, 13
Portfolio	9, 14
Journal	4, 12
Group	5, 10, 12
Review	15–18

▶ Helping with the Exercises

Exercise 1 Students may be surprised to see that when they multiply both sides of an equation by the same number the graph stays the same.

$$-9(6c + 14h) = -9(86.178) \rightarrow -54c - 126h = -775.602 \quad \text{Multiply both sides by } -9.$$

$$7(8c + 18h) = 7(114.232) \rightarrow \underline{56c + 126h = 799.624} \quad \text{Multiply both sides by } 7.$$

$$2c = 24.022 \quad \text{Add the equations.}$$

$$c = 12.011 \quad \text{Divide both sides by 2 and reduce.}$$

c. The solution to the system is (12.011, 1.008). So the atomic weight of carbon is 12.011 grams per mole and the atomic weight of hydrogen is 1.008 grams per mole. Check your answers by substituting them into the original equations.

$$8c + 18h = 114.232$$
$$8(12.011) + 18(1.008) \overset{?}{=} 114.232$$
$$96.088 + 18.144 \overset{?}{=} 114.232$$
$$114.232 = 114.232$$

$$6c + 14h = 86.178$$
$$6(12.011) + 14(1.008) \overset{?}{=} 86.178$$
$$72.066 + 14.112 \overset{?}{=} 86.178$$
$$86.178 = 86.178$$

Because you get true statements for both equations, the solution checks.

There is no single right order to the steps in solving a system of equations, so you can start by choosing a variable that's easy to eliminate. You can use both elimination and substitution if that's easiest. Always check your solution by substituting into the original system.

EXERCISES

You will need your graphing calculator for Exercises **9** and **12**.

▶ Practice Your Skills

1. Consider the equation $5x + 2y = 10$.

    a. Solve the equation for y and sketch the graph. ⓐ

    b. Multiply the equation $5x + 2y = 10$ by 3, and then solve for y. How does the graph of this equation compare with the graph of the original equation? Explain your answer. ⓐ

2. Use the equation $5x - 2y = 10$ to find the missing coordinate of each point.

    a. $(6, a)$ ⓗ $(6, 10)$ **b.** $(-4, b)$ ⓐ $(-4, -15)$ **c.** $(c, 25)$ $(12, 25)$ **d.** $(d, -5)$ $(0, -5)$

3. Solve each system of equations by elimination. Show your work.

    a. $\begin{cases} 6x + 5y = -20 \\ -6x - 10y = 25 \end{cases}$ **b.** $\begin{cases} 5x - 4y = 23 \\ 7x + 8y = 5 \end{cases}$

    You can simply add the equations as they are to eliminate the x-terms: $-5y = 5, y = -1$; $6x = -15, x = -2.5$. The solution is $(-2.5, -1)$.

    You can multiply the first equation by 2 to eliminate the y-terms: $17x = 51, x = 3$; $8y = -16, y = -2$. The solution is $(3, -2)$.

1a. $y = \dfrac{10 - 5x}{2}$, or $y = 5 - \dfrac{5x}{2}$

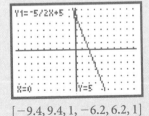

$[-9.4, 9.4, 1, -6.2, 6.2, 1]$

1b. $y = \dfrac{30 - 15x}{6}$, or $y = 5 - \dfrac{5x}{2}$

The graph is the same as the graph for 1a. Both equations are equivalent to $y = 5 - \frac{5}{2}x$.

4. Anisha turned in this quiz in her algebra class.

    a. What method did she use? substitution

    b. What is missing from her solution?

    c. Complete Anisha's solution.
        $y = -1; (4, -1)$

5. Consider this system of equations:

$$\begin{cases} 3x + 7y = -8 \\ 5x + 8y = -6 \end{cases}$$

In 5a and b, tell how you can eliminate each variable when you combine the equations by addition.

    a. the x-term @

    b. the y-term

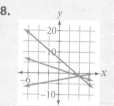

Anisha   Score _____

Solve this system: Solution:
$$y = x - 5$$
$$3y + 2x = 5$$

$$3(x - 5) + 2x = 5$$
$$3x - 15 + 2x = 5$$
$$5x = 20$$
$$x = 4$$

> ## Reason and Apply

6. List the different ways you have learned to solve the system. Then choose one method and find the solution. @   The solution is $(2, -2)$. You can

$$\begin{cases} 3x + 7y = -8 \\ 5x + 8y = -6 \end{cases}$$
  (1) solve for y and graph, then look for the point where the lines intersect;
  (2) solve for y, create tables, and zoom in to where the y-values are equal;
  (3) solve one equation for y (or x) and substitute into the other; or
  (4) multiply the equations and add them to eliminate x or y.

7. Solve each system using the elimination method.

    a. $\begin{cases} 2x + y = 10 \\ 5x - y = 18 \end{cases}$ $(4, 2)$ **b.** $\begin{cases} 3x + 5y = 4 \\ 3x + 7y = 2 \end{cases}$ $(3, -1)$ **c.** $\begin{cases} 2x + 9y = -15 \\ 5x + 9y = -24 \end{cases}$ $(-3, -1)$

8. In 8a–c, solve each equation for y and sketch a graph of the result on the same set of axes.

    a. $x - 2y = 6$ @ $y = -3 + 0.5x$

    b. $3x + 4y = 8$ @ $y = 2 - 0.75x$

    c. Graph the equation you get from adding the original two equations in 8a and b. @ $y = 7 - 2x$

    d. What does the graph tell you? @   The solution of the system is also a solution of the sum of the equations.

9. Refer to this system from Example A to answer each question.

$$\begin{cases} x + y = 163 \\ x - y = 33 \end{cases}$$

    a. Solve each equation for y and enter these new equations into your calculator. Use the window [0, 150, 10, 0, 150, 10] to graph this system. $y = 163 - x$ and $y = -33 + x$

    b. Use the elimination method to find the y-value of the solution. Enter the resulting equation into Y₃ and add it to your graph from 9a. @

    c. Use elimination to find the x-value of the solution. Draw a vertical line on the graph to represent the equation you found in 9b.

    d. Describe what you notice about the four lines on your screen and explain why this happens.   The four lines intersect at the same point, (98, 65); the solution to the system must satisfy all the equations—the original equations in the system and any new equations created by combining pairs of equations.

9b. $2y = 130, y = 65$

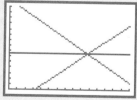

9c. $2x = 196, x = 98$

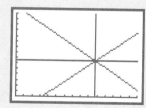

Exercise 4 Students might say that a check is part of what's missing. Encourage this kind of thinking.

4b. The y-value is missing from her solution.

5a. Multiply the first equation by -5 and the second equation by 3, or multiply the first equation by 5 and the second equation by -3.

5b. Multiply the first equation by -8 and the second equation by 7, or multiply the first equation by 8 and the second equation by -7.

8.

(graph)

Exercise 9 Students continue to explore the connections between the elimination method and the graphs representing the equations, and they discover that all the equations intersect in a single point.

In 9c, students are asked to draw a vertical line on their calculators. If they don't remember how to do this, refer them to Calculator Note 4B.

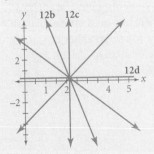
10. Part of Adam's homework paper is missing. If $(5, 2)$ is the only solution to the system shown, write a possible equation that completes the system. ⓗ

11. Consider this system of equations:

$$\begin{cases} 2x - 5y = 12 \\ 6x - 15y = 36 \end{cases}$$

   a. By what number can you multiply which equation to eliminate the x-term when you combine the equations by addition? Do this multiplication.

   b. What is the sum of these equations?

   c. What is the solution to the system?

   d. How can you predict this result by examining the original equations?

12. **Mini-Investigation** Consider the system

$$\begin{cases} 3x + 2y = 7 \\ 2x - y = 4 \end{cases}$$

keymath.com/DA

   a. Solve each equation for y and graph the result on your calculator. Sketch the graph on your paper.

   b. Add the two original equations and solve the resulting equation for y. Add this graph to your graph from 12a. What do you notice?

   c. Multiply the second original equation by 2, then add this to the first equation. Solve this equation for x and add its graph to your graph from 12a. What do you notice?

   d. Multiply the first original equation by 2 and the second by -3, then add the results. Solve this equation for y and add its graph to 12a. What do you notice?

   e. What is the solution to the system of equations? How does this point relate to the graphs you drew in 12a–d?

   f. Write a few sentences summarizing any conjectures you can make based on this exercise.

13. **APPLICATION** The school's photographer took pictures of couples at this year's prom. She charged $3.25 for wallet-size pictures and $10.50 for portrait-size pictures.

   a. Write a system of equations representing the fact that Crystal and Dan bought a total of 10 pictures for $61.50. ⓐ

   b. Solve this system and explain what your answer means.

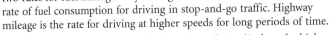

14. **APPLICATION** Automobile companies advertise two rates for fuel mileage. City mileage is the rate of fuel consumption for driving in stop-and-go traffic. Highway mileage is the rate for driving at higher speeds for long periods of time.

   Cynthia's new car gets 17 mi/gal in the city and 25 mi/gal on the highway. She drove 220 miles on 11 gallons of gas.

   a. Define variables and write a system of equations for the gallons burned at each mileage rate. ⓐ

b. Solve this system and explain the meaning of the solution. @ (6.875, 4.125); 6.875 gal in the city, 4.125 gal on the highway

c. Find the number of city miles and highway miles Cynthia drove. @

d. Check your answers. @

▶ Review

0.1 **15.** For each pair of fractions, name a fraction that lies between them.   Answers will vary. Samples are

a. $\frac{1}{2}$ and $\frac{3}{4}$ $\frac{5}{8}$ **b.** $\frac{2}{3}$ and $\frac{7}{8}$ $\frac{3}{4}$ **c.** $-\frac{1}{4}$ and $-\frac{1}{5}$ $-\frac{9}{40}$ **d.** $\frac{7}{11}$ and $\frac{5}{6}$ $\frac{2}{3}$

e. Describe a strategy for naming a fraction between any two fractions.

3.5 **16.** **APPLICATION** When you go up a mountain, the temperature drops about 4 degrees Fahrenheit for every 1000 feet you ascend.

a. While climbing a trail on Mt. McKinley in Alaska, Marsha intended to record the elevation and temperature at three locations. Complete the table for her.

Marsha's Climb

	Elevation (ft)	Temperature (°F)
Start	4,300	78
Rest station	7,800	64
Highest point	11,900	47.6

This mountain climber is ascending Mt. McKinley in Denali National Park, Alaska.

b. Write an equation to model the relationship between elevation and temperature. Explain the meanings of the slope and y-intercept.

c. Mt. McKinley is 20,320 feet tall. On the day Marsha was climbing, how cold was it at the summit? At the summit the temperature was 13.9°F.

4.3 **17.** Write an equation in point-slope form using the given information.

a. A line that passes through the point $(5, -3)$ and has slope -2. $y = -3 - 2(x - 5)$

b. A line that passes through the point $(-3, 7)$ and has slope 2.5. $y = 7 + 2.5(x + 3)$

5.1 **18.** The graph at right pictures distances from a motion sensor for two walkers. (Walker A starts at 0.5 ft and walks at 1 ft/s. Walker B waits at 10.5 ft until 1 second has passed and then walks at 0.5 ft/s.)

a. Write an equation for each walk. (*Hint:* Walker B's distance can be recorded in two segments. The first is $y = 10.5$ when $x \le 1$.)

b. When and where do they meet? They meet 7.5 ft from the sensor, when 7 s have passed.

c. When is Walker B farther from the sensor than Walker A?
Walker B is farther from the sensor than Walker A for all times up to, but not including, 7 s.

14c. $\dfrac{17 \text{ mi}}{\text{gal}} \cdot 6.875 \text{ gal} \approx$

117 city mi, $\dfrac{25 \text{ mi}}{\text{gal}} \cdot 4.125 \text{ gal} \approx$

103 hwy mi

14d. check:
$$\begin{cases} 6.875 + 4.125 = 11 \\ 17(6.875) + 25(4.125) = 220 \end{cases}$$
and $117 + 103 = 220$

15e. Sample answer: Find a common denominator, select a new numerator between the other two, and reduce.

16b. $T = 95.2 - 0.004E$; the slope is the rate of change in temperature for each increase of 1 ft in elevation, and the y-intercept (in this case, T-intercept) is the temperature that day at sea level in the same area.

18a. Walker A: $y = 0.5 + x$; Walker B: $y = 10.5$ when $x \le 1$ and $y = 10.5 - 0.5(x - 1)$, or $y = 11 - 0.5x$, when $x > 1$

LESSON

5.4

Solving Systems of Equations Using Matrices

The essence of mathematics is not to make simple things complicated but to make complicated things simple.

STANLEY GUDDER

In Lesson 1.8, you learned how to enter, display, and use matrices to organize and analyze data. In this lesson you will use matrices to solve systems of equations. This method of solving systems of equations is similar to the elimination method, but using matrices may be quicker because you can keep track of equations using a shorter notation. Computers and graphing calculators can solve complex systems of equations entered in matrix form.

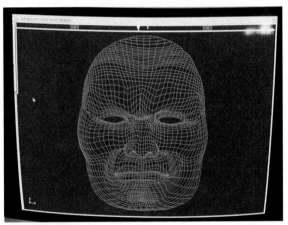

Software that renders 3-D computer-generated images uses matrices to organize data. This program graphs thousands of points and lines to draw the contours of a person's face.

If you look only at the numerals in a system of equations in standard form $ax + by = c$—that is, the coefficients of both variables and the constant terms—you have a matrix with two rows and three columns. If you have a system with both equations in standard form $ax + by = c$, you can write a matrix for the system:

$$\begin{cases} 5x + 3y = -1 \\ 2x - 6y = 50 \end{cases} \qquad \begin{bmatrix} 5 & 3 & -1 \\ 2 & -6 & 50 \end{bmatrix}$$

The numerals in the first equation match the numerals in the first row, and the numerals in the second equation match the numerals in the second row. But what does the solution look like in a matrix? The solution to the system above is $(4, -7)$, or $x = 4$ and $y = -7$. You want the rows of the solution matrix to represent the equations. So you can rewrite each equation to get the numerals for each row of the solution matrix:

$$\begin{array}{lll} x = 4 \\ y = -7 \end{array} \rightarrow \begin{array}{ll} x + 0y = 4 \\ 0x + y = -7 \end{array} \rightarrow \begin{bmatrix} 1 & 0 & 4 \\ 0 & 1 & -7 \end{bmatrix}$$

LESSON OBJECTIVES

- Represent a linear system with a matrix
- Use the method of Gaussian elimination for solving systems of linear equations
- Use the calculator to solve systems of linear equations

NCTM STANDARDS

CONTENT		PROCESS	
	Number	✔	Problem Solving
✔	Algebra	✔	Reasoning
	Geometry		Communication
	Measurement		Connections
	Data/Probability	✔	Representation

In the elimination method, you combined equations and multiplied them by numbers. In much the same way, you can modify the rows of a matrix by performing **row operations** on each number in those rows.

Row Operations in a Matrix

- ▶ Multiply (or divide) all numbers in a row by a nonzero number.
- ▶ Add all numbers in a row to corresponding numbers in another row.
- ▶ Add a multiple of the numbers in one row to the corresponding numbers in another row.
- ▶ Exchange two rows.

You can do these operations on the rows of a matrix to change the starting matrix into a solution matrix. The goal is to get a diagonal of 1's in the matrix with 0's above and below, like this:

$$\begin{bmatrix} 1 & 0 & a \\ 0 & 1 & b \end{bmatrix}$$

The ordered pair (a, b) is the solution, if one exists, to the system.

EXAMPLE A

Solve this system of equations using matrices:

$$\begin{cases} x - 2y = 3 \\ 3x + y = 23 \end{cases}$$

▶ **Solution**

Copy the numerals from each equation into each row of the matrix. Then use row operations to transform it into the solution matrix.

$$\begin{cases} x - 2y = 3 \\ 3x + y = 23 \end{cases} \longrightarrow \begin{bmatrix} 1 & -2 & 3 \\ 3 & 1 & 23 \end{bmatrix}$$

Add -3 times row 1 to row 2.

$$\begin{array}{rccc} -3 \text{ times row 1} & \rightarrow -3 & 6 & -9 \\ + \text{ row 2} & \rightarrow 3 & 1 & 23 \\ \hline \text{New row 2} & \rightarrow 0 & 7 & 14 \end{array} \quad \begin{bmatrix} 1 & -2 & 3 \\ 0 & 7 & 14 \end{bmatrix}$$

Divide row 2 by 7. $\longrightarrow \begin{bmatrix} 1 & -2 & 3 \\ 0 & 1 & 2 \end{bmatrix}$

Add 2 times row 2 to row 1.

$$\begin{array}{rccc} 2 \text{ times row 2} & \rightarrow 0 & 2 & 4 \\ + \text{ row 1} & \rightarrow 1 & -2 & 3 \\ \hline \text{New row 1} & \rightarrow 1 & 0 & 7 \end{array} \quad \begin{bmatrix} 1 & 0 & 7 \\ 0 & 1 & 2 \end{bmatrix}$$

One Step

Show students how to represent a system like $2x + y = 11$ and $6x - 5y = 9$ as a matrix of coefficients. Then challenge them to change the numbers in the matrix to indicate a solution to the system derived by elimination. As groups finish, suggest that they try the same approach on a system that has infinitely many or no solutions such as $y = 3x + 4$ and $2y - 6x = 8$ or $y = 2x + 1$ and $y - 2x = 3$. During Sharing, lead students to formalize the row operations and the diagonalization procedure.

INTRODUCTION

As needed, point out how the row operations mimic the operations on equations used in the previous lesson.

Implies Arrows

One bad habit some algebra students can begin to develop is writing a long string of equalities, such as

$$3x + 5 = 8 = 3x = 3 = x = 1$$

Among other inaccuracies, this statement claims that $8 = 1$. The equal signs have two different meanings. Some show equations, but the ones between equations mean *implies*. If indeed the solution is to be written on one line, have students write the word *implies* or use its abbreviation, an arrow:

$$3x + 5 = 8 \Rightarrow 3x = 3 \Rightarrow x = 1$$

Stress that implies arrows must be used carefully in mathematical statements. When the student text uses a regular arrow, it often means "next you do this." The first of the arrows used near the bottom of page 296 could be written as an implies arrow, but the second one should not be.

EXAMPLE A

This example illustrates how a system can be solved using row operations on a matrix.

[Language] A diagonalized matrix has the form

$$\begin{bmatrix} 1 & 0 & a \\ 0 & 1 & b \end{bmatrix}$$

Step 2 [Alert] Students often want to subtract 6 from all entries in row 2. Ask them to write out the corresponding equations to see that they've represented subtracting $6x$ and $6y$ from one side but 6 from the other side.

Step 2 Add -3 times row 1 to row 2 and record the sum in row 2 to get

$$\begin{bmatrix} 2 & 1 & 11 \\ 0 & -8 & -24 \end{bmatrix}.$$

Step 3 [Alert] Some students may try to add 9 to all entries in row 2.

Step 3 Divide row 2 by -8 to get

$$\begin{bmatrix} 2 & 1 & 11 \\ 0 & 1 & 3 \end{bmatrix}.$$

Step 4 Add -1 times row 2 to row 1 and write the answer in row 1:

$$\begin{bmatrix} 2 & 1 & 11 \\ 0 & 1 & 3 \end{bmatrix} \rightarrow \begin{bmatrix} 2 & 0 & 8 \\ 0 & 1 & 3 \end{bmatrix}$$

Step 5 Divide row 1 by 2 to get

$$\begin{bmatrix} 1 & 0 & 4 \\ 0 & 1 & 3 \end{bmatrix};$$ it means $x = 4$ and $y = 3$, so the solution is $(4, 3)$.

SHARING IDEAS

Point out the quotation opening the lesson. Ask in what sense using matrices is simplifying.

Have a group share their solution from Step 6. Ask the class to compare it to the matrix method.

Assessing Progress

You can assess students' familiarity with matrix-related terms such as row, column, and entry and their understanding of the elimination method and how to check a solution to a system of equations. You also will be able to tell how deeply they understand which systems have no solution and which have infinitely many solutions.

Step 1 $\begin{bmatrix} 2 & 1 & 11 \\ 6 & -5 & 9 \end{bmatrix};$ the numerals from the first equation; the numerals from the second equation

Step 6 Solution will mirror Steps 2–5; multiply the first equation by -3 and add it to the second equation to get $-8y = -24,$ or $y = 3;$ substitute $y = 3$ into the first equation and solve for x to get $x = 4.$

History
CONNECTION

German mathematician Carl Friedrich Gauss (1777–1855) made many contributions to mathematics, including developing the elementary row operations on matrices. In his honor the process of solving systems with matrices is sometimes called "Gaussian elimination." To learn more about Gauss, see **www.keymath.com/DA** .

Use the solution matrix to write the equations:

$$\begin{bmatrix} 1 & 0 & 7 \\ 0 & 1 & 2 \end{bmatrix} \rightarrow \begin{array}{l} 1x + 0y = 7 \quad \text{or} \quad x = 7 \\ 0x + 1y = 2 \quad \text{or} \quad y = 2 \end{array}$$

The solution to the system is $(7, 2)$.

 ## Investigation
Diagonalization

In this investigation you will see how to combine row operations in your solution process.

Consider the system of equations

$$\begin{cases} 2x + y = 11 \\ 6x - 5y = 9 \end{cases}$$

Step 1 Write the matrix for this system. What does the first row contain? The second row?

Step 2 Describe how to use row operations to get 0 as the first entry in the second row. Write this matrix.

Step 3 Next, get 1 as the second number in the second row of your matrix from Step 2.

Step 4 Use row operations on the matrix from Step 3 to get 0 as the second number in row 1.

Step 5 Next, get 1 as the first number of row 1 of your matrix from Step 4. Tell what this matrix means, and give the solution to the system.

Step 6 Check your solution using elimination. Eliminate x first.

Step 7 Look at the first three rules for Row Operations in a Matrix. How do they correspond to steps in the elimination process? In the elimination process, you can multiply an equation by a constant without affecting the solution. You can also add two equations together, ideally to eliminate a variable, without affecting the solution. And, you can also multiply one or both equations by a constant, then add them together.

Matrices are useful for solving systems involving large numbers. Here is another example.

EXAMPLE B

On Friday, 3247 people attended the county fair. The entrance fee for an adult was $5, and for a child 12 or under the fee was $3. The fair collected a total of $14,273. How many of the total attendees were adults and how many were children?

▶ **Solution**

Use A for the number of adults attending the fair and C for the number of children attending. Use these variables to write a system of equations and solve it using matrices. The attendance is the number of adults and children at the fair. So the first equation is $A + C = 3247$. The fair collected $5A$ dollars for A adults and $3C$ dollars for C children in attendance. The total collected is $5A + 3C$, so the second equation is $5A + 3C = 14273$.

With one equation describing attendance at the fair, and another describing ticket money collected, the system is

$$\begin{cases} A + C = 3247 \\ 5A + 3C = 14{,}273 \end{cases} \longrightarrow \begin{bmatrix} 1 & 1 & 3247 \\ 5 & 3 & 14{,}273 \end{bmatrix}$$

Use row operations to find the solution.

Add -5 times row 1 to row 2 to get new row 2. $\quad \begin{bmatrix} 1 & 1 & 3247 \\ 0 & -2 & -1962 \end{bmatrix}$ $\quad -5R_1 + R_2$

Divide row 2 by -2. $\quad \begin{bmatrix} 1 & 1 & 3247 \\ 0 & 1 & 981 \end{bmatrix}$ $\quad R_2/-2$

Add -1 times row 2 to row 1 to get new row 1. $\quad \begin{bmatrix} 1 & 0 & 2266 \\ 0 & 1 & 981 \end{bmatrix}$ $\quad -1R_2 + R_1$

The final matrix shows that $A = 2266$ and $C = 981$. So there were 2266 adults and 981 children at the fair on Friday.

To check this solution, substitute 2266 for A and 981 for C into the original equations.

$$A + C = 3247 \qquad\qquad 5A + 3C = 14{,}273$$
$$2266 + 981 \overset{?}{=} 3247 \qquad 5(2266) + 3(981) \overset{?}{=} 14{,}273$$
$$3247 = 3247 \qquad\qquad 11{,}330 + 2943 \overset{?}{=} 14{,}273$$
$$14{,}273 = 14{,}273$$

These are true statements, so the solution checks.

With row operations on matrices, you now have five methods to solve systems of linear equations. Like elimination and substitution, row operations on matrices give exact solutions. With practice, you will develop a sense of when it is easiest to use each solution method. The form of the equation often makes some methods easier to use than others. If an equation is solved for y, then it is easiest to use the substitution method. If the equations are in standard form, then it is probably easiest to solve by elimination or by using matrices.

EXERCISES

You will need your graphing calculator for Exercise **8.**

▶ Practice Your Skills

1. Write a system of equations whose matrix is

a. $\begin{bmatrix} 2 & 1.5 & 12.75 \\ -3 & 4 & 9 \end{bmatrix}$ @

b. $\begin{bmatrix} \frac{1}{2} & 0 & \frac{1}{2} \\ -1 & 2 & 0 \end{bmatrix} \begin{cases} \frac{1}{2}x = \frac{1}{2} \\ -x + 2y = 0 \end{cases}$

c. $\begin{bmatrix} 2 & 3 & 1 \\ 0 & 2 & 0 \end{bmatrix} \begin{cases} 2x + 3y = 1 \\ 2y = 0 \end{cases}$

2. Write the matrix for each system.

a. $\begin{cases} x + 4y = 3 \\ -x + 2y = 9 \end{cases}$ @ $\begin{bmatrix} 1 & 4 & 3 \\ -1 & 2 & 9 \end{bmatrix}$

b. $\begin{cases} 7x - y = 3 \\ 0.1x - 2.1y = 3 \end{cases} \begin{bmatrix} 7 & -1 & 3 \\ 0.1 & -2.1 & 3 \end{bmatrix}$

c. $\begin{cases} x + y = 3 \\ x + y = 6 \end{cases} \begin{bmatrix} 1 & 1 & 3 \\ 1 & 1 & 6 \end{bmatrix}$

3. Write each solution matrix as an ordered pair.

a. $\begin{bmatrix} 1 & 0 & 8.5 \\ 0 & 1 & 2.8 \end{bmatrix}$ @ $(8.5, 2.8)$

b. $\begin{bmatrix} 1 & 0 & \frac{1}{2} \\ 0 & 1 & \frac{13}{16} \end{bmatrix} \left(\frac{1}{2}, \frac{13}{16}\right)$

c. $\begin{bmatrix} 1 & 0 & 0 \\ 0 & 1 & 0 \end{bmatrix} (0,0)$

4. Use row operations to transform $\begin{bmatrix} 4.2 & 0 & 12.6 \\ 0 & -1 & 5.25 \end{bmatrix}$ into the form $\begin{bmatrix} 1 & 0 & a \\ 0 & 1 & b \end{bmatrix}$.

Write the solution as an ordered pair. ⓗ

5. Consider the system

$\begin{cases} y = 7 - 3x \\ y = 11 - 2(x - 5) \end{cases}$

a. Convert each equation to the standard form $ax + by = c$. @ $\begin{cases} 3x + y = 7 \\ 2x + y = 21 \end{cases}$

b. Write a matrix for the system. @ $\begin{bmatrix} 3 & 1 & 7 \\ 2 & 1 & 21 \end{bmatrix}$

▶ Reason and Apply

6. Give the missing description, matrix, and equations for each step of the process below. Give the solution as an ordered pair.

Description	Matrix	System equations
The matrix for $\begin{cases} 3x + 2y = 28.9 \\ 8x + 5y = 74.6 \end{cases}$	$\begin{bmatrix} 3 & 2 & 28.9 \\ 8 & 5 & 74.6 \end{bmatrix}$	$3x + 2y = 28.9$ $8x + 5y = 74.6$
Add 8 times row 1 to -3 times row 2 and put the result in row 2.	$\begin{bmatrix} 3 & 2 & 28.9 \\ 0 & 1 & 7.4 \end{bmatrix}$	$3x + 2y = 28.9$ $y = 7.4$
Add -2 times row 2 to row 1 and put the result in row 1.	$\begin{bmatrix} 3 & 0 & 14.1 \\ 0 & 1 & 7.4 \end{bmatrix}$	$3x = 14.1$ $y = 7.4$
Divide row 1 by 3. The solution is $(4.7, 7.4)$.	$\begin{bmatrix} 1 & 0 & 4.7 \\ 0 & 1 & 7.4 \end{bmatrix}$	$x = 4.7$ $y = 7.4$

7. APPLICATION Each day, Sal prepares a large basket of self-serve tortilla chips in his restaurant. On Monday, 40 adult patrons and 15 child patrons ate 10.8 kg of chips. On Tuesday, 35 adult patrons and 22 child patrons ate 12.29 kg of chips. Sal wants to know whether adults or children eat more chips on average.

a. Organize the information into a table. @

b. Define variables and write a system of equations. @

c. Write a matrix for the system.

d. Solve the system by transforming the matrix into the solution matrix $\begin{bmatrix} 1 & 0 & a \\ 0 & 1 & b \end{bmatrix}$.

e. Write a sentence that describes the real-world meaning of the solution to the system. Each adult ate an average of about 0.15 kg (150 g) of chips, and each child ate an average of 0.32 kg (320 g) of chips.

8. Your graphing calculator probably has built-in row operations to transform a matrix into its solution form. Transform this matrix using row operations on your calculator.

[▶ 🖥 See **Calculator Note 5A**. ◀]

$$\begin{bmatrix} 8 & 7 & -1 \\ 3 & -1 & -4 \end{bmatrix}$$

9. APPLICATION Zoe must ship 532 tubas and 284 kettledrums from her warehouse to a store across the country. A truck rental company offers two sizes of trucks. A small truck will hold 5 tubas and 7 kettledrums. A large truck will hold 12 tubas and 4 kettledrums. If she wants to fill each truck so that the cargo won't shift, how many small and large trucks should she rent?

a. Define variables and write a system of equations to find the number of small trucks and the number of large trucks Zoe needs to ship the instruments. (*Hint:* Write one equation for each instrument.) ⓗ

b. Write a matrix that represents the system. @

c. Perform row operations to transform the matrix into a solution matrix.

d. Write a sentence describing the real-world meaning of the solution. Zoe should order 20 small trucks and 36 large trucks.

10. APPLICATION Will is baking a new kind of bread. He has two different kinds of flour. Flour X is enriched with 0.12 mg of calcium per gram; Flour Y is enriched with 0.04 mg of calcium per gram. Each loaf has 300 g of flour, and Will wants each loaf to have 30 mg of calcium. How much of each type of flour should he use for each loaf?

a. Will wrote this system of equations:

$$\begin{cases} x + y = 300 \\ 0.12x + 0.04y = 30 \end{cases}$$

10a. x represents the number of grams of Flour X used in each loaf, and y represents the number of grams of Flour Y used in each loaf. The first equation sums the amount of each type of flour to get the total amount of flour in the loaf, and the second equation sums the amount of calcium contributed by each type of flour to get the total amount of calcium.

Give a real-world meaning to the variables x and y, and describe the meaning of each equation.

b. Write a matrix for the system. **10b.** $\begin{bmatrix} 1 & 1 & 300 \\ 0.12 & 0.04 & 30 \end{bmatrix}$ **10c.** $\begin{bmatrix} 1 & 0 & 225 \\ 0 & 1 & 75 \end{bmatrix}$

c. Find the solution matrix.

d. Explain the real-world meaning of the solution. Will should mix 225 g of Flour X with 75 g of Flour Y.

Exercise 7 Systems of equations show the power of algebra, which was developed to make arithmetical reasoning easier. Algebra is not needed for this problem:

> Each day Sal prepares a large basket of self-serve tortilla chips in his restaurant. One day, his 45 patrons ate 10.8 kg of chips. Sal knows from experience that each child eats 0.2 kg of chips and each adult eats 0.3 kg. How many adults and how many children patronized his restaurant that day?

In this case, you can think of dividing the 10.8 kg into portions of 0.2 kg each. There will be 54 of these portions. There were only 45 patrons, though, so 1.8 kg went to adults. Each adult eats 0.1 kg more than a child, so the 1.8 kg was distributed among 18 adults. The rest of the 45 patrons (27) must have been children.

However, for Exercise 7, Sal knows that on Monday 40 adults and 15 children ate a total of 10.8 kg of chips, and on Tuesday 35 adults and 22 children ate 12.29 kg of chips. Without using algebra, the thinking needed to solve this problem would be quite difficult.

Exercise 8 You may want to skip the calculator method if your students are using TI-73 or TI-82 calculators.

8.
```
[A]
    [[1 0 -1]
     [0 1 1 ]]
```

Exercise 9 If students have difficulty deciding what the equations should look like, ask what they want to find (to help them determine the variables) and what they know (to set up the equations).

9a–c. See page 302.

7a.

	Adults	Children	Total (kg)
Monday	40	15	10.8
Tuesday	35	22	12.29

7b. Let x represent the average weight of chips an adult eats and y represent the average weight of chips a child eats. The system is

$$\begin{cases} 40x + 15y = 10.8 \\ 35x + 22y = 12.29 \end{cases}$$

7c. $\begin{bmatrix} 40 & 15 & 10.8 \\ 35 & 22 & 12.29 \end{bmatrix}$

7d. Add -35 times row 1 to 40 times row 2 and put the result in row 2: $\begin{bmatrix} 40 & 15 & 10.8 \\ 0 & 355 & 113.6 \end{bmatrix}$.

Divide row 2 by 355: $\begin{bmatrix} 40 & 15 & 10.8 \\ 0 & 1 & 0.32 \end{bmatrix}$.

Add -15 times row 2 to row 1: $\begin{bmatrix} 40 & 0 & 6 \\ 0 & 1 & 0.32 \end{bmatrix}$.

Divide row 1 by 40: $\begin{bmatrix} 1 & 0 & 0.15 \\ 0 & 1 & 0.32 \end{bmatrix}$.

Exercise 11 This problem asks students to write a system of equations using three variables. Be sure students realize they need to use zeros as placeholders for missing variables when they write a system in matrix form.

11a. $\begin{cases} m + t + w = 286 \\ m - t \quad\;\; = 7 \\ \quad\;\; t - w = 24 \end{cases}$

11b. $\begin{bmatrix} 1 & 1 & 1 & 286 \\ 1 & -1 & 0 & 7 \\ 0 & 1 & -1 & 24 \end{bmatrix}$

The rows represent each equation. The columns represent the coefficients of each variable and the constants.

12a. $\begin{bmatrix} 72 & 65 \\ 55 & 55 \\ 45 & 35 \end{bmatrix} - \begin{bmatrix} 31 & 28 \\ 26 & 24 \\ 21 & 16 \end{bmatrix}$

$= \begin{bmatrix} 41 & 37 \\ 29 & 31 \\ 24 & 19 \end{bmatrix}$

12b. If you are planning to be in the park for 3 days, then the 3-day ticket is a much better deal. If you bought three 1-day tickets, the cost would be

$\begin{bmatrix} 93 & 84 \\ 78 & 72 \\ 21 & 48 \end{bmatrix}$.

12c. If you are going to be in the park for 2 days, the cost of two 1-day tickets would be

$\begin{bmatrix} 62 & 56 \\ 52 & 48 \\ 42 & 32 \end{bmatrix}$. This is less than the

cost of the 3-day ticket, so if you are going for only 2 days, you should buy two 1-day tickets.

---

11. APPLICATION On Monday a group of students started on a three-day bicycle tour covering a total of 286 km. On Tuesday they cycled 7 km less than on Monday. On Wednesday they traveled 24 km less than on Tuesday.

a. Write a system of three linear equations representing this trip. Use *m, t,* and *w* to represent the distances in kilometers they cycled on Monday, Tuesday, and Wednesday, respectively. Write each equation in the form $am + bt + cw = d$. ⓐ

b. Write a 3 × 4 matrix to model this system of equations. Describe what the rows and columns of your matrix represent. ⓐ

c. List and describe a sequence of matrix row operations that will produce a matrix of the form   The sequence of row operations will vary; the solution matrix is

$\begin{bmatrix} 1 & 0 & 0 & ? \\ 0 & 1 & 0 & ? \\ 0 & 0 & 1 & ? \end{bmatrix}$ $\begin{bmatrix} 1 & 0 & 0 & 108 \\ 0 & 1 & 0 & 101 \\ 0 & 0 & 1 & 77 \end{bmatrix}$.

d. What is the solution to this problem?
They cycled 108 km on Monday, 101 km on Tuesday, and 77 km on Wednesday.

▶ Review

1.8 **12. APPLICATION** These matrices show the cost, in dollars, of a 1-day ticket and a 3-day ticket for an adult, a teen, and a child at two amusement parks, Tivoli and Hill.

	1-day ticket		3-day ticket	
	Tivoli	Hill	Tivoli	Hill
Adult	31	28	72	65
Teen	26	24	55	55
Child	21	16	45	35

a. Write a matrix equation displaying the difference in cost between a 3-day ticket and a 1-day ticket.

b. Which type of ticket is the better deal and why?

c. Which type of ticket should you buy if you are in the park for only 2 days?

3.2 **13.** Write a recursive sequence for the *y*-coordinates of the points shown on each graph. On each graph one tick mark represents one unit. ⓗ

a. 4, Ans − 0.5
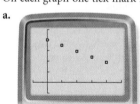

b. −3, Ans + 2

c. 1/2, Ans − 1

d. 0, Ans + 1
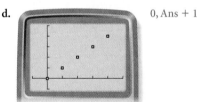

9a. Let *x* represent the number of small trucks and *y* represent the number of large trucks. The system is $\begin{cases} 5x + 12y = 532 \\ 7x + 4y = 284 \end{cases}$.

9b. $\begin{bmatrix} 5 & 12 & 532 \\ 7 & 4 & 284 \end{bmatrix}$

9c. Solution steps will vary; $\begin{bmatrix} 5 & 12 & 532 \\ 7 & 4 & 284 \end{bmatrix} \rightarrow$

$\begin{bmatrix} -16 & 0 & -320 \\ 0 & -64 & -2304 \end{bmatrix} \rightarrow \begin{bmatrix} 1 & 0 & 20 \\ 0 & 1 & 36 \end{bmatrix}$.

4.4 **14.** At the Coffee Stop, you can buy a mug for $25 and then pay only $0.75 per hot drink.

  a. What is the slope of the equation that models the total cost of refills? What is the real-world meaning of the slope? Slope: 0.75; the slope is the cost per drink once you've bought the mug.

  b. Use the point (33, 49.75) to write an equation in point-slope form that models this situation. $y = 49.75 + 0.75(x - 33)$

  c. Rewrite your equation in intercept form. What is the real-world meaning of the y-intercept? $y = 25 + 0.75x$; the y-intercept is the cost of buying the mug.

15. Over 2000 years ago the Chinese developed column equation matrices as a method to solve linear equations. The numerals of each equation are arranged in columns instead of rows. Then you use the biancheng (translated as "multiply throughout") and zhichu (translated as "direct reduction") rules of operation to solve the system.

Rules of Operation

  1. Biancheng: Multiply the numerals of the left column by the numeral at the top of the right column.
  2. Zhichu: Subtract the right column from the resulting left column repeatedly until you get a 0 at the top.

For example, represent this system as a column equation matrix.

$$\begin{cases} 2x + y = 11 \\ 6x - 5y = 9 \end{cases} \rightarrow \begin{bmatrix} 2 & 6 \\ 1 & -5 \\ 11 & 9 \end{bmatrix}$$

Biancheng: Multiply the first column by 6 (highest top row numeral).

  $2(6) \quad \rightarrow \quad 12$
  $1(6) \quad \rightarrow \quad 6$
  $11(6) \quad \rightarrow \quad 66$

Zhichu: Subtract the right column from the left column twice.

  $12 \ - \quad 6 \ - \quad 6 \ \rightarrow \quad 0$
  $6 \ - \ (-5) \ - \ (-5) \ \rightarrow \quad 16$
  $66 \ - \quad 9 \ - \quad 9 \ \rightarrow \quad 48$

Write a new equation and solve for y.

  $16y = 48$
  $y = 3$

Substitute and solve for x.

  $2x + 3 = 11$
  $x = 4$

Now use a Chinese column equation matrix to solve the system
$$\begin{cases} x - 2y = 3 \\ 3x + y = 23 \end{cases} \text{ⓐ}$$

$$\begin{bmatrix} 1 & 3 \\ -2 & 1 \\ 3 & 23 \end{bmatrix} \rightarrow \begin{matrix} 3 & -3 & 0 \\ -6 & -1 \\ 9 & -23 \end{matrix} \rightarrow \begin{matrix} 0 \\ -7 \\ -14 \end{matrix}$$

$-7y = -14, y = 2; x = 7$

(Jean-Claude Martzloff, *A History of Chinese Mathematics*, 1997, pp. 252–254; Lǐ Yǎn and Dù Shírán, *Chinese Mathematics, a Concise History*, 1987, pp. 46–48)

Exercise 15 This historical problem shows another way to solve a system of equations. Assign this exercise as enrichment for students who enjoy a challenge. It may confuse students who are just learning the regular row operations.

LESSON

5.5

Some material may be inappropriate for children under 13.

DESCRIPTION OF PG-13 RATING, MOTION PICTURE ASSOCIATION OF AMERICA

Inequalities in One Variable

Drink at least six glasses of water a day. Store milk at temperatures below 40°F. Eat snacks with fewer than 20 calories. Spend at most $10 for a gift. These are a few examples of inequalities in everyday life. In this lesson you will analyze situations involving inequalities in one variable and learn how to find and graph their solutions.

An **inequality** is a statement that one quantity is less than or greater than another. You write inequalities using these symbols:

less than	$<$	less than or equal to	$\leq$
greater than	$>$	greater than or equal to	$\geq$

Sometimes you need to translate everyday language into the phrases you see in the table above. Here are some examples.

History CONNECTION

Thomas Harriot (1560–1621) introduced the symbols of inequality $<$ and $>$. Pierre Bouguer (1698–1758) first used the symbols $\leq$ and $\geq$ about a century later.
(Florian Cajori, *A History of Mathematics*, 1985)

Everyday phrase	Translation	Inequality
at least six glasses	The number of glasses is greater than or equal to 6.	$g \geq 6$
below 40°	The temperature is less than 40°.	$t < 40$
fewer than 20 calories	The number of calories is less than 20.	$c < 20$
at most $10	The price of the gift is less than or equal to $10.	$p \leq 10$
between 35° and 120°	35° is less than the temperature and the temperature is less than 120°.	$35 < t < 120$

You solve inequalities very much like you solve equations. You use the same strategies—adding or subtracting the same quantity to both sides, multiplying both sides by the same number or expression, and so on. However, there is one exception you need to remember when solving inequalities. You will explore this exception in the investigation.

LESSON OBJECTIVES

- Write and solve one-variable inequalities and interpret the results based on real-world situations
- Graph solutions to one-variable inequalities on a number line, showing whether they are strict inequalities
- Interpret an interval graphed on a number line as an inequality sentence
- Learn the sign-change rule for multiplying or dividing both sides of a one-variable inequality by a negative number

NCTM STANDARDS

CONTENT		PROCESS	
✔	Number		Problem Solving
✔	Algebra	✔	Reasoning
✔	Geometry	✔	Communication
	Measurement	✔	Connections
	Data/Probability	✔	Representation

Investigation
Toe the Line

In this investigation you will analyze properties of inequalities and discover some interesting results.

First you'll act out operations on a number line.

You will need

- chalk or a tape measure to mark a segment

keymath.com/DA

Procedure Note

The announcer calls out operations for Walkers A and B. The walkers perform operations on their numbers by walking to the resulting values on the number line. The recorder logs the position of each walker after each operation.

Step 1 | In your group, choose an announcer, a recorder, and two walkers. The two walkers make a number line on the floor with marks from −10 to 10. The announcer and recorder make a table with these column headings and twelve rows. The operations to use as row headings are Starting number, Add 2, Subtract 3, Add −2, Subtract −4, Multiply by 2, Subtract 7, Multiply by −3, Add 5, Divide by −4, Subtract 2, and Multiply by −1.

Operation	Walker A's position	Inequality symbol	Walker B's position
Starting number	2		4
Add 2			

Step 2 | Read the Procedure Note. As a trial, act out the first operation in the table: Walker A simply stands at 2 on the number line, and Walker B stands at 4.

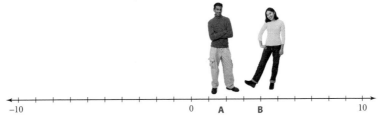

Enter the inequality symbol into the table that describes the relative position of Walkers A and B on the number line. Be sure you have written a true inequality.

Step 3 | Call out the operations. After the walkers calculate their new numbers, record the operation and walkers' positions in the next row.

Step 4 | As a group, discuss which inequality symbol to enter into each cell of the third column.

Next you'll analyze what each operation does to the inequality.

Step 5 | What happens to the walkers' relative positions on the number line when the operation adds or subtracts a positive number? A negative number? Does anything happen to the direction of the inequality symbol?

Step 6 | What happens to the walkers' relative positions on the number line when the operation multiplies or divides by a positive number? Does anything happen to the inequality symbol? *The walkers' positions stretch from side to side, but the walkers do not switch relative positions; the inequality doesn't change.*

Guiding the Investigation

One Step
Ask walkers to follow the directions in Step 1. Each group should write inequalities to describe the result of each step and then look for patterns. Encourage them to note when the direction of inequality changes.

Step 1 In a group consisting of only three members, one can serve as both recorder and announcer. If time is a problem, use ropes prepared ahead of time. If space is also a problem, use the Number Line worksheet and move two markers instead of two people.

Step 2 You may want to discuss the term *relative position*. It means the position of the walkers in relation to each other. The one on the right is greater. Relative position does not indicate how far apart the walkers are.

Step 4 Correct students who use the term *equation* to refer to an inequality.

Step 5 The walkers' positions shift right and left but maintain the same distance apart; the inequality symbol doesn't change.

Steps 1–4

Operation	A's position	Inequality symbol	B's position	Operation	A's position	Inequality symbol	B's position
Start	2	<	4	Subtract 7	−1	<	3
Add 2	4	<	6	Multiply by −3	3	>	−9
Subtract 3	1	<	3	Add 5	8	>	−4
Add −2	−1	<	1	Divide by −4	−2	<	1
Subtract −4	3	<	5	Subtract 2	−4	<	−1
Multiply by 2	6	<	10	Multiply by −1	4	>	1

Step 7 Students may recall that the change in direction of the inequality occurred when the two walkers passed each other.

Step 8 As needed, note that multiplying by −1 reflects a point across zero. You may want students to circle rows in the table where the inequality switches directions.

Step 9 Encourage students to continue using decimals and other fractions. If time permits, explore the effects of operations such as square roots and powers.

SHARING IDEAS

Note the opening quotation, and ask how it relates to the lesson. To bring out the strictness of the inequality, ask if 13-year-olds are included in the advice.

Ask students what patterns they saw in Step 9. Watch for confusion about the relative position of two negative numbers—that is, the one closer to 0 is larger although it has the smaller magnitude.

Inequalities with < or > are *strict* inequalities. Entertain the common but infrequently articulated question of why you'd ever need any other kind of inequality. After all, if two numbers are equal, you can use an equal sign. Students may get ideas about this question from the table in the introduction.

[Ask] "How might inequalities be graphed?" Encourage all participation, not just "right answers." Through repeatedly asking what makes one graphing method better than another, you may be able to get enough ideas from students to make Example A unnecessary.

Assessing Progress

Watch for comfort with negative integers and operations on them, especially subtraction of negatives. Assess familiarity with the number line, the ability to follow systematic instructions, and the willingness to look for patterns in data.

Step 7 The walkers switch relative positions; the inequality symbol reverses direction. **Step 7**

Step 8 Multiplying or dividing by a negative number reverses the direction of the inequality. All elementary operations—add, subtract, multiply, and divide—with positive numbers maintain the direction of the inequality. Adding or subtracting negative numbers also preserves the inequality. Multiplying by a number greater than 1 or dividing by a fraction between −1 and 1 increases the distance between walkers. **Step 8**

Step 9

What happens to the walkers' relative positions on the number line when the operation multiplies or divides by a negative number? Does the inequality symbol change directions?

Which operations on an inequality reverse the inequality symbol? Does it make any difference which numbers you use? Consider fractions and decimals as well as integers.

Check your findings about the effects of adding, subtracting, multiplying, and dividing by the same number on both sides of an inequality by creating your own table of operations and walkers' positions.

In square dancing, a caller tells the dancers which steps to take. Their maneuvers depend on their relative positions.

This example will show you how to graph solutions to inequalities.

EXAMPLE A

Graph each inequality on a number line.

a. $t > 5$

b. $x \leq -1$

c. $-2 \leq x < 4$

▶ **Solution**

a. Any number greater than 5 satisfies the inequality $t > 5$. So $5.0001 > 5$, $7\frac{1}{2} > 5$, and $1{,}000{,}000 > 5$ are all true statements. You show this by drawing an arrow through the values that are greater than 5.

The open circle at 5 excludes 5 from the solutions because $5 > 5$ is not a true statement.

b. The inequality $x \leq -1$ reads, "x is less than or equal to −1." The solid circle at −1 includes the value −1 in the solutions because $-1 \leq -1$ is a true statement.

EXAMPLE A

In this example, students see how to graph the solution of an inequality on a number line. Remind students that an open circle is used to represent the endpoint of a strict inequality and that a filled circle is used to represent the endpoint of an inequality that includes equality. Be sure students understand that the ray indicates an unbounded set of numbers.

c. This statement is a **compound inequality.** It says that -2 is less than or equal to x and that x is less than 4. So the graph includes all values that are greater than or equal to -2 but less than 4. The solid circle at -2 includes -2 in the solutions because $-2 \leq -2$ is true. The open circle at 4 excludes 4 from the solutions because $4 < 4$ is not true.

When you graph inequalities, always label 0 on the number line as a point of reference.

EXAMPLE B

Erin says, "I lose 15 minutes of sleep every time the dog barks. Last night I got less than 5 hours of sleep. I usually sleep 8 hours." Find the number of times Erin woke up.

To solve the problem, let x represent the number of times Erin woke up, and write an inequality.

Solve the inequality and graph your solutions.

▶ **Solution**

The number of hours Erin slept is 8 hours, minus $\frac{1}{4}$ hour times x, the number of times she woke up. The total is less than 5 hours. So the inequality is $8 - 0.25x < 5$.

Solve the inequality for x. Remember to reverse the inequality symbol if you multiply or divide by a negative number.

$8 - 0.25x < 5$	Original inequality.
$8 - 0.25x - 8 < 5 - 8$	Subtract 8 from both sides of the inequality.
$-0.25x < -3$	Evaluate.
$\dfrac{-0.25x}{-0.25} > \dfrac{-3}{-0.25}$	Divide both sides by -0.25, and reverse the inequality symbol.
$x > 12$	Divide.

The dog woke her up more than 12 times. However, Erin can only wake up a whole number of times, so the solution might be more accurately written as, "$x > 15$, where x is a whole number." The solution graph of this statement looks like this:

Is there a maximum number of times that Erin can be woken up during the night? You'll explore this question in Exercise 15.

EXAMPLE B

This example goes through the complete modeling process: representing a real-life problem with an inequality, solving the inequality, and interpreting the solution in the original context.

Writing the inequality may be the hardest step. Be sure students see the expression $8 - 0.25x$ as the amount of sleep Erin got. **[Ask]** "Why does the inequality include $0.25x$ instead of $15x$?" [The units of time need to be the same for every number in the expression.] As students read through the solution, be sure they notice that the direction of the inequality sign reverses.

Once students have seen the solution to the inequality, complete the modeling process by asking what solution it gives to the original problem.

Closing the Lesson

Inequalities help model problems for situations described by phrases such as *greater than, less than, no more than,* and *at least.* Solving inequalities is much like solving equations, except that multiplying or dividing by a negative number reverses the direction of the inequality. The solutions to an inequality can be represented by a ray, illustrating an unbounded set of numbers in the solution. If an open circle marks the ray's endpoint, the endpoint is not included in the solution. A solid circle indicates inclusion of the endpoint.

Working with inequalities is very much like working with equations. An equation shows a balance between two quantities, but an inequality shows an imbalance. The important thing to remember is that multiplying and dividing both sides of an equation by a negative number tips the scales in the opposite direction.

$a > b$ $\qquad\qquad\qquad$ $a < b$

EXERCISES

You will need your graphing calculator for Exercise **16.**

▶ Practice Your Skills

1. Tell what operation on the first inequality gives the second one, and give the answer using the correct inequality symbol.

   a. $3 < 7$ $\quad$ Multiply by 4; $12 < 28$.
   $4 \cdot 3 \;\square\; 7 \cdot 4$ @

   b. $5 \leq 12$ $\quad$ Multiply by -3; $-15 \geq -36$.
   $-3 \cdot 5 \;\square\; 12 \cdot -3$

   c. $-4 \geq x$ $\quad$ Add -10; $-14 \geq x - 10$.
   $-4 + (-10) \;\square\; x + (-10)$ @

   d. $b + 3 > 15$ $\quad$ Subtract 8; $b - 5 > 7$.
   $b + 3 - 8 \;\square\; 15 - 8$

   e. $24d < 32$ $\quad$ Divide by 3; $8d < 10\frac{2}{3}$.
   $\frac{24d}{3} \;\square\; \frac{32}{3}$ @

   f. $24x \leq 32$ $\quad$ Divide by -3; $-8x \geq -10\frac{2}{3}$.
   $\frac{24x}{-3} \;\square\; \frac{32}{-3}$

2. Find three values of the variable that satisfy each inequality.

   a. $5 + 2a > 21$ @

   b. $7 - 3b < 28$ $\quad$ Values must be > -7.

   c. $-11.6 + 2.5c < 8.2$ $\quad$ Values must be < 7.92.

   d. $4.7 - 3.25d > -25.3$

3. Give the inequality graphed on each number line.

   a. @
   $x \leq -1$

   b.
   $x > 0$

   c.
   $x \geq -2$

   d. @
   $-2 < x < 1$

   e.
   $0 < x \leq 2$

4. Translate each phrase into symbols.

   a. 3 is more than x $\quad$ $3 > x$

   b. y is at least -2 @ $\quad$ $y \geq -2$

   c. z is no more than 12 $\quad$ $z \leq 12$

   d. n is not greater than 7 $\quad$ $n \leq 7$

5. Solve each equation for y.

   a. $3x + 4y = 5.2$ $\quad$ $y = \frac{5.2 - 3x}{4} = 1.3 - 0.75x$

   b. $3(y - 5) = 2x$ $\quad$ $y = \frac{2x}{3} + 5$, or $\frac{2x + 15}{3}$

Reason and Apply

6. Solve each inequality and show your work.

a. $4.1 + 3.2x > 18$ ⓐ $x > 4.34375$, or $\frac{139}{32}$

b. $7.2 - 2.1b < 4.4$ $b > 1.\overline{3}$

c. $7 - 2(x - 3) \geq 25$ $x \leq -6$

d. $11.5 + 4.5(x + 1.8) \leq x$ $x \leq -5.6$

7. Solve each inequality and graph the solutions on a number line.

a. $3x - 2 \leq 7$

b. $4 - x > 6$ ⓐ

c. $3 + 2x \geq -3$

d. $10 \leq 2(5 - 3x)$

8. Ezra received $50 from his grandparents for his birthday. He makes $7.50 each week for odd jobs he does around the neighborhood. Since his birthday, he has saved more than enough to buy the $120 gift he wants to buy for his parents' 20th wedding anniversary. How many weeks ago was his birthday? ⓗ

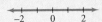

9. For each graph, tell what operation moves the two points in the inequality to their new positions. Write the new inequality, stating the position of the red dot first.

a. $1 < 2$ ⓐ Add 3 to both sides; $4 < 5$.

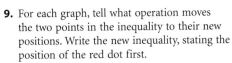

b. $6 > 2$ Divide both sides by 2 (or multiply by 0.5); $3 > 1$.

c. $-1 < 1$ Multiply both sides by -3; $3 > -3$.

d. $0 < 3$ Multiply both sides by 2; $0 < 6$.

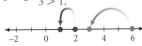

10. Tell whether each inequality is true or false for the given value.

a. $x - 14 < 9$, $x = 5$ $-9 < 9$ is true.

b. $3x \geq 51$, $x = 7$ $21 \geq 51$ is false.

c. $2x - 3 < 7$, $x = 5$ $7 < 7$ is false.

d. $4(x - 6) \geq 18$, $x = 12$ $24 \geq 18$ is true.

11. Solve each inequality. Explain the meaning of the result. On a number line, graph the values of x that make the original inequality true.

a. $2x - 3 > 5x - 3x + 3$ ⓐ

b. $-2.2(5x + 3) \geq -11x - 15$

12. Data collected by a motion sensor will vary slightly in accuracy. A given sensor has a known accuracy of ± 2 mm (0.002 m), and a distance is measured as 2.834 m. State this distance and accuracy as an inequality statement.

$2.834 - 0.002 \leq x \leq 2.834 + 0.002$; $2.832 \leq x \leq 2.836$ m

---

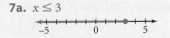

7a. $x \leq 3$

7b. $x < -2$

7c. $x \geq -3$

7d. $x \leq 0$

Exercise 8 A student who's very comfortable with dimensional analysis might go directly to the inequality $7.5w > 70$. Be encouraging.

8. $50 + 7.5w > 120$; $w > 9.\overline{3}$; Ezra has been saving for at least 10 wk.

Exercise 9 Here's another way to visualize operations on inequalities. You may want to model a problem like this one to be sure students understand that the directions of the arrows indicate movement of the two numbers relative to the number line.

11a. The variable x drops out of the inequality, leaving $-3 > 3$, which is never true. So the original inequality is not true for any number x. The graph would be an empty number line, with no points filled in.

11b. The variable x drops out of the inequality, leaving $-6.6 \geq -15$, which is always true. So the original inequality is true for any number x. The graph would be a line with arrows on both ends.

Exercise 12 This exercise reviews accuracy, introduced in Lesson 1.7. Students may need help writing the compound inequality.

13. You read the inequality symbols, $<$, $\le$, $>$, and $\ge$, as "is less than," "is less than or equal to," "is greater than," and "is greater than or equal to," respectively. But you describe everyday situations with different expressions. Identify the variable in each statement and give the inequality to describe each situation. ⓗ

   a. I'll spend no more than $30 on CDs this month.

   b. You must be at least 48 inches tall to go on this ride.

   c. Three or more people make a carpool. $p \ge 3$ (p for people in carpool)

   d. No one under age 17 will be admitted without a parent or guardian. $a \ge 17$ (a for age of person admitted)

14. The table gives equations that model the three vehicles' distances in the Investigation On the Road Again from Lesson 3.2. The variable x represents the time in minutes since all three vehicles began traveling, and y represents the distance in miles from Flint.

Equation	Vehicle
$y = 220 - 1.2x$	minivan
$y = 35 + 0.8x$	sports car
$y = 1.1x$	pickup truck

   a. What question is represented by the inequality statement $35 + 0.8x \ge 131$?   When is the sports car 131 or more miles away from Flint?

   b. What is the solution to the inequality $35 + 0.8x \ge 131$? $x \ge 120$

   c. What question is represented by the statement $220 - 1.2x < 35 + 0.8x$?

   d. What is the solution to the inequality $220 - 1.2x < 35 + 0.8x$? $x > 92.5$

15. In Example B, the inequality $8 - 0.25x < 5$ was written to represent the situation where Erin slept less than 5 hours, and her sleep time was 8 hours minus 0.25 hour for each time the dog barked. However, Erin can't sleep less than 0 hours, so a more accurate statement would be the compound inequality $0 \le 8 - 0.25x < 5$. You can solve a compound inequality in the same way you've solved other inequalities; you just need to make sure you do the same operation to all *three* parts. Solve this inequality for x and graph the solution.

▶ **Review**

2.7 16. List the order in which you would perform these operations to get the correct answer.

   a. $72 - 12 \cdot 3.2 = 33.6$ Multiply 12 by 3.2 to get 38.4. Subtract 38.4 from 72 to get 33.6.

   b. $2 + 1.5\left(3 - 5^2\right) = -31$

   c. $21 \div 7 - 6 \div 2 = 0$
      Divide 21 by 7 to get 3 and divide 6 by 2 to get 3. Subtract 3 from 3 to get 0.

3.2 **17.** The table shows the 2004 U.S. postal rates for letters, large envelopes, and small packages.

U.S. Postal Rates

Weight	Rate
First ounce or fraction of an ounce	$0.37
Each additional ounce or fraction	$0.23

(U.S. Postal Service, *www.usps.com*)

  a. Use a recursive routine to create a table that shows the cost of sending letters weighing from 0 to 11 ounces. @

  b. Use 1-ounce units on the horizontal axis to plot the postal costs. @

  c. Kasey has drawn a line through the points on her graph. What real-world meaning does this line have? Is a line useful in this situation? Why or why not? @

  d. What is the cost of sending a 10.5-ounce parcel? @ $2.67

4.4 **18.** Use the distributive property to rewrite each expression without using parentheses.

  a. $-2(x + 8)$ $-2x - 16$ **b.** $4(0.75 - y)$ $3 - 4y$
  c. $-(z - 5)$ $-z + 5$

17b.

Postage Costs

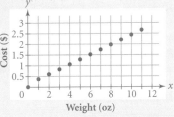

17c. A line would mean that the cost would pass through each amount between the different increments. For example, if a package weighed 0.5 oz, you would pay $0.185. However, the cost increases discretely. To show this, draw segments for each integral ounce. Note the open and closed circles.

Postage Costs

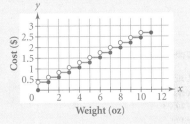

project

TEMPERATURES

Temperatures for your city vary depending on the time of day, season, and its location. Weather reports give the daily high and low temperatures and often compare them with the record temperatures in the past 100 years.

Research the range of temperatures for your geographic area. What are the record highs and lows? What are the record temperatures for a specific day, say, your birthday? How do the altitude and location of your area affect these temperatures?

Compare your results to temperatures on the moon. Research the temperatures of other planets such as Venus, Mars, and Pluto. What factors affect these data sets? Are the temperatures given in degrees Fahrenheit or degrees Celsius? Be sure to convert all data to the same units before comparing. Describe your findings with inequalities and graphs in a paper or give a presentation.

Your project should include

▸ Your hometown high and low temperatures.

▸ Algebraic expressions with compound inequalities.

▸ Clearly labeled graphs.

Some people think it may be possible to live on another planet or moon someday. Based on your findings, what do you think?

This view from the *Apollo II* spacecraft shows Earth above the lunar terrain.

Supporting the project

MOTIVATION

How do record temperatures in your geographic area compare with those on other planets or on the moon?

OUTCOMES

▸ Record highs and lows for the area overall, as well as temperatures for a specific day, are all given in the same units.

▸ The report comments on how the altitude and geographic location affect the temperatures.

▸ Temperatures for the moon or for other planets are given and compared.

▸ Factors influencing extraterrestrial temperatures are given.

▸ The paper or presentation includes clearly labeled graphs as well as inequalities, including compound inequalities.

▸ Claims about the possibility of living on another planet or on the moon are consistent with the data given.

LESSON

5.6

Graphing Inequalities in Two Variables

In Lesson 5.5, you learned to graph inequalities in one variable on a number line. However, some situations, such as the number of points a football team scores by touchdowns and field goals, require more than one variable. In this lesson you will learn to graph inequalities in two variables on a coordinate plane.

You have graphed equations like $y = 1 + 0.5x$. In the following investigation you will learn how to graph inequalities such as $y < 1 + 0.5x$ and $y > 1 + 0.5x$.

Investigation
Graphing Inequalities

You will need

- the worksheet Graphing Inequalities Grids

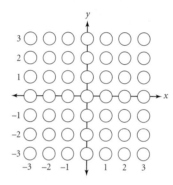

First you'll make a graph from one of four statements.

i. $y \,\square\, 1 + 0.5x$ **ii.** $y \,\square\, -1 - 2x$

iii. $y \,\square\, 1 - 0.5x$ **iv.** $y \,\square\, 1 - 2x$

Step 1   Each member of the group should choose a different statement from above.

Step 2   Evaluate the right side of your statement for $x = -3$. For each circle in the first column on the graph, fill in $>$ if the y-value of the point is greater than your value, $=$ if the values are equal, and $<$ if the y-value is less than your value. The first column for each graph should be filled in as shown in the answer for Step 3.

MATERIALS

- Graphing Inequalities Grids (W)
- Graphing Inequalities (T), *optional*
- Calculator Notes 5B, 5C
- Sketchpad demonstration Graphing Inequalities, *optional*

TEACHING

Solutions to inequalities involving two variables can be visualized as points in half-planes. If you have The Geometer's Sketchpad, you might introduce this lesson with the Sketchpad demonstration Graphing Inequalities.

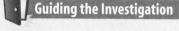

Guiding the Investigation

One Step
Ask students to divide statements i, ii, iii, and iv among group members. For each one, fill in each circle of the grid worksheet with the symbol $<$, $>$, or $=$ that should go into the box to make a true statement when that point's coordinates are substituted for x and y. Ask students to look for patterns. As you circulate, encourage students to check points with fractional coordinates, to redraw the graphs without the circles, and to use dotted lines as boundaries of strict inequalities.

LESSON OBJECTIVES

- Solve two-variable inequalities for y
- Graph inequalities on the coordinate plane and show the solutions as the intersection of two half-planes
- Interpret graphs of half-planes and write corresponding inequalities

NCTM STANDARDS

CONTENT		PROCESS	
	Number	✔	Problem Solving
✔	Algebra	✔	Reasoning
	Geometry	✔	Communication
	Measurement	✔	Connections
✔	Data/Probability	✔	Representation

Step 3 | Repeat Step 2 for $x = -2, -1, 0, 1, 2,$ and 3.

Next you'll analyze the results of your graph.

Step 4 The circles filled with equal signs form a line. The "greater than" symbols, $>$, are all above the line, and the "less than" symbols, $<$, are all below the line.

Step 5 Coordinates will vary. The symbol will be the same as the symbols on the same side of the line of equal signs.

Step 4 What do you notice about the circles filled with the equal sign? Describe any other patterns you see.

Step 5 Test a point with fractional or decimal coordinates that is not represented by a circle on the grid. Compare your result with the symbols on the same side of the line of equal signs as your point.

Step 6 Draw a set of xy-axes, with scales from -3 to 3 on each axis. Under the graph, write your statement with the "less than" symbol, $<$. Shade the region of points that makes your statement true. If the points on the line make an inequality true, draw a solid line through them. If not, draw a dashed line. Repeat this step for each of the remaining symbols ($>, \leq, \geq, =$).

Step 7 The graphs for the symbols $=, \leq,$ and $\geq$ require a solid line because points on the line satisfy the relationship; the strict inequalities, $<$ and $>$, require a dashed line.

Finally, you'll draw general conclusions by comparing graphs in your group.

Step 7 Compare your graphs with those of others in your group. What graphs require a solid line? A dashed line?

Step 8 What graphs require shading? Shading above the line? Below the line?

Step 9 Discuss how to use one point to check the graph of an inequality.

The graph of the solutions to a single inequality is called a **half-plane** because it includes all the points in the coordinate plane that fall on one side of the boundary line.

EXAMPLE A | Graph the inequality $2x - 3y > 3$, and check to see whether each point is part of the solution.

   i. $(3, -2)$

   ii. $(3, 1)$

   iii. $(-1, 2)$

   iv. $(-2, -3)$

▶ **Solution** | To graph the inequality, first solve it for y:

$$2x - 3y > 3 \qquad \text{Original inequality.}$$
$$-3y > 3 - 2x \qquad \text{Subtract } 2x \text{ from both sides.}$$
$$y < -1 + \frac{2}{3}x \qquad \text{Divide both sides by } -3 \text{ and reverse the inequality symbol.}$$

Step 1 If a group has only three members, have them reserve statement iv until they've finished the others. In a group with two members, each could take two statements, such as i and iii for one and ii and iv for the other.

Step 3 Graphs vary depending on statement chosen.

i.

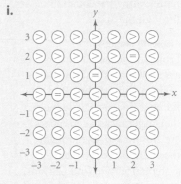

ii.

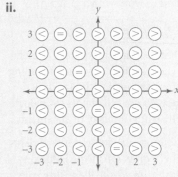

iii.

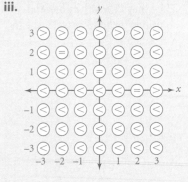

iv.

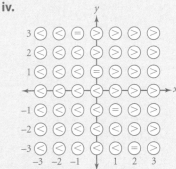

Step 7 [Ask] "Are broken lines and solid lines related to open circles and filled circles?" [Broken lines, like open circles, represent strict inequalities. Solid lines, like filled circles, include equality.]

Step 8 The graphs for the symbols $<, >, \leq,$ and $\geq$ require shading. For $>$ and $\geq$, shade above the line. Shade below the line for $<$ and $\leq$.

Step 9 Answers will vary. Substitute into the inequality the coordinates from one point on one side of the line, say $(0, 0)$. If the point satisfies the inequality, shade that side of the line. If not, shade the other side.

Ask students to describe the rules they derived for deciding which half-plane to shade, and prompt the class to critique them. Elicit the idea that the point $(0, 0)$ is the easiest point to check and that doing so will give the desired information unless the line representing the equation passes through the origin.

Assessing Progress

From your observations, you can assess students' understanding of inequality symbols and the number line, especially the fact that larger negative numbers are closer to 0. Also look for the ability to collect data systematically, to find patterns, and to work with a group.

EXAMPLE A

This example is good for students who had difficulty understanding the investigation. It also shows how to use calculators to evaluate the truth or falsity of statements.

You may need to remind students that points *satisfy* the inequality if they make the inequality true. They may check the potential solutions by hand as well as with a calculator.

Graph the line $y = -1 + \frac{2}{3}x$ with a dashed line to indicate that points on the line are not part of the solution to the inequality. Because the inequality in y is less than the expression in x on the right side, shade the region *below* the line. Points in this region will have y-values that are less than the expression in x.

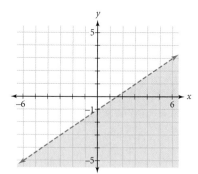

If you plot the given points, you'll see that the points that satisfy the inequality lie in the shaded part of the plane.

To check numerically whether the given points satisfy the inequality, substitute the x- and y-values from each given coordinate pair for x and y in the inequality $2x - 3y > 3$, and enter the inequality into your calculator. When you press $\boxed{\text{ENTER}}$, you'll see 1 if the inequality is true or 0 if the inequality is false, as shown on the calculator screen below. [▶ 🖥 See **Calculator Note 5B**. ◀]

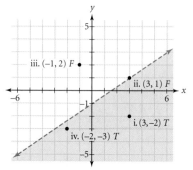

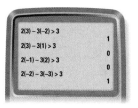

i. $2(3) - 3(-2) > 3 \longrightarrow 12 > 3 \longrightarrow$ True
ii. $2(3) - 3(1) > 3 \longrightarrow 3 > 3 \longrightarrow$ False
iii. $2(-1) - 3(2) > 3 \longrightarrow -8 > 3 \longrightarrow$ False
iv. $2(-2) - 3(-3) > 3 \longrightarrow 5 > 3 \longrightarrow$ True

Graphing Inequalities

▶ Draw a broken or dashed line on the boundary for inequalities with $>$ or $<$.
▶ Draw a solid line on the boundary for inequalities with $\geq$ or $\leq$.
▶ To graph inequalities in the form $y <$ or $y \leq$, shade below the boundary line.
▶ To graph inequalities in the form $y >$ or $y \geq$, shade above the boundary line.

[▶ 🖥 See **Calculator Note 5C** to graph inequalities in two variables on your calculator. ◀]

EXAMPLE B

Graph and shade each inequality.

a. $x > -2$
b. $3y \leq 1$
c. $-2x \geq 5$
d. $3 - y < 7$

▸ **Solution**

Solve for the variable in each inequality. Don't forget to switch the direction of the inequality when dividing by a negative!

a. $x > -2$

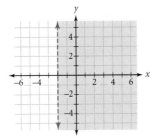

b. $3y \leq 1$ Divide each side by 3.
   $y \leq \dfrac{1}{3}$

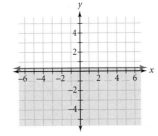

c. $-2x \geq 5$ Divide each side by -2.
   $x \leq -\dfrac{5}{2}$ or -2.5

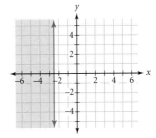

d. $3 - y < 7$ Subtract 3 from each side.
   $-y < 4$ Multiply each side by -1.
   $y > -4$

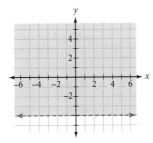

EXAMPLE B

This example gives students more experience with two-dimensional graphs of inequalities in one variable. Special cases like this may be notationally simpler than inequalities involving two variables, but they are conceptually more difficult for many students.

Closing the Lesson

To visualize solutions to inequalities involving two variables, you can graph the line that is represented by the equation and then shade in the side of that line (**half-plane**) on which the solutions to the inequality lie.

BUILDING UNDERSTANDING

Students practice working with inequalities in two variables.

ASSIGNING HOMEWORK

Essential	1–3, 4 or 5, 6–9
Performance assessment	6–8
Portfolio	8, 10
Journal	8, 13
Group	10, 11
Review	12–14

▶ Helping with the Exercises

Exercise 1 If students are having difficulty, suggest that they turn the inequality into an equation and graph the line that is the boundary for the solutions to the inequality. Some students may want to solve for y to have the equation in intercept form.

Exercise 3 This exercise reviews graphing inequalities on a number line. You may want to ask students to discuss the difference between inequalities graphed on a number line and those graphed on a coordinate plane. **[Ask]** "How would you graph an inequality like $x < 5$ on coordinate axes?" [Shade the half-plane to the left of the vertical line $x = n$ if $x < n$ or to the right of the line if $x > n$.]

3a.
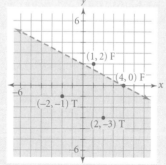

3b.

3c.

3d.

Exercises 4–6 [Alert] Check that students are using a broken line for strict inequalities and a solid line for others.

EXERCISES

▶ Practice Your Skills

1. Match each graph with an inequality.
   a. $y \le 3 + 2x$ iii
   b. $y \le 2 + 3x$ ii
   c. $2x + 3y \le 6$ @ i
   d. $2x + 3y \ge 6$ iv

   i.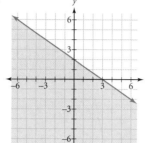

   ii.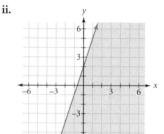

   iii.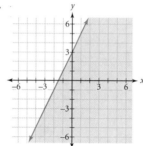

   iv.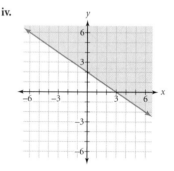

2. Solve each inequality for y.
   a. $84x + 7y \ge 70$ @ $y \ge -12x + 10$
   b. $4.8x - 0.12y < 7.2$ $y > 40x - 60$

3. Sketch each inequality on a number line.
   a. $x \le -5$
   b. $x > 2.5$
   c. $-3 \le x \le 3$ @
   d. $-1 \le x < 2$

4. Consider the inequality $y < 2 - 0.5x$.
   a. Graph the boundary line for the inequality on axes scaled from -6 to 6 on each axis. @
   b. Determine whether each given point satisfies $y < 2 - 0.5x$. Plot the point on the graph you drew in 4a. Label the point T (true) if it is part of the solution or F (false) if it is not part of the solution region. @
      i. $(1, 2)$
      ii. $(4, 0)$
      iii. $(2, -3)$
      iv. $(-2, -1)$
   c. Use your results from 4b to shade the half-plane that represents the inequality. @

5. Consider the inequality $y \ge 1 + 2x$.
   a. Graph the boundary line for the inequality on axes scaled from -6 to 6 on each axis.

4a–c.

b. Determine whether each given point satisfies $y \geq 1 + 2x$. Plot the point on the graph you drew in 5a, and label the point T (true) if it is part of the solution or F (false) if it is not part of the solution region.

 i. $(-2, 2)$ **ii.** $(3, 2)$ **iii.** $(-1, -1)$ **iv.** $(-4, -3)$

c. Use your results from 5b to shade the half-plane that represents the inequality.

▶ Reason and Apply

6. Sketch each inequality.

 a. $y \leq -3 + x$ ⓐ   **b.** $y > -2 - 1.5x$ **c.** $2x - y \geq 4$

7. Write the inequality for each graph. ⓗ

a.
ⓐ

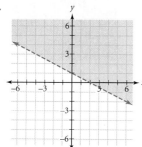

$y \leq 1 - 2x$

b.

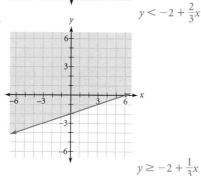

$y < -2 + \frac{2}{3}x$

c.

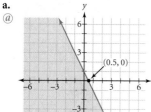

$y > 1 - 0.5x$

d.

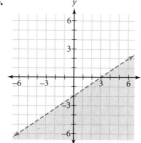

$y \geq -2 + \frac{1}{3}x$

e.
ⓐ

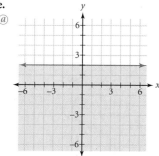

$y \leq 2$

f.

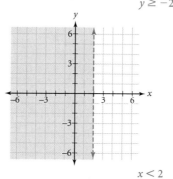

$x < 2$

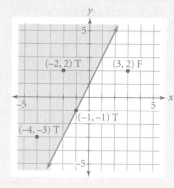

6a.

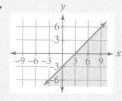

6b.

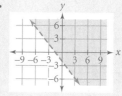

6c.

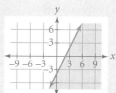

8a. $y = -3 + 1.5x$

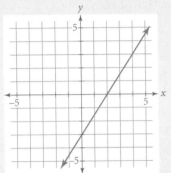

9a.

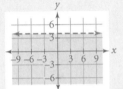

9b.

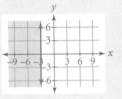

9c.

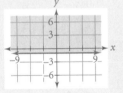

9d.

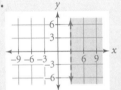

10c.

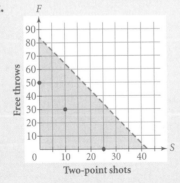

8. Mini-Investigation Consider the inequality $3x - 2y \le 6$.

   a. Solve the equation $3x - 2y = 6$ for y and graph the equation.

   b. Test the points $(1, 3)$ and $(1, -3)$. Which point makes the statement true? Does this indicate that you should shade above or below the line $3x - 2y = 6$? (1, 3); above

   c. You might think that the inequality $3x - 2y \le 6$ indicates that you should shade below the boundary line. Make a conjecture about when you must shade the side that is opposite what the inequality symbol implies. If the coefficient of y is negative, then shade the side opposite what the inequality symbol indicates.

9. Sketch each inequality on coordinate axes.

   a. $y < 4$ @   **b.** $x \le -3$ **c.** $y \ge -1$ **d.** $x > 3$

10. APPLICATION The total number of points from a combination of one-point free throws, F, and two-point shots, S, is less than 84 points.

$F + 2S < 84$ **a.** Write an inequality to represent this situation. @

$F + 2S = 84$ **b.** Write the equation for the boundary line of this situation. @

   c. Graph this inequality with S on the horizontal axis and F on the vertical axis. Show the scale on the axes.

   d. On your graph, indicate three possible combinations of free throws and two-point shots that give a point total of 50. Label the coordinates of these points. possible answer: $(0, 50), (10, 30), (25, 0)$

11. Graph the inequalities in Exercises 4 and 5 on your calculator. [▶ 🖥 See **Calculator Note 5C**. ◀]

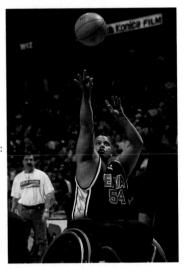

Raul Acosta plays wheelchair basketball for the Eastern Paralyzed Veterans Association in New Jersey.

▶ Review

4.2 **12.** These data are federal minimum wages of the past 70 years.

Federal Minimum Wages

Year	Minimum wage	2003 equivalent dollars
1938	0.25	3.26
1939	0.30	3.97
1945	0.40	4.09
1950	0.75	5.73
1956	1.00	6.76
1961	1.25	7.69
1967	1.40	7.71
1968	1.60	8.46
1974	2.00	7.46
1975	2.10	7.18

Federal Minimum Wages

Year	Minimum wage	2003 equivalent dollars
1976	2.30	7.44
1978	2.65	7.48
1979	2.90	7.35
1980	3.10	6.92
1981	3.35	6.78
1990	3.50	4.93
1991	4.25	5.74
1996	4.75	5.57
1997	5.15	5.90

(Department of Labor, *www.dol.gov*)

12a, d.

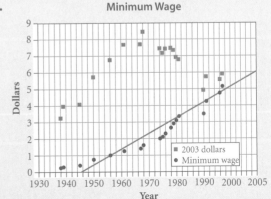

a. Graph the data from the table on the same set of axes. Use one color for minimum wage and another for 2003 dollars.

b. Which is better represented by a line, the hourly minimum wage or the 2003 dollar value?   minimum wage

c. Find the line of fit based on Q-points for the data points of the form (*year, minimum wage*).   Q-points: (1956, 1.00), (1981, 3.35); $y = -182.864 + 0.094x$

d. Graph the equation in 12c to verify that it is a good fit.

e. What is the real-world meaning of the slope? How does it compare with the 2003 dollars graph?

2.5   **13.** Ellie was talking with her grandmother about a trip she took this summer. Ellie made the trip in 2.5 h traveling at 65 mi/h. Ellie's grandmother remembers that she made the same trip in about 6 h when she was Ellie's age. ⓗ

a. What speed was Ellie's grandmother traveling when she made the trip?   about 27 mi/h

b. Explain how this is an application of inverse variation.

3.4   **14.** Solve each equation for y.

a. $7x - 3y = 22$ $y = \frac{7}{3}x - \frac{22}{3}$

b. $5x + 4y = -12$ $y = -\frac{5}{4}x - 3$

11.

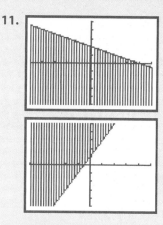

Exercise 12 This exercise is a follow-up to Chapter 4 Review, Exercise 10.

12e. The minimum wage increases 9¢ every year on average, but the actual dollar value was highest in 1968 and has decreased almost every year since then.

13b. Because $d = r \cdot t$ and the distance was the same for both Ellie and her grandmother, you can set these products equal to each other. If you let r represent Ellie's grandmother's speed, then $2.5(65) = 6r$.

IMPROVING YOUR VISUAL THINKING SKILLS

In this chapter you have seen three possible outcomes for a system of two equations in two variables. If one solution exists, it is the point of intersection. If no solution exists, the lines are parallel and there is no point of intersection. If infinitely many solutions exist, the two lines overlap.

But what do the solutions look like in a system of three linear equations in three unknowns? An equation like $3x + 2y = 12$ is a line, but an equation in three variables is a plane. Consider the graph of $3x + 2y + 6z = 12$. Imagine the x-axis coming out of the page. The shaded triangle indicates the part of the solution plane whose coordinates are all positive. The complete plane is infinite.

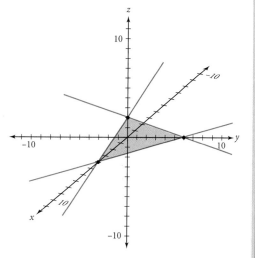

If you have two more planar equations, you have a system of three equations in three variables. There will be three planes on the graph. So the solutions to this system are where the planes intersect, if they do at all. Visualize how three planes could intersect to answer these questions.

▶ Can three planes intersect in one point? If so, how many solutions will this system have?

▶ If a system has infinitely many solutions, must all three equations be the same plane?

▶ If the system has no solutions, must the planes be parallel?

IMPROVING VISUAL THINKING SKILLS

If two planes aren't parallel, they intersect in a line. If three planes all intersect, the intersection of each pair is a line. Those lines might intersect in a point, which means the system will have one solution. Or the three lines might be the same line, in which case the system has infinitely many solutions even though the planes aren't the same.

Or the lines of intersection of pairs of planes might all be parallel, extending the edges of a triangular prism. Then the system will have no solution, but the planes themselves won't be parallel. If two of the planes are parallel, there will also be no solution.

LESSON
5.7

Systems of Inequalities

All mathematical truths are relative, conditional.

CHARLES PROTEUS STEINMETZ

You learned that the solution to a system of two linear equations, if there is exactly one solution, is the coordinates of the point where the two lines intersect. In this lesson you'll learn about **systems of inequalities** and their solutions. Many real-world situations can be described by a system of inequalities. When solving these problems, you'll need to write inequalities, often called **constraints,** and graph them. You'll then find a region, rather than a single point, that represents all solutions.

Translucent sheets of blue, red, and yellow intersect to form overlapping regions of new colors—orange, green, and purple.

PLANNING

LESSON OUTLINE

One day:

20 min Investigation

15 min Examples

5 min Sharing

5 min Closing

5 min Exercises

MATERIALS

- Cereal Sales and Profit (T)
- Calculator Note 5C
- Sketchpad demonstration Linear Programming, *optional*

TEACHING

The solution set for a system of inequalities is the intersection of the solution sets for the individual inequalities.

One Step

Tell students that a cereal company is letting the buyer of each box of cereal enter a drawing for a $1,000 scholarship. One scholarship will be given away each month. The company makes a profit of between $0.47 and $1.10 on each box of cereal, depending on how the cereal is priced at different locations. If the company sells 2000 boxes in a month, will it make enough to cover the $1,000 scholarship? Ask students to answer the question in as many ways as they can. As you circulate, be sure that one way they answer is through a system of inequalities.

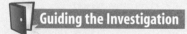
Guiding the Investigation

If you have a variety of envelopes that meet postal regulations, you might display them or even have

Investigation
A "Typical" Envelope

The U.S. Postal Service imposes several constraints on the acceptable sizes for an envelope. One constraint is that the ratio of length to width must be less than or equal to 2.5, and another is that this ratio must be greater than or equal to 1.3.

Step 1 Let l represent the length in inches and w represent the width in inches; $\frac{l}{w} \leq 2.5, \frac{l}{w} \geq 1.3$.

Step 2 $\begin{cases} l \leq 2.5w \\ l \geq 1.3w \end{cases}$; inequality is not reversed because w takes on only positive values.

Step 1 Define variables and write an inequality for each constraint.

Step 2 Solve each inequality for the variable representing length. Decide whether or not you have to reverse directions on the inequality symbols. Then write a system of inequalities to describe the Postal Service's constraints on envelope sizes.

Step 3 Decide on appropriate scales for each axis and label a set of axes. Decide if you should draw the boundaries of the system with solid or dashed lines. Graph each inequality on the same set of axes. Shade each half-plane with a different color or pattern.

Step 4 Where on the graph are the solutions to the system of inequalities? Discuss how to check that your answer is correct. Answers will vary. Check by substituting coordinates from the overlapping regions to see if they satisfy both inequalities.

LESSON OBJECTIVES

- Solve systems of inequalities by graphing
- Interpret the mathematical solutions in terms of the problem context
- Write inequalities to represent *constraints* in application problems

NCTM STANDARDS

CONTENT		PROCESS	
	Number	✓	Problem Solving
✓	Algebra	✓	Reasoning
✓	Geometry	✓	Communication
	Measurement	✓	Connections
	Data/Probability	✓	Representation

Step 5 | Decide if each envelope satisfies the constraints by locating the corresponding point on your graph.

a. 5 in. by 8 in. yes

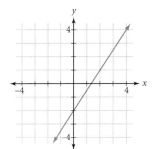

b. 3 in. by 3 in. no

c. 2.5 in. by 7.5 in. no

d. 5.5 in. by 7.5 in. yes

Step 6 | Do the coordinates of the origin satisfy this system of inequalities? Explain the real-world meaning of this point. What constraints can you add to more realistically model the Postal Service's acceptable envelope sizes? How do these additions affect the graph?

EXAMPLE A

Graph the system of inequalities

$$\begin{cases} y \le -2 + \frac{3}{2}x \\ y > 1 - x \end{cases}$$

Graph the boundary lines and shade the half-planes. Indicate the solution area as the darkest region.

▶ **Solution**

First, determine if the boundary lines are solid or dashed. Graph $y = -2 + \frac{3}{2}x$ with a solid line because points on the line satisfy the inequality. Graph $y = 1 - x$ with a dotted line because its points do not satisfy the inequality.

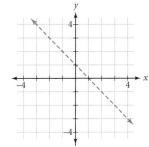

Shade the half-plane below the solid line $y = -2 + \frac{3}{2}x$ because its inequality has the "less than or equal to" symbol, $\le$. Shade above the dotted line $y = 1 - x$ because its inequality has the "greater than" symbol, $>$. Use different colors or patterns to distinguish each area shaded.

Step 6 Answers will vary. Yes, $(0, 0)$ satisfies the system. This means the envelope has no length or width. Minimum and maximum lengths and widths could be added as constraints. For example, the Postal Service lists $11\frac{1}{2}$ in. and $6\frac{1}{8}$ in. as the maximum length and width for an envelope with a 37¢ stamp. A sample system:

$$\begin{cases} l \le 2.5w \\ l \ge 1.3w \\ w \le 6.125 \\ l \le 11.5 \end{cases}$$

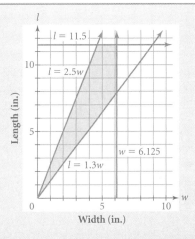

Width (in.)

students measure them, report their ratios, and try to guess the legal constraints.

Step 2 You may need to remind students to multiply each side of the inequality by w. Encourage the habit of thinking about the sign of the multiplier of an inequality. Here, if nothing were known about w, you'd have to consider the case of negative w as well as positive w. Because w represents the width of an envelope, w is positive, so the direction of the inequality isn't changed.

Step 3 It is often good for students to graph on a larger region than is needed. If they graph on a calculator, they may not be able to shade differently.

Step 3

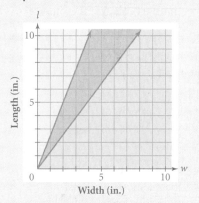

Width (in.)

Step 5

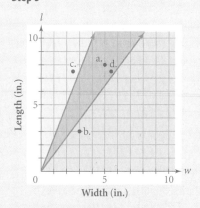

Width (in.)

Step 6 For information about other constraints, visit www.keymath.com/DA and see the link to the U.S. Postal Service. Tell students that, although the units in this ratio cancel, the Postal Service uses "inches" as its unit of measurement.

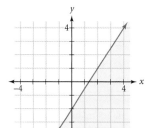
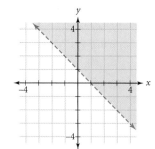
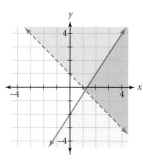

Each shaded area indicates the region of points that satisfy each inequality. The overlapping area bounded by $y \leq -2 + \frac{3}{2}x$ and $y > 1 - x$ satisfies both. Only the points that lie in both half-planes are the solutions to the system of inequalities.

EXAMPLE B

A cereal company is including a chance to win a $1,000 scholarship in each box of cereal. In this promotional campaign, it will give away one scholarship each month, regardless of the number of boxes sold. Because the cereal is priced differently at various locations, the profit from a single box is between $0.47 and $1.10. Graph the expected profit, given the initial cost of the scholarship, for up to 5000 boxes sold in a month. Show the solution region on a graph. Is it possible to sell 3000 boxes and make a profit of $1,000?

▶ Solution

Write a system of inequalities to model this situation. The lowest profit per box is $0.47. So $0.47x$ is the minimum profit when x boxes are sold. Subtract $1,000 for the scholarship given each month. So the profit y is at least $0.47x - 1000$ dollars for x boxes sold. This is given by the inequality

$$y \geq -1000 + 0.47x$$

Likewise, if the maximum profit is $1.10 per box, then the profit is at most $1.1x - 1000$ dollars. So the second inequality is

$$y \leq -1000 + 1.1x$$

The profit during each month is given by the system

$$\begin{cases} y \geq -1000 + 0.47x \\ y \leq -1000 + 1.1x \end{cases}$$

SHARING IDEAS

Have students briefly share their answers to Step 5 and then discuss how well the solution to the system applies to the real-world problem. If you or your students have looked up more constraints, bring those out.

Assessing Progress

Students will show their ability at graphing the solution set for an inequality in two variables and their understanding of the need to reverse the direction of an inequality when multiplying by a negative number.

EXAMPLE A

This example shows how to solve an abstract system of inequalities.

[Ask] "In how many points can two half-planes intersect?" [infinitely many if they intersect, and zero if they don't]

Analogously, a system of linear *equations* has zero solutions, one solution, or infinitely many solutions because two lines intersect in zero points, one point, or infinitely many points.

Students enjoy watching their calculators graph a system of inequalities. If you have a projection panel, you might demonstrate.

Students may wonder if the intersection of two half-planes is a "quarter-plane." Because the area of the intersection is infinite, it isn't really smaller than a half-plane in any measurable sense.

EXAMPLE B

This example provides a real-world application of a system of inequalities. If students don't understand how to set up the inequalities, ask what they want to find (to help them determine the variables) and what they know (to write the inequalities).

You might ask why anyone would want to know if it's possible to sell 3000 boxes and make $1,000. For example, the marketing staff might want to know if the $1,000 scholarship will be paid for by selling a projected number of boxes.

Pick various points in the solution region. Ask why they are solutions to each inequality and what real-world meaning they have. You might generate some good discussion if you pick a point with fractional coordinates. Students will need to realize that x is a number of boxes sold, so it must be an integer. The variable y is in dollars, so it can be fractional to an extent.

The Cereal Sales and Profit transparency shows the two graphs separately. If you cut the transparency apart, you can lay one graph on top of the other and get a result that looks like the third graph on page 323.

Each inequality is graphed for up to 5000 boxes on separate axes below.

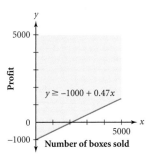
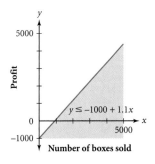

The possible profits are in the region where the two half-planes overlap.
[▶ 🖵 See **Calculator Note 5C** to graph systems of inequalities on your calculator. ◀]

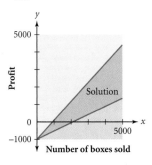

To see if it is possible to make $1,000 when 3000 boxes are sold, plot the point (3000, 1000) on the graph. The point is in the solution region, so the coordinates satisfy both inequalities.

You can also substitute 3000 for x and 1000 for y and see if you get true statements.

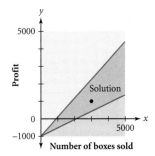

$$y \geq -1000 + 0.47x$$
$$1000 \ \square \ -1000 + 0.47(3000) \quad \text{and}$$
$$1000 \geq 410$$

$$y \leq -1000 + 1.1x$$
$$1000 \ \square \ -1000 + 1.1(3000)$$
$$1000 \leq 2300$$

Both inequalities are true, so it is possible to sell 3000 boxes and make $1,000.

With enough constraints the solution to a system of inequalities might resemble a geometric shape or polygon. No matter how small the region, there are infinitely many points that satisfy the system. In some cases, the solution to a system of inequalities might be only a line or a line segment, but a line or segment still represents infinitely many solutions. It is also possible for the solution region to be merely a single point, or for there to be no solution region at all.

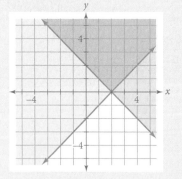
EXERCISES

▶ **Practice Your Skills**

1. Match each system of inequalities with its graph.

a. $\begin{cases} y < 3 \\ x \geq 2 \end{cases}$ iii

b. $\begin{cases} y > 2 + x \\ y > 1 - x \end{cases}$ i

c. $\begin{cases} 2x - y \leq 6 \\ 3x + 2y \geq 12 \end{cases}$ ii

i.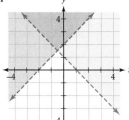

ii.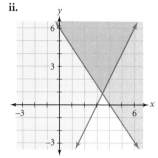

iii.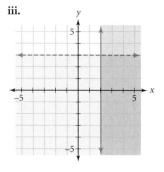

2. Here is the graph of this system of inequalities:

$$\begin{cases} y > x \\ y > 2 - \dfrac{1}{2}x \end{cases}$$

Is each point listed a solution to the system? Explain why or why not.

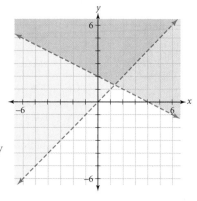

a. (1, 2) @

b. (3, 2)

c. $\left(\dfrac{4}{3}, \dfrac{4}{3} \right)$

No; for both inequalities, $\dfrac{4}{3} > \dfrac{4}{3}$ is not true.

d. (5, −3)

No; neither inequality is satisfied.

3. Consider these two inequalities together as a system.

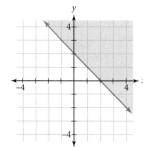   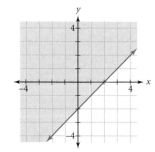

a. Name the inequality pictured in each graph. @ $y \geq -x + 2; y \geq x - 2$

b. Sketch a graph showing the solution to this system.

4. Sketch a graph showing the solution to each system.

    a. $y \le 2$ **b.** $x + y \le 4$

       $x < 2$ $x - y \le 4$

5. Write a system of inequalities for the solution shown on the graph.

$$\begin{cases} y > 2 - x \\ y < 2 \\ x < 3 \end{cases}$$

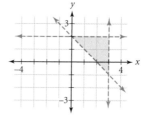

▶ Reason and Apply

6. APPLICATION The cereal company from Example B decides to raise the scholarship amount to $1,250. It also lowers the cereal's price so that the expected profit from a single box is between $0.40 and $1.00.

    a. Write the inequalities to represent this new situation. @ $y \ge -1250 + 0.40x, y \le -1250 + 1.00x, x \ge 0$

    b. Graph the expected revenue for up to 5000 boxes sold in a month. @

7. APPLICATION On Kids' Night, every adult admitted into a restaurant must be escorted by at least one child. The restaurant has a maximum seating capacity of 75 people.

7a.
$$\begin{cases} A \le C \\ A + C \le 75 \\ A \ge 0 \\ C \ge 0 \end{cases}$$

    a. Write a system of inequalities to represent the constraints in this situation. @

    b. Graph the solution. Is it possible for 50 children to escort 10 adults into the restaurant?

    c. Why might the restaurant reconsider the rules for Kids' Night? Add a new constraint to address these concerns. Draw a graph of the new solution.

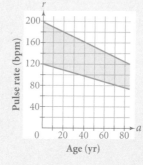

8. APPLICATION The American College of Sports Medicine considers age as one factor when it recommends low and high heart rates during workout sessions. For safe and efficient training, your heart rate should be between 55% and 90% of the maximum heart rate level. The maximum heart rate is calculated by subtracting a person's age from 220 beats per minute.

    a. Define variables and write an equation relating age and maximum heart rate during workouts.

    b. Write a system of inequalities to represent the recommended high and low heart rates during a workout. @

    c. Graph the solution to show a region of safe and efficient heart rates for people of any age.

    d. What constraints should you add to limit your region to show the safe and efficient heart rates for people between the ages of 14 and 40? @ $a \ge 14$ and $a \le 40$

    e. Graph the new solution for 8d.

Pulse rate

Age

7c. Answers will vary. It is possible to have all children and no adults at the restaurant. One possible additional constraint is that there must be at least one adult per five children, or $A \ge \frac{1}{5}C$. The solution for this set of constraints is the triangular region bounded by $A \le C, A + C \le 75$, and $A \ge 0.2C$.

8a. $r = 220 - a$, where a represents age in years and r represents the heart rate in beats per minute

8b. $\begin{cases} r \le 0.90(220 - a) \\ r \ge 0.55(220 - a) \end{cases}$ or $\begin{cases} r \le 198 - 0.90a \\ r \ge 121 - 0.55a \end{cases}$

8c.
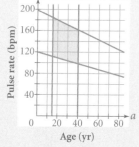
Age (yr)

8e.
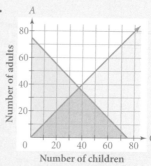
Age (yr)

4a.
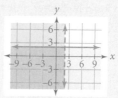

4b.
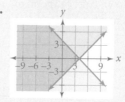

Exercise 6 Don't mark students wrong if they don't include the inequality $x \ge 0$. It is assumed but not stated in the example.

6b.
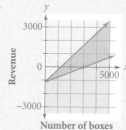
Number of boxes

Exercise 7 A common error is to translate "every adult must be escorted by at least one child" as $A \ge 1C$ or $A \ge C$. Rather than just announcing that the inequality is backward, try to engage students in a conversation about how A and C represent numbers of adults and children, not just the words *adult* and *child*. Students may not list the inequalities $A \ge 0$ and $C \ge 0$. The Sketchpad demonstration Linear Programming can be used to replace this exercise.

7b.

Number of children

All the points in the dark-shaded triangular region satisfy the two inequalities. The point (50, 10) represents the situation in which 50 children escort 10 adults.

keymath.com/DA

Exercises 9 and 10 Some students may find it difficult to work backward from the region to the inequalities, especially because they first have to find the equations of the lines. Suggest that they first write down a list of the steps and then follow their plan.

10. $AB: y \leq \frac{2}{3}x + \frac{5}{3}$;

$BC: y \leq -\frac{3}{5}x + \frac{59}{5}$;

$AC: y \geq \frac{1}{11}x + \frac{31}{11}$

11. The region is a pentagon.

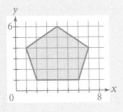

9. Write two inequalities that describe the shaded area below. Assume that the boundaries are solid lines and that each grid mark represents 1 unit.

$x \geq 3$ and $y \geq -2 + \frac{1}{2}x$

10. Write a system of inequalities to describe the shaded area on the graph at right. Write each slope as a fraction. ⓗ

11. Graph this system of inequalities on the same set of axes. Describe the shape of the region.

$$\begin{cases} y \leq 4 + \frac{2}{3}(x - 1) \\ y \leq 6 - \frac{2}{3}(x - 4) \\ y \geq -17 + 3x \\ y \geq 1 \\ y \geq 7 - 3x \end{cases}$$

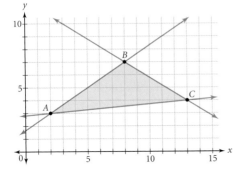

12. Write a system of inequalities that defines each shaded region of parallelogram $ABCD$ in the graph at right. ⓗ

Region 1: $\begin{cases} y \geq 3 \\ y \geq x - 2 \\ y \leq \frac{1}{3}x + \frac{8}{3} \end{cases}$ Region 2: $\begin{cases} y \leq 3 \\ y \leq x - 2 \\ y \geq \frac{1}{3}x \end{cases}$

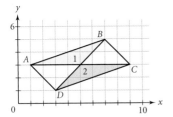

▶ **Review**

2.3 **13.** **APPLICATION** Manuel has a sales job at a local furniture store. Once a year, on Employees' Day, every item in the store is 15% off regular price. In addition, salespeople get to take home 25% commission on the items they sell as a bonus.

  a. A loft bed with a built-in desk and closet usually costs $839. What will it cost on Employees' Day? ⓐ $713.15

  b. At the end of the day, Manuel's bonus is $239.45. How many dollars worth of merchandise did he sell? ⓗ $957.80

2.8 **14.** Think about the number trick shown at right.

    a. Layla got a final number of 4. What was her original number? 4

    b. Robert got a final answer of 10. What was his original number? 10

    c. Let x represent the starting number. Write an algebraic expression to represent this sequence of operations. Then simplify the expression as much as possible.

x	_____
Ans · 3	_____
Ans + 12	_____
Ans / 5	_____
Ans − 1.4	_____
Ans · 10	_____
Ans − 10	_____
Ans / 6	_____

14c. $\dfrac{10\left(\frac{3x+12}{5}-1.4\right)-10}{6}$,

which simplifies to x

5.3 **15.** Solve each system of equations by using a symbolic method. Check that your solutions are correct.

    a. $\begin{cases} y = 4x - 3 \\ y = 2x + 9 \end{cases}$ **b.** $\begin{cases} 3x - 4y = -2 \\ -2x + 3y = 1 \end{cases}$

        $x = 6, y = 21$ $x = -2, y = -1$

5.2 **16.** Mr. Diaz makes an organic weed killer by mixing 8 ounces of distilled white vinegar with 20 ounces of special-strength pickling vinegar. Distilled white vinegar is 5% acid and Mr. Diaz's mixture is 15% acid. What is the acid concentration of the pickling vinegar? 19% acid

IMPROVING YOUR REASONING SKILLS

Suppose 9 crows each make 9 caws 9 times throughout the day. How many total caws are there?

Suppose 99 crows make 99 caws 99 separate times in one day. Now how many caws are there?

Answer the question again for 999 crows making 999 caws 999 times. If you continue this pattern of problems, at what number does your calculator round the answer? What is the exact number of caws in this case?

Write the answers to the first three questions and look for a pattern. Use it to find how many caws there are when the number is 99,999. With 86,400 seconds in a day, this means that each crow makes more than one caw per second every hour!

IMPROVING REASONING SKILLS

The calculators referred to in the calculator notes will use scientific notation for numerals with more than ten digits. Some more powerful calculators, such as the TI-89, will hold many more digits. At 9,999 crows, the TI-83 begins rounding.

Crows	Caws
9	729
99	970,299
999	997,002,999
9,999	999,700,029,999
99,999	999,970,000,299,999

In this chapter you learned to model many situations with a **system of equations** in two variables. You learned that systems of linear equations can have zero, one, or infinitely many solutions. You used tables, used graphs, and solved symbolically to find the solutions to systems. You discovered that the methods of **elimination, substitution,** and **row operations** on a matrix allow you to find exact solutions to problems, not just the approximations of graphs and tables.

Then you analyzed situations involving **inequalities** and discovered how to find their solutions using graphs, tables, and symbolic manipulation. The graph of an inequality in one variable is a part of a number line, and the graph of a linear inequality in two variables is a shaded **half-plane** that contains points whose coordinates make the inequality true. A **compound inequality** is the combination of two inequalities.

You discovered how to use inequalities to define **constraints** that limit the solution possibilities in real-world applications. You learned how to graph a **system of inequalities.**

EXERCISES

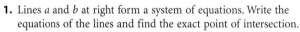

@ Answers are provided for all exercises in this set.

1. Lines *a* and *b* at right form a system of equations. Write the equations of the lines and find the exact point of intersection.

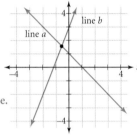

2. Find the point where the graphs of the equations intersect. Check your answer.

$$\begin{cases} 3x - 2y = 10 \\ x + 2y = 6 \end{cases}$$ The lines meet at the point $(4, 1)$; the equations $3(4) - 2(1) = 10$ and $(4) + 2(1) = 6$ are both true.

3. Graph this system of equations, and find the solution point.

$$\begin{cases} y = 5 - 0.5(x - 3) \\ y = -4 + 1.5(x + 2) \end{cases}$$

4. Show the steps involved in solving this system symbolically by the substitution method. Justify each step.

$$\begin{cases} y = 16 + 4.3(x - 5) \\ y = -7 + 4.2x \end{cases}$$

5. Complete each sentence. . . . the slopes are the same but the intercepts are different (the lines are parallel).

a. A system of two linear equations has no solution if . . .

b. A system of two linear equations has infinitely many solutions if . . .   . . . the slopes are the same and the intercepts are the same (the lines coincide).

c. A system of two linear equations has exactly one solution if . . .

. . . the slopes are different (the lines intersect in a single point).

3.

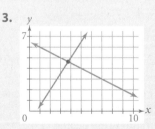

The point of intersection is $(3.75, 4.625)$.

6. Name the inequality that each graph represents.

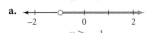

a.

$x > -1$

b.

$x < 2$

c.

$-2 \le x < 1$

7. Solve the inequality $5 \le 2 - 3x$ for x and graph the solution on a number line.

$x \le -1$

8. Write a system of inequalities to describe this shaded area.

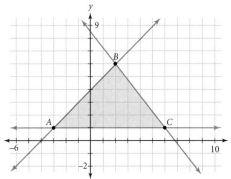

$$\begin{cases} y \le x + 4 \\ y \le -1.25x + 8.5 \\ y \ge 1 \end{cases}$$

9. APPLICATION Harold cuts lawns after school. He has a problem on Wednesdays when he cuts Mr. Fleming's lawn. His lawn mower has two speeds—at the higher speed he can get the job done quickly, but he always runs out of gas; at the lower speed he has plenty of gas, but it seems to take forever to get the job done. So he has collected this information.

- On Monday he cut a 15-meter-by-12-meter lawn at the higher speed in 18 minutes. He used a half tank of gas, or 0.6 liter.

- On Tuesday he cut a 20-meter-by-14-meter lawn at the lower speed in 40 minutes. He used a half tank of gas.

- Mr. Fleming's lawn measures 22 meters by 18 meters.

a. How many square meters of lawn can Harold cut per minute at the higher speed? At the lower speed?   10 m²/min; 7 m²/min

b. If Harold decides to cut Mr. Fleming's lawn using the higher speed for 10 minutes and the lower speed for 8 minutes, will he finish the job?   No; he will cut 156 m², and the lawn measures 396 m².

c. Let h represent the number of minutes cutting at higher speed, and let l represent the number of minutes cutting at lower speed. Write an equation that models completion of Mr. Fleming's lawn. $10h + 7l = 396$

d. How much gas does the lawn mower use in liters per minute at the higher speed? At the lower speed? $\frac{1}{30}$ L/min; $\frac{3}{200}$ L/min

e. Write an equation in terms of h and l that has Harold use all of his gas. $\frac{h}{30} + \frac{3l}{200} = 1.2$

f. Using the equations from 9c and e, solve the system and give a real-world meaning of the solution. $l = 14.4$ min, $h = 29.52$ min; if Harold cuts for 29.52 min at the higher speed and 14.4 min at the lower speed, he will finish Mr. Fleming's lawn and use one full tank of gas.

10. Use row operations to find the solution matrix for this system.

$$\begin{cases} 7x + 3y = -45 \\ x + 6y = -51 \end{cases} \begin{bmatrix} 1 & 0 & -3 \\ 0 & 1 & -8 \end{bmatrix}$$

4.

$16 + 4.3(x - 5) = -7 + 4.2x$	Set the right sides of the two equations equal to each other.
$16 + 4.3x - 21.5 = -7 + 4.2x$	Apply the distributive property.
$-5.5 + 4.3x = -7 + 4.2x$	Subtract.
$0.1x = -1.5$	Add $-4.2x$ and 5.5 to both sides.
$x = -15$	Divide both sides by 0.1.
$y = -7 + 4.2(-15)$	Substitute -15 for x to find y.
$y = -70$	Multiply and add.

The solution is $x = -15$ and $y = -70$.

Take Another Look

Linear programming problems like this one deal with many more variables and inequalities. An application might require that you maximize or minimize a linear function of the two variables, using only points in this region. The largest and smallest values of the function occur along the boundary of the region, usually at a corner. These problems are a major application of mathematics today.

$$\text{System:} \begin{cases} x \le 6000 \\ y \le 8000 \\ x + y \le 10,000 \\ x \ge 0 \\ y \ge 0 \end{cases}$$

The profit is given by $15x + 10y$. At (6000, 4000), the profit is the maximum, $130,000.

TAKE ANOTHER LOOK

Businesses use systems of equations and inequalities to determine how to maximize profits. A process called **linear programming** applies the concepts of constraints, points of intersection, and algebraic expressions to solve this very real application problem. Here is one example.

A company manufactures scooters and skateboards. The factory has the capacity to make at most 6000 scooters in one day, and the factory can make at most 8000 skateboards in one day. However, the factory can produce a combination of no more than 10,000 scooters and skateboards together. Define variables and write a system of three inequalities to describe these constraints. Label a set of axes and graph the solution. This is called a **feasible region.** What do the points in this shaded region represent? Find the points of intersection at the corners of this region.

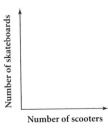

The company makes a profit of $15 per scooter and $10 per skateboard. How many of each should the company make to maximize its profits? To answer this question, use the variables defined earlier to write an expression to find the total profit the company makes from scooters and skateboards. Then substitute the coordinates of several points from the feasible region including the points of intersection. For example, if the company makes 5000 scooters and 5000 skateboards, substitute 5000 for x and 5000 for y into your expression to find the profit. Which point gave you the greatest profit?

Professional skateboarder Tony Hawk performs at the X Games.

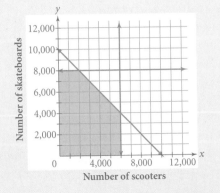

Assessing What You've Learned

In each of the five chapters from Chapter 0 to Chapter 4, you were introduced to a different way to assess what you learned. Maybe you have tried all five ways— keeping a portfolio, writing in your journal, organizing your notebook, giving a presentation, and doing a performance assessment. Maybe you have tried just a couple of these methods. Probably, your teacher has adapted these ideas to suit the needs of your class.

By now, you should realize that assessment is not just giving and taking tests. In the working world, performance in some occupations can be measured in tests, but in all occupations, there is a need to communicate what you know to coworkers. In all jobs, workers demonstrate to their employer or to their clients, patients, or customers that they are skilled in their fields. They need to show they are creative and flexible enough to apply what they've learned in new situations. Assessing your own understanding and letting others assess what you know gives you practice in this important life skill. It also helps you develop good study habits, and that, in turn, will help you advance in school and give you the best possible opportunities in your work life. Keep that in mind as you try one or more of these suggestions.

 UPDATE YOUR PORTFOLIO Choose your best graph of a system of inequalities from this chapter to add to your portfolio. Redraw the graph with a clearly labeled set of axes. Use color to highlight each inequality and its half-plane. Indicate the solution region with a visually pleasing design or pattern.

 WRITE IN YOUR JOURNAL Add to your journal by answering one of these prompts:
- You have learned five methods to find a solution to a system of equations. Which method do you like best? Which one is the most challenging to you? What are the advantages and disadvantages of each method?
- Describe in writing the difference between an inequality in one variable and an inequality in two variables. How do the graphs of the solutions differ? Compare these to the graph of a system of inequalities.

 ORGANIZE YOUR NOTEBOOK Update your notebook with an example, investigation, or exercise that demonstrates each solution method for a system of equations. Add one problem that demonstrates each of these concepts: inequalities in one variable, inequalities in two variables, and systems of inequalities.

 GIVE A PRESENTATION Write your own word problem for a system of equations or inequalities. Choose a setting that is meaningful to you or that you wish to know more about, and write a problem to model the situation. It can be about winning times for Olympic events, the point where two objects meet while traveling, percent mixture problems, or something new you created. Solve the problem using one of the methods you learned in this chapter. Make a poster of the problem and its solution, and present it to the class. Work with a partner or in a group.

 PERFORMANCE ASSESSMENT As a classmate, family member, or teacher watches, solve a system of equations using at least two different methods. Explain your process, and show how to check your solution.

For written assessment, use Constructive Assessment items for this chapter or one of the chapter tests from Assessment Resources. Or create your own test using the Test Generator CD, omitting matrices if you are not covering them.

FACILITATING SELF-ASSESSMENT

To help students complete the portfolio described in Assessing What You've Learned, suggest that they consider for evaluation their work in Lesson 5.1, Exercises 8 and 10; Lesson 5.2, Exercise 12; Lesson 5.3, Exercises 9 and 14; Lesson 5.4, Exercises 9–11; Lesson 5.5, Exercise 8; Lesson 5.6, Exercises 8 and 10; and Lesson 5.7, Exercises 8 and 11.

CHAPTER

6

Exponents and Exponential Models

Overview

For studying relationships between sets of numbers, the idea of a mathematical function is central. So far in *Discovering Algebra* students have been studying functions in the guise of linear equations and systems. Before studying the *concept* of function in Chapter 7, students encounter another special case in this chapter: exponential functions. In **Lesson 6.1,** students model exponential growth through recursion with constant multipliers. In **Lesson 6.2,** students discover how to write exponential equations to model the real-life growth being simulated by the recursive routines. Students review the multiplication property of exponents in **Lesson 6.3,** where they are also introduced to the power properties. In **Lesson 6.4,** the multiplication property of exponents is used to introduce and develop scientific notation for large numbers. In **Lesson 6.5,** students review the division property of exponents and then combine exponential expressions involving both multiplication and division. **Lesson 6.6** introduces students to nonpositive exponents as they learn how to use scientific notation for very small numbers. In **Lesson 6.7,** students fit an exponential model to a set of data. **Lesson 6.8** is an activity day in which students do one of two experiments related to exponential decay.

The Mathematics

Exponential Change

Up to this point in *Discovering Algebra,* the phenomena studied have exhibited a constant rate of change. That is, for every unit of change in x, the change in y has been constant. Values can be generated on a calculator by a recursive procedure involving *addition* of a constant at each step.

To model many real-life phenomena, however, values often are best generated on a calculator by recursively *multiplying* by a constant rather than by adding. Instead of consecutive terms having a constant *difference,* they have a constant *ratio.* (A sequence of terms generated by multiplying by a constant is known as a

geometric sequence, though this terminology isn't used.) The rate of change is not constant but rather is changing in a regular way. The most common examples of these phenomena are financial investments, populations, heating, cooling, and radioactive decay.

A constant rate of change can be represented by an equation of the form $y = a + bx$. The constant b is added to a repeatedly, x times. In contrast, with the multiplicative model, the equation is $y = ab^x$. The constant b multiplies a repeatedly, x times. In this case, the rate of change is not constant, and b isn't the rate of change. In the exponential model, b represents the *constant multiplier* or *growth factor* (even when b is less than 1, in which case the values of y are shrinking rather than growing).

The graph of $y = a + bx$ is a straight line, so the equation represents what is called *linear change.* Because the variable x is an exponent in $y = ab^x$, this kind of change is called *exponential change.* The slope of the graph of $y = ab^x$ is always changing.

For most phenomena exhibiting exponential change, we don't know the constant multiplier directly, but rather we know what portion of y is being added on or removed for each unit change in x. For example, a financial investment earns interest at an annual rate of 5%, or carbon-14 atoms decay at a rate of 35% every 1000 years. In these cases, the constant multiplier b is best written in terms of its relationship to 1. In the case of growth, we write $y = a(1 + r)^x$ and call r the *growth rate.* In the case of decay, we write $y = a(1 - r)^x$ and call r the *decay rate.* The quantities $(1 + r)^x$ and $(1 - r)^x$ are dimensionless numbers being multiplied by the initial value a, which has dimensions.

As a quick way to summarize exponential decay, especially of radioactive substances, scientists often refer to the *half-life* of a particle. The half-life is the amount of change in x that is required to halve the value of y. The fact that the half-life is independent of the initial value of y (it takes just as long to reduce y from 1000 to 500 as from 100 to 50) is an important feature of exponential change.

332A   CHAPTER 6 INTERLEAF Exponents and Exponential Models

Going Backward

Just as we often want to solve the linear equation $y = a + bx$ for x in order to predict when growth will reach a certain point, we frequently want to solve the exponential equation $y = ab^x$ for x. That is, we want to find the value of the exponent. There are several ways to do this. To get an approximate value of x, calculator graphs and tables are fine. So is the guess-and-check method—trying various values of x and gradually homing in on one that gives the desired value of y. For a more exact solution, logarithms can be used.

Scientific Notation and Significant Digits

The note on significant digits on page 357 will help you guide students in determining the digits to display in scientific notation or after a decimal point.

Using This Chapter

If your students are already proficient at using the rules of exponents and scientific notation, you can skim or skip Lessons 6.3–6.5. If your class is familiar with nonpositive exponents, you can skip Lesson 6.6. On the other hand, if students are very weak at exponents and you skipped Chapter 0, you might want to do Lessons 0.2 and 0.3 before embarking on this chapter.

Resources

Discovering Algebra Resources

Teaching and Worksheet Masters
Lessons 6.2, 6.3, 6.5, 6.6, 6.7, 6.8

Calculator Notes 0H, 3A, 6A, 6B, 6C, 6D

Fathom Demonstrations
Lessons 6.2, 6.7

CBL 2 Demonstration
Lesson 6.7

Dynamic Algebra Explorations online
Lessons 6.1, 6.2, 6.8

Assessment Resources
Quiz 1 (Lessons 6.1, 6.2)
Quiz 2 (Lessons 6.3–6.6)
Quiz 3 (Lesson 6.7)
Chapter 6 Test
Chapter 6 Constructive Assessment Options

More Practice Your Skills for Chapter 6

Condensed Lessons for Chapter 6

Other Resources

Powers of Ten. Santa Monica, California: Pyramid Film and Video, 1984.

Powers of Ten by Philip and Phylis Morrison.

Functional Melodies by Scott Beall.

Graphic Algebra by Gary Asp et al.

For complete references to these and other resources, see www.keypress.com/DA.

Materials

- graph paper
- paper plates
- protractors
- small counters
- balls
- metersticks
- empty soda cans
- string
- motion sensor, *optional*

Pacing Guide

	day 1	day 2	day 3	day 4	day 5	day 6	day 7	day 8	day 9	day 10
standard	6.1	6.2	6.2	quiz, 6.3	6.4	6.5	6.6	6.6	quiz, 6.7	6.7
enriched	6.1	6.2	6.2, project	quiz, 6.3	6.4	6.5	6.6	6.6	quiz, 6.7	6.7, project
block	6.1, 6.2	6.2, 6.3	6.4, 6.5	6.6	quiz, 6.7	6.8, review	assessment			

	day 11	day 12	day 13	day 14	day 15	day 16	day 17	day 18	day 19	day 20
standard	6.8	review	assessment							
enriched	6.8	review, TAL	assessment							

Exponents and Exponential Models

- Write the exponential form of a sequence generated recursively by a constant multiplier

- Review or learn the multiplication, division, and power properties of exponents

- Move between scientific notation (by hand and on a calculator) and standard notation for numbers

- Rewrite an expression with exponents as an expression with the opposite of those exponents

- Write exponential equations that model real-world growth and decay data

This "Chinese Horse" is part of a prehistoric cave painting in Lascaux, France. Scientific methods that use equations with exponents have determined that parts of the Lascaux cave paintings are more than 15,000 years old. For archaeologists, dating ancient artifacts helps them understand how civilizations evolved. Drawings and pieces of art help them understand what existed at that time and what was important to the civilization. You will see that exponents are useful in many other real-world settings too.

OBJECTIVES

In this chapter you will
- write recursive routines for nonlinear sequences
- learn an equation for exponential growth or decrease
- use properties of exponents to rewrite expressions
- write numbers in scientific notation
- model real-world data with exponential equations

A standard procedure for determining age is by carbon dating (as discussed in the chapter), but many of the paints used in Lascaux are metal-based and don't contain carbon. The claim that the paintings are 15,000 years old is based on carbon dating of paintings done in charcoal and on other artifacts at the site. Non-carbon-based methods indicate that the caves are about 17,000 years old. Students can find more details about these dating methods using the Internet links for Lesson 6.7 available at www.keymath.com/DA. Students might also want to investigate the deterioration of cultural treasures elsewhere, such as in Italy or Egypt.

Knowledge of ancient art has made many modern artists concerned about the durability of the materials they use. Deterioration due to exposure and the growth of organisms in organic fibers and pigments is usually exponential. Students may be interested in the archival methods and materials for preserving family photographs or books. Will the latest film you saw be around in 15,000 years?

LESSON

6.1

Recursive Routines

Have you ever noticed that it doesn't take very long for a cup of steaming hot chocolate to cool to sipping temperature? If so, then you've also noticed that it stays about the same temperature for a long time. Have you ever left food in your locker? It might look fine for several days, then suddenly some mold appears and a few days later it's covered with mold. The same mathematical principle describes both of these situations. Yet these patterns are different from the linear patterns you saw in rising elevators and shortening ropes— you modeled those situations with repeated addition or subtraction. Now you'll investigate a different type of pattern, a pattern seen in a population that increases very rapidly.

Slow buds the pink dawn
like a rose
From out night's gray and
cloudy sheath
Softly and still it grows
and grows
Petal by petal, leaf by leaf
SUSAN COOLIDGE

Investigation
Bugs, Bugs, Everywhere Bugs

You will need
- graph paper

Imagine that a bug population has invaded your classroom. One day you notice 16 bugs. Every day new bugs hatch, increasing the population by 50% each week. So, in the first week the population increases by 8 bugs.

Step 1 In a table like this one, record the total number of bugs at the end of each week for 4 weeks.

Bug Invasion

Weeks elapsed	Total number of bugs	Increase in number of bugs (rate of change per week)	Ratio of this week's total to last week's total
Start (0)	16	/////	/////
1	24	8	$\frac{24}{16} = \frac{3}{2} = 1.5$
2	36	12	$\frac{36}{24} = \frac{3}{2} = 1.5$
3	54	18	$\frac{54}{36} = \frac{3}{2} = 1.5$
4	81	27	$\frac{81}{54} = \frac{3}{2} = 1.5$

Step 2 The increase in the number of bugs each week is the population's rate of change per week. Calculate each rate of change and record it in your table. Does the rate of change show a linear pattern? Why or why not?

Step 3 Let x represent the number of weeks elapsed, and let y represent the total number of bugs. Graph the data using (0, 16) for the first point. Connect the points with line segments and describe how the slope changes from point to point.

NCTM STANDARDS

CONTENT		PROCESS	
✔	Number		Problem Solving
✔	Algebra	✔	Reasoning
	Geometry		Communication
	Measurement	✔	Connections
✔	Data/Probability	✔	Representation

LESSON OBJECTIVES

- Begin to investigate geometric sequences using recursive routines
- See examples of growth and decay that can be modeled recursively

PLANNING

LESSON OUTLINE

One day:
30 min	Investigation
5 min	Sharing
10 min	Examples
5 min	Closing

MATERIALS

- graph paper
- counters, *optional*
- Calculator Note 3A

TEACHING

In some situations values change through multiplying by a constant rather than through adding a constant.

Guiding the Investigation

One Step
"You have a colony of 16 bugs, and the number is increasing by 50% each week. Use your calculators to recursively generate the colony's population for four weeks and to graph the data points. Then decide on a good recursive routine to fit the data." Be sure at least one group thinks about multiplication and not just addition. While groups share a variety of ideas, elicit the notion of the constant multiplier.

Groups might model the growth using counters. Or you may work out the first stage or two with the class.

See page 724 for answers to Steps 2 and 3.

Step 2 Remind students that a rate of change has dimensions. **[Ask]** "What are the units for the rate of change?" [bugs per week] **[Alert]** If students think the pattern is linear because the rate of change shows a regular pattern, ask what the constant difference is.

Step 3 Students can also be challenged to graph rate of change (y) versus weeks (x) or to find the rate of change of the rate of change. The rate of change of exponential growth is also exponential.

Step 5 $\frac{3}{2}$ or 1.5; multiply the starting number by $\frac{3}{2}$ five times.

Step 6 {0, 16} sets the starting value (when 0 weeks have elapsed) at 16. {Ans (1) + 1, Ans (2) · 1.5} increases the number of weeks elapsed by 1 and multiplies the population value by 1.5.

Step 7 Students will get decimal values for weeks 5 to 8. **[Ask]** "What does a decimal mean when you are talking about population?" [A fraction of a bug cannot exist.] **[Alert]** If students have trouble entering this recursive routine, they may be entering parentheses for braces or vice versa. Remind them to use the 2nd key to make braces around the list {0, 16} and around the entire recursive expression.

Step 7

```
        {1 24}
        {2 36}
        {3 54}
        {4 81}
     {5 121.5}
    {6 182.25}
   {7 273.375}
  {8 410.0625}
```

SHARING IDEAS

Point out the quotation that opens the lesson. Susan Coolidge (1835–1905), also known as Sarah Chauncey Woolsey, was an author of children's literature. This stanza creates an image of growth, a central topic of this chapter.

Ask a student or group to present the table.

Step 4 The constant ratio of $\frac{3}{2}$ indicates that the bug population is multiplied by 1.5 each week. Recursive routines with repeated addition create linear patterns. But here the rate of change between two successive bug populations changes every week. The new values result from multiplication by a constant amount.

Step 8 After 20 wk: 53,204 bugs; after 30 wk: 3,068,017 bugs; possible answer: Natural factors—decreasing resources, death, migration—would cause the population to level off.

Step 4 Calculate the ratio of the number of bugs each week to the number of bugs the previous week, and record it in the table. For example, divide the population after 1 week has elapsed by the population when 0 weeks have elapsed. Repeat this process to complete your table. How do these ratios compare? Explain what the ratios tell you about the bug population growth.

Step 5 What is the **constant multiplier** for the bug population? How can you use this number to calculate the population when 5 weeks have elapsed?

Step 6 Model the population growth by writing a recursive routine that shows the growing number of bugs. [▶ 🖥 See **Calculator Note 3A** to review recursive routines. ◀] Describe what each part of this calculator command does.

Step 7 By pressing `ENTER` a few times, check that your recursive routine gives the sequence of values in your table (in the column "Total number of bugs"). Use the routine to find the bug population at the end of weeks 5 to 8.

Step 8 What is the bug population after 20 weeks have elapsed? After 30 weeks have elapsed? What happens in the long run?

In the investigation you found that repeated multiplication is the key to growth of the bug population. Populations of people, animals, and even bacteria show similar growth patterns. Many decreasing patterns, like cooling liquids and decay of substances, can also be described with repeated multiplication.

EXAMPLE A Maria has saved $10,000 and wants to invest it for her daughter's college tuition. She is considering two options. Plan A guarantees a payment, or return, of $550 each year. Plan B grows by 5% each year. With each plan, what would Maria's new balance be after 5 years? After 10 years?

▶ **Solution** With plan A, Maria's investment would grow by $550 each year.

Year	Current balance	+	Return	=	New balance
1	10,000	+	550	=	10,550
2	10,550	+	550	=	11,100
3	11,100	+	550	=	11,650

A recursive routine to do this on your calculator is

{0, 10000} `ENTER`

{Ans(1)+1, Ans(2)+550} `ENTER`

`ENTER` , `ENTER` , . . .

After 5 years the new balance is $12,750. After 10 years it is $15,500.

```
{3 11650}
{4 12200}
{5 12750}
{6 13300}
{7 13850}
{8 14400}
{9 14950}
{10 15500}
```

[Ask] "How does the population growth of the bugs differ from linear growth? Does it make sense that the more bugs there are, the more will be added each week?" [Yes, there are more bugs reproducing.]

See whether the class can think of other situations in which growth takes place in a "the more there are, the more you get" way. This is a good opportunity to ask students to explain their reasoning without

acknowledging the correctness of their answers right away. If someone mentions financial investments, you can go right into Example A.

Assessing Progress

The investigation allows you to assess students' understanding of 50% as $\frac{1}{2}$ and their ability to work with decimals, follow directions systematically, calculate ratios, and enter a recursive sequence.

With plan B, money earns *interest* each year. The amount of interest is 5% of the current balance. To find the new balance at the end of the first year, add the interest to the current balance. Notice that there is a factor of 10,000 in both the current balance and the interest. You can apply the distributive property to write the expression for the new balance in **factored form.**

Year	Current balance	+	Interest (balance × interest rate)	=	New balance (factored form)
1	10,000	+	10,000 × 0.05	=	10,000(1 + 0.05), or 10,500
2	10,500	+	10,500 × 0.05	=	10,500(1 + 0.05), or 11,025
3	11,025	+	11,025 × 0.05	=	11,025(1 + 0.05), or about 11,576

In the first year the balance grows by $500, to $10,500. To find the new balance for the next year, you need to add 5% of $10,500 to the current $10,500 balance in the account.

Each year, the balance grows by 5%. To find each new balance, you use the constant multiplier 1 + 0.05, or 1.05.

You can generate the sequence of balances from year to year on your calculator using this recursive routine:

{0, 10000} `ENTER`

{Ans(1)+1, Ans(2) · (1+0.05)} `ENTER`

`ENTER`, `ENTER`, . . .

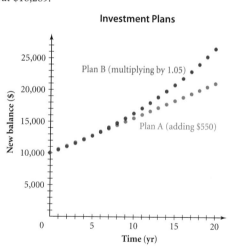

The calculator screen shows the sequence of new balances after the first 5 years. Notice that the balance grows by a larger amount each year. That's because each year you're finding a percent of a larger current balance than in the previous year. After 5 years the new balance is about $12,763. After 10 years it is about $16,289.

A graph illustrates how the investment plans compare. Given enough time, the balance from plan B, which is growing by a constant percent, will always outgrow the balance from plan A, which has only a constant amount added to it. After 20 years you see an even more significant difference: $26,533 compared to $21,000.

Investment Plans

Plan B (multiplying by 1.05)

Plan A (adding $550)

New balance ($) — Time (yr)

► **EXAMPLE A**

This example reinforces the concepts introduced in the investigation and shows how to write exponential growth in factored form. It also compares the results over time for linear and exponential growth. Be sure students understand that an exponential model represents much faster growth than a linear model.

The situation described is not very realistic, because interest is almost always compounded more frequently than once per year. Let students know that the student text is simplifying matters to help with understanding.

The starting balance is often called the *principal* and represented as *P*. Students can think of 1.05 as 105%, or 100% + 5% (principal + interest).

[Alert] Watch for difficulty with the factoring. Merely having students check it by distributing doesn't answer the question "How could I see how to do that?" Point out the occurrence of the same number in each term of the sum and ask what the result would be if you divided each term by that number.

[Ask] "How do banks actually round dollar amounts for balances? How does this compare with what your calculator does?" [A calculator will round up if the decimal represents more than half a cent, but many banks ignore fractions of a cent.]

You might point out that plan A is actually more profitable in the first two years. **[Ask]** "Which plan should Maria choose?" Encourage answers that are based on different assumptions.

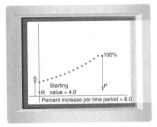
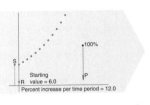

keymath.com/DA

[▶The graphs of growth defined by repeated multiplication share certain characteristics. You can use the **Dynamic Algebra Exploration** at www.keymath.com/DA to explore these graphs and to solve some of the exercises in this lesson. ◄]

It is helpful to think of a constant multiplier, like 1.05 in Example A, as a sum. The plus sign in $1 + 0.05$ shows that the pattern increases and 0.05 is the percent growth per year, written as a decimal. When a balance or population decreases, say, by 15% during a given time period, you write the constant multiplier as a difference, for example, $1 - 0.15$. The subtraction sign shows that the pattern decreases and 0.15 is the percent decrease per time period, written as a decimal.

Example B uses a proportion and a constant multiplier to calculate a marked-down price.

▶ EXAMPLE B

Encourage students to answer the final question posed in the solution by using a constant multiplier: $34.99(1 - 0.70) \approx 10.50$, so marking down by 70% once gives a different result from two 35% markdowns. Elicit the idea that the second markdown is taking 35% of a smaller amount. Exercise 12 revisits this idea.

EXAMPLE B

Birdbaths at the Feathered Friends store are marked down 35%. What is the cost of a birdbath that was originally priced $34.99? What is the cost if the birdbath is marked down 35% a second time?

▶ Solution

If an item is marked down 35%, then it must retain $100 - 35$ percent of its original price. That is, it will cost 65% of the original price. In Chapter 2, you learned how to set up a proportion using 65% and the ratio of cost, C, to original price.

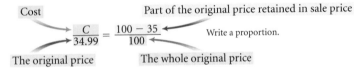

$$C = \frac{100 - 35}{100} \cdot 34.99 \quad \text{Multiply by 34.99 to undo the division.}$$

$$C \approx 22.74 \quad \text{Multiply and divide, and round to the nearest hundredth.}$$

So the cost after the 35% markdown is $22.74.

You can set up a proportion again to find the cost after the second markdown. Or, you can solve this problem using a constant multiplier. The cost after one 35% markdown is calculated like this:

$$34.99(1 - 0.35) \approx 22.74$$

Using a constant multiplier makes it easy to calculate the cost after the second markdown.

$$22.74(1 - 0.35) \approx 14.78$$

So the cost after two successive markdowns is \$14.78. Is this different than if the birdbath had been marked down 70% one time?

Constant multipliers can be positive or negative. These two sequences have the same starting value, but one has a multiplier of 2 and the other has a multiplier of −2.

3, 6, 12, 24, 48, . . .
3, −6, 12, −24, 48, . . .

How does the negative multiplier affect the sequence? The negative multiplier changes the sign on every other term. Every other term is the result of multiplying two negatives, and the other terms result from multiplying a negative and a positive.

EXERCISES

You will need your graphing calculator for Exercises **7** and **9**.

▶ Practice Your Skills

1. Give the starting value and constant multiplier for each sequence. Then find the 7th term of the sequence.
   a. 16, 20, 25, 31.25, . . . ⓐ starting value: 16; multiplier: 1.25; 7th term: 61.035
   b. 27, 18, 12, 8, . . . starting value: 27; multiplier: $\frac{2}{3}$, or $0.\overline{6}$; 7th term: $2.\overline{370}$, or $\frac{64}{27}$

2. Use a recursive routine to find the first six terms of a sequence that starts with 100 and has a constant multiplier of −1.6. Start with 100, then apply the rule Ans · −1.6; first six terms are 100, −160, 256, −409.6, 655.36, −1048.576.

3. Write each percent change as a ratio comparing the result to the original quantity. For example, a 3% increase is $\frac{103}{100}$. Then write it as a constant multiplier, for example, 1 + 0.03.
   a. 8% increase $\frac{108}{100}$; 1 + 0.08
   b. 11% decrease $\frac{89}{100}$; 1 − 0.11
   c. 12.5% growth ⓐ $\frac{1125}{1000}$, or $\frac{112.5}{100}$; 1 + 0.125
   d. $6\frac{1}{4}$% loss ⓐ $\frac{9,375}{10,000}$, or $\frac{93.75}{100}$; 1 − 0.0625
   e. x% increase $\frac{100 + x}{100}$; 1 + $\frac{x}{100}$
   f. y% decrease $\frac{100 - y}{100}$; 1 − $\frac{y}{100}$

4. Use the distributive property to rewrite each expression in an equivalent form. For example, you can write 500(1 + 0.05) as 500 + 500(0.05).
   a. 75 + 75(0.02)
   b. 1000 − 1000(0.18) ⓐ
   c. P + Pr ⓐ P(1 + r)
   d. 75(1 − 0.02) 75 − 75 · 0.02
   e. 80(1 − 0.24) 80 − 80 · 0.24
   f. A(1 − r) A − A · r

5. You may remember from Chapter 0 that the geometric pattern below is the beginning of a fractal called the *Sierpiński triangle*. The Stage 0 triangle below has a total shaded area of 32 square units. Write a recursive routine that generates the sequence of shaded areas in the pattern. Then use your routine to find the shaded area in Stages 2 and 5. ⓗ

Stage 0
Area = 32 square units

Stage 1
Area = 24 square units

Stage 2

Start with 32, then apply the rule Ans · 0.75; Stage 2 has a shaded area of 18 square units; Stage 5 has a shaded area of 7.59375 square units.

Exercise 4 *P* is commonly used in applications to mean *principal*. In 4f, *A* could mean *amount*. In both 4c and 4f, *r* could mean *rate*. If students try to write answers as single numbers, point out that they haven't factored or distributed.

4a. 75(1 + 0.02), or 75(1.02)
4b. 1000(1 − 0.18), or 1000(0.82)

Exercise 5 Students who have done Chapter 0 can draw Stage 3 (or higher) and calculate the shaded area of this figure. **[Ask]** "In Chapter 0, what mathematical operation did you use to express areas and lengths of fractals?"

Closing the Lesson

When values change through multiplying by a constant rather than through adding a constant, the constant is called a **constant multiplier.** The rate of change is not constant but increases as the amount increases. Examples include growth of populations and the growth of an interest-earning financial investment.

BUILDING UNDERSTANDING

Students practice recursive routines with constant multipliers.

ASSIGNING HOMEWORK

Essential	1–4, 6 or 7–9
Performance assessment	5, 7, 12
Portfolio	9
Journal	11
Group	6, 9
Review	13–16

▶ Helping with the Exercises

Exercise 1 The decay in 1b is represented by having a constant multiplier less than 1.

Exercise 2 In this sequence resulting from a negative multiplier, the terms are neither decreasing nor increasing—they go back and forth between negative and positive.

6a. Start with 20,000, then apply the rule Ans · (1 − 0.04).

6b. 5th term: 16,986.93; $16,982.93 is the selling price of the car after four price reductions.

Exercise 6c Students can solve problems like this by using graphs, calculator tables, or guess-and-check.

Exercise 7 [ELL] In the United States, a *billion* is a thousand millions. In other English-speaking countries, a billion is a million millions. "Round to the nearest 0.1 billion" means, in this text, round to the nearest hundred million.

7a. Start with 7.1, then apply the rule Ans · (1 + 0.117).

7c.

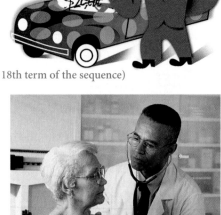

▶ **Reason and Apply**

6. APPLICATION Toward the end of the year, to make room for next year's models, a car dealer may decide to drop prices on this year's models. Imagine a car that has a sticker price of $20,000. The dealer lowers the price by 4% each week until the car sells.

a. Write a recursive routine to generate the sequence of decreasing prices. @

b. Find the 5th term and explain what your answer means in this situation. @

c. If the dealer paid $10,000 for the car, how many weeks would pass before the car's sale price would produce no profit for the dealer? 17 wk (the 18th term of the sequence)

7. APPLICATION Health care expenditures in the United States exceeded $1 trillion in the mid-1990s and are expected to exceed $2 trillion before 2010. Many elderly and disabled persons rely on Medicare benefits to help cover health care costs. According to the Centers for Medicare and Medicaid *2005 Annual Report,* Medicare expenditures were $7.1 billion in 1970.

a. Assume Medicare spending has increased by 11.7% per year since 1970. Write a recursive routine to generate the sequence of increasing Medicare spending. @

b. Use your recursive routine to find the missing table values. Round to the nearest $0.1 billion.

Medicare Spending

Year	1970	1975	1980	1985	1990	1995	2000	2005
Elapsed time (yr) x	0	5	10	15	20	25	30	35
Spending ($ billion) y	7.1	12.3	21.5	37.3	64.9	112.9	196.3	341.3

c. Plot the data points from your table and draw a smooth curve through them.

d. What does the shape of the curve suggest about Medicare spending? Do you think this is a realistic model? Answers will vary. The graph implies a smooth, ever-increasing amount of Medicare spending, which is probably not realistic.

8. APPLICATION Ima Shivring took a cup of hot cocoa outdoors where the temperature was 0°F. When she stepped outside, the cocoa was 115°F. The temperature in the cup dropped by 3% each minute.

a. Write a recursive routine to generate the sequence representing the temperature of the cocoa each minute. Start with 115, then apply the rule Ans · (1 − 0.03).

b. How many minutes does it take for the cocoa to cool to less than 80°F? 12 min

9. APPLICATION The advertisement for a Super-Duper Bouncing Ball says it rebounds to 85% of the height from which it is dropped.

a. If the ball is dropped from a starting height of 2 m, how high should it rebound on the first bounce? ⓐ 1.7 m

b. Write a recursive routine to generate the sequence of heights for the ball when it is dropped from a height of 2 m. ⓐ Start with 2, then apply the rule Ans · 0.85.

c. How high should the ball rebound on the sixth bounce? approximately 0.75 m

d. If the ball is dropped from a height of 10 ft, how high should it rebound on the tenth bounce? ⓗ approximately 1.97 ft

e. When the ball is dropped from a height of 10 ft, how many times will it bounce before the rebound height is less than 0.5 ft? 19 times

f. A collection of Super-Duper Bouncing Balls was tested. Each ball was dropped from a height of 2 m. The table shows the height of the first rebound for eight different balls. Do you think the advertisement's claim that the ball rebounds to 85% of the original height is fair? Explain your thinking.

Answers will vary. The mean is 1.7 m, or 85% of 2 m, and the median and mode are both 1.68 m, or 84% of 2 m. However, only two of the balls tested met or exceeded 85% of the drop height.

Balls Dropped from 2 m

Ball number	1	2	3	4	5	6	7	8
Height of rebound (m)	1.68	1.67	1.69	1.78	1.64	1.68	1.66	1.8

10. Look back at the six expressions in Exercise 4. Imagine that each expression represents the value of an antique that is increasing or decreasing in value each year. For each expression, identify whether it represents an increasing or decreasing situation, give the starting value, and give the percent increase or decrease per year. ⓗ

11. Grace manages a local charity. A wealthy benefactor has offered two options for making a donation over the next year. One option is to give $50 now and $25 each month after that. The second option is to give $1 now and twice that amount next month; each month afterward the benefactor would give twice the amount given the month before.

a. Determine how much Grace's charity would receive each month under each option. Use a table to show the values over the course of one year. ⓐ

b. Use another table to record the total amount Grace's charity will have received after each month.

c. Let x represent the number of the month (1 to 12), and let y represent the total amount Grace received after each month. On the same coordinate axes, graph the data for both options. How do the graphs compare?

d. Which option should Grace choose? Why?

Exercise 9 You might have students collect data for this exercise using motion sensors attached to calculators. See Lesson 6.8, Experiment 1.

10a. increasing; 75; 2%

10b. decreasing; 1000; 18%

10c. increasing; P; $100r\%$

10d. decreasing; 75; 2%

10e. decreasing; 80; 24%

10f. decreasing; A; $100r\%$

11c. The graph of the first plan is linear. The graph of the second is not; its slope increases between consecutive points.

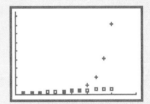

[0, 15, 3, 0, 4750, 500]

11d. Possible answer: Grace's charity will receive more total money with option 2. This option will also give the charity more income later in the year when the budget may be tighter.

11a.

	Jan	Feb	Mar	Apr	May	June	July	Aug	Sep	Oct	Nov	Dec
Option 1	$50	$25	$25	$25	$25	$25	$25	$25	$25	$25	$25	$25
Option 2	$1	$2	$4	$8	$16	$32	$64	$128	$256	$512	$1,024	$2,048

11b.

	Jan	Feb	Mar	Apr	May	June	July	Aug	Sep	Oct	Nov	Dec
Option 1	$50	$75	$100	$125	$150	$175	$200	$225	$250	$275	$300	$325
Option 2	$1	$3	$7	$15	$31	$63	$127	$255	$511	$1,023	$2,047	$4,095

Exercise 12 This exercise shows that a 3.5% increase followed by a 3.5% decrease does not get you back to where you started. Ask students to keep all the decimal places of their calculation on calculators so they won't think the small difference is due to round-off error. This is not an easy concept for students to under-stand. It highlights that you must always know 3.5% of what, not just 3.5%. Ask students having trouble to start with 200, increase by 10%, then decrease by 10%: $200 + 20 - 22$ is not 200. You might also draw a line segment, add 10% to it, and then point out that 10% of the new segment is longer than the amount that was added.

Exercise 14 This exercise reviews Lesson 4.3, but it asks for a line through points with non-integer coordinates.

16c. $y = 45$ for 600 min or less of use; $y = 45 + 0.55(x - 600)$ for more than 600 min of use.

16d. First plan: $67.50; second plan: $45.00 (she pays only the flat rate of $45.00). She should sign up for the second plan.

16e. First plan: $172.50; second plan: $182.50. He should sign up for the first plan.

12. APPLICATION Tamara works at a bookstore, where she earns $7.50 per hour.

a. Her employer is pleased with her work and gives her a 3.5% raise. What is her new hourly rate? $7.76

b. A few weeks later business drops off dramatically. The employer must reduce wages. He decreases Tamara's latest wage by 3.5%. What is her hourly rate now? $7.49

c. What is the final result of the two pay changes? Explain. ⓗ Her wage has dropped by $0.01/h because the increase was calculated as 3.5% of $7.50, but the decrease was based on $7.76.

▶ **Review**

4.3 **13.** Write an equation in point-slope form for a line with slope -1.2 that goes through the point (600, 0). Find the y-intercept. $y = -1.2(x - 600)$; y-intercept: (0, 720)

4.3 **14.** Find the equation of the line that passes through (2.2, 4.7) and (6.8, -3.9).
$y \approx 4.7 - 1.87(x - 2.2)$, or $y \approx -3.9 - 1.87(x - 6.8)$

3.4 **15.** Match the recursive routine to the equation.

a. $y = 3x + 7$ i
b. $y = -3x + 7$ iii
c. $y = 7x + 3$ ii
d. $y = -7x + 3$ iv

i. Start with 7, then apply the rule Ans $+ 3$.
ii. Start with 3, then apply the rule Ans $+ 7$.
iii. Start with 7, then apply the rule Ans $- 3$.
iv. Start with 3, then apply the rule Ans $- 7$.

5.2 **16. APPLICATION** A wireless phone service provider offers two calling plans. The first plan costs $50 per month and offers 500 minutes free per month; additional minutes cost 35¢ per minute. The second plan costs only $45 a month and offers 600 minutes free per month; but additional minutes cost more—55¢ per minute.

a. Define variables and write an equation for the first plan if you use it for 500 minutes or less. ⓐ Let x represent minutes of use and y represent cost; $y = 50$.

b. Write an equation for the first plan if you use it for more than 500 minutes. ⓐ $y = 50 + 0.35(x - 500)$

c. Write two equations for the second plan similar to those you wrote in 15a and b. Explain what each equation represents.

d. Sydney generally talks on her phone about 550 minutes per month. How much would each plan cost her? Which plan should she choose? ⓐ

e. Louis averages 850 minutes of phone use per month. How much would each plan cost him? Which plan should he choose?

f. For how many minutes of use will the cost of the plans be the same? How can you decide which of these two wireless plans is better for a new subscriber? ⓐ
The plans cost the same for 800 min of use. A new subscriber who will use more than 800 min should choose the first plan. If she will use 800 min or less, then the second plan is better.

Exponential Equations

Recursive routines are useful for seeing how a sequence develops and for generating the first few terms. But, as you learned in Chapter 3, if you're looking for the 50th term, you'll have to do many calculations to find your answer. For most of the sequences in Chapter 3, you found that the graphs of the points formed a linear pattern, so you learned how to write the equation of a line.

Recursive routines with a constant multiplier create a different type of increasing or decreasing pattern. In this lesson you'll discover the connection between these recursive routines and exponents. Then, with a new type of equation, you'll be able to find any term in a sequence based on a constant multiplier without having to find all the terms before it.

This sculpture, *Door to Door* (1995), was created by Filipino artist José Tence Ruiz (b 1956) from wood, cardboard, and other materials. The decreasing size of the boxes suggests an exponential pattern.

Investigation
Growth of the Koch Curve

You will need

- the worksheet Growth of the Koch Curve

keymath.com/DA

In this investigation you will look for patterns in the growth of a fractal. You may remember the *Koch curve* from Chapter 0. Here you will think about the relationship between the length of the Koch curve and the repeated multiplication you studied in Lesson 6.1. Stage 0 of the Koch curve is already drawn on the worksheet. It is a segment 27 units long.

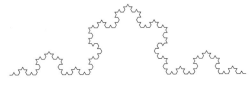

NCTM STANDARDS

CONTENT	PROCESS
✔ Number	Problem Solving
✔ Algebra	✔ Reasoning
✔ Geometry	✔ Communication
Measurement	✔ Connections
Data/Probability	✔ Representation

LESSON OBJECTIVES

- Explore exponential growth and decay patterns
- Discover the connection between recursive and exponential forms of geometric sequences

PLANNING

LESSON OUTLINE

First day:
40 min   Investigation
10 min   Sharing

Second day:
30 min   Examples
 5 min   Closing
15 min   Exercises

MATERIALS

- Growth of the Koch Curve (W)
- Koch Curve with Sketchpad (W), *optional*
- Calculator Note 6A
- Fathom demonstration Exponential Equations, *optional*

TEACHING

Values changing through multiplication by a constant can be represented using powers of the constant multiplier. The standard form of an exponential, $y = ab^x$, can be found from its linear counterpart $y = a + bx$ by changing the addition to multiplication and the multiplication to exponentiation.

One Step
Remind students of the Koch curve from Chapter 0, or introduce it. Ask them to find the constant multiplier for the length when moving from one stage of the curve to the next. Then have them use that multiplier to write expressions for the length of the curve at each of several stages. As you circulate, remind students to use exponents. During Sharing, ask for other examples of exponential growth and have the class make up a problem about a savings account.

Guiding the Investigation

You might want to explore the Koch curve and collect data for Step 2 with The Geometer's Sketchpad and the Koch Curve with Sketchpad worksheet or with the Dynamic Algebra Exploration Koch Curve Growth at www.keymath.com/DA.

Step 1 Students who did not do Chapter 0 may need help in seeing how to generate one stage from another. Have them write a rule. Students may describe something like "Remove the middle third and put a bottomless triangle on it." Alternatively, students can look back at page 14 in Lesson 0.3 to see further stages, or use the How Long Is This Fractal? worksheet from Lesson 0.3. Note that the Stage 0 Koch curve in Chapter 0 does not have length 27.

Step 3

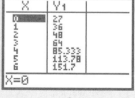

Stage 2

Stage 3

Step 5 Predictions will vary. Exact answers are Stage 4:
$27\left(\frac{4}{3}\right)\left(\frac{4}{3}\right)\left(\frac{4}{3}\right)\left(\frac{4}{3}\right) = 85.\overline{3}$,

and Stage 5:
$27\left(\frac{4}{3}\right)\left(\frac{4}{3}\right)\left(\frac{4}{3}\right)\left(\frac{4}{3}\right)\left(\frac{4}{3}\right) = 113.\overline{7}$.

Step 8 Some students may need to be reminded of what exponents are, especially if you skipped Chapter 0. Remember not to say that the exponent gives "the number of times the base is multiplied by itself," because if you multiply the number $\frac{4}{3}$ by itself two times, you'll get $\frac{4}{3} \times \frac{4}{3} \times \frac{4}{3}$, which is $\left(\frac{4}{3}\right)^3$. Rather, say that the exponent gives the number of times the base is a factor in the product.

Step 1 The figure should look like the one shown in the Student Edition, where each segment is 9 units long.

Step 1 Draw the Stage 1 figure below the Stage 0 figure. The first segment is drawn for you on the worksheet. As shown here, the Stage 1 figure has four segments, each $\frac{1}{3}$ the length of the Stage 0 segment.

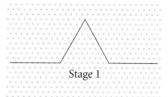

Stage 1

Step 2 Determine the total length at Stage 1 and record it in a table like this:

Stage number	Total length (units)	Ratio of this stage's length to previous stage's length
0	27	/////
1	36	$\frac{4}{3} = 1.\overline{3}$
2	48	$\frac{4}{3} = 1.\overline{3}$
3	64	$\frac{4}{3} = 1.\overline{3}$

Step 3 Draw the Stage 2 and Stage 3 figures of the fractal. Again, the first segment for each stage is drawn for you. Record the total length at each stage.

Step 4 Find the ratio of the total length at any stage to the total length at the previous stage. What is the constant multiplier? See table for ratios; $\frac{4}{3}$, or $1.\overline{3}$.

Step 5 Use your constant multiplier from Step 4 to predict the total lengths of this fractal at Stages 4 and 5.

Step 6 twice; $27\left(\frac{4}{3}\right)\left(\frac{4}{3}\right) = 27\left(\frac{4}{3}\right)^2$

Step 6 How many times do you multiply the original length at Stage 0 by the constant multiplier to get the length at Stage 2? Write an expression that calculates the length at Stage 2.

Step 7 three times; $27\left(\frac{4}{3}\right)\left(\frac{4}{3}\right)\left(\frac{4}{3}\right) = 27\left(\frac{4}{3}\right)^3$

Step 7 How many times do you multiply the length at Stage 0 by the constant multiplier to get the length at Stage 3? Write an expression that calculates the length at Stage 3.

Step 8 If your expressions in Steps 6 and 7 do not use exponents, rewrite them so that they do.

Step 9 Stage 5: $27\left(\frac{4}{3}\right)^5 = 113.\overline{7}$

Step 9 Use an exponent to write an expression that predicts the total length of the Stage 5 figure. Evaluate this expression using your calculator. Is the result the same as you predicted in Step 5?

Step 10 Let x represent the stage number, and let y represent the total length. Write an equation to model the total length of this fractal at any stage. Graph your equation and check that the calculator table contains the same values as your table.

Step 11 What does the graph tell you about the growth of the Koch curve?
Possible answer: The length of the Koch curve rapidly increases.

Step 10 [Ask] "Are all values of x and y meaningful in this equation?" [Only whole numbers can represent stage numbers and lengths of the first stage of these curves.]

[Alert] Be sure students understand the difference between the fractal itself and the graph that represents its growth.

Step 10 $y = 27\left(\frac{4}{3}\right)^x$

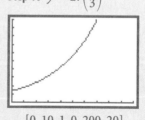
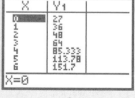

$[0, 10, 1, 0, 200, 20]$

A recursive routine that uses a constant multiplier represents a pattern that increases or decreases by a constant ratio or a constant percent. Because exponents are another way of writing repeated multiplication, you can use exponents to model these patterns. In the investigation you discovered how to calculate the length of the Koch curve at any stage by using this equation:

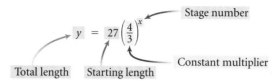

Equations like this are called **exponential equations** because a variable, in this case x, appears in the exponent. The standard form of an exponential equation is $y = a \cdot b^x$.

When you write out a repeated multiplication expression to show each factor, it is written in **expanded form.** When you show a repeated multiplication expression with an exponent, it is in **exponential form** and the factor being multiplied is called the **base.**

Expanded form		Exponential form
$27\left(\frac{4}{3}\right)\left(\frac{4}{3}\right)\left(\frac{4}{3}\right)$	$=$	$27\left(\frac{4}{3}\right)^3$

The exponent means there are three such factors of $\frac{4}{3}$.

There are three factors of $\frac{4}{3}$.

The base means you are multiplying factors of $\frac{4}{3}$.

EXAMPLE A

Write each expression in exponential form.

a. $(5)(5)(5)(5)(5)(5)$

b. $3(3)(2)(2)(2)(2)(2)(2)(2)(2)$

c. the current balance of a savings account that was opened 7 years ago with $200 earning 2.5% interest per year

▶ **Solution**

The exponent tells how many times each base is a factor.

a. 5^6

b. There are two factors of 3 and nine factors of 2, so you write

$3^2 \cdot 2^9$

You can't combine 3^2 and 2^9 any further because they have different bases.

c. There will be seven factors of $(1 + 0.025)$ multiplied by the starting value of $200, so you write

$200(1 + 0.025)^7$

Step 11 Have students consider the slope of the line between consecutive points. They should find that the rate of change is always increasing.

SHARING IDEAS

Select students to share their ideas about Steps 10 and 11.

Assessing Progress

Watch for students' familiarity with fractions and exponents.

▶ **EXAMPLE A**

This example reviews the meaning of exponents as repeated multiplication.

When the exponent must be a whole number, the variable n is sometimes used instead of x.

You can replace this example with the Fathom demonstration Exponential Equations. This example is useful for students who didn't come up with an equation to graph during the investigation. It is also good for refining students' skill at "chunking," seeing a collection of symbols as a single entity. Some students have difficulty seeing $(1 + 0.05)$ as a single quantity that's being multiplied by itself repeatedly. Temporarily rewriting the number as 1.05 might help, but the form $(1 + 0.05)$ emphasizes the fact that the multiplier is more than 1 and the account's value is increasing by 5%.

Students may ask why the constant multiplier is $(1 + 0.05)$ rather than just 0.05. Suggest that they look at $200(0.05)^x$ for several values of x. Then ask them to explain why the 1 is part of the expression.

All dollar values are rounded to the nearest cent. Students' calculators may show different numbers of decimal places, depending on how the mode is set.

Help students distinguish between the growth rate r and the rate of change. The number r is constant and has no units. The rate of change is the amount of increase in y for each unit of increase in x, and it has units.

Closing the Lesson

When values are increasing through multiplication by a constant that's greater than 1, we say that we have **exponential growth** and represent the values by the equation $y = A(1 + r)^x$. You might want to make a bulletin board display of the exponential growth equation.

EXAMPLE B

Seth deposits $200 in a savings account. The account pays 5% annual interest. Assuming that he makes no more deposits and no withdrawals, calculate his new balance after 10 years.

▶ **Solution**

The interest represents a 5% rate of growth per year, so the constant multiplier is $(1 + 0.05)$. Now find an equation that you can use to find the new balance after any number of years by considering these yearly calculations and results:

	Expanded form	Exponential form	New balance
Starting balance:	$200		$= \$200.00$
After 1 year:	$200(1 + 0.05)$	$= \$200(1 + 0.05)^1$	$= \$210.00$
After 2 years:	$200(1 + 0.05)(1 + 0.05)$	$= \$200(1 + 0.05)^2$	$= \$220.50$
After 3 years:	$200(1 + 0.05)(1 + 0.05)(1 + 0.05)$	$= \$200(1 + 0.05)^3$	$= \$231.53$
After x years:	$200(1 + 0.05)(1 + 0.05) \ldots (1 + 0.05)$	$= \$200(1 + 0.05)^x$	

You can now use the equation $y = 200(1 + 0.05)^x$, where x represents time in years and y represents the balance in dollars, to find the balance after 10 years.

$$y = 200(1 + 0.5)^x \qquad \text{Original equation.}$$

$$y = 200(1 + 0.05)^{10} \qquad \text{Substitute 10 for } x.$$

$$y \approx 325.78 \qquad \text{Use your calculator to evaluate the exponential expression.}$$

The balance after 10 years will be $325.78.

Amounts that increase by a constant percent, like the savings account in the example, have **exponential growth.**

Exponential Growth

Any constant percent growth can be modeled by the exponential equation

$$y = A(1 + r)^x$$

where A is the starting value, r is the rate of growth written as a positive decimal or fraction, x is the number of time periods elapsed, and y is the final value.

You can model amounts that decrease by a constant percent with a similar equation. What would need to change in the exponential equation to show a constant percent decrease?

EXERCISES

You will need your graphing calculator for Exercises **5, 7, 9, 11,** and **13.**

Practice Your Skills

1. Rewrite each expression with exponents.

a. (7)(7)(7)(7)(7)(7)(7)(7) 7^8

b. (3)(3)(3)(3)(5)(5)(5)(5)(5) $3^4 \cdot 5^5$

c. $(1 + 0.12)(1 + 0.12)(1 + 0.12)(1 + 0.12)$ @ $(1 + 0.12)^4$

2. A bacteria culture grows at a rate of 20% each day. There are 450 bacteria today. How many will there be

a. Tomorrow? @ $450(1 + 0.2) = 540$ bacteria

b. One week from now?
$450(1 + 0.2)^7 \approx 1612$ bacteria

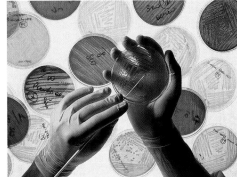

A technician puts bacteria in several petri dishes of agar. Agar is a gelatin-like substance made from algae. The agar holds the bacteria in place on the petri dish and provides nutrients for growth of the bacteria.

3. Match each equation with a table of values.

a. $y = 4(2)^x$ ii **b.** $y = 4(0.5)^x$ iii **c.** $y = 2(4)^x$ iv **d.** $y = 2(0.25)^x$ i

i.

x	y
0	2
1	0.5
2	0.12
3	0.03

ii.

x	y
0	4
1	8
2	16
3	32

iii.

x	y
0	4
1	2
2	1
3	0.5

iv.

x	y
0	2
1	8
2	32
3	128

4. Match each recursive routine with the equation that gives the same values.

iv **a.** 1.05 ENTER
Ans · (0.95) ENTER

ii **b.** 1.05 ENTER
Ans + Ans · 0.05 ENTER

i **c.** 0.95 ENTER
Ans · (1+0.05) ENTER

iii **d.** 0.95 ENTER
Ans · (1−0.05) ENTER

i. $y = 0.95(1.05)^x$

ii. $y = 1.05(1 + 0.05)^x$

iii. $y = 0.95(0.95)^x$

iv. $y = 1.05(1 - 0.05)^x$

BUILDING UNDERSTANDING

Students make connections between recursive routines, explicit definitions, calculator lists, and tables of values.

ASSIGNING HOMEWORK

Essential	**2–5, 9, 12**
Performance assessment	**8, 10, 14**
Portfolio	**9, 12**
Journal	**6, 7, 13, 14**
Group	**12, 13**
Review	**1, 10, 16**

6. The initial deposit is $500. The account earns 4% interest per year; thus the constant multiplier is $(1 + 0.04)$. The variable x represents the number of years since the initial deposit. The variable y represents the balance after x years.

Exercise 7 In this game, students are deriving only the right-hand expression $A(1 + r)^x$. Yet on paper they should include the $y =$.

Exercise 9 Make sure students are aware that in actuality, depreciation is not always a constant rate—a car may depreciate 20% one year and 30% another year. Students doing Exercise 13 will see that some goods, such as artwork and antiques, gain in value, or *appreciate*.

9a. $9,200

9b. Start with 11,500, then apply the rule Ans $\cdot (1 - 0.2)$.

9d. $y = 11,500(1 - 0.2)^x$

9e.

$[0, 10, 1, 0, 12000, 2000]$

---

5. For each table, find the value of the constants a and b such that $y = a \cdot b^x$. (*Hint:* To check your answer, enter your equation into Y_1 on your calculator. Then see if a table of values matches the table in the book.)

a.

x	y
0	1.2
1	2.4
2	4.8
3	9.6
4	19.2

$y = 1.2 \cdot 2^x$

b. @

x	y
0	500
2	20
3	4
5	0.16
7	0.0064

$y = 500 \cdot 0.2^x$

c.

x	y
3	8
1	50
5	1.28
2	20
7	0.2048

$y = 125 \cdot 0.4^x$

6. The equation $y = 500(1 + 0.04)^x$ models the amount of money in a savings account that earns annual interest. Explain what each number and variable in this expression means.

7. Run the calculator program INOUTEXP and play the easy-level game five times. Each time you play, write down the input and output values you were given and the exponential equation that models those values. [►▢ See **Calculator Note 6A** for instructions on running the program INOUTEXP. ◄] You may wish to team up with another student and use one calculator to run the program while using another calculator to find the constant multiplier. Students will self-check their work as they run the program.

► **Reason and Apply**

8. APPLICATION A credit card account is essentially a loan. A constant percent interest is added to the balance. Stanley buys $100 worth of groceries with his credit card. The balance then grows by 1.75% interest each month. How much will he owe if he makes no payments in 4 months? Write the expression you used to do this calculation in expanded form and also in exponential form. @
$100(1 + 0.0175)(1 + 0.0175)(1 + 0.0175)(1 + 0.0175) = 100(1 + 0.0175)^4$; about $107.19

9. APPLICATION Phil purchases a used truck for $11,500. The value of the truck is expected to decrease by 20% each year. (A decrease in monetary value over time is sometimes called *depreciation*.)

  a. Find the truck's value after 1 year.

  b. Write a recursive routine that generates the value of the truck after each year.

  c. Create a table showing the value of the truck when Phil purchases it and after each of the next 4 years.

  d. Write an equation in the form $y = A(1 - r)^x$ to calculate the value, y, of the truck after x years.

  e. Graph the equation from 9d, showing the value of the truck up to an age of 10 years.

Many people, like these ranch workers in Montana, rely on a truck for work and leisure.

9c.

Time elapsed (yr)	0	1	2	3	4
Value ($)	11,500	9,200	7,360	5,888	4,710.40

10. Draw a "starting" line segment 2 cm long on a sheet of paper.

    a. Draw a segment 3 times as long as the starting segment. How long is this segment? 6 cm

    b. Draw a segment 3 times as long as the segment in 10a. How long is this segment? 18 cm

    c. Use the starting length and an exponent to write an expression that gives the length in centimeters of the next segment you would draw. @ $2(3)^3$

    d. Use the starting length and an exponent to write an expression that gives the length in centimeters of the longest segment you could draw on a 100 m soccer field. $2(3)^7$

11. Run the calculator program INOUTEXP and play the medium- or difficult-level game five times. Each time you play, write down the input and output values you were given and the exponential equation that models those values. [▶ ☐ See **Calculator Note 6A** for instructions on running the program INOUTEXP. ◀] You may wish to team up with another student and use one calculator to run the program while using another calculator to find the constant multiplier.

Students will self-check their work as they run the program.

12. Fold a sheet of paper in half. You should have two layers. Fold it in half again so that there are four layers. Do this as many times as you can. Make a table and record the number of folds and number of layers.

    a. As you fold the paper in half each time, what happens to the number of layers?

    b. Estimate the number of folds you would have to make before you have about the same number of layers as the number of pages in this textbook.

    c. Calculate the answer for 12b. You may use a recursive routine, the graph or table of an equation, or a trial-and-error method.

Origami is the Japanese art of paper folding. To learn more about the history and mathematics of origami, see the links at www.keymath.com/DA .

13. **APPLICATION** Phil's friend Shawna buys an antique car for $5,000. She estimates that it will increase in value (*appreciate*) by 5% each year.

    a. Write an equation to calculate the value, y, of Shawna's car after x years. @ $y = 5000(1 + 0.05)^x$

    b. Simultaneously graph the equation in 13a and the equation you found in 9d. Where do the two graphs intersect? What is the meaning of this point of intersection? @

14. Invent a situation that could be modeled by each equation below. Sketch a graph of each equation, and describe similarities and differences between the two models.

$$y = 400 + 20x$$
$$y = 400(1 + 0.05)^x$$

15. Consider the recursive routine

    {0, 100} (ENTER)

    {Ans(1)+1, Ans(2) · (1−0.035)} (ENTER)

    a. Invent a situation that this routine could model. Answers will vary.

    b. Create a problem related to your situation. Carefully describe the meaning of the numbers in your problem. Answers will vary.

    c. Use an exponential equation to solve your problem.
    Answers will vary. The solution should use $y = 100(1 − 0.035)^x$.

14. Possible answer: The first equation could model a principal of $400 to which $20 is added each time period; the second equation could model a starting bank balance of $400, with 5% interest added to the balance each time period. Both models have the same starting value, 400. In both models, $y = 420$ when $x = 1$. For x greater than 1, y increases much more quickly in the second model.

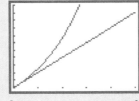

[0, 50, 10, 400, 1500, 100]

12a. The number of layers doubles with each fold.

12b. Estimates will vary.

12c. Methods will vary. Eight folds give 256 layers (512 pages), and nine folds give 512 layers (1024 pages).

Exercise 13 This is the first time students may notice that in $y = A(1 + r)^x$ the value of x can be fractional. The graph of the equation is continuous, not discrete.

Students may not know how to convert a decimal number of years to years and months. They can multiply 3.06 years by 12 months per year to get approximately 37 months, or 3 years and 1 month.

If students use trace to find the intersection of the graphs to answer 13b, the width of the pixels on the screen may prevent them from finding the exact position.

13b.

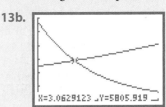

X=3.0629123 Y=5805.919

[0, 10, 1, 0, 12000, 2000]

The intersection point represents the time and the value of both cars when their value will be the same. By tracing the graph shown, students should see that both cars will be worth approximately $5,800 after a little less than 3 years 1 month.

Exercise 16 This situation can be modeled with colored tiles or centimeter cubes.

16a.

Number of steps x	1	2	3	4
Perimeter (cm) y	4	8	12	16

16b.

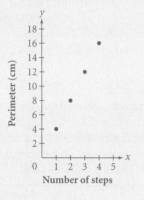

Student Data for Project
Data should be collected from *Kelly Blue Book* or reliable online resources with consideration given to features of the car (should be similar for all years) and mileage (should increase as age increases). Students may tend to notice a linear pattern, depending on the actual rate of depreciation and how far back the data go. If factors such as mileage and features are not closely considered, the data may appear to have no pattern.

▶ **Review**

3.1 **16.** Look at this "step" pattern. In the first figure, which has one step, each side of the block is 1 cm long.

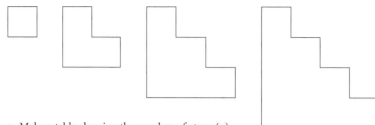

a. Make a table showing the number of steps (x) and the perimeter (y) of each figure. ⓐ

b. On a graph, plot the coordinates your table represents.

c. Write an equation that relates the perimeter of these figures to the number of steps. $y = 4x$

d. Use your equation to predict the perimeter of a figure with 47 steps. 188 cm

e. Is there a figure with a perimeter of 74 cm? If so, how many steps does it have? If not, why not? A perimeter of 74 cm is not possible because it would require 18.5 steps.

project

AUTOMOBILE DEPRECIATION

Cars usually lose value as they get older. Dealers and buyers may rely on books or Internet resources to help them find out how much a used car is worth. But many people don't understand what type of math is used to make these judgments.

Choose a model of automobile that has been manufactured for several years. Research the new-car value now. Then research how much the same model would be worth now if it were manufactured last year, the year before that, and so on. Do your data show a pattern? If so, write an equation that models your data.

Your project should include

▶ Data for at least 10 consecutive years.

▶ A scatter plot comparing age and value.

▶ The rate of change (if your data appear linear) or the rate of depreciation as a percent (if your data look exponential).

▶ An equation that fits your data.

▶ A summary of your procedures and findings; include how you collected your data and how well your equation fits the data.

You might want to ask a local auto dealership how it determines a car's value. Does it use the same rate of depreciation for all cars? And how do special features, like a custom stereo, affect the value?

Supporting the project

MOTIVATION

The cost of driving a car includes more than gas and repairs. It also includes the depreciation, the difference between what was paid for the car and what it can be sold for.

OUTCOMES

▶ The data and scatter plot correctly illustrate the findings.

▶ The report includes a summary of procedures and findings, including information about how the data were found.

▶ An equation in the form $y = a + bx$ or $y = A(1 - r)^x$ should be stated and shown to be a good model of the data.

▶ The report includes the rate of depreciation.

• Appropriate adjustments are made to the equations to achieve a good fit.

• The report includes extended research on the equations actually employed in the used-car industry and how they are applied.

Multiplication and Exponents

Growth for the sake of growth is the ideology of the cancer cell.
EDWARD ABBEY

In Lesson 6.2, you learned that the exponential expression $200(1 + 0.05)^3$ can model a situation with a starting value of 200 and a rate of growth of 5% over three time periods. How would you change the expression to model five time periods, seven time periods, or more? In this lesson you will explore that question and discover how the answer is related to a rule for showing multiplication with exponents.

Every year, the population of the United States increases. This photo shows Grand Central Station in New York City, which is the most populated U.S. city.

Social Science CONNECTION

The U.S. Bureau of the Census only collects population information every 10 years. It uses mathematical models, like exponential equations, to make population predictions between census years.

Suppose the population of a town is 12,800 and the town's population grows at a rate of 2.5% each year.

An expression for the population 3 years from now is $12,800(1 + 0.025)^3$. To represent one more year, you can write the expression $12,800(1 + 0.025)^4$. You can also think about the growth from 3 years to 4 years recursively. Because the rate of growth is constant, multiply the expression for 3 years by one more constant multiplier to get $12,800(1 + 0.025)^3 \cdot (1 + 0.025)^1$.

This means that

$$12,800(1 + 0.025)^3 \cdot (1 + 0.025)^1 = 12,800(1 + 0.025)^4$$

Both methods make sense and both evaluate to the same result.

So you can advance exponential growth one time period either by multiplying the previous amount by the base (the constant multiplier) or by increasing the exponent by one. Every time you increase by one the number of times the base is used as a factor, the exponent increases by one. But what happens when you want to advance the growth by more than one time period? In the next investigation you will discover a shortcut for multiplying exponential expressions.

NCTM STANDARDS

CONTENT		PROCESS	
✔	Number		Problem Solving
✔	Algebra	✔	Reasoning
	Geometry		Communication
	Measurement	✔	Connections
	Data/Probability	✔	Representation

LESSON OBJECTIVES

- Review or learn the multiplication property of exponents
- Review or learn the power properties of exponents

PLANNING

LESSON OUTLINE

One day:
5 min	Introduction
15 min	Investigation
5 min	Sharing
15 min	Examples
5 min	Closing
5 min	Exercises

MATERIALS

- Properties of Exponents (T), *optional*
- Calculator Note 6B

TEACHING

Exponential growth models motivate rules for exponents when multiplying quantities with the same bases and when raising a power to a power.

INTRODUCTION

To estimate a population between actual counts, the growth rate is assumed to be the same between the counts. Theoretically, the graph of a population is a step function, because the population is counted by whole numbers. Because the steps would be so small in the graph, the best model assumes that the population takes on non-integer values and grows continuously. In estimating the population, students should round to the nearest integer.

[Alert] Some students may have forgotten that $(1 + 0.025)^1$ equals $1 + 0.025$. It's sometimes useful to write a number as itself to the first power when trying to see or demonstrate a pattern.

One Step

Say that the number of ants in a colony has been growing exponentially for 5 wk and has reached a value of $16(1 + 0.5)^5$. Assuming that the growth will continue at the same rate, what will the population be 3 wk from now? As you circulate, ask students to write an expression for that population in at least two ways—$16(1 + 0.5)^5(1 + 0.5)^3$ and $16(1 + 0.5)^8$. **[Ask]** "Can you always add exponents when multiplying?" [Bring out the necessity of having the same base.] Ask students to make up and solve some similar problems with which to challenge each other.

Step 1 Having students go through the "expanded form" will help them make sense of and remember the multiplication property of exponents. Students may have difficulty seeing $1 + 0.05$, the base, as a "chunk."

Step 2 You may want to extend this instruction to include "Write an explanation of this pattern for a friend who is absent today."

Step 3 [Ask] "What would happen in something like a^3b^2?" [Exponents can't be added if the bases differ. If the bases are the same, we say they are *like bases*.]

Step 4 The real-world contexts help students develop understanding of the multiplication rule for exponents. The contexts should also help students make the connection with the exponential growth and decay models.

Investigation
Moving Ahead

Step 1 Rewrite each product below in expanded form, and then rewrite it in exponential form with a single base. Use your calculator to check your answers.

a. $3^4 \cdot 3^2$ $(3 \cdot 3 \cdot 3 \cdot 3) \cdot (3 \cdot 3) = 3^6$

b. $x^3 \cdot x^5$ $(x \cdot x \cdot x) \cdot (x \cdot x \cdot x \cdot x \cdot x) = x^8$

c. $(1 + 0.05)^2 \cdot (1 + 0.05)^4$

d. $10^3 \cdot 10^6$ $(10 \cdot 10 \cdot 10) \cdot (10 \cdot 10 \cdot 10 \cdot 10 \cdot 10 \cdot 10) = 10^9$

Step 1c $[(1 + 0.05) \cdot (1 \cdot 0.05)] \cdot [(1 + 0.05) \cdot (1 + 0.05) \cdot (1 + 0.05) \cdot (1 + 0.05)] = (1 + 0.05)^6$

Step 2 Compare the exponents in each final expression you got in Step 1 to the exponents in the original product. Describe a way to find the exponents in the final expression without using expanded form.

Step 2 Sample answer: You add the original exponents to get the exponent on the final expression.

Step 3 Generalize your observations in Step 2 by filling in the blank.

$b^m \cdot b^n = b^{\square}$ $m + n$

Step 4 Apply what you have discovered about multiplying expressions with exponents.

a. The number of ants in a colony after 5 weeks is $16(1 + 0.5)^5$. What does the expression $16(1 + 0.5)^5 \cdot (1 + 0.5)^3$ mean in this situation? Rewrite the expression with a single exponent. the population after 3 more weeks; $16(1 + 0.5)^8$

All ants live in colonies.

b. The depreciating value of a truck after 7 years is $11,500(1 - 0.2)^7$. What does the expression $11,500(1 - 0.2)^7 \cdot (1 - 0.2)^2$ mean in this situation? Rewrite the expression with a single exponent. the value of the truck after 2 more years; $11,500(1 - 0.2)^9$

c. The expression $A(1 + r)^n$ can model n time periods of exponential growth. What does the expression $A(1 + r)^{n+m}$ model? the growth after m more time periods

Step 5 How does looking ahead in time with an exponential model relate to multiplying expressions with exponents?
Sample answer: Multiplying by $(1 + r)^m$ represents looking ahead m time periods.

SHARING IDEAS

Have students share and critique answers to Step 4c.

Draw students' attention to the quotation that opens the lesson. The growth and reproduction of cells is one of many situations that can be modeled by exponential equations.

Ask how good they think predictions will be if made from exponential models of a population. What factors are not taken into account with an exponential model of the town's growth or of the growing cancer cells mentioned in the introduction? In general, exponential models neglect to consider limits on resources (such as the availability of food, jobs, or land) and external interventions (such as immigration or treatments that kill cancer cells).

Assessing Progress

Look for understanding of constant multipliers and of exponents as showing repeated multiplication.

In the investigation you discovered the **multiplication property of exponents.**

> ### Multiplication Property of Exponents
>
> For any nonzero value of b and any integer values of m and n,
>
> $$b^m \cdot b^n = b^{m+n}$$

This property is very handy for rewriting exponential expressions. However, you can add exponents to multiply numbers only when the bases are the same.

EXAMPLE A

Cal and Al got different answers when asked to write $3^4 \cdot 2^2$ in another exponential form. Who was right and why?

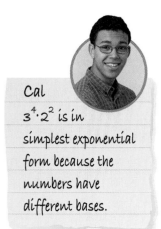

Cal

$3^4 \cdot 2^2$ is in simplest exponential form because the numbers have different bases.

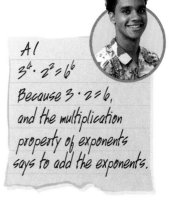

Al

$3^4 \cdot 2^2 = 6^6$

Because $3 \cdot 2 = 6$, and the multiplication property of exponents says to add the exponents.

▶ **Solution**

Rewrite the original expression in expanded form.

$$3 \cdot 3 \cdot 3 \cdot 3 \cdot 2 \cdot 2 \;=\; 3^4 \cdot 2^2$$

4 factors of 3   2 factors of 2

The factors are not all the same, so the multiplication property of exponents does not allow you to write this expression with a single exponent. Cal was right. Use your calculator to check that $3^4 \cdot 2^2$ and 6^6 are not equivalent.

EXAMPLE B

Rewrite each expression without parentheses.

a. $(4^5)^2$

b. $(x^3)^4$

c. $(5^m)^n$

d. $(xy)^3$

▶ **Solution**

a. Here, a number with an exponent has another exponent. You can say that 4^5 is **raised to the power** of 2. Begin by writing $(4^5)^2$ as two factors of 4^5.

$$(4^5)^2 = 4^5 \cdot 4^5 = 4^{5+5} = 4^{10}$$

There is a total of $5 \cdot 2$, or 10, factors of 4.

b. $(x^3)^4 = x^3 \cdot x^3 \cdot x^3 \cdot x^3 = x^{3+3+3+3} = x^{12}$

There is a total of $3 \cdot 4$, or 12, factors of x.

c. Based on parts a and b, when you raise an exponential expression to a power, you multiply the exponents.

$$(5^m)^n = 5^{mn}$$

d. Here, a product is raised to a power. Begin by writing $(xy)^3$ as 3 factors of xy.

$$(xy)^3 = xy \cdot xy \cdot xy = x \cdot x \cdot x \cdot y \cdot y \cdot y = x^3y^3$$

Do you remember which property allows you to write $xy \cdot xy \cdot xy$ as $x \cdot x \cdot x \cdot y \cdot y \cdot y$?

This example has illustrated two more properties of exponents.

Power Properties of Exponents

For any nonzero values of a and b and any integer values of m and n,

$$(b^m)^n = b^{mn}$$
$$(ab)^n = a^nb^n$$

EXERCISES

You will need your graphing calculator for Exercises **1, 8, 9,** and **13.**

▶ ## Practice Your Skills

1. Use the properties of exponents to rewrite each expression. Use your calculator to check that your expression is equivalent to the original expression. [▶ 🖳 See **Calculator Note 6B** to learn how to check equivalent expressions. ◀]

  a. $(5)(x)(x)(x)(x)$ @ $5x^4$ b. $3x^4 \cdot 5x^6$ $15x^{10}$ c. $4x^7 \cdot 2x^3$ $8x^{10}$ d. $(-2x^2)(x^2 + x^4)$ @ $-2x^4 - 2x^6$

2. Write each expression in expanded form. Then rewrite the product in exponential form.

  a. $3^5 \cdot 3^8$ b. $7^3 \cdot 7^4$ @ c. $x^6 \cdot x^2$ d. y^8y^5 e. $x^2y^4 \cdot xy^3$

3. Rewrite each expression with a single exponent.

  a. $(3^5)^8$ 3^{40} b. $(7^3)^4$ 7^{12} c. $(x^6)^2$ x^{12} d. $(y^8)^5$ y^{40}

4. Use the properties of exponents to rewrite each expression.

  a. $(rt)^2$ r^2t^2 b. $(x^2y)^3$ x^6y^3 c. $(4x)^5$ $1024x^5$ d. $(2x^4y^2z^5)^3$ $8x^{12}y^6z^{15}$

Reason and Apply

5. An algebra class had this problem on a quiz: "Find the value of $2x^2$ when $x = 3$."
Two students reasoned differently.

   Student 1 Two times three is six. Six squared is thirty-six.
   Student 2 Three squared is nine. Two times nine is eighteen.

   Who was correct? Explain why. ⓗ Student 2 was correct; according to the order of operations, squaring should be done before multiplication.

6. Match expressions from this list that are equivalent but written in different exponential forms. There can be multiple matches.

   a. $(4x^4)(3x)$ **b.** $(8x^2)(3x^2)$ **c.** $(12x)(4x)$ **d.** $(6x^3)(2x^2)$

   e. $12x^6$ **f.** $24x^4$ **g.** $12x^5$ **h.** $48x^2$

   a, d, and g; b and f; c and h; e has no match.

7. Evaluate each expression in Exercise 6 using an x-value of 4.7.
   a, d, and g: 27,521.40084; b and f: 11,711.2344; c and h: 1,060.32; e: 129,350.5839

8. Use the properties of exponents to rewrite each expression. Use your calculator to check that your expression is equivalent to the original expression. [▶ 🖥 See **Calculator Note 6B** to learn how to check equivalent expressions. ◀]

   a. $3x^2 \cdot 2x^4 \;\; 6x^6$ **b.** $5x^2y^3 \cdot 4x^4y^5 \;\; 20x^6y^8$ **c.** $2x^2 \cdot 3x^3y^4 \;\; 6x^5y^4$ **d.** $x^3 \cdot 4x^4 \;\; 4x^7$

9. Cal and Al's teacher asked them, "What do you get when you square negative five?" Al said, "Negative five times negative five is positive twenty-five." Cal replied, "My calculator says negative twenty-five. Doesn't my calculator know how to do exponents?" Experiment with your calculator to see if you can find a way for Cal to get the correct answer.

10. Evaluate $2x^2 + 3x + 1$ for each x-value.

    a. $x = 3$ ⓐ 28   **b.** $x = 5$ 66   **c.** $x = -2$ 3   **d.** $x = 0$ 1

11. The properties you learned in this section involve adding and multiplying exponents and applying an exponent to more than one factor. Possible answers:

    a. Write and solve a problem that requires adding exponents. $x^3 \cdot x^5 = x^8$

    b. Write and solve a problem that requires multiplying exponents. $\left(x^3\right)^5 = x^{15}$

    c. Write and solve a problem that requires applying an exponent to two factors. $(3x)^5 = 3^5x^5 = 243x^5$

    d. Write a few sentences describing when to add exponents, when to multiply exponents, and when to apply an exponent to more than one factor.

12. **APPLICATION** Lara buys a $500 sofa at a furniture store. She buys the sofa with a new credit card that charges 1.5% interest per month, with an offer for "no payments for a year."

    a. What balance will Lara's credit card bill show after 6 months? Write an exponential expression and evaluate it. ⓐ
    $500(1 + 0.015)^6$; $546.72

Exercises 5 and 8 Students may not recall that the conventional order of operations has exponentiation before multiplication. That is, ab^c means $a(b^c)$ rather than $(ab)^c$. ("Powers have more power.")

Exercise 8 You might ask students to write each expression in *simplest form*. Ask students if there are any common bases remaining in their expression. Make sure that they have multiplied any coefficients to give a final expression with only one coefficient.

9. Enclose the -5 in parentheses.

Exercise 11 Students might also write and solve word problems for 11a–c.

11d. Exponents are added when you multiply two exponential expressions with the same base. Exponents are multiplied when an exponential expression is raised to a power. An exponent is distributed when a product is raised to a power.

b. How much total interest will be added after 6 months? ⓐ $46.72

c. What balance will Lara's credit card bill show after 12 months? Write an exponential expression and evaluate it. $500(1 + 0.015)^{12}$; $597.81

d. How much more interest will be added between 6 and 12 months? $51.09

e. Explain why more interest builds up between 6 and 12 months than between 0 and 6 months. Answers will vary. The increase is greater between 6 and 12 months because the interest each month is a percentage of a greater current balance.

13. Use the distributive property and the properties of exponents to write an equivalent expression without parentheses. Use your calculator to check your answers, as you did in Exercise 1.

    a. $x(x^3 + x^4)$ $x^4 + x^5$ **b.** $(-2x^2)(x^2 + x^4)$ $-2x^4 - 2x^6$ **c.** $2.5x^4(6.8x^3 + 3.4x^4)$ ⓗ
                                                                                                 $17x^7 + 8.5x^8$

14. Write an equivalent expression in the form $a \cdot b^n$. ⓗ

    a. $3x \cdot 5x^3$ $15x^4$ **b.** $x \cdot x^5$ x^6 **c.** $2x^3 \cdot 2x^3$ $4x^6$
    d. $3.5(x + 0.15)^4 \cdot (x + 0.15)^2$ **e.** $(2x^3)^3$ $8x^9$ **f.** $[3(x + 0.05)^3]^2$ $9(x + 0.05)^6$
       $3.5(x + 0.15)^6$

▶ Review

5.5 **15.** Jack Frost started a snow-shoveling business. He spent $47 on a new shovel and gloves. Jack plans to charge $4.50 for every sidewalk he shovels.

    a. Write an expression for Jack's profit from shoveling x sidewalks. (*Hint:* Don't forget his expenses.) ⓐ $4.5x - 47$

    b. Write and solve an inequality to find how many sidewalks Jack must shovel before he makes enough money to earn back the amount he spent on his equipment.

    c. How many sidewalks must Jack shovel before he makes enough money to buy a $100 used lawn mower for his summer business? Write and solve an inequality to find out.
    $4.5x - 47 > 100$; $x > 32.\overline{6}$; he must shovel 33 sidewalks to pay for his expenses and buy a lawn mower.

5.3 **16.** Solve each system.

    a. $\begin{cases} y = 7.3 + 2.5(x - 8) \\ y = 4.4 - 1.5(x - 2.9) \end{cases}$ $(5.3625, 0.70625)$ **b.** $\begin{cases} 2x + 5y = 10 \\ 3x - 3y = 7 \end{cases}$ ⓐ   approximately $(3.095, 0.762)$

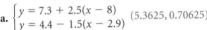

Exercise 15 As an alternative solution for 15b, students can graph the equation $y = 4.5x - 47$, where y represents profit. The x-intercept is Jack's "break-even" point of approximately 11 sidewalks. The point $(33, 101.5)$ represents 33 sidewalks needed to make more than $100 profit.

15b. $4.5x - 47 > 0$; $x > 10.\overline{4}$; he must shovel 11 sidewalks to pay for his equipment.

Exercise 16 This exercise reviews Lesson 5.3, but each solution is a point with non-integer coordinates.

LESSON
6.4

Scientific Notation for Large Numbers

In fact, everything that can be known has number, for it is not possible to conceive of or to know anything that has not.

PHILOLAUS

Did you know that there are approximately 75,000 genes in each human cell and more than 50 trillion cells in the human body? This means that $75,000 \cdot 50,000,000,000,000$ is a low estimate of the number of genes in your body!

Whether you use paper and pencil, an old-fashioned slide rule, or your calculator, exponents are useful when you work with very large numbers. For example, instead of writing 3,750,000,000,000,000,000 genes, scientists write this number more compactly as 3.75×10^{18}. This compact method of writing numbers is called **scientific notation.** You will learn how to use this notation for large numbers—numbers far from 0 on a number line. The properties of exponents you've learned will help you work with numbers in scientific notation.

This is a computer model of a DNA strand. Many strands of DNA combine to form the genetic information in each cell.

Investigation
A Scientific Quandary

Consider these two lists of numbers:

In scientific notation	Not in scientific notation
3.4×10^5	27×10^4
7.04×10^3	$120,000,000$
6.023×10^{17}	42.682×10^{29}
8×10^1	4.2×12^6
1.6×10^2	$4^2 \times 10^2$

Step 1

Step 2 Possible answer: The number is factored so that the first factor is a number between 1 and 10 and the second **Step 2** factor is a power of 10.

Classify each of these numbers as in scientific notation or not. If a number is not in scientific notation, tell why not.

a. 4.7×10^3 yes
b. 32×10^5
c. $2^4 \times 10^6$
d. 1.107×10^{13} yes
e. 0.28×10^{11} no; should be 2.8×10^{10}

Define what it means for a number to be in scientific notation.

NCTM STANDARDS

CONTENT	PROCESS
✔ Number	Problem Solving
✔ Algebra	Reasoning
Geometry	✔ Communication
✔ Measurement	✔ Connections
Data/Probability	✔ Representation

LESSON OBJECTIVES

- Write in scientific notation numbers far from zero
- Rewrite in standard notation numbers that are in scientific notation
- Learn how calculators represent scientific notation

LESSON
6.4

PLANNING

LESSON OUTLINE

One day:

5 min	Introduction
20 min	Investigation
5 min	Sharing
5 min	Example
5 min	Closing
10 min	Exercises

MATERIALS

- Calculator Note 6C

TEACHING

This lesson introduces students to scientific notation, both as it's written by hand and as it's represented on a calculator.

One Step

Give the problem from the example and let students struggle for a while with writing all the zeros. Then call them together and ask for ideas about simpler notation. If no one suggests scientific notation, introduce it, have students solve the problem, and let them experiment with scientific notation mode on their calculators to see how to work with it there.

INTRODUCTION

All cells have matching genes, so not all of the 3.75×10^{18} genes in the body are different. The scientific notation assumes that the number of genes given has three significant digits. See page 357 of this teacher's edition for a discussion of significant digits. Page 357 of the student book has a picture of a slide rule.

Step 1b no; should be 3.2×10^6
Step 1c No; the only exponent should be on 10; should be 1.6×10^7.

Step 1 Scientific notation commonly uses × instead of · to indicate multiplication by a power of 10, because typically numbers rather than letters are being multiplied.

If students aren't familiar with the fact that multiplying by 10 appends zeros or moves the decimal point, you may want to show them a list like this:

$4 \times 10 = 4 \times 10^1 = 40$
$4 \times 10 \times 10 = 4 \times 10^2 = 400$
$4 \times 10 \times 10 \times 10 = 4 \times 10^3$
$= 4000$

Step 3 *Standard notation* means using numerals and decimal points, with no exponents. You may want to have students also set the number of decimal places from floating to fixed 3. Then 4.7×10^8 will be 4.700E8.

Steps 4 and 5 Many students should do these steps by hand before pulling out their calculators. Calculator displays will vary. Some use E (in place of 10) followed by the exponent. Help students translate their display to written scientific notation.

Step 6 [Alert] Some students may need more experience with the number of digits in various powers of 10.

SHARING IDEAS

Ask students to share their instructions for Steps 7 and 8. Writing precise instructions is very difficult for many students, so be sympathetic. On the other hand, be sure that weaknesses in the instructions are noted. Work toward the definition that follows Step 8. If appropriate, you might elicit the fact that the condition on *a* can be written as $1 \le |a| < 10$.

See page 724 for answers to Steps 4 and 5.

Step 6 Answers will vary. The exponent on 10 is the number of digits following the first digit in the original number. The digits before the 10 show the significant digits in the original number. If the number is negative in standard notation, the decimal number will likewise be negative in scientific notation and the minus sign will appear before the digits factor.

Step 7 Possible answer: Write the digits 415 with one digit before the decimal point: 4.15. Determine how many places the decimal point needs to move to have 4.15 become 415,000,000, and make this the exponent on 10. The scientific notation is 4.15×10^8.

Step 8 Possible answer: Move the decimal point in 6.4 five places to the right as represented in 10^5. The standard notation is 640,000.

Use your calculator's scientific notation mode to help you figure out how to convert standard notation to scientific notation and vice versa.

Step 3
Step 4

Set your calculator to scientific notation mode. [▶ 🖥 See **Calculator Note 6C.** ◀]

Enter the number 5000 and press (ENTER). Your calculator will display its version, 5×10^3. Use a table to record the standard notation for this number, 5000, and the equivalent scientific notation.

Step 5

Repeat Step 4 for these numbers:

a. 250   **b.** −5,530
c. 14,000   **d.** 7,000,000
e. 18   **f.** −470,000

Step 6

In scientific notation, how is the exponent on the 10 related to the number in standard notation? How are the digits before the 10 related to the number in standard notation? If the number in standard notation is negative, how does that show up in scientific notation?

Step 7

Write a set of instructions for converting 415,000,000 from standard notation to scientific notation.

Step 8

Write a set of instructions for converting 6.4×10^5 from scientific notation to standard notation.

Physicist Suzanne Willis repairs a particle detector at Fermi National Accelerator Lab in Batavia, Illinois. When working with the physics of atomic particles, physicists need scientific notation to write quantities such as 2 trillion electron volts.

A number in scientific notation has the form $a \times 10^n$ where $1 \le a < 10$ or $-10 < a \le -1$ and *n* is an integer. In other words, the number is written as a number with one nonzero digit to the left of the decimal point multiplied by a power of 10. The number of digits to the right of the decimal point in *a* depends on the degree of precision you want to show.

EXAMPLE

Meredith is doing a report on stars and wants an estimate for the total number of stars in the universe. She reads that astronomers estimate there are at least 125 billion galaxies in the universe. An encyclopedia says that the Milky Way, Earth's galaxy, is estimated to contain more than 100 billion stars. Estimate the total number of stars in the universe. Give your answer in scientific notation.

Maria Mitchell (1818–1889) was the first female professional astronomer in the United States.

[Ask] "What real-world quantities could be negative?" [Negative quantities might represent temperatures, location or velocity relative to a fixed point, time before a given time, electrical charges, or acceleration (deceleration).]

Point out the quote introducing the lesson. Philolaus was a philosopher from 475 B.C.E. who lived in what is now southern Italy. Ask students if they agree that everything that can be known for sure can be

counted or measured. Scientific notation provides convenient names for numbers far from zero. To motivate Lesson 6.6, you might challenge students to think about how to use scientific notation to describe numbers close to zero.

Assessing Progress

As you observe, you can assess students' skill at seeing patterns, following instructions, applying careful thinking, and working with groups.

► **Solution**

History
CONNECTION

A slide rule is a mechanical device that uses a scale related to exponential notation. Slide rules were widely used for calculating with large numbers until electronic calculators became readily available in the 1970s. To learn more about slide rules, see the links at www.keymath.com/DA .

One billion is 1,000,000,000, or 10^9. Write the numbers in the example using powers of 10 and multiply them.

$\left(125 \times 10^9\right)\left(100 \times 10^9\right)$ 125 billion (galaxies) times 100 billion (stars per galaxy).

$125 \times 100 \times 10^9 \times 10^9$ Regroup using the associative and commutative properties of multiplication.

$125 \times 10^2 \times 10^9 \times 10^9$ Express 100 as 10^2.

125×10^{20} Use the multiplication property of exponents.

Because 125 is greater than 10, the answer is not yet in scientific notation.

$1.25 \times 10^2 \times 10^{20}$ Convert 125 to scientific notation.

1.25×10^{22} Use the multiplication property of exponents.

So the universe contains more than 1.25×10^{22} stars.

Notice in this example that you used exponential expressions that were not in scientific notation. Numbers like 125 billion, 100×10^{18}, or 0.03×10^{12} can come up in calculations, and sometimes these numbers make comparisons easier. Scientific notation is one of several ways to write large numbers.

EXERCISES

You will need your graphing calculator for Exercises **8, 10,** and **14.**

► **Practice Your Skills**

1. Write each number in scientific notation.
   a. 34,000,000,000 @ 3.4×10^{10} **b.** −2,100,000 -2.1×10^6 **c.** 10,060 1.006×10^4

2. Write each number in standard notation.
   a. 7.4×10^4 @ 74,000   **b.** -2.134×10^6 −2,134,000   **c.** 4.01×10^3 4010

3. Use the properties of exponents to rewrite each expression.
   a. $3x^5(4x)$ $12x^6$ **b.** $y^8\left(7y^8\right)$ @ $7y^{16}$
   c. $b^4\left(2b^2 + b\right)$ $2b^6 + b^5$ **d.** $2x\left(5x^3 - 3x\right)$ $10x^4 - 6x^2$

4. Use the properties of exponents to rewrite each expression.
   a. $3x^2 \cdot 4x^3$ $12x^5$ **b.** $\left(3y^3\right)^4$ @ $81y^{12}$
   c. $2x^3\left(5x^4\right)^2$ $50x^{11}$ **d.** $\left(3m^2n^3\right)^3$ $27m^6n^9$

5. Owen insists on reading his calculator's display as "three point five to the seventh." Bethany tells him that he should read it as "three point five times ten to the seventh." He says, "They are the same thing. Why say all those extra words?" Write Owen's and Bethany's expressions in expanded form, and evaluate each to show Owen why they are not the same thing.

$3.5 \times 10^7 = 3.5 \cdot 10 \cdot 10 \cdot 10 \cdot 10 \cdot 10 \cdot 10 \cdot 10 = 35,000,000;$
$3.5^7 = 3.5 \cdot 3.5 \cdot 3.5 \cdot 3.5 \cdot 3.5 \cdot 3.5 \cdot 3.5 = 6433.9296875$

► **EXAMPLE**

[ELL] Remind students that in the United States the term *billion* means a thousand millions.

Have students check the solution with their calculators. Improving Your Reasoning Skills in Lesson 6.6 will introduce engineering notation, an alternative to scientific notation.

Significant Digits
Significant digits allow you to communicate the degree of rounding in a measurement. For example, if your measuring device showed you only that the length of an object was between 3 and 4 cm, and closer to 3 cm, then you'd report the length as 3 cm. If your device showed you that the length was between 3.0 and 3.1 cm, though, and closer to 3.0, you'd report the length as 3.0 cm.

Using significant digits to report the accuracy of a measurement can be tricky for whole numbers ending in 0. For example, what if your measurement gave you a value between 1200 and 1210, but closer to 1200? You would write 1200. But isn't that also what you'd write if your measurement were between 1200 and 1201, but closer to 1200? Or if your measurement were between 1200 and 1300, but closer to 1200? Just writing 1200 doesn't communicate the number of significant digits.

Here's where scientific notation comes to the rescue. To communicate that 1200 has only two significant digits, you'd write 1.2×10^3. If 1200 has three significant digits, you'd write 1.20×10^3. And to say that it has four significant digits, you'd write 1.200×10^3.

Closing the Lesson

Scientific notation provides a way of naming numbers consistently and is especially useful for numbers that are very close to or far from zero. When written, the notation consists of a number between 1 and 10 (possibly 1 but not 10), or between −1 and −10, multiplied by a power of 10. Calculators use other representations.

ASSIGNING HOMEWORK

Essential	1, 2, 5, 8–10
Performance assessment	6, 11–13
Portfolio	7, 14
Journal	5, 9, 10
Group	14
Review	3, 4, 14, 15

▶ Helping with the Exercises

Exercises 3 and 4 Remind students to rewrite each expression in simplest form.

Exercise 6 Some students may want to use their calculators here. They don't need to use scientific notation mode. They can enter 5.58*10^23, for example, or on some calculators they can enter 5.58 EE23.

Exercise 9 Neither answer is better because the problem doesn't ask for a result in scientific notation.

9a. yes, because they are both equal to 51,800,000,000

9d. Rewrite the digits before the 10 in scientific notation, then use the multiplication property of exponents to add the exponents on the 10's. In this case, $4.325 \times 10^2 \times 10^3 = 4.325 \times 10^5$.

10b. Regroup, multiply the numbers, and multiply the powers of 10 by adding the exponents.

▶ Reason and Apply

6. There are approximately 5.58×10^{21} atoms in a gram of silver. How many atoms are there in 3 kilograms of silver? Express your answer in scientific notation. @ 1.674×10^{25}

7. Because the number of molecules in a given amount of a compound is usually a very large number, scientists often work with a quantity called a *mole*. One mole is about 6.02×10^{23} molecules.

  a. A liter of water has about 55.5 moles of H_2O. How many molecules is this? Write your answer in scientific notation. 3.3411×10^{25}

  b. How many molecules are in 6.02×10^{23} moles of a compound? Write your answer in scientific notation. approximately 3.6×10^{47}

8. Write each number in scientific notation. How does your calculator show each answer? Answers will vary based on the model of calculator used.

  a. 250 2.5×10^2; 2.5E2

  b. 7,420,000,000,000 7.42×10^{12}; 7.42E12

  c. −18 -1.8×10^1; −1.8E1

9. Cal and Al were assigned this multiplication problem for homework:

$$(3.5 \times 10^4)(14.8 \times 10^5)$$

Cal got an answer of 51.8×10^9, and Al got 5.18×10^{10}.

  a. Are Cal's and Al's answers equivalent? Explain why or why not. @

  b. Whose answer is in scientific notation? @ Al's answer

  c. Find another exponential expression equivalent to Cal's and Al's answers. @ possible answer: 518×10^8

  d. Explain how you can rewrite a number such as 432.5×10^3 in scientific notation. @

10. Consider these multiplication expressions:

  i. $(2 \times 10^5)(3 \times 10^8)$ 6×10^{13} **ii.** $(6.5 \times 10^3)(2.0 \times 10^5)$ 1.3×10^9

  a. Set your calculator in scientific notation mode and multiply each expression.

  b. Explain how you could do the multiplication in 10a without using a calculator. ⓗ

  c. Find the product $(4 \times 10^5)(6 \times 10^7)$ and write it in scientific notation without using your calculator.
$(4 \times 10^5)(6 \times 10^7) = 4 \times 6 \times 10^5 \times 10^7 = 24 \times 10^{12} = 2.4 \times 10^1 \times 10^{12} = 2.4 \times 10^{13}$

11. Americans make almost 2 billion telephone calls each day. (*www.britannica.com*)

  a. Write this number in standard notation and in scientific notation. 2,000,000,000; 2×10^9

  b. How many phone calls do Americans make in one year? (Assume that there are 365 days in a year.) Write your answer in scientific notation. 7.3×10^{11} calls per year

The number of molecules in one mole is called *Avogadro's number*. The number is named after the Italian chemist and physicist Amadeo Avogadro (1776–1856).

12. On average a person sheds 1 million dead skin cells every 40 minutes. (*The World in One Day,* 1997, p. 16)

   a. How many dead skin cells does a person shed in an hour? Write your answer in scientific notation. ⓗ

   b. How many dead skin cells does a person shed in a year? (Assume that there are 365 days in a year.) Write your answer in scientific notation.
   1.314×10^{10} cells per year

Dead skin cells are one of the components of dust.

13. A *light-year* is the distance light can travel in one year. This distance is approximately 9,460 billion kilometers. The Milky Way galaxy is estimated to be about 100,000 light-years in diameter.

   a. Write both distances in scientific notation. 9.46×10^{12} km; 1.0×10^5 light-years

   b. Find the diameter of the Milky Way in kilometers. Use scientific notation. 9.46×10^{17} km

   c. Scientists estimate the diameter of Earth is greater than 1.27×10^4 km. How many times larger is the diameter of the Milky Way? $\dfrac{(9.46 \times 10^{17})}{(1.27 \times 10^4)} = 7.45 \times 10^{13}$

 Review

6.2 **14.** **APPLICATION** The exponential equation $P = 3.8(1 + 0.017)^t$ approximates Australia's annual population (in millions) since 1900.

   a. Explain the real-world meaning of each number and variable in the equation. ⓐ

   b. What interval of *t*-values will give information up to the current year? ⓐ

   c. Graph $P = 3.8(1 + 0.017)^t$ over the time interval you named in 14b.

   d. What population does the model predict for the year 1950? ⓐ   approximately 8.8 million

   e. Use the equation to predict today's population. ⓗ
   Answers will vary depending on the current year; $P = 3.8(1 + 0.017)^{current\ year - 1900}$.

5.6 **15.** Graph $y \le -2(x - 5)$.

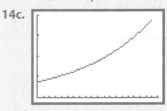
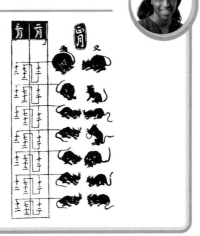
Exercises 12 and 13 Encourage the use of dimensional analysis.

12a. 1.5×10^6 cells per hour

Exercise 13 This exercise, which reviews Lesson 6.3, can be used to foreshadow division with exponents in Lesson 6.5. That is, $10^{17} \div 10^4 = 10^{13}$.

Exercise 14 Because the equation was written to fit data, it might not provide the exact population at any point. In particular, it predicts today's population a little higher than the actual population now.

This exercise is from *Graphic Algebra* (Key Curriculum Press), a good resource for other problems.

14a. 3.8 is the population (in millions) in 1900; 0.017 is the annual growth rate; *t* is the elapsed time in years since 1900; *P* is the population (in millions) *t* years after 1900.

14b. Answers will vary depending on the current year; $0 \le t \le$ (*current year* − 1900).

14c.

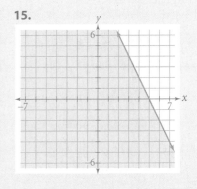

[0, 100, 5, 0, 20, 5]

15.

LESSON

6.5

The eye that directs a needle in the delicate meshes of embroidery, will equally well bisect a star with the spider web of the micrometer.

MARIA MITCHELL

Looking Back with Exponents

You've learned that looking ahead in time to predict future growth with an exponential model is related to the multiplication property of exponents. In this lesson you'll discover a rule for dividing expressions with exponents. Then you'll see how dividing expressions with exponents is like looking *back* in time.

PLANNING

LESSON OUTLINE

One day:

20 min	Investigation
5 min	Sharing
10 min	Examples
5 min	Closing
10 min	Exercises

MATERIALS

- Properties of Exponents (T), *optional*

TEACHING

Real-world situations give insight into why exponents are subtracted when powers of like bases are divided.

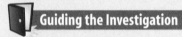 Guiding the Investigation

One Step

Pose this problem: "Six years ago Anne paid $18,500 for a van for her flower delivery service. Its value has been depreciating at a rate of 9% per year, so the van is currently worth $18,500(1 − 0.09)^6$ dollars. How much was it worth two years ago?" As you circulate, encourage students to write the value in at least two different ways: $\frac{18,500(1-0.09)^6}{(1-0.09)^2}$ and $18,500(1-0.09)^4$. Ask students if they think they can always subtract exponents when dividing, bring out the idea of having like bases, and ask them to make up and solve some related problems with which to challenge each other.

See page 724 for answers to Step 1.

Investigation
The Division Property of Exponents

Step 1   Write the numerator and the denominator of each quotient in expanded form. Then reduce to eliminate common factors. Rewrite the factors that remain with exponents. Use your calculator to check your answers.

    a. $\dfrac{5^9}{5^6}$ **b.** $\dfrac{3^3 \cdot 5^3}{3 \cdot 5^2}$ **c.** $\dfrac{4^4 x^6}{4^2 x^3}$

Step 2   Compare the exponents in each final expression you got in Step 1 to the exponents in the original quotient. Describe a way to find the exponents in the final expression without using expanded form.

Step 2 Descriptions should include subtracting the exponent in the denominator from the exponents in the numerator.

Step 3   Use your method from Step 2 to rewrite this expression so that it is not a fraction. You can leave $\frac{0.08}{12}$ as a fraction.

$$\frac{5^{15}\left(1 + \dfrac{0.08}{12}\right)^{24}}{5^{11}\left(1 + \dfrac{0.08}{12}\right)^{18}} \qquad 5^{(15-11)}\left(1 + \dfrac{0.08}{12}\right)^{(24-18)} = 5^4\left(1 + \dfrac{0.08}{12}\right)^6$$

Recall that exponential growth is related to repeated multiplication. When you look ahead in time you multiply by repeated constant multipliers, or increase the exponent. To look back in time you will need to undo some of the constant multipliers, or divide.

LESSON OBJECTIVE

- Review or learn the division property of exponents

NCTM STANDARDS

CONTENT		PROCESS	
✔	Number	✔	Problem Solving
✔	Algebra	✔	Reasoning
	Geometry	✔	Communication
	Measurement	✔	Connections
	Data/Probability	✔	Representation

Step 4 | Apply what you have discovered about dividing expressions with exponents.

a. After 7 years the balance in a savings account is $500(1 + 0.04)^7$. What does the expression $\frac{500(1 + 0.04)^7}{(1 + 0.04)^3}$ mean in this situation? Rewrite this expression with a single exponent. the balance 3 yr prior; $500(1 + 0.04)^4$

b. After 9 years of depreciation, the value of a car is $21,300(1 - 0.12)^9$. What does the expression $\frac{21,300(1 - 0.12)^9}{(1 - 0.12)^5}$ mean in this situation? Rewrite this expression with a single exponent. the balance 5 yr prior; $21,300(1 - 0.12)^4$

c. After 5 weeks the population of a bug colony is $32(1 + 0.50)^5$. Write a division expression to show the population 2 weeks earlier. Rewrite your expression with a single exponent. $\frac{32(1 + 0.50)^5}{(1 + 0.50)^2} = 32(1 + 0.50)^3$

d. The expression $A(1 + r)^n$ can model n time periods of exponential growth. What expression models the growth m time periods earlier? $A(1 + r)^{n-m}$

Step 5 | How does looking back in time with an exponential model relate to dividing expressions with exponents? Dividing by $(1 + r)^m$ represents looking back m time periods.

Expanded form helps you understand many properties of exponents. It also helps you understand how the properties work together.

EXAMPLE A | Use the properties of exponents to rewrite each expression.

a. $\frac{6x^9}{5x^4}$ **b.** $\frac{(3x^2)(8x^4)}{-4x^3}$ **c.** $\frac{7.5 \times 10^8}{1.5 \times 10^3}$

▶ **Solution** | **a.**

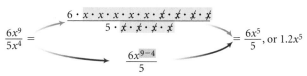

Use expanded form and reduce.

$$\frac{6x^9}{5x^4} = \frac{6 \cdot x \cdot x \cdot x \cdot x \cdot x \cdot \cancel{x} \cdot \cancel{x} \cdot \cancel{x} \cdot \cancel{x}}{5 \cdot \cancel{x} \cdot \cancel{x} \cdot \cancel{x} \cdot \cancel{x}} = \frac{6x^5}{5}, \text{ or } 1.2x^5$$

$$\frac{6x^{9-4}}{5}$$

In expanded form, 4 factors of x are removed in the numerator and denominator. That leaves $9 - 4$, or 5, factors of x in the numerator.

b.

Use expanded form and reduce.

$$\frac{(3x^2)(8x^4)}{-4x^3} = \frac{3 \cdot 8 \cdot x^2 \cdot x^4}{-4 \cdot x^3} = \frac{3 \cdot 8}{-4} \cdot \frac{x \cdot x \cdot x \cdot \cancel{x} \cdot \cancel{x} \cdot \cancel{x}}{\cancel{x} \cdot \cancel{x} \cdot \cancel{x}} = -6x^3$$

$$\frac{3 \cdot 8}{-4} \cdot x^{(2+4)-3}$$

In expanded form, 2 factors of x are combined with 4 factors of x in the numerator. Then 3 factors of x are removed in the numerator and denominator. That leaves $(2 + 4) - 3$, or 3, factors of x in the numerator.

Step 1 Encourage students to write exponents of 1. Doing so will aid them in devising a rule in Step 2.

Step 3 Division by a power of 5 as well as the other power might confuse some students. Remind them that division is the opposite of multiplication, so that they can think of dividing 5^{15} by 5^{11}.

Step 4 If students are having difficulty expressing their ideas in parts a and b, suggest that they look at the wording in parts c and d.

SHARING IDEAS

Ask students to share their ideas about Step 2. Try to get them to formulate the division property of exponents. Students can look on page 362, or you might want to display the division property shown on the Properties of Exponents transparency. **[Ask]** "Why must b not equal zero?" [Division by zero is undefined.] "Why doesn't the statement exclude m or n from being zero?" Getting students to conjecture about the value of b^0 motivates Lesson 6.6.

Assessing Progress

Look for understanding that exponents represent repeated multiplication, understanding that the fraction bar represents division, and the ability to see "chunks."

▶ ***EXAMPLE A***

This example is good for extending the division property beyond powers on a single base. If students are having trouble, keep stressing that they can write out the terms in expanded form, such as

$$\frac{6x^9}{5x^4} = \frac{6 \cdot x \cdot x \cdot x \cdot x \cdot x \cdot x \cdot x \cdot x \cdot x}{5 \cdot x \cdot x \cdot x \cdot x},$$

and then eliminate factors equivalent to 1, in this case getting $\frac{6x^5}{5}$.

c.

$$\frac{7.5 \times 10^8}{1.5 \times 10^3} = \frac{7.5}{1.5} \times \frac{10 \cdot 10 \cdot 10 \cdot 10 \cdot 10 \cdot \cancel{10} \cdot \cancel{10} \cdot \cancel{10}}{\cancel{10} \cdot \cancel{10} \cdot \cancel{10}} = 5.0 \times 10^5$$

$$\frac{7.5}{1.5} \times 10^{8-3}$$

So, division involving scientific notation can be done just like any other expression with exponents.

The investigation and example have introduced the **division property of exponents.**

> ### Division Property of Exponents
>
> For any nonzero value of b and any integer values of m and n,
>
> $$\frac{b^n}{b^m} = b^{n-m}$$

The division property of exponents lets you divide expressions with exponents simply by subtracting the exponents.

EXAMPLE B

Six years ago, Anne bought a van for $18,500 for her flower delivery service. Based on the prices of similar used vans, she estimates a rate of depreciation of 9% per year.

a. How much is the van worth now?

b. How much was it worth last year?

c. How much was it worth 2 years ago?

► **Solution**

The original price was $18,500, and the rate of depreciation as a decimal is 0.09. Use the expression $A(1 - r)^x$.

a. Right now the value of the van has been decreasing for 6 years.

$$A(1 - r)^x = 18{,}500(1 - 0.09)^6 \approx 10{,}505.58$$

The van is currently worth $10,505.58.

b. A year ago, the van was 5 years old. One approach is to use 5 as the exponent.

$$18{,}500(1 - 0.09)^5 \approx 11{,}544.59$$

Another approach is to undo the multiplication in part a by using division.

$$\frac{18{,}500(1 - 0.09)^6}{(1 - 0.09)} = 18{,}500(1 - 0.09)^5$$

The numerator on the left side of this equation represents the starting value multiplied by 6 factors of the constant multiplier $(1 - 0.09)$. Dividing by the constant multiplier once leaves you with an expression representing 5 years of exponential depreciation. Either way, the exponent is decreased by 1. The van was worth $11,544.59 last year.

If b is positive, the division property of exponents works for all real values of m and n.

► **EXAMPLE B**

This example provides another case of a decreasing exponential situation, especially useful for students who had difficulties with Step 4b of the investigation.

Closing the Lesson

Considering the value of an exponentially growing quantity at one time and at an earlier time can show that, when powers of like bases are divided, the exponents are subtracted.

c. To find the value 2 years ago, decrease the exponent in part a by 2.

$$18{,}500(1 - 0.09)^{6-2} = 18{,}500(1 - 0.09)^4 \approx 12{,}686.37$$

Subtracting 2 from the exponent gives the same result as undoing two multiplications. The van was worth $12,686.37 two years ago.

EXERCISES

▶ Practice Your Skills

1. Eliminate factors equivalent to 1 and rewrite the right side of this equation.

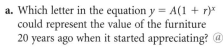

$$\frac{x^5 y^4}{x^2 y^3} = \frac{x \cdot x \cdot x \cdot x \cdot x \cdot y \cdot y \cdot y \cdot y}{x \cdot x \cdot y \cdot y \cdot y} \quad x^3 y$$

2. Use the properties of exponents to rewrite each expression.

   a. $\dfrac{7^{12}}{7^4}$ @ 7^8 **b.** $\dfrac{x^{11}}{x^5}$ x^6 **c.** $\dfrac{12x^5}{3x^2}$ @ $4x^3$ **d.** $\dfrac{7x^6 y^3}{14x^3 y}$ $0.5x^3 y^2$

3. Cal says that $\frac{3^6}{3^2}$ equals 1^4 because you divide the 3's and subtract the exponents. Al knows Cal is incorrect, but he doesn't know how to explain it. Write an explanation so that Cal will understand why he is wrong and how he can get the correct answer. ⓗ

4. APPLICATION Webster owns a set of antique dining-room furniture that has been in his family for many years. The historical society tells him that furniture similar to his has been appreciating in value at 10% per year for the last 20 years and that his furniture could be worth $10,000 now.

   a. Which letter in the equation $y = A(1 + r)^x$ could represent the value of the furniture 20 years ago when it started appreciating? @

   b. Substitute the other given information into the equation $y = A(1 + r)^x$. @

   c. Solve your equation in 4b to find how much Webster's furniture was worth 20 years ago. Show your work. @

5. Use the properties of exponents to rewrite each expression.

   a. $(2x)^3 \cdot (3x^2)^4$ $648x^{11}$ **b.** $\dfrac{(5x)^7}{(5x)^5}$ $25x^2$ **c.** $\dfrac{(2x)^5}{-8x^3}$ @ $-4x^2$ **d.** $(4x^2 y^5) \cdot (-3xy^3)^3$
                                                                       $-108x^5 y^{14}$

▶ Reason and Apply

6. Earth is 1.5×10^{11} m from the Sun. Light travels at a speed of 3×10^8 m/s. How long does it take light to travel from the Sun to Earth? Answer to the nearest minute.
It takes 500 s, or approximately 8 min.

4a. *A* represents the starting value.

4b. $10{,}000 = A(1 + 0.1)^{20}$

4c. $10{,}000 = A(1 + 0.1)^{20}$

$\dfrac{10{,}000}{(1 + 0.1)^{20}} = A$

   $1486.43 \approx A$

The furniture was worth about $1,486 twenty years ago.

Exercises 6 and 7 Encourage the use of dimensional analysis in setting up the quotient. If students use a calculator to do the calculations, point out that they can also do some of the calculations using the division property of exponents.

▶ Helping with the Exercises

Exercise 2a If students write this as 1^8, urge them to write out the 7's and then remove values of 1. There will be eight 7's left.

Exercise 3 This exercise gives students a chance to confront a common error. [Ask] "Why can't you divide the common bases?" Encourage students to write the numerator and denominator in expanded form and then remove values equivalent to 1. To challenge students who understand this very well, [Ask] "Are there any conditions under which you could divide the common bases?" [If the same bases have the same power, then the ratio is 1. Dividing the bases to get a base of 1 will yield that ratio.]

3. Possible answer: $\frac{3^6}{3^2}$ means there are six factors of 3 in the numerator and two factors of 3 in the denominator. So there are two factors of 1, or $\frac{3}{3}$, in the entire expression, leaving four factors of 3 in the numerator, or 3^4.

Exercise 4 At this point students can solve the equation by using graphing or tables. Students will see in Lesson 6.6 that the equation can also be solved using negative exponents: $A = 10{,}000(1 + 0.1)^{-20}$.

7. **APPLICATION** **Population density** is the number of people per square mile. That is, if the population of a country were spread out evenly across an entire nation, the population density would be the number of people in each square mile.

a. In 2004, the population of Mexico was about 1.0×10^8. Mexico has a land area of about 7.6×10^5 square miles. What was the population density of Mexico in 2004? (Central Intelligence Agency, *www.cia.gov*) ⓐ about 132 people per square mile

b. In 2004, the population of Japan was about 1.3×10^8. Japan has a land area of about 1.5×10^5 square miles. What was the population density of Japan in 2004? (Central Intelligence Agency, *www.cia.gov*) about 867 people per square mile

c. How did the population densities of Mexico and Japan compare in 2004?

7c. The population of Japan was about 6.6 times denser than that of Mexico.

8. **APPLICATION** Eight months ago, Tori's parents put $5,000 into a savings account that earns 3% annual interest. Now, her dentist has suggested that she get braces.

a. If the interest is calculated each month, what is the monthly interest rate? ⓐ 0.25%

b. If Tori's parents use the money in their savings account, how much do they have? $5,100.88

c. If Tori's dentist had suggested braces 3 months ago, how much money would have been in her parents' savings account? $5,062.81

d. Tori's dentist says she can probably wait up to 2 months before having the braces fitted. How much will be in her parents' savings account if she waits? $5,126.42

Orthodontic treatment can cost between $4,000 and $6,000 depending on the extent of the procedure. An estimated 5 million people were treated by orthodontists in the United States in 2000.

Exercise 9 Students could also use the equation $20 = 864(3)^x$, thus previewing negative exponents in Lesson 6.6.

9. **APPLICATION** During its early stages, a disease can spread exponentially as those already infected come in contact with others. Assume that the number of people infected by a disease approximately triples every day. At one point in time, 864 people are infected. How many days earlier had fewer than 20 people been infected? Show two different methods for solving this problem. ⓗ

9. Four days earlier;

Method 1: Use a recursive routine:
864 ⏎ , Ans/3 ⏎ ,
⏎ , ⏎ , ⏎ .

Method 2: Use an equation:
$y = 864\left(\frac{1}{3}\right)^x$; look at the table to find x when y is less than 20.

10. The population of a city has been growing at a rate of 2% for the last 5 years. The population is now 120,000. Find the population 5 years ago. approximately 108,688

11. APPLICATION In the course of a mammal's lifetime, its heart beats about 800 million times, regardless of the mammal's size or weight. (This excludes humans.)

a. An elephant's heart beats approximately 25 times a minute. How many years would you expect an elephant to live? Use scientific notation to calculate your answer. @ approximately 61 yr

b. A pygmy shrew's heart beats approximately 1150 times a minute. How many years would you expect a pygmy shrew to live? approximately 1.3 yr

c. If this relationship were true for humans, how many years would you expect a human being with a heart rate of 60 bpm to live? approximately 25.4 yr

Pygmy shrews may be the world's smallest mammal, as small as 5 cm from nose to tail.

12. More than 57,000 tons of cotton are produced in the world each day. It takes about 8 ounces of cotton to make a T-shirt. The population of the United States in 2000 was estimated to be more than 275 million. If all the available cotton were used to make T-shirts, how many T-shirts could have been manufactured every day for each person in the United States in 2000? Write your answer in scientific notation. (*www.cotton.net*) approximately 8.3×10^{-1} T-shirt per person

13. Each day, bees sip the nectar from approximately 3 trillion flowers to make 3300 tons of honey. How many flowers does it take to make 8 ounces of honey? Write your answer in scientific notation. (*The World in One Day,* 1997, p. 21) ⓗ approximately 2.272×10^5 flowers

▶ Review

2.3 **14.** On his birthday Jon figured out that he was 441,504,000 seconds old. Find Jon's age in years. (Assume that there are 365 days per year.) 14 yr

2.3, **15.** Halley is doing a report on the solar system and wants to make models
6.4 of the Sun and the planets showing relative size. She decides that Pluto, the smallest planet, should have a model diameter of 2 cm.

a. Using the table, find the diameters of the other models she would have to make. ⓗ

b. What advice would you give Halley on her project?

Possible answer: Halley should make her models much smaller because Jupiter is 1 m in diameter and the Sun is greater than 11 m in diameter; it would be better to leave the Sun out of her models altogether. If she makes Pluto with a diameter of 0.2 cm, Jupiter will be only about 12 cm in diameter.

Size of Planets and Sun

Planet	Diameter (mi)
Mercury	3.1×10^3
Venus	7.5×10^3
Earth	7.9×10^3
Mars	4.2×10^3
Jupiter	8.8×10^4
Saturn	7.1×10^4
Uranus	5.2×10^4
Neptune	3.1×10^4
Pluto	1.5×10^3
Sun	8.64×10^5

Exercise 11 Encourage students to use dimensional analysis. As needed, remind them that bpm means *beats per minute.*

Exercises 12 and 13 Urge students to use dimensional analysis carefully. Students may not know that 1 ton is 2000 lb and 1 lb is 16 oz.

Exercise 15 This exercise requires division of exponential expressions.

15a. (answers recorded to tenths) Mercury: 4.1 cm; Venus: 10 cm; Earth: 10.5 cm; Mars: 5.6 cm; Jupiter: 117.3 cm; Saturn: 94.7 cm; Uranus: 69.3 cm; Neptune: 41.3 cm; Pluto: 2 cm; Sun: 1152 cm

PLANNING

LESSON OUTLINE

First day:

40 min   Investigation

10 min   Sharing

Second day:

30 min   Examples

 5 min   Closing

15 min   Exercises

MATERIALS

• Properties of Exponents (T), *optional*

TEACHING

Negative exponents are used in scientific notation for numbers very close to zero. They provide an alternative way to solve problems involving division of powers.

  Guiding the Investigation

One Step

Pose this problem: "Assume that the diameter of a pin point is 0.0010 cm and that each atom has diameter 0.00000001 cm. How would you represent these numbers with scientific notation, and how many atoms are on the point of a pin?" As students work, remind them that the positive exponent in scientific notation is one fewer than the number of digits to the left of the decimal point. After they get the quotient $\frac{1.0 \times 10^{-3}}{10^{-8}}$, you may need to remind them how to subtract a negative number from another negative number.

Step 4 Possible answer: A base raised to a negative exponent means the same thing as the reciprocal of the base raised to the same exponent with the sign changed to positive.

It is not knowledge which is dangerous, but the poor use of it.

HROTSWITHA

Zero and Negative Exponents

Have you noticed that so far in this chapter the exponents have been positive integers? In this lesson you will learn what a zero or a negative integer means as an exponent.

Investigation
More Exponents

Step 1   Use the division property of exponents to rewrite each of these expressions with a single exponent. Use your calculator to check your answers.

    a. $\frac{y^7}{y^2}$ y^5 **b.** $\frac{3^2}{3^4}$ 3^{-2} **c.** $\frac{7^4}{7^4}$ 7^0 **d.** $\frac{2}{2^5}$ 2^{-4} **e.** $\frac{x^3}{x^6}$ x^{-3}

    f. $\frac{z^8}{z}$ z^7 **g.** $\frac{2^3}{2^3}$ 2^0 **h.** $\frac{x^5}{x^5}$ x^0 **i.** $\frac{m^6}{m^3}$ m^3 **j.** $\frac{5^3}{5^5}$ 5^{-2}

Some of your answers in Step 1 should have positive exponents, some should have negative exponents, and some should have a zero exponent.

Step 2
Possible answer: Expressions resulting in positive exponents have a larger exponent in the numerator; expressions resulting in negative exponents have larger exponents in the denominator; expressions resulting in zero exponents have equal exponents in the numerator and denominator.

Step 2   How can you tell what type of exponent will result simply by looking at the original expression?

Step 3   Go back to the expressions in Step 1 that resulted in a negative exponent. Write each in expanded form. Then reduce them.   **b.** $\frac{1}{9}$ **d.** $\frac{1}{16}$ **e.** $\frac{1}{x^3}$ **j.** $\frac{1}{25}$

Step 4   Compare your answers from Step 3 and Step 1. Tell what a base raised to a negative exponent means.

Step 5   Go back to the expressions in Step 1 that resulted in an exponent of zero. Write each in expanded form. Then reduce them.   c, g, and h; 1

Step 6   Compare your answers from Step 5 and Step 1. Tell what a base raised to an exponent of zero means.
Possible answer: A base raised to a zero exponent is always equal to 1.

LESSON OBJECTIVES

• Investigate the meaning of nonpositive exponents

• Write a number with a negative exponent in a form that has a positive exponent and write a number with a positive exponent in a form that has a negative exponent

• Write in scientific notation numbers close to zero

NCTM STANDARDS

CONTENT		PROCESS	
✔	Number		Problem Solving
✔	Algebra	✔	Reasoning
	Geometry	✔	Communication
✔	Measurement	✔	Connections
	Data/Probability	✔	Representation

Step 7 Use what you have learned about negative exponents to rewrite each of these expressions with positive exponents and only one fraction bar.

a. $\frac{5^{-2}}{1}$ $\frac{1}{5^2}$ b. $\frac{1}{3^{-8}}$ $\frac{1}{\frac{1}{3^8}}$, or $\frac{3^8}{1}$ c. $\frac{4x^{-2}}{z^2y^{-5}}$ $\frac{4y^5}{z^2x^2}$

Step 8 In one or two sentences, explain how to rewrite a fraction with a negative exponent in the numerator or denominator as a fraction with positive exponents. Possible answer: An expression with an exponent can be moved between the numerator and denominator of a fraction as long as the sign of the exponent is changed with each move.

This table supports what you have learned about negative exponents and zero exponents. To go down either column of the table, you divide by 3. Notice that each time you divide, the exponent decreases by 1. (Likewise, to go up either column of the table, you multiply by 3 and the exponent increases by 1.) In order to continue the pattern, 3^0 must have the value 1. As the exponents become negative, the base 3 appears in the denominator with a positive exponent.

Exponential form	Fraction form
3^3	27
3^2	9
3^1	3
3^0	1
3^{-1}	$\frac{1}{3}$
3^{-2}	$\frac{1}{9}$
3^{-3}	$\frac{1}{27}$

$$3^1 \div 3 = \frac{3^1}{3^1} = 3^{1-1} = 3^0 \qquad 3 \div 3 = \frac{3}{3} = 1$$

$$3^{-1} \div 3 = \frac{3^{-1}}{3^1} = 3^{-1-1} = 3^{-2} \qquad \frac{1}{3} \div 3 = \frac{1}{3} \cdot \frac{1}{3} = \frac{1}{3^2} = \frac{1}{9}$$

Negative Exponents and Zero Exponents

For any nonzero value of b and for any value of n,

$$b^{-n} = \frac{1}{b^n} \quad \text{and} \quad \frac{1}{b^{-n}} = b^n$$

$$b^0 = 1$$

EXAMPLE A

Use the properties of exponents to rewrite each expression without a fraction bar.

a. $\frac{3^5}{4^7}$ b. $\frac{25}{x^8}$

c. $\frac{5^{-3}}{2^{-8}}$ d. $\frac{3(17)^8}{17^8}$

Step 7 Some students may see that a negative exponent on a term in the numerator moves that term to the denominator with a positive exponent but not see that the process works in reverse. Suggest that they write the denominator in part b as a fraction and then multiply the numerator and denominator of the complex fraction by 3^8. The same idea applies to y^{-5} in part c.

Step 8 [Ask] "Do your findings extend to rewriting an expression with positive exponents as a fraction with negative exponents?"

SHARING IDEAS

Ask for ideas from Step 8. Work with the class to come up with a precise method. **[Ask]** "Why does the method work?" [One justification might be through patterns, as found in the table in the student text.]

Have the class critique the boxed definition in the student text. Ask why b must be "nonzero." Help students see that if b were zero, then you'd have $0 = \frac{1}{0^n}$, but division by zero is undefined. When students realize the importance of the phrase "for any value of n," they may raise questions about the case of $n = 0$. In that case, both sides of the equation are 1.

Elicit the question of the value of 0^0. Arguments for two different values can be made: zero to any other power is zero, but any other number to the zero power is one. Mathematicians say 0^0 is *indeterminate,* meaning that it's undefined. If students are interested, they might graph the equation $y = x^x$ on their calculators and see what value it gets close to as x approaches zero.

Note the quotation introducing the lesson. Hrotswitha of Gansersheim (935–1000 C.E.) is the first recorded female German writer. She included some mathematics in her plays. She was also a Benedictine nun. You could use this quote to warn against the "dangers" of misapplying the various properties of exponents, though she undoubtedly had in mind a deeper social meaning.

Assessing Progress

You can assess students' understanding of exponents as indicators of repeated multiplication, their understanding of subtraction of exponents when dividing like bases, and their ability to subtract a larger integer from a smaller one.

► **Solution**

a. $\dfrac{3^5}{4^7} = 3^5 \cdot \dfrac{1}{4^7}$ Think of the original expression as having two separate factors.

$= 3^5 \cdot 4^{-7}$ Use the definition of negative exponents.

b. $\dfrac{25}{x^8} = 25 \cdot \dfrac{1}{x^8} = 25 \cdot x^{-8} = 25x^{-8}$

c. $\dfrac{5^{-3}}{2^{-8}} = 5^{-3} \cdot \dfrac{1}{2^{-8}} = 5^{-3} \cdot 2^8$

d. $\dfrac{3(17)^8}{17^8} = 3 \cdot 17^0$ Use the division property of exponents.

$= 3 \cdot 1$ Use the definition of zero exponents.

$= 3$ Multiply.

You can also use negative exponents to look back in time with increasing or decreasing exponential situations.

EXAMPLE B   Solomon bought a used car for $5,600. He estimates that it has been decreasing in value by 15% each year.

a. If his estimate of the rate of depreciation is correct, how much was the car worth 3 years ago?

b. If the car is 7 years old, what was the original price of the car?

► **Solution**

a. You can solve this problem by considering $5,600 to be the starting value and then looking back 3 years.

$y = A(1 - r)^x$ The general form of the equation.

$y = 5,600(1 - 0.15)^{-3}$ Substitute the given information in the equation. -3 means you look back 3 years.

$y \approx 9,118.66$

The value of the car 3 years ago was approximately $9,118.66.

b. The original price is the value of the car 7 years ago.

$$y = 5{,}600(1 - 0.15)^{-7}$$

$$y \approx 17{,}468.50$$

The original price was approximately $17,468.50.

You can also use negative exponents to write numbers close to 0 in scientific notation. Just as positive powers of 10 help you rewrite numbers with lots of zeros, negative powers of 10 help you rewrite numbers with lots of zeros between the decimal point and a nonzero digit.

EXAMPLE C

These particle tracks show the paths of particles like protons, electrons, and mesons during a nuclear reaction.

Convert each number to standard notation from scientific notation, or vice versa.

a. A pi meson, an unstable particle released in a nuclear reaction, "lives" only 0.000000026 s.

b. The number 6.67×10^{-11} is the gravitational constant in the metric system used to calculate the gravitational attraction between two objects that have given masses and are a given distance apart.

c. The mass of an electron is 9.1×10^{-31} kg.

▶ **Solution**

a. $0.000000026 = \dfrac{2.6}{100{,}000{,}000} = \dfrac{2.6}{10^8} = 2.6 \times 10^{-8}$

Notice that the decimal point in the original number was moved to the right eight places to get a number between 1 and 10, in this case, 2.6. To undo that, you must multiply 2.6 by 10^{-8}.

b. $6.67 \times 10^{-11} = \dfrac{6.67}{10^{11}} = \dfrac{6.67}{100{,}000{,}000{,}000} = 0.0000000000667$

Multiplying 6.67 by 10^{-11} moves the decimal point 11 places to the left, requiring 10 zeros after the decimal point—the first move of the decimal point changes 6.67 to 0.667.

c. Generalize the method in part b. To write 9.1×10^{-31} in standard notation you move the decimal point 31 places to the left, requiring 30 zeros after the decimal point.

$$9.1 \times 10^{-31} = 0.00000000000000000000000000000091$$

▶ **EXAMPLE C**

[Language] The term *pi meson* is pronounced pie′-may′-zon.

The gravitational constant is popularly known as *G*. Newton's law of universal gravitation states that every particle in the universe attracts every other particle with a force directly proportional to the product of the masses of the two particles and inversely proportional to the square of the distance between their centers of mass. In symbols, $F = \dfrac{Gm_1m_2}{s^2}$, where *F* is the force of attraction in newtons, m_1 and m_2 are the masses in kilograms (kg), and *s* is the distance in meters (m). For units to cancel in dimensional analysis, *G* is in $\dfrac{\text{newton-m}^2}{\text{kg}^2}$.

Because the student text refers to moving decimal places, if you haven't done so already you may want to review the effects on the decimal point of multiplying and dividing by 10. Multiplying by 10 moves the decimal to the right one place, and dividing by 10 moves the decimal to the left one place. Some students remember this with a number line—negatives to the left, positives to the right.

Exponents can be decimals or other fractions as well as integers. **[Ask]** "What have you seen already in this chapter that indicates the existence of fractional and decimal exponents?" [The graphs of equations of the form $y = A(1 + r)^x$ are smooth curves, indicating that *x* can have noninteger values.]

Closing the Lesson

As needed, say that negative exponents are used in scientific notation for numbers very close to zero and provide an alternative way of solving problems involving division of powers.

BUILDING UNDERSTANDING

Students practice working with nonpositive exponents.

ASSIGNING HOMEWORK

Essential	1–4, 6, 7, 9
Performance assessment	8, 14
Portfolio	12
Journal	5, 14
Group	9, 10–13
Review	14, 15

▶ Helping with the Exercises

Exercise 2 [Alert] This exercise tests students' number sense because they have to identify the order relationship between pairs of numbers. If students have difficulty with parts b and d, suggest that they treat the numbers as positive first and then multiply through by -1, changing the direction of the inequality.

Exercise 3b [Alert] Students need to be very careful: As they decrease 46 to 4.6, they add 1 to the negative exponent.

Exercise 4 Even students who would immediately recognize that $(1 + 0.028)^0$ equals 1 might be confused by needing to go backward.

Exercise 7 This exercise is about inflation, so the constant multiplier is more than 1, but the situation calls for thinking back in time, so the exponent is negative. **[Alert]** Students might write a quotient instead of using a negative exponent.

7a. $3500(1 + 0.04)^{-4}$; about $2,992

7c. $25(1 + 0.04)^{-5}$; about $21

EXERCISES

You will need your graphing calculator for Exercise **15**.

▶ Practice Your Skills

1. Rewrite each expression using only positive exponents.

  a. 2^{-3} @ $\frac{1}{2^3}$
  b. 5^{-2} $\frac{1}{5^2}$
  c. 1.35×10^{-4} @ $\frac{1.35}{10^4}$

2. Insert the appropriate symbol ($<$, $=$, or $>$) between each pair of numbers.

  a. 6.35×10^5 $\boxed{=}$ 63.5×10^4 @
    b. -5.24×10^{-7} $\boxed{<}$ -5.2×10^{-7}

  c. 2.674×10^{-5} $\boxed{>}$ 2.674×10^{-6}
    d. -2.7×10^{-4} $\boxed{>}$ -2.8×10^{-3}

3. Find the exponent of 10 that you need to write each expression in scientific notation.

  a. $0.0000412 = 4.12 \times 10^{\square}$ @ -5 **b.** $46 \times 10^{-5} = 4.6 \times 10^{\square}$ -4 **c.** $0.00046 = 4.6 \times 10^{\square}$ -4

4. The population of a town is currently 45,647. It has been growing at a rate of about 2.8% per year.

  a. Write an expression in the form $45{,}647(1 + 0.028)^x$ for the current population. @ $45{,}647(1 + 0.028)^0$

  b. What does the expression $45{,}647(1 + 0.028)^{-12}$ represent in this situation? @ the population 12 yr ago

  c. Write and evaluate an expression for the population 8 years ago. @ $45{,}647(1 + 0.028)^{-8} \approx 36{,}599$

  d. Write expressions without negative exponents that are equivalent to the exponential expressions from 4b and c. @ $\dfrac{45{,}647}{(1 + 0.028)^{12}}, \dfrac{45{,}647}{(1 + 0.028)^8}$

5. Juan says that 6^{-3} is the same as -6^3. Write an explanation of how Juan should interpret 6^{-3}, then show him how each expression results in a different value. Possible answer:
Negative exponents mean to use a reciprocal base with the exponent positive; $6^{-3} = \frac{1}{6^3} = \frac{1}{216}$, $-6^3 = -216$.

▶ Reason and Apply

6. Use the properties of exponents to rewrite each expression without negative exponents.

  a. $\left(2x^3\right)^2\left(3x^4\right)$ $12x^{10}$
    b. $\left(5x^4\right)^0\left(2x^2\right)$ $2x^2$

  c. $3(2x)^3(3x)^{-2}$ @ $\frac{8x}{3}$
    d. $\left(\dfrac{2x^4}{3x}\right)^{-3}$ $\dfrac{27}{8x^9}$

7. APPLICATION Suppose the annual rate of inflation is about 4%. This means that the cost of an item increases by about 4% each year. Write and evaluate an exponential expression to find the answers to these questions. ⓗ

  a. If a piano costs $3,500 today, what did it cost 4 years ago?

  b. If a vacuum cleaner costs $250 today, what did the same model cost 3 years ago? $250(1 + 0.04)^{-3}$; about $222

  c. If tickets to a college basketball game cost $25 today, what did they cost 5 years ago?

  d. The median price of a house in the United States in October 2004 was $187,000. What was the median price 30 years ago?
  (National Association of Realtors, *www.realtor.org*)
  $187{,}000(1 + 0.04)^{-30}$; about $57,656

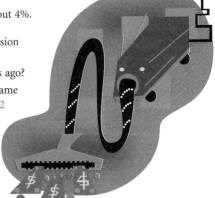

8. APPLICATION The population of Japan in 2004 was about 1.3×10^8. Japan has a land area of about 1.5×10^5 square miles. (Central Intelligence Agency, www.cia.gov)

  a. On average, how much land in square miles is there per person? (*Note:* This is a different problem from the one you may have solved in Lesson 6.5.) approximately 1.2×10^{-3} square mile per person

  b. Convert your answer from 8a to square feet per person. approximately 3.35×10^4 square feet per person (or 3.22×10^4 square feet per person if the answer from 8a is used without rounding)

9. Decide whether each statement is true or false. Use expanded form to show either that the statement is true or what the correct statement should be.

  a. $\left(2^3\right)^2 = 2^6$ **b.** $\left(3^0\right)^4 = 3^4$

  c. $\left(10^{-2}\right)^4 = -10^8$ ⓐ   **d.** $\left(5^{-3}\right)^{-4} = 5^{12}$

10. A large ball of string originally held 1 mile of string. Abigail cut off a piece of string one-tenth of that length. Barbara then cut a piece of string that was one-tenth as long as the piece Abigail had cut. Cruz came along and cut a piece that was one-tenth the length of what Barbara had cut.

  a. Write each length of string in miles in scientific notation.

  b. If the process continues, how long a piece will the next person, Damien, cut off? 1×10^{-4} mi

  c. Do any of the people have a piece of string too short to use as a shoelace? ⓗ Convert to inches; Damien's string is too short (6.3 in.).

11. Suppose $36(1 + 0.5)^4$ represents the number of bacteria cells in a sample after 4 hours of growth at a rate of 50% per hour. Write an exponential expression for the number of cells 6 hours earlier. $36(1 + 0.5)^{4-6}$, or $36(1 + 0.5)^{-2}$

10a. original: 1×10^0;
Abigail: 1×10^{-1};
Barbara: 1×10^{-2};
Cruz: 1×10^{-3}

12. APPLICATION Camila received a $1,200 prize for one of her essays. She decides to invest $1,000 of it for college. Her bank offers two options. The first is a regular savings account that pays 2.5% interest every 6 months. The second is a certificate of deposit that pays 5% interest each year.

  a. With the savings account, how much would Camila have after 1 year? After 2 years? ⓐ $1,050.63; $1,103.81

  b. With the certificate of deposit, how much would Camila have after 1 year? After 2 years? ⓐ $1,050; $1,102.50

  c. Explain why you get different results for 12a and b. ⓐ Possible answer: In the savings account, interest is added at 6 mo, so the interest earns interest. The 1 yr interest is $(1 + 0.025)^2$, or 1.050625; that is more than 5%.

13. *Mini-Investigation* In the last few lessons, you have worked with equations that have a variable exponent, and you have dealt with positive, negative, and zero exponents. An equation in which *variables* are raised only to nonnegative integer exponents is called a **polynomial equation.** Identify these equations as exponential, polynomial, or neither. ⓗ

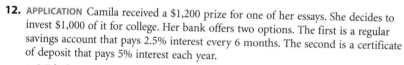

$y = 4x^3$ $y = -3(1 + 0.4)^x$ $y = x^x + x^2$ $y = 2x^5 - 3x^2 + 4x + 2$

$y = 2 \cdot 3^x$ $y = 2x + 7$ $y = -6 + 2x + 3x^2$ $y = 3$

Exercise 13 The role of a constant is ambiguous. For example, the constant 3 could be thought of as $3x^0$ (a polynomial) or as $3 \cdot 0^x$ (an exponential). The convention is to consider a constant as a polynomial so that when it's added to a polynomial the result is still a polynomial. Polynomials will come up again in Chapter 9.

 Review

6.2 **14.** APPLICATION A capacitor is charged with a nine-volt battery. The equation $y = 9.4(1 - 0.043)^x$ models the charge of a capacitor after it is connected to a load. The variable x is in seconds since the capacitor is connected, and y is in volts.

  a. Is the voltage of the capacitor increasing or decreasing? Explain.
    The voltage is decreasing because the base, 0.957, is less than 1.

13. exponential:
$y = -3(1 + 0.4)^x, y = 2 \cdot 3^x$;
polynomial: $y = 4x^3$,
$y = 2x^5 - 3x^2 + 4x + 2$,
$y = 2x + 7, y = -6 + 2x + 3x^2$,
$y = 3$; neither: $y = x^x + x^2$

9a. true; $\left(2^3\right)^2 = 2^3 \cdot 2^3 = 2 \cdot 2 \cdot 2 \cdot 2 \cdot 2 \cdot 2 = 2^6$

9b. false; $\left(3^0\right)^4 = \left(1\right)^4 = 1$

9c. false; $\left(10^{-2}\right)^4 = \left(\dfrac{1}{10^2}\right)^4 = \left(\dfrac{1}{10 \cdot 10}\right)\left(\dfrac{1}{10 \cdot 10}\right)\left(\dfrac{1}{10 \cdot 10}\right)\left(\dfrac{1}{10 \cdot 10}\right) = \dfrac{1}{10^8} = 10^{-8}$

9d. true; $\left(5^{-3}\right)^{-4} = \left(\dfrac{1}{5^3}\right)^{-4} = \dfrac{1}{\left(\dfrac{1}{5^3}\right)^4} = \dfrac{1}{\left(\dfrac{1}{5 \cdot 5 \cdot 5}\right)\left(\dfrac{1}{5 \cdot 5 \cdot 5}\right)\left(\dfrac{1}{5 \cdot 5 \cdot 5}\right)\left(\dfrac{1}{5 \cdot 5 \cdot 5}\right)} = \dfrac{1}{\dfrac{1}{5^{12}}} = \dfrac{1}{5^{-12}} = 5^{12}$

14b. 9.4 is the voltage at time 0. Each second, 4.3% of the previous voltage is lost.

14c.

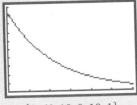

[0, 60, 10, 0, 10, 1]

14d. When $x > 15.77$ s; possible answer: The exponential graph is below the graph of $y = 4.7$ for $x > 15.77$ s. (The exponential graph intersects the graph of $y = 4.7$ at $x \approx 15.7706$, but students will not solve to this precision.)

Exercise 15 **[Alert]** Students may forget to use parentheses when entering the denominators into their calculators. For example, in 15a, they may enter 8*10^8/2*10^3 instead of 8*10^8/(2*10^3). Remind them that the numerator is divided by each factor in the denominator. In fact, they can avoid parentheses by entering 8*10^8/2/10^3. Be sure they explain their reasoning in 15c.

15b. Possible answer: Divide the coefficients of the powers of 10, and then divide the powers of 10 (subtract the exponents).

b. What is the meaning of the numbers 9.4 and 0.043 in the equation?

c. Draw a graph of this model for the first minute after disconnecting the battery.

d. When is y less than or equal to 4.7 volts? Explain how you found this answer.

6.4 **15.** Set your calculator in scientific notation mode for this problem.

    a. Use your calculator to do each division.

      i. $\dfrac{8 \times 10^8}{2 \times 10^3}$ 4×10^5 **ii.** $\dfrac{9.3 \times 10^{13}}{3 \times 10^3}$ 3.1×10^{10} **iii.** $\dfrac{4.84 \times 10^9}{4 \times 10^4}$ 1.21×10^5 **iv.** $\dfrac{6.2 \times 10^4}{3.1 \times 10^8}$ 2×10^{-4}

    b. Describe how you could do the calculations in 15a without using a calculator.

    c. Find the answer to the quotient $\dfrac{4.8 \times 10^7}{8 \times 10^2}$ without using your calculator.

      0.6×10^5, or 6×10^4 in scientific notation

IMPROVING YOUR REASONING SKILLS

You have learned about scientific notation in this chapter. There is another convention for writing numbers called **engineering notation.**

Engineering notation	Not in engineering notation
2.5×10^9	2500×10^3
630×10^{-3}	630×10^{-2}
12×10^0	1.5×10^5
400×10^3	0.4×10^6
10.8×10^6	1.08×10^7

1. Write a definition for engineering notation based on the numbers in the lists. If your calculator has an engineering notation mode, you can enter more numbers to help support your definition.

2. Convert these numbers to engineering notation.

    a. 78,000,000   **b.** 9,450

    c. 130,000,000,000   **d.** 0.0034

    e. 0.31   **f.** 1.4×10^8

3. You may have seen these symbols used as shorthand for numbers:

    n ("nano," or times $\frac{1}{1,000,000,000}$)

    μ ("micro," or times $\frac{1}{1,000,000}$)

    k ("kilo," or times 1,000)

    M ("mega," or times 1,000,000)

    G ("giga," or times 1,000,000,000)

Explain how engineering notation is related to these symbols.

This tool, a micrometer, is used to accurately measure very small distances. Measurements made with it may be recorded in engineering notation.

IMPROVING REASONING SKILLS

1. If students are having difficulty, suggest they get a hint from part 3. A possible definition of engineering notation that models the definition of scientific notation is $a \times 10^n$, where $1 \le a < 1000$ or $-1000 < a \le -1$ and n is a multiple of 3. As needed, point out that 0 is a multiple of 3, specifically, $3 \cdot 0$.

2. a. 78×10^6 **b.** 9.45×10^3
    c. 130×10^9 **d.** 3.4×10^{-3}
    e. 310×10^{-3} **f.** 140×10^6

Answers that append zeros to the first parts are acceptable. (For example, 2a may be 78.0×10^6 or 78.00×10^6.)

3. Engineering notation is related to the groups of three digits separated by commas in decimal numbers; that is, n = 10^{-9}, μ = 10^{-6}, k = 10^3, M = 10^6, G = 10^9.

Students may be interested in expanding this to a project by researching careers and applications that use engineering notation.

LESSON
6.7

Fitting Exponential Models to Data

In broken mathematics
We estimate our prize
Vast—in its fading ratio
To our penurious eyes!

EMILY DICKINSON

Victoria Julian has been collecting data on changes in median house prices in her area over the past 10 years. She plans to buy a house 5 years from now and wants to know how much money she needs to save each month toward the down payment. How can she make an intelligent prediction of what a house might cost in the future? What assumptions will she have to make?

Sale pending

Charming Mock Tudor on 1/2 acre

6 bedrms, 3 baths, stone fireplace, marquetry floors throughout, 2-car garage, huge landscaped lot. Best offer.

Lovely Westside Bungalow
Newly remodeled, 2 bedroom, 1.5 bath, off-street parking, laundry, porch, hdwd floors and fireplace, charming back patio

Affordable Brownstone

• 3 floors
• 3 bed/2 bath
• spacious
• charming details
• street parking
• needs only minor repairs
• walk to shops and park
• accepting offers starting Wed

In the real world, situations like population growth, price inflation, and the decay of substances often tend to approximate an exponential pattern over time. With an appropriate exponential model, you can sometimes predict what might happen in the future.

In Chapter 4, you learned about fitting linear models to data. In this lesson you'll learn how to find an exponential model to fit data.

Investigation
Radioactive Decay

You will need
• a paper plate
• a protractor
• a supply of small counters

The particles that make up an atom of some elements, like uranium, are unstable. Over a period of time specific to the element, the particles will change so that the atom eventually will become a different element. This process is called **radioactive decay.**

In this investigation your counters represent atoms of a radioactive substance. Draw an angle from the center of your plate, as illustrated. Counters that fall inside the angle represent atoms that have decayed.

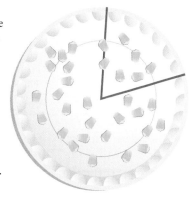

NCTM STANDARDS

CONTENT		PROCESS	
✔	Number	✔	Problem Solving
✔	Algebra	✔	Reasoning
✔	Geometry		Communication
✔	Measurement	✔	Connections
✔	Data/Probability	✔	Representation

LESSON OBJECTIVE
• Write exponential equations that model real-world growth and decay data

LESSON OUTLINE

First day:
| 5 min | Introduction |
| 45 min | Investigation |

Second day:
20 min	Sharing
10 min	Example
5 min	Closing
15 min	Exercises

MATERIALS

• paper plates
• protractors
• small flat counters that don't roll, such as lentils, split peas, popcorn kernels, or flat candies (about 100 per group)
• 100 Grid (W or T), *optional*
• Protractors (T), *optional*
• Radioactive Decay Sample Data (W), *optional*
• Moore's Law Sample Data (W), *optional*
• Calculator Note 0H
• Fathom demonstration Fitting Exponential Models to Data, *optional*
• CBL 2 demonstration Cool It, *optional*

TEACHING

Exponential models can help make predictions in many real-world situations.

INTRODUCTION

To make an intelligent prediction, Victoria must assume that prices will continue to increase at the same rate.

One Step

Have students generate the data as in the investigation. Then ask them to find an equation that models the data. As you circulate, encourage groups to find ratios and come up with an exponential equation. Also ask how their angles relate to those ratios.

To avoid using materials in Steps 1–3, have each group start with a 100 grid as their starting collection of atoms and then use a calculator to generate 15 random numbers to represent decayed atoms (see Calculator Note 0H). Duplicates may occur. They cross those numbers off the grid and record how many numbers are not crossed off. They generate another 15 random numbers, cross off new ones, and again count the remaining numbers. They repeat until fewer than ten numbers remain. If you use this method, skip Steps 11 and 12.

With the plates, students should use protractors to make an angle of less than 90°, but not too small. They can approximate the center by using a ruler to find the midpoints of several diameters.

Step 2 To have the counters fall randomly, students should avoid aiming. The objective is to have the counters spread evenly and quickly.

An acceptable plan would be to count counters on the line as being within the angle and to count those that fall outside the plate, but within the extended rays of the angle, as being within the angle.

Students may get a kinesthetic feeling for decay by eating candy counters.

See page 724 for answers to Steps 1, 2, 3, 4, 9, and 10.

Step 1 Count the number of counters. Record this in a table as the number of "atoms" after 0 years of decay. Pick up all of the counters.

Step 2 Drop the counters on the plate. Count and remove the counters that fall inside the angle—these atoms have decayed. Subtract from the previous value and record the number remaining after 1 year of decay. Pick up the remaining counters.

Step 3 Repeat Step 2 until you have fewer than ten atoms that have not decayed. Each drop will represent another year of decay. Record the number of atoms remaining each time.

Step 5 See table of Steps 1–3 (page 724) for sample data. The ratios should be approximately the same.

Step 6 Answers will vary. Students could give reasons for selecting the mean, the median, or another value. In these sample data, the mean is 0.802.

Step 7 For these sample data, using 0.802, the rate of decay is 19.8% per year.

Step 8 For this sample, $y = 201(1 - 0.198)^x$.

Step 4 Let x represent elapsed time in years, and let y represent the number of atoms remaining. Make a scatter plot of the data. What do you notice about the graph?

Step 5 Calculate the ratios of atoms remaining between successive years. That is, divide the number of atoms after 1 year by the number of atoms after 0 years; then divide the number of atoms after 2 years by the number of atoms after 1 year; and so on. How do the ratios compare?

Step 6 Choose one representative ratio. Explain how and why you made your choice.

Step 7 At what rate did your atoms decay?

Step 8 Write an exponential equation that models the relationship between time elapsed and the number of atoms remaining.

Step 9 Graph the equation with the scatter plot. How well does it fit the data?

Step 10 If the equation does not fit well, which values could you try to adjust to give a better fit? Record your final equation when you are satisfied.

Step 11 The ratio of the angle measure to 360° should be approximately the same as r. In the sample data, $\frac{68}{360} \approx 0.19$, which is close to the r-value used in Step 8.

Step 12 $y = 400\left(1 - \frac{60}{360}\right)^x$; answers will vary. Factors might include how evenly the counters are distributed on the plate, what you do when a counter is on an angle side, and how you treat counters that fall outside the plate.

Step 11 Measure the angle on your plate. Describe a connection between your angle and the numbers in your equation.

Step 12 Based on what you've learned and the procedures outlined in this investigation, write an equation that would model the decay of 400 counters, using a central angle of 60°. What are some of the factors that might cause differences between actual data and values predicted by your equation?

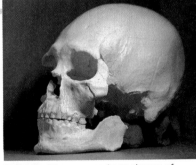

Archaeologists can approximate the age of artifacts with *carbon dating*. This process uses the rate of radioactive decay of carbon-14. Carbon is found in all living things, so the amount left in a bone, for example, is an indicator of the bone's age. This is a plastic casting of a skull found in 1997 in Richland, Washington. Carbon dating has dated the skull as 9200 years old.

Step 3 Rather than counting the remaining counters each time, students may find it easier to count the number decayed and subtract from the previous amount to find the number remaining.

Step 5 Suggest that students add a column of data for recording the ratios.

Step 7 You may need to encourage students to look at their constant multiplier in the form of $(1 - r)$. That is, a ratio of $\frac{3}{4}$ would be $(1 - 0.25)$.

Steps 11 and 12 If students are not experienced at using protractors, use the Protractors transparency to model how to measure angles and how to draw an angle with a given measure.

Step 11 [Ask] "What is the ratio of your angle measure to the whole plate?"

Step 12 You may want to discuss theoretical value versus observed data. The starting value of the best fit might not be the actual starting value of the data.

The steps of finding an equation in the investigation provide a good method for finding an exponential equation that models data that display an exponential pattern, either increasing or decreasing. These situations are often generated recursively by multiplying by a constant ratio. Thinking of the constant multiplier in the form $1 + r$ or $1 - r$ leads to these familiar equations:

$$y = A(1 + r)^x$$
$$y = A(1 - r)^x$$

You can then fine-tune the fit of your model by slightly adjusting the values of A and r.

EXAMPLE

Every musical note has an associated frequency measured in hertz (Hz), or vibrations per second. The table shows the approximate frequencies of the notes in the octave from middle C up to the next C on a piano. (In this scale, E# is the same as F and B# is the same as C.)

Piano Notes

Note name	Note number above middle C	Frequency (Hz)
Middle C	0	262
C#	1	277
D	2	294
D#	3	311
E	4	330
F	5	349
F#	6	370
G	7	392
G#	8	415
A	9	440
A#	10	466
B	11	494
C above middle C	12	523

The arrangement of strings in a piano shows an exponential-like curve.

a. Find a model that fits the data.

b. Use the model to find the frequency of the note two octaves above middle C (note 24).

c. Find the note with a frequency of 600 Hz.

C above middle C

Middle C

You might use the Fathom demonstration Fitting Exponential Models to Data to supplement the investigation. You might also have students write a lab report.

SHARING IDEAS

Have several groups present their data, scatter plots, equations, and graphs for class critique and suggestions. In the equation $y = A(1 - r)^x$, the number A is the y-intercept of the graph, so students might adjust A to shift the graph vertically. For graphs of exponential equations, vertical shifts can also be thought of as horizontal shifts. To stretch the graph, students will tinker with the decay rate, r.

Ask if anyone can explain radioactive decay and its uses. In general, a neutron of an atom is stable only when paired with a sufficient number of protons. Elements with either too few or too many protons per neutron are unstable. The nuclei of unstable elements can decay in a variety of ways. The half-life of different radioactive nuclei can be anywhere from 10^{-9} s up to 10^{20} yr.

Because carbon-14 atoms occur in all living things, knowing about their decay is extremely useful in determining the age of very old remains of life. It takes about 5730 yr for half of their excess neutrons to decay. Therefore, if one bone has half the amount of carbon-14 as a similar bone, the first bone is 5730 yr older.

[Ask] "Would there ever be zero atoms remaining?" [In the exponential equation, the value of y will never decrease all the way to zero. The counters and even protons are discrete units, however, so they will all decay eventually.]

You may want to have students generalize the steps they used in writing an equation:

1. Find the ratios between successive y-values.

2. Select a representative ratio, possibly a mean or median.

3. Think of the ratio in the form of $(1 - r)$ if the values are decreasing and $(1 + r)$ if they're increasing.

4. Use the starting value, A, to write an equation in the form $y = A(1 - r)^x$ or $y = A(1 + r)^x$.

5. Adjust the values of A and r to get a better fit.

Point out the opening quotation. It is the second stanza of an untitled poem from about 1859. The first stanza is

As by the dead we love to sit
Become so wondrous dear

As for the lost we grapple
Tho' all the rest are here.

[Language] *Penurious* means extremely stingy or poor. One interpretation is that the relationship between what we want and what we see that we currently have is an inverse relationship—the more we want, the less we see value in what we have. Another interpretation is that what we want decays exponentially with respect to how well we see what we have.

Watch for skill at handling geometric tools (ruler, protractor),
collecting data, making a scatter
plot, and graphing exponential
equations.

▶ **EXAMPLE**

This example shows exponential
growth in a different context. You
might ask students who have a
musical background to elaborate
on the notation. The symbol # in
the table means *sharp,* or one-half
step above the note; C# is one-
half step above C. *Functional
Melodies* (Key Curriculum Press)
has additional activities involving
the Pythagorean and even-
tempered scales.

The solution in part c brings in a
new way to solve an equation:
graph the two sides of the equation and find the intersection
point of the graphs.

Closing the Lesson

At the heart of finding the equation modeling exponential
growth or decay is finding a ratio
to use as a constant multiplier.

Music
● ━━ **CONNECTION** ━━ ●

Before the 17th century, there
were many ways to tune an
instrument. The most popular,
developed by the ancient Greek
philosopher Pythagoras, used
different tuning ratios between
each pair of adjacent notes.
This made some scales, like
the scale of C, sound good but
others, like the scale of A-flat,
sound bad. Modern Western
tuning now uses *even
temperament,* based on an
equal tuning ratio between
adjacent notes, which leads to
an exponential model.

▶ **Solution**

a. Let x represent the note number above middle C, and let y represent the
frequency. A scatter plot shows the exponential-like pattern. To find the
exponential model, first calculate the ratios between successive data points.
The mean of the ratios is 1.0593. So the frequency of the notes increases by
about 5.93% each time you move up one note on the keyboard. The starting
frequency is 262 Hz. So an equation is

$$y = 262(1 + 0.0593)^x$$

The graph shows a very good fit.

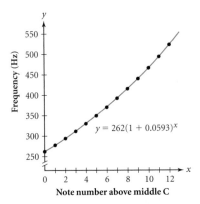

b. To find the frequency of the C two octaves above middle C (note 24),
substitute 24 for x in the model.

$$y = 262(1 + 0.0593)^{24} \approx 1044$$

By this model, the frequency of note 24 is 1044 Hz.

c. To find the note with a frequency of 600 Hz,
substitute 600 for y in the model.

$$600 = 262(1 + 0.0593)^x$$

Enter $262(1 + 0.0593)^x$ into Y₁ and 600 into
Y₂ on your calculator. Graph both equations
and trace to approximate the intersection
point. Or you could look at a table to see
where Y₁ = Y₂.

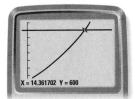

[0, 18, 10, 250, 650, 50]

Both the graph and the table show an
x-value between 14 and 15. The 14th note
above middle C is a D and the 15th note is
a D#. Because the piano notes correspond
only to whole numbers, you cannot make
a note with a frequency of 600 Hz on
this piano.

If you wanted to find the frequency of notes below middle C, you would need to
use negative values for x. The frequencies found using this equation will be fairly
accurate because the data fit the equation so well. If the piano were very out of
tune, the equation probably would not fit so nicely, and the model might be less
valuable for predicting.

EXERCISES

You will need your graphing calculator for Exercises **5, 6, 8, 9, 10,** and **11.**

▶ Practice Your Skills

1. Rewrite each value as either $1 + r$ or $1 - r$. Then state the rate of increase or decrease as a percent.

   a. 1.15 ⓐ $1 + 0.15$; rate of increase: 15% **b.** 1.08 $1 + 0.08$; rate of increase: 8% **c.** 0.76 ⓐ $1 - 0.24$; rate of decrease: 24%

   d. 0.998 $1 - 0.002$; rate of decrease: 0.2% **e.** 2.5 $1 + 1.5$; rate of increase: 150%

2. Use the equation $y = 47(1 - 0.12)^x$ to answer each question.

   a. Does this equation model an increasing or decreasing pattern? ⓗ decreasing

   b. What is the rate of increase or decrease? 12%

   c. What is the y-value when x is 13? $y \approx 8.92$

   d. What happens to the y-values as the x-values get very large? The y-values approach zero.

3. Write an equation to model the growth of an initial deposit of $250 in a savings account that pays 4.25% annual interest. Let B represent the balance in the account, and let t represent the number of years the money has been in the account. ⓐ $B = 250(1 + 0.0425)^t$

4. Use the properties of exponents to rewrite each expression with only positive exponents.

   a. $4x^3 \cdot (3x^5)^3$ $108x^{18}$ **b.** $\dfrac{60x^8y^4}{15x^3y}$ ⓐ $4x^5y^3$ **c.** $3^2 \cdot 2^3$ 72 **d.** $\dfrac{(8x^3)^2}{(4x^2)^3}$ ⓐ 1

   e. $x^{-3}y^4$ $\dfrac{y^4}{x^3}$ **f.** $(2x)^{-3}$ $\dfrac{1}{8x^3}$ **g.** $2x^{-3}$ $\dfrac{2}{x^3}$ **h.** $\dfrac{2x^{-4}}{(3y^2)^{-3}}$ $\dfrac{54y^6}{x^4}$

▶ Reason and Apply

5. Mya placed a cup of hot water in a freezer. Then she recorded the temperature of the water each minute.

   Water Temperature

Time (min) x	0	1	2	3	4	5	6	7	8	9	10
Temperature (°C) y	47	45	43	41.5	40	38.5	37	35.5	34	33	31.5

   [Data sets: **FZTIM, FZTMP**]

   a. Find the ratios between successive temperatures. ⓐ

   b. Find the mean of the ratios in 5a. ⓐ approximately 0.96

   c. Write the ratio from 5b in the form $1 - r$. ⓐ $1 - 0.04$

   d. Use your answer from 5c and the starting temperature to write an equation in the form $y = A(1 - r)^x$. ⓐ $y = 47(1 - 0.04)^x$

   e. Graph your equation with a scatter plot of the data. Adjust the values of A or r until you get a satisfactory fit.

   f. Use your equation to predict how long it will take for the water temperature to drop below 5°C.

5f. 55 min

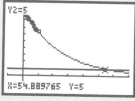

$[-10, 70, 10, -10, 50, 5]$

LESSON 6.7 Fitting Exponential Models to Data **377**

▶ Helping with the Exercises

Exercise 1e Some students may not realize that a number that's more than 1 is more than 100%.

Exercise 2d This question brings in the idea of limit, as discussed in Chapter 0. **[Ask]** "Why do powers of positive numbers less than 1 get smaller and smaller?" [Multiplying a positive number by a positive number less than 1 yields a smaller positive number.]

Exercises 5 and 6 Students can use a CBL 2 to collect data for these exercises. You can use the CBL 2 demonstration Cool It as an extension for Exercise 5.

5a. The ratios are 0.957, 0.956, 0.965, 0.964, 0.963, 0.961, 0.959, 0.958, 0.971, and 0.955.

5e.

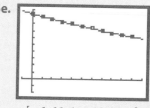

$[-1, 11, 1, -10, 50, 5]$

Adjustments to A or r are not necessary—the fit is good as is.

Exercise 5f Ask if the temperature will ever drop to freezing (0°C). Theoretically, an exponential expression will never actually get to zero, though in real life water freezes.

6. In science class Phylis used a light sensor to measure the intensity of light (in lumens per square meter, or lux) that passes through layers of colored plastic. The table below shows her readings.

Light Experiment

Number of layers	0	1	2	3	4	5	6
Intensity of light (lux)	431	316	233	174	128	98	73

[Data sets: LTLAY, LTINT]

a. Write an exponential equation to model Phylis's data. Let x represent the number of layers, and let y represent the intensity of light in lux. ⓗ

b. What does your r-value represent?

c. If Phylis's sensor cannot register readings below 30 lux, how many layers can she add before the sensor stops registering?

7. Suppose that on Sunday you see 32 mosquitoes in your room. On Monday you count 48 mosquitoes. On Tuesday there are 72 mosquitoes. Assume that the population will continue to grow exponentially.

a. What is the percent rate of growth? @ 50%

b. Write an equation that models the number of mosquitoes, y, after x days. $y = 32(1 + 0.5)^x$

c. Graph your equation and use it to find the number of mosquitoes after 5 days, after 2 weeks, and after 4 weeks. 243 mosquitoes; 9,342 mosquitoes; 2,727,126 mosquitoes

d. Name at least one real-life factor that would cause the population of mosquitoes not to grow exponentially. Answers will vary. Possibilities include lack of resources, overcrowding, and extermination.

8. There are many stories in children's literature that involve magic pots. An Italian variation goes something like this: A woman puts a pot of water on the stove to boil. She says some special words, and the pot begins filling with pasta. Then she says another set of special words, and the pot stops filling up.

Suppose someone overhears the first words, takes the pot, and starts it in its pasta-creating mode. Two liters of pasta are created. Then the pot continues to create more pasta because the impostor doesn't know the second set of words. The volume continues to increase 50% per minute.

a. Write an equation that models the amount of pasta in liters, y, after x minutes. @ $y = 2(1 + 0.5)^x$

b. How much pasta will there be after 30 seconds?

c. How much pasta will there be after 10 minutes?

d. How long, to the nearest second, will it be until the entire house, which can hold 450,000 liters, is full of pasta? after about 30.4 min, or 30 min 24 s

---

6a. possible answer:
$y = 431(1 - 0.26)^x$, where 0.26 is derived from the mean ratio of about 0.74

6b. With each layer of plastic, the amount of light is reduced 26%.

6c. With 9 layers, the reading would be below 30.

Exercise 7 This data set is artificial. You might encourage students to research similar data for their own town or make their own projections.

Exercise 8 "Magic pot" stories have developed in the folklore of several cultures, including India, Italy, and China. Titles include *The Magic Porridge Pot, The Magic Pasta Pot,* and simply *The Magic Pot. The Sorcerer's Apprentice* has a similar theme.

8b. $y = 2(1 + 0.5)^{0.5} \approx 2.45$; approximately 2.45 L

8c. approximately 115 L

9. APPLICATION Recall Victoria from the opening of this lesson. She has collected this table of data on median house prices for her area.

a. Define variables and find an exponential equation to model Victoria's data. @

b. Victoria plans to buy a house 5 years from now. What median price should she expect then?

c. Victoria plans to make a down payment of 10% of the purchase price. Based on your answer to 9b, how much money will she need for her down payment?

d. If Victoria saves the same amount each year for the next 5 years (without interest), how much will she need to save each month for her down payment?

Median House Prices

Year	Years since 2000	Median price ($)
2000	0	135,500
2001	1	144,000
2002	2	152,500
2003	3	161,500
2004	4	171,500
2005	5	181,500
2006	6	192,250

[Data sets: **HSEYR, HSEYS, HSEPR**]

9a. Possible answer: Let x represent years since 2000 and y represent median price in dollars. An equation is $y = 135,500(1 + 0.06)^x$, where 0.06 is derived from the mean ratio of about 1.06.

10. The equation $y = 262(1 + 0.0593)^x$ models the frequency in hertz of various notes on the piano, with middle C considered as note 0. The average human ear can detect frequencies between 20 and 20,000 hertz. If a piano keyboard were extended, the highest and lowest notes audible to the average human ear would be how far above and below middle C? @ Note 75 above middle C (a D#) would be the highest audible note; note −44 (an E 44 notes below middle C) would be the lowest audible note.

11. Mini-Investigation In this exercise you will explore the equation $y = 10(1 − 0.25)^x$.

a. Find y for some large positive values of x, such as 100, 500, and 1000. What happens to y as x gets larger and larger? *y gets closer and closer to zero.*

b. The calculator will say y is 0 when x equals 10,000. Is this correct? Explain why or why not. *No, because y can never equal zero. The number is just smaller than the calculator is able to represent.*

c. Find y for some large negative values of x, such as −100, −500, and −1000. What happens to y as x moves farther and farther from 0 in the negative direction? *y approaches infinity.*

Exercise 10 [Language] *Audible* means capable of being heard. A standard keyboard has 88 keys.

▶ Review

6.6 12. Very small amounts of time much less than a second have special names. Some of these names may be familiar to you, such as a millisecond, or 0.001 second. Have you heard of a nanosecond or a microsecond? A nanosecond is 1×10^{-9} second, and a microsecond is 1×10^{-6} second. How many nanoseconds are in a microsecond? *1000 nanoseconds per microsecond*

6.2 13. APPLICATION Lila researched tuition costs at several colleges she's interested in. The data are listed below. Costs are predicted to go up 3.7% each year.

[Data set: **TUITN**]

$2,860 $3,580 $8,240 $9,460
$11,420 $22,500 $26,780

a. What will the costs be next year? *Answers are rounded to the nearest $10: $2,970, $3,710, $8,540, $9,810, $11,840, $23,330, $27,770.*

b. Find the estimated cost for each school five years from now. *Answers are rounded to the nearest $10: $3,430, $4,290, $9,880, $11,340, $13,690, $26,980, $32,110.*

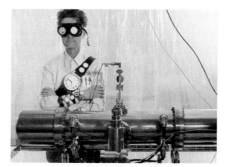

This is Jim Gray, keeper of the NBS-4 atomic clock. Atomic clocks gain or lose less than a microsecond each year. For more information, see the links at **www.keymath.com/DA** .

Exercise 12 Students may recall *nano* and *micro* from Lesson 6.6, Improving Your Reasoning Skills, about engineering notation. As needed, offer help with subtracting a negative number.

9b–d. Answers will vary depending on year. See the table for possible answers.

Year	9b. Median price ($)	9c. Down payment ($)	9d. Savings ($/mo)
2011	257,219	25,722	429
2012	272,653	27,265	454
2013	289,012	28,901	482
2014	306,352	30,635	511
2015	324,734	32,473	541
2016	344,218	34,422	574
2017	364,871	36,487	608

Exercise 14 A *joule* is the SI (International System of Units) unit for the amount of work done by a force of 1 newton acting over a distance of 1 m. It is equivalent to 1 watt-second, so a 100-watt bulb burning for an hour produces 360,000 joules of energy.

14. One of the most famous formulas in science is

$$E = mc^2$$

This equation, formulated by Albert Einstein in 1905, describes the relationship between mass (*m*, measured in kilograms) and energy (*E*, measured in joules) and shows how they can be converted from one to the other. The variable *c* is the speed of light, 3×10^8 meters per second. How much energy could be created from a 5-kilogram bowling ball? Express your answer in scientific notation.

$5(3 \times 10^8)^2 = 5(9 \times 10^{16}) = 45 \times 10^{16}$, or 4.5×10^{17} joules

James Joule (1818–1889) was one of the first scientists to study how energy was related to heat. At the time of his experiments, many scientists thought heat was a gas that seeped in and out of objects. The SI (metric) unit of energy was named in his honor.

Other Laws
Machrone's Law states that the machine you want always costs $5,000 (for example, the purchase price of transistors is cut in half every 2 yr, so as the number of transistors doubles, the price stays the same). Rock's Law states that the cost of equipment to build semiconductors doubles every 4 yr.

project

MOORE'S LAW

In 1965 Gordon Moore, the co-founder of Intel Corporation, observed that the number of transistors on a computer chip doubled approximately every 2 years. Because a computer processor's speed and power are proportional to the number of transistors on it, computers should get twice as powerful every 2 years.

Has "Moore's Law" come true since 1965? Research technical specifications for various computer processors and find an exponential model that relates time and number of transistors. You can research data in magazines or at www.keymath.com/DA . How many years or months has it taken for computers to double in power? At what rate has the power of computers increased each year?

Your project should include

▶ A scatter plot of your data.

▶ An exponential equation that models the data and an explanation of each number and variable in your equation.

▶ A report summarizing your findings.

You may want to research news items that give recent projections and see if computer chip manufacturers are continuing to meet or exceed Moore's Law. You may also want to research other theories on computer production that examine variables such as purchase price or equipment required for production.

Fathom
With Fathom you can easily graph an exponential equation through data points. You can use a slider to make small adjustments in your equation until it fits. You can graph multiple models each with its own slider to compare different exponential equations.

Supporting the project

MOTIVATION

This project challenges students by requiring evaluation of data whose *x*-values are not likely to be sequential. (Students may use the Moore's Law Sample Data worksheet.)

OUTCOMES

▶ The report gives evidence that the relationship between time and number of transistors is roughly exponential, as Moore's Law predicts.

▶ Analysis (for the sample data) shows that a good model is $y = 2300(1 + 0.38)^x$, where *x* is time in years since 1971 and *y* is number of transistors.

▶ The report shows that, by the same model, the number of transistors doubles in a little over 2 yr.

• The presentation may show an alternative model: $y = 2300(2)^{x/2.15}$. Here, the base, 2, represents doubling, and dividing *x* by 2.15 means that the number of transistors will double in 2.15 yr.

LESSON 6.8

Activity Day

Decreasing Exponential Models and Half-Life

keymath.com/DA

In Lesson 6.7, you learned that data can sometimes be modeled using the exponential equation $y = A(1 - r)^x$. In this lesson you will do an experiment, write an equation that models the decreasing exponential pattern, and find the **half-life**—the amount of time needed for a substance or an activity to decrease to one-half its starting value. To find the half-life, approximate the value of x that makes y equal to $\frac{1}{2} \cdot A$.

In the previous investigation, if your plate was marked with a 72° angle and you started with 200 "atoms," a model for the data could be $y = 200(1 - 0.20)^x$. This is because the ratio of the angle to the whole plate is $\frac{72}{360}$, or 0.20. To determine the half-life of your atoms, you would need to find out how many drops you would expect to do before you had 100 atoms remaining. Hence, you could solve the equation $100 = 200(1 - 0.20)^x$ for x using a graph or a calculator table. The x-value in this situation is approximately 3, which means your atoms have a half-life of about 3 years.

Technology
CONNECTION

You can see simulations of atomic half-life with a link at **www.keymath.com/DA** .

Activity
Bouncing and Swinging

You will need
- a motion sensor
- a meterstick
- a ball
- string
- a soda can half-filled with water

There are two experiments described in this activity. Each group should choose at least one, collect and analyze data, and prepare a presentation of results.

PLANNING

LESSON OUTLINE

One day:
5 min	Introduction
35 min	Activity
10 min	Sharing

MATERIALS

- balls
- metersticks
- motion sensor, *optional*
- soda cans half-filled with water
- string
- Bounce Sample Data (W), *optional*
- Pendulum Sample Data (W), *optional*
- Calculator Note 6D

TEACHING

Exponential decay equations can model processes that slow down.

Guiding the Activity

It is not mandatory to have all of the materials. The motion sensor can be supplanted with careful low-tech data collection. The bouncing ball is needed only for Experiment 1, and the string and can are needed only for Experiment 2. In place of tying a string around the pull tab of a soda can, you might tie the string around the neck of a water bottle.

If the materials in general are problematic, try the 100-grid alternative explained in Lesson 6.7. Sample data for each experiment are available on the worksheets and on the Programs and Data CD.

NCTM STANDARDS

CONTENT		PROCESS	
✔	Number		Problem Solving
✔	Algebra	✔	Reasoning
	Geometry		Communication
✔	Measurement	✔	Connections
✔	Data/Probability	✔	Representation

LESSON OBJECTIVE

- Write exponential equations that model real-world decay data

Step 3 The location of the pendulum bob is harmonic, but its maximum distance from the resting position is roughly exponential.

Step 4 Students who collect pendulum data by eye will need to account for collecting data every fifth swing. One option is $y = A(1 + r)^{x/5}$, where x is the number of swings.

Step 4 for sample data:
Exp. 1: $y = 1(1 - 0.33)^x$

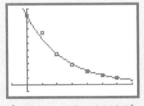

$[-1, 7, 1, -0.1, 1.1, 0.1]$

Exp. 2: $y = 0.50(1 - 0.04)^x$

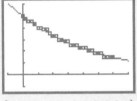

$[-5, 35, 5, -0.1, 0.6, 0.1]$

Step 6 You might want to introduce the equation $y = A\left(\frac{1}{2}\right)^{x/t}$, where t is the half-life. Students can see that the graph of this equation is similar to that of their equation in the form $y = A(1 - r)^x$. Ask them to think about why the graphs are the same. [Looking at special cases, when $x = t$, the quantity A is multiplied by $\frac{1}{2}$. When $x = 2t$, $\left(\frac{1}{2}\right)A$ is multiplied by $\frac{1}{2}$, to make $\frac{1}{4}A$. And so on. Symbolically, by definition of half-life, $b^t = \frac{1}{2}$, so raising both sides to the $\frac{x}{t}$ power gives $b^x = \left(\frac{1}{2}\right)^{x/t}$.]

SHARING IDEAS

Groups can share their summaries from Step 7. The class can discuss the reasons for differences in data and equations that model the data.

Step 3 The scatter plot should show an exponential pattern.

Step 5 One method is to graph $Y_2 = \frac{1}{2} \cdot A$ and find the intersection with $Y_1 = A(1 - r)^x$. Using sample data, half-lives are
Exp. 1: about 2 bounces,
Exp. 2: about 17 swings.

Assessing Progress

Watch for students' ability to collect data systematically, to define variables, to make a scatter plot, to find common ratios and write an appropriate exponential decay equation, and to find the half-life.

Step 1 Select one of these two experiments.

Experiment 1: Ball Bounce

Drop a ball from a height of about 1 m and measure its rebound height for at least 6 bounces. You can collect data "by eye" using a meterstick, or you can use a motion sensor. [▶ 🖳 See **Calculator Note 6D.** ◀] If you use a motion sensor, hold it $\frac{1}{2}$ m above the ball and collect data for about 8 s; trace the resulting scatter plot of data points to find the maximum rebound heights.

Experiment 2: Pendulum Swing

Make a pendulum with a soda can half-filled with water tied to at least 1 m of string—use the pull tab on the can to connect it to the string. Pull the can back about $\frac{1}{2}$ m from its resting position and then release it. Measure how far the can swings from the resting position for several swings. You can collect data "by eye" using a meterstick (you may have to collect data for every fifth swing in this case), or you can use a motion sensor. [▶ 🖳 See **Calculator Note 6D.** ◀] If you use a motion sensor, position it 1 m from the can along the path of the swing; the program will collect the maximum distance from the resting position for 30 swings.

Resting position

Step 2 Set up your experiment and collect data. Based on your results, you might want to modify your setup and repeat your data collection.

Step 3 Define variables and make a scatter plot of your data on your calculator. (If you used a motion sensor, you should have this already.) Draw the scatter plot accurately on your paper. Does the graph show an exponential pattern?

Step 4 Find an equation in the form $y = A(1 - r)^x$ that models your data. Graph this equation with your scatter plot and adjust the values if a better fit is needed.

Step 5 Find the half-life of your data. Explain what the half-life means for the situation in your experiment. (Read page 381 to review the calculation of half-life.)

Step 6 Find the y-value after 1 half-life, 2 half-lives, and 3 half-lives. How do these values compare? With each consecutive half-life, the value of y will be half the previous value of y.

Step 7 Write a summary of your results. Include descriptions of how you found your exponential model, what the rate r means in your equation, and how you found the half-life. You might want to include ways you could improve your setup and data collection.

In the real world, eventually your ball will stop bouncing or your pendulum will stop swinging. Your exponential model, however, will never reach a y-value of zero. Remember that any mathematical model is, at best, an approximation and will therefore have limitations.

Closing the Lesson

As needed, point out that the term *exponential decay* refers to slowing processes other than radioactive decay.

CHAPTER
6
REVIEW

6

You started this chapter by creating sequences that increase or decrease when you multiply each term by a constant factor. Repeated multiplication causes the rate of change between successive terms to increase or decrease. So the graphs of these sequences curve, getting steeper and steeper or less and less steep. You then discovered that **exponential equations** model these sequences, in which the constant multiplier is the **base** and the number of the term in the sequence is the **exponent.**

By writing exponential expressions in both **expanded form** and **exponential form,** you learned the **multiplication, division,** and **power properties of exponents,** and you explored the meanings of zero and negative exponents. You applied these properties to **scientific notation,** a way to express numbers with powers of 10.

When modeling data, you can often use an equation to make predictions. You now have two kinds of models for real-world data—linear equations and exponential equations. Many real-world quantities that increase can be modeled as **exponential growth** with an equation in the form $y = A(1 + r)^x$. You can model many quantities that decrease, like **radioactive decay,** with an equation in the form $y = A(1 - r)^x$.

PLANNING

LESSON OUTLINE

One day:

10 min	Introduction
15 min	Exercises
10 min	Checking work
15 min	Student self-assessment

REVIEWING

Refer students to Lesson 6.2, Exercise 13. **[Ask]** "What is the equation asked for in 13a?" $[y = 5000(1 + 0.05)^x]$ "By this model, how much will the car be worth in 5 years?" [$6,381] "How much will it be worth 3 years after that?" [$7,387] "What about 2 years before that?" [After 6 years from the time she purchased the car, it will be worth $6,700.] Review the addition of exponents when multiplying powers of the same base and the subtraction of exponents when dividing powers of the same base. Then ask how much the car was worth 5 years ago. Model the problem using negative exponents, and discuss the fact that a model is not always accurate. **[Ask]** "What would the car be worth 5 years from now if, contrary to Shawna's hopes, it depreciates at 7% per year instead of appreciating?" [$3,478]

ASSIGNING HOMEWORK

You might assign the even-numbered problems (2–10) for homework and allow students to work on the odd-numbered problems in class while you take time to work individually with students who have questions.

EXERCISES

You will need your graphing calculator for Exercises **2, 3,** and **10.**

@ Answers are provided for all exercises in this set.

1. Write each number in exponential form with base 3.

   a. 81 3^4 **b.** 27 3^3 **c.** 9 3^2

   d. $\frac{1}{3}$ 3^{-1} **e.** $\frac{1}{9}$ 3^{-2} **f.** 1 3^0

2. Use the properties of exponents to rewrite each expression. Your final answer should have only positive exponents. Use calculator tables to check that your expression is equivalent to the original expression.

   a. $\dfrac{x \cdot x \cdot x}{x}$ x^2 **b.** $2x^{-1}$ $\dfrac{2}{x}$ **c.** $\dfrac{6.273x^8}{5.1x^3}$ $1.23x^5$ **d.** 3^{-x} $\dfrac{1}{3^x}$

   e. $3x^0$ 3   **f.** $x^2 \cdot x^5$ x^7 **g.** $\left(3^4\right)^x$ 3^{4x} **h.** $\dfrac{1}{x^{-2}}$ x^2

3. Consider this exponential equation:

   $y = 300(1 - 0.15)^x$

   a. Invent a real-world situation that you can model with this equation. Give the meaning of 300 and of 0.15 in your situation.

   b. What would the inequality $75 \le 300(1 - 0.15)^x$ mean for your situation in 3a?

   c. Find all integer values of x such that $75 \le 300(1 - 0.15)^x$. Answers will vary given the context of 3a. $x \le 8$ or $0 \le x \le 8$ (some integers may be excluded by the real-life situation).

▶ Helping with the Exercises

Exercise 3 This exercise reviews inequality along with exponential equations.

3a. Possible answer: A $300 microwave depreciates at a rate of 15% per year.

3b. the years (x) for which the depreciating value of the microwave is at least $75

4. Answers will vary. Possible answer: $\frac{3^x}{3^x} = 3^{x-x} = 3^0$. The result of any number divided by itself is 1.

4. Proaga says, "Three to the power of zero must be zero. An exponent tells you how many times to multiply the base, and if you multiply zero times you would have nothing!" Give her a convincing argument that 3^0 equals 1.

5. For each table, find the value of the constants A and r such that $y = A(1 + r)^x$ or $y = A(1 - r)^x$. Then use your equations to find the missing values.

a.

x	y
0	200
1	280
2	392
3	548.8
4	768.32
5	1075.648
6	1505.9072

$y = 200(1 + 0.4)^x$

b.

x	y
−2	1176.4706
−1	1000.0000
0	850
1	722.5
2	614.125
3	522.00625
4	443.7053

$y = 850(1 - 0.15)^x$

6. Convert each number from scientific notation to standard notation, or vice versa.

a. -2.4×10^6 $-2,400,000$

b. 3.25×10^{-4} 0.000325

c. 37,140,000,000 3.714×10^{10}

d. 0.00000008011 8.011×10^{-8}

Exercise 7 Encourage students to use dimensional analysis.

7. A person blinks about 9365 times a day. Each blink lasts about 0.15 second. If one person lives 72 years, how many years will be spent with his or her eyes closed while blinking? Write your answer in scientific notation. approximately 1.17×10^0 yr

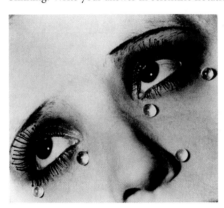

One of the purposes of blinking is to spread tears over the eye. The American photographer Man Ray (1890–1976) is well-known for this photo titled *Glass Tear*.

Exercise 8 Encourage a variety of approaches, including recursion. This exercise provides a good chance to ask students about reasonable values of y. The equation $y = 1.00(1 + 0.03)^x$ can yield any positive real value of y. But if, for example, the smallest denomination of coin accepted by the machine is a nickel, then only multiples of 0.05 fit the real-world situation.

8. **APPLICATION** In 2004, a can of soda cost $1.00 in a vending machine. If prices increase about 3% per year, in what year will the cost first exceed $2? after 24 yr, or in 2028

9. Classify each equation as true or false. If false, explain why and change the right side of the equation to make it true.

a. $\left(3x^2\right)^3 = 9x^6$

b. $3^2 \cdot 2^3 = 6^5$

c. $2x^{-2} = \frac{1}{2x^2}$

d. $\left(\frac{x^2}{y^3}\right)^3 = \frac{x^5}{y^6}$

9a. False; 3 to the power of 3 is not 9; $27x^6$.

9b. False; you can't use the multiplication property of exponents if the bases are different; $9 \cdot 8$, or 72.

9c. False; the exponent -2 applies only to x; $\frac{2}{x^2}$.

9d. False; the power property of exponents says to multiply exponents; $\frac{x^6}{y^9}$.

10. APPLICATION A pendulum is pulled back 80 centimeters horizontally from its resting position and then released. The maximum distance of the swing from the resting position is recorded after each minute for 5 minutes.

Pendulum Swings

Time elapsed (min)	0	1	2	3	4	5
Maximum distance from resting position (cm)	80	66	55	46	38	32

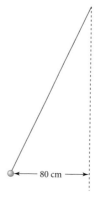

← 80 cm →

a. Define variables and write an equation that models the maximum distance of the swing after each minute.

b. What is the maximum distance from the resting position after 9 minutes? approximately 15.0 cm

c. After how many minutes will the maximum distance from the resting position be less than 5 centimeters? 15 min

TAKE ANOTHER LOOK

▶ Scientific notation gives scientists and mathematicians one way to express extremely large and extremely small numbers. Sometimes scientists focus on only the power of 10 to describe size or quantity, calling this the **order of magnitude.**

Consider that the average distance from Earth to the Sun is 9.29×10^7 miles. Unless a scientist is going to calculate with this figure, she may simply say the distance in miles from Earth to the Sun is *on the order of 10^7*. By stating only the power of 10, what range of values is the scientist including?

Order of magnitude is also used to compare numbers. Suppose a sample of bacteria grows from several hundred to several thousand cells overnight. How many times larger is the sample now? A scientist may say the number of cells in the sample *increased by one order of magnitude,* because $\frac{10^3}{10^2}$ equals 10^1. What would the scientist say when the sample grows from several hundred cells to several hundred thousand cells? What fraction of cells would remain if the sample *decreased* by two orders of magnitude? (*Note:* The units must be equal to compare orders of magnitude.)

Think about the relative size of our universe as you answer these questions:

1. Explain what it means for the typical size of a cell in meters to be on the order of 10^{-6}.

2. Explain what it means for the length of a cow in meters to be on the order of 10^0.

3. The distance in meters from Earth to the nearest star (other than the Sun) is on the order of 10^{17}. Is it correct to compare the distance from Earth to the Sun and the distance from Earth to the nearest star as an increase by 10 orders of magnitude, because $\frac{10^{17}}{10^7}$ equals 10^{10}?

Exercise 10 As mentioned in Lesson 6.8, pendulum motion is fundamentally harmonic. But the aspect that this exercise simulates can be roughly modeled with an exponential equation. However, that doesn't mean it is truly exponential.

10a. Possible answer: $y = 80(1 - 0.17)^x$, where x is the time elapsed in minutes and y is the maximum distance in centimeters; $(1 - 0.17)$ is derived from the mean ratio of approximately 0.83.

▶ **Take Another Look**

Students may better understand order of magnitude if they relate it to maximum place value and can describe orders of magnitude with words. (For example, 10^7 means the maximum place value is the ten millions.)

By stating the order of 10^7, the scientist is including a range of values of at least 10,000,000 and less than 100,000,000.

If a sample grows from several hundred cells to several thousand cells, it has increased roughly 10 times.

If the sample grows from several hundred cells to several hundred thousand cells, it has increased by three orders of magnitude. If the cells decrease by two orders of magnitude, about $\frac{1}{100}$ remain.

1. The size of a cell includes a range of values of at least 0.000001 and less than 0.00001.

2. The length of a cow is at least 1 m and less than 10 m.

3. This is incorrect because the units are not equivalent (meters versus miles).

4. This is an increase by 26 orders of magnitude.

An increase by 100% does not represent an increase in order of magnitude. An increase of 100% means the quantity doubles, whereas an increase in an order of magnitude means that the quantity is multiplied by about 10.

4. The diameter in meters of the Milky Way galaxy is 10^{20}. Describe the increase in order of magnitude between the size of a cell and the size of the galaxy.

When something increases 100%, should it be described as an increase in order of magnitude? Give an example to support your conclusion.

Assessing What You've Learned

WRITE IN YOUR JOURNAL Add to your journal by considering one of these prompts:
▶ Why is scientific notation convenient for writing extremely large or extremely small numbers? Are there numbers that you find to be less convenient to write in scientific notation? Does scientific notation help you to understand why our standard number system is called a "base 10" system?
▶ Compare and contrast linear and exponential data. How do the graphs differ? If you weren't specifically told to find either a linear or an exponential equation to fit a graph of data, how would you decide which to try? How do the methods of fitting linear and exponential models compare?

PERFORMANCE ASSESSMENT Show a classmate, a family member, or your teacher that you know how to find an exponential model in the form $y = A(1 + r)^x$. You may want to go back and use the data sets from Lesson 6.7 or Lesson 6.8, or use data that you have collected from a project. Explain why you think the data are exponential, and when and why you would want to adjust the value of A or r.

GIVE A PRESENTATION Review the properties of exponents that you learned in this chapter. Think about the techniques you have used to remember these properties, or ask your peers, teachers, or family members how they remember these properties. Prepare a presentation for your class and demonstrate the memory methods you have learned. Your presentation will help your classmates remember the properties of exponents too!

7

Functions

Overview

Having seen two kinds of functions, linear and exponential, students are now ready to generalize to the unifying mathematical concept of function. In Chapter 7, they encounter the squaring, square root, and absolute-value functions. In Chapter 8, they'll study transformations in anticipation of a more extensive consideration of quadratic functions in Chapter 9.

Secret codes highlight **Lesson 7.1.** Students learn that unambiguous encoding requires a code that's a function. Functions are defined in **Lesson 7.2** as students learn about properties and geometric representations of functions. In **Lesson 7.3,** to learn the difference between independent and dependent variables, students construct and interpret simple graphs that describe real-world situations. **Lesson 7.4** focuses on function notation and its relationship to input and output variables. In **Lesson 7.5,** students learn several ways to define absolute value and then construct and interpret graphs of absolute-value functions. **Lesson 7.6** features the squaring and square root functions; students graph parabolas and relate the squaring function to finding the area of a square.

The Mathematics

Functions

Originally, calculus was developed to study geometric figures as described by equations. The notion of a function evolved to put calculus on a firm logical footing. Leonhard Euler, who introduced the modern function notation in the middle of the 1700s, thought of functions as algebraic expressions corresponding to curves.

As work progressed, the geometry of calculus gradually became less important, and the notion of function became more abstract. Although several different approaches are used today, the most common one is that of a function as a set of ordered pairs of objects (such as letters, numbers, or figures) in which no first element of an ordered pair can correspond to more than one second element. When you think of functions of numbers, you can envision a two-column table, perhaps infinite, with no number occurring twice in the first column. If you think of the ordered pairs of numbers as representing points on the plane, no vertical line will pass through the graph more than once.

Although graphing functions helps us understand them, many graphs of geometric figures (for example, circles) don't pass the vertical line test. The importance of the function concept is evident in graphing calculators, which most easily graph functions rather than these other figures.

Squares and Square Roots

The *square* of a number is the product of that number multiplied by itself. The term comes from the geometric square, whose area is the product of the length of one edge multiplied by itself. The notation for the square of number x is x^2. Most calculators have a key to find the square of a number. You can also enter $x\wedge 2$. A number x and its opposite $(-x)$ have the same square.

Each number has only one square, so $y = x^2$ is a function. Its graph is a curve known as a *parabola*. The parabola is one of the *conic sections,* so named because they are formed by the intersection of an infinite cone with a plane.

To go from the area of a square to the length of one edge, you use the *square root function,* symbolized by $\sqrt{}$. This function gives the *nonnegative* number whose square is the given number. For example, $\sqrt{4} = 2$.

Both 2 and -2 have the square 4, and both are considered *square roots* of 4. The nonnegative value is called the *principal square root,* and it is the value returned by the square root function.

Absolute Value

Absolute values arise from a need to talk about distances, which are never negative. If we want the *difference* between numbers a and b, we simply subtract: $a - b$. If we want the *distance* between them, we don't want a negative number. If $a - b$ is negative, we want $b - a$ instead, because it's positive. We

refer to the distance as the *absolute value* of $a - b$, represented $|a - b|$. It's the same as $|b - a|$.

The absolute value of a single number x, then, is its distance from zero. If $x < 0$, we say that $|x|$ is $-x$, which will be a positive number. If $x \geq 0$, then $|x|$ is simply x itself.

Because the square root function returns the non-negative square root, we can say that $\sqrt{x^2} = |x|$, whether x is positive or negative.

Using This Chapter

Because students need to understand the definition of function, to be familiar with the absolute-value and squaring functions, and to have experience relating situations to graphs, you will want to do all the lessons in this chapter. You might want to use several of the one-step investigations to give students more opportunity to explore.

Resources

Discovering Algebra Resources

Teaching and Worksheet Masters
Lessons 7.1, 7.2, 7.3, 7.4, 7.5

Calculator Notes 1C, 1F, 1J, 7A, 7B, 7C, 7D

Sketchpad Demonstrations
Lesson 7.5, Chapter Review

Fathom Demonstration
Lesson 7.5

CBR Demonstration
Lesson 7.5

Dynamic Algebra Explorations online
Lessons 7.4, 7.6

Assessment Resources
Quiz 1 (Lessons 7.1, 7.2)
Quiz 2 (Lessons 7.3, 7.4)
Quiz 3 (Lessons 7.5, 7.6)
Chapter 7 Test
Chapter 7 Constructive Assessment Options
Chapters 4–7 Exam

More Practice Your Skills for Chapter 7

Condensed Lessons for Chapter 7

Other Resources

Green Globs and Graphing Equations. New York: Sunburst Technology, 2004. (Both Macintosh and Windows versions are available.)

For complete references to this and other resources, see www.keypress.com/DA.

Pacing Guide

	day 1	day 2	day 3	day 4	day 5	day 6	day 7	day 8	day 9	day 10
standard	7.1	7.1	7.2	quiz, 7.3	7.4	7.5	7.5	7.6	review	assessment
enriched	7.1	7.1, project	7.2	quiz, 7.3	7.4	7.5	7.5	7.6	review, TAL	assessment
block	7.1	7.2, 7.3	7.4	quiz, 7.5	7.6, review	assessment, mixed review	exam			

	day 11	day 12	day 13	day 14	day 15	day 16	day 17	day 18	day 19	day 20
standard	mixed review	exam								
enriched	mixed review	exam								

Functions

The musician in
The Lute Player by an
unknown artist called the
Master of the Half Figures
plays her lute while reading
sheet music. When music is
composed or transcribed, it is
written on a staff as notes in standard
notation or as numbers in tablature.
Playing music from notation and writing
notation from music are very much like
the relationships between input and
output in mathematical functions.

CHAPTER 7 OBJECTIVES

- Investigate the concept, definition, notation, properties, and graphs of functions
- Learn the terminology of independent and dependent variables
- Describe, read, and interpret graphs of real-world situations using the terms *linear*, *nonlinear*, *increasing*, *decreasing*, *rate of change*, *continuous*, and *discrete*
- Construct and interpret graphs and functions that describe real-world situations
- Evaluate functions by substitution, by using the graphing calculator, and by using graphs
- Learn to work with absolute values and with the absolute-value function and its graph
- Learn to work with the squaring and square root functions and the parabolic graph of the squaring function.

OBJECTIVES

In this chapter you will
- learn strategies for coding and code breaking
- learn how to determine whether a relationship is a function
- graph functions of real-world situations
- learn about function notation and vocabulary
- learn the absolute-value and squaring functions

Relationships between musical notation and musical pitch can be modeled mathematically. A piano player reading standard musical notation (input) plays the key that corresponds to each written note (output). Discuss with students whether playing the piano from sheet music is an example of a relationship in which each input has only one output. [It is.] Ask if translating piano playing to standard musical notation is that same kind of relationship. [Yes; there is exactly one musical notation for each piano key.]

Other stringed instruments differ from the piano in this respect. The same pitch may be played in different ways. For example, on a guitar a high F can be played on the first string at the first fret, on the second string at the sixth fret, or on the third string at the tenth fret. Ask if guitar playing from music written in standard notation is a relationship with a single output for each input. [No; this is not a *function,* a word students will learn the meaning of in this chapter.]

In tablature, however, each method of producing a musical pitch has its own musical notation. Lute tablature defines a function rule that tells which notes to play on which strings. A player reading lute tablature (input) has only one choice of how to play the note (output). Discuss the relationship of writing tablature (output) from a lutist's playing (input). [This is a function.]

LESSON OUTLINE

First day:

50 min   Investigation

Second day:

5 min   Investigation

20 min   Sharing

15 min   Example

5 min   Closing

5 min   Exercises

MATERIALS

- Coding Grid (W)
- TFDSFU DPEFT (T), *optional*

TEACHING

Schemes for writing secret codes provide an introduction to mathematical functions. Take advantage of the fact that many students are intrigued by secret codes.

Guiding the Investigation

[ELL] Explain *code* and *decode* in terms of doing and undoing.

[Language] Other words for coding and decoding are *encryption* and *decryption*.

One Step

Use the TFDSFU DPEFT transparency to show how to encode a word, and then ask each pair to create its own code with a regular pattern on the Coding Grid worksheet and to encode a message for other pairs to decode. As you circulate, bring out the idea that for coding, the pattern should have only one output for each input, and for decoding, the

Secret Codes

The study of secret codes is called *cryptography*. Early examples of codes go back 4000 years to Egypt. Writing messages in code plays an important role in history and in technology. Today you can find applications of codes at ATMs, in communications, and on the Internet.

Cryptography is an intellectual battle between the code-maker and the code-breaker.

SIMON SINGH

The Rosetta Stone, found near Rashid, Egypt, in 1799, bears inscriptions in Greek, Egyptian hieroglyphics, and demotic (everyday) Egyptian. Having these three versions of the same text helped language researchers "break the code" of hieroglyphics.

In this investigation you will learn some of the mathematics behind secret codes.

Investigation
TFDSFU DPEFT

You will need

- the worksheet Coding Grid

The table below shows that the letter A is coded into the letter Q, the letter B is coded into R, and so on. It also shows that the letter U is coded into the letter K. This code is an example of a *letter-shift code*. Can you see why? How would you use the code to write a message?

Original input	A	B	C	D	E	F	G	H	I	J	K	L	M	N	O	P	Q	R	S	T	U	V	W	X	Y	Z
Coded output	Q	R	S	T	U	V	W	X	Y	Z	A	B	C	D	E	F	G	H	I	J	K	L	M	N	O	P

LESSON OBJECTIVE

- Investigate the concept of function through secret codes

NCTM STANDARDS

CONTENT		PROCESS	
	Number	✓	Problem Solving
✓	Algebra	✓	Reasoning
	Geometry	✓	Communication
	Measurement	✓	Connections
	Data/Probability	✓	Representation

You can also represent the code with a grid. Note that the input letters run across (horizontally). To code a letter, look for the colored square directly above it. Then find the coded output by looking across to the letters that run up (vertically).

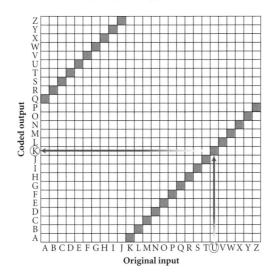

Coded output (vertical axis)
Original input (horizontal axis)

Step 1

Use the coding grid to write a two-word or three-word message.

Step 2

Exchange your coded message with a partner. Use this grid to decode each other's messages.

Next you'll invent your own letter-shift code.

Step 3 Create a new code by writing a rule that shifts letters a certain specified number of places. Put the code on a grid like the one shown above. Do not allow your partner to see this grid.

Step 4 Use your new grid to code the same message you wrote in Step 1.

Step 5 Exchange your newly coded message with your partner. Use it along with the message in the first code to try to figure out each other's new codes. Write a rule or create a coding grid to represent your partner's new code.

Step 6 Compare your grid to your classmates' new grids. In what ways are the grids the same? How are they different? For any one grid, how many coded outputs are possible for one input letter? How many ways are there to decode any one letter in a coded message?

Step 7 Use the grid on the next page to send a new two- or three-word message to your partner. Exchange and decode each other's messages.

Step 8 Did your partner successfully decode your message? Why or why not?
There may be several ways to decode one message. HI can be decoded as AB, RS, AS, or RB.

Step 1 sample answers:
input: MATH;
output: CQJX
input: NUMBER;
output: DKCRUH
input: LETTER;
output: BUJJUH

Steps 3–6 All possible letter-shift codes should appear on the grid as two parallel diagonal lines sloping upward. Possible codes might have different intercepts. Neither line segment will be directly above the other or across from the other at any point.

Step 7 Answers will vary. Each letter between K and S has two possible codes. So MOP can be coded eight different ways—CEF, CEW, CVF, CVW, TEF, TEW, TVF, TVW.

---

reverse should be the case. The thinking processes of developing codes and trying to decode are more important than any answers the students get. During Sharing, introduce the term *function*.

For this investigation, students are in pairs.

Step 1 If necessary, use the transparency to demonstrate how to encode a word. In making sense of graphs of equations, students have probably thought in terms of moving from the origin to the right (or left) and then up (or down). When considering the graph of a function, it's good to think of beginning with input on the *x*-axis, moving up (or down) to the graphed line or curve, and then moving horizontally to the *y*-axis for the corresponding output. Coding with a grid helps establish this way of thinking.

Watch for inappropriate words.

Step 3 Give students the Coding Grid worksheet to make grids for their codes.

Step 6 The grid scheme helps students see how various codes are similar and different. Provided that students have followed directions and written the alphabet in order, all code graphs should consist of two linear segments with positive slopes. The graph should have no more than one point (one shaded square) in any one vertical or horizontal line.

Step 7 Students may be confused because there's more than one way to encode most messages. To motivate Step 9, ask them what characteristic of the graph makes it confusing.

Step 11 Codes created here may look somewhat random or have some other pattern. However, they should all have only one coded letter value for each original letter.

SHARING IDEAS

Have selected students present their code grids and answers to the questions in Step 11. This is a good chance for students to shine who are more comfortable with language than mathematics. As the idea arises of one output for each input, introduce the terms *function, domain,* and *range.*

Begin writing out complete sentences on the board and insist that students do the same. For example, they should write "If the input is 1, then the output is 4," rather than some shorthand. The inconvenience of doing this will motivate function notation in Lesson 7.4.

Draw attention to the quotation introducing the lesson, and ask what the difference is between breaking a code and decoding. Ask how difficult it would be to break each of the codes they created in the investigation—that is, to figure out the corresponding grids. The advantage to less organized grids is their security against code breakers. The disadvantage is that more information has to be transmitted for decoders to work and this information may be intercepted. Modern mathematics has led to methods in which no information must be transmitted for decoding but whose complexity makes cracking the code virtually impossible. The quote is from a journalist who specializes in mathematics and science. He has written books on codes and on the origin of the universe.

Use this code for Steps 7 to 10.

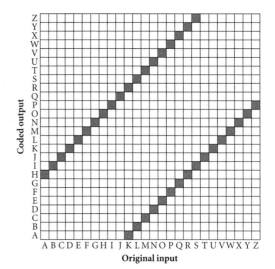

Original input

Step 9 This coding grid's overlapping lines allow eight ways to code FUNC-TION. N and O (letters between K and S) each can be coded as **Step 9** two different letters.

Step 10 The grid **Step 10** in Step 1 is easier for decoding; each coded letter between H **Step 11** and P corresponds to two input letters.

How is the grid above different from the grid in Step 1? Code the word FUNCTION to help you answer this question.

Which grid makes it easier to decode messages? Which coded output letters are difficult to decode into their original input letters?

Create a new coding scheme by shading squares that don't touch each other on the grid. Make the grid so that there is exactly one output for each input. How is it similar to the grid in Step 1? How is it different? Coding grids will be similar to the grid in Step 1 in that no two shaded squares will be in the same column or row.

Letter-shift codes are relationships—any relationship between two variables is called a **relation.** You can also think of a relation as a set of ordered pairs. Codes that have exactly one output letter for every input letter are examples of **functions.** The set of values that are inputs for a relation or function is called its **domain.** In the investigation the domain is the set of all letters of the alphabet. The **range** of a relation or function is the set of all its possible output values for these codes. The range happens to be all the letters of the alphabet as well. But often the domain contains many values different from those in the range. Here is an example.

Domain	A	B	C	D	E	F	G	H	I	J	K	L	M
Range	65	66	67	68	69	70	71	72	73	74	75	76	77

Domain	N	O	P	Q	R	S	T	U	V	W	X	Y	Z
Range	78	79	80	81	82	83	84	85	86	87	88	89	90

Computers store letters as numbers. In the preceding example, the letter A is coded as the number 65, B as 66, and so on. In this case, the domain is the letters of the alphabet, but the range is the set of whole numbers from 65 through 90. Notice that each letter in the domain matches no more than one number in the range. This is what makes the code a function.

EXAMPLE

Tell whether each table of values represents a function. Give the domain and range of each relation.

Table A

Input	Output
1	2
2	4
3	6

Table B

Input	1	0	1
Output	1	2	5

Table C

Input	1	2	3	4	5	6
Output	0	0	0	0	0	0

▶ Solution

To be a function, each input must have exactly one output. It is helpful to use arrows to show which input value matches which output value.

Table A

Each input value matches one output value. So this relation is a function. The domain is {1, 2, 3}, and the range is {2, 4, 6}.

Input: 1   2   3

Output: 2   4   6

Table B

The input value 1 has two outputs, 1 and 5. This relation is not a function because there is an input value with more than one output value. The domain is {0, 1}, and the range is {1, 2, 5}.

Input: 0   1

Output: 1   2   5

Table C

Each input value has exactly one output value. So this relation is a function, even though all the inputs have the same output. The domain is {1, 2, 3, 4, 5, 6}, and the range is {0}.

Input: 1   2   3   4   5   6

Output: 0

You can represent a relation with a table, a graph, an equation, symbols, a diagram, or even a written rule or description. Many of the relations you have studied in this book are functions. You will revisit some of them as you learn more about functions in this chapter.

Have students look at the table of computer codes following the investigation. Ask for a description of the set of input values, and use the term *domain*. Do the same for the output values and *range*. This code is called ASCII (pronounced ASK-ee), which stands for American Standard Code for Information Interchange. Special characters, symbols, and numbers are represented by numbers 0 through 64 in ASCII, so the alphabet begins with 65.

▶ EXAMPLE

This example isolates the ideas of function, domain, and range. Assume that the entire domain and entire range are listed in the tables.

Making the Connection

The History Connection refers to the Enigma machine. This machine used rotors to perform a different shift for each letter of the code, according to a prearranged keyword. For example, if the keyword was ENCODE, the first letter of the message would shift by 5 (because E is the fifth letter in the alphabet), the second letter would shift by 14 (because N is the fourteenth letter), and so on. The Enigma machine could handle very long "keywords" that were not really words at all. Because the Allies were very careful in how they responded to information gained by decoding German messages, the Germans were not aware that their code had been cracked and didn't make their methods more secure.

Assessing Progress

Through your observations, you can assess students' ability to describe a mathematical procedure in English, to follow directions, and to work with a partner.

Closing the Lesson

A **function** is a relationship between two sets, called the **domain** and **range** of the function, such that every element of the domain is associated with one and only one element of the range. The domain can be thought of as the set of input values, and the range as the set of output values.

A function might be defined by a table, arrow diagram, formula, equation, written description, or graph. Many functions are best defined by a table rather than by a formula or an equation.

EXERCISES

You will need your graphing calculator for Exercise **7.**

▶ Practice Your Skills

1. Use this table to code each word.

Input	A	B	C	D	E	F	G	H	I	J	K	L	M	N	O	P	Q	R	S	T	U	V	W	X	Y	Z
Coded output	B	C	D	E	F	G	H	I	J	K	L	M	N	O	P	Q	R	S	T	U	V	W	X	Y	Z	A

a. RANGE @ SBOHF   **b.** DOMAIN EPNBJO   **c.** TABLE UBCMF   **d.** GRAPH HSBQI

2. Use the grid at right to decode each word.
  a. SXZED INPUT
  b. YEDZED OUTPUT
  c. BOVKDSYXCRSZ @ RELATIONSHIP
  d. BEVO RULE

3. The title of the investigation, TFDSFU DPEFT, is the output of a one-letter-shift code.
  a. Decode TFDSFU DPEFT. @ SECRET CODES
  b. Write the rule or create the coding grid for the code. The coding scheme is a letter shift of +1.

4. Use the coding grid below to answer 4a–c.
  a. What are the possible input values?
  b. What are the possible output values?
  c. Is this code a function? Explain why or why not. No; the letters B, E, G, I, K, M, and Q each have more than one output.

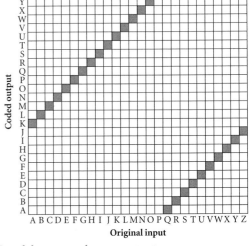

5. The table converts standard time to military time.

Standard time (A.M.)	1:00	2:00	3:00	4:00	5:00	6:00	7:00	8:00	9:00	10:00	11:00	12:00
Military time	0100	0200	0300	0400	0500	0600	0700	0800	0900	1000	1100	1200

Standard time (P.M.)	1:00	2:00	3:00	4:00	5:00	6:00	7:00	8:00	9:00	10:00	11:00	12:00
Military time	1300	1400	1500	1600	1700	1800	1900	2000	2100	2200	2300	2400

a. Describe the domain. ⓐ {1:00, 2:00, 3:00, 4:00, 5:00, 6:00, 7:00, 8:00, 9:00, 10:00, 11:00, 12:00} or {1:00 A.M., 1:00 P.M., ..., 12:00 A.M., 12:00 P.M.}

b. Describe the range. ⓐ

c. Does the table represent a function? Explain why or why not. ⓐ It is not a function because each standard time designation has two military time designations. If students distinguish A.M. from P.M. times, then it is a function.

Reason and Apply

6. Use the letter-shift grid at right to

a. Find the output when the input is W. G

b. Find the input when the output is W. M

c. Code a Q. A

d. Decode a K. A

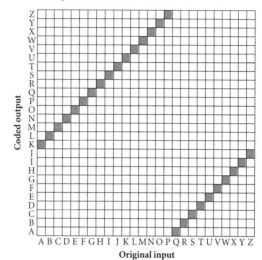

Coded output (vertical axis: Z Y X W V U T S R Q P O N M L K J I H G F E D C B A)

Original input (horizontal axis: A B C D E F G H I J K L M N O P Q R S T U V W X Y Z)

7. APPLICATION Think of the letters A through Z as the numbers 1 through 26.

a. Enter the position for each letter in the word FUNCTIONS into list L₁. Use your calculator to add 9 to each value. Store the results in list L₂. ⓐ

b. What must you do to some of these numbers before coding them back into letters? Enter the results in list L₃. ⓗ

c. Use the results from 7b to code the word FUNCTIONS. ODWLCRXWB

d. Plot pairs in the form (*input position, output position*) for this code.

e. If you design a different letter-shift code, what letter-shift values should you avoid so that FUNCTIONS is not coded as itself? Avoid any multiple of 26, such as 0, ±26, ±52, and so on.

8. Sylvana creates a code that doubles the position number of each letter in the alphabet. Then she subtracts 26 from the new positions that do not correspond to a letter in the alphabet. She stores the input values in list L₁ and the output values in list L₂.

a. What numbers are in list L₁? L₁ = {1, 2, ..., 26}

b. What numbers are in list L₂? L₂ = {2, 4, ..., 26, 2, 4, 6, 8, ..., 26}

c. Plot Sylvana's code.

d. Will she have difficulty coding or decoding messages? Answers will vary. The graphs show that the 26 letters of the alphabet are coded into 13 letters. Sylvana will have difficulty decoding because each coded letter has two possible inputs.

8c.

[−10, 37, 0, −5, 31, 0]

Exercise 9 There are 54 possibilities, but only one is a word. Students might write all possible decoded letters next to the coded one to aid in their solution.

10a. Each input codes to a single output, but each output does not decode to a single input. There are two decoding choices for B.

10b. Coding would be easier.

10c. Every output letter on the vertical axis should match only one input letter on the horizontal axis. Possible answer: Change the code so that D encodes as A.

12a. Double the position of the letter and add 1. If the result is greater than 26, subtract 26. This number is the position of the coded letter.

13. Yes, it could represent a function even though different inputs have the same output; domain: $\{-2, 0, 1, 3\}$; range: $\{-2, 3\}$.

9. Use the coding grid at right to decode CEOKEQC into a word. ALGEBRA

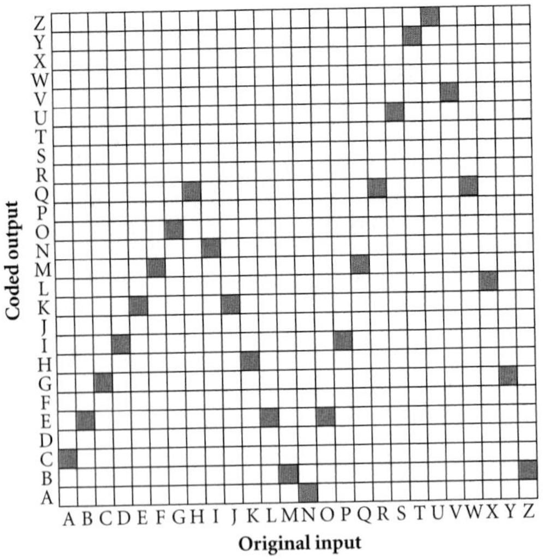

10. Here is a corner of a coding grid.

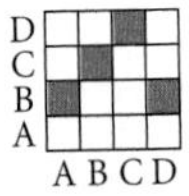

a. Does each input letter code to a single output? Does each output letter decode to a single input? @

b. Which is easier, coding or decoding?

c. How would you change this grid to make the other part of coding in 10b easier?

11. For each diagram, give the domain and range and then tell whether each relation is a function.

a. @

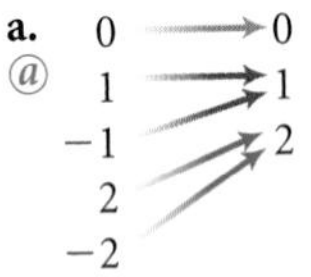

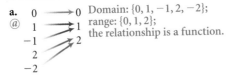

Domain: $\{0, 1, -1, 2, -2\}$; range: $\{0, 1, 2\}$; the relationship is a function.

b.

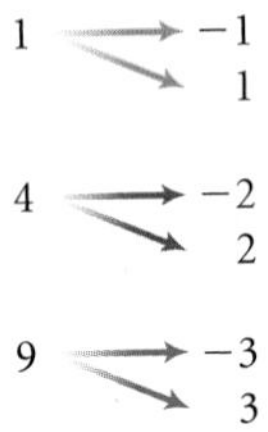

Domain: $\{1, 4, 9\}$; range: $\{1, -1, 2, -2, 3, -3\}$; the relationship is not a function.

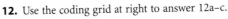

12. Use the coding grid at right to answer 12a–c.

a. Write a rule for this coding grid.

b. Code the word CODE. GEIK

c. Can you decode the word SPY? Explain why or why not. You cannot decode SPY because the letter P is not in the range.

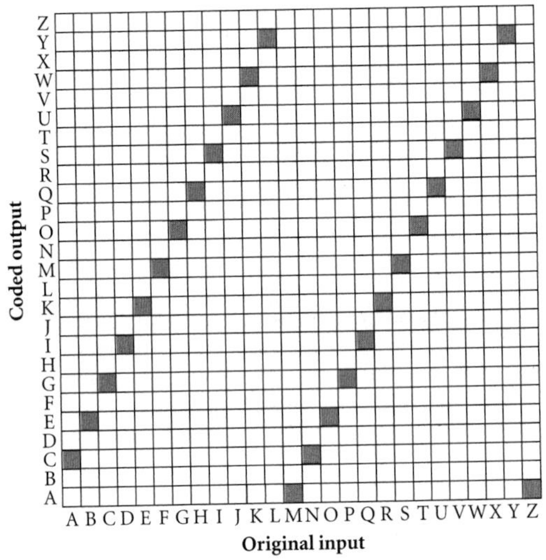

13. Could this set of ordered pairs represent a function? If so, what are its domain and range values?

$(-2, 3), (3, -2), (1, 3), (0, -2)$ @

14. Could this set of ordered pairs represent a function? Explain your reasoning.

$(3, -2), (-2, 3), (3, 1), (-2, 0)$

No; the input -2 has two different outputs, 3 and 0, and the input 3 has two different outputs, 1 and -2.

15. The grid at right shows an ancient Hebrew code called "atbash." For more information about this and other codes, see

www.keymath.com/DA .

("A Short History of Cryptography," Fred Cohen, all.net/books/ip/Chap2-1.html)

a. Create a rule for the atbash code. @

b. Is this code a function? Explain why or why not.   Yes; each input matches no more than one output.

c. Use the atbash code to code your name.   Sample: LISA codes as ORHZ.

16. If you know that TIPGKFXIRGYP is the study of coding and decoding, what is the rule for breaking this code? What is the original message?   Subtract 9 from the letter's position, or add 17, so that your result is between 1 and 26, inclusive. The original message is CRYPTOGRAPHY.

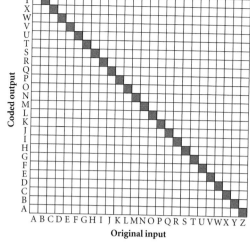

Coded output / Original input

ABCDEFGHIJKLMNOPQRSTUVWXYZ

15a. Subtract the input letter's position from 27 to get the output letter's position.

▶ Review

6.3, 6.5
17. If possible, perform the indicated operation.

a. $(4b^3)(7b^3)$ $28b^6$

b. $4a^3 + 7a^3$ $11a^3$

c. $\dfrac{7c^3}{4c^3}$ 1.75

d. $4(7d^3)^3$ $1372d^9$

e. $2a^3 + 3b^2$ not possible

f. $(2x^3)(2x^2)$ $4x^5$

2.3
18. If 1 calorie is 4.1868 joules, then how many calories is 470 joules?

$\dfrac{1 \text{ cal}}{4.1868 \text{ J}} = \dfrac{x \text{ cal}}{470 \text{ J}}$, so $x = \dfrac{470}{4.1868} \approx 112$ cal

COMPUTER NUMBER SYSTEMS

A computer stores alphanumeric symbols—letters, digits, and special characters—as a sequence of 1's and 0's in its memory. These numbers are called **binary numbers,** or base-2 numbers, because they contain only two digits—1 and 0. The number system that people use is a base-10 decimal system because it contains the ten digits from 0 through 9. How does a computer store 10 numerical digits, 26 letters, and several other characters using only two digits?

Research the binary number system and its use in computer memory. Are there other number systems that computers also use? How do computers convert letters into numbers? Is there a standard code that most systems follow?

Your project should include

▶ Sample conversions of base-10 numbers to binary numbers, and vice versa.

▶ A table that shows how to code letters and special characters.

Supporting the project

MOTIVATION

Dramatic improvements in the size and speed of computer memory enable the technology behind all digital media, including the Internet, CDs and MP3s, DVDs, video games, and cell phones.

OUTCOMES

▶ A sample showing conversions between bases 2 and 10 is clearly explained.

▶ The report includes an ASCII table.

• The hexadecimal (base 16) system is mentioned, and its relation to base 2 is explained.

• The ASCII table includes decimal, binary, and hexadecimal representations for each letter or symbol.

• Use of the binary system in computers is put in the context of the history of computers and programming.

LESSON OUTLINE

One day:

20 min   Investigation

5 min   Sharing

15 min   Example

5 min   Closing

5 min   Exercises

MATERIALS

- Function or Not? (T), *optional*
- Calculator Note 1J

The vertical line test is one method to determine whether a graph represents a function. Continue to use—and insist that students use—complete sentences when writing up the mathematics.

One Step

Show the Function or Not? transparency. Ask students which graphs represent functions, reviewing the fact that a function has only one output value for every input value. Then ask what the graphs of functions have in common that distinguish them from graphs of non-functions. As students think together, encourage them as necessary to use straightedges to help explain their ideas to each other.

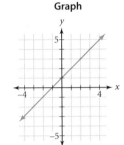

LESSON

7.2

Functions and Graphs

In Lesson 7.1, you learned that you can write rules for some of the coding grids. You can also write rules, often in the form of equations, to transform numbers into other numbers. One simple example is "Add one to each number." You can represent this rule with a table, an equation, a graph, or even a diagram.

Table

Input x	Output y
7	8
-47	-46
10.28	11.28
x	$x + 1$

Equation

$y = x + 1$

Graph

Diagram

Domain		Range
-47	$\longrightarrow$	-46
7	$\longrightarrow$	8
10.28	$\longrightarrow$	11.28

This rule turns 7 into 8, -47 into -46, 10.28 into 11.28, and x into $x + 1$.

When you explored relations in previous chapters, you used recursive routines, graphs, and equations to relate input and output data. To tell whether a relationship between input and output data is a function, there is a test that you can apply to the relation's graph on the xy-plane.

The Spanish painter Pablo Picasso (1881–1973) was one of the originators of the art movement Cubism. Cubists were interested in creating a new visual language, translating realism into a different way of seeing.

This painting is titled *Guitare et Journal.*

LESSON OBJECTIVES

- Learn a definition of function
- Learn about properties and geometric representations of functions

NCTM STANDARDS

CONTENT		PROCESS	
	Number		Problem Solving
✓	Algebra	✓	Reasoning
	Geometry		Communication
	Measurement		Connections
	Data/Probability	✓	Representation

Investigation
Testing for Functions

In this investigation you will use various kinds of evidence to determine whether relations are functions.

Step 1 Each table represents a relation. Based on the tables, which relations are functions and which are not? Give reasons for your answers.

Table 1	
Input *x*	Output *y*
−2	−3
−1	−1
0	1
1	3
2	5
3	7
4	9

Table 2	
Input *x*	Output *y*
4	−2
1	−1
0	0
1	1
4	2
9	3
16	4

Table 3	
Input *x*	Output *y*
−2	0.44
−1	0.67
0	1
1	1.5
2	2.25
3	3.37
4	5.06

Table 4	
Input *x*	Output *y*
−2	−3
−1	−5
1	−1
1	−3
2	−10
3	−2
3	−8

Step 2 Each algebraic statement below represents a relation. Based on the equations, which relations are functions and which are not? Give reasons for your answers.

Statement 1	Statement 2	Statement 3	Statement 4
$y = 1 + 2x$	$y^2 = x$	$y = 1.5^x$	$y < -1 + \frac{2}{3}x$

Step 3 Each graph below represents a relation. Move a vertical line, such as the edge of a ruler, from side to side on the graph. Based on the graph and your vertical line, which relations are functions and which are not? Give reasons for your answers.

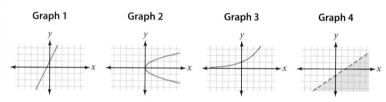

Graph 1   Graph 2   Graph 3   Graph 4

Step 4 Use your results in Step 3 to write a rule explaining how you can determine whether a relation is a function, based only on its graph.

A function is a relation between input and output values. Each input has exactly one output. The **vertical line test** helps you determine if a relation is a function. If all possible vertical lines cross the graph once or not at all, then the graph represents a function. The graph does not represent a function if you can draw even one vertical line that crosses the graph two or more times.

Step 1 Tables 1 and 3 represent functions because each *x*-value has only one *y*-value paired with it. Tables 2 and 4 do not represent functions because an *x*-value can have multiple *y*-values, for example, (4, −2) and (4, 2) in Table 2 and (1, −1) and (1, −3) in Table 4.

Step 2

Step 3 Graphs 1 and 3 represent functions because a vertical line never intersects the curve more than once. Graphs 2 and 4 do not represent functions because a vertical line can contact more than one point on the graph.

Step 4 If a graph represents a function, then a vertical line will never intersect the graph at more than one point.

Guiding the Investigation

Step 2 Statements 1 and 3 represent functions because each *x*-value produces a unique *y*-value. Statements 2 and 4 do not represent functions because there are *x*-values that result in more than one *y*-value.

Step 3 You might have students sketch the graphs and label two points that demonstrate that Graphs 2 and 4 are not functions. For example, if students choose the points (4, 2) and (4, −2) for Graph 2, they can see that the vertical line $x = 4$ will intersect the graph at both points.

SHARING IDEAS

Ask students to share their ideas on how to tell whether a graph represents a function. Connect the vertical line test to the definition of function: For each input value, there's only one output value.

[Ask] "What does the function $y = x + 1$ do to numbers like 7?" [adds 1] "What does it do to *t*?" [$t + 1$] "To $a + 5$?" [$a + 6$]

[Ask] "Is the inequality $x < 5$ a function?" [Some students may think of the graph on a number line, which is a horizontal line and passes the vertical line test. Remind students that we're dealing with two variables and that the two-variable equivalent of $x < 5$ is $0y + x < 5$. The graph of this inequality is a half-plane, which does not pass the vertical line test.]

Assessing Progress

You can assess students' ability to create a table, graph, or equation representation of a function from one of the other forms and to plot points and graph functions on a calculator.

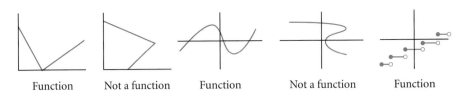

Function   Not a function   Function   Not a function   Function

You have learned many forms of linear equations. In the example you will see whether all lines represent functions.

► EXAMPLE

Part b Remind students that the slope-intercept form of a linear equation is similar to the intercept form, but the constant term appears last.

Writing the equation $x = 9$ as $0y + x = 9$ emphasizes that no matter what value is substituted for y, the first term will be 0. So, for the input value of 9, there are infinitely many output values. Set an example for raising thoughtful questions. Other good questions here are "What about horizontal lines? Are they graphs of functions?"

EXAMPLE | Name the form of each linear equation or inequality, and use a graph to explain why it is or is not a function.

a. $y = 1 - 3x$ b. $y = 0.5x + 2$ c. $y = \frac{3}{4}x$ d. $2x + 3y = 6$

e. $y = 5 + 2(x - 8)$ f. $y = 7$ g. $x = 9$ h. $2x - 4y \leq 12$

► Solution | Each equation is written in one of the forms you have learned in this course. If you graph the equations, you can see that all of them except the graphs for parts g and h pass the vertical line test. So all the equations represent functions except for the ones in parts g and h.

a. This equation is in the intercept form $y = a + bx$.

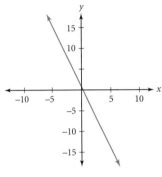

b. This equation is in the slope-intercept form $y = mx + b$.

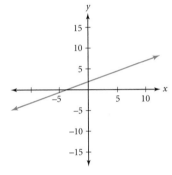

c. This equation is a direct variation in the form $y = kx$.

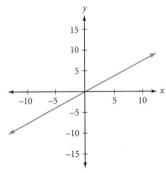

d. This equation is in the standard form $ax + by = c$.

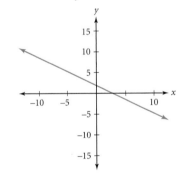

e. This equation is in the point-slope form $y = y_1 + b(x - x_1)$.

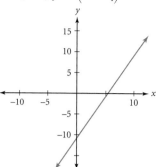

f. This equation is a horizontal line in the form $y = k$.

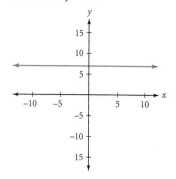

g. This equation is a vertical line in the form $x = k$.

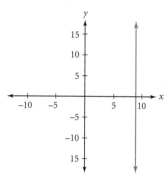

h. The boundary of this inequality, $2x - 4y = 12$, is in the standard form $ax + by = c$.

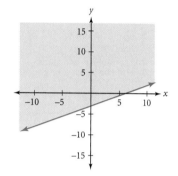

The graphs of $x = 9$ and $2x - 4y \leq 12$ fail the vertical line test. In both cases you can match infinitely many output values of y to a single input value of x. So, $x = 9$ and $2x - 4y \leq 12$ do not represent functions. In fact, graphs of all vertical lines and linear inequalities fail the vertical line test, and are therefore not functions. All nonvertical lines are functions.

As you work more with functions, you will be able to tell if a relationship is a function without having to consider its graph on the xy-plane. If the graph is shown, use the vertical line test. Otherwise, see if there is more than one output value for any single input value.

Carpenters use a tool called a "level" to determine if support beams are truly vertical.

BUILDING UNDERSTANDING

Students practice determining whether graphs represent functions. Remind students to use complete sentences when writing out their assignment.

ASSIGNING HOMEWORK

Essential	**1–4, 6, 11**
Performance assessment	**9, 10, 12, 14**
Portfolio	**10**
Journal	**6, 8, 14**
Group	**5–8, 13**
Review	**15–17**

▶ **Helping with the Exercises**

2.

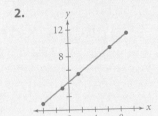

3.

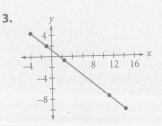

Exercise 4 This exercise depends on the previous three exercises. Be sure students justify their answers.

Exercise 5 [Ask] "Will every set of walking instructions represent a function?"

EXERCISES

▶ **Practice Your Skills**

1. Use the equations to find the missing entries in each table.

a. $y = 4.2 + 0.8x$

@	Input x	Output y
	−4	1
	−1	3.4
	1.5	5.4
	6.4	9.32
	9	11.4

b. $y = 1.2 − 0.8x$

Domain x	Range y
−4	4.4
−1	2
2.4	−0.72
11	−7.6
14	−10

2. On the same set of axes, plot the points in the table and graph the equation in Exercise 1a.

3. On the same set of axes, plot the points in the table and graph the equation in Exercise 1b.

4. Use the tables and graphs in Exercises 1–3 to tell whether the relationships in Exercise 1 are functions. @ Answers will vary. In the table, every input value produces exactly one output value. Both graphs in Exercises 2 and 3 pass the vertical line test. Both rules are functions.

▶ **Reason and Apply**

5. The graph at right describes another student's distance from you. What are the walking instructions for the graph? Does it represent a function? @

6. Find whether each graph below represents a function. Does it pass the vertical line test?

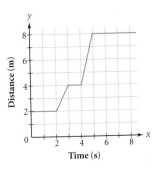

a.   yes

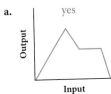

b.

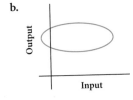

c. ⓗ

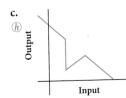

d.   yes

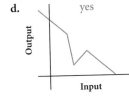

e.

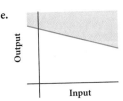

No; each input value has infinitely many output values.

5. Sample answer: Start at the 2 m mark and stand still for 2 s. Walk toward the 4 m mark at 2 m/s for 1 s. Stand still for another second. Walk toward the 8 m mark at 4 m/s for 1 s. Then stand still for 3 s. Yes, the graph represents a function.

6b. No; many input values have two different output values.

6c. No; there is a vertical segment. All the points on the vertical segment have the same input value but different output values.

7. Does each relationship in the form (*input, output*) represent a function? If the relationship does not represent a function, find an example of one input that has two or more outputs. This is called a **counterexample.**

   a. (*city, ZIP Code*) ⓗ

   b. (*person, birth date*)

   c. (*last name, first name*) ⓐ

   d. (*state, capital*)
     Yes; each state has only
     one capital.

8. Here are the graphs of seven walks showing distance from a motion sensor.

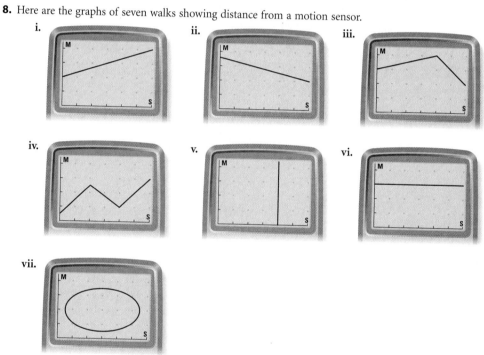

   a. Which graphs represent functions? i, ii, iii, iv, and vi

   b. For which graphs is it not possible to write walking instructions? v and vii

   c. What conclusion can you make?
     Sample conclusion: It is not possible to walk a graph that does not represent a function.

Exercise 7 [Language] Make sure students understand that a *counterexample* is an example that proves a statement false. You might give another example. **[Ask]** "Is the relation (*musical note name, pitch*) a function?" [It depends. If several different notes are all called C, then the note name will have many different pitches, so it won't be a function. If the different C's have different names, like C′ and C″, then it will be a function.] You can also extend this exercise and preview the Take Another Look activity at the end of the chapter by looking at inverse functions. **[Ask]** "If we interchange the input and output values, do we still have a function?" [(*ZIP Code, city*), no; (*birth date, person*), no; (*first name, last name*), no; (*capital, state*), yes]

7a. No; Los Angeles, for example, has more than one ZIP Code (90001, 90002, . . .).

7b. Yes; each person has only one birth date.

7c. No; the same last name will correspond to many different first names.

Exercise 9 **[Ask]** "How can the table in part a be changed to make it a function?"

9a. Not a function; the *x*-value 3 has two different *y*-values, 10 and 8.

9b. A function; each *x*-value corresponds to only one *y*-value.

9c. A function; each *x*-value corresponds to only one *y*-value.

Exercises 10 and 11 Both noncontinuous and continuous functions are acceptable. You might have students present a variety of answers.

Exercise 12 If students have difficulty filling in the tables, especially in 12c, encourage them to solve the equations for *y* in terms of *x*. In 12c, *x* is a function of *y*, but *y* is not a function of *x*.

12a.

12b.

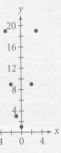

12c.

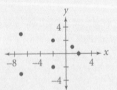

12d.

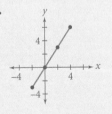

9. Find whether each table of *x*- and *y*-values represents a function. Explain your reasoning.

a.

Domain x	Range y
0	5
1	7
3	10
7	9
5	7
4	5
3	8

b.

Domain x	Range y
3	7
4	9
8	4
5	5
9	3
11	9
7	6

c.

Domain x	Range y
2	8
3	11
5	12
7	3
9	5
8	7
4	11

10. On graph paper, draw a graph that is a function and has these three properties:

▶ Domain of *x*-values satisfying $-3 \leq x \leq 5$
▶ Range of *y*-values satisfying $-4 \leq y \leq 4$
▶ Includes the points $(-2, 3)$ and $(3, -2)$ @

Graphs must pass the vertical line test, have the correct domain and range, and pass through the points $(-2, 3)$ and $(3, -2)$.

11. On graph paper, draw a graph that is *not* a function and has these three properties:

▶ Domain of *x*-values satisfying $-3 \leq x \leq 5$
▶ Range of *y*-values satisfying $-4 \leq y \leq 4$
▶ Includes the points $(-2, 3)$ and $(3, -2)$

Graphs will not pass a vertical line test, but they should include points $(-2, 3)$ and $(3, -2)$ and have the correct domain and range. Graphs of inequalities are possible.

12. Complete the table of values for each equation. Let *x* represent domain values, and let *y* represent range values. Graph the points and find whether the equation describes a function. Explain your reasoning.

a. $x - 3y = 5$ @

x	2	8	−4	−1	0	5
y	−1	1	−3	−2	$-\frac{5}{3}$	0

The graph is a line. This is a function; each *x*-value is paired with only one *y*-value.

b. $y = 2x^2 + 1$

x	−2	3	0	−3	−1	±2
y	9	19	1	19	3	9

This is a function; each *x*-value is paired with only one *y*-value.

c. $x + y^2 = 2$

x	−7	1	−2	−7	−2	2
y	±3	1	−2	−3	±2	0

The equation does not represent a function because there are two different *y*-values for some *x*-values.

d. $x + 2y = 4x$

x					
y					

Tables will vary. Sample: $(0, 0), (2, 3), (-2, -3), (4, 6)$. The graph is a line and represents a function because each *x*-value is paired with only one *y*-value.

13. Identify all numbers in the domain and range of each graph.

a.

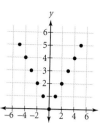

b.

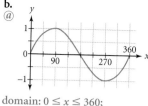

domain: $0 \leq x \leq 360$;
range: $-1 \leq y \leq 1$

c.

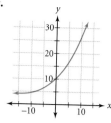

14. Consider the capital letters in our alphabet.

a. Draw two capital letters that do not represent the graph of a function. Explain. ⓗ

b. Draw two capital letters that do represent the graph of a function. Explain.

▶ Review

5.1 **15.** If x represents actual temperature and y represents wind chill temperature, the equation

$$y = -29 + 1.4x$$

approximates the wind chill temperatures for a wind speed of 40 mi/h. Enter this equation into Y₁ on your calculator and find the requested x- and y-values.

a. What x-value gives a y-value of $-15°$? Explain how you use the calculator table function to find this answer.

b. Enter

$$y = -15$$

into Y₂ on your calculator. Graph both equations. Explain how to use the graph to answer 15a.

2.8 **16.** Show how you can use an undoing process to solve these equations.

a. $\dfrac{4(x-7)-8}{3} = 20$

b. $\dfrac{4.5}{x-3} = \dfrac{2}{3}$ ⓗ

5.2 **17.** Find the solution to each system.

a. $\begin{cases} y = 3x - 5 \\ y = -2.5x + 9 \end{cases}$ ⓐ $\left(\dfrac{28}{11}, \dfrac{29}{11}\right) \approx (2.55, 2.64)$

b. $\begin{cases} y = 2(x-4) + 15 \\ y = 15(x+5) - 12 \end{cases}$ $\left(-\dfrac{56}{13}, -\dfrac{21}{13}\right) \approx (-4.31, -1.62)$

Exercise 13 The arrows on graph c indicate that the input values extend indefinitely. The output may or may not become zero or negative.

13a. domain: $\{-5, -4, -3, -2, -1, 0, 1, 2, 3, 4, 5\}$; range: $\{0, 1, 2, 3, 4, 5\}$

13c. Answers may vary; possible domain: all numbers x; possible range: all numbers y.

14a. Letters such as A, B, and C are not functions because a vertical line could intersect them at more than one point.

14b. Letters such as V and W are functions because no vertical line could intersect them at more than one point.

Exercise 15 Have copies of Calculator Note 1J available for students who need to review graphing two equations.

15a. When $x = 10, y = -15$. Answers will vary. Zoom in on the table by changing the start values and the table increments (ΔTbl).

15b. Answers will vary. The lines intersect at the solution point.

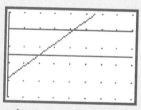

$[0, 40, 5, -40, 10, 10]$

16a. Multiply by 3, add 8, divide by 4, add 7; $x = 24$.

16b. Invert the proportion to get $\dfrac{x-3}{4.5} = \dfrac{3}{2}$, multiply by 4.5, add 3; $x = 9.75$.

LESSON OUTLINE

One day:

5 min	Example A
20 min	Investigation
10 min	Sharing
5 min	Example B
5 min	Closing
5 min	Exercises

MATERIALS

- large sheets of paper and markers (one set per group)
- Real-World Situations (W), *optional*
- Water Depth (T), *optional*

TEACHING

A graph can be thought of as telling a story about how variables change values. Continue to model—and have students model—the use of complete sentences when writing about the mathematics.

Some students will be more comfortable with the terms *x-axis* and *y-axis* than with *horizontal axis* and *vertical axis.*

One Step

Assign each group one of the situations on the Real-World Situations worksheet (also on page 406 of the student text) and ask students to represent the situation with a graph, drawn on a large sheet of paper. As you circulate, plant the idea (if necessary) in one or two groups that their graphs may need to be discrete. Post the sheets of paper, and ask the groups to come up with words describing the graphs so that they can be compared and contrasted. During the discussion, focus on the terms *linear,*

Graphs of Real-World Situations

One picture is worth ten thousand words.

FRED R. BARNARD

Like pictures, graphs communicate a lot of information. So you need to be able to interpret, draw, and communicate about graphs. In previous chapters you learned to use bar graphs, histograms, and box plots. Then you learned to graph data from recursive routines and equations. Most graphs you've seen represent functions—some of these graphs were lines, or **linear,** and others were curves, or **nonlinear.**

In this lesson you will learn vocabulary for describing graphs (like linear and nonlinear), and you'll interpret graphs of some real-world situations.

EXAMPLE A

This graph shows the depth of the water in a leaky swimming pool. Tell what quantities are varying and how they are related. Give possible real-world events in your explanation.

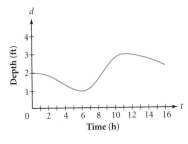

▶ **Solution**

The graph shows that the water level, or depth, changes over a 15-hour time period. At the beginning, when no time has passed, $t = 0$, and the water in the pool is 2 feet deep, so $d = 2$. During the first 6-hour interval ($0 \leq t \leq 6$), the water level drops. The leak seems to get worse as time passes. When $t = 6$ and $d = 1$, it seems that someone starts to refill the pool. The water level rises for the next 5 hours, during the interval $6 \leq t \leq 11$. At $t = 11$, the water reaches its highest level at just about 3 feet, so $d = 3$. At the 11-hour mark, the in-flowing water is apparently turned off. The pool still has a leak, so the water level starts to drop again.

In the example the depth of the water is a function of time. That is, the depth depends on how much time has passed. So, in this case, depth is called the **dependent variable.** Time is the **independent variable.** When you draw a graph, put the independent variable on the horizontal axis and put the dependent variable on the vertical axis.

LESSON OBJECTIVES

- Construct and interpret graphs that describe real-world situations
- Learn the terminology of independent and dependent variables
- Describe, read, and interpret graphs of real-world situations using the terms *linear, nonlinear, increasing, decreasing, rate of change, continuous,* and *discrete*

NCTM STANDARDS

CONTENT		PROCESS	
	Number	✓	Problem Solving
✓	Algebra	✓	Reasoning
	Geometry	✓	Communication
✓	Measurement	✓	Connections
	Data/Probability	✓	Representation

In the graph of the function in Example A, you can see domain values that are possible for the independent variable. The domain is the set of all times from 0 through 16 hours. You express this interval as $0 \leq x \leq 16$, where x is the independent variable representing time.

You can also see the values that are possible for the dependent variable. The range appears to be the set of all numbers from 1 through 3. You express this as $1 \leq y \leq 3$, where y is the dependent variable representing the depth of the water. Notice that the lowest value for the range does not have to be the starting value when x is zero.

While sections of the graph in Example A may appear linear, such as on the interval $8 \leq x \leq 10$, the function is nonlinear overall. This means that as x changes at a constant rate, the function values change at a varying rate. In the investigation that follows, Graphs A and D show linear functions—as x increases at a constant rate, the function values also change at a constant rate. In the investigation you'll discover another aspect of functions and you'll use graphs of functions to describe real-world situations.

 ## Investigation
Matching Up

First, you'll consider the concepts of increasing and decreasing functions.

Step 1 | These are graphs of *increasing functions*. What do the three graphs have in common? How would you describe the rate of change in each?

Graph A

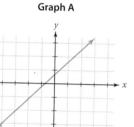

Graph B

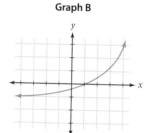

Graph C

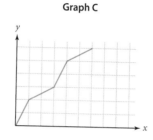

Step 2 | These are graphs of *decreasing functions*. What do they have in common? How are they different from those in Step 1? How would you describe the rate of change in these graphs?

Graph D

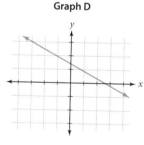

Graph E

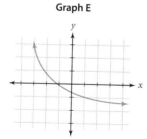

Graph F

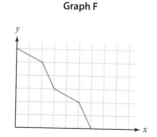

Step 2 Sample answer: All three graphs fall from left to right. Unlike in Step 1, the function values decrease as the x-values increase. The rate of change can be constant or can vary, but it is negative.

nonlinear, increasing, decreasing, rate of change, continuous, and discrete.

▶ **EXAMPLE A**

This example illustrates how a graph can tell a story. Use the Water Depth transparency as you ask students about the various time periods. Be sure they understand that the different rates are depicted as slopes. Identify the variables to emphasize further the concepts of independent (input) and dependent (output) variables and domain and range.

Be careful that your language doesn't equate "the graph" with "the function." The graph is a picture, but the function is a relationship between sets.

You might want to revisit this example after students do the investigation. You need not insist on distinctions between strict and nonstrict inequalities. Help students find the correct direction of the inequality sign.

For review, you might ask whether every line is the graph of some function. Be patient. Wait at least 40 seconds before answering the question yourself. Accept all answers, and have the class critique them. Vertical lines are not graphs of functions, but all other lines are. Some students may think that horizontal lines are not. Constant functions, such as $f(x) = -3$, which give the same output value for every input value, may not be very interesting, but they are functions.

Guiding the Investigation

Step 1 Sample answer: All three graphs rise from left to right. The function values increase as the x-values increase. The rate of change can be constant or can vary, but it is positive.

Step 3 Situation A: Time is independent, number of deer is dependent. Situation B: Time is independent, amount of daylight is dependent. Situation C: Width is independent, area is dependent. Situation D: Time is independent, temperature difference is dependent.

Step 4 Encourage students to create graph descriptions that are more than a repetition of the situation in the description in the student text.

Steps 4 and 5 Sample description: Situation A matches Graph 5, which is increasing with a faster and faster rate of change, then slows to become linear with no change. Situation B matches Graph 3, which starts with a slow rate of change that speeds up, levels off and peaks, decreases quickly at first, then decreases more slowly and levels off again. Situation C matches Graph 1, which increases with a steep rate of change that slows, levels off and peaks, then decreases, at first with a slow rate of change and then faster and faster. Situation D matches Graph 4, which decreases, first at a fast rate of change and then more slowly.

SHARING IDEAS

[Language] Model correct use of the adjectives *increasing* and *decreasing* as well as the verbs *increase* and *decrease*. It might be helpful to show students that they already know that "*x* increases" as you move right on the *x*-axis and that "*y* increases" as you go up on the *y*-axis.

Do students agree with the quotation that opens the lesson? Are the graphs pictures that are worth ten thousand words? How many words are needed to set the context for the pictures? As students share their descriptions, clarify that "the function increases" means that the *function values* increase. Because we always read a graph from left to right,

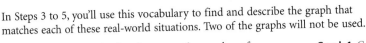

In Steps 3 to 5, you'll use this vocabulary to find and describe the graph that matches each of these real-world situations. Two of the graphs will not be used.

Situation A During the first few years, the number of deer on the island increased by a steady percentage. As food became less plentiful, the growth rate started slowing down. Now, the number of births and deaths is about the same.

Situation B In the Northern Hemisphere the amount of daylight increases slowly from January through February, faster until mid-May, and then slowly until the maximum in June. Then it decreases slowly though July, faster from August until mid-November, and then slowly until the year's end.

Situation C If you have a fixed amount of fencing, the width of your rectangular garden determines its area. If the width is very short, the garden won't have much area. As the width increases, the area also increases. The area increases more slowly until it reaches a maximum. As the width continues to increase, the area becomes smaller more quickly until it is zero.

Situation D Your cup of tea is very hot. The difference between the tea temperature and the room temperature decreases quickly at first as the tea starts to cool to room temperature. But when the two temperatures are close together, the cooling rate slows down. It actually takes a long time for the tea to finally reach room temperature.

Step 3 In Situation A decide which quantities are varying. Also decide which variable is independent and which is dependent.

Step 4 Match and describe the graph that best fits the situation. Write a description of the function and its graph using words such as *linear, nonlinear, increasing, decreasing, rate of change, maximum* or *greatest value,* and *minimum* or *least value.* Tell why you think the graph and your description match the situation.

Step 5 Repeat Steps 3 and 4 for the other three situations.

Graph 1 C
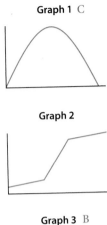

Graph 2
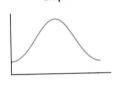

Graph 3 B
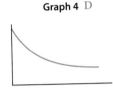

Graph 4 D
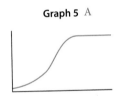

Graph 5 A
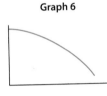

Graph 6

"as *x* increases" is often an assumed condition when using the terms *increasing function* and *decreasing function.*

[Ask] "How do the first two situations differ from the last two?" Be open to lots of ideas. As needed, bring out the idea that a *discrete function* has separate, unconnected points in its domain or range, as in Situations A and B.

Although Situations A and B are discrete, they can be conveniently modeled with *continuous functions.*

Point out that it is always important to *interpret* the mathematical model in terms of the original situation.

[Ask] "What kind of growth is represented in Situations A and D?" [Situation A begins as exponential growth, and Situation D shows exponential decay.]

Situation B is trigonometric (a sinusoidal curve). Be sure students understand what the graph looks like, because it's a model for Exercise 9.

In the investigation you learned how to describe real-world situations with graphs and some function vocabulary. A function is **increasing** when the variables change in the same way—that is, the *y*-values *grow* when reading the graph from left to right. A function is **decreasing** when the variables change in different directions—that is, the *y*-values *drop* when reading the graph from left to right.

Sometimes it is useful to name a part of the domain for which a function has a certain characteristic.

EXAMPLE B

Describe this graph, telling how the quantities in the graph relate to each other.

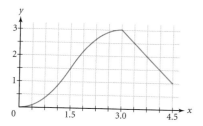

▶ **Solution**

Use the intervals marked on the *x*-axis to help you discuss where the function is increasing or decreasing and where it is linear or nonlinear.

On the interval $0 \leq x < 3.0$, the function is nonlinear and increasing. As *x* increases steadily, *y* changes at a varying rate, so the graph is nonlinear. When read from left to right, the graph rises. So the *y*-values grow and the function is increasing.

On the interval $3.0 \leq x \leq 4.5$, the function appears linear and is decreasing. Because *y* appears to change at a constant rate on the graph, the function is linear. When read from left to right, the graph falls. So the *y*-values drop and the function is decreasing.

Situations C and D in the investigation are represented by **continuous** functions because there are no breaks in the domain or range. Many functions that are not continuous involve quantities that are counted or measured in whole numbers—for instance, people, cars, or stories of a building. In the investigation you have already seen two functions like this—the number of deer in Situation A and the number of days in Situation B. These are called **discrete** functions. When graphing the amount of daylight for every day of the year, the graph should really be a set of 365 points, as in the graph below. There is no value for day 47.35. Likewise, there may not be a day with exactly 11 hours 1 minute of daylight. But it's easier to draw this relationship as a smooth curve than to plot 365 points.

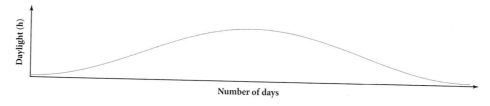

▶ **EXAMPLE B**

This example is good for students who were having difficulty describing graphs in the investigation. Students will study the nature of a function at the boundary points of the intervals in calculus.

Assessing Progress

Look for ability to graph and for understanding of domain and range.

Closing the Lesson

Graphs tell a story about how the **dependent** (output) **variable** depends on the **independent** (input) **variable**. A function **increases** if its *y*-values get larger as its *x*-values increase. Graphically, its graph rises from left to right. A function **decreases** if its *y*-values get smaller as its *x*-values increase. Its graph falls from left to right. A function's rate of change increases if the slope of the graph becomes larger, and it decreases if the slope becomes smaller.

BUILDING UNDERSTANDING

Students work with graphs of functions representing real-world situations and practice identifying dependent and independent variables. Remind students to use complete sentences when writing up assignments, both to motivate function notation in Lesson 7.4 and to deepen their understanding of mathematical ideas.

ASSIGNING HOMEWORK

Essential	**2–6**
Performance assessment	**9–12**
Portfolio	**13**
Journal	**2, 13**
Group	**7, 8, 10–12**
Review	**14–16**

Helping with the Exercises

Exercises 2 and 4 Here, "slower and slower" means slopes becoming closer to zero, with a graph becoming flatter. "Faster and faster" means slopes farther from zero, with a graph becoming steeper.

2a.

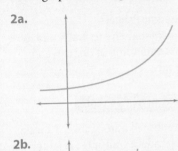

2b.

2c.

2d.

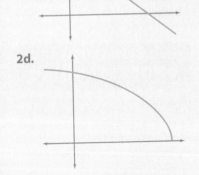

EXERCISES

▶ Practice Your Skills

1. Sketch a reasonable graph and label the axes for each situation described. Write a few sentences explaining each graph.

   a. The more students who help to decorate for the homecoming dance, the less time it will take to decorate. @

   b. The more you charge for T-shirts, the fewer T-shirts you will sell.

   c. The more you spend on advertising, the more product you will sell.

2. Sketch a graph of a continuous function to fit each description.

   a. always increasing with a faster and faster rate of change

   b. decreasing with a slower and slower rate of change, then increasing with a faster and faster rate of change @

   c. linear and decreasing

   d. decreasing with a faster and faster rate of change @

3. Use the number line to write an inequality for each interval in 3a–e. Include the least point in each interval and exclude the greatest point in each interval.

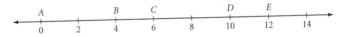

   a. *A* to *B* @
   $0 \leq x < 4$

   b. *B* to *C*
   $4 \leq x < 6$

   c. *B* to *D*
   $4 \leq x < 10$

   d. *C* to *E*
   $6 \leq x < 12$

   e. *A* to *E*
   $0 \leq x < 12$

4. Sketch a discrete function graph to fit each description.

   a. always increasing with a slower and slower rate of change @

   b. linear with a constant rate of change equal to zero

   c. linear and decreasing

   d. decreasing with a faster and faster rate of change

5. For each relationship, identify the independent variable and the dependent variable.

   a. the weight of your dog and the reading on the scale

   b. the amount of time you spend in an airplane and the distance between your departure and your destination

   c. the number of times you dip a wick into hot wax and the diameter of a handmade candle

   The wax sticks to the candle wick each time you dip it, so the number of dips is the independent variable and the diameter of the candle is the dependent variable.

Traders on the floor of the New York Stock Exchange use graphs to show stock prices.

1. Sample answers:

1a.

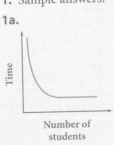

The graph shows an inverse relationship. It is not possible to take 0 hr to decorate, no matter how many students help.

1b.

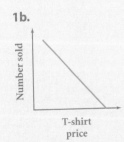

This graph shows an inverse relationship. There is a price so high that no one will buy T-shirts.

1c.

This graph shows a linear relationship. Some product will be sold without any advertising. Eventually the amount of product sold will level off, but that isn't shown on the graph.

Reason and Apply

6. The graph describes another student's distance from you.

   a. Is the relationship a function? Explain your reasoning.

   b. What is the domain?   The domain is $0 \leq x \leq 8$.

   c. What is the range?   The range is $2 \leq y \leq 8$.

   d. Explain what $(0, 2)$ means in this situation.

   e. Find the missing coordinate in each ordered pair.

     $(3.5, y)$ $(5, y)$ $(x, 3)$ $y = 4; y = 8; x = 2.5$

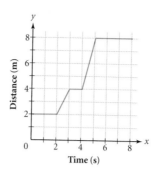

7. **APPLICATION** The diagram below shows a side view of a swimming pool that is being filled. The water enters the pool at a constant rate. Sketch a graph of your interpretation of the relationship between depth and time as the pool is being filled. Explain your graph. ⓗ

Student graphs should consist of three line segments, each less steep than the one before it.

8. **APPLICATION** This graph shows Anne's blood pressure level during a morning at school. Give the points or intervals when her blood pressure

   a. Reached its highest level. about 11:00 A.M.

   b. Was rising the fastest. between 10:10 and 10:40 A.M.

   c. Was decreasing. between 9:00 and 9:45 A.M. and then again after 11:00 A.M.

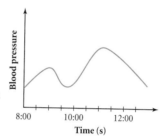

9. This graph shows the air temperature in a 24-hour period from midnight to midnight. Write a description of this graph, giving the intervals over which the graph changed in different ways. The temperature dropped slowly from midnight until 6 A.M. and was fairly constant through the morning. At about 10 A.M., the temperature began a dramatic rise for 2 hr. Then the temperature continued to rise more slowly for another 7 hr until 7 P.M. The temperature dropped only slightly from 7 P.M. until midnight.

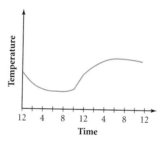

5a. The reading on the scale depends on the weight of the dog, so the dog's weight is the independent variable and the reading on the scale is the dependent variable.

5b. The amount of time you spend in the plane depends on the distance you fly, so the distance between the cities is the independent variable and the amount of time in the plane is the dependent variable.

6a. Yes; the graph passes the vertical line test and the student cannot be at two different places at the same time.

6d. Before any time has elapsed, the distance is 2 m.

Exercise 7 The depth of the pool is measured at the deep end.

7.

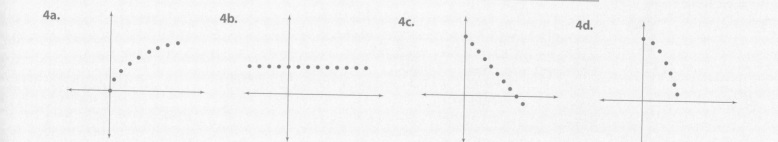

4a.   4b.   4c.   4d.

Exercise 10 **[Alert]** Watch for confusion here as students try to see how the graph tells a story of the race. **[Ask]** "What does it mean for one curve to be higher than the other?" [That runner has gone farther in the time so far and so is ahead.] Students may say that where the curves cross, the runners are "at the same place but not at the same time," thus neglecting to take into account both variables. **[Ask]** "What's special about where the curves cross?" [The girls are passing each other.]

10c. They were tied at approximately 3 s, at 5.5 s, from 10 to 10.5 s, and just before the end of the race.

Exercise 11 **[Alert]** Some students may still be having difficulty representing motion on a graph. Be patient. Even if a student asks a question you have just answered, be grateful that the student is trying to make sense of the idea. Often people don't hear answers to questions they haven't asked.

Exercise 12a Students may find it difficult to imagine a scenario here. They may try to think of a situation in which distance, rather than velocity, jumps among −2, 0, and 2. Or they may point out that in real life velocity won't take on discrete values, without acceleration. Encourage approximations, such as rocking a car that's stuck in snow or sand. Students may think of a walker going in one direction then turning and going in the other direction.

12a. Answers will vary. A sample graph is shown. It should be made up of at least three horizontal segments at heights 0, 2, and −2.

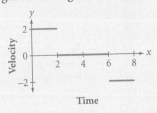

10. The graph pictures the performance of Erica and Eileen in a 100-meter dash.

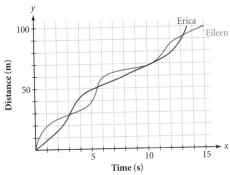

Erica won in about 13.5 s.

a. Who won the race and in how many seconds? Explain. *@*

b. Who was ahead at the 60-meter mark? *@* Eileen

c. At what approximate times were the runners tied? *@*

d. When was Eileen in the lead? *@* from approximately 0 to 3 s, from 5.5 to 10 s, and from 10.5 to about 13.2 s.

11. A turtle crawls steadily from its pond across the lawn. Then a small dog picks up the turtle and runs with it across the lawn. The dog slows down and finally drops the turtle. The turtle rests for a few minutes after this excitement. Then a young boy comes along, picks up the turtle, and slowly carries it back to the pond. Which of the graphs describes the turtle's distance from the pond? Graph B

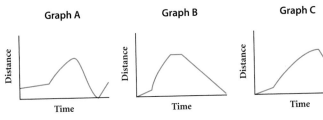

12. Sketch a graph and describe a reasonable scenario for each statement.

a. a domain for the independent variable, *time,* of 0 to 8 seconds and a range for the dependent variable, *velocity,* of {0, 2, −2} meters per second *@*

b. your speed while you are riding or driving in a car following a school bus

c. the height of a basketball during a free throw shot

d. the height of the grass in a yard over the summer

e. the number of buses needed to take different numbers of students on a field trip

12b. A sample graph is shown. As the school bus leaves a stop, its speed increases. It travels for a while at a constant speed. Then it slows down briefly and speeds up again to a faster speed than before it slowed down. It travels at a constant speed for a while, then slows down and stops as it lets some students off. It speeds up again and levels off at a constant speed.

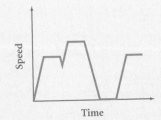

13. Each graph shows the distance of a person from a fixed point for a 4-second interval. Answer both questions for each graph.

    i. Is the person moving toward or away from the point?

    ii. Is the person speeding up, slowing down, or moving at a constant speed?

a.

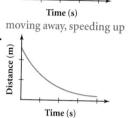

moving away, speeding up

b.

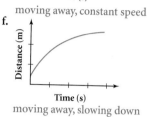

moving toward, speeding up

c.

moving away, constant speed

d.

moving toward, slowing down

e.

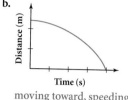

moving toward, constant speed

f.

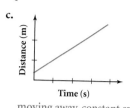

moving away, slowing down

> ## Review

4.2, **14.** It is possible for two different functions to have coordinates in common.
6.2

    a. Write the equation of a line through the points $(0, 8)$ and $(1, 10)$. $y = 8 + 2x$

    b. Write an exponential equation of a function whose graph goes through the points $(0, 8)$ and $(1, 10)$.   The equation is $y = 8(1 + 0.25)^x$.

2.8, **15.** Solve each equation for x using any method. Use another method to check your
3.6   answer.

    a. $\dfrac{2x - 4}{3} + 7 = 4$ -2.5 **b.** $\dfrac{5(3 - x)}{-2} = -17.5$ -4 **c.** $\dfrac{2}{x - 1} = 3$ $\frac{5}{3}$

4.4 **16.** Consider the equation $y = -12.4 - 2.5(x + 5.4)$.

    a. Write the equation in intercept form. $y = -25.9 - 2.5x$

    b. Name the slope and y-intercept of the equation in 16a.   The slope is -2.5, and the y-intercept is -25.9.

IMPROVING YOUR **GEOMETRY** SKILLS

Use 16 toothpicks to make this pattern. Then remove 4 toothpicks so that you have 4 congruent triangles.

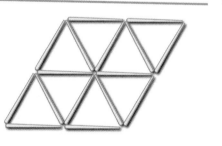

IMPROVING **GEOMETRY** SKILLS

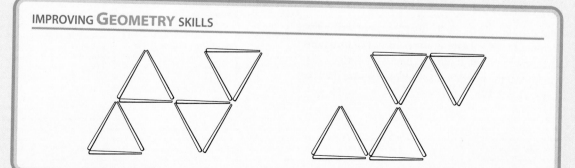

12c. Graphs and descriptions will vary. One possible graph is shown.

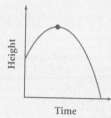

12d. A sample graph is shown. The height of the grass is quite short after it has been mowed, then grows taller until it is mowed again.

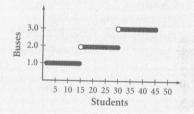

12e. A sample graph is shown. The number of students and the number of buses can only be integers, so the graph is made up of dots rather than lines. After a bus is full, students get into the next bus.

Exercise 13 [Alert] Some students may think that the point is at the origin or y-intercept. Remind them that the graph is not the path of the moving person and that the height of the graph represents the distance of that person from the fixed point.

Exercise 14b [Ask] "What are the starting value and constant multiplier?" [The starting value is 8, and the constant multiplier is $\frac{10}{8}$, or $1 + 0.25$.] Or students can get the values through symbolic manipulation: Because the equation $y = ab^x$ goes through $(0, 8)$, you can conclude that $8 = ab^0$, so a must be 8. Because the graph goes through $(1, 10)$, you have $10 = 8b^1$, so b must be $\frac{10}{8}$.

LESSON

7.4

Function Notation

The theory that has had the greatest development in recent times is without any doubt the theory of functions.

VITO VOLTERRA

Every function defines a relationship between an input (independent) variable and an output (dependent) variable. **Function notation** uses parentheses to name the input, or independent, variable for the function. For instance, $y = f(x)$, which you read as "y equals f of x," says "y is a function of x" or "y depends on x." (In function notation, the parentheses do *not* mean multiplication.)

Albert Einstein writes mathematical notation in a lecture to scientists in 1931.

You can show some functions with an equation. For example, the equation $y = 2x + 4$ represents a function, so you can write it as $f(x) = 2x + 4$. The notation $f(3)$ tells you to substitute 3 for x in the equation $y = 2x + 4$. So, $f(3) = 2(3) + 4$. The value of $f(x)$ when $x = 3$ is 10. By itself, f is the name of the function. In this case, its rule is $2x + 4$.

Not all functions are expressed as equations. The graph below shows a new function, $f(x)$. No rule or equation is given, but you can still use function notation to find output values. For example, on the graph below, the point at $x = 4$ has the coordinates $(4, f(4))$ or $(4, 1)$. The value of y when x is 4 is $f(4)$. So, $f(4) = 1$. Check that $f(2)$ is 4. What is the value of $f(6)$? Can you find two x-values for which $f(x) = 1$?

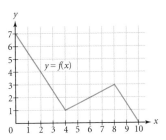

In the next investigation you will learn more about using function notation with graphs.

Teaching Sidebar (left column)

INTRODUCTION

Remind students of the inconvenience of writing out accurate statements about the behavior of functions, and show them the standard function notation. As you look at the graph with students, be sure they see that $f(6) = 2$. When $f(x) = 1$, x is 4 or about 9.3.

Investigation
A Graphic Message

In this investigation you will apply function notation to learn the identity of the mathematician who introduced functions.

Step 1   Describe the domain and range of the function f in the graph.

Step 2   Use the graph to find each function value in the table. Then do the indicated operations.

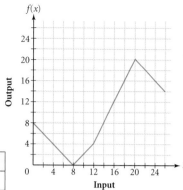

Notation	Value
$f(3)$	5
$f(18) + f(3)$	21
$f(5) \cdot f(4)$	12
$f(15) / f(6)$	5
$f(20) - f(10)$	18

Step 3   Use the rules for the order of operations to evaluate these expressions that involve function values. Do any operations inside parentheses first. Then use the graph to find the function values before doing the remaining operations. Write your answers in a table.

Notation	Value
$f(0) + f(1) - 3$	12
$5 \cdot f(9)$	5
x when $f(x) = 10$	15
$f(9 + 8)$	14
x when $f(x) = 0$	8
$f(8 \cdot 3) - 5 \cdot f(11)$	1
$f(4 \cdot 5 - 1)$	18
$f(12)$	4

Step 4   Think of the numbers 1 through 26 as the letters A through Z. Find the letters that match your answers to Step 2 to learn the mathematician's last name. Find the letters that match your answers to Step 3 to discover the first name.

Step 2: EULER; Step 3: LEONHARD

The mathematician whose name you decoded was the inventor of much of the mathematical notation in use today. To learn more about this mathematician, see the links at **www.keymath.com/DA** . In the example that follows, you will practice function notation with an equation.

NCTM STANDARDS

CONTENT		PROCESS	
	Number		Problem Solving
✓	Algebra	✓	Reasoning
	Geometry		Communication
	Measurement		Connections
	Data/Probability	✓	Representation

LESSON OBJECTIVES

• Learn function notation

• Evaluate functions by substitution, by using the graphs drawn by hand, and on the graphing calculator

• Write and interpret functions that describe real-world data

This example gives students more practice with function notation. Using the calculator to check answers will reinforce the idea that the number inside the parentheses denotes the x-value (input) that is substituted into the function expression to get the y-value (output). Have Calculator Note 7A available for students. You might extend the example to ask about $f(-40)$. A temperature of $-40°C$ is the same as $-40°F$.

Most TI models allow you to evaluate functions by using the notation $Y_1(x)$. However, Casio calculators interpret the parentheses as multiplication between the value in Y_1 and the value currently stored in x. Consult the calculator manual to see how to enter and evaluate functions on your calculator.

Closing the Lesson

Using notation such as $f(x) = 5x - 4$ to describe a function allows saying "$f(3) = 5(3) - 4 = 11$" instead of "the value of $y = 5x - 4$ is 11 when $x = 3$."

BUILDING UNDERSTANDING

Students practice using function notation and evaluating functions.

ASSIGNING HOMEWORK

Essential	1–5, 11
Performance assessment	6, 10
Portfolio	7
Journal	11, 12
Group	9, 11
Review	8, 13–15

► Helping with the Exercises

Exercise 1 If students are confused by $g(x)$, direct them to the paragraph after the example.

EXAMPLE

You can use the function $f(x) = \frac{9}{5}x + 32$ to find the temperature $f(x)$ in degrees Fahrenheit for any given temperature x in degrees Celsius. Find the specified value.

a. $f(15)$ **b.** $f(-10)$

c. x when $f(x) = 41$ **d.** x when $f(x) = -4$

► **Solution**

In a and b, substitute the value in parentheses for x in the function. In c and d, substitute the given value for $f(x)$.

a. $f(15) = \frac{9}{5}(15) + 32$
$f(15) = 27 + 32$
$f(15) = 59$

b. $f(-10) = \frac{9}{5}(-10) + 32$
$f(-10) = -18 + 32$
$f(-10) = 14$

c. $41 = \frac{9}{5}x + 32$
$9 = \frac{9}{5}x$
$5 = x$

d. $-4 = \frac{9}{5}x + 32$
$-36 = \frac{9}{5}x$
$-20 = x$

[▷ 🖥] See **Calculator Note 7A** to learn how to evaluate functions on your calculator. ◁

Note that you don't have to always call a function f, and the input doesn't have to be x. You can call a function $g(x)$, $h(t)$, or any letters you prefer. Sometimes you'll choose letters that represent the variables, such as t for time and h for height. But when you use your calculator, you'll usually need to translate into x and y. Most calculators use the notation $Y_1(x)$.

EXERCISES

You will need your graphing calculator for Exercises **1, 2, 8,** and **11.**

► Practice Your Skills

1. Find each value for $f(x) = 3x + 2$ and $g(x) = x^2 - 1$ without using your calculator. Then enter the equations for $f(x)$ and $g(x)$ into Y_1 and Y_2. Use function notation on your calculator to check your answers. [▷ 🖥] See **Calculator Note 7A.** ◁

a. $f(3)$ **b.** x when $f(x) = 2$ @   **c.** $g(5)$ **d.** $g(-3)$

2. Find the y-coordinate corresponding to each x-coordinate if the functions are $f(x) = -2x - 5$ and $g(x) = 3.75(2.5)^x$. Check your answers with your calculator.

a. $f(6)$ @   **b.** $f(0)$ **c.** $g(2)$ **d.** $g(-2)$ $3.75(2.5)^{-2} = 0.6$
$-2(6) - 5 = -17$ $-2(0) - 5 = -5$ $3.75(2.5)^2 = 23.4375$

3. Use the graph of $y = f(x)$ at right to answer each question.

a. What is the value of $f(4)$? @ $f(4) = 0$

b. What is the value of $f(6)$? $f(6) = 4$

c. For what value or values of x does $f(x)$ equal 2? @

d. For what value or values of x does $f(x)$ equal 1?

e. How many x-values make the statement $f(x) = 0.5$ true? @ three

f. For what x-values is $f(x)$ greater than 2? $x > 5$

g. What are the domain and range shown on the graph?
domain: $-1 \le x \le 7$; range: $0 \le y \le 6$

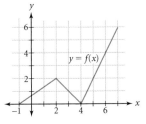

1a. $3(3) + 2 = 11$; $Y_1(3) = 11$

1b. $3x + 2 = 2, x = 0$; $Y_1(0) = 2$

1c. $(5)^2 - 1 = 24$; $Y_2(5) = 24$

1d. $(-3)^2 - 1 = 8$; $Y_2(-3) = 8$

Exercise 3f Students may find this exercise confusing. Remind them that the $f(x)$ values are vertical heights in the graph.

3c. $f(2) = 2, f(5) = 2$

3d. $f(0.5) = 1, f(3) = 1, f(4.5) = 1$

4. APPLICATION The graph of the function $y = f(x)$ below shows the temperature y outside at different times x over a 24-hour period.

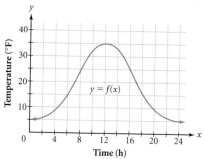

a. What are the dependent and independent variables? @

b. What are the domain and range shown on the graph? @   domain: $0 \le x \le 24$; range: $5 \le y \le 35$

c. Use function notation to represent the temperature at 10 h. @ $f(10)$

d. Use function notation to represent the time at which the temperature is 10°F. @ $f(x) = 10$

5. Use function notation to write the equation of a line through each pair of points.

a. $(0, 5)$ and $(1, 12)$ @ $f(x) = 7x + 5$

b. $(1, 5)$ and $(2, 12)$ $f(x) = 5 + 7(x - 1)$

Reason and Apply

6. The function $f(x)$ gives the lake level over the past year, with x measured in days and y, that is, the $f(x)$-values, measured in inches above last year's mean height. ⓗ

a. What is the real-world meaning of $f(60)$?   the level of the lake on the 60th day of the year

b. What is the real-world meaning of $f(x) = -3$?   At a certain time, the level was 3 in. below last year's mean.

c. What is an interpretation of $f(x) = f(150)$?   On certain days the level was the same as it was on day 150.

7. The graph shows part of the function $f(x) = 500(0.80)^x$.

a. What is the dependent variable and what are its units? @ amount of medication in milligrams

b. What is the independent variable and what are its units? @ time in hours

c. What part of the domain is pictured? What is the domain of the function? @ $0 \le x \le 10$; all real numbers x

d. What part of the range is pictured? What is the range of the function? @ $53 < y \le 500, y > 0$

e. What is $f(0)$ for this graph? @ 500

f. Find the value of x when $f(x) = 200$. @ about 4 h

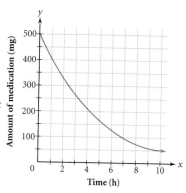

4a. The dependent variable, y, is temperature in degrees Fahrenheit; the independent variable, x, is time in hours.

Exercise 6c Students may find this difficult. Encourage them to think about it, taking it apart. **[Ask]** "What's $f(150)$? What if you rewrite the equation with that number in place of $f(150)$?" [$f(150)$ is the height of the lake on day 150.] "Does function f have two output values for some input value, making it not a function after all?" [No; it has two input values that give the same output value, but there is only one output value for an input value.]

Exercise 7d At $x = 10, y > 53$, but looking at the graph, students might say the range pictured is between 50 and 500. Students may need to think to realize that the range includes all positive numbers. Remind them that x can be negative.

8b. domain: $x \geq 0$, range: $0 < y \leq 650$

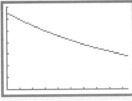

$[0, 9.4, 1, 0, 700, 100]$

8c. The point of intersection is (7.8, 325).

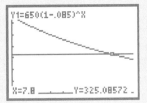

8. **APPLICATION** A bacteria population decreases at the rate of 8.5% per hour. There are 650 bacteria present at the start.

   a. Write an equation that describes this population decay. What domain and range values make sense for this situation? $f(x) = 650(1 - 0.085)^x$

   b. On your calculator, graph the function you wrote in 8a.

   c. The time it takes for the population to decrease to half its original size is called its half-life. Graph the horizontal line that represents half the starting amount of bacteria. Find the point of intersection of this line with the population decay function.

   d. What is the real-world meaning of your answer in 8b? After 7.8 h, there are 325 bacteria present. The half-life is about 7.8 h.

9. Use the function $f(x) = \frac{5}{9}(x - 32)$ to convert temperatures in degrees Fahrenheit (x-values) to temperatures in degrees Celsius ($f(x)$-values), and vice versa.

   a. 72°F @
   $f(72) \approx 22.2°C$

   b. −10°F
   $f(-10) \approx -23.3°C$

   c. 20°C @
   $f(x) = 20; x = 68°F$

   d. −5°C
   $f(x) = -5; x = 23°F$

10. Use the graph of $f(x)$ at right to evaluate each expression. Write your answers as a number sequence. Then think of the numbers 1 through 26 as the letters A through Z to decode a message.

    a. $f(8) + 6$ @ 6

    b. $f(20) + 1$ 21

    c. the sum of two x-values that give $f(x) = 8$ @ 14

    d. $f(0) - 4$ 4

    e. $f(7)$ 1

    f. x when x is an integer and $f(x) = 15$ 25

    g. $f(18) + f(5)$ 19

    h. (the sum of two x-values that give $f(x) = 16) \div 42$ 1

    i. (x when $f(x) = 12) - 8$ 8

    j. $\dfrac{f(25)}{3}$ 5

    k. $f(7) + f(8)$ 1

    l. the largest domain value − the largest range value − 2 4

FUN DAYS AHEAD

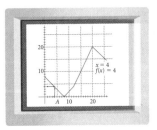
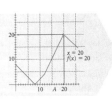

[▶ You can use the **Dynamic Algebra Exploration** at **www.keymath.com/DA** to explore input and output values of the function in Exercise 10. ◀]

keymath.com/DA

11. Many of the commands in your calculator are programmed as functions. Try each command several times with a variety of inputs. Describe the allowable input and corresponding output of each command. If you think the command is a function, describe its domain and range. [▶ 🖳 See **Calculator Note 7B** to access and use these commands. ◀]

    a. the square (x^2) command

    b. the square root $(\sqrt{\ })$ command

    c. the sum of a list command

    d. the random command

12. The graphs of $f(x)$ and $g(x)$ below show two different aspects of an object dropped straight down from the Tower of Pisa.

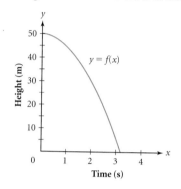

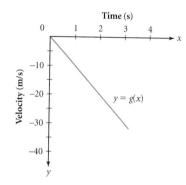

Answer these questions for the graph of each function.

    a. What are the dependent and independent variables? @

    b. What are the domain and range? @

    c. Describe a real-world sequence of events for each graph. @

    d. About how far does the ball drop in the 1st second (from $x = 0$ to $x = 1$)? @

    e. About how far does the ball drop in the 2nd second (from $x = 1$ to $x = 2$)?

    f. At what speed does the object hit the ground? @

▶ Review

6.6 **13.** Write each expression in exponential form without using negative exponents.

    a. $(a^3)^{-3}$ $\dfrac{1}{a^9}$ **b.** $(b^2)^5$ b^{10} **c.** $(a^4b^2)^3$ $a^{12}b^6$ **d.** $(c^2d^3)^{-4}$ $\dfrac{1}{c^8d^{12}}$

4.1 **14.** Find the slope of the line through each pair of points.

    a. $(1, 3)$ and $(-2, 6)$ @ -1 **b.** $(-4, -5)$ and $(7, 0)$ $\dfrac{5}{11}$ **c.** $(-3, 6)$ and $(9, 6)$ 0

3.6 **15.** Solve each equation.

    a. $2x - 5 = 7x + 15$ $x = -4$ **b.** $3(x + 6) = 12 - 5x$ **c.** $\dfrac{7(8 - x)}{4} = x + 3$ $x = 4$
                                                            $x = -0.75$

12b. for $f(x)$: domain $0 \le x \le 3.2$, range $0 \le y \le 50$; for $g(x)$: domain $0 \le x \le 3.2$, range $-31 \le y \le 0$

12c. Answers will vary. For the graph of $f(x)$, the ball is dropped from an initial height of 50 m. It hits the ground after about 3.2 s. At the moment the ball is dropped, its velocity is 0 m/s. For the graph of $g(x)$, the velocity starts at 0 m/s and changes at a constant rate, becoming more and more negative.

12d. In the 1st second, the ball falls about 5 m, from 50 m at $x = 0$ to about 45 m at $x = 1$.

12e. In the 2nd second, the ball falls about 15 m, from about 45 m at $x = 1$ to about 30 m at $x = 2$.

12f. From the graph of $f(x)$, the ball hits the ground after about 3.2 s. From the graph of $g(x)$, at $x \approx 3.2$ s the velocity is about -31 m/s.

MATERIALS

- Pulse Rate Sample Data 2 (T), *optional*
- Calculator Notes 1C, 1F, 7C, 7D
- Sketchpad demonstration Solving Absolute-Value Equations, *optional*
- Fathom demonstration Deviations from the Mean, *optional*
- CBR demonstration Back and Forth, *optional*

TEACHING

The absolute-value function is very useful for converting differences between values into distances, which can't be negative.

One Step

Remind students of how the spread of a data set was measured in Chapter 1: the range, the interquartile range, and the five-number summary. Ask them to generate and plot a set of data (as in Step 1 of the investigation) and to use differences from the mean to devise a method for describing the spread. Some groups will find the mean of differences, but others will see that differences cancel each other and may instead use distances, which are not negative. You might plant ideas in some groups to ensure variety. During Sharing, have several measures presented

Defining the Absolute-Value Function

Cal and Al both live 3.2 miles from school, but in opposite directions. If you assign the number 0 to the school, you can show that Cal and Al live in opposite directions from it by assigning +3.2 to Al's house and −3.2 to Cal's apartment. For both Cal and Al, the distance from school is 3.2 miles.

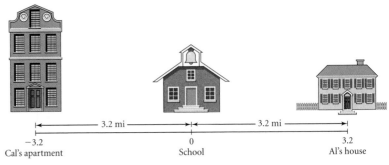

−3.2	0	3.2
Cal's apartment	School	Al's house

Distance is never negative, but distance is often found by subtracting, which sometimes gives a negative result. For this reason, it is useful to have a function that turns opposite numbers into the same positive number. The **absolute value** of a number is its size, or magnitude, regardless of whether the number is positive or negative.

A way to visualize the absolute value of a number is to picture its distance from zero on a number line. A number and its opposite have the same magnitude, or absolute value, because they're the same distance from zero. For example, 3.2 and −3.2 are both 3.2 units from zero, so they both have an absolute value of 3.2.

The notation $|x|$ is used to write absolute-value expressions. So you would write $|3.2| = 3.2$ and $|-3.2| = 3.2$.

EXAMPLE A

Evaluate each expression.

a. $|5| + |-5|$ b. $2|-17| + 3$ c. $\dfrac{|-4|}{|4|}$

d. $|-6| - |-6|$ e. $-|8|$ f. $|0|$

▶ **Solution**

Substitute the magnitude of the number for each absolute value.

a. $|5| + |-5| = 5 + 5 = 10$ b. $2|-17| + 3 = 2(17) + 3 = 37$

c. $\dfrac{|-4|}{|4|} = \dfrac{4}{4} = 1$ d. $|-6| - |-6| = 6 - 6 = 0$

e. $-|8| = -8$ f. $|0| = 0$

Absolute value is useful for answering questions about distance, pulse rates, test scores, and other data values that lie on opposite sides of a central point such as a mean. The difference of a data point from the mean of its data set is called its *deviation from the mean*.

LESSON OBJECTIVES

- Investigate the concept of absolute value
- Construct and interpret graphs of absolute-value functions
- Learn the piecewise definition of the absolute-value function
- Evaluate expressions containing absolute values

NCTM STANDARDS

CONTENT		PROCESS	
	Number		Problem Solving
✔	Algebra	✔	Reasoning
	Geometry	✔	Communication
✔	Measurement		Connections
✔	Data/Probability	✔	Representation

Investigation
Deviations from the Mean

In this investigation you will learn how the absolute-value function tells how much an item of data or a whole set of data deviates from the mean.

Step 1 Collect at least 10 pulse rates from your class. Record the data in a table and enter the numbers into list L1 on your calculator.

Step 2 Find the difference between each data point and the mean of the data in list L1. [▶ 🖳 See **Calculator Note 1C** to review finding the mean of a list. ◀] Record these numbers in a second column of your table and enter them into list L2. What do these numbers represent? *deviations, or positive and negative differences, from the mean*

Step 3 Make a dot plot of the list L1 data and note the distance from each data point to the mean. Record your results in a third column and enter them into list L3. How are these entries different from those in list L2? How are they alike? *These numbers have the same magnitudes, but all are positive.*

Step 4 Next, plot points in the form (L2, L3). [▶ 🖳 See **Calculator Note 1F** to review scatter plots. ◀] What numbers are in the domain and range of the graph?

Step 4 *Answers will vary depending on the data. Any number can be in the domain. Only positive numbers and zero (nonnegative numbers) will be in the range.*

Step 5 Use the trace function on your calculator and use the arrow keys to step through the data points. Which input numbers are unchanged as output numbers? *Positive domain values are unchanged.*

Step 6 Which input numbers are changed, and how? *Negative domain values are changed to their positive opposites.*

Step 7 Does it make sense to connect these points with a continuous graph? Why or why not? *yes, because a data point can be any decimal distance from the mean*

Step 8 How does this graph compare to the graph of Y1 = abs(x) on your calculator? [▶ 🖳 See **Calculator Note 7C** to access the abs command. ◀] *The graph of Y1 = abs(x) passes through all the points on the graph.*

Step 9 Find the mean of the deviations stored in list L2. Compare it to the mean of the distances stored in list L3. Which do you think is a better measure of the spread of the data?

Step 9 *The mean in list L3, the absolute value of the deviations from the mean, is the better measure. Otherwise, negative numbers in the deviation reduce the value of the mean of the deviations to zero. By definition of mean, the mean difference will always be zero.*

Step 10 In your own words, write the rule for the function you graphed in Step 8. What number is output as y when the input, x, is positive or equal to zero? What number is output when x is negative? How can you use operations to change these numbers? *Sample explanation: If x is positive or zero, output the same number as y. If x is negative, output the positive number by multiplying x by −1.*

Despite deviations from each other in appearance, each impersonator clearly portrays Elvis Presley. This photo was taken at Graceland, the late singer's home in Memphis, Tennessee.

Step 10 Students may have difficulty jumping from "just make it positive" or "take away the negation sign" to "output the opposite if the input is negative."

You might have students write a lab report for this investigation.

and critiqued (perhaps differences first), and introduce the idea of absolute value.

▶ EXAMPLE A

This example gives students practice with finding the absolute values of a variety of integers.

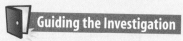

[Language] Remind students that a *difference* is the result of subtraction and may be negative, whereas a *distance* is never negative. A deviation is a difference and might be negative. Model correct usage of both the noun (*deviation*) and the verb.

You can use the Fathom demonstration Deviations from the Mean to replace this investigation.

Step 1 To get enough data, you may choose to have the class do this investigation together. If students work in groups, they must collect data from at least ten people. Or you can assign the data collection as part of the previous night's homework. To save time, you may display the Pulse Rate Sample Data 2 transparency or pass out copies of the data as a worksheet.

Step 2 Some students may need help breaking this down into the two parts: finding the mean and then entering the expression L1 − (*mean*) into list L2. You might want to demonstrate part of this process for a smaller data set. You also might want students to do this and the next two steps by hand before they work with the graphing calculator.

Step 3 Students may need to be reminded of what a dot plot is. See Lesson 1.1. Be sure that the distances recorded are never negative.

Students might think that $-x$ is always a negative number. Remind them that $-x$ is "the opposite of x." Use that term rather than "the negative of x" or "negative x." You might say that the graph of $y = |x|$ is *piecewise linear*.

SHARING IDEAS

After presentation of results, you might mention that a more standard measure of spread is the *standard deviation*. To calculate the standard deviation, squares of the differences are taken (instead of the absolute value) to make positive quantities, the squares are added, the sum is divided by one less than the number of data points, and then the square root is taken. Take Another Look activity 2 at the end of this chapter introduces standard deviation.

[Ask] "Is $\sqrt{x^2}$ the same as $|x|$?" Don't answer the question; it previews Lesson 7.6.

Assessing Progress

Assess students' skill at gathering data systematically, entering calculator lists, and plotting points. Also see how well they remember dot plots.

▶ EXAMPLE B

For part c, to determine which intervals contain the solutions, students might test specific values. For example, $x = 0$ is not a solution, so x-values between -3 and 7 are not solutions.

Ask students to find examples of absolute-value equations with just one solution or no solution. The equation $|x| + 5 = 5$ has only the solution $x = 0$. The equation $|x| + 5 = 4.9$ has no solution, because a solution would imply that $|x|$ could be negative. You might have students solve each of these equations graphically. Students will see absolute-value equations with one or no solution in Exercises 10 and 14. For more practice solving absolute-value

The **absolute-value function** is defined by two rules. The first rule says to output the same number when the input value is positive or zero. The second rule says to output the opposite number when the input value is negative. You express these rules like this:

$$|x| = \begin{cases} x & \text{if } x \geq 0 \\ -x & \text{if } x < 0 \end{cases}$$

For instance, if x is 3, then $|x|$ is also 3. On the other hand, if x is -3, then multiply by -1 to get 3 again. So there are two solutions to the equation $|x| = 3$.

EXAMPLE B

Solve each equation or inequality symbolically.

a. $|x| + 7 = 12$ b. $|x - 2| + 7 = 12$ c. $|x - 2| + 7 \geq 12$

▶ **Solution**

The process for symbolically solving equations and inequalities that involve absolute value is a bit different because there is no function for "undoing" the absolute value—and there is often more than one solution.

a. You might use a graph to estimate your solutions.

$[-8, 8, 1, -1, 14, 1]$

The graphs appear to intersect when $x = 5$ and $x = -5$.

Here's how to solve the equation symbolically:

$\|x\| + 7 = 12$	Original equation.
$\|x\| = 5$	Subtract 7 from both sides of the equation.
$x = 5$ or $x = -5$	The two numbers whose absolute value is 5.

b.
$\|x - 2\| + 7 = 12$	Original equation.
$\|x - 2\| = 5$	Subtract 7 from both sides of the equation.
$x - 2 = 5$ or $x - 2 = -5$	$x - 2$ is equal to either 5 or -5.
$x = 7$ or $x = -3$	Add 2 to both sides of each equation.

c. Again, you might use a graph to help with your solution.

 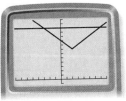

$[-8, 8, 1, -1, 14, 1]$

equations with graphs, you might use the Sketchpad demonstration Solving Absolute-Value Equations.

Another Example

You might want to ask students to generate the graph of (*distance from the east goal line, yard line on the football field*). **[Ask]** "What are the domain and range of this function?" [domain: $0 \leq$ *distance from the east goal line* ≤ 100, range: $0 \leq$ *yard line on the football field* ≤ 50] "How does the graph of this function compare with that of the absolute-value function?"

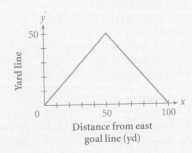

Distance from east goal line (yd)

From part b, you know that $|x - 2| + 7 = 12$ when $x = 7$ or -3. The graph of $y = |x - 2| + 7$ is at or above the graph of $y = 12$ when $x \geq 7$ or $x \leq -3$. So the solution is $x \geq 7$ or $x \leq -3$.

Whatever method you use to solve an absolute-value equation, you always have to be sure that you are finding all possible solutions. In general, an absolute-value equation has two solutions, one solution, or no solution.

If you're not sure how many solutions an equation should have, look at the graph of the situation first and then decide which method you want to use to solve the equation.

EXERCISES

You will need your graphing calculator for Exercises **1**, **3**, and **5**.

▶ Practice Your Skills

1. Find the value of each expression without using a calculator. Check your results with your calculator. [▶ ▣ See **Calculator Note 7C**. ◀]

   a. $|-7|$ 7

   b. $|0.5|$ 0.5

   c. $|-7 + 2|$ 5

   d. $|-7| + |2|$ 9

   e. $-|5|$ -5

   f. $-|-5|$ @ -5

   g. $|-4| \cdot |3|$ 12

   h. $\dfrac{|-6|}{|2|}$ 3

2. Find the x-values that satisfy each statement.

   a. $|x| = 10$ $x = 10$ or $x = -10$

   b. $|x| > 4$ $x > 4$ or $x < -4$

3. Evaluate both sides of each statement to determine whether to replace the box with $=$, $<$, or $>$. Use your calculator to check your answers.

   a. $|5| + |7|$ ☐ $|5 + 7|$ $12 = 12$

   b. $|-5| \cdot |8|$ ☐ $|-40|$ $40 = 40$

   c. $|-12 - 3|$ ☐ $|-12| - |3|$ @ $15 > 9$

   d. $|-2 + 11|$ ☐ $|-2| + |11|$ $9 < 13$

   e. $\dfrac{|36|}{|-9|}$ ☐ $\left|\dfrac{36}{-9}\right|$ $4 = 4$

   f. $|4|^{|-2|}$ ☐ $|4^{-2}|$ $16 > \dfrac{1}{16}$

4. Consider the functions $f(x) = 3x - 5$ and $g(x) = |x - 3|$. Find each value.

   a. $f(5)$ @ 10

   b. $f(-2.5)$ -12.5

   c. $g(-5)$ @ 8

   d. $g(1)$ 2

5. Plot the function $y = |x|$ (or $Y_1 = \text{abs}(x)$). Use a friendly window. [▶ ▣ See **Calculator Note 7D** to learn about friendly windows. ◀] Use the trace feature to evaluate $|2.8|$ and $|-1.5|$.

▶ Reason and Apply

6. Create this graph on graph paper: When $x \geq 0$, graph the line $y = x$. When $x < 0$, graph the line $y = -x$. What single function has this same graph? $y = |x|$, the absolute-value function

7. Solve this system of equations:
$$\begin{cases} y = |x| \\ y = 2.85 \end{cases} \text{@}$$

5. $|2.8| = 2.8, |-1.5| = 1.5$

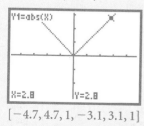

$[-4.7, 4.7, 1, -3.1, 3.1, 1]$

6.

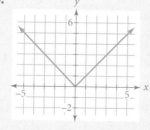

7. The solutions are $(2.85, 2.85)$ and $(-2.85, 2.85)$.

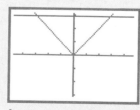

$[-4.7, 4.7, 1, -3.2, 3.2, 1]$

Closing the Lesson

The **absolute-value function** converts differences between values into distances, which can't be negative, by outputting the opposite of negative numbers (and the number itself if it's not negative). It can be used to describe the spread of a data set by converting deviations, or differences, from the mean into distances and then finding the mean of the distances.

BUILDING UNDERSTANDING

Students find absolute values and work with the absolute-value function and its graph.

ASSIGNING HOMEWORK

Essential	**1–8, 11, 13**
Performance assessment	**12, 14**
Portfolio	**13**
Journal	**9, 12**
Group	**10, 11, 13**
Review	**15, 16**

▶ Helping with the Exercises

Exercise 2 Be sure students see both values. They might think of x as positive in the expression $|x|$.

Exercise 3 Some students may need to write down the values they get for both sides of the statement. A good form for writing up 3c, for example, is

$|-12 - 3| = |-15| = 15$
$|-12| - |3| = 12 - 3 = 9$
$15 > 9$

Exercise 6 This is another example of a piecewise linear graph.

Exercise 9 For an extension of this exercise, you might use the CBR demonstration Back and Forth, which has students use a CBR to walk absolute-value graphs.

Exercises 10 and 14 Exercises 10 and 14c and d address absolute-value equations with one or no solution. If students have trouble with 14c and d, have them solve graphically, as shown in Example B.

8. Solve each equation for x.

    a. $|x| = 12$ $x = -12$ or $x = 12$

    b. $10 = |x| + 4$ $x = -6$ or $x = 6$

    c. $10 = 2|x| + 6$ @ $x = 2$ or $x = -2$

    d. $4 = 2(|x| + 2)$ $x = 0$

9. Write specific directions for the walk represented by this calculator graph. Include time, speed, position, and direction. Each mark on the *x*-axis represents 1 second, and each mark on the *y*-axis represents 1 meter.

The walker starts 5 m away from the motion sensor and walks toward the motion sensor at a rate of 1 m/s for 4 s and then walks away from the motion sensor at the same rate.

10. The graph in Example B, part a, shows two solutions for *x*.

    a. Replace $Y_2 = 12$ with a horizontal line that gives exactly one solution for *x*. ⓗ $Y_2 = 7$

    b. Replace $Y_2 = 12$ with a horizontal line that gives no solution for *x*. $Y_2 =$ any number less than 7

11. In 11a–d, identify which function, $f(x)$, $g(x)$, or $h(x)$, is used in each (*input, output*) pair.

    $f(x) = 7 + 4x$ $g(x) = |x| + 6$ $h(x) = 18(1 + 0.5)^x$

    a. (5, 11) @ $g(5) = |5| + 6 = 11$

    b. (1, 27) $h(1) = 18(1.5) = 27$

    c. (−2, 8)
       $g(-2) = |-2| + 6 = 8; h(-2) = 18(1.5)^{-2} = 8$

    d. (3, 19) $f(3) = 7 + 4 \cdot 3 = 19$

12. The solutions to the equation $|x - 4| + 3 = 17$ are −10 and 18.

    a. Explain why the equation has two solutions.

    b. What are the solutions to $|x - 4| + 3 \le 17$? Explain. @

    c. What are the solutions to $|x - 4| + 3 > 17$? Explain.

13. **APPLICATION** The table shows the weights of fish caught by wildlife biologists in Spider Lake and Doll Lake. In which lake did the fish weights vary more from the mean? Explain how you arrived at your answer. ⓗ

Weights of Fish

Spider Lake (lb)	Doll Lake (lb)
1.2	0.9
2.1	1.1
0.8	1.6
1.4	1.9
2.7	2.1
1.0	1.4
0.4	1.4
2.4	2.2

[Data sets: FSHSL, FSHDL]

Find the mean of the absolute values of the deviations for each lake. Spider Lake: 0.675 lb; Doll Lake: 0.375 lb. The fish weights varied more in Spider Lake.

Exercise 13 Some students might reason that the range is greater in the Spider Lake data, so there is more variation from the mean. This approach works for this data set, but challenge students to find a data set where it doesn't work. **[Ask]** "Find a pair of data sets of equal size in which one has a larger range and the other has more deviation from the mean." [An example is {1, 5, 5, 5, 5, 5, 9} and {2, 2, 2, 5, 8, 8, 8}.]

Exercise 12 You may want to present the symbolic method of solving inequalities involving absolute value, as shown here for 12c. Have students verify the solution by testing some values in the original inequality.

$\|x - 4\| + 3 > 17$	Original equation.
$\|x - 4\| > 14$	Subtract 3 from both sides.
$x - 4 > 14$ or $-(x - 4) > 14$	Definition of absolute value.
$x > 18$ or $x - 4 < -14$	Add 4 to both sides; multiply both sides by −1.
$x > 18$ or $x < -10$	Add 4 to both sides.

12a. Answers will vary. Possible answer: The graphs of $y = 17$ and $y = |x - 4| + 3$ intersect twice, at $x = -10$ and $x = 18$.

12b. $-10 \le x \le 18$; when $-10 \le x \le 18$, the graph of $y = |x - 4| + 3$ is at or below the graph of $y = 17$.

12c. $x < -10$ or $x > 18$; when $x < -10$ or $x > 18$, the graph of $y = |x - 4| + 3$ is above the graph of $y = 17$.

14. If possible, solve each equation for x. Check your answer by substituting the value or values into the original equation.

a. $|x + 1| = 7$ ⓐ $x = 6$ or $x = -8$

b. $2|3x - 1| = 4$ $x = 1$ or $x = -\frac{1}{3}$

c. $|2x - 4.2| - 3 = -3$ $x = 2.1$

d. $3|x + 2| = -6$ ⓗ no solution

▶ Review

5.2, 5.3 **15.** Solve each system of equations using the method of your choice. For each, tell which method you chose and why.

a. $\begin{cases} -2x + 3y = 12 \\ 4x - 3y = -21 \end{cases}$ $(-4.5, 1)$

b. $\begin{cases} 5x + y = 12 \\ 2x - 3y = 15 \end{cases}$ $(3, -3)$

5.5 **16.** Solve each inequality and graph the solution on a number line.

a. $-2 < 6x + 8$ ⓐ $-1\frac{2}{3} < x$, or $x > -1\frac{2}{3}$

b. $3(2 - x) + 4 \geq 13$ ⓐ $x \leq -1$

c. $-0.5 \geq -1.5x + 2(x - 4)$

$15 \geq x$, or $x \leq 15$

IMPROVING YOUR REASONING SKILLS

Consider the table of the squares of numbers between 0 and 50 that end in 5.

Number	5	15	25	35	45
Square	25	225	625	1225	2025

Do you notice a pattern that helps you mentally calculate these kinds of square numbers quickly? Can you square 65 in your head? When you think you have discovered the pattern, check your results with a calculator. Then try reversing the process to find the square root of 7225.

Practice this pattern and then race someone using a calculator to see who is quicker at computing a square number ending in 5. Will this pattern work for all numbers ending in 5? Why or why not? Are there numbers that make this pattern too difficult to use?

IMPROVING REASONING SKILLS

To square a positive integer that ends in 5, take the number before the 5 and multiply it by one more than itself. Put 25 on the end of that product. For example, to square 115, find that $(11)(12) = 132$ and append 25 to get 13,225. This procedure will always be successful.

To find the square root of 7225, find consecutive positive integers (8 and 9) whose product is 72. Put a 5 after the smaller of these integers, to get $\sqrt{7225} = 85$. This procedure will be successful whenever the number preceding the 25 is the product of two consecutive integers.

PLANNING

LESSON OUTLINE

One day:

5 min	Introduction
20 min	Investigation
5 min	Sharing
10 min	Example
5 min	Closing
5 min	Exercises

MATERIALS

• Calculator Notes 1F, 7B

TEACHING

The relationship between numbers and their squares (or lengths of geometric squares and their areas) is a function whose graph is a parabola. There's also a function that relates the areas of squares to the lengths of their sides.

Students can use geometry software to construct squares based on a line segment between the origin and a moving point on the *x*-axis. If they plot (*x-coordinate of moving point, area of square*), they can trace points on the graph and then test functions to generate graphs through those points.

One Step

Ask whether there's a function that relates the length of the side of a square to its area. After consideration of congruent squares, students will probably decide that the squaring function qualifies. Ask them to graph the function and describe its shape, using terms from Lesson 7.3. Encourage them to look at its mirror symmetry and to note the point that's the square of only one number. Then ask whether there's a function to go from the square's

Squares, Squaring, and Parabolas

Think of a number between 1 and 10. Multiply it by itself. What number did you get? Try it again with the opposite of your number. Did you get the same result? This result is called the **square** of a number. The process of multiplying a number by itself is called **squaring.** The square of a number *x* is "*x* squared," and you write it as *x* to the power of 2, or x^2. When squaring numbers on your calculator, remember the order of operations. Try entering -3^2 and $(-3)^2$ on your calculator. Which result is the square of -3?

Many real-world situations, such as calculating area of squares and circles, involve squaring. Do you think that the rule for squaring is a function? In order to answer this question, you will graph the relationship between numbers and their squares.

History
● CONNECTION ●

The mathematical process of squaring takes its name from the application of finding a square's area. From the Latin *quadrare*, which means to make square, we also have the word "quadratic" to describe x^2.

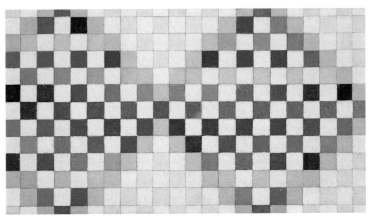

Charmion Von Wiegand, *Advancing Magic Squares*, ca. 1958.
The National Museum of Women in the Arts, Washington, D.C.

Investigation
Graphing a Parabola

In this investigation you will explore connections between any number *x* and its square by graphing the coordinate pairs (x, x^2).

Step 1 Make a table with column headings like the ones shown. Put the numbers -10 through 10 in the first column, and then enter these numbers into list L1 on your calculator.

Number (*x*)	Square (x^2)

Step 2 Without a calculator, find the square of each number and place it in the second column. Check your results by squaring list L1 with the x^2 key. [▶ 🖳 See **Calculator Note 7B.** ◀] Store these numbers in list L2.

Steps 1 and 2 number column: $\{-10, -9, -8, \ldots, -1, 0, 1, 2, \ldots, 8, 9, 10\}$;
square column: $\{100, 81, 64, \ldots, 1, 0, 1, 4, \ldots, 64, 81, 100\}$

area to the length of a side. The idea of the square root function ($\sqrt{}$) should come out. Help students describe its graph.

INTRODUCTION

Remind students that the opposite of a number *x*, written $-x$, is the result of multiplying *x* by -1.

Refer students to the list of the conventional order of operations in Lesson 0.1. Expressions in parentheses are evaluated first, so $(-3)^2 = 9$. But powers are

evaluated before multiplication and therefore before taking opposites. So $-3^2 = -9$.

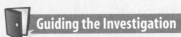

Guiding the Investigation

Step 1 [Ask] "What might the square of a number represent?" At least the idea of the area of a square should come up.

Step 2 As needed, remind students that a negative times a negative is positive.

Step 3 How do the squares of numbers and their opposites compare? What is the relationship between the positive numbers and their squares? Between the negative numbers and their squares? *The output values are nonnegative integers. The square of any number is equal to the square of its opposite.*

Step 4 Choose an appropriate window and plot points in the form (L1, L2). ▶ 🖥 See **Calculator Note 1F** to review scatter plots. ◀ Graph Y1 = x^2 on the same set of axes. What relationship does this graph show?

Step 5 Is the graph of $y = x^2$ the graph of a function? If so, describe the domain and range. If not, explain why not. *yes; domain: all numbers, range: $y \geq 0$*

The graph of $y = x^2$ is called a **parabola.** In later chapters you will learn how to create other parabolas based on variations of this basic equation.

Step 6 The points of the parabola for $y = x^2$ are in what quadrants? *Quadrants I and II and the origin (0, 0)*

Step 7 What makes the point (0, 0) on your curve unique? Where is this point on the parabola?

keymath.com/DA

Step 7 *The output value 0 has only one input value, which is also 0.* **Step 8** *The point (0, 0) is at the bottom of the parabola.*

Step 8 Draw a vertical line through the point (0, 0). How is this line like a mirror?

Step 9 Compare your parabola with the graph of the absolute value function, $y = |x|$. How are they alike and how are they different?

Step 10 Which x- and y-values in your parabola could represent side lengths and areas of squares?

The parabolic shape of the SETI (Search for Extraterrestrial Intelligence) radio telescope at Harvard University in Massachusetts collects radio signals from space. You can learn about the use of parabolas in the real world with the links at **www.keymath.com/DA** .

In the investigation you learned that on the graph of $y = x^2$ two different input values can have the same output. For instance, the square of -3 and the square of 3 are both equal to 9. What happens when you try to "undo" the squaring? If you want to find a number whose square is 9, is 3 the answer? Or -3? Or are both the answer? In the example you will learn about a function that undoes squaring.

EXAMPLE

Find the side of the square whose area is 6.25 square centimeters (cm^2). Use a graph to check your answer.

▶ **Solution**

Let x represent the side of the square in centimeters. To find it, solve the equation $x^2 = 6.25$.

6.25 cm² — x

x

NCTM STANDARDS

CONTENT		PROCESS	
✔	Number	✔	Problem Solving
✔	Algebra	✔	Reasoning
✔	Geometry	✔	Communication
	Measurement	✔	Connections
	Data/Probability	✔	Representation

LESSON OBJECTIVES

- Learn about the squaring and square root functions
- Graph parabolas
- Compare the squaring function with other functions
- Relate the squaring function to finding the area of a square

Step 3 Students may say that the square of every number equals the square of its absolute value.

Step 5 After students determine that the graph is that of a function (by the vertical line test), **[Ask]** "Does it make sense that the relationship between the length of a side of a square and the area of that square is a function?" That is, do all congruent squares have the same area?

Step 7 You might introduce the term *vertex* to describe the turning point.

Step 8 Mirror symmetry, or reflective symmetry, is often called simply *symmetry*.

SHARING IDEAS

Arrange for sharing any unusual ideas. Answers to Steps 9 and 10 might be especially interesting.

As needed, mention the terms *parabola* and its *vertex*. As a follow-up to Step 10, you might ask how to find the length of a square's side given its area. If only one idea arises, ask for more. You can thus get into discussion of the ideas of the example.

Assessing Progress

Check for students' ability to enter and operate on calculator lists, to make scatter plots, and to apply the vertical line test.

▶ ***EXAMPLE***

The ordered pair (x, x^2) here represents (*side of a square, square's area*). Because of the context of the problem, only positive values of x are reasonable. Both the domain and the range of the function are nonnegative numbers.

Students frequently are confused about the difference between the square roots of a number and the square root function (whose output is only the nonnegative square root, often called the

See page 725 for answers to Steps 4, 8, 9, and 10.

principal square root). The square root symbol refers to the output of the square root function. So it's incorrect, for example, to say $\sqrt{4}$ equals -2. If you want to refer to both square roots, you use the notation $\pm\sqrt{\ }$ precisely because $\sqrt{\ }$ alone means only the positive root.

Closing the Lesson

The graph of the **squaring** function is a **parabola.** Although every positive number has two square roots, the **square root function** ($\sqrt{\ }$) gives only the positive square root.

BUILDING UNDERSTANDING

Students practice using squares and square roots.

ASSIGNING HOMEWORK

Essential	1–7, 8, 10
Performance assessment	8, 10, 11
Portfolio	9
Journal	8, 12
Group	9–11
Review	13–15

Helping with the Exercises

Exercise 1 If students are having difficulty, suggest that they draw pictures.

Exercise 2 You may want to introduce the notation $\pm\sqrt{\ }$ here.

Exercise 3 Be sure students explain their answers, especially why there's no real solution to the equation in 3b.

$x^2 = 6.25$ Original equation.

$\sqrt{x^2} = \sqrt{6.25}$ To solve for x, take the **square root** of both sides.

$|x| = 2.5$ See Exercise 7.

$x = 2.5$ or $x = -2.5$ There are two solutions.

The equation has two solutions, but because the side of a square must be positive, the only realistic solution is 2.5 cm.

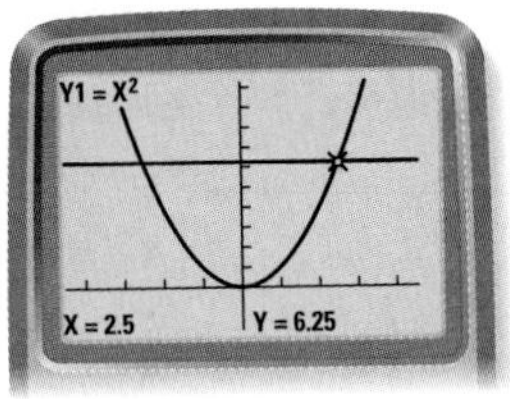

Graph the line $y = 6.25$ and the parabola $y = x^2$. The graphs intersect at two points.

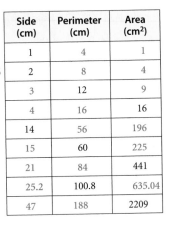

Your calculator will not give the negative solution when you press the square root key. The **square root function,** $f(x) = \sqrt{x}$, gives only the positive solution.

EXERCISES

You will need your graphing calculator for Exercises **4, 5,** and **10.**

Practice Your Skills

1. Complete the table by filling in the missing values for the side, perimeter, and area of each square.

Side (cm)	Perimeter (cm)	Area (cm²)
1	4	1
2	8	4
3	12	9
4	16	16
14	56	196
15	60	225
21	84	441
25.2	100.8	635.04
47	188	2209

2. Solve each equation for x.

a. $|x| = 6$ @ $x = \pm 6$

b. $x^2 = 36$ @ $x = \pm 6$

c. $|x| = 3.8$ $x = \pm 3.8$

d. $x^2 = 14.44$ $x = \pm 3.8$

3. Solve each equation, if possible.

a. $4.7 = |x| - 2.8$ $x = 7.5$ or $x = -7.5$

b. $-41 = x^2 - 28$ @ no real solution

c. $11 = x^2 - 14$ $x = 5$ or $x = -5$

4. Solve each equation for x. Use a calculator graph to check your answers.

a. $|x - 2| = 4$ @

b. $(x - 2)^2 = 16$ @

c. $|x + 3| = 7$

d. $(x + 3)^2 = 49$

Reason and Apply

5. For what values of x is $|x| \geq x^2$? To check your answer, graph $Y_1 = |x|$ and $Y_2 = x^2$ on the same set of axes. $-1 \leq x \leq 1$. Good graphing window answers will vary. One possibility is a TI-83 friendly window like $[-2.35, 2.35, 1, 0, 3.1, 1]$.

6. For what values of y does the equation $y = x^2$ have

a. No real solutions? @ $y < 0$

b. Only one solution? $y = 0$

c. Two solutions? $y > 0$

4a. $x = 6$ or $x = -2$

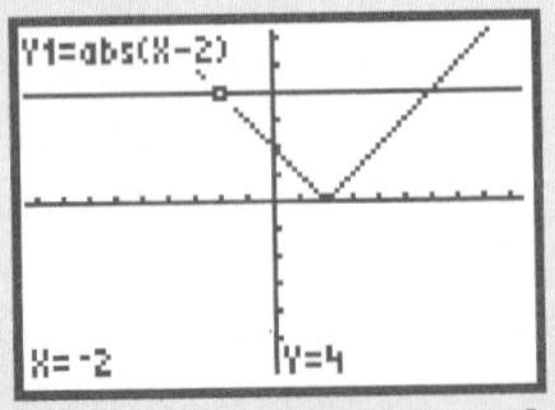

$[-9.4, 9.4, 1, -6.2, 6.2, 1]$

4b. $x = 6$ or $x = -2$

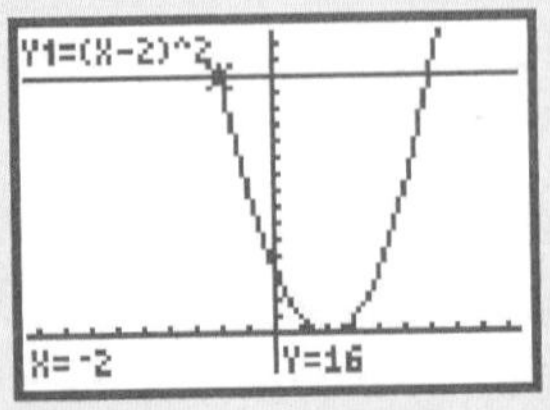

$[-9.4, 9.4, 1, -2.2, 18.6, 1]$

4c. $x = 4$ or $x = -10$

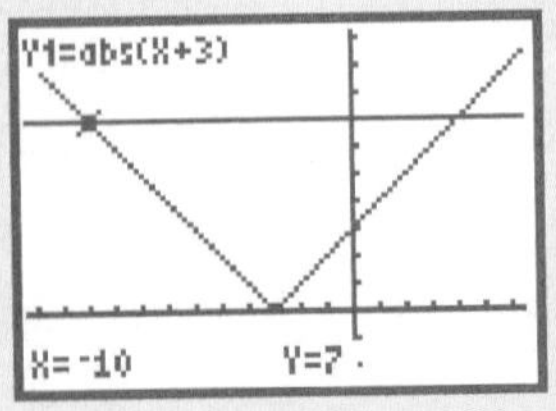

$[-12.4, 6.4, 1, -2.2, 10.2, 1]$

4d. $x = 4$ or $x = -10$

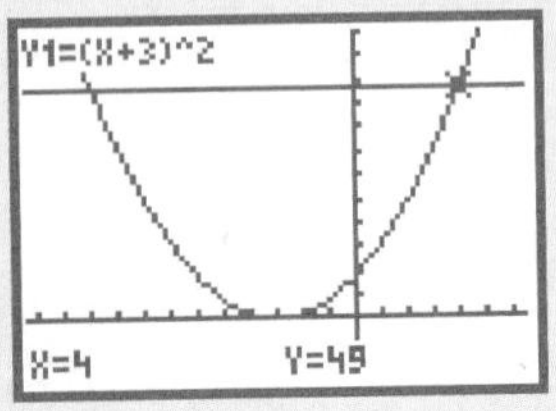

$[-12.4, 6.4, 1, -11, 60, 5]$

7. Graph the function $f(x) = \sqrt{x^2}$. What other equation produces the same graph? *@* $y = |x|$

8. Look at the table of squares in the Investigation Graphing a Parabola. Use values from this table to explain why $y = x^2$ is nonlinear. Answers will vary. One explanation is that the slope between $x = 0$ and $x = 1$ is 1, but the slope from $x = 1$ to $x = 2$ is 3. The rate of change varies.

9. *Mini-Investigation* Find the sum of each set of numbers in 9a–c.

a. the first five odd positive integers $1 + 3 + 5 + 7 + 9 = 25$, or 5^2

b. the first 15 odd positive integers $1 + 3 + 5 + 7 + 9 + \cdots + 29 = 225$, or 15^2

c. the first n odd positive integers *@* The sum of the first n positive odd integers is n^2.

d. Use the diagram to explain the connection among the sum of odd integers, square numbers, and these square figures.

10. Write an equation for the function represented in each table. Use your calculator to check your answers.

a.

x	−3	−1	0	1	4	6
y	14	10	8	6	0	−4

b.

x	−3	−1	0	1	4	6
y	9	1	0	1	16	36

c.

x	−3	−1	0	1	4	6
y	3	1	0	1	4	6

10a. $y = 8 - 2x$

10b. $y = x^2$

10c. $y = |x|$

11. This 4-by-4 grid contains squares of different sizes.

a. How many of each size square are there? Include overlapping squares. *@*

b. How many total squares would a 3-by-3 grid contain? A 2-by-2 grid? A 1-by-1 grid?

c. Find a pattern to determine how many squares an n-by-n grid contains. Use your pattern to predict the number of squares in a 5-by-5 grid.

12. Explain why the equation $x^2 = -4$ has no solutions. *ⓗ*

► Review

6.2 **13.** The table shows exponential data.

a. What equation in the form $y = ab^x$ can you use to model the data in the table? *@* $y = 400(0.75)^x$

b. Use your equation to find the missing values.

x	y
0	400
4	126.5625
3	168.75
1	300
≈ -3.19	1000

12. Answers will vary. It's impossible for x^2 to be negative. If x is a negative number, x^2 is a negative times a negative, which is positive. If x is a positive number, x^2 is a positive times a positive, which is also positive. If $x = 0$, then $x^2 = 0$. So x^2 must be positive or zero, no matter what x is.

Exercise 5 Some students may need help interpreting inequality on the graph.

Exercise 6 You may want to discuss the difference between real and imaginary numbers. Imaginary numbers are square roots of negative numbers. They were originally investigated because they were useful in finding solutions to cubic equations (equations that involve x^3).

9d. Each larger square is created by adding a border of small squares on two sides. The number of small squares added on each time is the next odd number. The resulting figure is the next square number.

Exercise 10 Students might find it helpful to graph the data and to think of input and output values. 10c is a good example of a case that might prove difficult because of its simplicity.

Exercise 11 Don't expect students to find a closed-form expression for the sum of squares of positive integers up to n. That formula is $\dfrac{n(n + 1)(2n + 1)}{6}$.

11a. sixteen 1-by-1 squares, nine 2-by-2 squares, four 3-by-3 squares, and one 4-by-4 square

11b. A 3-by-3 grid has fourteen squares: nine 1-by-1 squares, four 2-by-2 squares, and one 3-by-3 square. A 2-by-2 grid has five squares: four 1-by-1 squares and one 2-by-2 square. A 1-by-1 grid has one 1-by-1 square.

11c. Answers will vary. One possible response: There are n^2 1-by-1 squares, $(n - 1)^2$ 2-by-2 squares, $(n - 2)^2$ 3-by-3 squares, and so on. There would be 55 squares in a 5-by-5 grid.

15.

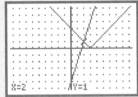

$[-9.4, 9.4, 1, -6.2, 6.2, 1]$

Answers will vary. The graphs tell us that there is exactly one solution and that the x-value that makes the equation true is $x = 2$.

6.6 **14.** Use properties of exponents to find an equivalent expression in the form ax^n, if possible. Use positive exponents.

a. $24x^6 \cdot 2x^3$ @ $48x^9$

b. $(-15x^4)(-2x^4)$ $30x^8$

c. $\dfrac{72x^{11}}{3x^2}$ $24x^9$

d. $4x^2(2.5x^4)^3$ $62.5x^{14}$

e. $\dfrac{15x^5}{-6x^2}$ $-2.5x^3$

f. $(-3x^3)(4x^4)^2$ $-48x^{11}$

g. $\dfrac{42x^{-6}y^2}{7y^{-4}}$ $\dfrac{6y^6}{x^6}$

h. $3(5xy^2)^3$ $375x^3y^6$

7.5 **15.** Graph the functions $f(x) = 3x - 5$ and $g(x) = |x - 3|$. What do the two graphs tell you about the equation $3x - 5 = |x - 3|$?

IMPROVING YOUR **VISUAL THINKING** SKILLS

Square numbers are so named because they result from the geometric application of finding the area of a square. A square of side length 3 has an area equal to 3^2, or 9. You can represent 9, and other *perfect square* numbers, with diagrams like this:

1   2   3   4   5

What numbers result when you represent them with cubes instead of squares? Use sugar cubes to make these shapes:

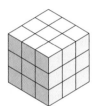
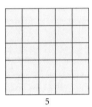

How many sugar cubes does it take to make each figure? What is the relationship between the side length (measured in sugar cubes) and the total number of cubes needed for each figure? If you double the side length of a cubic figure, how many times larger is its resulting volume? If you triple the side length?

IMPROVING **VISUAL THINKING** SKILLS

The cubes consist of 1, 8, and 27 sugar cubes. These are their volumes, measured in cubic units. The volume of a cube of length n is $n \cdot n \cdot n$, which is n^3 or n *cubed*.

The last two questions lead to a profound result, so let students play with them. If the length of one side is doubled, the volume is multiplied by 8, which is 2^3. If the length of a side is tripled, the volume is multiplied by 27, which is 3^3. In general, if the length is multiplied by k, the volume is multiplied by k^3. Even more generally, if all lengths in an n-dimensional figure are multiplied by k, the "size" (either length, area, volume, or the equivalent for n dimensions) is multiplied by k^n.

CHAPTER
7
REVIEW

In this chapter you used functions to describe real-world relationships. You began by designing and decoding secret messages. You discovered that the easiest way to code is to use a **function**—it codes each input into a single output.

You investigated functions represented by rules, equations, tables, and graphs. You learned to tell whether a relationship is a function by applying the **vertical line test.** On a graph, this means that no vertical line can intersect the graph of a function at more than one point.

You learned how to use function notation $f(x)$ and some new vocabulary—**independent variable, dependent variable, domain,** and **range.** You learned when a function is **increasing** or **decreasing, linear** or **nonlinear,** and the difference between a **discrete** and **continuous** graph. You explored the **absolute-value function,** $f(x) = |x|$, and the **squaring function,** $f(x) = x^2$, and their graphs. You learned that these two functions can have zero, one, or two solutions. You learned how to graph a **parabola.** You also used the **square root function** to undo the squaring function and get only the positive square root.

EXERCISES

You will need your graphing calculator for Exercises **10, 13, 19,** and **20.**

▶ @ Answers are provided for all exercises in this set.

1. Answer each question for the graph of $f(x)$.

   a. What is the domain of the function? $-2 \le x \le 4$

   b. What is the range of the function? $1 \le f(x) \le 3$

   c. What is $f(3)$? 1

   d. For what values of x does $f(x) = 1$?

     -1 and 3

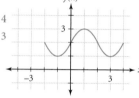

2. Which of these tables of x- and y-values represent functions? Explain your answers.

a.

x	y
0	5
1	7
3	10
7	9
5	7
4	5
2	8

b.

x	y
3	7
4	9
8	4
3	5
9	3
11	9
7	6

c.

x	y
2	8
3	11
5	12
7	3
9	5
8	7
4	11

ASSIGNING HOMEWORK

You might let students work on the even-numbered exercises in groups in class and do the other exercises individually as homework. Groups could share and discuss their answers to Exercise 10. Assign the Mixed Review before giving a test that covers Chapters 4–7.

2a. A function; each x-value corresponds to only one y-value.

2b. Not a function; the input $x = 3$ has two different output values, 5 and 7.

2c. A function; each x-value corresponds to only one y-value.

LESSON OUTLINE

One day:

10 min	Introduction
15 min	Exercises
10 min	Checking work
15 min	Student self-assessment

MATERIALS

- Sketchpad demonstration Functions, *optional*

Ask students to critique this coding scheme: Translate each letter to an integer 1 through 26, square it, subtract 26 repeatedly until you get a number between 1 and 26, and then translate back to a letter. (If there's time, students might make a coding grid.) Because every input value has a single output value, the method involves a function. The method would lead to difficulties in decoding, however, because more than one input value is taken to the same output value. In fact, the integers n and $26 - n$ will be paired with the same output, just as integers and their opposites have the same square. **[Ask]** "If n and $26 - n$ are opposites, does the absolute value of a number equal the positive square root of the number squared, as it does without wrapping?" [It does if "positive" integers are defined to be integers from 1 to 13 and if integers from 14 to 26 are considered their opposites.]

The Sketchpad demonstration Functions reviews function notation and linear, quadratic, square root, and absolute-value functions using dynagraphs.

▶ Helping with the Exercises

3. The graph is a horizontal line segment at 0.5 m/s.

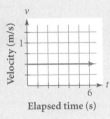

Elapsed time (s)

Exercise 4 Archimedes (ca. 287–212 B.C.E.), a Greek philosopher and inventor, wrote about volume, pi, and spirals.

René Descartes (1596–1650), a French mathematician and philosopher, invented the coordinate system.

Hypatia (ca. 370–415 C.E.) was a Greek philosopher and mathematician. She was the head of the Platonist school at Alexandria.

Euclid (ca. 300 B.C.E.) was a Greek geometer whose *Elements* was the chief source of geometric reasoning until the 19th century.

4d. This code shifts 20 spaces forward, or 6 spaces back, in the alphabet.

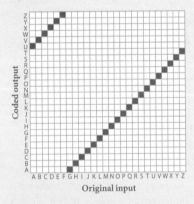

Original input

Exercise 5 Students may say that the three girls reach the same point after 20 s, but the graph shows only that they reach the same velocity. A good question is whether they do in fact arrive at the same point. In fact, Caitlin's average velocity is less than Bea's, which is less than Abby's, so they won't be at the same point. Actually, the distances traveled are given by the areas between the curves and the

3. The graph at right shows the relationship between time in seconds and an object's distance from a motion sensor in meters. Sketch a graph to represent the velocity of this object, dependent on time *t*.

Elapsed time (s)

4. In a letter-shift code, ARCHIMEDES codes into ULWBCGYXYM. Use this information to determine the names of famous mathematicians in 4a–c.

   a. XYMWULNYM DESCARTES

   b. BSJUNCU HYPATIA

   c. YOWFCX EUCLID

   d. Create a grid and state a rule for this code.

5. The graph below shows the velocities of three girls inline skating over a given time interval. Assume that they start at the same place at the same time.

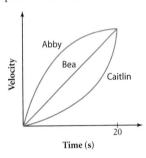

Time (s)

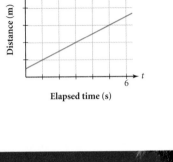

   a. Create a story about these three girls that explains the graph.

   b. Are Caitlin and Bea ever in front of Abby? Explain.

6. **APPLICATION** A recent catalog price for tennis balls was $4.25 for a can with three balls. The shipping charge per order was $1.00.

   a. Write an equation that you can use to project the costs for ordering different numbers of cans. $y = 4.25x + 1.00$

   b. Draw a graph showing this relationship.

   c. How does raising the shipping charge by 50¢ affect the graph? It shifts the graph up 0.50 unit on the *y*-axis.

   d. What equation models the cost situation in 6c?
$$y = 4.25x + 1.50$$

7. Draw graphs that fit these descriptions:

   a. a function that has a domain of $-5 \leq x \leq 1$, a range of $-4 \leq y \leq 4$, and $f(-2) = 1$

   b. a relationship that is not a function and that has inputs on the interval $-6 \leq x \leq 4$ and outputs on the interval $0 \leq y \leq 5$
Answers will vary. The graph will fail the vertical line test.

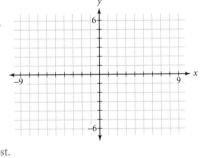

horizontal axis (in *velocity · time* units, which are distance units), so they differ considerably.

5a. Stories will vary. At the 20 s mark, each girl is moving at the same velocity. Bea's velocity increases steadily in a linear fashion. Caitlin's velocity increases very slowly at first and then becomes faster and faster. Abby's velocity increases very quickly at first and then increases at a slower rate.

5b. No; because Abby starts out moving faster than both Bea and Caitlin, even when she slows down to their speed she stays ahead.

6b.

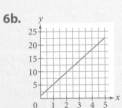

7a. Answers will vary. The graph will pass the vertical line test.

8. Cody's code multiplies each letter's position by 2. Complete a table like the one shown. If a number is greater than 26, subtract 26 from it so that it represents a letter of the alphabet. Is the code a function? Is the rule for decoding a function?

A	B	C	D	E
1	2	3	4	5
2	4	6		

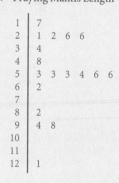

9. Consider the function $f(x) = |x|$.
   a. What is $f(-3)$? $f(-3) = |-3| = 3$
   b. What is $f(2)$? $f(2) = |2| = 2$
   c. For what x-value(s) does $f(x) = 10$? 10 and −10

10. Use your calculator for 10a–c.
   a. Graph the functions $y = \sqrt{x}$ and $y = x^2$ in a friendly window.
   b. Compare the graphs. How are they similar? How are they different?
   c. Explain why the graph of $y = \sqrt{x}$ has only one "branch."
   d. Sketch the graph of $y^2 = x$. Is this the graph of a function? Explain why or why not.

MIXED REVIEW

5.3
11. Three sisters went shopping for T-shirts and sweatshirts at an outlet store. They paid $6 for each T-shirt and $10 for each sweatshirt. They bought 12 shirts in all and the total cost was $88.
   a. Define variables and write a system of equations to represent this situation.
   b. Solve the system symbolically. How many shirts of each kind did the sisters buy? 8 T-shirts and 4 sweatshirts

1.4 **12.** **APPLICATION** Mr. Lee's science class received a collection of praying mantises from a local entomologist. The students measured the mantises' lengths in centimeters.

Praying Mantis Lengths (cm)

5.6, 9.4, 1.7, 3.4, 5.3, 6.2, 8.2, 2.1, 5.3, 2.6, 5.6, 2.6, 5.4, 12.1, 5.3, 2.2, 4.8, 9.8

[Data set: **PMLTH**]

   a. Organize the data in a stem plot.
   b. What is the range of the data? 10.4 cm
   c. What are the measures of center? Which do you think best represents the data? Explain your thinking.
   Mean: approximately 5.4 cm; median: 5.3 cm; mode: 5.3 cm. Choice and explanations will vary.

Praying mantises use their front legs to capture other insects.

8. The domain of the 26 letters is coded to a range of the 13 even-number-positioned letters—{B, D, F, . . . , Z}. The code is a function because every original letter is coded to a unique single letter. The rule for decoding is not a function because there are two choices for every letter in the coded message. For example, the letter B could be decoded to either A or N.

Exercise 10 Students may think that the graph in 10d is like that of 10c. Point out that 10d includes negative values of y. In this case, x is a function of y, but y is not a function of x. To do 10d on a calculator, enter $\sqrt{x}$ into Y1 and $-\sqrt{x}$ into Y2.

Exercises 11–21 These exercises can be used to review for a multi-unit exam.

11a. Let t be the number of T-shirts, and let s be the number of sweatshirts.
$t + s = 12$
$6t + 10s = 88$

Exercise 12 [Language] An *entomologist* is one who studies or collects insects.

12a. Praying Mantis Length

1	7
2	1 2 6 6
3	4
4	8
5	3 3 3 4 6 6
6	2
7	
8	2
9	4 8
10	
11	
12	1

Key

1 | 7 means 1.7 cm

10a.

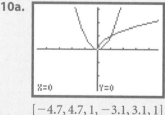

X=0   Y=0

$[-4.7, 4.7, 1, -3.1, 3.1, 1]$

10b. The graph of $y = \sqrt{x}$ looks like half of the graph of $y = x^2$ lying on its side.

10c. The graph of $y = \sqrt{x}$ has only one branch because it gives only positive solutions.

10d. This equation does not represent a function, because a given input can have two different outputs. For example, if $x = 4$, then $y = 2$ or $y = -2$.

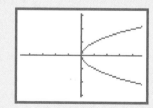

13a. Start with 21, then apply the rule Ans − 4; 10th term = −15.

13b. Start with −5, then apply the rule Ans · (−3); 10th term = 98,415.

13c. Start with 2, then apply the rule Ans + 7; 10th term = 65.

Exercise 14b If students multiply the second equation by 1.5, they will see that the two equations are equivalent.

15a. $y = 1.6x$, where x is a measurement in miles and y is a measurement in kilometers

16. right triangle

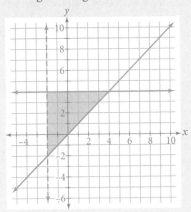

3.1   **13.** Write a recursive routine to generate each sequence. Then use your routine to find the 10th term of the sequence.

     a. 21, 17, 13, 9, . . .   **b.** −5, 15, −45, 135, . . .   **c.** 2, 9, 16, 23, . . .

5.2,   **14.** Solve each system of equations.
5.3

     a. $\begin{cases} y = 6x - 3 \\ y = 1.2x + 6 \end{cases}$ $\begin{array}{l} x = 1.875, \\ y = 8.25 \end{array}$ **b.** $\begin{cases} 3x - 1.5y = -12.3 \\ 2x - y = -8.2 \end{cases}$ infinitely many solutions

2.4   **15.** Angie has some guests visiting from Italy, and they are planning to drive from her house to Washington, D.C. Angie wants her friends to understand how far they will need to drive.

     a. Write a direct variation equation to convert miles to kilometers (1 mi ≈ 1.6 km).

     b. Angie's house is about 250 miles from Washington, D.C. How many kilometers will her friends have to drive?   400 km

     c. The hotel her friends are staying at says it is 2 miles from the Washington Monument. How far is that in kilometers?   3.2 km

     d. The Washington Monument is taller than 555 feet. How tall is this in meters (1 m ≈ 3.3 ft)?   approximately 168 m

The Washington Monument was built between 1848 and 1884. It was the tallest structure in the world until the Eiffel Tower was built in 1889.

5.7   **16.** Sketch a graph showing these three inequalities on the same coordinate axes. What shape do you get?

$$\begin{cases} x > -2 \\ y \geq x \\ y \leq 4 \end{cases}$$

3.6   **17.** Solve each equation using the method of your choice. Then use a different method to verify your answer.

     a. $-2(4 - d) + 3 = -13$ −4   **b.** $42 - 7(d - 8) = 7$ 13

     c. $0.5(d - 2) - 3 = -10$ −12   **d.** $3d - 5 + d = 0.5d + 2$ 2

4.1   **18.** Find the slope and y-intercept of the line through each pair of points.

     a. $(3, 2), (1, -3)$ **b.** $(-1, 4), (-1, 8)$ **c.** $(-11, 3), (-9, 2)$

6.6   **19.** **APPLICATION** When Anton started his career as an assistant manager of a tutoring center, his salary was $18,500 per year. He was told that he would get a 2.25% raise every year. Anton has now been with the company for 3 years.

     a. Find Anton's current salary in whole dollars. $19,777

     b. What will Anton's salary be in another 5 years? $22,104

     c. Anton's coworker Kobra has been with the company for 10 years. She can't remember her starting salary but knows that she got the same 2.25% raise for each of her first 8 years and then got a 3.5% raise during each of the last 2 years. She now makes $23,039. Write and solve an equation to find Kobra's starting salary.

        $y = 23{,}039(1 + 0.0225)^{-8}(1 + 0.035)^{-2}$; approximately $18,000

18a. slope: $\frac{5}{2}$; y-intercept: $-\frac{11}{2}$

18b. slope: undefined; y-intercept: none

18c. slope: $-\frac{1}{2}$; y-intercept: $-\frac{5}{2}$

4.7 **20.** Does someone use the same amount of soap each day when he or she showers? Rex Boggs of Glenmore State High School in Queensland, Australia, decided to find out. He collected data for three weeks.

a. Make a scatter plot and find a linear equation that fits the data. Use any method that you prefer.

b. Write your equation in intercept form. $y = 124.5 - 5.7x$

c. Using your equation, after how many days would Rex's soap weigh 34 grams? approximately 16 days

d. How would your equation in 20b change if Rex starts with a family-size soap bar that weighs 200 grams? Write an equation for a family-size soap bar. (Assume the soap is used at the same rate.)

e. If Rex starts with a family-size soap bar, how much will it weigh after 20 days have elapsed? 86 g

Soap Usage

Number of days elapsed	Weight of bar of soap (grams)
0	124
1	121
4	103
5	96
6	90
7	84
8	78
9	71
11	58
12	50
17	27
19	16
20	12
21	8
22	6

(Rex Boggs, *www.statsci.org/data/oz/soap*) [Data sets: SPDYS, SPWGT]

7.3 **21.** For each relationship, identify the independent and dependent variables. Then describe each relationship as *increasing* or *decreasing*, and *continuous* or *discrete*. Sketch a graph, with the independent variable on the horizontal axis and the dependent variable on the vertical axis.

a. the mass of a spherical lollipop and the number of times it has been licked

b. the number of scoops in an ice cream cone and the cost of the cone

c. the distance a rubber band will fly and the amount you stretch it before you release it

d. the number of coins you flip and the number of heads

21d. independent: number of coins flipped; dependent: number of heads; increasing, discrete

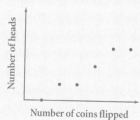

20. Answers will vary depending on the method used. The following possible answers used the Q-point method and a decimal approximation of the slope.

20a. $y = 96 - 5.7(x - 5)$

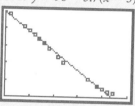

[0, 25, 5, 0, 125, 25]

20d. The *y*-intercept would become 200; $y = 200 - 5.7x$.

21a. independent: number of licks; dependent: mass; decreasing, discrete

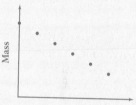

21b. independent: number of scoops; dependent: cost; increasing, discrete

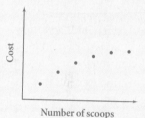

21c. independent: amount of stretch; dependent: flying distance; increasing, continuous

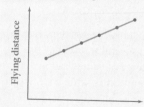

Take Another Look

1. The inverse of the equation that converts temperatures from degrees Celsius to degrees Fahrenheit is a function. Encourage exploration of several functions, both algebraically and with graphs. A function has an inverse that's a function if its graph passes the horizontal line test: No horizontal line crosses the graph at more than one point. Equivalently, some students may say that the graph "doesn't turn around." That is, it's either always increasing or always decreasing. Students should also realize that the inverse of a constant function or a step function will not be a function.

Often a function is restricted to a domain over which it's only increasing or decreasing in order to have an inverse function. For example, when $y = x^2$ is restricted to the domain of positive values of x, it has the inverse function $y = \sqrt{x}$.

2. You may want to skip this activity unless you need to cover standard deviation. *Discovering Advanced Algebra* covers standard deviation in detail.

For 2b, remind students that adding the squares and then finding the square root will not give the same result as adding the absolute values of the original numbers. **[Ask]** "Does $3 + 4$ equal $\sqrt{3^2 + 4^2}$?" [No, 7 does not equal $\sqrt{25}$, or 5.]

Help students express their results for 2c in several ways. They might give a range of values, saying that most community-wide trash bag weights will fall within 5.5 lb of the mean or that most trash bag weights will fall between 7 lb and 18 lb.

TAKE ANOTHER LOOK

1. You learned to solve linear equations by "undoing" the order of operations in them. You learned to code and decode secret messages. Both are examples of reversing the order of a process, or finding an **inverse.**

How do you find the inverse of a function? The equation $y = \frac{9}{5}x + 32$ converts temperatures from x in degrees Celsius to y in degrees Fahrenheit.

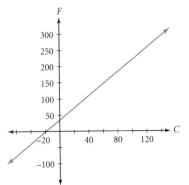

If you want to write an equation that converts temperature from degrees Fahrenheit to degrees Celsius, you can swap the two variables in the equation and solve for y.

$$y = \frac{9}{5}x + 32 \qquad \text{Original equation.}$$

$$x = \frac{9}{5}y + 32 \qquad \text{Interchange } x \text{ and } y.$$

$$x - 32 = \frac{9}{5}y \qquad \text{Subtract 32 from both sides.}$$

$$5(x - 32) = 9y \qquad \text{Multiply both sides by 5.}$$

$$\frac{5}{9}(x - 32) = y \qquad \text{Divide both sides by 9.}$$

$$y = \frac{5}{9}(x - 32) \qquad \text{Isolate } y \text{ on the left side.}$$

Note that after the switch, x represents degrees in Fahrenheit and y represents degrees in Celsius. The domain of the inverse is the range of the original function, and vice versa. Is this a function? Does each input in °F give exactly one output in °C?

How can you tell from the graph of a function whether it has an inverse that's a function? Does every linear function in the form $y = a + bx$ have an inverse function? Does the squaring function or the absolute-value function have an inverse function? Look for patterns in the graphs of these functions and others. Can you restrict the values on the domain of a function so that the inverse is a function?

Learn more about inverse functions with the links at **www.keymath.com/DA** .

2. In the investigation in Lesson 7.5, you learned one way to measure spread, by averaging the absolute values of the differences between each data value and the mean. The absolute values gave you positive numbers for distance from data point to mean. In this activity, you'll learn another way to measure spread.

The members of the Math Club did a highway trash pickup. Each student cleaned 0.2 mile. Then they weighed the trash bags, and rounded to the nearest pound.

Weight (lb): 15, 7, 11, 25, 4, 11, 18, 9, 13, 13, 16, 9 [Data set: TRASH]

a. Enter the trash bag weights into list L₁ on your calculator and calculate the mean. In list L₂, calculate the deviations by subtracting the mean from the values in the first list. Calculate the mean absolute deviation, as you did in the Lesson 7.5 investigation. What does this measure tell you about the data?

2a. The mean is about 12.6 and the mean absolute deviation is about 4.1. The mean absolute deviation indicates that the data values are generally spread within about 4.1 lb of 12.6 lb, so they are mostly between 8.5 and 16.7 lb.

b. Now you'll calculate another measure of spread, called the **standard deviation.** As you saw in Lesson 7.6, another method of ensuring that numbers are positive is to square them. In list L_3, square the deviations. Then find the mean of list L_3. Finally, to undo the effects of squaring, take the square root. Is this standard deviation close to the mean absolute deviation?

c. In 2b, you calculated the mean and standard deviation for the Math Club's trash bag weights. Suppose you want to use this information to predict the weights of trash bags collected community-wide. Statisticians have found that the mean of the community-wide data will be about the same as the sample mean, but the standard deviation calculated from a sample will be slightly smaller than that of the community. To deal with that, instead of finding the mean of the squares (in which you sum the squares and divide by the number of data points, in this case, 12), you sum the squares and divide by one less than the number of data points (in this case, 11). Repeat the calculation from 2b with this modification. What can you predict about community-wide trash bag weights?

Assessing What You've Learned

UPDATE YOUR PORTFOLIO Choose your best explanation of a graph of a real-world situation from this chapter to add to your portfolio. Identify the independent and dependent variables of the situation. Describe all possible domain and range values as shown in the graph. Discuss whether the graph should be continuous or discrete.

WRITE IN YOUR JOURNAL Add to your journal by answering one of these prompts:
▶ You have seen many forms of equations—direct and indirect variation, linear relationships, and exponential modeling. Do you think all equations represent functions? Can you represent all functions as equations?
▶ Is function notation, $f(x)$, helpful to you or do you find it challenging? When do parentheses ( ) mean multiplication, and when do they show the independent variable in function notation?

ORGANIZE YOUR NOTEBOOK Update your notebook with an example, investigation, or exercise that best demonstrates the concept of a function. Also, add one problem that illustrates the absolute-value function and one that shows the squaring function.

GIVE A PRESENTATION Create your own code for making secret messages. Explain the rule for your code with a grid or an equation or both. Is your code a function? Is it simple to code? Is it hard to decode? How does the concept of functions apply to code making and code breaking?

2b. The standard deviation is about 5.3 lb. This is somewhat close to the mean absolute deviation.

2c. The community's standard deviation is about 5.5 lb. The community's trash bags will have a mean weight of about 12.6 lb, and will mostly be spread within about 5.5 lb of the mean. That is, most will weigh between 7.1 lb and 18.1 lb.

ASSESSING

If you have given the quizzes for this chapter, you may decide to skip the Chapter Test and instead have students turn in a portfolio. Or use the Assessment Resources or the test generator to create a written assessment.

FACILITATING SELF-ASSESSMENT

To help students complete the portfolio described in Assessing What You've Learned, suggest that they consider for evaluation their work on Lesson 7.1, Exercise 7 or 8; Lesson 7.2, Exercise 10; Lesson 7.3, Exercise 13; Lesson 7.4, Exercise 7; Lesson 7.5, Exercise 13; and Lesson 7.6, Exercise 9.

CHAPTER 8

Transformations

Overview

In this chapter students consider transformations of functions, building valuable skills for the study of quadratic functions in Chapter 9. Students study vertical and horizontal translations in **Lessons 8.1** and **8.2** by changing coordinates of polygons in the plane and then by modifying equations. They learn about reflections in **Lesson 8.3** and vertical stretches and shrinks in **Lesson 8.4**. In **Lesson 8.5**, students perform experiments to generate data that can be modeled by transformed linear and exponential functions. In **Lesson 8.6**, students study rational functions by transforming the basic function $y = \frac{1}{x}$. **Lesson 8.7** concludes the chapter with the study of how matrices can be used to represent transformations, including some rotations, of geometric figures.

The Mathematics

Transformations

This chapter includes the study of four ways of transforming geometric figures and equations: translating (shifting), reflecting (across a line), stretching and shrinking, and, briefly, rotating about the origin. Many students are intrigued by the application of transformations to computer graphics, so you might tie each lesson to that topic.

The chapter considers transformations from two points of view. Students first consider moving polygons by working with the coordinates of their vertices. But nonpolygonal figures must be treated differently. Students study those that can be represented by equations to see the effects of various kinds of transformations on those equations.

Students often don't understand the relationship between the two points of view and resort to memorization. For example, they may not understand why you accomplish the same horizontal translation by *adding* to the x-coordinates of a polygon's vertices but *subtracting* from the variable x

in an equation. Similarly, the operations involved in vertical translations and in stretches and shrinks seem backward. For example, if you're trying to stretch or shrink a polygon vertically by a factor of 3, you multiply the y-coordinates of its vertices by 3. But if you're trying to vertically stretch the graph of $y = x^2$, you replace y with $\frac{y}{3}$ (and then solve for y as needed to get $y = 3x^2$). Why?

To find the equation of the transformed graph, the strategy is to use the equation of the original graph. The x and y in the transformed equation will be coordinates of points lying on the transformed graph. So, if the transformation stretches everything vertically by 3, then points with coordinates $\left(x, \frac{y}{3}\right)$ lie on the original graph and therefore satisfy the original equation, meaning that $\frac{y}{3} = x^2$.

Similarly, if the graph of $y = |x|$ is translated 2 units to the right, to find the equation relating the coordinates (x, y) of the transformed graph you use the fact that point $(x - 2, y)$ lies on the original graph, so $y = |x - 2|$.

Double Duty

You might encourage students who enjoy looking for relationships to explore how different transformations of some functions yield the same result.

The parent linear function $y = x$ has the interesting property that horizontal transformations are also vertical transformations. The graph of $y = x + a$ can be thought of as a shift of $y = x$ either a units to the left or a units up.

Horizontal translations of the parent exponential functions are vertical stretches. For example, $y = 3^{x+2}$ is the same as $y = 3^2 \cdot 3^x = 9 \cdot 3^x$.

Vertical stretches of $y = x^2$ are horizontal shrinks. For example, $y = 16x^2$ can also be thought of as $y = (4x)^2$. And vertical stretches of $y = \frac{1}{x}$ are also horizontal stretches. For example, $y = \frac{4}{x}$ is the same as $y = \frac{1}{\frac{1}{4}x}$.

Matrices of Transformations

In computer graphics, points are moved by multiplying by matrices. If a point is represented by the matrix $\begin{bmatrix} x \\ y \end{bmatrix}$, then multiplying it on the left by the matrix $\begin{bmatrix} a & b \\ c & d \end{bmatrix}$ produces the point $\begin{bmatrix} ax + by \\ cx + dy \end{bmatrix}$. If b and c are 0 and d is 1, this transformation is a horizontal stretch or shrink or reflection.

Multiplying by any 2×2 matrix always takes the origin to itself, so such a matrix can't represent a translation. Computer graphics programs instead use three coordinates for points in the plane and 3×3 matrices for transformations. They represent each point as $\begin{bmatrix} x \\ y \\ 1 \end{bmatrix}$. Multiplying by

$\begin{bmatrix} 1 & 0 & 3 \\ 0 & 1 & -2 \\ 0 & 0 & 1 \end{bmatrix}$ gives $\begin{bmatrix} x + 3 \\ y - 2 \\ 1 \end{bmatrix}$, representing a translation.

Using This Chapter

The activities of Lesson 8.5 apply the ideas of previous lessons rather than introducing new material. Lesson 8.6 may be skipped if rational functions are not included in your standards. And use Lesson 8.7 only if your class is studying matrices.

Resources

Discovering Algebra Resources

Teaching and Worksheet Masters
Lessons 8.1–8.5

Calculator Notes 1H, 1P, 3B, 7D, 8A, 8B, 8C, 8D

Sketchpad Demonstrations
Lessons 8.1, 8.3

Fathom Demonstrations
Lessons 8.2, 8.6

CBL 2 Demonstration
Lesson 8.4

Dynamic Algebra Explorations online
Lessons 8.2–8.4

Assessment Resources
Quiz 1 (Lessons 8.1, 8.2)
Quiz 2 (Lessons 8.3, 8.4)
Quiz 3 (Lessons 8.6, 8.7)
Chapter 8 Test
Chapter 8 Constructive Assessment Options

More Practice Your Skills for Chapter 8

Condensed Lessons for Chapter 8

Other Resources

Transforming Functions to Fit Data by Ronald J. Carlson and Mary Jean Winter.

For complete references to this and other resources, see www.keypress.com/DA.

Materials

- graph paper
- patty paper, *optional*
- large marbles
- poster board
- metersticks or yardsticks
- tape
- sheets of paper
- paper cups
- books
- tables and chairs
- motion sensor
- cables for linking calculators
- stopwatches or watches with second hand

Pacing Guide

	day 1	day 2	day 3	day 4	day 5	day 6	day 7	day 8	day 9	day 10
standard	8.1	8.1	8.2	quiz, 8.3	8.4	8.5	8.5, quiz	8.6	8.7, quiz	review
enriched	8.1	8.1, project	8.2	quiz, 8.3	8.4	8.5	quiz, 8.6	8.7	project, quiz	review, TAL
block	8.1	8.2, 8.3	quiz, 8.4	8.5, 8.6	8.7, quiz	review, assessment				

	day 11	day 12	day 13	day 14	day 15	day 16	day 17	day 18	day 19	day 20
standard	assessment									
enriched	assessment									

Transformations

- Learn how to graph polygons on the graphing calculator

- Write list definitions to describe transformations (translations, reflections, stretches and shrinks) of points

- Learn to recognize and graph transformations on graph paper

- Write equations of transformed functions and graph them

- Explore the concept of a parent function and its family

- Model real-world data with transformed equations

- Investigate rational functions of the form $f(x) = \frac{a}{x}$ and explore basic transformations of this function

- Model real-world data with rational functions

- Use matrices to represent transformations of polygons

The Dome of the Rock is a famous site in Jerusalem. Built in the 7th century, it is well known for its beautiful tile work. Moving a small design left, right, up, or down could create some of the large patterns you see. Flipping or turning a design could create yet other patterns. Moving, flipping, or turning a design is important in creating many art forms. As you will see, changes like these are equally important in mathematics.

OBJECTIVES

In this chapter you will

- move a polygon by changing its vertices' coordinates
- learn to change, or transform, graphs by moving, flipping, shrinking, or stretching
- write a new equation to describe the changed, or transformed, graph
- model real-world data with equations of transformations
- use matrices to transform the vertices of a polygon

Challenge students to find the smallest unit that can be repeated in the row of tilted squares at the top. That unit is analogous to a parent, and every other incidence of it can be thought of as a child of the parent. There is more than one way to visualize the parent unit. For instance, students can trap a light-colored diamond in a square and call that the parent, or they can visualize a square that captures a bow-tie-shaped figure.

A design that repeats to fill the plane is called a *tessellation*. The patterns pictured here are based on squares, but tessellations can be derived from any plane-filling figure. The parent unit, called a *tessera*, is translated, reflected, or rotated in several directions.

You might ask students to think of other art forms that use transformations. Examples include fabric designs and some forms of cubism and pop art.

You may want to make a distinction between symmetry and transformation. Complete sections of the Dome of the Rock facade could be described as having reflective symmetry (one half of the section looks like the other half). The designer of the facade may have used a reflection transformation to create the second half.

Translating Points

In computer animation, many individual points define each figure. You animate a figure by moving these points around the screen, little by little, through a series of frames. When you see the frames one after the other, the entire figure appears to move. This is the principle behind computer-animated movies and video games.

In mathematics, changing or moving a figure is called a **transformation.** So, every frame of an animation is a transformation of the one before it.

If one is lucky, a solitary fantasy can totally transform one million realities.

MAYA ANGELOU

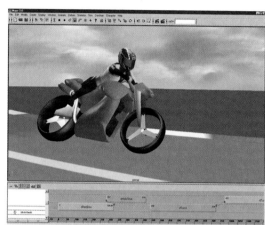

This computer-animated motorcycle was created with software called Maya. The "skeleton" of the motorcycle would look like the face in the photo on page 296. The software allows an animator to move the motorcycle by transforming the points of the underlying skeleton.

Investigation
Figures in Motion

In this investigation you will learn how to move a polygon around the coordinate plane. You will first view what happens when you change the *y*-coordinates of the vertices.

> **Procedure Note**
>
> For this investigation, use a friendly window with a factor of 2.
> [▶ 🖥 See **Calculator Note 7D** to review friendly windows. ◀]

Step 1 Name the coordinates of the vertices of this triangle.

Step 2 Enter the *x*-coordinates of the vertices into list L1 and the corresponding *y*-coordinates of the vertices into list L2. Enter the first coordinate pair again at the end of each list. Graph the triangle by connecting the vertices.
[▶ 🖥 See **Calculator Note 1H** to review connected graphs. ◀]

NCTM STANDARDS

CONTENT		PROCESS	
✔	Number		Problem Solving
✔	Algebra	✔	Reasoning
✔	Geometry	✔	Communication
	Measurement		Connections
	Data/Probability	✔	Representation

LESSON OBJECTIVES

- Learn how to graph polygons on the graphing calculator
- Write list definitions to describe translations of points
- Learn to recognize and graph translations on graph paper

Step 1 (2, 1), (2, 4), (6, 1)

Ask one member of each group to do the investigation on graph paper.

Step 2 The connected graphs shown use the small dot mark.

Steps 2 and 3

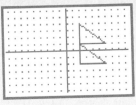

$[-9.4, 9.4, 1, -6.2, 6.2, 1]$

Step 3 This definition can take place in the STAT EDIT menu or using the STO key on the home screen: $L_1 \rightarrow L_3$ (ENTER) and $L_2 - 3 \rightarrow L_4$ (ENTER).

Step 5 Students will not need to keep entering $L_3 = L_1$, but they should be reminded that the x-coordinates are not changing.

Step 5a

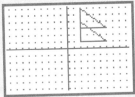

Step 5b

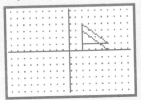

Step 6 [ELL] Some students may not realize that the phrase "in terms of" means "using."

Step 7 As needed, remind students that a quadrilateral is a four-sided figure. The calculator will produce a strange figure if students enter the coordinates in an order other than clockwise or counterclockwise around the figure. Let them learn from their error rather than trying to prevent it. Also, they must enter the first coordinate again at the end to close the figure.

Step 4 $(2, -2), (2, 1),$ and $(6, -2)$; the triangle moves down 3 units; the y-coordinates are reduced by 3.

Step 7 $(1, 2), (2, -2),$ $(-3, -1), (-2, 1)$

Step 10 $(-2, 2), (-1, -2),$ $(-6, -1),$ and $(-5, 1)$; the quadrilateral moves left 3 units; the x-coordinates are reduced by 3.

Step 11a $(3, 2), (4, -2),$ $(-1, -1),$ and $(0, 1)$; the quadrilateral moves right 2 units; the x-coordinates are increased by 2.

Step 11b $(0, 5), (1, 1), (-4, 2),$ and $(-3, 4)$; the quadrilateral moves left 1 unit and up 3 units; the x-coordinates are reduced by 1, and the y-coordinates are increased by 3.

Steps 9 and 11 Ask any group you may be observing when they begin this step if they can predict the result before going to the calculator. Students need not enter $L_4 = L_2$ more than once, but they should be aware that the y-coordinates are not changing.

Step 3

Define list L_3 and list L_4 as follows:

$L_3 = L_1$
$L_4 = L_2 - 3$

Graph a second triangle using list L_3 for the x-coordinates of the vertices and list L_4 for the y-coordinates of the vertices.

Step 4 Name the coordinates of the vertices of the new triangle. Tell how the original triangle has moved. How did the coordinates of the vertices change?

Step 5 Repeat Steps 3 and 4 with these definitions.

$(2, 0), (2, 3),$ and $(6, 0)$; the triangle moves down 1 unit; the y-coordinates are reduced by 1.

a. $L_3 = L_1$
$L_4 = L_2 + 2$

$(2, 3), (2, 6),$ and $(6, 3)$; the triangle moves up 2 units; the y-coordinates are increased by 2.

b. $L_3 = L_1$
$L_4 = L_2 - 1$

Step 6 Write definitions for list L_3 and list L_4 in terms of list L_1 and list L_2 to create each graph below. Check your definitions by graphing on your calculator.

a.

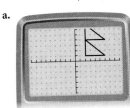

$L_3 = L_1;\ L_4 = L_2 + 3$

b.

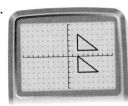

$L_3 = L_1;\ L_4 = L_2 - 4$

c.

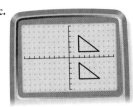

$L_3 = L_1;\ L_4 = L_2 - 5$

Next, you will include changes to the x-coordinates too.

Step 7 Name the coordinates of the vertices of this quadrilateral.

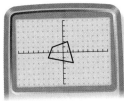

Step 8 Graph the quadrilateral using list L_1 for the x-coordinates of the vertices and list L_2 for the y-coordinates of the vertices.

Step 9 Define list L_3 and list L_4 as follows:

$L_3 = L_1 - 3$
$L_4 = L_2$

Graph a second quadrilateral using list L_3 for the x-coordinates of the vertices and list L_4 for the y-coordinates of the vertices.

Step 10 Name the coordinates of the vertices of this new quadrilateral. Describe how the original quadrilateral moved. How did the coordinates of the vertices change?

Step 11 Repeat Steps 9 and 10 with these definitions.

a. $L_3 = L_1 + 2$
$L_4 = L_2$

b. $L_3 = L_1 - 1$
$L_4 = L_2 + 3$

Steps 8 and 9

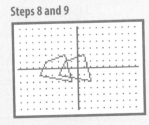

Step 11a

Step 12 | Write definitions for list L₃ and list L₄ in terms of list L₁ and list L₂ to create each graph below. Check your definitions by graphing on your calculator.

a.

$L_3 = L_1 + 6; \ L_4 = L_2$

b.

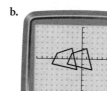

$L_3 = L_1 - 3; \ L_4 = L_2$

c.

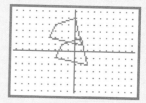

$L_3 = L_1 - 5; \ L_4 = L_2 + 3$

Step 13 | Summarize what you have learned about moving a figure around the coordinate plane.

In the investigation, each new polygon is the result of transforming the original polygon by moving it left, right, up, or down, or combinations of these movements. The figure that results from a transformation is called the **image** of the original figure. Transformations that move a figure horizontally, vertically, or both are called **translations.** You can define the translation of a point simply by adding to or subtracting from its coordinates.

EXAMPLE

Sketch the image of this figure after a translation right 4 units and down 3 units. Define the coordinates of any point in the image using (x, y) as the coordinates of any point in the original figure.

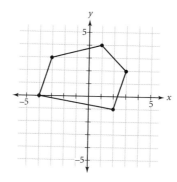

▶ Solution

Translate every point right 4 units and down 3 units. For example, move the vertex at $(1, 4)$ to $(5, 1)$. This is the same as adding 4 to the x-coordinate and subtracting 3 from the y-coordinate. That is, $(1 + 4, 4 - 3)$ gives $(5, 1)$.

A definition for any point in the image is

$$(x + 4, y - 3)$$

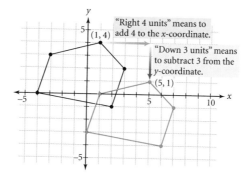

"Right 4 units" means to add 4 to the x-coordinate.

"Down 3 units" means to subtract 3 from the y-coordinate.

▶ EXAMPLE

This example shows how the variables x and y are used to define the translation. It is good for students who haven't yet grasped how to translate a point in two directions, as in Step 11b.

You might use the Sketchpad demonstration Translation of Figures as another example for students.

Step 11b

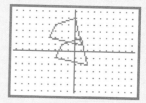

Step 13 Sample answer: Adding to or subtracting from the x-coordinates moves the figure right or left, respectively. Adding to or subtracting from the y-coordinates moves the figure up or down, respectively.

SHARING IDEAS

[Language] *Transformation* and *translation* are defined as nouns, but they have verb forms also: "Translate the point."

Ask several students to report their ideas from Step 13. As always, aim for variety to enrich the discussion. Watch students' faces and body language and respond appropriately. Students may get the idea that you read minds! Or, if you're smooth enough, you can have the satisfaction of their not even noticing that you asked for their opinion right when they had an idea.

Remind the class that they have been looking at transformations of the geometric figures. Draw their attention to the quotation at the beginning of the lesson and ask how that use of the word *transform* is similar to and different from the mathematical meaning. Introduce the term *translation* for the kind of transformation they've been observing, and mention that the resulting figure is called the *image* of the original under the transformation. Ask how a geometric translation like this is similar to and different from a translation between languages.

Assessing Progress

Through observing groups and presentations, you can assess students' ability to name coordinates of points, enter data into calculator lists, and operate on calculator lists.

On your calculator, you can put the coordinates of the vertices of the original pentagon into list L_1 and list L_2. Then define list L_3 as $L_3 = L_1 + 4$ and list L_4 as $L_4 = L_2 - 3$.

Graphing confirms that your definition works.

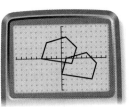

Science CONNECTION

Many scientists support the theory of plate tectonics. According to this theory, the continents of the world were, at one time, together as a single continent. The German geophysicist and meteorologist Alfred Wegener (1880–1930) called this mass of land Pangaea. Over thousands of years, the individual continents drifted (or translated) to their current locations.

EXERCISES

You will need your graphing calculator for Exercise **7.**

▶ Practice Your Skills

1. Name the coordinates of the vertices of each figure.

a.

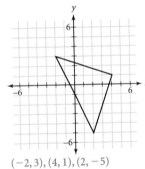

$(-2, 3), (4, 1), (2, -5)$

b.

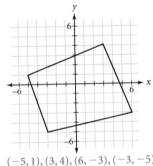

$(-5, 1), (3, 4), (6, -3), (-3, -5)$

2. The *x*-coordinates of the vertices of a triangle are entered into list L_1. The *y*-coordinates are entered into list L_2. Describe the transformation for each definition.

a. $L_3 = L_1 - 5$ ⓐ
$L_4 = L_2$
a translation left 5 units

b. $L_3 = L_1 + 1$
$L_4 = L_2 + 2$
a translation right 1 unit and up 2 units

3. The red triangle at right is the image of the black triangle after a transformation.

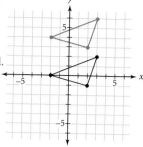

    a. Describe the transformation. ⓐ a translation up 4 units

    b. Tell how the *x*-coordinates of the vertices change between the original figure and the image. ⓐ The *x*-coordinates are unchanged.

    c. Tell how the *y*-coordinates of the vertices change.
       The *y*-coordinates are increased by 4.

▶ **Helping with the Exercises**

4. Consider the square at right.

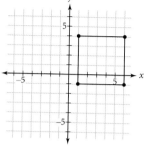

    a. Sketch the image of the figure after a translation left 2 units.

    b. Define the coordinates of any point in the image using (x, y) as the coordinates of any point in the original figure. ⓐ $(x - 2, y)$

4a.

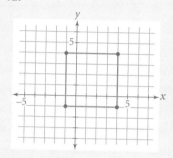

5. The "spider" in the upper left has its *x*-coordinates in list L_1 and its *y*-coordinates in list L_2.

$[-9.4, 9.4, 1, -6.2, 6.2, 1]$

    a. Describe the transformation to create the image in the lower right.   a translation right 10 units and down 8 units

    b. Write definitions for list L_3 and list L_4 in terms of list L_1 and list L_2. $L_3 = L_1 + 10, L_4 = L_2 - 8$

    c. How would your answer to 5b change if the "spider" in the lower right were the original figure and the figure in the upper left were the image? ⓐ
       The signs would change: $L_3 = L_1 - 10, L_4 = L_2 + 8$.

▶ Reason and Apply

6. Consider the triangle on the calculator screen at right.

    a. Describe how to graph this triangle on your calculator.

    b. For each graph below, describe the transformation made to the original triangle.

$[-9.4, 9.4, 1, -6.2, 6.2, 1]$

6a. Possible answer: Enter the *x*-coordinates into list L_1 and the *y*-coordinates into list L_2: $L_1 = \{2, 5, 1, 2\}$ and $L_2 = \{-1, 0, 2, -1\}$. Then make a connected graph.

    i.

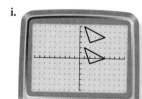

    a translation up 4 units

    ii.

    a translation left 5 units

    iii.

    a translation right 3 units and down 2 units

7a.

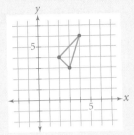

7b.

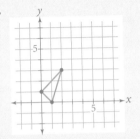

7c.

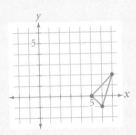

8a. a translation right 12 units and up 7 units

Exercise 9 The original figure is frame 0. Hence, by the 10th frame, the definition of the translation, $(x - 0.25, y + 0.05)$, has been used 10 times.

Exercise 11 11c and d may be the first time students evaluate a function for a variable expression. You might want to describe it as "substituting $x + 2$ for x." They will do this again in Lesson 8.2, Exercise 1.

---

7. The coordinates of the vertices of a triangle are (2, 1), (4, 3), and (3, 0). Sketch the image that results from each definition. Use calculator lists to check your work.

  a. $(x, y + 3)$ @   **b.** $(x - 2, y)$ **c.** $(x + 3, y - 1)$

8. APPLICATION Lisa is designing a computer animation. She has a set of coordinates for the arrow in the lower left. She wants the arrow to move to the upper-right position.

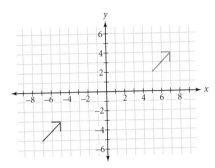

  a. Describe the transformation that moves the arrow to the upper-right position.

  b. Define the coordinates of any point in the image using (x, y) as the coordinates of any point in the original figure. @ $(x + 12, y + 7)$

  c. Lisa decides that a single move is too sudden. She thinks that moving the arrow little by little, in 20 frames, would look better. How should she define the coordinates of any point in each new image using (x, y) as the coordinates of any point in the figure in the previous frame? ⓗ $\left(x + \dfrac{12}{20}, y + \dfrac{7}{20}\right)$, or $(x + 0.6, y + 0.35)$

9. APPLICATION Nick is also designing a computer animation program. His program first draws a letter N by connecting the points (7, 1), (7, 2), (8, 1), and (8, 2). Then, in each subsequent frame, the previous N is erased and an image is drawn whose coordinates are defined by $(x - 0.25, y + 0.05)$. The program uses recursion to do this over and over again.

What will be the coordinates of the N in the

  a. 10th new frame? @   **b.** 25th new frame?   **c.** 40th new frame?
  (4.5, 1.5), (4.5, 2.5), (5.5, 1.5), (5.5, 2.5)   (0.75, 2.25), (0.75, 3.25), $(-3, 3), (-3, 4),$
                                    (1.75, 2.25), (1.75, 3.25) $(-2, 3), (-2, 4)$

▶ **Review**

7.6 **10.** Complete this table of values for $g(x) = |x - 3|$ and $h(x) = (x - 3)^2$.

x	0	1	2	3	4	5	6
$g(x)$	3	2	1	0	1	2	3
$h(x)$	9	4	1	0	1	4	9

7.4 **11.** Use $f(x) = 2 + 3x$ to find

  a. $f(5)$ 17   **b.** x when $f(x) = -10$ @ $x = -4$ **c.** $f(x + 2)$ $8 + 3x$ **d.** $f(2x - 1)$ @ $-1 + 6x$

3.6 **12.** Solve each equation.

  a. $5 = -3 + 2x$ $x = 4$ **b.** $-4 = -8 + 3(x - 2)$ $x = 3.\overline{3}$ **c.** $7 + 2x = 3 + x$ $x = -4$

6.2,
7.5
13. Find an equation for each graph.

a.

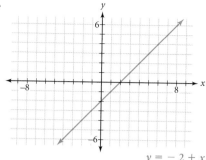

$$y = -2 + x$$

b.

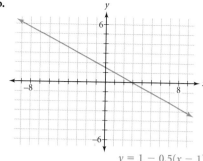

$$y = 1 - 0.5(x - 1)$$

c.

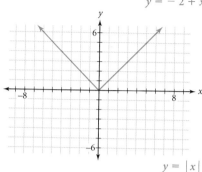

$$y = |x|$$

d.

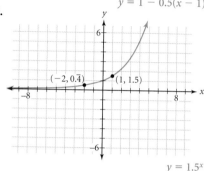

$(-2, 0.\overline{4})$ $(1, 1.5)$

$$y = 1.5^x$$

Exercise 13 To help students with 13d, you might write an exponential equation from a graph. Give the points (0, 1) and (1, 1.5) so they can calculate the constant multiplier.

Alternative Project

For students for whom this project is inaccessible (because they don't have access to a computer or calculator or they find the logic of programming languages confusing), you might want to suggest a research paper on professional animation software.

project

ANIMATING WITH TRANSFORMATIONS

As you've learned in this lesson, you can use transformations to create computer animation. Programs use mathematics to transform the points of a figure little by little. For example, Lisa's arrow in Exercise 8 appears to move because it makes 20 very small translations.

Now it's your turn to be the computer animator. Use a computer programming language to create an animation of any figure you choose. You can even use your calculator. [▶ 💻 See **Calculator Note 8A** for a calculator program that moves Lisa's arrow. ◀]

Your project should include

▶ The steps of your program.

▶ An explanation of what each step of the program does.

▶ A description of the transformations used.

▶ A sketch of your original figure and the final image.

As you learn about other transformations in this chapter, you can try including them in your project too. You might also want to research the programming languages and software that professional animators use.

Supporting the project

MOTIVATION

Many students who think they can't write computer programs become very excited when they discover how to move a figure across the screen of a graphing calculator, so don't be too quick to give in to protests.

OUTCOMES

▶ The program does not have any obvious errors (such as unclosed loops) that would keep it from running.

▶ Each step is described in easy-to-understand terms using proper terminology. ("This step stores the coordinates of the vertices." "This step produces a translation to the right 0.5 unit and up 0.4 unit.")

▶ The sketch accurately shows the original and final figure on a coordinate grid.

• Student uses elaborate figures or many different transformations.

• Student has researched and learned a new computer programming language.

• Student has used internet animation languages like Java, Shockwave, or Flash.

PLANNING

LESSON OUTLINE

One day:

25 min Investigation
5 min Sharing
10 min Examples
5 min Closing
5 min Exercises

MATERIALS

- Moving Absolute Values (W), *optional*
- Calculator Note 8B
- Fathom demonstration The Uncool Sandwich, *optional*

TEACHING

To transform graphs that aren't polygons, you can't just connect images of vertices. Rather, you need to see how the equations of these graphs are affected by transformations.

Students have learned to write linear equations in intercept form with the constant term first: $y = a + bx$. Nonlinear equations will be written with the constant term last, as in $y = (x - 4)^2 + 2$, $y = |x - 7| + 2.5$, and $y = 3^{x+1} - 2$.

 Guiding the Investigation

One Step
Give each group the Moving Absolute Values worksheet and ask them to alter the calculator function $Y_1 = abs(x)$ to create the lighter graph. Let them experiment with adding and subtracting in various ways.

Step 1 You may need to remind students of the meaning of absolute value.

See page 725 for answers to Steps 1 and 2.

444 CHAPTER 8 Transformations

Translating Graphs

There are infinitely many linear and exponential functions. In previous chapters, you wrote many of them "from scratch" using points, the y-intercept, the slope, the starting value, or the constant multiplier.

Poetry is what gets lost in translation.
ROBERT FROST

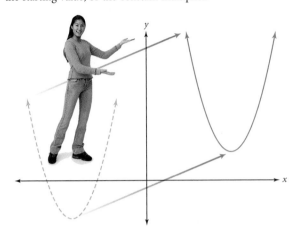

There are also infinitely many absolute-value and squaring functions. But rather than starting from scratch, you can transform $y = |x|$ and $y = x^2$ to create many different equations. In this investigation you will use what you know about translating points to translate functions. If you discover any unexpected transformations along the way, make a note so that you can use them later in the chapter.

 ## Investigation
Translations of Functions

First you'll transform the absolute-value function by making changes to x.

Procedure Note
For this investigation, use a friendly window with a factor of 2.

Step 1 Enter $y = |x|$ into Y1 and graph it on your calculator.

Step 2 If you replace x with $x - 3$ in the function $y = |x|$, you get $y = |x - 3|$. Enter $y = |x - 3|$ into Y2 and graph it.

Step 3 Think of the graph of $y = |x|$ as the original figure and the graph of $y = |x - 3|$ as its image. How have you transformed the graph of $y = |x|$?
a translation right 3 units

The **vertex** of an absolute-value graph is the point where the function changes from decreasing to increasing or from increasing to decreasing.

Step 4 Name the coordinates of the vertex of the graph of $y = |x|$. Name the coordinates of the vertex of the graph of $y = |x - 3|$. How do these two points help verify the transformation you found in Step 3?
$(0, 0)$; $(3, 0)$; the vertex is translated right 3 units.

LESSON OBJECTIVES

- Write equations to describe translations of the absolute-value and squaring functions
- Graph and recognize translations of the absolute-value and squaring functions
- Explore the concept of a family of functions

NCTM STANDARDS

CONTENT		PROCESS	
	Number		Problem Solving
✔	Algebra	✔	Reasoning
✔	Geometry	✔	Communication
	Measurement	✔	Connections
	Data/Probability	✔	Representation

Step 5 | Find a function for Y2 that will translate the graph of $y = |x|$ left 4 units. What is the function? In the equation $y = |x|$, what did you replace x with to get your new function? $y = |x - (-4)|$, or $y = |x + 4|$; replace x with $x + 4$.

Step 6 | Write a function for Y2 to create each graph below. Check your work by graphing both Y1 and Y2.

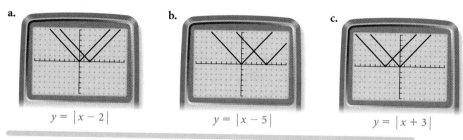

a. $y = |x - 2|$ b. $y = |x - 5|$ c. $y = |x + 3|$

Next, you'll transform the absolute-value function by making changes to y.

Step 7 | Clear all of the functions in your Y= menu. Enter $y = |x|$ into Y1 and graph it.

Step 8 | If you replace y with $y - 3$ in the function $y = |x|$, you get $y - 3 = |x|$. Solve for y and you get $y = |x| + 3$. Enter $y = |x| + 3$ into Y2 and graph it.

Step 9 | Think of the graph of $y = |x|$ as the original figure and the graph of $y = |x| + 3$ as its image. How have you transformed the graph of $y = |x|$?
a translation up 3 units

Step 10 | Name the coordinates of the vertex of the graph of $y = |x|$. Name the coordinates of the vertex of the graph of $y = |x| + 3$. How do these two points help verify the transformation you found in Step 9?
$(0, 0)$; $(0, 3)$; the vertex is translated up 3 units.

Step 11 | Find a function for Y2 that will translate the graph of $y = |x|$ down 3 units. What is the function? In the function $y = |x|$, what did you replace y with to get your new function? $y = |x| - 3$; replace y with $y - (-3)$, or $y + 3$.

Step 12 | Write a function for Y2 to create each graph below. Check your work by graphing both Y1 and Y2.

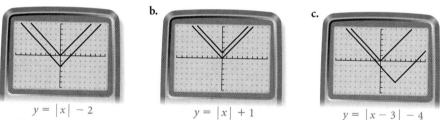

a. $y = |x| - 2$ b. $y = |x| + 1$ c. $y = |x - 3| - 4$

Step 13 | Summarize what you have learned about translating the absolute-value graph vertically and horizontally.

Remind students of Step 8: $y = |x| + 3$ is equivalent to $y - 3 = |x|$; either form is a translation 3 units up from $y = |x|$. Students may ask why subtracting a positive number from the y-coordinate of a point translates that point *down,* but subtracting a positive number from the variable y in the equation $y = |x|$ translates the graph *up.* It may help to compare the tables of $y = |x|$ and $y = |x| + 3$ to see that the y-values are greater by 3 for the second

equation. As usual, the longer you can wait before explaining, the more students will think about the ideas.

Ask how the vertex of an absolute-value function is like and unlike the vertex of a polygon. Answers are unimportant. Your goal is to help students become more familiar with the term *vertex.*

Step 4 Students may be confused by the fact that, to translate a point to the right, you add to the x-coordinate, but in an equation you ultimately subtract from x. Challenge them to think about reasons to discuss during Sharing.

Step 6 Suggest to students having trouble that they look at individual points.

Steps 7 and 8

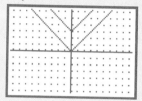

Step 13 Sample answer: To translate h ($h > 0$) units to the right, replace x with $x - h$. To translate h units to the left, replace x with $x + h$. When y is replaced with $y + h$, the graph is translated down h units. When y is replaced with $y - h$, the graph is translated up h units. Another sample answer: To translate the graph horizontally, subtract from x in the function (subtracting a positive number translates right; subtracting a negative number translates left). To translate the graph vertically, add to the entire function (adding a positive number translates up; adding a negative number translates down).

SHARING IDEAS

[Language] Point out that the plural of *vertex* is *vertices* and that the singular of *vertices* is not *verticie.*

The quotation introducing the lesson, as well as the Science Connection on page 446, can be used to initiate discussion of the multiple meanings of *translation.* Robert Frost (1874–1963) was an American poet.

Have three or more groups report on the parts of Step 12.

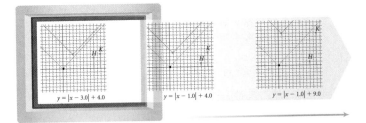

$y = |x - 3.0| + 4.0$ $y = |x - 1.0| + 4.0$ $y = |x - 1.0| + 9.0$

keymath.com/DA

[▶ You can explore transformations interactively using the **Dynamic Algebra Exploration** at **www.keymath.com/DA** . ◀]

The most basic form of a function is often called a **parent function.** By transforming the graph of a parent function, you can create infinitely many new functions, or a **family of functions.** Functions like $y = |x - 3|$ and $y = |x| + 3$ are members of the absolute-value family of functions, with $y = |x|$ as the parent. Other families of functions include the linear family, with $y = x$ as the parent, the squaring family, with $y = x^2$ as the parent, and the base-3 exponential family, with $y = 3^x$ as the parent.

Learning how to create a family of functions will help you to see relationships between equations and graphs. The translations you learned in the investigation apply to any function.

Anni Albers (1899–1994), a German-American artist, used many transformations of a single triangle to create this serigraph. Can you find some translations?
Anni Albers, *Untitled*, ca. 1969. The National Museum of Women in the Arts, Washington, D.C.

Science
CONNECTION

Earthquakes often translate Earth's crust along a *fault.* You can see faults most easily when buildings and other structures are translated too. These cable car tracks were bent by a fault during the 1906 earthquake in San Francisco, California. Learn more about earthquakes and faults with the links at **www.keymath.com/DA** .

Dip-slip fault

Strike-slip fault

Parent Functions

Introduce the terms *parent function* and *family of functions* and ask what equation would represent a translation of the parent function $y = x^2$ two units to the right and four units down. This leads into Example A.

You may want to use and display more formal notation for translations, such as $y = f(x - h) + k$, where h represents a horizontal translation and k represents a vertical translation. The constants h and k will be used in Chapter 9.

Assessing Progress

Watch for students' understanding of translation and their ability to graph functions.

EXAMPLE A

The graph of the parent function $y = x^2$ is shown in black. Its image after a transformation is shown in red. Describe the transformation. Then write an equation for the image.

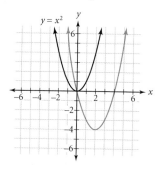

▶ **Solution**

The **vertex** of a parabola is the point where the squaring function changes from decreasing to increasing or increasing to decreasing. The vertex of the graph of $y = x^2$ is $(0, 0)$. The vertex of the image is $(2, -4)$. So the graph of $y = x^2$ is translated right 2 units and down 4 units to create the red image. You can check this with any other point. For example, the image of the point $(2, 4)$ is $(4, 0)$, which is also a translation right 2 units and down 4 units.

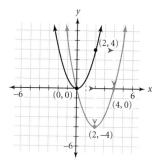

Every point on $y = x^2$ is translated right 2 units and down 4 units.

The equation of the image is

$$y - (-4) = (x - 2)^2$$

or

$$y = (x - 2)^2 - 4$$

Use the translation to write an equation for the red image.

$y = x^2$ Equation of the original parabola.

$y = (x - 2)^2$ Replace x with $x - 2$ to translate the graph right 2 units.

$y - (-4) = (x - 2)^2$ Replace y with $y - (-4)$, or $y + 4$, to translate the graph down 4 units.

$y = (x - 2)^2 - 4$ Solve for y.

The equation of the image is $y = (x - 2)^2 - 4$. You can graph this on your calculator to check your work.

In the next example you'll see how to translate an exponential function. Later you will use these skills to fit a function to a set of data.

▶ **EXAMPLE A**

This example shows how to translate the squaring parent function in two directions. As needed, remind students of the meaning of squaring.

You can use this example to reinforce students' understanding of the graph of the parent quadratic equation. Have students work through the example themselves on graph paper, so that they have experience accurately sketching $y = x^2$.

▶ EXAMPLE B

Here an exponential function is translated horizontally to model a real-world situation. Some students may think the graph is a translation down rather than to the right. If they try drawing vertical lines between points, they will see there is not a uniform translation vertically.

If students ask why subtraction in the equation is the same as adding to the coordinate, have students look at the tables for each equation. Point out that points $(-4, 32.9)$ and $(0, 94)$ lie on the graph of $y = 94(1 + 0.30)^x$. **[Ask]** "What points on the graph of $y = 94(1 + 0.30)^{x-4}$ have y-values of 32.9 and 94? What is the position of these points relative to the original points?" $[(0, 32.9)$ and $(4, 94)$. These points are four units to the right of the original points.]

Ask whether students think the function $y = 33(1 + 0.30)^x$ is of the same family as the original function. Have students develop the algebraic derivation requested in the student text:

$$y = 94(1 + 0.30)^{x-4}$$
$$= 94(1 + 0.30)^{-4}(1 + 0.30)^x$$
$$\approx 33(1 + 0.30)^x$$

On one hand, the expression for the transformed graph is an equivalent expression for the shift of the first function, so the functions would appear to be part of the same family. On the other hand, students may argue that the functions are not of the same family because they have different starting values. Don't answer the question yet. It motivates Lesson 8.4, in which students will see that both functions are stretches of the parent function $y = (1 + 0.30)^x$.

An alternate approach to the problem would be to solve the equation $94 = a(1.3)^4$ for a (about 33) and then write $y = 33(1 + 0.3)^x$. Although this method does not illustrate the use of translations, it requires sophisticated use of algebra, so congratulate any students who come up with it.

448 CHAPTER 8 Transformations

EXAMPLE B | The starting number of bacteria in a culture dish is unknown, but the number grows by approximately 30% each hour. After 4 hours there are 94 bacteria present. Write an equation to model this situation. Then find the starting number of bacteria.

▶ **Solution** | The starting number is not known, but you can find it by assuming that you're beginning with 94 bacteria, and then shifting back in time. If you were beginning with 94 bacteria, the function would be $y = 94(1 + 0.30)^x$, in which x represents time elapsed in hours and y represents the number of bacteria.

However, there were 94 bacteria after 4 hours, not at 0 hours. So translate the point $(0, 94)$ right 4 units to $(4, 94)$. To translate the whole graph right 4 units, replace x with $x - 4$ in the function. You get

$$y = 94(1 + 0.30)^{x-4}$$

The graph shows how the new function translates every point in the graph right 4 units.

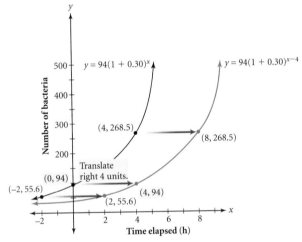

To find the starting number of bacteria, substitute 0 for x in the new function.

$$94(1 + 0.30)^{0-4} = 94(1 + 0.30)^{-4} \approx 33$$

The starting number was approximately 33 bacteria.

Using the starting value you found in the example, you could now write the function $y = 33(1 + 0.30)^x$. How can you use properties of exponents to show that $y = 94(1 + 0.30)^{x-4}$ is approximately equivalent to $y = 33(1 + 0.30)^x$? Do you think these functions would be considered members of the same family of functions? Why or why not?

Closing the Lesson

Numbers are added to coordinates of points to indicate translations up or to the right (adding negative numbers for translations in the opposite directions), but those same numbers are subtracted from the variables to transform an equation of the graph similarly. The strategy is to build on the equation of the original function to create the equation of the transformed function.

Basic functions such as $y = x^2$, $y = |x|$, $y = x$, and $y = 3^x$ are called **parent functions,** and all transformations of these functions make up **families of functions.** The origin is a **vertex** of the graphs of $y = x^2$ and $y = |x|$. The graph of a family member that is the image of the parent function under a transformation has as its vertex the image of the origin under the same transformation.

EXERCISES

You will need your graphing calculator for Exercises **4, 6, 8, 11,** and **12.**

Practice Your Skills

1. Use $f(x) = 2|x + 4| + 1$ to find

   a. $f(5)$ 19
   b. $f(-6)$ @   5
   c. $f(-2) + 3$ 8
   d. $f(x + 2)$ @ $2|x + 6| + 1$

2. List L₁ and list L₂ contain coordinates for three points on the graph of $f(x)$. List L₃ and list L₄ contain coordinates for the three points after a transformation of f.

L₁ x	L₂ y
−1	3
3	5
2	4

L₃ x	L₄ y
7	−1
11	1
10	0

   a. Write definitions for list L₃ and list L₄ in terms of list L₁ and list L₂.   L₃ = L₁ + 8; L₄ = L₂ − 4
   b. Describe the transformation.   a translation right 8 units and down 4 units

3. Give the coordinates of the vertex for each graph.

   a.
   @
   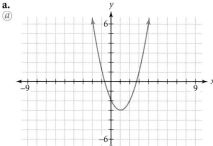
   $(1, -3)$

   b.
   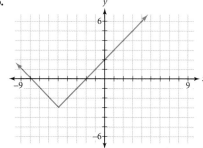
   $(-5, -3)$

   c.
   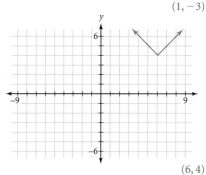
   $(6, 4)$

   d.
   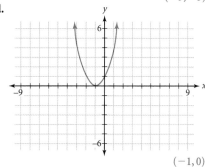
   $(-1, 0)$

4. Use a calculator to graph each equation. Describe the graph as a transformation of $y = |x|$, $y = x^2$, or $y = 3^x$.

   a. $y + 2.5 = |x - 1.5|$ @
   b. $y = (x + 3)^2$
   c. $y - 3.5 = |x|$
   d. $y - 2 = 3^{x+1}$ @

4d. a translation of $y = 3^x$ left 1 unit and up 2 units

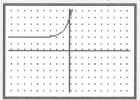

▶ Helping with the Exercises

Exercise 1 You might ask what the parent function is and how it has been transformed. [The parent function $y = |x|$ has been translated left 4 units and up 1 unit.]

4a. a translation of $y = |x|$ right 1.5 units and down 2.5 units

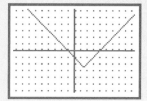

4b. a translation of $y = x^2$ left 3 units

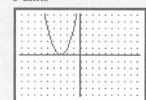

4c. a translation of $y = |x|$ up 3.5 units

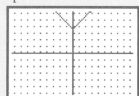

6a. a translation of $y = x^2$ right 1 unit and down 3 units; $y = (x - 1)^2 - 3$

6b. a translation of $y = |x|$ left 5 units and down 3 units; $y = |x + 5| - 3$

6c. a translation of $y = |x|$ right 6 units and up 4 units; $y = |x - 6| + 4$

6d. a translation of $y = x^2$ left 1 unit; $y = (x + 1)^2$

7a. The input variable is time; the output variable is distance.

7b. Time is in seconds and distance is in meters.

7c. domain: $0 \le t \le 5$, where t is time in seconds; range: $1 \le d \le 4$, where d is distance in meters

7d. Possible answer: Beth starts 3 m from her teacher and walks toward the teacher at 1 m/s for 2 s. When she turns in the test, she is 1 m from the teacher. Beth then turns and walks away from the teacher at 1 m/s for 3 s.

Exercise 8 Calculator syntax varies. For example, some calculators interpret $Y_1(x - 4)$ as composition of functions, while others interpret it as multiplication. Calculator Note 8B is therefore mandatory for this exercise. You might want to challenge students to determine whether their calculators do composition or multiplication. They might try simple functions. For example, if $Y_1 = x$ and $Y_2 = Y_1(x)$, identical graphs would indicate composition.

8a. a translation down 4 units

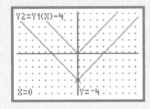

5. Write an equation for each of these transformations.
  a. Translate the graph of $y = x^2$ down 2 units. $y = x^2 - 2$
  b. Translate the graph of $y = 4^x$ right 5 units. @ $y = 4^{x-5}$
  c. Translate the graph of $y = |x|$ left 4 units and up 1 unit. $y = |x + 4| + 1$

Reason and Apply

6. Describe each graph in Exercise 3 as a transformation of $y = |x|$ or $y = x^2$. Then write its equation. Use your calculator to check your answers.

7. This graph shows Beth's distance from her teacher as she turns in her test.
  a. What are the input and output variables?
  b. What are the units of the variables?
  c. What are the domain and range shown in the graph?
  d. Describe the situation.
  e. Write a function that models this situation.
     $d = |t - 2| + 1$

Beth's Walk

(graph: Distance from teacher (m) vs Time (s))

8. Graph $Y_1(x) = abs(x)$ on your calculator. Predict what each graph will look like. Check by comparing the graphs on your calculator.
  [▶ See **Calculator Note 8B** for specific instructions for your calculator. ◀] ⓗ
  a. $Y_2(x) = Y_1(x) - 4$ **b.** $Y_2(x) = Y_1(x - 4)$

9. Describe how the graph of $y = x^2$ will be transformed if you replace
  a. x with $(x - 3)$ a translation right 3 units   **b.** x with $(x + 2)$ @ a translation left 2 units
  c. y with $(y + 2)$ @ a translation down 2 units   **d.** y with $(y - 3)$ a translation up 3 units

10. **APPLICATION** The equation $y = a \cdot b^x$ models the decreasing voltage of a charged capacitor when connected to a load. Measurements for a particular 9-volt battery are recorded in the table.

Time (s)	10	11	12	13	14	15	16
Voltage (volts)	6.579	6.285	5.992	5.738	5.484	5.230	4.995

[Data sets: **CAPTM, CAPVT**]

10b. approximately 0.955 volt/s; the value of b is 0.955.

  a. The voltages are given beginning at time $t = 10$ s rather than $t = 0$ s. How can the equation $y = a \cdot b^x$ be changed to account for this? @ $y = a \cdot b^{x-10}$
  b. To model the data, you need values of a and b. For the value of b, what is the average ratio between consecutive voltages?
  c. Find the value of a and write the equation that models these data. ⓗ $a = 6.579$; $y = 6.579(0.955)^{x-10}$
  d. Use your equation to predict the voltage at time 0.
  e. Use your equation to predict when the voltage is less than 1.
     approximately 51 s after the capacitor is disconnected

8b. a translation right 4 units

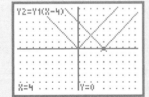

Exercise 10 Don't assign this problem if you haven't covered exponential equations from Chapter 6. For 10d, it might be interesting to note that most 9-volt batteries actually start out with about 9.5 volts.

10d. $y = 6.579(0.955)^{0-10} \approx 10.426$ volts

Exercise 11 [Ask] "Why is r subtracted from 1 instead of added?" [To model decreasing growth, you use a base that's less than 1 (but more than 0). Powers of numbers less than 1 get smaller and smaller.]

You might use the Fathom demonstration The Uncool Sandwich to replace this exercise.

11. Mini-Investigation Recall that an exponential equation in the form $y = A(1 - r)^x$ models some decreasing patterns. As you increase the value of x, the **long-run value** of y gets closer and closer to zero. Some situations, however, do not decrease all the way to zero. For example, as a cup of hot chocolate cools, the coolest it can get is room temperature. The long-run value will not be 0°C. Consider this table of data.

Time (min)	0	1	2	3	4	5	6
Temperature (°C)	68	52	41	34	30	27	25

[Data sets: **HCTIM, HCTMP**]

a. Define variables and make a scatter plot of the data. What type of function would fit the data? @

b. Find the ratio of each temperature to the previous temperature. Do these ratios support your answer to 11a?

Assume the temperature of the room in this situation is 21°C. This means the long-run value of these data will also be 21°C.

c. Make a new table by subtracting 21 from each temperature. Then make a scatter plot of the changed data. How have the points been transformed? What will be the long-run value? @

d. For your data in 11c, find the ratios of temperatures between successive readings. How do the ratios compare? What is the mean of these ratios? @

e. Write an exponential equation in the form $y = A(1 - r)^x$ that models the data in 11c. $y = 47(1 - 0.34)^x$

f. In 11c you subtracted 21 from each temperature. What transformation takes these data back to the original data? @ a translation up 21 units

g. Your equation in 11e models translated data. Change that equation so that it models the original data. Check the fit by graphing on your calculator.

12. APPLICATION In 2004, the world population was estimated to be 6.4 billion, with an annual growth rate of 1.14%. (Central Intelligence Agency, *www.cia.gov*)

a. Define input and output variables for this situation.

b. Without finding an equation, sketch a graph of this situation for 1995 to 2015.

c. What one point on the graph do you know for sure? (2004, 6.4)

d. Write a function that models this situation. Graph your function on your calculator and name an appropriate window.

e. Use your graph to estimate the population to the nearest tenth of a billion in 1995 and 2015. (Assume a constant growth rate during this period.) 1995: 5.8 billion; 2015: 7.2 billion

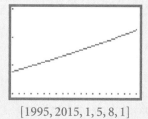
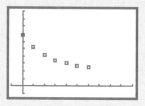
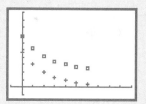
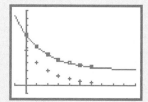

Exercise 13 It could surprise students that vertical translations of the graph of $y = bx$ are the same as horizontal translations. For example, the vertical upward shift given by $y - 3 = 2x$ gives the same graph as $y = 2(x + 1.5)$, which can be seen as a translation to the left. This property is a characteristic of straight lines.

13. The graph of a linear equation of the form $y = bx$ passes through $(0, 0)$.

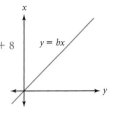

a. Suppose the graph of $y = bx$ is translated right 4 units and up 8 units. Name a point on the new graph. $(4, 8)$

$y = b(x - 4) + 8$

b. Write an equation for the line in 13a after the transformation. @

c. Suppose the graph of $y = bx$ is translated horizontally H units and vertically V units. Name a point on the new graph. @ (H, V)

d. Write an equation for the line in 13c after the transformation.
$y = b(x - H) + V$

▶ **Review**

2.2 **14.** Drew's teacher gives skill-building quizzes at the start of each class.

a. On Monday, Drew got 77 problems correct out of 85. What is her percent correct? 90.6%

b. On Tuesday, Drew got 100% on a quiz that had only 10 problems. Estimate her percent correct for the two-day total. Answers will vary.

c. Calculate her percent correct for the two-day total. 91.6%

5.3 **15.** Solve each system of equations.

a. $\begin{cases} y = 5 + 2x \\ y = 8 - 2x \end{cases}$

$x = 0.75, y = 6.5$

b. $\begin{cases} y = -2 + 3(x - 4) \\ y = 3 + 5(x - 2) \end{cases}$

$x = -3.5, y = -24.5$

c. $\begin{cases} 2x + 7y = 13 \\ 5x - 14y = 1 \end{cases}$

$x = 3, y = 1$

IMPROVING YOUR VISUAL THINKING SKILLS

Tammy and José are working on Exercise 13a on this page. They each decide to graph a linear equation in the form $y = bx$ to help visualize the question. They translate their graphs right 4 units and up 8 units. Their results are surprisingly different.

José's Graph

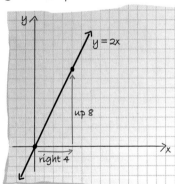

$y = 2x$

up 8

right 4

Tammy's Graph

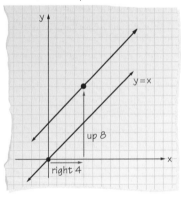

$y = x$

up 8

right 4

Why did José get the same graph after the translation?

If the graph of an equation in the form $y = bx$ is translated horizontally H units and vertically V units, when would you get the same graph after the translation?

IMPROVING VISUAL THINKING SKILLS

The vertical shift divided by the horizontal shift is the same as the slope of José's line, so the line was in effect shifted along itself to lie on top of itself. You might ask what shift would have shifted Tammy's line onto itself. Students may be surprised to discover that any translation by the same amount horizontally and vertically will leave Tammy's line unchanged. A translation horizontally H units and vertically V units will leave the line with slope $\frac{V}{H}$ unchanged. Ask if this could happen to figures other than lines, to help students appreciate the importance of lines' constant slope.

Reflecting Points and Graphs

The art of a people is a true mirror to their minds.

JAWAHARLAL NEHRU

Translations move points and graphs around the coordinate plane. Have you noticed that the image of the translation always looks like the original figure? Although the image of a translation moves, it doesn't flip, turn, or change size. To get these changes, you need other types of transformations.

Investigation
Flipping Graphs

In this investigation you will explore the relationships between the graph of an equation and its image when you flip it two different ways.

Step 1 $(1, 5), (3, 1),$ and $(6, 2)$

Step 1 Name the coordinates of the vertices of this triangle.

> **Procedure Note**
> For this investigation, use a friendly window with a factor of 2.

Step 2 Graph the triangle on your calculator. Use list L1 for the x-coordinates of the vertices and list L2 for the y-coordinates of the vertices.

Step 3 Define list L3 and list L4 as follows:

$$L3 = -L1$$
$$L4 = L2$$

Step 4 $(-1, 5), (-3, 1),$ and $(-6, 2)$; the triangle is flipped across the y-axis; the x-coordinates of the new triangle become negative.

Graph a second triangle using list L3 for the x-coordinates of the vertices and list L4 for the y-coordinates of the vertices.

Step 4 Name the coordinates of the vertices of the new triangle. Describe the transformation. How did the coordinates of the vertices change?

Step 5a $(1, -5), (3, -1),$ and $(6, -2)$; the triangle is flipped across the x-axis; the y-coordinates of the new triangle become negative.

Step 5 Repeat Steps 3 and 4 with these definitions.

a. $L3 = L1$
  $L4 = -L2$

b. $L3 = -L1$
  $L4 = -L2$

$(-1, -5), (-3, -1),$ and $(-6, -2)$; the triangle is flipped across the x- and y-axes; the signs change for both the x- and y-coordinates.

Next, you'll see if what you have learned about flipping points is true for graphs of functions.

Step 6 Graph $y = 2^x$ on your calculator.

Step 7 Replace x with $-x$ in the function. Graph this second function. Describe how the second graph is related to the graph of $y = 2^x$. $y = 2^{-x}$; a flip across the y-axis

reflection and the congruence between the reflected image and the original.

Some students may recognize that in part b, a reflection across the x-axis and then across the y-axis is equivalent to a 180° rotation about the origin.

Step 5a

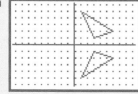

Step 5b

PLANNING

LESSON OUTLINE

One day:
20 min	Investigation
5 min	Sharing
10 min	Examples
5 min	Closing
10 min	Exercises

MATERIALS

- graph paper
- patty paper, *optional*
- Flipping a Letter (T), *optional*
- Calculator Note 8B
- Sketchpad demonstration Transforming Graphs, *optional*

TEACHING

Another kind of transformation is the reflection. Here we look at reflections across the axes.

 Guiding the Investigation

One Step
Show the Flipping a Letter transparency. Ask students what operations they should apply to the coordinates of the corners of the darker letter to achieve the lighter letter. Students might use their calculators to test their theories. As groups finish, have them experiment to reflect the graph of a function of their choice across the x-axis and the y-axis.

Step 5 Each time students repeat Step 3, they are to work with the original triangle. They might use graph paper or patty paper. The graph can be folded and held up to the light to see both the line of

See page 725 for answers to Steps 2, 3, 6, 7, 8, and 10.

Step 8 Encourage students to write out all the details.

SHARING IDEAS

Groups could report their ideas from Steps 9 and 10. Students may be surprised that the reflections of the graph of $y = x$ across the two axes are the same. Ask whether that's the case for other graphs. [It's true only for figures that are rotated onto themselves by a 180° rotation about the origin.] Be sure the term *reflection* is used.

A mathematical *reflection* across a line moves a figure to where it would *appear* to be if the line were a mirror. The term *flipping* for a reflection indicates that you can think of the figure as leaving the plane and being flipped across the line of reflection.

Ask whether the opening quotation uses the idea of a mirror in the same way as a mathematical reflection. Nehru (1889–1964), a leader in India's liberation from British rule, went on to become India's first prime minister.

To write the equation of a translation, students went backward from what they did to coordinates of vertices. Some students may notice that with reflections, they seem to be doing the same thing to both the variable in the equation and the coordinate of a vertex: taking the opposite, or changing the sign. **[Ask]** "Why does translation seem different from reflection in this respect?" [Elicit the idea that, whereas going backward from adding 4 is subtracting 4, going backward from taking the opposite is still taking the opposite.]

Step 8 $y = -2^x$;   Step 8
a flip across the x-axis

Step 9a   Step 9
$y = (-x - 1)^2$ flips across the y-axis; $y = -(x - 1)^2$ flips across the x-axis.

          Step 10

Now replace y with $-y$ in the function $y = 2^x$ and solve for y. Graph this third function. Describe how its graph is related to the graph of $y = 2^x$.

Repeat Steps 6–8 using these functions. Make a note of anything unusual that you find.   **Step 9b** $y = -|x|$ flips across the y-axis, although it appears
a. $y = (x - 1)^2$ unchanged due to the vertical symmetry of the graph;
b. $y = |x|$ $y = -|x|$ flips across the x-axis.
c. $y = x$ **Step 9c** $y = -x$ can be considered a flip either across the x-axis or
                        across the y-axis due to diagonal symmetry of the graph.

Summarize what you have learned about flipping graphs.

A transformation that flips a figure to create a mirror image is called a **reflection.** A point is **reflected across the x-axis,** or *vertically reflected,* when you change the sign of its y-coordinate. A point is **reflected across the y-axis,** or *horizontally reflected,* when you change the sign of its x-coordinate. You saw both types of reflections in the investigation. Similar reflections result when you change the sign of x or y in a function.

You can combine reflections with other transformations. Sometimes, different combinations will give the same result.

EXAMPLE A

The graph of a parent function is shown in black. Its image after a transformation is shown in red. Describe the transformation and then write a function for the image.

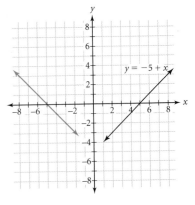

▶ **Solution**

This is a reflection across the y-axis. The image is produced by replacing each x-value in the original function with $-x$.

$$y = -5 + (-x)$$
or
$$y = -5 - x$$

The sign of the x-coordinates changes. So the graph reflects across the y-axis.

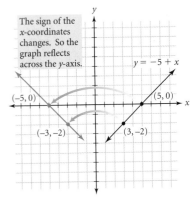

LESSON OBJECTIVES

- Explore reflections and combinations of reflections and translations
- Write equations for these transformations and list definitions that describe them

NCTM STANDARDS

CONTENT		PROCESS	
	Number		Problem Solving
✓	Algebra	✓	Reasoning
✓	Geometry		Communication
	Measurement	✓	Connections
	Data/Probability	✓	Representation

EXAMPLE B

The graph of a parent function is shown in black. Its image after a transformation is shown in red. Describe the transformation and then write a function for the image.

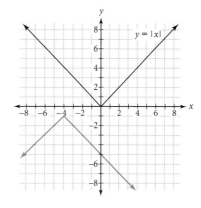

▶ **Solution**

Here is one possible solution. Reflect the graph of the function across the *x*-axis, then translate it left 4 units and down 1 unit. To write the equation of the image, change the original function in the same order.

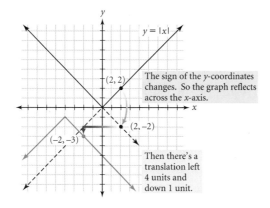

The sign of the *y*-coordinates changes. So the graph reflects across the *x*-axis.

Then there's a translation left 4 units and down 1 unit.

$$y = |x|$$ Original equation.

$$-y = |x|$$ Replace *y* with $-y$ to reflect across the *x*-axis.

$$y = -|x|$$ Solve for *y*.

$$y = -|x + 4|$$ Replace *x* with $x + 4$ to translate left 4 units.

$$y + 1 = -|x + 4|$$ Replace *y* with $y + 1$ to translate down 1 unit.

$$y = -|x + 4| - 1$$ Solve for *y*.

A function for the image is $y = -|x + 4| - 1$.

[▶ You can practice writing a function for a translated and reflected graph, or graphing a translated and reflected function, using the **Dynamic Algebra Exploration** at **www.keymath.com/DA** . ◀]

Assessing Progress

Watch for the ability to read coordinates of points, enter coordinates into lists, graph polygons on a calculator, graph equations on a calculator, and recognize translations.

▶ **EXAMPLE A**

This example illustrates going from the graph to the transformation.

▶ **EXAMPLE B**

Some students may prefer to see $x + 4$ rewritten as $x - (-4)$.

Extension Questions

If you have time, ask extension questions. **[Ask]** "What effect does a horizontal or vertical reflection have on the slope of a straight line?" [It negates the slope.] "What one point does not change due to the reflection?" [the intercept with the line of reflection] "What order of transformations, applied to the parent absolute-value function, produces $y = -\left(|-x - 4| + 1\right)$?" [one answer: a translation right 4 units and up 1 unit, followed by a reflection across the *y*-axis, followed by a reflection across the *x*-axis]

► **EXAMPLE C**

The two halves of the graphs $y = f(x)$ and $y = f(x - 8) - 6$ are mirror images. Each graph is *symmetric*. **[Ask]** "Are there any other graphs you have learned about that are mirror images of themselves?" [parabolas, absolute-value functions, horizontal and vertical lines] "Is it possible for a *function's* graph to show no apparent change after a reflection across the *x*-axis?" [For this to be the case, the top half of the graph would have to be a mirror image of the bottom half. Unless the function were $f(x) = 0$, the graph would then fail the vertical line test.] You might also **[Ask]** "When can translations be replaced by reflections?" [Every translation can be accomplished with two reflections, though not necessarily across axes. If the graph is appropriately symmetric, the translation can be accomplished with just one reflection.] These ideas preview Exercise 11 and Take Another Look.

Closing the Lesson

Taking the opposite (changing the sign) of a *y*-coordinate or the variable *y* results in a **reflection** across the *x*-axis. Similarly, taking the opposite of an *x*-coordinate or the variable *x* results in a reflection across the *y*-axis.

BUILDING UNDERSTANDING

Students work with combinations of reflections and translations.

ASSIGNING HOMEWORK

Essential	1, 4–6, 12
Performance assessment	2, 7
Portfolio	8, 9
Journal	10
Group	3, 11
Review	12–14

EXAMPLE C

The graph of a parent function is shown in black. Its image after a transformation is shown in red. Describe two different transformations and then write functions for the image.

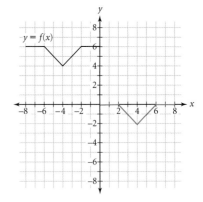

► **Solution**

As in Example B, you can think of this transformation in several ways. One solution is to translate right 8 units and down 6 units, as shown in the graph on the left below. That gives the function $y = f(x - 8) - 6$.

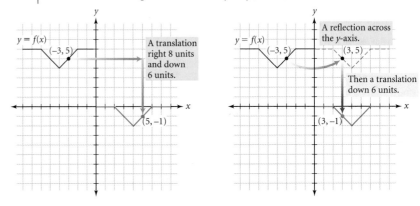

Another solution is to reflect the graph across the *y*-axis and then translate down 6 units, as shown in the graph on the right above. That gives the function $y = f(-x) - 6$.

In the investigation you probably saw no change when you reflected the graph of $y = |x|$ across the *y*-axis. In Example C, a reflection across the *y*-axis has the same result as a horizontal translation. Do you notice anything special about these graphs that could explain these strange results?

EXERCISES

You will need your graphing calculator for Exercises **2, 4, 5,** and **12**.

▶ **Practice Your Skills**

1. Use $f(x) = 0.5(x - 3)^2 - 3$ to find

  a. $f(5)$ −1 **b.** $f(-6)$ ⓐ 37.5 **c.** $4 \cdot f(2)$ −10 **d.** $f(-x)$ $0.5(-x - 3)^2 - 3$ **e.** $-f(x)$ ⓐ $-0.5(x - 3)^2 + 3$

2. Describe each graph as a transformation of $y = |x|$ or $y = x^2$. Then write its equation. Check your answers by graphing on your calculator.

a.
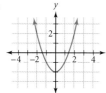
a translation of the graph of $y = x^2$ down 2 units; $y = x^2 - 2$

b.
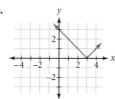
a translation of the graph of $y = |x|$ right 3 units; $y = |x - 3|$

c.
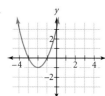
a translation of the graph of $y = x^2$ left 2 units and down 1 unit; $y = (x + 2)^2 - 1$

d.
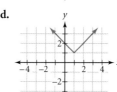
a translation of the graph of $y = |x|$ right 1 unit and up 1 unit; $y = |x - 1| + 1$

3. Describe each graph below as a transformation of $y = |x + 3|$, shown at right.

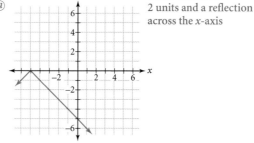
$y = |x + 3|$

a.
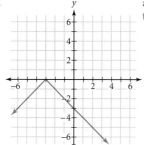
a reflection across the x-axis

b. @
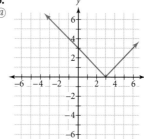
a translation right 6 units or a reflection across the y-axis

c.
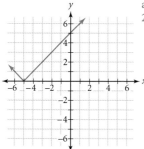
a translation left 2 units

d. @
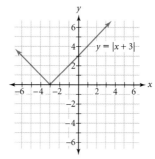
a translation left 2 units and a reflection across the x-axis

► **Helping with the Exercises**

Exercise 2 Now that students know about reflections, they might insert reflections to give a variety of transformations.

Exercise 3 Some students may be confused by being asked to identify the transformation of a function that is already a transformation of a parent function.

You might use the Sketchpad demonstration Transforming Graphs to give students more practice with translations and reflections.

Exercise 4 [Alert] As in Lesson 8.2, Exercise 8, make sure students know how their calculators behave. On some calculators, $Y_1(-x)$ will multiply rather than give a composition of functions.

4a. a reflection across the y-axis

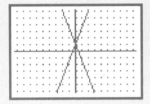

4b. a reflection across the x-axis

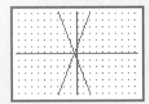

Exercise 5 Some students may need to be reminded that the order of operations calls for $-x^2$ to mean $-(x^2)$ rather than $(-x)^2$.

Order is crucial in 5c. A translation followed by a reflection would be represented by the equation $y = -(x^2 + 3)$.

In 5d, because the graph of $y = x^2$ has vertical symmetry, the resulting graph will appear only to have been translated. You may want to ask students why $(-x)^2 + 3$ would be equivalent to $x^2 + 3$, to review $(-x)^2 = x^2$.

5a. a reflection across the x-axis

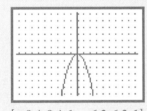

$[-9.4, 9.4, 1, -6.2, 6.2, 1]$

5b. a translation left 3 units and a reflection across the x-axis

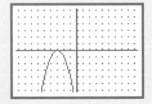

4. Graph $Y_1(x) = 1 + 2.5x$ on your calculator. Predict what each graph will look like. Check by comparing graphs on your calculator. [▶ 🖳 See **Calculator Note 8B** for specific instructions for your calculator. ◀]

   a. $Y_2(x) = Y_1(-x)$

   b. $Y_2(x) = -Y_1(x)$

5. Describe the graph of each function below as a transformation of the graph of the parent function $y = x^2$. Check your answers by graphing on your calculator. (You'll need to solve for y first.)

   a. $y = -x^2$

   b. $-y = (x + 3)^2$

   c. $y = -x^2 + 3$ ⓐ

   d. $y - 3 = (-x)^2$ ⓐ

▶ **Reason and Apply**

6a. Possible answer: Enter the x-coordinates into list L1 and the y-coordinates into list L2: L1 = $\{2, 7, 7, 2\}$ and L2 = $\{2, 2, 4, 2\}$. Then make a connected graph.

6. Consider the triangle at right.

   a. Describe how you can graph this triangle on your calculator.

   b. How could you make these graphs?

$[-9.4, 9.4, 1, -6.2, 6.2, 1]$

  i. 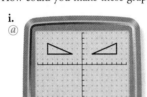   Define L3 = $-$L1 and L4 = L2. **ii.**    Define L3 = $-$L1 and L4 = $-$L2.

  iii. 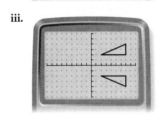   Define L3 = L1 and L4 = $-$L2. **iv.**    Define L3 = L1 + 2 and L4 = $-$L2.

7. The points in this table form a star when you connect them in order. Describe the transformation that results when you change the points to

   a. $(-x, y)$ a reflection across the y-axis

   b. $(x, -y)$ a reflection across the x-axis

7c. a translation left 8 units and a reflection across the x-axis

   c. $(x - 8, -y)$

   d. $(x + 2, y - 4)$ ⓐ   a translation right 2 units and down 4 units

   e. $(-x, -y)$ ⓐ   a reflection across the x- and y-axes

   f. (y, x) ⓗ   a reflection across the line $y = x$

x	y
6.0	2.0
2.4	3.2
4.6	0.1
4.6	3.9
2.4	0.8
6.0	2.0

5c. a reflection across the x-axis followed by a translation up 3 units

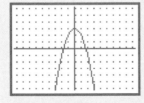

5d. a reflection across the y-axis and a translation up 3 units (or just a translation up 3 units)

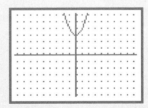

Exercise 6b Students should use list definitions to create the new graphs, rather than entering the coordinates for individual points.

8. Anthony and Cheryl are using a motion sensor for a "walker" investigation.

a. This graph shows data that Cheryl collected when Anthony walked. Write an equation that models his walk. $y = |x - 4| + 1$

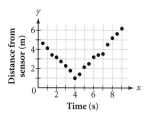

Anthony's Walk

b. Here is a description of Cheryl's walk.

Begin at a distance of 0.5 meter from the sensor. Walk away from the sensor at 1 meter per second for 3 seconds. Then walk toward the sensor at the same rate for 3 seconds.

Write an equation to model her walk. ⓗ $y = -|x - 3| + 3.5$

c. Give the domain and range for the function that models Cheryl's walk.
domain: $0 \le x \le 6$; range: $0.5 \le y \le 3.5$

9. APPLICATION Bo is designing a computer animation program. She wants the star on the left to move to the position of the star on the right using 11 frames. She also wants the star to flip top to bottom in each frame. Define the coordinates of each image based on the coordinates of the previous figure. ⓐ

$$(x + 1, -y)$$

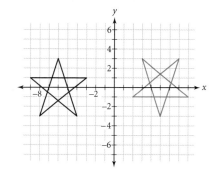

10. For a and b, the graph of a parent function is shown in black. Describe the transformation that creates the red image. Then write a function for the image.

a.

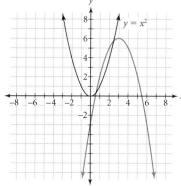

possible answer: $y = -(x - 3)^2 + 6$

b.

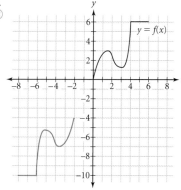

possible answer: $y = -f(-(x + 2)) - 4$

Exercise 11 Graph iv can be thought of in several ways. For 11a, the graph can be thought of in four ways: as a reflection across the y-axis followed by a translation either left 8 units or down 16 units, and as a reflection across the x-axis followed by a translation either down 8 units or left 4 units. All are equivalent to $y = -12 - 2x$. For 11b, the reflection in graph iv can be either horizontal or vertical.

11a. i. $y = -x^2 - 4$

ii. $y = -|x| + 7$

iii. $y = 2^{-(x-6)}$

iv. $y = 2[-(x + 8)] + 4$;
$y = [4 + 2(-x)] - 16$;
$y = -(4 + 2x) - 8$; or
$y = -[4 + 2(x + 4)]$

11b. i. $y = -2$

ii. $y = 3.5$

iii. $x = 3$

iv. $x = -4$ or $y = -4$

11c. If the line of reflection is $x = a$ or $y = b$, the amount of translation is twice a or twice b.

11. *Mini-Investigation* A line of reflection does not have to be the x- or y-axis. Consider this example in which $y = |x|$ is reflected across the line $x = 4$.

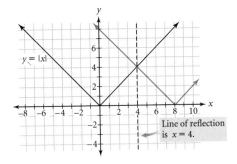

Line of reflection is $x = 4$.

a. Write an equation for the red image in each graph. ⓐ

i.

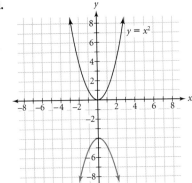

$y = x^2$

ii.

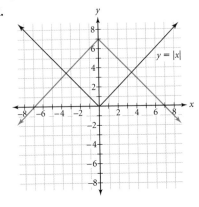

$y = |x|$

iii.

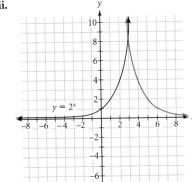

$y = 2^x$

iv.

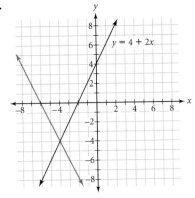

$y = 4 + 2x$

b. Think about each of the transformations in 11a as a single reflection. What is the line of reflection in each case? ⓐ

c. What is the relationship between the line of reflection and the translation in your equation?

d. The graph of $y = f(x)$ is reflected across the horizontal line $y = b$. What is the equation of the image? ⓐ $y = -f(x) + 2b$

e. The graph of a function $y = f(x)$ is reflected across the vertical line $x = a$. What is the equation of the image? ⓗ $y = f(-x + 2a)$

6.2 **12.** A chemical reaction consumes 12% of the reactant per minute. A scientist begins with 500 grams of one reactant. So the equation $y = 500(0.88)^x$ gives the amount of reactant, y, remaining after x minutes.

  a. What does the number 0.88 tell you? There is a 12% decrease per minute; $(1 - 0.12 = 0.88)$.

  b. What is the long-run value of y? What is the real-world meaning of this value?

  c. What is the long-run value of y for the equation $y = 500(0.88)^x + 100$? What is the real-world meaning of this value?   100 g; not all the reactant will be used.

  d. Graph $y = 500(0.88)^x$ and $y = 500(0.88)^x + 100$. How are these graphs the same? How are they different?

2.3 **13.** Convert 47 tablespoons to quarts. (16 tablespoons = 1 cup; 1 quart = 4 cups) Ⓗ

4.6 **14.** This table shows the temperature of water in a pan set on a stove.

  a. Find the equation of a line that models these data.

  b. How long will it take for the water to boil (100°C)? approximately 22 min

Time (min)	0	2	4	6	8	10	12	14	16	18
Temperature (°C)	22	29	36	44	51	58	65	72	80	87

[Data sets: PANTM, PANTP]

IMPROVING YOUR REASONING SKILLS

The ancient Mayan civilization occupied parts of Mexico and Central America as early as 1500 B.C.E. The Maya had a number system based on 20. They are also the earliest known civilization to use zero.

Below are the 20 numerals in the Mayan number system. Can you decode the numerals and label them with the numbers 0 to 19? A few are labeled to get you started.

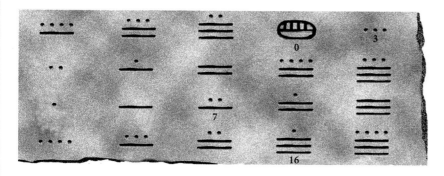

Exercise 12 [ELL] A *reaction* is a chemical change. A *reactant* is the chemical that changes.

12b. 0 g; all the reactant will be used.

12d. Both graphs are decreasing exponential graphs. The graph of $y = 500(0.88)^x$ shows a starting amount of 500 g reactant; the graph of $y = 500(0.88)^x + 100$ shows a starting amount of 600 g reactant. The second graph is a translation of the first graph up 100 units.

13. $47\,\text{T} \cdot \dfrac{1\text{ cup}}{16\text{ T}} \cdot \dfrac{1\text{ quart}}{4\text{ cups}}$
$= \dfrac{47}{64}$ quarts ≈ 0.734 quart

14a. possible answers using Q-points: $y = 36 + 3.6(x - 4)$ or $y = 72 + 3.6(x - 14)$

IMPROVING REASONING SKILLS

The components of the Mayan number system are often described as *dots* and *rods*. Each rod represents 5 and each dot represents 1. The symbol for 0 is often called a *shell*, yet different sources draw it differently.

The base-10 Hindu-Arabic system we use today has 10 digits, 0 through 9. Every other numeral is formed by a placement of these digits. For example, each digit in the numeral 349 represents multiplication by a different power of 10.

In the Mayan number system, the 20 digits, equivalent to our 0 to 19, were used in a top-to-bottom positional number system in which each digit represented a different power of 20. The answers are:

9	13	17	0	3
2	6	10	14	18
1	5	7	11	15
4	8	12	16	19

LESSON

8.4

PLANNING

LESSON OUTLINE

One day:

25 min   Investigation

5 min   Sharing

10 min   Examples

5 min   Closing

5 min   Exercises

MATERIALS

- graph paper, *optional*
- Stretching a Polygon (T or W), *optional*
- Calculator Notes 8B, 8C, 8D
- CBL 2 demonstration Warming Up, *optional*

TEACHING

Our transformation toolbox is expanded to include vertical stretches and shrinks.

Using the Quote

Oliver Heaviside was an English telegrapher who made important advances in the field of electro-magnetism. He predicted the existence of a layer in the atmosphere that allowed radio waves to follow the curvature of Earth. This layer was later proved to exist and named the Heaviside layer. Interested students might research current scientific theories on the size of the universe using the links at www.keymath.com/DA.

Stretching and Shrinking Graphs

There is no absolute scale of size in the Universe, for it is boundless towards the great and also boundless towards the small.

OLIVER HEAVISIDE

Imagine what happens to the shape of a picture drawn on a rubber sheet as you **stretch** the sheet vertically.

The width remains the same, but the height changes. You can also **shrink** a picture vertically. This makes the picture appear to have been flattened.

You know how to translate and reflect graphs on a coordinate plane. Now let's see how to change their shape.

LESSON OBJECTIVES

- Discover how to change the shape of polygons and functions
- Explore vertical stretches and shrinks of polygons and graphs of equations
- Write equations for graphs resulting from stretches and shrinks

NCTM STANDARDS

CONTENT		PROCESS	
	Number		Problem Solving
✓	Algebra		Reasoning
✓	Geometry	✓	Communication
	Measurement	✓	Connections
	Data/Probability	✓	Representation

The German painter Hans Holbein II (1497–1543) used a technique called anamorphosis to hide a stretched skull in his portrait *The Ambassadors* (1533). You can see the skull in the original painting if you look across the page from the lower left. The painting was originally hung above a doorway so that people would notice the skull as they walked through the door. Holbein may have been making a political statement about these two French ambassadors, who were members of England's court of King Henry VIII.

Investigation
Changing the Shape of a Graph

In this investigation you will learn how to stretch or shrink a graph vertically.

Step 1

Step 1 $(1, 3), (2, -1),$
$(-3, 0),$ and $(-2, 2)$

Step 4 For $a = 2$, the quadrilateral is stretched vertically by a factor of 2. For $a = 3$, the quadrilateral is stretched vertically by a factor of 3. For $a = 0.5$, the quadrilateral is **Step 2** shrunk vertically by a factor of 0.5. For $a = -2$, the quadrilateral **Step 3** is stretched vertically by 2 and reflected across the x-axis. For each vertex, the y-coordinate of the vertex is multiplied by a factor of a.

Step 4

Step 5 $(1, 4.5), (2, -1.5),$
$(-3, 0), (-2, 3)$; the quadrilateral will **Step 5** stretch vertically slightly, by a factor of 1.5; **Step 6** the vertex $(-3, 0)$ will not move.

Name the coordinates of the vertices of this quadrilateral.

> **Procedure Note**
>
> For this investigation, use a friendly window with a factor of 2.

Graph the quadrilateral on your calculator. Use list L1 for the x-coordinates of the vertices and list L2 for the y-coordinates of the vertices.

Each member of your group should choose one of these values of a: 2, 3, 0.5, or -2. Use your value of a to define list L3 and list L4 as follows:

L3 = L1
L4 = $a \cdot$ L2

Graph a second quadrilateral using list L3 for the x-coordinates of the vertices and list L4 for the y-coordinates of the vertices.

Share your results from Step 3. For each value of a, describe the transformation of the quadrilateral in Step 2. What was the result for each vertex?

Predict the location of each vertex if the value of a is 1.5. Describe how you think the overall appearance of the quadrilateral will change.

Make a conjecture about how a graph will be affected when its y-values are multiplied by values greater than 1, between 0 and 1, and less than 0.

Step 4 possible answer:

Value of a	The whole graph	Points above the x-axis	Points below the x-axis	Points on the x-axis
$a = 2, a = 3$	A vertical stretch	Go farther up, away from the x-axis	Go farther down, away from the x-axis	Unchanged
$a = 0.5$	A vertical shrink	Go down closer to the x-axis	Go up closer to the x-axis	Unchanged
$a = -2$	A stretch or a shrink reflected across the x-axis	As above but reflected across the x-axis	As above but reflected across the x-axis	Unchanged

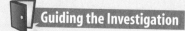
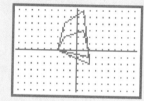
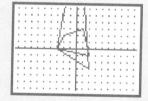
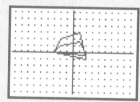
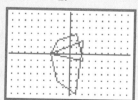

Step 6 For a factor greater than 1, the graph stretches vertically. For a factor less than 1, the graph shrinks vertically. For a factor less than 0, the graph stretches or shrinks vertically (depending on whether a is less than -1 or between -1 and 0) and is reflected across the x-axis. Points on the x-axis do not move.

Step 8 As written, the equation in part b indicates a stretch followed by a translation. Students entering $L_3 = 2 * (L_2 - 2)$ will see a translation followed by a stretch, with a different result. If any students make this mistake, ask them to present it later so that the class can learn from the idea.

Step 8a a vertical shrink by a factor of 0.5, then a reflection across the x-axis

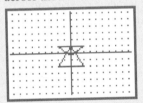

Step 8b a vertical stretch by a factor of 2, then a translation down 2 units

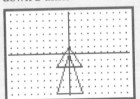

Step 9 Each of these images is obtained by stretching and then perhaps translating the figure in Step 7. If students are confused, help them identify the stretch factor. **[Ask]** "How tall is the original triangle? The transformed triangle is how many times as tall?"

Step 10 If a group has fewer than four members, the first student to finish with one equation should repeat the procedure with an unused equation.

Steps 11 and 13 Students may be confused because they're transforming functions that are not

Step 7 Graph should look like that shown on the student page;
$L_1 = \{2, -2, 0, 2\}$,
$L_2 = \{-2, -2, 1, -2\}$.

Step 9a
$L_3 = L_1$,
$L_4 = 3 \cdot L_2$

Step 9b
$L_3 = L_1$,
$L_4 = 2 \cdot L_2 + 3$

Steps 10 and 11 Graphs depend on equation chosen.

Step 12 The y-values for Y_2 will be twice the y-values for Y_1. This results in a vertical stretch so that the positive range is 2 times higher and the negative range is 2 times lower.

Step 13a The y-values for Y_2 will be one-half the y-values for Y_1; a vertical shrink.

Step 13b The y-values for Y_2 will be 3 times the y-values for Y_1; a vertical stretch.

Step 13c The y-values for Y_2 will be 2 times the y-values for Y_1 and then negated; a vertical stretch and reflection.

Step 7

Step 8

Step 9

Step 10

Step 11

Step 12

Step 13

Step 14

Graph this triangle on your calculator. Use list L_1 for the x-coordinates of the vertices and list L_2 for the y-coordinates of the vertices.

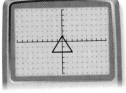

Describe how the definitions in Steps 8a–b below transform the triangle. Use list L_3 for the x-coordinates of the vertices of the image and list L_4 for the y-coordinates of the vertices of the image. Check your answers by graphing on your calculator.

a. $L_3 = L_1$
$L_4 = -0.5 \cdot L_2$

b. $L_3 = L_1$
$L_4 = 2 \cdot L_2 - 2$

Write definitions for list L_3 and list L_4 in terms of list L_1 and list L_2 to create each image below. Check your definitions by graphing on your calculator.

a.

b.

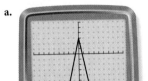

Next, see how you can stretch and shrink the graph of a function.

Each member of your group should choose an equation from the list below. Enter your equation into Y_1 and graph it on your calculator.

$Y_1(x) = -1 + 0.5x$ $Y_1(x) = |x| - 2$
$Y_1(x) = -x^2 + 1$ $Y_1(x) = 1.4^x$

Enter $Y_2(x) = 2 \cdot Y_1(x)$ and graph it. [▶ 🖥 See **Calculator Note 8B** for specific instructions for your calculator. ◀]

Look at a table on your calculator and compare the y-values for Y_1 and Y_2.

Repeat Steps 11 and 12, but use these equations for Y_2.

a. $Y_2(x) = 0.5 \cdot Y_1(x)$ **b.** $Y_2(x) = 3 \cdot Y_1(x)$ **c.** $Y_2(x) = -2 \cdot Y_1(x)$

Write an equation for $R(x)$ in terms of $B(x)$. Then write an equation for $B(x)$ in terms of $R(x)$.

a.

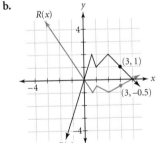

$R(x) = 3 \cdot B(x)$;
$B(x) = \frac{1}{3} \cdot R(x)$

b.

$R(x) = -\frac{1}{2} \cdot B(x)$;
$B(x) = -2 \cdot R(x)$

parent functions. Calculators vary in syntax. Have Calculator Note 8B handy.

SHARING IDEAS

Ask students to report ideas from Steps 6, 9, and 13.

Remind students that, for translations and reflections, the change to a variable in an equation was backward from the change to the corresponding coordinate of a point. **[Ask]** "Is that the case for a vertical stretch or shrink? How and why?"

As a prelude to Improving Your Reasoning Skills, ask about horizontal stretches and shrinks. **[Ask]** "How would you change the coefficients of a point? How would you change the equation?"

If you were able to generate some controversy in Lesson 8.2 about whether the functions $y = 33(1 + 0.30)^x$ and $y = 92(1 + 0.30)^x$ were in the same family, you might ask the question again. Elicit the idea that they are both vertical stretches of the function $y = (1 + 0.30)^x$, so they're in the same family.

To vertically stretch or shrink a polygon, you multiply the y-coordinates of the vertices by a constant factor. To vertically stretch or shrink the graph of a function, you again have to multiply the function by a factor.

EXAMPLE A

Describe how the graph of $y = 0.5|x|$ relates to the graph of $y = |x|$. Then graph both functions.

▶ **Solution**

Tables of values for both functions show that $y = 0.5|x|$ is a vertical shrink. Each y-value for $y = 0.5|x|$ is one-half the corresponding y-value for $y = |x|$. Multiplying the function by 0.5 has the same effect as multiplying the y-coordinate of every point on the graph of $y = |x|$ by 0.5.

x	$y = |x|$	$y = 0.5|x|$
2	2	1
0	0	0
1	1	0.5
5	5	2.5

Technology
CONNECTION

Many computer applications allow you to change the size and shape of clip art. Some applications have commands to change only the horizontal or the vertical scale. If you change only one scale, you distort the picture with a stretch or a shrink. If you change both scales by the same factor, you create a larger or smaller picture that is geometrically similar to the original.

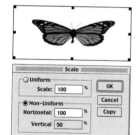

keymath.com/DA

Graphing the functions together also shows a vertical shrink by a factor of 0.5. Each point on the graph of $y = 0.5|x|$ is one-half the distance from the x-axis of the corresponding point on $y = |x|$.

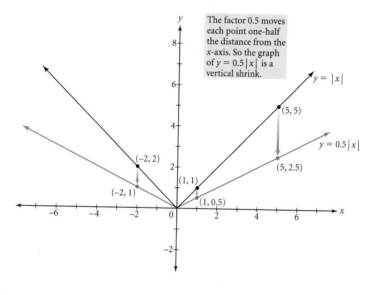

The factor 0.5 moves each point one-half the distance from the x-axis. So the graph of $y = 0.5|x|$ is a vertical shrink.

[▶ You can explore stretches and shrinks interactively using the **Dynamic Algebra Exploration** at **www.keymath.com/DA** . ◀]

Assessing Progress
Watch for students' ability to name the coordinates of a point, graph a polygon, operate on calculator lists, and recognize and describe translations and reflections.

▶ **EXAMPLE A**

This example describes a vertical shrink in terms of a ratio of distances from the x-axis.

MAKING THE CONNECTION

If a figure is stretched or shrunk by the same factor both horizontally and vertically, the image is geometrically similar to the original. This is called a *dilation*. If you have a projector and a computer with a drawing program, you could illustrate this.

This example shows how to find the factor by which a graph is stretched vertically. The solution considers the stretch of the graph first, although a translation is most apparent. The reason is twofold. First, like order of operations, it is customary to approach multiplication (stretches, shrinks, and reflections) before addition (translations). Second, applying the stretch factor after translating could erroneously result in

$$y = 1.5[(x + 4)^2 + 2]$$
$$= 1.5(x + 4)^2 + 3.$$

One method to check that you have found the correct function is to substitute several points that can be approximated on the graph, such as $(-4, 2)$, $(-2, 8)$, and $(-5, 3.5)$. Another method is to enter the function into the calculator and see whether a table of values corresponds to the graph in the student text.

For an additional example, you might use the CBL 2 demonstration Warming Up, which has students transform an exponential function to fit data.

EXAMPLE B Find an equation for the function shown in this graph.

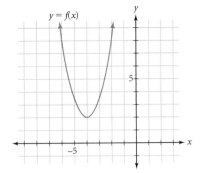

► **Solution** The graph is a parabola, so the parent function is $y = x^2$. First determine if a vertical stretch or shrink is necessary. An informal way to do this is to think about corresponding points on the graphs of $y = x^2$ and $y = f(x)$.

The parent function, $y = x^2$
When you move 1 unit left of the vertex, you move 1 unit up to find a point on the graph. When you move 2 units right of the vertex, you move 4 units up to find a point on the graph.

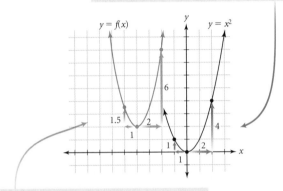

The image function, $y = f(x)$
When you move 1 unit left of the vertex, you move 1.5 units up to find a point on the graph. When you move 2 units right of the vertex, you move 6 units up to find a point on the graph.

For the same x-distances from the vertex on each graph, the corresponding y-distances from the vertex on the image graph, $y = f(x)$, are 1.5 times the y-distances on the parent graph, $y = x^2$. So the stretch factor is 1.5.

x-distance from vertex	y-distance from vertex of parent function, $y = x^2$	y-distance from vertex of image function, $y = f(x)$	Stretch factor calculation
1	1	1.5	$\frac{1.5}{1} = 1.5$
2	4	6	$\frac{6}{4} = 1.5$

$$y = x^2$$

Equation of the parent function.

$$y = 1.5x^2$$

Multiply the parent function, x^2, by a factor of 1.5 for the vertical stretch.

The vertex of the graph of $y = f(x)$ is $(-4, 2)$. So you must now change the equation to show a translation left 4 units and up 2 units.

$$y = 1.5(x + 4)^2$$

Replace x with $x - (-4)$, or $x + 4$, to translate the graph left 4 units.

$$y - 2 = 1.5(x + 4)^2$$

Replace y with $y - 2$ to translate the graph up 2 units.

$$y = 1.5(x + 4)^2 + 2$$

Solve for y.

The equation for the function is $y = 1.5(x + 4)^2 + 2$.

How can you check that this equation is correct?

Now that you've learned how to translate, reflect, and vertically stretch or shrink a graph, you can transform a function into many forms. This skill gives you a lot of power in mathematics. You can look at a complicated equation and see it as a variation of a simpler function. This skill also allows you to adjust the fit of mathematical models for many situations.

EXERCISES

You will need your graphing calculator for Exercises **4, 5, 7,** and **12.**

▶ **Practice Your Skills**

1. Ted and Ching-I are using a motion sensor for a "walker" investigation. They find that the graph at right models data for Ted's walk. Write an equation for this graph. @ $y = |x - 5|$

2. Ching-I walks so that her distance from the sensor is always twice Ted's distance from the sensor.
   a. Sketch a graph that models Ching-I's walk. @
   b. Write an equation for the graph in 2a. $y = 2|x - 5|$

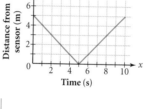

3. Ted walks so that the data can be modeled by this graph. $y = -1.2|x - 5| + 6$
   a. Write an equation for this graph. @
   b. Describe how Ted walked to create this graph.

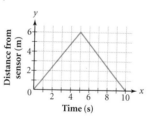

4. Run the ABS program five times. On your paper, sketch a graph of each randomly generated absolute-value function. Find an equation for each graph. [▶ 🖵 See **Calculator Note 8C** to learn how to use the ABS program. ◀] Answers will vary.

5. Run the PARAB program five times. On your paper, sketch a graph of each randomly generated parabola. Find an equation for each graph. [▶ 🖵 See **Calculator Note 8D** to learn how to use the PARAB program. ◀] Answers will vary.

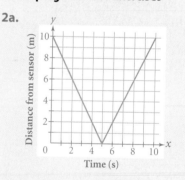

7a. a vertical stretch of $y = x^2$ by a factor of 2

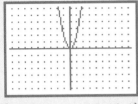

$[-9.4, 9.4, 1, -6.2, 6.2, 1]$

7b. a vertical shrink of $y = |x|$ by a factor of 0.25, then a translation right 2 units and up 1 unit

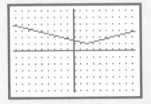

7c. a reflection of $y = x^2$ across the x-axis, then a translation left 4 units and down 1 unit

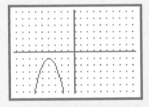

7d. a vertical stretch of $y = |x|$ by a factor of 2 and a reflection across the x-axis, then a translation right 3 units and up 4 units

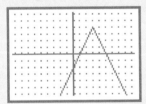

Exercise 9 This is a good exercise for reviewing all of the transformations learned in this chapter.

Exercise 10 Order will not change the answer in 10a. In 10b, the order of the vertical shrink and horizontal translation will not change the answer, but the vertical translation must occur last or the resulting graph will be wrong.

See page 725 for answers to Exercises 11a–c.

▶ **Reason and Apply**

6. This table lists the vertices of a triangle. Name the vertex or vertices that will not be affected by doing a vertical stretch. ⓗ
$(2, 0)$

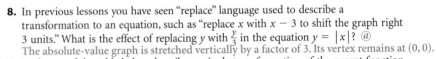

x	y
2	0
4	2
0	1

7. Graph each function on your calculator. Then describe how each graph relates to the graph of $y = |x|$ or $y = x^2$. Use the words *translation*, *reflection*, *vertical stretch*, and *vertical shrink*.

a. $y = 2x^2$ **b.** $y = 0.25|x - 2| + 1$ ⓐ

c. $y = -(x + 4)^2 - 1$ **d.** $y = -2|x - 3| + 4$

8. In previous lessons you have seen "replace" language used to describe a transformation to an equation, such as "replace x with $x - 3$ to shift the graph right 3 units." What is the effect of replacing y with $\frac{y}{3}$ in the equation $y = |x|$? ⓐ
The absolute-value graph is stretched vertically by a factor of 3. Its vertex remains at $(0, 0)$.

9. Each row of the table below describes a single transformation of the parent function $y = |x|$. Copy and complete the table.

Change to the equation $y = |x|$	New equation in $y =$ form	Transformation of the graph of $y = |x|$
Replace x with $x - 3$	$y = |x - 3|$	Translation right 3 units
Replace y with $y + 2$	$y = |x| - 2$	Translation down 2 units
Replace y with $-y$	$y = -|x|$	Reflection across the x-axis
Replace y with $y - 2$	$y = |x| + 2$	Translation up 2 units
Replace y with $\frac{y}{0.5}$	$y = 0.5|x|$	Vertical shrink by a factor of 0.5
Replace x with $x + 4$	$y = |x + 4|$	Translation left 4 units
Replace y with $\frac{y}{1.5}$	$y = 1.5|x|$	Vertical stretch by a factor of 1.5
Replace x with $x - 1$	$y = |x - 1|$	Translation right 1 unit
Replace y with $\frac{y}{3}$	$y = 3|x|$	Vertical stretch by a factor of 3

10. Describe the order of transformations of the graph of $y = x^2$ represented by

a. $y = -(x + 3)^2$ ⓗ a reflection across the x-axis and a translation left 3 units   **b.** $y = 0.5(x - 2)^2 + 1$ ⓗ possible answer: a vertical shrink by a factor of 0.5, then a translation right 2 units and up 1 unit

11. Draw this J on graph paper or on your calculator. Then draw the image defined by each of the definitions in 11a–c. Describe how each image relates to the original figure. (If you use graph paper, give yourself a lot of room or make five individual graphs. If you use a calculator, adjust your friendly window so that you can see both figures at the same time.)

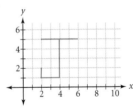

a. $(3x, y)$ a horizontal stretch by a factor of 3

b. $(3x, 3y)$ a horizontal and vertical stretch by a factor of 3

c. $(0.5x, 0.5y)$ a horizontal and vertical shrink by a factor of 0.5

d. Explain why the transformations in 11b and c are often called "size transformations." These transformations increase or decrease the overall size of the object without changing its shape.

Exercise 11 If students use a calculator, good lists for creating the original figure are $L_1 = \{2, 2, 4, 4, 6, 2\}$ and $L_2 = \{2, 1, 1, 5, 5, 5\}$. Then lists L_3 and L_4 can be used to define and plot the images.

The horizontal stretch in 11a is the first students have seen. Students will encounter horizontal stretches and shrinks in Improving Your Reasoning Skills and in the investigation in Lesson 8.7.

In 11b, some students may note that the figures are geometrically similar.

In 11d, a size transformation results in similar figures, whereas a single vertical or horizontal stretch distorts the figure in one direction.

12. Graph $Y_1(x) = abs(x)$ on your calculator. Predict what each graph will look like. Check by comparing the graphs on your calculator. [▶ 🖥 See **Calculator Note 8B** for specific instructions for your calculator. ◀]

   a. $Y_2(x) = -0.5\,Y_1(x)$

   b. $Y_2(x) = 2\,Y_1(x - 4)$

   c. $Y_2(x) = -3\,Y_1(x + 2) + 4$

13. In Interlochen, Michigan, it begins to snow in early November. The depth of snow increases over the winter. When winter ends, the snow melts and the depth decreases. This table shows data collected in Interlochen.

Snow in Interlochen

Date	Nov 1	Dec 1	Jan 1	Feb 1	Mar 1	Apr 1
Depth of snow (cm)	25	50	70	60	35	10

   a. Plot the data. For the dependent variable, let Nov 1 = 1, Dec 1 = 2, and so on. Find a function that models the data. @

   b. Use your function to find $f(2.5)$. Explain what this value represents.

   c. Find x if $f(x) = 47$. Explain what this x-value represents.

   d. According to your model, when was the snow the deepest? How deep was it at that time?   *after 3.2 months (early January); about 80 cm*

January snow covers the seats of the outdoor theater at Interlochen Center for the Arts.

14. APPLICATION Deshawn is designing a computer animation program. She has a set of coordinates for the tree shown on the right side. She wants to use 13 frames to move the tree from the right to the left. In each frame, she wants the tree height to shrink by 80%. How should she define the coordinates of each image using the coordinates from the previous frame? @ $(x - 1, 0.8y)$

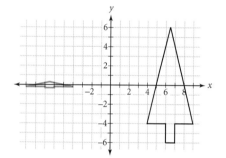

15. Byron says,

> If the graph of a function is stretched vertically, but not translated, the factor a is the same as the y-value when x equals 1.

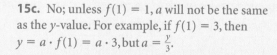

Does Byron's conjecture work for every function in the forms shown below? Explain why or why not.

   a. $y = a \cdot x^2$ @   Yes; when you substitute 1 for x, you get $y = a \cdot 1^2 = a$.

   b. $y = a \cdot |x|$ Yes; when you substitute 1 for x, you get $y = a \cdot |1| = a$.

   c. $y = a \cdot f(x)$

13b. Using the equation in 13a: $f(2.5) = 62.5$; the depth of the snow after 2.5 months (mid-December) would be about 62.5 cm.

13c. Using the equation in 13a: $x = 1.88$ or $x = 4.52$; the depth of the snow would be 47 cm after 1.88 months (end of November) or after 4.52 months (mid-February).

15c. No; unless $f(1) = 1$, a will not be the same as the y-value. For example, if $f(1) = 3$, then $y = a \cdot f(1) = a \cdot 3$, but $a = \frac{y}{3}$.

12a. a vertical shrink by a factor of 0.5 and a reflection across the x-axis

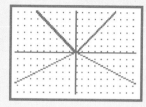

12b. a vertical stretch by a factor of 2 and a translation right 4 units

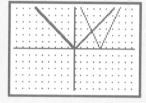

12c. a vertical stretch by a factor of 3 and a reflection across the x-axis, then a translation left 2 units and up 4 units

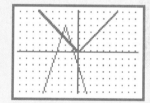

Exercise 13 Here students model a real-world situation with an absolute-value function or parabola. Students having difficulty can be advised to first identify the vertex and then estimate the scale factor. By adjusting the scale factor, students can get a better-fitting equation.

In 13a, if students assume the vertex is at January 1, they may get $f(x) = -20|x - 3| + 70$ or $f(x) = -9.3(x - 3.3)^2 + 70$.

13a. possible answer: $f(x) = -25|x - 3.2| + 80$

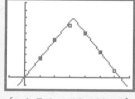

$[-1, 7, 1, -10, 100, 10]$

▶ Review

6.6 **16.** Use the properties of exponents to rewrite each expression without negative exponents.

    a. $\left(2^3\right)^{-3}$ @ $\frac{1}{2^9}$ **b.** $\left(5^2\right)^5$ 5^{10}

    c. $\left(2^4 \cdot 3^2\right)^3$ $2^{12} \cdot 3^6$ **d.** $\left(3^2 \cdot x^3\right)^{-4}$ $\frac{1}{3^8 \cdot x^{12}}$

3.4 **17.** The equation $y = -29 + 1.4x$ approximates the wind chill temperature in degrees Fahrenheit for a wind speed of 40 miles per hour.

    a. Which variable represents the actual temperature? Which variable represents the wind chill temperature? *x* represents actual temperature, and *y* represents wind chill temperature.

    b. What *x*-value gives a *y*-value of −15? Explain what your answer means in the context of this problem. 10; when the wind chill temperature is −15°F with a wind speed of 40 mi/h, the actual temperature is approximately 10°F.

2.1, **18.** Solve each equation for *x*. Substitute your answer into the original equation to verify
3.6   your solution.

    a. $\frac{1}{x+3} = \frac{1}{2x}$ $x = 3$ **b.** $\frac{20}{x} = \frac{15}{x-4}$ $x = 16$

    c. $\frac{5}{2x} + \frac{1}{2} = \frac{9}{4}$ $x = \frac{10}{7}$, or about 1.4   **d.** $-95 = \frac{5}{x-10} - 100$ $x = 11$

IMPROVING YOUR **REASONING** SKILLS

In this lesson you learned how to transform points and functions with a vertical stretch or shrink. In Exercise 11 in this set of exercises, you also saw how to transform points with a horizontal stretch or shrink. It is also possible to change the equation of a function to show a horizontal stretch or shrink.

Consider the graph of $y = x^2$ and its image after a horizontal stretch by a factor of 2. Write an equation for the image.

Describe the image in terms of a vertical stretch or shrink. Write an equation that shows this transformation. Is this equation equivalent to the one that shows a horizontal stretch?

When you vertically stretch or shrink the graph of $y = f(x)$ by a factor of *a*, you get a graph of $y = a \cdot f(x)$. If you horizontally stretch or shrink the graph of $y = f(x)$ by a factor of *b*, you will get the graph of what equation?

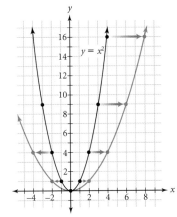

IMPROVING **REASONING** SKILLS

Possible equations to represent the horizontal stretch include $y = \left(\frac{x}{2}\right)^2$ and $y = (0.5x)^2$. Because these equations are equivalent to $y = 0.25x^2$, the horizontal stretch can also be considered a vertical shrink by a factor of 0.25. Just as a vertical stretch or shrink of $f(x)$ by a factor of *a* is given by $\frac{y}{a} = f(x)$, a horizontal stretch or shrink

by a factor of *b* can be represented generically by $y = f\left(\frac{x}{b}\right)$. You may want to ask why the variable *x* is divided by the factor *b*. [For a point (x, y) on the transformed equation, the point $\left(\frac{x}{b}, y\right)$ satisfies the original equation, so the new graph has the equation $y = f\left(\frac{x}{b}\right)$.]

Exercise 18 You might review inverting proportions if students are stumped. For 18c and d, they will need to collect like terms before inverting.

Using Transformations to Model Data

In this lesson you'll do experiments to gather data, and then you'll find a function to model the data. To fit the model, you'll first need to identify a parent function. Then you'll transform the parent function and fit the image function to the data.

There are three experiments to choose from. Your group should choose one experiment. Do the other experiments if time permits.

Activity

Roll, Walk, or Sum

Experiment 1: The Rolling Marble

In this experiment you'll write the equation for the path of a falling marble. Then you'll catch the marble at a point you calculate using your equation.

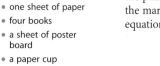

You will need

- a large marble
- tape
- one sheet of paper
- four books
- a sheet of poster board
- a paper cup
- a meterstick or a yardstick
- a table and chair
- a motion sensor
- a stopwatch or a watch with a second hand

> **Procedure Note**
>
> Use the books and poster board to build a ramp whose bottom is about 30 cm from the edge of the table. Fold the sheet of paper into fan pleats—the smaller the pleats, the better. This paper, when unfolded, will help you locate where the marble hits the floor.

NCTM STANDARDS

CONTENT		PROCESS	
	Number		Problem Solving
✔	Algebra	✔	Reasoning
✔	Geometry	✔	Communication
✔	Measurement	✔	Connections
✔	Data/Probability	✔	Representation

LESSON OBJECTIVE

- Use transformations of functions $y = x$, $y = |x|$, and $y = x^2$ to model real-world data

Experiment 1

Step 2 The marble will often dent the pleats at the place where it hits the floor.

Step 3 The Rolling Marble transparency models the setup with sample coordinates. An open notebook can be used for the ramp instead of poster board.

Step 5 As needed, point out to students that they will get only one chance to try to intercept the marble, so they should be very careful with measurements and calculations.

Step 6 When each group is ready to make its try, you might have the entire class gather around to watch.

Experiment 2

Step 2 Use cables to connect the calculators for distributing the data.

Step 2
sample graph:

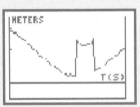

Step 3 These data points actually fit a branch of a hyperbola, but an absolute-value function (made up of the hyperbola's asymptotes) is a good fit.

Other walking patterns will produce more clearly visible absolute-value graphs. For example, students might walk directly toward the sensor and then turn abruptly and walk directly away from it.

Step 4 Using the points in Step 3, an equation is $y = -\frac{1}{7}x^2 + 28$. That is a vertical shrink of the graph of $y = x^2$ by a factor of $\frac{1}{7}$ and a reflection across the x-axis, then a translation up 28 units.

Step 5 Students should substitute the seat's height for y in the equation they wrote in Step 4. The value of x will then be the horizontal distance the cup must be from the table.

Step 1 Do a trial run. Roll the marble from the top edge of the ramp. Let it roll down the ramp and across the table and drop to the floor. Spot the place where it hits the floor (approximately). Tape the folded paper to the floor in this area.

Step 2 Now collect data to identify the drop point more precisely. Roll the marble two or three times, and mark the point where it hits the paper each time. Each roll should be as much like the other rolls as you can make it. So start each marble roll at the same place, and release it the same way each time.

Step 3 Next, find the coordinates of points for a graph. Let x represent horizontal distance, and let y represent vertical distance. Locate the point on the floor directly below the *edge* of the table. Call this point $(0, 0)$. Measure from $(0, 0)$ up to the point at the edge of the table where the marble rolls off. Name the coordinates of this point. Lastly, measure from $(0, 0)$ to each point where the marble hit the floor. Find the average coordinates for these points on the floor. Using the sample setup, points are $(0, 0)$, $(0, 28)$, and $(14, 0)$.

Step 4 As your marble falls, it will follow the path of a parabola. The point where it leaves the table is the vertex of the parabola. Define variables and write an equation in the form $y = ax^2 + b$ that fits your two points.

Next, you'll test your model by using it to calculate a point on the path of the marble. See if you can catch the marble at that point.

Step 5 Measure the height of the chair seat. Put the chair next to the table and place a small cup on the chair. Use your calculations to adjust the position of the cup so that when you roll the marble, it will land in the cup.

Step 6 You have only one chance to land in the cup. Release the marble as you did in Step 2. Good luck!

Experiment 2: Walking

In this experiment you'll walk past a motion sensor and model the data you collect.

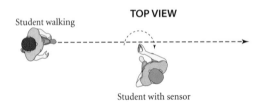

TOP VIEW

Student walking

Student with sensor

Step 1 Walk steadily in the same direction toward the sensor. Pass it and go about 3 meters farther. Record data for the entire walking time.

Step 2 Download the data to each person's calculator. You should expect some erratic data points while the walker is close to the sensor.

Step 3 Fit the data using function transformations. If the vertex is "missing" from the data, estimate its location. The equation should be in the form $y = a|x - h|$, in which a is the speed of the walkers in m/s and h is the starting distance between the two students.

Another Experiment

An alternative experiment that generates a parabola uses two metersticks or yardsticks and about 1 m of string. Holding one end of the string at zero on the meterstick and the other end at various points, students straighten the string to form rectangles. They measure the length and width and calculate the area of each rectangle. After ten rectangles, they can find an equation that fits the (*length, area*) data they have collected.

Step 4a Start 1.2 m **Step 4** | Write walking instructions for each of these functions. In your instructions say
from the person holding | where to start, how fast to go, and when to pass the sensor.
the sensor. Walk at 1.5 m/s.
Pass the sensor at 0.8 s.
Step 5

a. $f(x) = 1.5 |x - 1.2|$ **b.** $f(x) = 2.1 |x - 0.85|$

If time permits, try following your instructions from Step 4 to see if your data
fits the graph.

Step 4b Start 0.85 m from the person holding the sensor. Walk at 2.1 m/s. Pass the sensor at about 0.4 s.

Experiment 3: Calculating

Who is the fastest calculator operator (CO) in
your group? The COs had better warm up their
fingers!

> **Procedure Note**
>
> You must start with
> $1 + 2 + 3 \ldots$ each time. It is
> not fair to use the last result!

Step 1

Step 4 The data are likely
to give a direct variation in
the form $y = kx$, in which
k is the amount of time
required to enter one
number and the plus sign.

The CO should carefully calculate sums a–g.
Record the answers.

a. $1 + 2 + 3 + \cdots + 8 + 9 + 10$

b. $1 + 2 + 3 + \cdots + 13 + 14 + 15$

c. $1 + 2 + 3 + \cdots + 18 + 19 + 20$

Step 5 Students should
substitute 47 for x in their
equations from Step 4. The
value of y is the
time required.

d. $1 + 2 + 3 + \cdots + 23 + 24 + 25$

e. $1 + 2 + 3 + \cdots + 28 + 29 + 30$

f. $1 + 2 + 3 + \cdots + 33 + 34 + 35$

g. $1 + 2 + 3 + \cdots + 38 + 39 + 40$

Step 2

Step 6 If students **Step 3**
found a direct variation,
then the y-intercept
will be 0, which **Step 4**
means it takes no
time to add no **Step 5**
numbers. If students did
find a y-intercept, **Step 6**
answers will vary.

Next, the CO calculates the first sum, 1 to 10, again *while being timed*. (Record
the time only if the CO gets the correct answer. If not, run the trial again.)

Repeat Step 2 for sums b–g, that is, 1 to 15, 1 to 20, . . . , 1 to 40. You should have
seven data points in the form (*number of numbers added, time*).

Find an equation to model the data. Transform it as needed for a better fit.

Use your model to predict the time it would take to sum the numbers from 1 to
47. Test your prediction and record the results.

What is the y-intercept of your model? Does this value have any real-world
meaning? If yes, then what is the meaning? If no, then why not?

Discuss your results with the class. How were the experiments alike? How were they
different? How could you recognize the parent function in the data?

Experiment 3
Many jobs require testing for
speed and accuracy in typing or
in numeric keypad entry.

Step 1 This step is for answer
checking and for warming up
students' fingers. If students know
the expression $\frac{n(n + 1)}{2}$ for the
sum of the first n positive
integers, they can use it to
double-check their answers.

Step 4 Encourage students to use
transformations of the line $y = x$
rather than methods learned in
Chapter 4, Fitting a Line to Data.

Step 5 Students may point out
that averaging several times for
the same summation would yield
better predictions. It's probably
better for groups to spend the
time on a different experiment.

SHARING IDEAS

Have a group report results of
each experiment, especially if not
all groups worked on each one.

Assessing Progress
This is an excellent opportunity
to see how well students understand the effect on equations of
translations, reflections, and
stretches and shrinks, as well as
their ability to work with the
parent quadratic, absolute-value,
and linear functions.

Closing the Lesson

Knowledge of how transformations affect equations can be very
useful in making predictions.

Introduction to Rational Functions

 Guiding the Investigation

In Chapter 2, you learned that some relationships are modeled by inverse variation. The simplest inverse variation equation is $y = \frac{1}{x}$. Look at the graph of this equation.

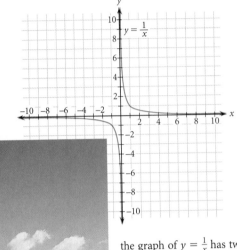

Notice that the graph of $y = \frac{1}{x}$ has two parts. One part is in Quadrant I, and the other is in Quadrant III. In Chapter 2, you wrote inverse variation equations for countable and measurable quantities, such as number of nickels and distance in inches. Because these quantities are always positive, you worked only with the part of the graph in Quadrant I.

Notice that as the x-values get closer and closer to 0, the graph gets closer and closer to the y-axis. As the x-values get farther and farther from 0, the graph gets closer and closer to the x-axis. An **asymptote** is a line that a graph approaches more and more closely. So the graph of $y = \frac{1}{x}$ has two asymptotes: the lines $x = 0$ and $y = 0$. Can you explain why the x- and y-axes are asymptotes for this graph?

Also notice that $y = \frac{1}{x}$ is a function because it passes the vertical line test. You can use the inverse variation function as a parent function to understand many other functions.

Some amusement parks have free-fall rides shaped like a first-quadrant inverse variation graph. This is the Demon Drop at Cedar Point Amusement Park in Ohio.

 ## Investigation
I'm Trying to Be Rational

In the first part of this investigation, you will explore transformations of the parent function $y = \frac{1}{x}$.

Step 1 | Graph the parent function $y = \frac{1}{x}$ on your calculator.

Step 2 | Use what you have learned about transformations to predict what the graphs of these functions will look like.

a. $\frac{y}{-3} = \frac{1}{x}$ **b.** $\frac{y-3}{2} = \frac{1}{x}$ **c.** $y = \frac{1}{x-2}$ **d.** $y + 2 = \frac{1}{x+1}$

LESSON OBJECTIVES

- Investigate basic transformations of the inverse variation function $f(x) = \frac{1}{x}$
- Model real-world data with rational functions
- Write rational expressions in lowest terms

NCTM STANDARDS

CONTENT		PROCESS	
	Number	✔	Problem Solving
✔	Algebra	✔	Reasoning
	Geometry	✔	Communication
	Measurement		Connections
	Data/Probability	✔	Representation

Mathematicians often explore similarities in patterns. **Rational expressions** look similar to fractions, but include variables as well as numbers. When you studied fractions, you reduced and did arithmetic; can the same thing be done with rational expressions? In the next example you'll do operations with rational expressions in the same way you've done them with fractions, and you'll use your graphing calculator to provide evidence that the same methods apply.

EXAMPLE B

A rational expression is reduced to **lowest terms** when the numerator and denominator have no factors in common other than 1.

a. Reduce these rational expressions to lowest terms.

  i. $\dfrac{45x^2}{60x}$ **ii.** $\dfrac{5x^2 - 100x}{35x}$

b. Perform the indicated operation and reduce the results to lowest terms.

  i. $\dfrac{6}{x} \cdot \dfrac{4x^3}{15}$

  ii. $\dfrac{2x^5}{5y^2} \div \dfrac{6x^4}{20y}$

  iii. $\dfrac{2x}{3} + \dfrac{5}{2}$

  iv. $\dfrac{x - 2}{4} - \dfrac{x - 5}{2x}$

▶ **Solution**

a. You can reduce a rational expression to lowest terms in the same way that you reduce a numerical fraction to lowest terms. Find the common factors, then divide them out.

i. $\dfrac{45x^2}{60x} = \dfrac{3 \cdot 3 \cdot 5 \cdot x \cdot x}{3 \cdot 4 \cdot 5 \cdot x}$ Rewrite each expression as a product of its factors.

$= \dfrac{\cancel{3} \cdot 3 \cdot \cancel{5} \cdot \cancel{x} \cdot x}{\cancel{3} \cdot 4 \cdot \cancel{5} \cdot \cancel{x}}$ Remove fractions equal to 1: $\frac{3}{3}$, $\frac{5}{5}$, and $\frac{x}{x}$.

$= \dfrac{3x}{4}$ Combine the remaining factors to write as a rational expression in lowest terms.

You can check this answer by looking at table values for your original and final expressions.

Notice that all values of x except 0 give the same values for y. The expression $\frac{45x^2}{60x}$ is undefined when $x = 0$ because you can't divide by zero. However, x can be equal to 0 in the expression $\frac{3x}{4}$. So, $\frac{45x^2}{60x}$ is equal to $\frac{3x}{4}$ for all values of x except 0. This value is called an **excluded value** or a **restriction on the variable.** You can write $\frac{45x^2}{60x} = \frac{3x}{4}$, where $x \neq 0$.

If you have time, you might suggest that students rework the example with x representing the total amount of water rather than the amount added. In that case they can work with the direct variation $y = \frac{0.2}{x}$, or $xy = 0.2$, and get $x = 8$ when $y = 0.025$. They must then subtract the initial liter of water to find the amount added.

You can use the Fathom demonstration Salt Concentrations to replace this example.

▶ **EXAMPLE B**

If your state standards don't cover rational expressions, you can skip Example B and Exercises 6 and 11–13. Depending on students' comfort with performing operations with fractions, you may need more or less discussion about operations with rational expressions. For example, your class might need a review of how to find common factors or of how to find a least common denominator. Also, if you didn't cover Lessons 6.3 and 6.5, which introduced the multiplication and division rules of exponents, you may want to cover them here.

In Lesson 4.4, students were introduced to factoring a monomial from a binomial (the distributive property in reverse). You might remind them of that work.

In Chapter 9, Quadratic Models, students will learn more about factoring polynomials. Operations with rational expressions will be revisited in that chapter, especially in Lesson 9.8.

[Alert] Some students may have difficulty seeing 1 as the ratio $\frac{x}{x}$, as opposed to a ratio of numbers.

For part bii, you can substitute 0 for x in the original equation to show that it will cause division by zero, so $x \neq 0$ is a *restriction* on the variable.

ii. $\dfrac{5x^2 - 100x}{35x} = \dfrac{5 \cdot x \cdot (x - 20)}{5 \cdot 7 \cdot x}$

Rewrite each expression as a product of its factors. In the numerator, you'll need to identify factors that are common to both terms.

$= \dfrac{\not{5} \cdot \not{x} \cdot (x - 20)}{\not{5} \cdot 7 \cdot \not{x}}$

Remove the 1's.

$= \dfrac{x - 20}{7}$, where $x \neq 0$

Write as a rational expression in lowest terms.

Again, be sure to note any values of x that are undefined in the original expression. These values must also be excluded from the domain of the reduced expression. In this case, $x \neq 0$.

b. You can add, subtract, multiply, and divide rational expressions following the same procedures you use with fractions.

i. $\dfrac{6}{x} \cdot \dfrac{4x^3}{15} = \dfrac{6 \cdot 4x^3}{x \cdot 15}$

Multiply the numerators and denominators.

$= \dfrac{3 \cdot 2 \cdot 2 \cdot 2 \cdot x^3}{x \cdot 3 \cdot 5}$

Rewrite each expression as a product of its factors.

$= \dfrac{8x^2}{5}$, where $x \neq 0$

Remove the 1's and write as a rational expression in lowest terms. You can use the multiplication and division properties of exponents that you learned in Chapter 6 to help you. State restrictions on the variable.

Again, you can check table values of the original and final expressions. This table suggests that all defined values of x give the same result for y.

ii. $\dfrac{2x^5}{5y^2} \div \dfrac{6x^4}{20y} = \dfrac{2x^5}{5y^2} \cdot \dfrac{20y}{6x^4}$

Rewrite the division as multiplication by a reciprocal.

You may now be able to eliminate common factors by observation, or you might prefer to combine the numerators and denominators and write them as products of factors.

$= \dfrac{2 \cdot 2 \cdot 2 \cdot 5 \cdot x^5 \cdot y}{2 \cdot 3 \cdot 5 \cdot x^4 \cdot y^2}$

$= \dfrac{4x}{3y}$, where $x \neq 0$ and $y \neq 0$

Write as a rational expression in lowest terms and state restrictions on the variables.

The restrictions must include $x \neq 0$ because the divisor, $\dfrac{6x^4}{20y}$, is zero when $x = 0$.

iii. To add fractions or rational expressions, you first find a common denominator.

$$\frac{2x}{3} + \frac{5}{2} = \frac{2}{2} \cdot \frac{2x}{3} + \frac{3}{3} \cdot \frac{5}{2}$$

The common denominator is 6, so multiply the first and second expressions by 1, in the form of $\frac{2}{2}$ and $\frac{3}{3}$.

$$= \frac{4x}{6} + \frac{15}{6}$$

Multiply. Now that you have a common denominator, you can combine the numerators.

$$= \frac{4x + 15}{6}$$

There are no restrictions on the variable.

iv. To subtract fractions or rational expressions, you also begin by finding a common denominator.

$$\frac{x-2}{4} - \frac{x-5}{2x} = \frac{x}{x} \cdot \frac{x-2}{4} - \frac{2}{2} \cdot \frac{x-5}{2x}$$

The least common denominator is 4x, so multiply each expression by an appropriate fraction equal to 1.

$$= \frac{x^2 - 2x}{4x} - \frac{2x - 10}{4x}$$

Multiply.

$$= \frac{(x^2 - 2x) - (2x - 10)}{4x}$$

Combine the fractions.

$$= \frac{x^2 - 4x + 10}{4x}, \text{ where } x \neq 0$$

Subtract. State restrictions on the variable.

EXERCISES

You will need your graphing calculator for Exercises **11**, **12**, **13**, and **15**.

Practice Your Skills

1. Describe each graph as a transformation of the graph of the parent function $y = |x|$ or $y = x^2$. Then write its equation.

a.

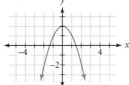

b.

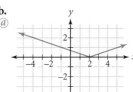

c.

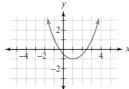

d.

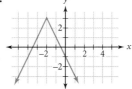

2. Write an equation that generates this table of values. @
$y = \frac{2}{x}$

x	-4	-3	-2	-1	0	1	2	3	4
y	$-\frac{1}{2}$	$-\frac{2}{3}$	-1	-2	Undefined	2	1	$\frac{2}{3}$	$\frac{1}{2}$

Closing the Lesson

Any translation of the parent inverse variation $y = \frac{1}{x}$ has horizontal and vertical **asymptotes** through the image of the origin under the same transformation. In more general terms, a **rational function** $\frac{f(x)}{g(x)}$ has a horizontal asymptote at $y = L$ if there's a number L to which the values of the function get closer and closer as x gets farther from zero. The graph has a vertical asymptote at $x = L$ if $g(L) = 0$ but $f(L) \neq 0$. If it doesn't have a vertical asymptote at $x = L$ and if $f(L)$ and $g(L)$ are *both* zero, then the graph has a hole at a point with x-coordinate L. Rational expressions can be **reduced to lowest terms** by dividing out common factors and noting any **restrictions on the variable.**

BUILDING UNDERSTANDING

Students work with transformations and applications of inverse variations and simplify rational expressions.

ASSIGNING HOMEWORK

Essential	1–5, 10
Performance assessment	9
Portfolio	8, 12
Journal	4
Group	6, 7, 11–13
Review	14–17

▶ **Helping with the Exercises**

Ask students to use the Y= menu and tables to support and verify their work and answers in these exercises.

Exercise 1 In 1c, the translation right can be done before the shrink, but the translation down must be done after the shrink. In 1d, the stretch, the reflection, and the translation left can be done in any order, but the translation up must be done after the reflection and stretch.

1a. a reflection of the graph of $y = x^2$ across the x-axis, then a translation up 2 units (or translation then reflection); $y = -x^2 + 2$

1b. a vertical shrink of the graph of $y = |x|$ by a factor of $\frac{1}{3}$ and a translation right 2 units; $y = \frac{1}{3}|x - 2|$

1c. possible answer: a vertical shrink of the graph of $y = x^2$ by a factor of 0.5, then a translation right 1 unit and down 1 unit; $y = 0.5(x - 1)^2 - 1$

1d. possible answer: a vertical stretch of the graph of $y = |x|$ by a factor of 2 and a reflection across the x-axis, then a translation left 2 units and up 3 units; $y = -2|x + 2| + 3$

5a. a vertical stretch by a factor of 4; domain: $x \neq 0$

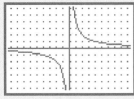

$[-9.4, 9.4, 1, -6.2, 6.2, 1]$

5b. a translation right 5 units and down 2 units; domain: $x \neq 5$

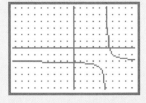

5c. a vertical shrink by a factor of 0.5, then a translation up 3 units; domain: $x \neq 0$

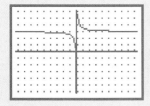

5d. a vertical stretch by a factor of 3, a reflection across the x-axis, and a translation left 3 units; domain: $x \neq -3$

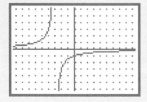

6. If the expressions were equivalent, the two graphs would be the same. The graph shows that they are not. You can only cancel *factors*, and $3x + 7$ and $x + 7$ don't have any common factors.

3. Write an equation for this graph in the form $y = \frac{a}{x}$. @ $y = -\frac{5}{x}$

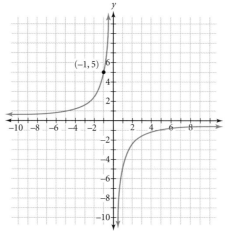

$(-1, 5)$

4. The two curves shown are $f(x) = \frac{4}{x}$ and $g(x) = \frac{8}{x}$. Which equation describes the red curve? The blue curve? Explain.

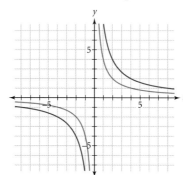

The red curve is described by $f(x) = \frac{4}{x}$, and the blue curve is described by $g(x) = \frac{8}{x}$. Explanations will vary. Possible explanations: The red curve is closer to the origin, and $f(x) = \frac{4}{x}$ indicates less vertical stretch; or $f(1) = 4$, which is a point on the red curve, whereas $g(1) = 8$.

5. Describe each function as a transformation of the graph of the parent function $y = \frac{1}{x}$. Then sketch a graph of each function and list values that are not part of the domain.

a. $y = \frac{4}{x}$ @   **b.** $y = \frac{1}{x - 5} - 2$ **c.** $y = \frac{0.5}{x} + 3$ **d.** $y = \frac{-3}{x + 3}$

▶ Reason and Apply

6. Imelda reduced the rational expression $\frac{3x + 7}{x + 7}$ like this:

$$\frac{3x + 7}{x + 7} = \frac{3\cancel{x} + \cancel{7}}{\cancel{x} + \cancel{7}} = 3$$

She then graphed $Y_1 = \frac{3x + 7}{x + 7}$ and $Y_2 = 3$ to verify that the two expressions are equivalent. Her graph is shown. How does the graph show that $\frac{3x + 7}{x + 7}$ is not equal to 3? What did Imelda do incorrectly?

$Y_2 = 3$

$X = -5$ $Y = 3$

$[-15, 5, 1, -10, 10, 1]$

7. Write an equation for each graph. Each calculator screen shows a friendly window with a factor of 1.

a. 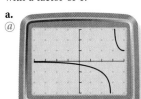 $y = \dfrac{1}{x - 3}$

b.  $y = \dfrac{1}{x + 2}$

c. $y = \dfrac{1}{x - 1} + 1$

d. 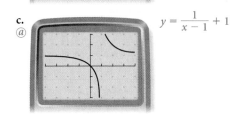 $y = \dfrac{1}{x - 1} - 2$

8. Consider the graph of the inverse variation function $f(x) = \frac{1}{x}$. (See page 474.)

   a. Write an equation that reflects the graph across the x-axis. Sketch the image.

   b. Write an equation that reflects the graph across the y-axis. Sketch the image.

   c. Compare your sketches from 8a and b. Explain what you find.

9. APPLICATION A nurse needs to treat a patient's eye with a 1% saline solution (salt solution). She finds only a half-liter bottle of 5% saline solution. Write an equation and use it to calculate how much water she should add to create a 1% solution. @

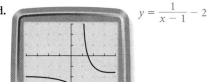

The saline solution that is used to clean contact lenses is usually a 1% salt solution.

10. APPLICATION A business group wants to rent a meeting hall for its job fair during the week of spring break. The rent is $3,500, which will be divided among the businesses that agree to participate. So far, only five businesses have signed up.

   a. At this time, what is the cost for each business? $700

   b. Make a table to show what happens to the cost per business as the additional businesses agree to participate.

   c. Write a function for the cost per business related to the number of additional businesses that agree to participate.

   d. How many additional businesses must agree to participate before the cost per business is less than $150? $150 = \frac{3500}{5 + x}$; $x = 18.\overline{3}$; 19 additional businesses

11. Reduce each rational expression to lowest terms by dividing out common factors, and state any restrictions on the variable. Use your calculator's table feature to verify your answer.

   a. $\dfrac{120x^4}{24x^5}$ $\frac{5}{x}$, where $x \neq 0$

   b. $\dfrac{(5x^3)(16x^2)}{80x^3}$ x^2, where $x \neq 0$

   c. $\dfrac{28x^2(x - 5)}{7(x - 5)^2}$ $\frac{4x^2}{x - 5}$, where $x \neq 5$

   d. $\dfrac{4 + 20x}{20x}$ $\frac{1 + 5x}{5x}$, where $x \neq 0$

   e. $\dfrac{5x - 15x^4}{5x}$ @ $1 - 3x^3$, where $x \neq 0$

8a. $y = -f(x)$, or $y = -\dfrac{1}{x}$

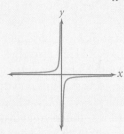

8b. $y = f(-x)$, or $y = \dfrac{1}{-x}$; see sketch above.

8c. Either reflection produces the same graph because $\dfrac{1}{-x} = -\dfrac{1}{x}$.

9. Let x represent the amount of water to add and y represent the concentration of salt. The amount of salt is $0.05(0.5) = 0.025$.

$y = \dfrac{0.025}{0.5 + x}$; $0.01 = \dfrac{0.025}{0.5 + x}$; $x = 2$; 2 L

Exercise 10 Some students may use $y = \dfrac{3500}{x}$. This is okay if they subtract 5 from the value of x that they will get in 10d.

10b.

Additional businesses	0	5	10	15	20
Cost per business ($)	700.00	350.00	233.33	175.00	140.00

10c. $y = \dfrac{3500}{5 + x}$, where x is the number of additional businesses that have signed up and y is the cost per business

Exercise 15 As needed, help students realize that the vertex of the graph of $y = (x - h)^2 + k$ is located at (h, k), an idea informally explored in Lesson 8.2 that will be more formally stated in Chapter 9. As students find the y-coordinates of points whose x-coordinate differs from that of the vertex by 1, they may see that the amount the graph has risen in that unit corresponds to the vertical stretch factor. You might ask why. Encourage students to see that in the original graph the amount of increase over this interval was just 1.

Exercise 16 Don't assign this exercise if you aren't teaching matrices. However, it will be a good review for students if you are covering Lesson 8.7.

16a. $\begin{bmatrix} 39 & 34 \\ 17 & 24 \\ 11 & 13 \end{bmatrix}$; these are the total numbers of baked goods sold, in dozens, for the past two years.

16b. $\begin{bmatrix} 20.50 & 24.10 \\ 90.25 & 102.75 \end{bmatrix}$; the first row is the total cost for fall and spring this year, and the second row is the total income from sales for fall and spring this year.

12. Find the lowest common denominator, perform the indicated operation, and reduce the result to lowest terms. State any restrictions on the variable. Use your calculator to verify your answers.

   a. $\dfrac{6x}{5} - \dfrac{x}{5}$ $\quad x$

   b. $\dfrac{5}{12x} + \dfrac{1}{6x}$ @ $\dfrac{7}{12x}$, where $x \neq 0$

   c. $\dfrac{5}{2x} - \dfrac{5}{3}$ $\dfrac{15 - 10x}{6x}$, where $x \neq 0$

   d. $\dfrac{5}{x - 5} + \dfrac{2}{x + 2}$ $\dfrac{7x}{(x - 5)(x + 2)}$, where $x \neq 5$ and $x \neq -2$

13. Perform the indicated operation and reduce the result to lowest terms. State any restrictions on the variable. Use your calculator to verify your answers.

   a. $\dfrac{4x^3}{24x^6} \cdot \dfrac{12x^4}{15x}$ $\dfrac{2}{15}$, where $x \neq 0$

   b. $\dfrac{3(x - 6)}{18} \cdot \dfrac{4(x + 6)}{8(x - 6)}$ @ $\dfrac{x + 6}{12}$, where $x \neq 6$

   c. $\dfrac{4xy^3}{(2x)^3} \div \dfrac{2y^2}{1\frac{y}{4x^2}}$, where $x \neq 0$ and $y \neq 0$

   d. $\dfrac{3(x + 4)}{5x} \cdot \dfrac{20x^2}{6x^2 + 24x}$ 2, where $x \neq 0$ and $x \neq -4$

▶ **Review**

5.5 14. Solve each inequality.

   a. $4 - 2x > 8$ @ $x < -2$

   b. $-8 + 3(x - 2) \geq -20$ $x \geq -2$

   c. $7 + 2x \leq 3 + 3x$ $x \geq 4$

8.2, 8.4 15. Name the coordinates of the vertex of the graph of $y = 2(x - 3)^2 + 1$. Without graphing, name the points on the parabola whose x-coordinates are 1 unit more or less than the x-coordinate of the vertex. Check your answers by graphing on your calculator. vertex: $(3, 1)$; point to the left: $(2, 3)$; point to the right: $(4, 3)$

1.8 16. In the fall and spring each year, the math club holds a bake sale to raise money to buy new calculators. Information from these sales has been recorded in three matrices. The values have units of dozens or dollars per dozen.

Last year	Fall	Spring
Cookies (dozen)	18	15
Brownies (dozen)	9	12
Cupcakes (dozen)	6	6

Matrix A

This year	Fall	Spring
Cookies (dozen)	21	19
Brownies (dozen)	8	12
Cupcakes (dozen)	5	7

Matrix B

	Cookies	Brownies	Cupcakes
Expenses ($/dozen)	0.50	0.75	0.80
Price charged ($/dozen)	2.50	3.00	2.75

Matrix C

   a. Add $[A] + [B]$ and describe the meaning of the result.

   b. Multiply $[C] \cdot [B]$ and describe the meaning of the result. @

7.3 **17.** Jack lives in a cabin at the bottom of a hill. At the top of the hill, directly behind his cabin, is an observation tower. There is a creek at the bottom of the hill on the side opposite Jack's cabin.

Match each description in a–c to one of the graphs below. Then answer part d. The horizontal axis in each graph shows time, and the vertical axis shows distance from the *top* of the hill.

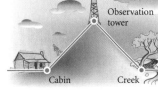
Observation tower
Cabin   Creek

a. Jack walks steadily from the cabin to the observation tower. i

b. Jack walks steadily from the observation tower to the creek. ii

c. Jack walks steadily from the cabin to the creek. iv

d. Create a walking context and story for the unmatched graph.

Answers will vary as students create a scenario for graph iii.

i.
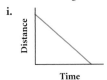
Distance | Time

ii.

Distance | Time

iii.

Distance | Time

iv.

Distance | Time

IMPROVING YOUR VISUAL THINKING SKILLS

Describe each striped or plaid fabric pattern as a set of transformations. Which patterns are translations? Which are reflections?

Fabric A

Fabric B

Fabric C

Fabric D

What is the smallest rectangular "unit" that repeats throughout each pattern? Can there be more than one "unit" for a pattern? Suppose a tailor is making a shirt from each fabric pattern. Which shirt should be most expensive? Why?

IMPROVING VISUAL THINKING SKILLS

The stripes in Fabric A exhibit a 123123… pattern. The smallest unit that repeats (through translation) consists of three adjacent stripes.

Fabric B has a 123212321… pattern. You can think of it as generated from reflections or from the unit of four adjacent stripes repeatedly translated.

Fabric C has a 1232112321… pattern of vertical stripes, as well as a 2121… pattern of horizontal stripes. You can interpret the pattern as generated by a horizontal or vertical translation or as repeatedly reflecting horizontally.

Fabric D has the same pattern along its length and across its width as Fabric A, generated by translations. There is no reflection.

It's not possible to cut symmetrical pieces like shirt fronts from a folded piece of Fabric D. Hence there would be more fabric waste as pieces are individually positioned, and more time would be required.

Transformations with Matrices

Say what you know, do what you must, come what may.

SOFIA KOVALEVSKAYA

You can use a matrix to organize the coordinates of a geometric figure. You can represent this quadrilateral with a 2 × 4 matrix.

$$\begin{bmatrix} 1 & -2 & -3 & 2 \\ 2 & 1 & -1 & -2 \end{bmatrix}$$

Each column contains the *x*- and *y*-coordinates of a vertex. The first row contains all the *x*-coordinates, and the second row contains all the *y*-coordinates. All four vertices are in consecutive order in the matrix. When you add or multiply this matrix, the coordinates change. So matrices are useful when you transform coordinates.

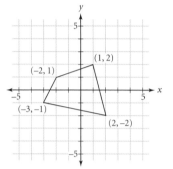

Many textiles, such as this Turkish carpet, use transformations to create interesting patterns.

Investigation
Matrix Transformations

You will need

- graph paper

In this investigation you'll use matrix addition and multiplication to create some familiar transformations.

Step 1 Create a set of coordinate axes on graph paper. Draw the triangle that is represented by this matrix:

$$[A] = \begin{bmatrix} -4 & 3 & 2 \\ -1 & 4 & 0 \end{bmatrix}$$

Step 2 Add.

$$[A] + \begin{bmatrix} 5 & 5 & 5 \\ 0 & 0 & 0 \end{bmatrix} \begin{bmatrix} 1 & 8 & 7 \\ -1 & 4 & 0 \end{bmatrix}$$

LESSON OBJECTIVES

- Review matrix addition and multiplication
- Use matrices to represent transformations of polygons
- Solve problems using matrix models

NCTM STANDARDS

CONTENT		PROCESS	
✔	Number	✔	Problem Solving
✔	Algebra	✔	Reasoning
	Geometry		Communication
	Measurement	✔	Connections
	Data/Probability	✔	Representation

Step 3 | Draw the image represented by your answer in Step 2. Describe the transformation.

Step 4 Possible answer: The transformation adds 5 to each *x*-coordinate, and the matrix that you added has all 5's in the *x*-coordinate row.

Step 4 | How is the transformation related to the matrix that you added?

Step 5 | Repeat Steps 1–4, but in Step 2 change what you add to matrix [A] each time as described in a–c. Use a new set of coordinate axes for each transformation.

a. $[A] + \begin{bmatrix} 0 & 0 & 0 \\ -4 & -4 & -4 \end{bmatrix}$ b. $[A] + \begin{bmatrix} 5 & 5 & 5 \\ -4 & -4 & -4 \end{bmatrix}$

c. $[A] + \begin{bmatrix} -6 & -6 & -6 \\ 4 & 4 & 4 \end{bmatrix}$

Next, see if you can work backward.

Step 6 | Write matrix equations to represent these translations.

a.

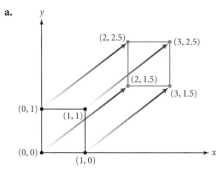

$\begin{bmatrix} 0 & 0 & 1 & 1 \\ 0 & 1 & 1 & 0 \end{bmatrix}$

$+ \begin{bmatrix} 2 & 2 & 2 & 2 \\ 1.5 & 1.5 & 1.5 & 1.5 \end{bmatrix}$

$= \begin{bmatrix} 2 & 2 & 3 & 3 \\ 1.5 & 2.5 & 2.5 & 1.5 \end{bmatrix}$

b.

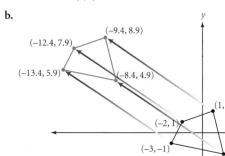

$\begin{bmatrix} -3 & -2 & 1 & 2 \\ -1 & 1 & 2 & -2 \end{bmatrix}$

$+ \begin{bmatrix} -10.4 & -10.4 & -10.4 & -10.4 \\ 6.9 & 6.9 & 6.9 & 6.9 \end{bmatrix}$

$= \begin{bmatrix} -13.4 & -12.4 & -9.4 & -8.4 \\ 5.9 & 7.9 & 8.9 & 4.9 \end{bmatrix}$

Now, see what effect multiplication has.

Step 7 The graph should look like the one shown in the book. Possible answer:
$\begin{bmatrix} 2 & 3 & 6 & 7 & x \\ 2 & 4 & 5 & 1 & y \end{bmatrix}$.

Step 7 | Draw this quadrilateral on your own graph paper. Write the coordinates of the vertices in a matrix, [B]. Add a fifth column to your matrix to represent any point of the form (x, y).

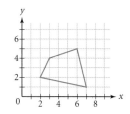

Step 8 | Multiply.

$\begin{bmatrix} 1 & 0 \\ 0 & -1 \end{bmatrix} \cdot [B]$ $\begin{bmatrix} 2 & 3 & 6 & 7 & x \\ -2 & -4 & -5 & -1 & -y \end{bmatrix}$

Step 5b $\begin{bmatrix} 1 & 8 & 7 \\ -5 & 0 & -4 \end{bmatrix}$; a translation right 5 units and down 4 units

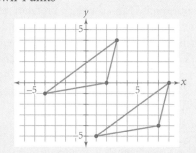

Step 5c $\begin{bmatrix} -10 & -3 & -4 \\ 3 & 8 & 4 \end{bmatrix}$; a translation left 6 units and up 4 units

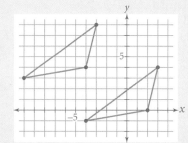

Guiding the Investigation

Steps 1–5 Some students might want to see how to do these matrix calculations on a calculator. They could also use a calculator to draw the original and transformed figures. You might challenge some students to use matrices in calculator programs that move figures across the screen, as in the project of Lesson 8.1.

Step 1

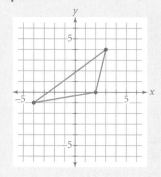

Step 3 a translation right 5 units

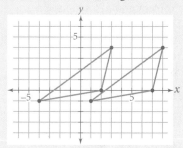

Step 5a $\begin{bmatrix} -4 & 3 & 2 \\ -5 & 0 & -4 \end{bmatrix}$; a translation down 4 units

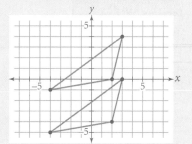

Steps 7 and 8 Some students may not feel secure about having letters (*x* and *y*) in matrices. Suggest that they just go ahead and see what happens.

Step 9 The last column will not be part of the image but rather will show the general transformation in Step 10.

SHARING IDEAS

Have students report their results from Steps 6, 11, and 12.

[Ask] "Does it matter in what order the matrices are multiplied?" [A 2 × 3 matrix representing a triangle must be multiplied by a 2 × 2 matrix on the left.]

"What transformation matrix would produce a reflection across both the x- and y-axes?" [It would be $\begin{bmatrix} -1 & 0 \\ 0 & -1 \end{bmatrix}$.] This double reflection accomplishes a rotation through 180°.

The opening quotation by Sofia Kovalevskaya (1850–1891), a Russian mathematician, was the motto on her paper "On the Problem of the Rotation of a Solid Body about a Fixed Point." In Exercise 9, students will see rotations through angles other than 180°.

Assessing Progress

You can assess students' abilities at adding and multiplying matrices and at recognizing translations, reflections, and stretches or shrinks of graphs.

Closing the Lesson

You can represent a polygon by putting the coordinates of its vertices into the columns of a matrix. To achieve a translation, you add another matrix. To achieve a reflection, stretch, or shrink, you multiply on the left by a 2 × 2 matrix.

BUILDING UNDERSTANDING

Students work with matrices representing transformations.

See page 726 for answers to Steps 9, 11a–c, and 12, and to Exercise 1a.

486 CHAPTER 8 Transformations

Step 9

Step 10 Possible answer: In Step 5a of the Flipping Graphs Investigation (Lesson 8.3), when $L_4 = -L_2$, all of the y-coordinates were negated, creating a reflection across the x-axis.

Step 9 Draw the image represented by your answer in Step 8. Describe the resulting transformation. a reflection across the x-axis

Step 10 How is the last column of the image matrix related to the transformations you made using lists in this chapter?

Step 11 Repeat Steps 7–10, but in Step 8 change what you multiply by matrix $[B]$ each time. Use a new set of coordinate axes for each transformation.

a. $\begin{bmatrix} -1 & 0 \\ 0 & 1 \end{bmatrix} \cdot [B]$
b. $\begin{bmatrix} 1 & 0 \\ 0 & 0.5 \end{bmatrix} \cdot [B]$
c. $\begin{bmatrix} 0.5 & 0 \\ 0 & 2 \end{bmatrix} \cdot [B]$

Step 12 Make a conjecture about the relationship between the matrix multiplied by $[B]$ and the resulting transformation.

EXERCISES

You will need your graphing calculator for Exercise **5**.

▶ **Practice Your Skills**

1. The matrix $\begin{bmatrix} -2 & 1 & -2 \\ 2 & 2 & 6 \end{bmatrix}$ represents a triangle.

  a. Name the coordinates and draw the triangle. $(-2, 2), (1, 2), (-2, 6)$ $\begin{bmatrix} 0 & 0 & 0 \\ -3 & -3 & -3 \end{bmatrix}$

  b. What matrix would you add to translate the triangle down 3 units? @

  c. Calculate the matrix for the image if you translate the triangle down 3 units. @ $\begin{bmatrix} -2 & 1 & -2 \\ -1 & -1 & 3 \end{bmatrix}$

2. Refer to these triangles.

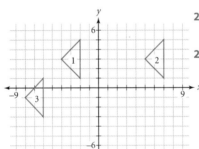

2b. $\begin{bmatrix} -4 & -2 & -2 \\ 3 & 5 & 1 \end{bmatrix} + \begin{bmatrix} 9 & 9 & 9 \\ 0 & 0 & 0 \end{bmatrix} = \begin{bmatrix} 5 & 7 & 7 \\ 3 & 5 & 1 \end{bmatrix}$

2c. $\begin{bmatrix} -4 & -2 & -2 \\ 3 & 5 & 1 \end{bmatrix} + \begin{bmatrix} -4 & -4 & -4 \\ -4 & -4 & -4 \end{bmatrix} = \begin{bmatrix} -8 & -6 & -6 \\ -1 & 1 & -3 \end{bmatrix}$

  a. Write a matrix to represent triangle 1.   possible answer: $\begin{bmatrix} -4 & -2 & -2 \\ 3 & 5 & 1 \end{bmatrix}$

  b. Write the matrix equation to translate from triangle 1 to triangle 2. @

  c. Write the matrix equation to translate from triangle 1 to triangle 3.

3. Add or multiply.

  a. $[4 \quad 7] + [2 \quad 8]$ @ $[6 \quad 15]$ **b.** $\begin{bmatrix} 4 \\ 7 \end{bmatrix} + \begin{bmatrix} 2 \\ 8 \end{bmatrix}$ $\begin{bmatrix} 6 \\ 15 \end{bmatrix}$ **c.** $[4 \quad 7] \cdot \begin{bmatrix} 2 \\ 8 \end{bmatrix}$ @ $[64]$ **d.** $\begin{bmatrix} 4 \\ 7 \end{bmatrix} \cdot [2 \quad 8]$ $\begin{bmatrix} 8 & 32 \\ 14 & 56 \end{bmatrix}$

4. In the investigation you saw that matrix multiplication can result in a reflection.

  a. What matrix reflects a figure across the y-axis? $\begin{bmatrix} -1 & 0 \\ 0 & 1 \end{bmatrix}$

4b. $\begin{bmatrix} 1 & 0 \\ 0 & -1 \end{bmatrix}$ **b.** What matrix reflects a figure across the x-axis?

ASSIGNING HOMEWORK

Essential	1, 5–7
Performance assessment	4, 5
Portfolio	8
Journal	6, 7
Group	2, 9
Review	3, 10–12

▶ **Helping with the Exercises**

Exercise 3 Because calculators are best used when the focus of an exercise is on solving a problem rather than on learning skills, calculators would not be appropriate here. In fact, you might ask students to write out their calculations in each entry of the solution matrix. In 3d, students may not realize that the product of a 2 × 1 matrix and a 1 × 2 matrix is a 2 × 2 matrix.

▶ Reason and Apply

5. The matrix $\begin{bmatrix} -1 & 2 & 1 & -2 \\ 2 & -1 & -2 & 1 \end{bmatrix}$ represents a quadrilateral.

   a. What kind of quadrilateral is it? ⓗ   a rectangle

   b. Without using your calculator, tell how to find the image of the point $(2, -1)$

     when you multiply $\begin{bmatrix} 1 & 0 \\ 0 & 2 \end{bmatrix} \cdot \begin{bmatrix} -1 & 2 & 1 & -2 \\ 2 & -1 & -2 & 1 \end{bmatrix}$. What are the coordinates of

     this point's image? In what row and column of the image matrix will you find the new x-coordinate? The new y-coordinate? ⓐ

   c. Multiply $\begin{bmatrix} 1 & 0 \\ 0 & 2 \end{bmatrix} \cdot \begin{bmatrix} -1 & 2 & 1 & -2 \\ 2 & -1 & -2 & 1 \end{bmatrix}$. Check your work with your calculator.

     [▶ 🖥 See **Calculator Note 1P** to review matrix multiplication. ◀] ⓐ $\begin{bmatrix} -1 & 2 & 1 & -2 \\ 4 & -2 & -4 & 2 \end{bmatrix}$

   d. Draw the image represented by your answer to 5c. What kind of polygon is it?   a parallelogram

6. Consider this square.

   a. Write a matrix, $[S]$, to represent it. $[S] = \begin{bmatrix} 0 & 1 & 1 & 0 \\ 0 & 0 & 1 & 1 \end{bmatrix}$

   b. Describe the transformation when you calculate

     i. $\begin{bmatrix} 1 & 0 \\ 0 & 3 \end{bmatrix} \cdot [S]$ **ii.** $\begin{bmatrix} 1 & 0 \\ 0 & -3 \end{bmatrix} \cdot [S]$

     iii. $\begin{bmatrix} 4 & 0 \\ 0 & 2 \end{bmatrix} \cdot [S]$ **iv.** $[S] + \begin{bmatrix} 4 & 4 & 4 & 4 \\ 2 & 2 & 2 & 2 \end{bmatrix}$

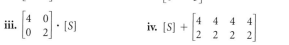

7. Consider this quadrilateral.

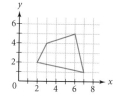

7b. $\begin{bmatrix} 1 & 0 \\ 0 & 0.5 \end{bmatrix} \cdot [Q] = \begin{bmatrix} 2 & 3 & 6 & 7 \\ 1 & 2 & 2.5 & 0.5 \end{bmatrix}$

   a. Write a matrix, $[Q]$, to represent it. ⓐ   possible answer: $[Q] = \begin{bmatrix} 2 & 3 & 6 & 7 \\ 2 & 4 & 5 & 1 \end{bmatrix}$

   b. Write a matrix multiplication equation that will vertically shrink the quadrilateral by a factor of 0.5. ⓐ

   c. Write a matrix multiplication equation that will both vertically and horizontally shrink the quadrilateral by a factor of 0.5. $\begin{bmatrix} 0.5 & 0 \\ 0 & 0.5 \end{bmatrix} \cdot [Q] = \begin{bmatrix} 1 & 1.5 & 3 & 3.5 \\ 1 & 2 & 2.5 & 0.5 \end{bmatrix}$

   d. Multiply $\begin{bmatrix} 1 & 0 \\ 0 & -1 \end{bmatrix} \cdot \begin{bmatrix} -1 & 0 \\ 0 & 1 \end{bmatrix}$. Then multiply the result by matrix $[Q]$. Draw the image of the quadrilateral. Describe the resulting transformation. How is

     the transformation related to the matrices $\begin{bmatrix} 1 & 0 \\ 0 & -1 \end{bmatrix}$ and $\begin{bmatrix} -1 & 0 \\ 0 & 1 \end{bmatrix}$?

   e. Multiply $\begin{bmatrix} 0 & -1 \\ 1 & 0 \end{bmatrix} \cdot [Q]$. Draw the image. Describe the transformation.

     $\begin{bmatrix} -2 & -4 & -5 & -1 \\ 2 & 3 & 6 & 7 \end{bmatrix}$; a quarter-turn counterclockwise

7d. $\begin{bmatrix} -1 & 0 \\ 0 & -1 \end{bmatrix}; \begin{bmatrix} -1 & 0 \\ 0 & -1 \end{bmatrix} \cdot [Q]$

$= \begin{bmatrix} -2 & -3 & -6 & -7 \\ -2 & -4 & -5 & -1 \end{bmatrix};$

a reflection across both the x- and y-axes; alone,

$\begin{bmatrix} 1 & 0 \\ 0 & -1 \end{bmatrix}$ results in a reflection across the x-axis, and

$\begin{bmatrix} -1 & 0 \\ 0 & 1 \end{bmatrix}$ results in a reflection across the y-axis.

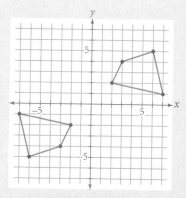

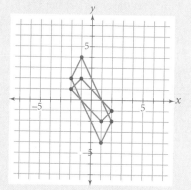

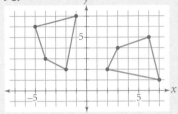

Exercise 8 [Ask] "How are the 3's and 2's in the transformation matrix in 8c related to the transformation and the equation of the image?" [The transformation matrix shows a translation to the right 3 units and a translation up 2 units; in the equation, the 3 is subtracted from x before it is squared, and the 2 is the constant term.]

In 8d, suggest that students draw the graph of the transformed equation. [Ask] "Why does it look like the original graph, even though the image matrix is different from the original matrix?" [The graph of $y = (-x)^2$ is visually identical to the graph of $y = x^2$.]

Exercise 9 This exercise will challenge many students on different levels. The concept of rotation might be new, and students may have difficulty determining the 60° rotation. Prior experience with angle measures is useful. It may help some students if you ask, "What fraction of a circle was the polygon rotated through?" Students might benefit from using a polygon that has one edge on the x-axis, as in the sample answers, and then determining the rotation of this one edge.

See pages 726–727 for answers to Exercises 9a–f, 10a, and 11b.

8. The points $(-2, 4)$, $(-1, 1)$, $(0, 0)$, $(1, 1)$, and $(2, 4)$ are on a parabola.

  a. What is the equation of the parabola that passes through these points? $y = x^2$

  b. Write a matrix, $[P]$, to represent the coordinates of these points. $[P] = \begin{bmatrix} -2 & -1 & 0 & 1 & 2 \\ 4 & 1 & 0 & 1 & 4 \end{bmatrix}$

  c. Add $[P] + \begin{bmatrix} 3 & 3 & 3 & 3 & 3 \\ 2 & 2 & 2 & 2 & 2 \end{bmatrix}$. Write an equation of the parabola that passes through the points represented in the image matrix. @ $\begin{bmatrix} 1 & 2 & 3 & 4 & 5 \\ 6 & 3 & 2 & 3 & 6 \end{bmatrix}$; $y = (x - 3)^2 + 2$

  d. Multiply $\begin{bmatrix} -1 & 0 \\ 0 & 1 \end{bmatrix} \cdot [P]$. Write an equation of the parabola that passes through the points represented in the image matrix. $\begin{bmatrix} 2 & 1 & 0 & -1 & -2 \\ 4 & 1 & 0 & 1 & 4 \end{bmatrix}$; $y = (-x)^2$

9. *Mini-Investigation* In Exercise 7e, you saw a transformation called a **rotation**. A rotation turns a figure about a point called the *center*. The center of a rotation can be inside, outside, or on the figure that is rotated.

  a. Draw a polygon of your own design on graph paper. Represent your polygon with a matrix, $[R]$.

  b. Multiply $\begin{bmatrix} 0.5 & -0.866 \\ 0.866 & 0.5 \end{bmatrix} \cdot [R]$. Draw the image of your polygon.

  c. The transformation matrix in 9b rotates the polygon. How many degrees is it rotated? What point is the center of the rotation?

  d. Multiply $\begin{bmatrix} 0.5 & -0.866 \\ 0.866 & 0.5 \end{bmatrix} \cdot \begin{bmatrix} 0.5 & -0.866 \\ 0.866 & 0.5 \end{bmatrix}$ and round the entries in the answer matrix to the nearest thousandth. Then multiply the result by matrix $[R]$. Draw the image of the polygon. Describe the transformation.

  e. Describe how you could rotate your polygon 180° (a half-turn).

  f. Describe how you could rotate your polygon 360° so that the image is the same as the original polygon.

Did you know that you use rotations every day? Opening a door, turning a faucet, tightening a bolt with a wrench—all of these require rotations. The rotational force you use to do these things is called *torque*. Think of other everyday situations that require rotations.

▶ **Review**

8.4 **10.** Tacoma and Jared are doing a "walker" investigation. Tacoma starts 2 m from the motion sensor. He walks away at a rate of 0.5 m/s for 6 s. Then he walks back toward the sensor at a rate of 0.5 m/s for 3 s.

  a. Sketch a time-distance graph for Tacoma's walk.

  b. Write an equation that fits the graph. $y = 5 - 0.5|x - 6|$

1.3 **11.** This table shows the approximate population of the ten most populated countries in 2004.

  a. Give the five-number summary. in millions: 127, 141, 171.5, 293, 1299

  b. Make a box plot of the data.

  c. Are there any outliers? yes, China and India

Most Populated Countries, 2004

Country	Population (millions)
China	1,299
India	1,065
United States	293
Indonesia	238
Brazil	184
Pakistan	159
Russia	144
Bangladesh	141
Nigeria	137
Japan	127

(Central Intelligence Agency, *www.cia.gov*)

[Alert] Students may also have trouble accurately calculating with the decimals in this problem. Students' graphing abilities will be tested by having to identify the location of points with decimal coordinates such as $(-0.232, 3.598)$.

In the transformation matrix, 0.866 is an approximation of $\frac{\sqrt{3}}{2}$, derived from a 30°-60°-90° triangle with hypotenuse 1 unit. Because students have not yet seen square roots that are irrational numbers, have them use the approximation 0.866 and round subsequent answers to three decimal places.

For 9e, some students may recall from 7d that $\begin{bmatrix} -1 & 0 \\ 0 & -1 \end{bmatrix} \cdot [R]$ will also accomplish a rotation through 180°.

2.8 **12.** Use an undo table to solve the equation given. Notice that several steps have been filled in for you.

$x = 0$ or $x = 6$

Equation: $4(x - 3)^2 + 1 = 37$		
Description	Undo	Result
Pick x.		$0, 6$
$-(3)$	$+(3)$	± 3
$( )^2$	$\pm \sqrt{}$	9
$\cdot (4)$	$/(4)$	36
$+(1)$	$-(1)$	37

project

TILES

Some floor tiles are simple polygons, like squares. Others have more complex shapes, with curves or unusual angles. But all tiles have one thing in common—they fit together without gaps or overlap.

You can use transformations to create your own tile shape. Start with a polygon that works as a tile. For example, you can start with a rhombus and use transformations to create a complex shape that still works as a tile. In this example, a design drawn on the right side of the rhombus is translated and copied on the left side; a translation is also used for the top and bottom. The result is an interesting shape that still fits together.

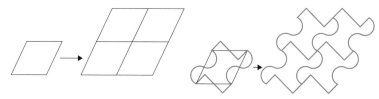

Your project should include

▶ Your tile pattern. Show what a single tile looks like and how several tiles look when they are joined together.

▶ A report of how you created your tile. What polygon did you start with? What transformations did you use?

For an extra challenge, start with a polygon that is not a quadrilateral, like a triangle. Or try other transformations or combinations of transformations. Dot paper, graph paper, a computer drawing program, or The Geometer's Sketchpad software are useful tools for this project.

Learn more about the mathematics of tilings with the Internet links at
www.keymath.com/DA .

THE GEOMETER'S SKETCHPAD

The Geometer's Sketchpad was used to create these tiles. Sketchpad has tools to help you create simple polygons and apply transformations. Learn how to use these tools to create your own tiling pattern.

Supporting the project

MOTIVATION

Tessellation is the mathematical term for a tiling or a collection of shapes that tile the plane. *Tessellation* comes from *tessera*, the Latin word for "tile." Students will have more extensive exposure to creating tessellations with transformations in *Discovering Geometry*.

OUTCOMES

▶ Project includes the required elements and uses correct vocabulary.
• A tile is created from a polygon other than a quadrilateral (possibilities: all triangles, hexagons with opposite sides parallel, or a combination of shapes, such as a regular octagon and a square).
• A tile is created from transformations other

than translations. (In the example shown in the student text, each side is created by a rotation about the side's midpoint.)
• The student does extensive investigation into which polygons tile the plane and can explain why certain polygons work.
• The student creates a tile that looks like an object, as in the art of M. C. Escher.

PLANNING

LESSON OUTLINE

One day:

5 min	Introduction
15 min	Exercises and helping individuals
15 min	Checking work and helping individuals
15 min	Student self-assessment

REVIEWING

Refer students to Lesson 8.3, Exercise 9, in which Bo is moving a star by translations and reflections. Work through the exercise as given. Then add the condition that the star is to shrink vertically by a factor of 0.8 in each frame. Change it to a vertical stretch by a factor of 1.3 in each frame. Then begin with the star centered at the origin and move it vertically the same distance, reflecting and stretching or shrinking horizontally. If you've done Lesson 8.7, review how to accomplish each of these transformations with a matrix. Finally, begin with the graph of $y = |x|$ or $y = \frac{1}{x}$ and write equations for moving it horizontally or vertically 11 units in 11 frames, in each of which it reflects and stretches or shrinks. Depending on the amount of time you have, you or the students might demonstrate these moves using a calculator program.

ASSIGNING HOMEWORK

You might assign even-numbered exercises for homework and have students work alone or in groups on the odd-numbered exercises in class. Assign Exercise 12 only if you are covering matrices.

In this chapter you moved individual points, polygons, and graphs of functions with **transformations.** You learned to **translate, reflect, stretch,** and **shrink** a **parent function** to create a **family of functions** based on it. For example, if you know what the graph of $y = x^2$ looks like, understanding transformations gives you the power to know what the graph of $y = 3(x + 2)^2 - 4$ looks like.

You transformed the graphs of the parent functions $y = |x|$ and $y = x^2$ to create many different absolute-value and squaring functions. You can apply the same transformations to the graphs of other parent functions, like $y = x$ or $y = 2^x$, to create many different linear or exponential functions. You can even fit an equation to data by transforming a simple graph.

You learned that the inverse variation function, $y = \frac{1}{x}$, is one type of **rational function.** The graphs of transformations of the parent function $y = \frac{1}{x}$ have one vertical **asymptote** and one horizontal asymptote—understanding transformations helps you know where asymptotes will occur. You also learned how to perform arithmetic with **rational expressions.**

Finally, you used matrices to organize the coordinates of points and to do transformations. You can use matrices to do translations, reflections, stretches, shrinks, and **rotations.**

EXERCISES

You will need your graphing calculator for Exercises **4** and **7.**

@ Answers are provided for all exercises in this set.

For Exercises 1 and 2, consider the black pentagon below as the original figure.

1. The image of the black pentagon after a transformation is shown in red.

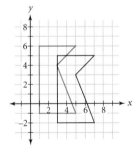

a. Describe the transformation. a translation left 2 units and up 1 unit

b. Define the coordinates of any point in the image using (x, y) as the coordinates of any point in the original figure. $(x - 2, y + 1)$

2. Here are three more transformations of the black pentagon from Exercise 1.

   i.

   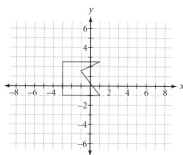

   ii.

   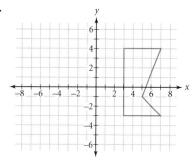

   iii.

   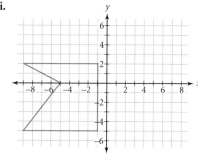

   a. Describe the transformations.

   b. Patty plots the original pentagon on her calculator. She uses list L₁ for the x-coordinates of the vertices and list L₂ for the y-coordinates. Tell Patty how to define list L₃ and list L₄ for each image shown above.

3. You can create this figure on a calculator by connecting four points. Assume the x-coordinates of each point are entered into list L₁ and the corresponding y-coordinates are entered into list L₂. Explain how to make an image that is

   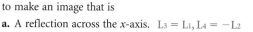

   a. A reflection across the x-axis. $L_3 = L_1, L_4 = -L_2$

   b. A reflection across the y-axis. $L_3 = -L_1, L_4 = L_2$

   c. A reflection across the x-axis and a translation right 3 units.
   $L_3 = L_1 + 3, L_4 = -L_2$

4. Describe each function as a transformation of the graph of the parent function $y = |x|$ or $y = x^2$. Then sketch a graph of each function. Check your answers by graphing on your calculator.

   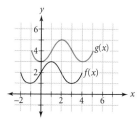

   a. $y = 2|x| + 1$ **b.** $y = -|x + 2| + 2$

   c. $y = 0.5(-x)^2 - 1$ **d.** $y = -(x - 2)^2 + 1$

5. At right, the graph of $g(x)$ is a transformation of the graph of $f(x)$. Write an equation for $g(x)$ in terms of $f(x)$. $g(x) = f(x - 1) + 2$

   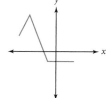

▶ **Helping with the Exercises**

2a. i. a vertical shrink by a factor of 0.5 and a translation left 6 units

2a. ii. possible answer: a reflection across the x-axis, then a translation up 2 units

2a. iii. possible answer: a horizontal stretch by a factor of 2 and a reflection across the y-axis, then a translation right 5 units and down 3 units

2b. i. $L_3 = L_1 - 6, L_4 = 0.5 \cdot L_2$

2b. ii. possible answer: $L_3 = L_1$, $L_4 = -L_2 + 2$

2b. iii. possible answer: $L_3 = -2 \cdot L_1 + 5, L_4 = L_2 - 3$

3. Answers will vary. For these possible answers, list L₃ and list L₄ are used for the x- and y-coordinates, respectively, of each image.

4a. a vertical stretch of the graph of $y = |x|$ by a factor of 2, then a translation up 1 unit

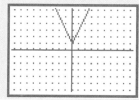

$[-9.4, 9.4, 1, -6.2, 6.2, 1]$

4b. a reflection of the graph of $y = |x|$ across the x-axis, then a translation left 2 units and up 2 units

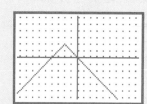

4c. possible answer: a vertical shrink of the graph of $y = x^2$ by a factor of 0.5, then a reflection across the y-axis (which doesn't show, because the graph is symmetrical) then a translation down 1 unit

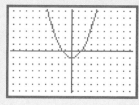

4d. possible answer: a reflection of the graph of $y = x^2$ across the x-axis, then a translation right 2 units and up 1 unit

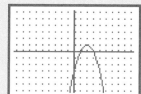

7a. The graph should have the same x-intercept as $f(x)$. The y-intercept should be the opposite of that for $f(x)$.

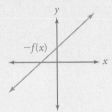

7b. Answers will vary. Possible answer for a friendly window with a factor of 1: If $Y_1 = -x - 2$, then $Y_2 = -Y_1$ reflects the graph across the x-axis (because the calculator interprets $-Y_1$ as $-(-x - 2)$, or $x + 2$); this supports the answer to 7a.

8a. a translation right 3 units; asymptotes: $x = 3, y = 0$

8b. a vertical stretch by a factor of 3 and then a translation left 2 units; asymptotes: $x = -2$, $y = 0$

8c. a translation right 5 units and down 2 units; asymptotes: $x = 5, y = -2$

Exercise 9 In physics, intensity is the same as brightness. You may want to define this as an "inverse square function." You may wish to explore this topic further with the CBL 2 demonstration Light Intensity from Chapter 2.

---

6. Write the equation for each graph.

a. $y \quad y = -|x| + 3$

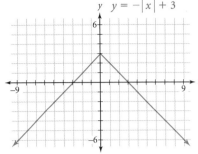

b. $y \quad y = (x + 4)^2 - 2$

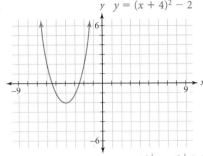

c. $y \quad y = 0.5x^2 - 5$

d. $y = -2|x - 3| + 1$

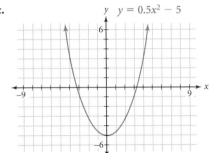

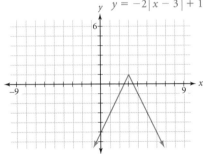

7. Consider the graph of $f(x)$ at right.
  a. Sketch the graph of $-f(x)$.
  b. Enter a linear function into Y_1 on your calculator to create a graph like $f(x)$. Enter $Y_2 = -Y_1$ and graph it too. Describe your results.

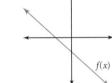

8. Describe each function as a transformation of the graph of the parent function $y = \frac{1}{x}$. Give equations for the asymptotes.

  a. $y = \dfrac{1}{x - 3}$
  b. $y = \dfrac{3}{x + 2}$
  c. $y = \dfrac{1}{x - 5} - 2$

9. APPLICATION The intensity, I, of a 100-watt lightbulb is related to the distance, d, from which it is measured. This rational function shows the relationship when intensity is measured in lux (lumens per square meter) and distance is measured in meters.

$$I = \frac{90}{d^2}$$

  a. Find the intensity of the light 4 meters from the bulb. 5.625 lumens
  b. Find the distance from the bulb if the intensity of the light measures 20 lux. approximately 2.12 m

10. Describe each graph as a transformation of the graph of the parent function $y = 2^x$ or $y = \frac{1}{x}$. Then write an equation for each graph.

a.

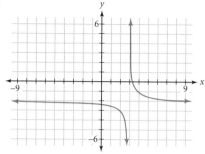

b.

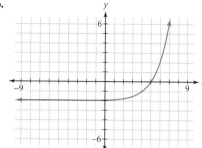

c.

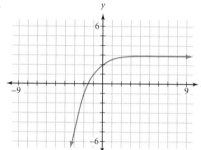

d.

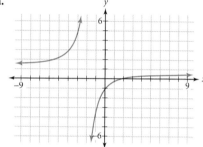

11. Perform the indicated operation and reduce the result to lowest terms. State any restrictions on the variable.

a. $\dfrac{x}{2x - 3} - \dfrac{2x + 3}{8x - 12}$ $\frac{1}{4}$, where $x \neq \frac{3}{2}$

b. $\dfrac{42x^2}{x - 3} \div \dfrac{3}{2x - 6}$ $28x^2$, where $x \neq 3$

12. Consider this square.

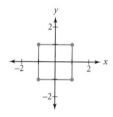

a. Write a matrix, $[A]$, that represents this square.

b. Describe the transformation when you calculate

i. $\begin{bmatrix} 1 & 0 \\ 0 & 1 \end{bmatrix} \cdot [A]$

ii. $\begin{bmatrix} -1 & 0 \\ 0 & -1 \end{bmatrix} \cdot [A]$

iii. $\begin{bmatrix} 1 & 0 \\ 0 & 3 \end{bmatrix} \cdot [A]$

iv. $[A] + \begin{bmatrix} 1 & 1 & 1 & 1 \\ 1 & 1 & 1 & 1 \end{bmatrix}$

Exercise 10 10b and 10c may be challenging, because exposure to exponential functions has been limited in this chapter. Help students recognize that transformations can be applied to any function. It may also help to show that $y = 2^x$ has an asymptote at $y = 0$ and passes through the point $(0, 1)$. These facts can then be used to help students determine what translations have occurred.

10a. a translation of the graph of $y = \frac{1}{x}$ right 3 units and down 2 units; $y = \frac{1}{x - 3} - 2$

10b. a translation of the graph of $y = 2^x$ right 4 units and down 2 units; $y = 2^{x-4} - 2$

10c. possible answer: a reflection of the graph of $y = 2^x$ across the x-axis and across the y-axis, followed by a translation up 3 units; the reflection across the y-axis can be done at any time, but the translation up must be done after the reflection across the x-axis; $y = -2^{-x} + 3$

10d. possible answer: a vertical stretch of the graph of $y = \frac{1}{x}$ by a factor of 4 and a reflection across the x-axis, followed by a translation up 1 unit and left 2 units; $y = -\frac{4}{x + 2} + 1$

Exercise 12b If students actually graph the image, they may say that nothing has happened. Because of symmetry, the image will look identical to the original square. However, actually calculating the image matrix will show that the vertices do move, indicating some change.

12a. possible answer:
$[A] = \begin{bmatrix} -1 & 1 & 1 & -1 \\ 1 & 1 & -1 & -1 \end{bmatrix}$

12b. i. Nothing; the image is identical to the original square.

12b. ii. a reflection across the x-axis and across the y-axis, or a rotation through $180°$

12b. iii. a vertical stretch by a factor of 3

12b. iv. a translation right 1 unit and up 1 unit

▶ Take Another Look

The equation of the line of reflection is $y = x$. Students should find that the coordinates of each point are interchanged after the reflection. For example, the image of $(2, 4)$ is $(4, 2)$. The image of this function is not a function. An example of a function whose inverse is also a function is $y = 2x$. An example of a function whose inverse is not a function is $y = x^2$. The coordinates of the image are defined as (y, x).

[Ask] "Is any function its own inverse?" [Yes, if its graph is symmetric to the graph of $y = x$; for example, $y = \frac{1}{x}$ and $y = -x$ are their own inverses, as is the function $y = x$ itself.]

You may also want to have students pick an example of a function $f(x)$ whose inverse is also a function. Call the inverse $g(x)$, and ask students to evaluate $f(g(2)), g(f(0))$, and $f(g(x))$.

ASSESSING

For a written assessment, you can choose Form A or B of the Chapter 8 test from Assessment Resources, use two or three Constructive Assessment items, or select a combination of short-answer and deeper questions from the test generator.

FACILITATING SELF-ASSESSMENT

To help students complete the portfolio described in Assessing What You've Learned, suggest that they consider for evaluation their work on Lesson 8.1, Exercise 9; Lesson 8.2, Exercise 11; Lesson 8.3, Exercises 8 and 9; Lesson 8.4, Exercise 9; Lesson 8.6, Exercises 8 and 12; and Lesson 8.7, Exercise 8.

TAKE ANOTHER LOOK

 In this chapter you saw reflections across the x-axis and across the y-axis. You also saw reflections across other vertical and horizontal lines (see Exercise 11 in Lesson 8.3). Let's examine another very important line of reflection.

Here is the graph of a function in black. The red image was created by a reflection across the dotted line. What is the equation of the line of reflection?

Identify at least three points on the graph of $y = f(x)$. Then name the image of each point after the reflection. How would you define the coordinates of the image based on the coordinates of the original graph?

The image that results from this type of reflection is called an **inverse.** Is the inverse of a function necessarily a function too? Find an example of a function whose inverse is also a function. Find an example of a function whose inverse is not a function.

Learn more about inverse functions with the links at www.keymath.com/DA .

Mirrors are used to create reflections. This mirror helps drivers see around a corner on an Italian street.

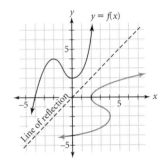

Assessing What You've Learned

 UPDATE YOUR PORTFOLIO Choose one piece of work that illustrates each transformation that you have studied in this chapter. Add these to your portfolio. Describe each work in a cover sheet, giving the objective, the result, and what you might have done differently.

ORGANIZE YOUR NOTEBOOK Organize your notes on each type of transformation that you have learned about. Review how each transformation affects individual points and how it changes the equation of a function. Then create a table that summarizes your notes. Use rows for each type of transformation and columns to show effects on points and equations. You can use subrows and subcolumns to further organize the information. For example, you might want to use one row for reflections across the x-axis and another row for reflections across the y-axis. You might want to use one column for changes to $y = f(x)$ and other columns for changes to specific functions like $y = x^2, y = |x|$, or $y = \frac{1}{x}$.

 PERFORMANCE ASSESSMENT Show a classmate, a family member, or your teacher how you can transform a single parent function into a whole family of functions. Explain how you can write a function for a graph by identifying the transformations. In contrast, show how you can sketch a graph just by looking at the equation.

Quadratic Models

Overview

Students have studied linear and exponential growth and have abstracted to the concept of a function. In Chapter 8, they considered transformations of functions. Now they're ready to apply transformations to the study of quadratic functions.

Lesson 9.1 introduces quadratic equations and their graphs in the context of a real-world problem. Students use the equation of a transformed basic parabola to identify the vertex of the parabola. They also solve quadratic equations symbolically and by using graphs and tables. In **Lesson 9.2,** they use a quadratic function to model a real-world problem and learn to find the vertex form from knowing the x-intercepts of a parabola. In **Lesson 9.3,** students learn to change a quadratic equation from vertex form to general form by squaring binomials (using rectangle diagrams). In **Lesson 9.4,** students learn that the roots of a quadratic equation can be found quickly from its factored form, and they explore the relationships among the three forms of a quadratic equation. During Activity Day **Lesson 9.5,** students collect motion data that they then model with quadratic equations. In **Lesson 9.6,** students learn to solve quadratic equations in general form by completing the square. Students study the derivation of the quadratic formula and learn to apply it in **Lesson 9.7. Lesson 9.8** describes cubic functions—their general patterns, characteristics, and graphs.

The Mathematics

A quadratic function is a transformation of the parent function $y = x^2$. It has an x^2 term and possibly linear (x) and constant terms.

Three Forms

The **vertex form** $y = a(x - h)^2 + k$ appeared in Chapter 8 as the general transformation of the parent function $y = x^2$. This form is most useful for finding the vertex of the parabolic graph. The roots (x-intercepts) of any equation expressed in this form can be found symbolically by undoing or balancing. Finding the y-intercept requires some calculation.

The **factored form** $y = a(x - r_1)(x - r_2)$ clearly shows the roots r_1 and r_2. The vertex of the parabola can be found from the average of r_1 and r_2. Finding the y-intercept also requires some calculation.

The **general form,** or standard form, is $y = ax^2 + bx + c$. Here the y-intercept is the coefficient c. If the equation is representing the height y of a projectile x seconds after it began moving, the coefficient a is $-\frac{1}{2}$ times the acceleration due to gravity force, and the coefficient b is the initial velocity. Finding the vertex or roots of the general form requires, in effect, changing to one of the other forms.

Changing Forms

To change from vertex form to general form requires squaring the binomial $(x - h)$ and combining like terms. Similarly, to get from the factored form to the general form, you multiply the binomials $(x - r_1)$ and $(x - r_2)$. Students will understand squaring or multiplying binomials more deeply through diagrams than from memorizing the FOIL (first, outside, inside, last) method.

The primary reason to change quadratic equations from general form is to solve them. In some cases changing to factored form is easy, especially with rectangle diagrams. Then the roots are apparent. In other cases, completing the square (again with a rectangle diagram) can yield vertex form, which can be solved symbolically. The algorithm called the *quadratic formula* is derived this way.

Cubics and Finding Coefficients

The **degree** of a polynomial in variable x is the highest power of x. A polynomial of degree 3 is called a *cubic*.

A polynomial of degree 2 (a quadratic) has three coefficients. If you know three points through which you want a parabola to pass, you can substitute to obtain a system of three equations in three unknowns (the three coefficients) that has a unique solution, meaning that only one parabola will pass through those three points. If you're given the vertex of the parabola, however, knowing just one other point through which the parabola passes will determine the parabola, because the figure must also pass through a third point that is a reflection of the second point across the axis of the parabola. Hence the vertex-form equation $y = a(x - h)^2 + k$ can be found from knowing only the vertex (h, k) and one other point, which determines the stretch or shrink factor a. Such symmetry is not useful for general polynomials of degree n. Without further conditions, to determine a graph uniquely you need to know $n + 1$ points through which the graph will pass.

Using This Chapter

If your curriculum doesn't call for factoring, you could omit part of Lesson 9.4. A light treatment of Lessons 9.6 and 9.7 is possible with curricula that don't require completing the square or the quadratic formula. Lesson 9.8 is needed only to be sure students see cube roots and perfect cubes and to revisit the connection between roots and the factored form of an equation.

Resources

Discovering Algebra Resources

Teaching and Worksheet Masters
  Lessons 9.1, 9.2 (from Chapter 1), 9.6–9.8

Sketchpad Demonstrations
  Lessons 9.2, 9.3

Fathom Demonstrations
  Lessons 9.4, 9.8

CBR Demonstration
  Lesson 9.4

Dynamic Algebra Explorations online
  Lessons 9.4, 9.5

Calculator Notes 2A, 6B, 7A, 9A, 9B

Assessment Resources
  Quiz 1 (Lessons 9.1, 9.2)
  Quiz 2 (Lessons 9.3, 9.4)
  Quiz 3 (Lessons 9.6–9.8)
  Chapter 9 Test
  Chapter 9 Constructive Assessment Options

More Practice Your Skills for Chapter 9

Condensed Lessons for Chapter 9

Other Resources

www.keypress.com/DA

Materials

- graph paper
- several 24 cm lengths of string
- motion sensors
- empty coffee can
- long table

Pacing Guide

	day 1	day 2	day 3	day 4	day 5	day 6	day 7	day 8	day 9	day 10
standard	9.1	9.2	quiz, 9.3	9.3	9.4	9.5	quiz, 9.6	9.6	9.7	9.8
enriched	9.1	9.2	quiz, 9.3	9.3	9.4	9.5	quiz, project	9.6	9.7	9.8
block	9.1, 9.2	quiz, 9.3	9.4, 9.5	quiz, 9.6, 9.7	9.8 review	assessment				

	day 11	day 12	day 13	day 14	day 15	day 16	day 17	day 18	day 19	day 20
standard	review	assessment								
enriched	review, TAL	assessment								

Quadratic Models

- Use quadratic functions to model and solve equations based on (*time, height*) relationships for projectiles

- Solve quadratic equations using graphs, tables, and symbolic methods

- Write quadratic equations that model other real-world data

- Find the *x*-intercepts and vertex of a parabola by graphical and symbolic methods

- Convert quadratic equations among the vertex, factored, and general forms

- Learn to multiply binomials and factor trinomials using rectangle diagrams

- Explore cubes, cube roots, and transformations of the parent cubic function

Buckingham Fountain in Chicago's Grant Park contains 1.5 million gallons of water. When pumped through one of the fountain's 133 jets, the water forms the shape of a parabola as it falls back into the pool. The central spout shoots 135 feet in the air. The relationship between time and the height of free-falling objects in the air is described by quadratic equations.

OBJECTIVES

In this chapter you will
- model applications with quadratic functions
- compare features of parabolas to their quadratic equations
- learn strategies for solving quadratic equations
- learn how to combine and factor polynomials
- make connections between some new polynomial functions and their graphs

As you and your students look at the many streams of water in the photo of Buckingham Fountain, ask them to describe the parabolas that they see. **[Ask]** "What determines the shape of the parabolas?" [both the angle and the force at which the water is projected] Compare streams projected straight up with those that leave the fountain at different angles. [If the force behind two fountains is the same, the water from the spout with the steeper angle will go higher, but the water will

not land as far from the spout as it will for a spout with a shallower angle.] For one of the streams, you know the height. **[Ask]** "What besides the height would you need to know to determine the equation that describes the parabolic path of a drop of water?" [You would also need the point at which the water falls back into the pool. Imagine a coordinate axis with the *y*-axis through the highest point of the stream of water and the *x*-axis through the spout that shoots the water. The equa-

tions could be determined from three points: the maximum height of the water, the horizontal distance from the spout to the highest point, and the reflection across the *y*-axis of that point.]

The fountain, made of pink Georgia marble, is modeled after the Latona Basin in the gardens of Louis XIV's palace in Versailles, France. Kate Sturges Buckingham gave it to the city of Chicago in 1927.

LESSON

9.1

Solving Quadratic Equations

PLANNING

LESSON OUTLINE

One day:

5 min	Example A
20 min	Investigation
5 min	Sharing
5 min	Example B
5 min	Closing
10 min	Exercises

MATERIALS

- graph paper, *optional*
- Coordinate Plane (T, one per group), *optional*
- Number System Venn Diagram (T), *optional*
- Calculator Note 7A

TEACHING

The height of a projectile is given by a transformation of the squaring function. When the function is written in a form that shows that transformation, an equation involving it can be solved by undoing or balancing.

One Step

Pose this problem: "A ball is hit straight up. It reaches a height of 68 ft. Four seconds after it is hit, the ball reaches the ground. Sketch a graph of the ball's height, in feet, in terms of its flight time in seconds." Some students may draw a vertical line, confusing the height function with the path of the ball. Others may conjecture that the graph is that of an absolute-value function. **[Ask]** "Does the ball keep the same speed while going up and then suddenly switch to going down at a constant speed?" After students decide the graph should be a parabola, ask when they think it reaches its peak, 68 ft. You may need to ask when they think it will return to the height from which it was hit, giving rise to their making some assumptions. As time allows, ask them to write an equation of the graph as a transformation of the function $y = x^2$. They'll need to find the (negative) stretch factor to make the graph go through the point $(4, 0)$.

We especially need imagination in science; it is not all mathematics, nor all logic, but it is somewhat beauty and poetry.

MARIA MITCHELL

When you throw a ball straight up into the air, its height depends on three major factors—its starting position, the velocity at which it leaves your hand, and the force of **gravity.** Earth's gravity causes objects to accelerate downward, gathering speed every second. This acceleration due to gravity, called *g*, is 32 ft/s². It means that the object's downward speed increases 32 ft/s *for each second* in flight. If you plot the height of the ball at each instant of time, the graph of the data is a parabola.

EXAMPLE A

A baseball batter pops a ball straight up. The ball reaches a height of 68 ft before falling back down. Roughly 4 s after it is hit, the ball bounces off home plate. Sketch a graph that models the ball's height in feet during its flight time in seconds. When is the ball 68 ft high? How many times will it be 20 ft high?

LESSON OBJECTIVES

- Use quadratic functions to model and solve equations based on (*time, height*) relationships for projectiles
- Solve quadratic equations using graphs, tables, and symbolic methods
- Describe real-world meanings related to quadratic models

▶ **Solution**

The sketch at right pictures the ball's height from the time it is hit to when it lands on the ground. When the bat hits the ball, it is a few feet above the ground. So the y-intercept is just above the origin. The ball's height is 0 when it hits the ground just over 4 s later. So the parabola crosses the x-axis near the coordinates $(4, 0)$. The ball is at its maximum height of 68 ft after about 2 s, or halfway through its flight time. So the vertex of the parabola is near $(2, 68)$.

The ball reaches a height of 20 ft twice—once on its way up and again on its way down. If you sketch $y = 20$ on the same set of axes, you'll see that this line crosses the parabola at two points.

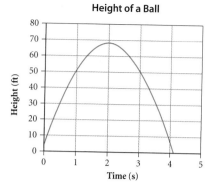

Height of a Ball

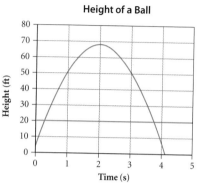

Height of a Ball

▶ **EXAMPLE A**

[Language] The word *quadratic* comes from the Latin *quadrare* and means "to make square." In a quadratic equation, the variable is squared; it is raised to the power of 2. The root *quad* means "four," as in *quadrilateral*.

This example shows students that the graph of the equation giving the height of a projectile is a parabola and tells them how to interpret such an equation.

Reassure students unfamiliar with baseball terms that the ball is simply rising straight up and then falling back down. The pull of gravity changes the speed of the ball; gravity slows down the ball as it goes up and speeds up the ball as it falls. [Alert] Some students may confuse the shape of the graph with the path of the ball. (The path is also parabolic and is discussed in Exercise 7.)

The parabola in Example A is a transformation of the equation $y = x^2$. The function $f(x) = x^2$ and transformations of it are called **quadratic functions**, because the highest power of x is x-squared. The Latin word meaning "to square" is *quadrare*. The function that describes the motion of a ball, and many other projectiles, is a quadratic function. You will learn more about this function in the investigation.

Investigation
Rocket Science

A model rocket blasts off and its engine shuts down when it is 25 m above the ground. Its velocity at that time is 50 m/s. Assume that it travels straight up and that the only force acting on it is the downward pull of gravity. In the metric system, the acceleration due to gravity is 9.8 m/s². The quadratic function $h(t) = \frac{1}{2}(-9.8)t^2 + 50t + 25$ describes the rocket's **projectile motion**.

Known as the father of rocketry, Robert Hutchings Goddard fired the first successful liquid-fueled rocket in 1926. Learn more about Goddard at www.keymath.com/DA .

NCTM STANDARDS

CONTENT	PROCESS
Number	✔ Problem Solving
✔ Algebra	✔ Reasoning
Geometry	✔ Communication
✔ Measurement	✔ Connections
Data/Probability	✔ Representation

Step 1 Encourage the use of dimensional analysis: 25 is in meters, and 50 is in meters per second (m/s). So when the latter is multiplied by t (in seconds), the result is in meters. The gravitational acceleration -9.8 is in meters per second squared (m/s^2), so when it is multiplied by t^2, in seconds squared (s^2), the result again is in meters. The $\frac{1}{2}$ has no dimensions.

The equation is not a perfect model for the real world. It is based on the invalid assumptions that there is no air resistance and that the value of g is constant (g decreases with distance from the center of Earth).

Step 3 Some students may think that g should be -32 rather than -9.8. They're thinking of g in the English system, measured in feet per second squared (ft/s^2).

Step 4 Again, watch for confusion between the shape of the graph and the path of the ball.

SHARING IDEAS

Ask students to present their ideas about Steps 3, 6, 7, 8, 9, and 10, perhaps using the Coordinate Plane transparency.

Elicit ideas about what each term in the projectile motion equation represents. In general, the height of a projectile (neglecting air resistance) in meters is given by $h(t) = \frac{1}{2}(-g)t^2 + v_0 t + h_0$, where g is acceleration due to gravity, v_0 is the initial velocity, and h_0 is the initial height. In this case, 25 m is the initial height, and $50t$ is the number of meters gained in t seconds. The initial term, $\frac{1}{2}(-9.8)t^2$, or $-4.9t^2$, represents the downward component of the motion. When t is small, $\frac{1}{2}(-9.8)t^2$ is less than $v_0 t + h_0$, so the object gains in height. When t

See page 727 for graphs for Steps 4, 5, 9, and 10.

Step 1 Let t represent the time in seconds since the engine shut down. Let $h(t)$ be the function value that gives the height, in meters, of the rocket at time t.

Step 1 Define the function variables and their units of measure for this situation.

Step 2 What is the real-world meaning of $h(0) = 25$? When $t = 0$ s, the height of the rocket is 25 m.

Step 3 How is the acceleration due to gravity, or g, represented in the equation? How does the equation show that this force is *downward*? The factor -9.8 is the downward (negative) acceleration due to gravity.

Next you'll make a graph of the situation.

Step 4 Graph the function $h(t)$. What viewing window shows all the important parts of the parabola?

Step 5 How high does the rocket fly before falling back to Earth? When does it reach this point? approximately 152.55 m; after approximately 5.10 s

Step 6 How much time passes while the rocket is in flight, after the engine shuts down? approximately 10.68 s

Step 7 What domain and range values make sense in this situation? possible answers: domain: $0 \le t \le 10.68$; range: $10 \le h \le 152.55$

Step 8 Write the equation you must solve to find when $h(t) = 60$. $60 = \frac{1}{2}(-9.8)t^2 + 50t + 25$

Step 9 When is the rocket 60 m above the ground? Use a calculator table to approximate your answers to the nearest tenth of a second. at about 0.8 s and at about 9.4 or 9.5 s

Step 10 Describe how to answer Step 8 graphically. Sample answer: Graph $y = h(t)$ and $y = 60$ on the the same set of axes. Find points of intersection.

In the investigation you approximated solutions to a quadratic equation using tables and graphs. Later in this chapter you will learn to solve quadratic equations in the **general form,** $y = ax^2 + bx + c$, using symbolic manipulation. Until then, quadratic equations must be in a certain form for you to solve them symbolically. You will combine the "undo" and "balance" methods on this form in the next example.

EXAMPLE B

Solve $5(x + 2)^2 - 10 = 47$ symbolically. Check your answers with a graph and a table.

▶ **Solution**

Undo each operation as you would when solving a linear equation. To undo the squaring operation, take the square root of both sides. You will get two possible answers.

$5(x + 2)^2 - 10 = 47$	Original equation.
$5(x + 2)^2 = 57$	Add 10 to undo the subtraction.
$(x + 2)^2 = 11.4$	Divide by 5 to undo the multiplication.
$\sqrt{(x + 2)^2} = \sqrt{11.4}$	Take the square root to undo the squaring.
$|x + 2| = \sqrt{11.4}$	Definition of absolute value.
$x + 2 = \pm\sqrt{11.4}$	Use $\pm$ to undo the absolute value.
$x = -2 \pm \sqrt{11.4}$	Subtract 2.

The two solutions are $-2 + \sqrt{11.4}$, or approximately 1.38, and $-2 - \sqrt{11.4}$, or approximately -5.38.

gets large enough, the first term begins to dominate the sum of the other two terms, and the object begins to fall.

Ask students if they agree with the opening quotation. Mitchell seems to make the assumption that mathematics is calculation and logic, rather than beauty and poetry. Have students seen something other than calculations in this mathematics course? Try to emphasize that mathematics is more a way of thinking than a way of calculating.

To illustrate your point, this might be a good time to have students pose extension problems. Some good ones are "What if the object were dropped from a height instead of beginning on the ground?" "What if it were thrown down from a height?" "Is g the same no matter where you are?" "We know g is, in effect, zero in space. Does it gradually change from Earth to space, or is there a sudden drop?" The purpose is not to answer these questions but to show that doing mathematics involves posing many problems for future exploration.

The calculator screens of the graph and the table support each solution.

 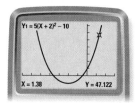

$$[-7, 3, 1, -10, 70, 10]$$

You can also confirm your answer by using your calculator to evaluate $y = 5(x + 2)^2 - 10$ for each solution, and verifying that the result is 47.

[▶ See **Calculator Note 7A** to review how to evaluate a function. ◀]

As you practice solving quadratic equations symbolically, first think about the order of operations. Then concentrate on how to undo this order. In some situations only one of the solutions you find has a real-world meaning. Always ask yourself whether the answers you find make sense in real-world situations.

A symbolic approach allows you to find the exact solutions rather than just approximations from a table or a graph. Exact solutions such as $x = -2 \pm \sqrt{11.4}$ are called **radical expressions** because they contain the square root symbol, $\sqrt{}$, and "radical" comes from the Latin word for "root."

Most numbers that, when simplified, contain the square root symbol are **irrational numbers**. An irrational number is a number that cannot be written as a ratio of two integers. The *Venn diagram* at right shows the relationship among several sets of numbers that you may be familiar with. The inner region is the *natural* or *counting numbers*—1, 2, 3, and so

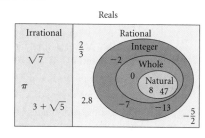

on. The set of *whole numbers* includes the natural numbers and zero. The set of numbers that includes the whole numbers and their negatives is the *integers*. The set of *rational numbers* includes all the integers and any number that can be written as a ratio of integers. The **real numbers** include all rational and irrational numbers.

EXERCISES

You will need your graphing calculator for Exercises **1, 5, 6, 8,** and **9**.

▶ Practice Your Skills

1. Use a graph and table to approximate solutions for each equation, to the nearest hundredth.

   a. $x^2 + 3x - 7 = 11$

   b. $-x^2 + x + 4 = 7$ ⓐ

   c. $x^2 - 6x + 14 = 5$

   d. $-3x^2 - 5x - 2 = -5$ ⓐ

[Language] *Radical* comes from the Latin *radix*, meaning "root." You might ask students whether they think a radical, or extreme, opinion always gets to the root, or source, of a problem. The number $\sqrt{11.4}$ is sometimes read "radical 11.4," although the word *radical* refers to any root.

You might display the Number System Venn Diagram transparency and ask students for examples for each set of numbers.

Closing the Lesson

The height of a projectile in meters is given by the **quadratic function** $h(t) = -4.9t^2 + v_0 t + h_0$, where t is the number of seconds after launch, v_0 is the initial velocity, and h_0 is the initial height. This is a transformation of the squaring function. When the function is written in the familiar form that shows the transformation, an equation involving it can be solved by undoing or balancing. There are often two solutions, and frequently their exact forms are **radical expressions**.

Assessing Progress
Watch for the ability to use dimensional analysis, to interpret an expression, to graph a function, and to solve an equation with graphing and with a calculator table.

▶ **EXAMPLE B**
This example shows students how to solve a quadratic equation that is written in the form $a(x - h)^2 + k = c$. (In the next lesson students will see that form called the *vertex form*.) They can think either of undoing to get from c back to x (subtract k, divide by a, take square roots, add h) or of balancing, doing the same thing to both sides of the equation. You might encourage the use of an undo table to help students organize these steps. The steps are the same, but the thought process is somewhat different. For solving linear equations, some students might still rely on representing the undoing process with arrow diagrams. Help those students see that arrow diagrams can be used to represent undoing a quadratic equation of this form, as long as they allow a split to find the two square roots.

Some students may ask, "How big is $\sqrt{11.4}$?" They probably want a decimal name for that number. Even while stressing that $\sqrt{11.4}$ is a perfectly good name—in fact, an accurate name—for the number, point out that 11.4 is between 9 and 16, so its positive square root is between 3 and 4.

Tracing the graph on the window specified in the example gives slightly different values. To obtain the x- and y-values shown, have the calculator evaluate the function from the graph screen for $x = 1.38$.

See pages 727–728 for complete answers to Exercise 1.

2. Classify each number by specifying all of the number sets of which it is a member. Consider the sets: real, irrational, rational, integer, whole, and natural numbers.

   a. $-\dfrac{17}{4}$ real, rational   **b.** -8 ⓐ   **c.** $\sqrt{\dfrac{5}{4}}$ real, irrational   **d.** 2047   real, rational, integer, whole number, natural number

      real, rational, integer

3. Use a symbolic method to solve each equation. Show each solution exactly as a rational or a radical expression.

   a. $x^2 = 18$ **b.** $x^2 + 3 = 52$ **c.** $(x - 2)^2 = 25$ **d.** $2(x + 1)^2 - 4 = 10$ ⓐ
      $x = \pm\sqrt{18}$ $x^2 = 49, x = \pm 7$ $x - 2 = \pm 5, x = 7$ or $x = -3$

4. Sketch the graph of a quadratic function with

   a. One x-intercept.   **b.** Two x-intercepts.   **c.** Zero x-intercepts.

   d. The vertex in the first quadrant and two x-intercepts.

▶ Reason and Apply

5. A baseball is dropped from the top of a very tall building. The ball's height, in meters, t seconds after it has been released is $h(t) = -4.9t^2 + 147$.

   a. Find $h(0)$ and give a real-world meaning for this value.

   b. Solve $h(t) = 20$ symbolically and graphically.

   c. Does your answer to 5b mean the ball is 20 m above the ground twice? Explain your reasoning.

   d. During what interval of time is the ball less than 20 m above the ground? ⓐ $t > 5.09$ s

   e. When does the ball hit the ground? Justify your answer with a graph. ⓐ   The ball hits the ground when $t \approx 5.48$ s because the positive x-intercept is near the point $(5.48, 0)$.

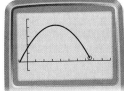

6. **APPLICATION** A flare is fired into the air from the ground. It reaches its highest point, 108 m, at 4.70 s. It falls back to the ground at 9.40 s.

   a. Name three points that the graph goes through. $(0, 0), (4.7, 108), (9.4, 0)$

   b. Name a graphing window that lets you see those three points. sample answer: $[-1, 10, 1, -10, 120, 10]$

   c. What are the coordinates of the vertex of this parabola? $(4.7, 108)$

   d. Find an equation in the form $y = a(x - h)^2 + k$ that fits the three known points. You may need to guess and check to find the value of a. ⓗ $h(t) = -4.9(t - 4.7)^2 + 108$

   e. Find $h(3)$ and give a real-world meaning for this value. approximately 94 m; at 3 s, the flare is about 94 m above the ground

   f. Find the t-values for $h(t) = 47$, and describe the real-world meaning for these values.

7. The path of a ball in flight is given by $p(x) = -0.23(x - 3.4)^2 + 4.2$, where x is the horizontal distance in meters and $p(x)$ is the vertical height in meters. Note that in this case the graph is the path of the ball, not the graph of the ball's height over time.

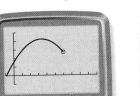

$[-1, 10, 1, -1, 5, 1]$

5a. $h(0) = -4.9(0)^2 + 147 = 147$; it is the starting height of the ball, when $t = 0$ s.

5b. Solve the equation $20 = -4.9t^2 + 147$ symbolically to get $\pm\sqrt{\dfrac{20 - 147}{-4.9}}$, or approximately ± 5.09.
The graph shows two solution points: $(5.09, 20)$ and $(-5.09, 20)$.

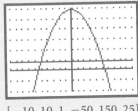

$[-10, 10, 1, -50, 150, 25]$

5c. No; only the solution $(5.09, 20)$ makes sense, because the time t must be positive.

a. Find $p(2)$ and give a real-world meaning for this value.

b. Find the x-values for $p(x) = 2$, and describe their real-world meanings.

c. How high is the ball when it is released? When $x = 0$, the height is 1.5412 m.

d. How far will the ball travel horizontally before it hits the ground? When $p(x) = 0$, the horizontal distance is $3.4 + \sqrt{\frac{420}{23}}$, or approximately 7.67 m.

8. Solve the equation $4 = -2(x - 3)^2 + 4$ using

  a. A graph.   b. A table.   c. A symbolic method.

9. **APPLICATION** The graph at right shows the graph of $h(t) = -4.9t^2 + 50t - 97.5$. The variable t represents time in seconds, and $h(t)$ represents the height in meters of a projectile.

  a. What is a real-world meaning for the x-intercepts in the graph? ⓐ

  b. Find the x-intercepts to the nearest 0.01 second. ⓐ 2.63 s and 7.58 s

  c. How can you use 9b to find the vertex of this parabola? ⓗ

  d. What is a real-world meaning for the vertex in the graph?

  e. What does $h(3.2)$ tell you? $h(3.2) = 12.324$ m; this is the height at 3.2 s.

  f. When is the projectile 12.5 m high? Explain how to find these solutions on a graph.

$[0, 10, 1, -5, 35, 5]$

10. *Mini-Investigation* In each equation the variable x represents time and y represents the height of a projectile.

  a. $y = -16(x - 3)^2 + 20$ b. $y = -4.9(x - 4.2)^2 + 12$

For each equation:

  i. Describe the transformations of the graph of $y = x^2$. ⓗ

  ii. Name the vertex of the parabola. a. $(3, 20)$ b. $(4.2, 12)$

  iii. What is the real-world meaning for each number in the equation?

▶ Review

5.5 11. Show a step-by-step symbolic solution of the inequality $-3x + 4 > 16$. ⓐ

5.6 12. The solid line in the graph passes through $(0, 6)$ and $(6, 1)$. Write an inequality to describe the shaded region. The slope is $\frac{1 - 6}{6 - 0} = \frac{-5}{6}$. An intercept form of the inequality is $y \geq 6 - \frac{5}{6}x$.

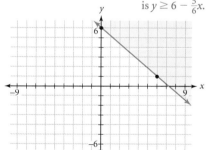

10a. i. a vertical stretch of 16 units, a reflection across the x-axis, a horizontal translation right 3 units, and a vertical translation of 20 units

10a. iii. -16 or $\frac{1}{2}(-32)$ ft/s^2 is the effect of gravity, the maximum height occurs at 3 s, and the maximum height is 20 ft.

10b. i. a vertical stretch of 4.9 units, a reflection across the x-axis, a horizontal translation right 4.2 units, and a vertical translation of 12 units

10b. iii. -4.9 or $\frac{1}{2}(-9.8)$ m/s^2 is the effect of gravity, the maximum height occurs at 4.2 s, and the maximum height is 12 m.

11. $-3x + 4 > 16$ The given inequality.
       $-3x > 12$ Subtract 4 from both sides.
         $x < -4$ Divide both sides by -3 and reverse the inequality symbol.

Exercise 7 [Alert] Be sure students realize that in this case the graph represents a (*distance, height*) relationship and not (*time, height*). They may wonder why the initial coefficient is not -4.9. The equation for $p(x)$ in this form tells you that the ball reaches its maximum height (the vertex of the parabola) when it is 3.4 m away horizontally from where it started. Substitution allows you to find $p(3.4)$ to be 4.2 m.

7a. After the ball has gone 2 m horizontally, it will be approximately 3.75 m above the ground.

7b. The ball will be 2 m above the ground once it has gone about 0.31 m horizontally and again once it has gone about 6.49 m horizontally. Exact solutions are

$$x = 3.4 \pm \sqrt{\frac{220}{23}}.$$

Exercise 8 There's more than one way to solve this equation using a graph. For example, students might graph the function $Y_1 = -2(x - 3)^2 + 4$ and then trace to find a y-value of 4. Or they might graph Y_1 and then also graph $Y_2 = 4$ and trace to find the point of intersection.

8c. $4 = -2(x - 3)^2 + 4$
    $0 = -2(x - 3)^2$
    $0 = (x - 3)^2$
    $0 = x - 3$
    $3 = x$

Exercise 9 This exercise foreshadows work with the general form in Lesson 9.3. If students are stuck on 9c, suggest that they use their answer to 9b.

9a. The x-intercepts indicate when the projectile is at ground level.

9c. Find the average of 2.63 and 7.58, which is 5.105; $h(5.105) \approx 30.051$.

9d. After 5.105 s, the projectile is 30.051 m above the ground, its maximum height.

See page 728 for answers to Exercises 8a and b and 9f.

LESSON
9.2

Finding the Roots and the Vertex

In this lesson you will discover that quadratic functions can model relationships other than projectile motion. You will explore relationships between parabolas and their equations. You will practice writing equations, finding *x*-intercepts, and determining real-world meanings for the *x*-intercepts and the vertex of a parabola.

Investigation
Making the Most of It

You will need
- graph paper

Suppose you have 24 meters of fencing material and you want to use it to enclose a rectangular space for your vegetable garden. Naturally, you want to have the largest area possible for your vegetables. What dimensions should you use for your garden?

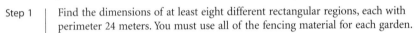

Step 1 Find the dimensions of at least eight different rectangular regions, each with perimeter 24 meters. You must use all of the fencing material for each garden.

Step 2 Find the area of each garden. Make a table to record the width, length, and area of the possible gardens. It's okay to have widths that are greater than their corresponding lengths.

Width (m)	Length (m)	Area (m²)

Step 3 Enter the data for the possible widths into list L1. Enter the area measures into list L2. Which garden width values would give no area? Add these points to your lists.

Step 4 Label a set of axes and plot points in the form (*x*, *y*), with *x* representing width in meters and *y* representing area in square meters. Describe as completely as possible what the graph looks like. Does it make sense to connect the points with a smooth curve?

Step 5 Where does your graph reach its highest point? Which rectangular garden has the largest area? What are its dimensions? The graph reaches its highest point at (6, 36). The 6-by-6 rectangle, a square, has the largest area.

Next you'll write an equation to describe this relationship.

Step 6 Create a graph of (*width, length*) data. What is the length of the garden that has width 2 meters? Width 4.3 meters? Write an expression for length in terms of width *x*. 10 m; 7.7 m; $12 - x$ m

Step 7 Using your expression for the length from Step 6, write an equation for the area of the garden. Enter this equation into Y1 and graph it. Does the graph confirm your answer to Step 5?

---

patterns and then to write a quadratic equation to fit the data. Ask how to approximate the *x*-intercepts (the roots of the equation *y* = 0) and wonder aloud how they might find the vertex from knowing the roots. Then ask them to rewrite the equation to show how the parent quadratic function would be transformed to get this one.

Step 1 Students can draw the rectangles if they have trouble visualizing. Use 24 cm lengths of string for kinesthetic learners. A width or length of zero is not

acceptable as a measurement, but these are useful values to list.

Step 6

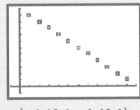

$[-1, 12, 1, -1, 12, 1]$

Step 8	Locate the points where the graph crosses the x-axis. What is the real-world meaning for these points? *x-intercepts are at (0, 0) and (12, 0); the rectangle has no area if the width is 0 or 12.*
Step 9	Do you think the general shape of a garden with maximum area would change for different perimeters? Explain your answer. *Sample answer: A maximum-area garden will always be square.*

In the investigation you found three important points on the graph. The two points on the x-axis are the *x-intercepts.* The x-values of those points are the solutions to the equation $y = f(x)$ when the function value is equal to zero. These solutions are the **roots** of the equation $f(x) = 0$.

In the investigation the roots are the widths that make the garden area equal to zero. The roots help you to find a third important point—the vertex of the parabola.

In Lesson 9.1, you symbolically solved quadratic equations written in the form $y = a(x - h)^2 + k$. In the next example you will learn to approximate roots of the quadratic equation, $0 = ax^2 + bx + c$.

EXAMPLE A

Use a graph and your calculator's table function to approximate the roots of

$$0 = x^2 + 3x - 5$$

▶ Solution

Graph $y = x^2 + 3x - 5$ and find the x-intercepts. On the graph you can see that there are two roots—one appears to be a little less than −4, and the other a little greater than 1.

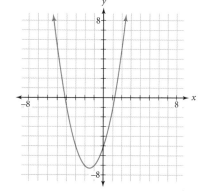

Search in your calculator's table for the positive x-value that makes the y-value equal to zero. Continue zooming in until you find the positive root, which is about 1.193. [▶ See **Calculator Note 2A** to review zooming in on a table. ◀] Repeat this process for the negative root, which you'll find to be about −4.193.

The line through the vertex that cuts a parabola into two mirror images is called the **line of symmetry.** If you know the roots, you can find the vertex and the line of symmetry.

NCTM STANDARDS

CONTENT	PROCESS
✔ Number	✔ Problem Solving
✔ Algebra	✔ Reasoning
✔ Geometry	Communication
✔ Measurement	✔ Connections
Data/Probability	✔ Representation

LESSON OBJECTIVES

• Introduce the general form of a quadratic equation

• Write quadratic equations that model real-world data

• Approximate the x-intercepts and other points on a parabola using graphs, tables, and symbolic methods

• Find the vertex of a parabola from knowing its x-intercepts

• Model real-world situations with the vertex form of a quadratic equation

Step 2 [Language] *Length* of a rectangle is often defined as its longer dimension. Some students may note that the table begins to repeat, that it will have symmetry, and they may stop because they want to keep the width shorter than the length. If they stop with half the data, their graph won't be a parabola. Say that for this investigation, *width* and *length* refer to the lengths of two edges of the rectangle. As the dimensions change, the width column will sometimes contain the longer measurement. Students who see immediately how to calculate the lengths from the widths may enter lengths into list L2 (by formula) and areas into list L3.

Step 4 You might have each group plot its points on a copy of the Coordinate Plane transparency. Then during Sharing you can combine the data points to counter any conjectures that the graph represents an absolute-value function. Note any groups that plot (*width, length*) instead of (*width, area*). During Sharing display their plot with the others and let them critique it with the class.

Step 6 Some students may benefit from solving the equation $2L + 2W = 24$ for *L*. **[Ask]** "Does the pattern *length* $= 12 - width$ make sense?" [Yes; the sum of one length and one width is half the perimeter of 24.]

SHARING IDEAS

If groups plotted their data on transparencies, have them all share those. Then ask for ideas about Steps 7 and 9.

Return to the original question of the investigation. **[Ask]** "What dimensions should you use for your garden?" Probably most will say the dimensions that give maximum area. But others may make suggestions such as that the best dimensions are those that allow easier access from the edges or have greater length facing the

sun. Point out that the utility of a mathematical model depends on assumptions made about the problem.

Real-life problems that involve finding the largest or smallest of something are called *optimization* problems. Before the advent of graphing calculators, solutions to such problems, especially for functions of degree higher than 2, were most easily found through calculus.

Assessing Progress

Observe students' understanding of area and perimeter of a rectangle and their ability to enter lists, plot points, graph functions, and trace graphs on the calculator.

▶ **EXAMPLE A**

This example shows that the *roots* of an equation $f(x) = 0$ are the *x*-intercepts of the graph of $f(x)$. Roots of an equation are also called *zeros* of the corresponding function. Note that roots in this sense are not necessarily square roots or cube roots.

The exact roots of this quadratic equation are $x = \dfrac{-3 \pm \sqrt{29}}{2}$. The calculator may have a feature allowing students to find these *x*-intercepts (roots) directly from the calculator's graph screen.

▶ **EXAMPLE B**

This example shows how to use the roots of a quadratic equation to find the equation of the line of symmetry and the vertex form of the equation for the parabola. The procedure requires several steps. Keep reminding students of the goal: to find values of *h*, *k*, and *a*.

[Alert] Some students may not be aware that the number halfway between two numbers is their mean, or average. Averaging the exact roots also results in −1.5.

As needed, point out that $h = -1.5$ implies $x - h = x + 1.5$.

EXAMPLE B | Find the equation of the line of symmetry, and find the coordinates (*h*, *k*) of the vertex of the parabola $y = x^2 + 3x - 5$. Then write the equation in the form $y = a(x - h)^2 + k$.

▶ **Solution** | This parabola crosses the *x*-axis twice and has a vertical line of symmetry. The *x*-coordinate of the vertex lies on the line of symmetry, halfway between the roots. From Example A, you know the two roots are approximately 1.193 and −4.193. Averaging the two roots gives −1.5. The graph shows that the line of symmetry passes through this *x*-value. The equation of the line of symmetry is $x = -1.5$.

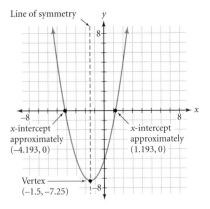

The *x*-coordinate of the vertex is −1.5. Now use the equation of the parabola, $y = x^2 + 3x - 5$, to find the *y*-coordinate of the vertex.

$$y = x^2 + 3x - 5 \qquad \text{Equation of the parabola.}$$
$$= (-1.5)^2 + 3(-1.5) - 5 \qquad \text{Substitute } -1.5 \text{ for } x.$$
$$= 2.25 - 4.5 - 5 \qquad \text{Multiply.}$$
$$= -7.25 \qquad \text{Subtract.}$$

So the vertex is (−1.5, −7.25). Sometimes you can find the vertex and see the symmetry in a table of values.

In the table, this point appears to be the lowest point on the parabola.  The symmetry of the curve shows up in the repeated *y*-values on either side of the vertex.

The graph is a transformation of the parent function, $f(x) = x^2$. The vertex, (*h*, *k*), is (−1.5, −7.25), so there is a translation left 1.5 units and down 7.25 units. Substitute the values *h* and *k* into the equation to get $y = (x + 1.5)^2 - 7.25$. Enter the equation into Y₂ and graph it.

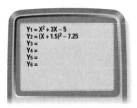 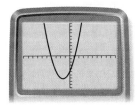 

[−10, 10, 1, −10, 10, 1]

Closing the Lesson

Finding the vertex of the parabolic graph of a quadratic equation can allow you to solve real-world optimization problems. You can get a quadratic equation into **vertex form** by approximating its **roots,** finding the vertex from the mean of the roots, and adjusting the dilation factor.

You can see from the graph and the table that the equations $y = x^2 + 3x - 5$ and $y = (x + 1.5)^2 - 7.25$ are equivalent. So the value of a is 1. The equation $y = 1(x + 1.5)^2 - 7.25$ is in the **vertex form,** $y = a(x - h)^2 + k$. It tells you that $(-1.5, -7.25)$ is the vertex.

EXERCISES

You will need your graphing calculator for Exercises **4, 8,** and **11.**

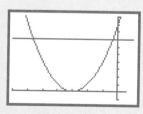

▶ Practice Your Skills

1. This parabola has x-intercepts 3 and -2. What is the equation of the line of symmetry? What is the x-coordinate of the vertex? @ The average of 3 and -2 is $\frac{3 + -2}{2}$, or 0.5. So the axis of symmetry is $x = 0.5$, and the vertex has an x-coordinate of 0.5.

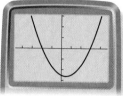

$[-4.7, 4.7, 1, -3.1, 3.1, 1]$

2. The equation of the parabola in Exercise 1 is $y = 0.4x^2 - 0.4x - 2.4$. Use the x-coordinate you found in Exercise 1 to find the y-coordinate of the vertex. $y = 0.4(0.5)^2 - 0.4(0.5) - 2.4$, or $y = -2.5$.

3. Solve $0 = (x + 1.5)^2 - 7.25$ symbolically. Show each step. Compare your solutions with the approximations from Examples A and B. @

4. Find the roots of each equation to the nearest thousandth by looking at a graph, zooming in on a table, or both.

   a. $0 = x^2 + 2x - 2$ @ $x \approx -2.732$ and $x \approx 0.732$

   b. $0 = -3x^2 - 4x + 3$ $x \approx -1.869$ and $x \approx 0.535$

5. Solve each equation symbolically and check your answer.

   a. $(x + 3)^2 = 7$

   b. $(x - 2)^2 - 8 = 13$

6. Graph $y = (x + 3)^2$ and $y = 7$. What is the relationship between your solution to Exercise 5a and these graphs? @

▶ Reason and Apply

7. The height of a golf ball is given by $h = -16t^2 + 48t$, where t is in seconds and h is in feet.

   a. At what times is the golf ball on the ground?

   b. At what time is the golf ball at its highest point?

   c. How high does the golf ball go? When $t = 1.5, h = 36$, so the ball goes 36 ft high.

   d. What domain and range values make sense in this situation?
      domain: $0 \le t \le 3$; range: $0 \le h \le 36$

3.

$$0 = (x + 1.5)^2 - 7.25$$
$$7.25 = (x + 1.5)^2$$
$$\pm\sqrt{7.25} = x + 1.5$$
$$-1.5 \pm\sqrt{7.25} = x$$
$$x \approx 1.193 \text{ or } x \approx -4.193$$

7a. The ball is on the ground when $h = 0$. This happens at $t = 0$ s and $t = 3$ s.

7b. The ball is at its highest point at $t = 1.5$ s, halfway through its flight.

BUILDING UNDERSTANDING

The exercises provide practice in approximating roots and in real-world optimization through finding vertices of parabolas.

ASSIGNING HOMEWORK

Essential	1–5, 7, 11
Performance assessment	6, 7, 11
Portfolio	7, 9
Journal	9, 10, 12
Group	8, 9
Review	13

▶ Helping with the Exercises

Exercises 3 and 5 Students can use either undoing or balancing.

Exercise 4 Allow students who ask about the root or zero calculator command to use it.

Exercise 5 Students might check their answers using one of the methods given in Example B, Lesson 9.1.

5a. $(x + 3) = \pm\sqrt{7}$
$$x = -3 \pm\sqrt{7}$$
$$x \approx -5.646 \text{ or}$$
$$x \approx -0.354$$

5b. $(x - 2)^2 = 21$
$$x = 2 \pm\sqrt{21}$$
$$x \approx -2.583 \text{ or}$$
$$x \approx 6.583$$

6. Answers will vary. The graph of $y = (x + 3)^2$ intersects the graph of $y = 7$ at $(-5.646, 7)$ and $(-0.354, 7)$.

$[-7, 1, 1, -1, 10, 1]$

Exercise 8 The initial velocity v_0 is 58 ft/s. The starting position of the ball is 3 ft above the ground.

8a. between 3.67 s when the height is still positive and 3.68 s when the height is negative

8b. Starting the table at 3.67 and setting ΔTbl equal to 0.001 gives the answer 3.676 s.

8c. The maximum height occurs between 1.81 and 1.82 s when the height of the ball is at least 55.562 ft.

Exercise 9 Students may be confused by the idea of negative velocity. Velocity is a vector quantity with both magnitude (the speed) and direction. In this case a negative sign indicates that the ball is traveling downward.

9a. Answers will vary. The ball is thrown from an initial height of 8 m. It reaches its maximum height, about 25 m, in 2 s and hits the ground at about 4.3 s.

9b. The ball starts at a velocity of 20 m/s and slows down at a constant rate. At 2 s it is not moving. Then it starts falling and is moving down at 22 m/s when it hits the ground.

9c. When the velocity is negative, the ball is falling.

9d. This is when the ball is at its maximum height and, at that instant not moving. Its velocity is zero.

9e. These are the two times when the height of the ball is about 13 m.

Exercise 10 Be sure students understand that they don't have enough information to decide how far or how high the ball travels. Gale's ball might have gone higher than Bo's or farther than Bo's.

10a. Bo's ball is at its highest point 0.5(3.4) s, or 1.7 s, after it is hit. Gale's is at its highest 0.5(4.7) s, or 2.35 s, after it is hit.

8. **APPLICATION** Taylor hits a baseball, and its height in the air at time x is given by the equation $y = -16x^2 + 58x + 3$, where x is in seconds and y is in feet. Use the graph and tables to help you answer these questions.

X	Y₁
3.65	1.54
3.66	.9504
3.67	.3576
3.68	−.2384
3.69	−.8376
3.7	−1.44
3.71	−2.046

Y1⬛−16X² + 58X + 3

X	Y₁
1.78	55.546
1.79	55.554
1.8	55.56
1.81	55.562
1.82	55.562
1.83	55.558
1.84	55.55

Y1⬛−16X² + 58X + 3

$[-1, 5, 1, -10, 60, 10]$

a. When does the ball hit the ground?

b. Use your calculator table to find the answer to 8a to three decimal places. ⓐ

c. According to the table above, during what time interval is the ball at its highest points? At what time (to the nearest hundredth of a second) is the ball at its highest point, and how high is it?

9. The two graphs at right show aspects of a ball thrown into the air. The first graph shows its height h in meters at any time t in seconds. The second graph shows its velocity v in meters per second at any time t.

a. What does the first graph tell you about the situation? Use numbers to be as specific as you can.

b. What does the second graph tell you about the situation? Use numbers to be as specific as you can. ⓗ

c. Give a real-world meaning in this context for the negative values on the lower graph. ⓐ

d. What can you say about the ball when the graph of the velocity line intersects the x-axis? ⓐ

e. What can you say about the height of the ball when the velocity is 15 meters per second and when it is −15 meters per second?

f. What are realistic domain and range intervals for the graphs?
domain: $0 \le t \le 4.3$; range: $0 \le h(t) \le 26$; $-22 \le v(t) \le 20$

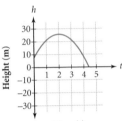

Time (s)

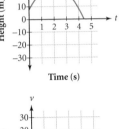

Time (s)

10. Bo and Gale are playing golf. Bo hits his ball, and it is in flight for 3.4 seconds. Gale's ball is in flight for 4.7 seconds.

a. At what time does each ball reach its highest point? ⓗ

b. Can you tell whose ball goes farther or higher? Explain.

11. The table at right shows the coordinates of a parabola.

a. On your calculator, plot the points in the table.

b. What is the equation of the line of symmetry for this graph? $x = 4.5$

c. Name the vertex of this graph. (4.5, 19)

d. Use your knowledge of transformations to write the equation of this parabola in the vertex form, $y = a(x - h)^2 + k$. Check your answer graphically.
$y = -3(x - 4.5)^2 + 19$

x	y
1.5	−8
2.5	7
3.5	16
4.5	19
5.5	16
6.5	7
7.5	−8

[Data sets: **PARAX, PARAY**]

10b. You can't tell whose ball goes farther. Even though Gale's is in the air longer, it might just go higher and not as far as Bo's.

11a.

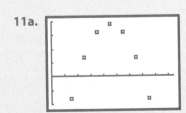

$[0, 9.4, 1, -10, 20, 5]$

12. The (*time, height*) graph $y = a(x - h)^2 + k$ of a small projectile contains the vertex $(2, 67)$ and the points $(0, 3)$ and $(4, 3)$. You can find the particular equation of this graph by substituting $(2, 67)$ for (h, k) in the equation, then finding the value of a by substituting the coordinates of one of the other points for x and y. What is the particular equation? @ $y = -16(x - 2)^2 + 67$

▶ **Review**

4.2 **13.** Write an equation in the form $y = a + bx$ for each of these graphs. One tick mark represents one unit.

a.  $y = 2 + \frac{1}{3}x$

b.  $y = 3.5 - \frac{1}{4}x$

IMPROVING YOUR VISUAL THINKING SKILLS

A parabola is an example of a **conic section.** The Greek geometer Apollonius (255–170 B.C.E.) defined conic sections by intersecting a double cone with a plane.

   Plane section   Double cone

The plane is a flat surface that extends into infinity. Likewise, both halves of the double cone widen infinitely in opposite directions. To form a parabola, Apollonius sliced the cone with a plane parallel to the cone's edge.

—Edge

Other examples of conic sections are circles, ellipses, and hyperbolas. How can you intersect a plane with a cone to form these shapes? Are there any other ways that a plane can intersect a double cone?

Parabolic section

   Circle   Ellipse   Hyperbola

Make a drawing that shows how to form each conic section. Can you form any other shapes? If so, describe them.

Conic Sections
   Circular section

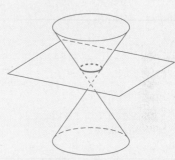

   Elliptical section

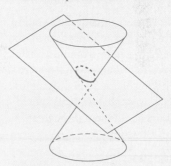

   Hyperbolic section

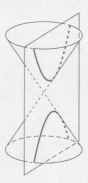

IMPROVING VISUAL THINKING SKILLS

A plane through the cone's vertex might intersect the cone in a point or a pair of lines (if the plane contains the axis). These figures are called *degenerate conics.* Planes not through the vertex intersect the cone in the conic sections described. A plane perpendicular to the axis will form a circle, a special case of an ellipse, in which the plane is tilted but not to the extent that it becomes parallel to the edge, when it forms a parabola. Any greater tilt of the plane, including the illustrated hyperbolic section with plane parallel to the cone's axis, will intersect both pieces of the cone and form a hyperbola.

Attempt the impossible in order to improve your work.

BETTE DAVIS

From Vertex to General Form

You have learned two forms of a quadratic equation. The vertex form, $y = a(x - h)^2 + k$, gives you information about transformations of the parent function, $y = x^2$. You used the general form, $y = ax^2 + bx + c$, to model many projectile motion situations. In this lesson you will learn how to convert an equation from the vertex form to the general form.

The general form, $y = ax^2 + bx + c$, is the sum of three terms—ax^2, bx, and c. A **term** is an algebraic expression that represents only multiplication and division between variables and constants. Recall that a sum of terms with nonnegative integer exponents is called a **polynomial.** Variables cannot appear as exponents in a polynomial.

Here are some examples of polynomials.

$$17x \qquad 4.7x^3 + 3x \qquad x^2 + 3x + 7 \qquad 47x^4 - 6x^3 + 0.28x + 7$$

The expression $17x$ has only one term, so it is called a **monomial.** The second expression has two terms and is called a **binomial.** The third expression is a **trinomial** because it has three terms. If there are more than three terms, the expression is generally referred to as a polynomial.

Recall that terms whose variable parts are identical, such as $3x$ and $2x$, are *like terms.* Terms such as $2x^2$ and x^4 are not like terms, because their variable components are different.

EXAMPLE A

Is each algebraic expression a polynomial? If so, combine like terms and state how many terms it has. If not, give a reason why it is not a polynomial.

a. $3x^2 + 4x^{-1} + 7$ **b.** $2^x - 7.5x + 18$

c. $\dfrac{47}{x} + 28$ **d.** $3x + 1 + 2x$

e. $x^2 - x^{10}$ **f.** $-2x^3 \cdot 3x^2$

▶ **Solution**

Expression	Is it a polynomial?
a. $3x^2 + 4x^{-1} + 7$	No, because the term $4x^{-1}$ has a negative exponent.
b. $2^x - 7.5x + 18$	No, because 2^x has a variable as the exponent.
c. $\dfrac{47}{x} + 28$	No, because the term $\frac{47}{x}$ is equivalent to $47x^{-1}$.
d. $3x + 1 + 2x$	Yes, it is a polynomial. It is equivalent to the binomial $1 + 5x$, which has two terms.
e. $x^2 - x^{10}$	Yes. It has two terms and is a binomial.
f. $-2x^3 \cdot 3x^2$	Yes. It involves only multiplication of constants and variables. It is equivalent to the monomial $-6x^5$.

In the investigation you will combine like terms when you convert an equation from the vertex form to the general form.

PLANNING

LESSON OUTLINE

First day:

5 min	Introduction
20 min	Example A
25 min	Investigation

Second day:

20 min	Investigation
10 min	Sharing
5 min	Example B
5 min	Closing
10 min	Exercises

MATERIALS

- graph paper
- Calculator Note 6B
- Sketchpad demonstration Quadratic Equations, *optional*

TEACHING

To convert a quadratic equation from vertex to general form, you need to square a binomial. The rectangle diagrams introduced in this lesson are so important for later work that students should learn about them through an investigation.

One Step

Sometimes you want to convert from vertex to general form to find a *y*-intercept easily. Doing so requires squaring the sum, called a *binomial,* to get a trinomial. Ask groups to derive methods for squaring the binomials $x + 3$ and $x - 2$. As you observe, challenge students to substitute numbers for x, suggest drawing rectangles, and have groups make up their own equation in vertex form to convert to general form.

INTRODUCTION

[Language] The prefix *poly-* means "many." Help students relate new vocabulary to words they know. Words like *monorail, monocle, bicycle,* and *tricycle* can help students relate *mono-* to "one," *bi-* to "two," and *tri-* to "three."

Students may confuse letters representing *constants* (a, h, k, b, c) with letters representing *variables* (x, y).

LESSON OBJECTIVES

- Change a quadratic equation from vertex form to general form
- Learn to square a binomial and factor perfect-square expressions using rectangle diagrams
- Solve problems using a quadratic equation that models projectile motion

Investigation
Sneaky Squares

There are many different, yet equivalent, expressions for a number. For example, 7 is the same as $3 + 4$ and as $10 - 3$. In this investigation you will use these equivalent expressions to model squaring binomials with rectangle diagrams.

Step 1

Step 1
$(3 + 4)^2 = 9 + 2(12) + 16$
$= 49; 49; 7^2 = (3 + 4)^2$

This diagram shows how to express 7^2 as $(3 + 4)^2$. Find the area of each of the inner rectangles. What is the sum of the rectangular areas? What is the area of the overall square? What conclusions can you make?

Step 2

For each expression below, draw a diagram on your graph paper like the one in Step 1. Label the area of each rectangle and find the total area of the overall square.

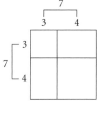

a. $(5 + 3)^2$ 64   **b.** $(4 + 2)^2$ 36   **c.** $(10 + 3)^2$ 169   **d.** $(20 + 5)^2$ 625

Even though lengths and areas are not negative, you can use the same kind of rectangle diagram to square an expression involving subtraction. You can use different colors, such as red and blue, to distinguish between the negative and the positive numbers. For example, this diagram shows 7^2 as $(10 - 3)^2$.

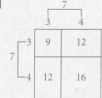

Step 3

Draw a rectangle diagram representing each expression. Label each inner rectangle and find the sum.

a. $(5 - 2)^2$ 9   **b.** $(7 - 3)^2$ 16   **c.** $(20 - 2)^2$ 324   **d.** $(50 - 3)^2$ 2209

You can make the same type of rectangle diagram to square an expression involving variables.

Step 4

Draw a rectangle diagram for each expression. Label each inner rectangle and find the total sum. Combine any like terms you see and express your answer as a trinomial.

a. $(x + 5)^2$ **b.** $(x - 3)^2$ **c.** $(x + 11)^2$ **d.** $(x - 13)^2$
    $x^2 + 10x + 25$ $x^2 - 6x + 9$ $x^2 + 22x + 121$ $x^2 - 26x + 169$

NCTM STANDARDS

CONTENT	PROCESS
Number	Problem Solving
✔ Algebra	✔ Reasoning
Geometry	Communication
Measurement	Connections
Data/Probability	✔ Representation

A *term* is something that's added or subtracted. (In contrast, a *factor* is something that's multiplied or divided.) Terms are not necessarily restricted to positive integer exponents. For example, $4x^{-1}$ might be a term in some expression, but that expression would not be a polynomial.

▶ **EXAMPLE A**

This example illustrates the concept of a polynomial by giving examples and non-examples. Note that before the number of terms is counted, products are taken and like terms are combined. *Polynomials* and types of polynomials were introduced previously in Lesson 6.6, Exercise 13. *Combining like terms* was introduced in Lesson 3.6.

Guiding the Investigation

To save time, you might have groups divide the labor in Steps 2 and 3.

Step 1

Step 2

Step 3 [Alert] Some students might need reminding that a positive number multiplied by a negative is negative, and a negative multiplied by a negative is positive. Others might question how an area can be

---

negative. Point out that those rectangles with -30 inside are representing a negative number and that the rectangles' actual areas (which, like all areas, are positive) don't matter. Students can check their work by finding the square of each sum. For example, with $(5 - 2)^2$, students probably immediately know that $3^2 = 9$, so they can expect the sum of the numbers in their diagram to be 9.

Steps 3 and 4 See page 510.

Step 3

$$
\begin{array}{c|c|c}
 & 5 & -2 \\
\hline
5 & 25 & -10 \\
\hline
-2 & -10 & 4 \\
\end{array}
\qquad
\begin{array}{c|c|c}
 & 7 & -3 \\
\hline
7 & 49 & -21 \\
\hline
-3 & -21 & 9 \\
\end{array}
$$

$$
\begin{array}{c|c|c}
 & 20 & -2 \\
\hline
20 & 400 & -40 \\
\hline
-2 & -40 & 4 \\
\end{array}
\qquad
\begin{array}{c|c|c}
 & 50 & -3 \\
\hline
50 & 2500 & -150 \\
\hline
-3 & -150 & 9 \\
\end{array}
$$

Step 4

$$
\begin{array}{c|c|c}
 & x & 5 \\
\hline
x & x^2 & 5x \\
\hline
5 & 5x & 25 \\
\end{array}
\qquad
\begin{array}{c|c|c}
 & x & -3 \\
\hline
x & x^2 & -3x \\
\hline
-3 & -3x & 9 \\
\end{array}
$$

$$
\begin{array}{c|c|c}
 & x & 11 \\
\hline
x & x^2 & 11x \\
\hline
11 & 11x & 121 \\
\end{array}
\qquad
\begin{array}{c|c|c}
 & x & -13 \\
\hline
x & x^2 & -13x \\
\hline
-13 & -13x & 169 \\
\end{array}
$$

Step 5

$$
\begin{array}{c|c|c}
 & x & 3 \\
\hline
x & x^2 & 3x \\
\hline
3 & 3x & 9 \\
\end{array}
\qquad
\begin{array}{c|c|c}
 & x & -5 \\
\hline
x & x^2 & -5x \\
\hline
-5 & -5x & 25 \\
\end{array}
$$

$$
\begin{array}{c|c|c}
 & x & 4 \\
\hline
x & x^2 & 4x \\
\hline
4 & 4x & 16 \\
\end{array}
\qquad
\begin{array}{c|c|c}
 & x & -6 \\
\hline
x & x^2 & -6x \\
\hline
-6 & -6x & 36 \\
\end{array}
$$

Step 6a $(x + 3)^2 = 49$;
$x + 3 = \pm\sqrt{49}$; $x = -3 \pm 7$;
$x = -10$ or $x = 4$

Step 6b $(x - 5)^2 = 81$;
$x - 5 = \pm\sqrt{81}$;
$x = 5 \pm 9$; $x = -4$ or $x = 14$

Step 6c $(x + 4)^2 = 121$;
$x + 4 = \pm\sqrt{121}$;
$x = -4 \pm 11$; $x = -15$ or $x = 7$

Step 6d $(x - 6)^2 = 64$; $x = 6 \pm 8$;
$x = -2$ or $x = 14$

Step 7 Students can make rectangle diagrams to help.

Step 8 You may want to challenge students by asking about a trinomial like $4x^2 + 12x + 9$, which is the square of $2x + 3$.

Now use what you have learned to create a rectangle diagram for a trinomial.

Step 5 You must divide the middle term by 2.

Step 5 Make a rectangle diagram for each trinomial. In so doing, what must you do with the middle term? Label each side of the overall square in your diagram, and write the equivalent expression in the form $(x + h)^2$.

a. $x^2 + 6x + 9$ $(x + 3)^2$
b. $x^2 - 10x + 25$ $(x - 5)^2$
c. $x^2 + 8x + 16$ $(x + 4)^2$
d. $x^2 - 12x + 36$ $(x - 6)^2$

Step 6 Use your results from Step 5 to solve each new equation symbolically. Remember, quadratic equations can have two solutions.

a. $x^2 + 6x + 9 = 49$
b. $x^2 - 10x + 25 = 81$
c. $x^2 + 8x + 16 = 121$
d. $x^2 - 12x + 36 = 64$

Numbers like 49 are called **perfect squares** because they are the squares of integers, in this case 7 or -7. The trinomial $x^2 + 6x + 9$ is the square of $x + 3$. So it is also called a perfect square.

Step 7 Which of these trinomials are perfect squares?

a. $x^2 + 14x + 49$ yes; $(x + 7)^2$
b. $x^2 - 18x + 81$ yes; $(x - 9)^2$
c. $x^2 + 20x + 25$ no
d. $x^2 - 12x - 36$ no

Step 8 When the coefficient of x^2 is 1, the last term is the square of half the coefficient of x.

Step 8 Explain how you can recognize a perfect-square trinomial when the coefficient of x^2 is 1. What is the connection between the middle term and the last term?

Step 9 $x^2 + 2hx + h^2$; possible answer: Double h to get the coefficient of x and square h to get the constant term.

Step 9 Square the expression $(x + h)^2$ by making a rectangle diagram. Then describe a shortcut for this process that makes sense to you.

Knowing how to square a binomial is a useful skill. It allows you to convert equations from vertex form to general form.

EXAMPLE B | Rewrite $y = 2(x + 3)^2 - 5$ in the general form, $y = ax^2 + bx + c$.

▶ **Solution**

$y = 2(x + 3)^2 - 5$	Original equation.
$y = 2(x^2 + 6x + 9) - 5$	Square the binomial using a rectangle diagram, as shown.
$y = 2x^2 + 12x + 18 - 5$	Use the distributive property.
$y = 2x^2 + 12x + 13$	Combine like terms.

$$
\begin{array}{c|c|c}
 & x & 3 \\
\hline
x & x^2 & 3x \\
\hline
3 & 3x & 9 \\
\end{array}
$$

SHARING IDEAS

Ask for results from Step 6, but, as usual, emphasize the process over the solutions.

Have students share their ideas about shortcuts in Step 9. Some may enjoy the game of seeing how fast they can say "The square of a binomial is the square of the first plus twice the product of the first and the second plus the square of the second."

You might point out that the square of a sum is not usually the sum of the squares. **[Ask]** "Under what conditions is it?" [If one term is zero; here is a simple proof: Assume $(x + y)^2 = x^2 + y^2$; then $x^2 + y^2 = x^2 + 2xy + y^2$, so $2xy = 0$. Either x or y must be zero.]

Assessing Progress

Assess general facility with arithmetic and order of operations.

You can use a graph or a table on your calculator to verify that the vertex form and the general form of this equation are equivalent. [▶ 🖵 See **Calculator Note 6B** to review checking different forms of an equation. ◀]

In the example you **expand** $(x + 3)^2$ when you rewrite it as $x^2 + 6x + 9$ in finding the general form. The vertex form tells you about translations, reflections, stretches, and shrinks of the graph of the parent function, $y = x^2$. The general form tells you the initial position, the velocity, and the force due to gravity in projectile motion applications. Later in this chapter you will learn to convert the general form to the vertex form. Then you'll be able to solve all forms of quadratic equations symbolically.

EXERCISES

You will need your graphing calculator for Exercises **2, 4, 8, 11,** and **16.**

▶ Practice Your Skills

1. Is each algebraic expression a polynomial? If so, how many terms does it have? If it is not, give a reason why it is not a polynomial.

    a. $x^2 + 3x - 8$ yes; three terms (trinomial)

    b. $2x - \dfrac{4}{5}$ ⓐ yes; two terms (binomial)

    c. $5x^{-1} - 2x^2$ No; the first term has a negative exponent.

    d. $\dfrac{3}{x^2} - 5x + 2$ ⓐ No; the first term is equivalent to $3x^{-2}$, which has a negative exponent.

    e. $6x$ yes; one term (monomial)

    f. $\dfrac{x^2}{3^{-2}} + 5x - 8$ ⓗ yes; three terms (trinomial)

    g. $10x^3 + 5x^2$ yes; two terms (binomial)

    h. $3(x - 2)$ ⓐ Not a polynomial as written, but it is equivalent to $3x - 6$, a binomial.

2. Expand each expression. On your calculator, enter the original expression into Y_1 and the expanded expression into Y_2. With a graph or a table, check that both forms are equivalent.

    a. $(x + 5)^2$ ⓐ $x^2 + 10x + 25$

    b. $(x - 7)^2$ $x^2 - 14x + 49$

    c. $3(x - 2)^2$ $3(x^2 - 4x + 4)$ or $3x^2 - 12x + 12$

3. Copy each rectangle diagram and fill in the missing values. Then write a squared binomial and an equivalent trinomial that both represent the total area of each diagram.

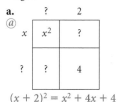

   $(x + 2)^2 = x^2 + 4x + 4$ $(x + 12)^2 = x^2 + 24x + 144$ $(x - 7)^2 = x^2 - 14x + 49$

4. Convert each equation from vertex form to general form. Check your answers by entering both expressions into the $Y=$ screen on your calculator, then graphing.

    a. $y = (x + 5)^2 + 4$ $y = x^2 + 10x + 29$

    b. $y = 2(x - 7)^2 - 8$ $y = 2x^2 - 28x + 90$

    c. $y = -3(x + 4)^2 + 1$ ⓐ $y = -3x^2 - 24x - 47$

    d. $y = 0.5(x - 3)^2 - 4.5$ $y = 0.5x^2 - 3x$

▶ Helping with the Exercises

Exercise 1 The expression in 1f is equivalent to the trinomial $9x^2 + 5x - 8$. You may have posted the new words from the lesson introduction. Students can refer to them and give specific names for the polynomials.

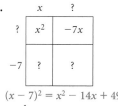

This example shows how to change an equation from vertex form to general form. You could point out that the general form shows the y-intercept easily, although it can be found from the vertex form by substituting 0 for x.

Reinforcing Relationships
A chart can help students summarize and see relationships. Students can make a chart with six columns headed *equation, graph, vertex, line of symmetry, roots,* and *compare with $y = x^2$.* Students can then list examples of quadratic equations in both the vertex form and the general form, filling in all six columns for each equation.

You might use the Sketchpad demonstration Quadratic Equations to explore how varying each coefficient of quadratic equations in vertex and in general form affects their graphs.

Closing the Lesson

To convert a quadratic equation from vertex form to general form, you need to square a **binomial.** That can be done with the help of a rectangle diagram, even if the binomial includes subtraction.

BUILDING UNDERSTANDING

Students practice squaring binomials, multiplying one binomial by another, and applying the vertex form of a quadratic equation.

ASSIGNING HOMEWORK

Essential	1–6, 9, 10
Performance assessment	6, 8
Portfolio	11
Journal	7, 13
Group	5, 8, 12
Review	14–16

5a.

	x	2
x	x^2	$2x$
4	$4x$	8

$(x + 2)(x + 4) = x^2 + 6x + 8$

5b.

	x	3
x	x^2	$3x$
5	$5x$	15

$(x + 3)(x + 5) = x^2 + 8x + 15$

5c.

	x	2
x	x^2	$2x$
-5	$-5x$	-10

$(x + 2)(x - 5) = x^2 - 3x - 10$

5d.

	x
x	x^2
-3	$-3x$

$x(x - 3) = x^2 - 3x$

5e.

	x	2
$2x$	$2x^2$	$4x$
5	$5x$	10

$(x + 2)(2x + 5) = 2x^2 + 9x + 10$

5f.

	$3x$	-1
$2x$	$6x^2$	$-2x$
3	$9x$	-3

$(3x - 1)(2x + 3) = 6x^2 + 7x - 3$

Exercise 7 Press for an explanation of why it is not correct.

7. No; by squaring the values inside the parentheses, Heather is accounting for only two of the four rectangles in a rectangle diagram. She needs to add the terms in the two rectangles that sum to the middle term.

Reason and Apply

5. Draw a rectangle diagram to represent each expression. Then write an equation showing the product of the two binomials and the equivalent polynomial in general form.

   a. $(x + 2)(x + 4)$ **b.** $(x + 3)(x + 5)$

   c. $(x + 2)(x - 5)$ **d.** $x(x - 3)$ ⓐ

   e. $(x + 2)(2x + 5)$ ⓐ   **f.** $(3x - 1)(2x + 3)$

6. Consider the graph of the parabola $y = x^2 - 4x + 7$.

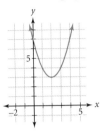

   a. What are the coordinates of the vertex? $(2, 3)$

   b. Write the equation in vertex form. $y = (x - 2)^2 + 3$

   c. Check that the equation you wrote in 6b is correct by expanding it to general form.
      $x^2 - 4x + 4 + 3 = x^2 - 4x + 7$

7. Heather thinks she has found a shortcut to the rectangle diagram method of squaring a binomial. She says that you can just square everything inside the parentheses. That is, $(x + 8)^2$ would be $x^2 + 64$. Is Heather's method correct? Explain.

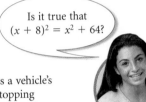

Is it true that $(x + 8)^2 = x^2 + 64$?

8. **APPLICATION** The quadratic equation $y = 0.0056x^2 + 0.14x$ relates a vehicle's stopping distance to its speed. In this equation, y represents the stopping distance in meters and x represents the vehicle's speed in kilometers per hour.

   a. Find the stopping distance for a vehicle traveling 100 km/h. 70 m

   b. Write an equation to find the speed of a vehicle that took 50 m to stop. Use a calculator graph or table to solve the equation. $50 = 0.0056x^2 + 0.14x$; $x \approx 83$ km/h

9. The function $h(t) = -4.9(t - 0.4)^2 + 2.5$ describes the height of a softball thrown by a pitcher, where $h(t)$ is in meters and t is in seconds.

   a. How high does the ball go? ⓗ

   b. What is an equivalent function in general form?

   c. At what height did the pitcher release the ball when t was 0 s? ⓐ The pitcher released the ball at a height of 1.716 m.

   d. What domain and range values make sense in this situation? domain: $0 \le t \le 1.1$; range: $0 \le h \le 2.5$

Catherine Osterman of the USA softball team pitches at the 2004 Olympics in Athens, Greece.

Exercise 8 [Language] Students may be confused by the phrase "relates ... to. ...." We say that an equation "relates y to x." Students can solve the equation in several ways. One method is to approximate the x-coordinate of the rightmost intersection point of $Y_1 = 50$ and $Y_2 = 0.0056x^2 + 0.14x$.

9a. The vertex is at $(0.4, 2.5)$, so the ball reaches a maximum height of 2.5 m.

9b. $h(t) = -4.9t^2 + 3.92t + 1.716$

10. Is the expression on the right equivalent to the expression on the left? If not, correct the right side to make it equivalent.

   a. $(x + 7.5)^2 - 3 \overset{?}{=} x^2 + 15x + 53.25$ yes

   b. $2(x - 4.7)^2 + 2.8 \overset{?}{=} 2x^2 - 9.4x - 41.38$ No; the right side should be $2x^2 - 18.8x + 46.98$.

   c. $-3.5(x + 1.6)^2 - 2.04 \overset{?}{=} -3.5x^2 + 11.2x - 11$ No; the right side should be $-3.5x^2 - 11.2x - 11$.

   d. $-4.9(x - 5.6)^2 + 8.9 \overset{?}{=} -4.9x^2 + 54.88x - 144.764$ yes

11. APPLICATION The Yo-yo Warehouse uses the equation $y = -85x^2 + 552.5x$ to model the relationship between income and price for one of its top-selling yo-yos. In this model, y represents income in dollars and x represents the selling price in dollars of one item.

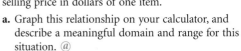

   a. Graph this relationship on your calculator, and describe a meaningful domain and range for this situation. @

   b. Describe a method for finding the vertex of the graph of this relationship. What is the vertex?

   c. What are the real-world meanings of the coordinates of the vertex?

   d. What is the real-world meaning of the two x-intercepts of the graph? The prices $0.00 and $6.50 produce no income.

   e. Interpret the meaning of this model if $x = 5$.
      If the warehouse charges $5 per item, income will be $637.50.

12. Use a three-by-three rectangle diagram to square each trinomial.

   a. $(x + y + 3)^2$ @

   b. $(2x - y + 5)^2$

13. What is the general form of $y = (x + 4)^2$? Write a paragraph describing several ways to rewrite this expression in general form. $y = x^2 + 8x + 16$; answers will vary.

Review

7.2 14. Is this parabola a graph of a function?   No; it doesn't pass a vertical line test.

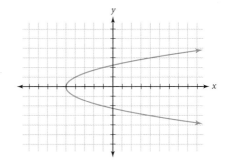

Exercise 10 One way to check the equivalence of two expressions is to enter one as Y₁ and the other as Y₂ and compare their graphs or tables.

Exercise 11 As the price rises above about $3.25, enough fewer people buy that the income goes down. As needed, help students find a good viewing window.

11a. meaningful domain: $0 \le x \le 6.5$; meaningful range: $0 \le y \le 897.81$

$[0, 9.4, 1, -100, 1000, 100]$

11b. Possible answer: Average the two x-intercepts, then substitute this value into the equation to find the y-coordinate of the vertex. The vertex is at $(3.25, 897.8125)$.

11c. The price $3.25 gives the maximum income, $897.81.

Exercise 13 Students will probably describe the rectangle diagram method, the use of the distributive property, or the use of the pattern $(a + b)^2 = a^2 + 2ab + b^2$.

12a.

	x	y	3
x	x^2	xy	$3x$
y	xy	y^2	$3y$
3	$3x$	$3y$	9

$x^2 + y^2 + 2xy + 6x + 6y + 9$

12b.

	$2x$	$-y$	5
$2x$	$4x^2$	$-2xy$	$10x$
$-y$	$-2xy$	y^2	$-5y$
5	$10x$	$-5y$	25

$4x^2 + y^2 - 4xy + 20x - 10y + 25$

7.4   **15.** Use the graph of $f(x)$ to evaluate each expression. Then think of the numbers 1 through 26 as the letters A through Z to decode a message.   The message is POLYNOMIALS.

a. $f(18)$ 16; P
b. $3 \cdot f(3)$ 15; O
c. $f(4^2)$ @ 12; L
d. $[f(3)]^2$ 25; Y
e. the greater x-value when $f(x) = 8$ 14; N
f. $f(25)$ 15; O
g. $f(5) + f(15)$ 13; M
h. the greater x-value when $f(x) = 1$ @ 9; I
i. $f(1) - f(2)$ 1; A
j. $f(4) \cdot f(5)$ 12; L
k. $f(5^2 - 2^2)$ 19; S

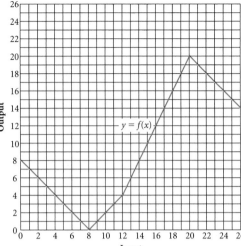

9.1   **16.** The equation $y = -0.0024x^2 + 0.81x + 2.0$ models the path of a golf ball hit by Tiger Woods. In the equation, x represents the horizontal distance from the tee, in yards, and y is the height of the ball above the ground, in yards.

a. Name a graphing window that allows you to see the entire path of the ball.   possible answer: $[0, 400, 50, -20, 100, 10]$
b. What domain values make sense in this situation? $0 \le x \le 340$
c. What range values make sense in this situation? $0 \le y \le 70.3$

Factored Form

*Mathematicians assume the
right to choose, within the
limits of logical contradiction,
what path they please in
reaching their results.*

HENRY ADAMS

So far you have worked with quadratic equations in vertex form and general form. This lesson will introduce you to another form of quadratic equation, the **factored form:**

$$y = a(x - r_1)(x - r_2)$$

This form helps you identify the roots, r_1 and r_2, of an equation. In the investigation you'll discover connections between the equation in factored form and its graph. You'll also use rectangle diagrams to convert the factored form to the general form and vice versa. Then in the example you'll learn how to use a special property to find the roots of an equation.

Investigation
Getting to the Root of the Matter

You will need
- graph paper

First you'll find the roots of an equation in factored form from its graph.

Step 1	On your calculator, graph the equations $y = x + 3$ and $y = x - 4$ at the same time.
Step 2	What is the x-intercept of each equation you graphed in Step 1? $x = -3$ and $x = 4$
Step 3	Graph $y = (x + 3)(x - 4)$ on the same set of axes as before. Describe the graph. Where are the x-intercepts of this graph?
Step 4	Expand $y = (x + 3)(x - 4)$ to general form. Graph the equation in general form on the same set of axes. What do you notice about this parabola and its x-intercepts? Is the graph of $y = (x + 3)(x - 4)$ a parabola?

Step 4
$y = x^2 - x - 12$; the graph
of $y = x^2 - x - 12$
is the same as that
of $y = (x + 3)(x - 4)$
and has identical
x-intercepts. So the graph of $y = (x + 3)(x - 4)$ is a parabola.

NCTM STANDARDS

CONTENT		PROCESS	
✔	Number		Problem Solving
✔	Algebra	✔	Reasoning
	Geometry	✔	Communication
	Measurement	✔	Connections
	Data/Probability	✔	Representation

LESSON OBJECTIVES

- Learn that the roots of a quadratic equation can be found quickly from its factored form
- Study factoring of the general form of a quadratic equation
- Explore the relationships among the three forms of a quadratic equation: factored form, vertex form, and general form
- Solve equations using the zero-product property
- Reduce rational expressions by factoring

PLANNING

LESSON OUTLINE

One day:
20 min   Investigation
5 min   Sharing
15 min   Examples
5 min   Closing
5 min   Exercises

MATERIALS

- graph paper
- Fathom demonstration Booming Babies, *optional*
- CBR demonstration Bounce Back, *optional*

TEACHING

The factored form of a quadratic equation is useful for finding roots (x-intercepts) quickly. It can be converted to and derived from the other two forms.

Guiding the Investigation

One Step
[Ask] "What are two numbers that have the product zero?" Entertain all ideas, being sure that products of opposites or reciprocals are rejected. Introduce the term *zero-product property*. **[Ask]** "What can you conclude about x if you know that $(x + 3)(x - 4) = 0$?" Note that if you have a quadratic equation in this *factored form*, you can find the roots easily. Then challenge the groups to find the factored form of the equation $x^2 + 5x + 6 = 0$. Encourage the use of rectangle diagrams and have students check their conjectures with graphs. Some students may do the factoring by graphing and finding the x-intercepts.

See page 729 for answers to Steps 1 and 3.

LESSON 9.4 Factored Form **515**

Step 2 Encourage students to determine these x-values without tracing.

Step 3 At this point students have no definitive evidence that the graph of $y = (x + 3)(x - 4)$ is a parabola.

Step 4 This kind of expanding was done in Lesson 9.3. Because students know the graph of $y = x^2 - x - 12$ is a parabola and because the equations are equivalent, students are assured that $y = (x + 3)(x - 4)$ does indeed graph as a parabola. They can double-check that the equations are equivalent by comparing calculator tables.

Step 6 As needed, remind students of the introduction's definition of *factored form*.

Step 6 $(x + 3)(x + 2)$. Enter $x^2 + 5x + 6$ into Y1 and $(x + 3)(x + 2)$ into Y2; a graph or table confirms equivalency.

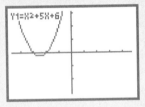

$$[-5, 5, 1, -3, 3, 1]$$

You might use the Fathom demonstration Booming Babies to give students more practice with factored form.

8a. $(x - 5)(x - 2)$; $x = 5$ and $x = 2$

8b. $(x - 2)(x + 8)$; $x = 2$ and $x = -8$

SHARING IDEAS

Have groups present their results from Step 8. Introduce the term *to factor* a trinomial and point out that students should expect to guess and check when factoring. (Although there are algorithmic

methods for factoring, students will gain deeper understanding by checking with rectangle diagrams or distribution.)

If you have time, you might show the two graphs from Step 1 of the investigation and ask whether students could predict where the graph of $y = (x + 3)(x - 4)$ is positive and negative by looking at the two linear graphs.

Now you'll learn how to find the roots from the general form.

Step 5 Complete the rectangle diagram whose sum is $x^2 + 5x + 6$. A few parts on the diagram have been labeled to get you started.

	x	3
x	x^2	$3x$
2	$2x$	6

Step 6 Write the multiplication expression of the rectangle diagram in factored form. Use a graph or table to check that this form is equivalent to the original expression.

Step 7 Find the roots of the equation $0 = x^2 + 5x + 6$ from its factored form.
$x = -3$ and $x = -2$

Step 8 Rewrite each equation in factored form by completing a rectangle diagram. Then find the roots of each. Check your work by making a graph.

a. $0 = x^2 - 7x + 10$

b. $0 = x^2 + 6x - 16$

c. $0 = x^2 + 2x - 48$
$(x - 6)(x + 8)$; $x = 6$ and $x = -8$

d. $0 = x^2 - 11x + 28$
$(x - 7)(x - 4)$; $x = 7$ and $x = 4$

Now you have learned three forms of a quadratic equation. You can enter each of these forms into your calculator to check that they are equivalent. Here are three equivalent equations that describe the height in meters, y, of an object in motion for x seconds after being thrown upward. Each equation gives different information about the object.

Vertex form	$y = -4.9(x - 1.7)^2 + 15.876$
General form	$y = -4.9x^2 + 16.66x + 1.715$
Factored form	$y = -4.9(x + 0.1)(x - 3.5)$

Which form is best? The answer depends on what you want to know. The vertex form tells you the maximum height and when it occurs—in this case, 15.876 meters after 1.7 seconds (the vertex). The general form tells you that the object started at a height of 1.715 meters (the y-intercept). The coefficients of x and x^2 give some information about the starting velocity and acceleration. The factored form tells you the times at which the object's height is zero (the roots).

You have already learned how to convert to and from the general form of a quadratic equation. Example A will show you how to get the vertex form from the factored form.

EXAMPLE A | Write the equation for this parabola in vertex form, factored form, and general form.

▶ Solution | From the graph you can see that the x-intercepts are 3 and -5. So the factored form contains the binomial expressions $(x - 3)$ and $(x + 5)$.

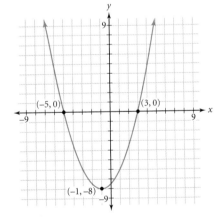

Three Forms

For the projectile motion described, ask what the roots mean. Only one root, 3.5, is meaningful, because a negative root refers to a time before the object was thrown. Posting examples of the three forms of quadratic equations will help many students grasp these concepts. In the CBR demonstration Bounce Back, students use each of the three forms to model one bounce of a ball.

If you graph $y = (x - 3)(x + 5)$ on your calculator, you'll see it has the same x-intercepts as the graph shown here, but a different vertex. The new vertex is $(-1, -16)$.

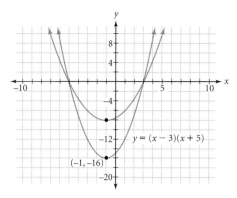

The new vertex needs to be closer to the x-axis, so you need to find the vertical shrink factor a.

The original vertex of the graph shown is $(-1, -8)$. So the graph of the function must have a vertical shrink by a factor of $\frac{-8}{-16}$, or 0.5. The factored form is $y = 0.5(x - 3)(x + 5)$. A calculator graph of this equation looks like the desired parabola.

$[-15, 15, 1, -10, 10, 1]$

Now you know that the value of a is 0.5 and that the vertex is $(-1, -8)$. Substitute this information into the vertex form to get $y = 0.5(x + 1)^2 - 8$.

Expand either form to find the general form.

$y = 0.5(x - 3)(x + 5)$	Original equations.
$y = 0.5(x^2 - 3x + 5x - 15)$	Expand using rectangle diagrams.

	x	-3
x	x^2	$-3x$
5	$5x$	-15

$y = 0.5(x^2 + 2x - 15)$	Combine like terms.
$y = 0.5x^2 + x - 7.5$	Distribute and combine.

$y = 0.5(x + 1)^2 - 8$

$y = 0.5(x^2 + 1x + 1x + 1) - 8$

	x	1
x	x^2	$1x$
1	$1x$	1

$y = 0.5(x^2 + 2x + 1) - 8$

$y = 0.5x^2 + x - 7.5$

So the three forms of the quadratic equation are

Vertex form	$y = 0.5(x + 1)^2 - 8$
General form	$y = 0.5x^2 + x - 7.5$
Factored form	$y = 0.5(x - 3)(x + 5)$

Assessing Progress

Keep an eye out for the ability to graph equations, solve linear equations, find x-intercepts by tracing, and multiply two binomials.

USING THE QUOTE

The text following the investigation contrasts the usefulness of the three forms of quadratic equations. Draw the class's attention to the quotation opening the lesson and ask whether it applies to the current topic. Point out the three forms of quadratic equations in the student text. Ask which of these three "paths" they might choose to reach which results.

▶ *EXAMPLE A*

You might ask students what numbers they can multiply to get zero. Some may suggest opposites until they realize they are thinking of adding. Some may suggest reciprocals, thinking of the product 1. The goal is to dramatize the *zero-product property*—if a product is zero, then at least one of the factors must be zero.

To obtain the vertex coordinates shown on the screen, evaluate the function at $x = -1$ from the graph screen.

When finding roots it is helpful to use the factored form. In Example A, one root is 3 because 3 is the value that makes $(x - 3)$ equal to 0. The other root is -5 because it makes $(x + 5)$ equal to 0. Think of numbers that multiply to zero. If $ab = 0$ or $abc = 0$, the **zero-product property** tells you that a, or b, or c must be 0. In an equation like $(x + 3)(x - 5) = 0$, *at least one of the factors must be zero.* The roots of an equation are sometimes called the **zeros** of a function because they make the value of the function equal to zero.

keymath.com/DA

[▶ You can further explore the relationship between factored form, roots, and *x*-intercepts using the **Dynamic Algebra Exploration** at www.keymath.com/DA . ◄]

The ability to factor polynomials is also useful when simplifying rational expressions, as you'll see in the next example. When a polynomial equation is in factored form, and reduced, it's much easier to predict or identify characteristics such as *x*-intercepts and asymptotes.

EXAMPLE B

A rational expression can be reduced if there is a common factor in both the numerator and denominator. Reduce the expression $\frac{x^2 + 2x - 24}{x^2 + 7x + 6}$ by factoring. Then check your answer with a graph.

▶ **Solution**

First factor the quadratic expressions in the numerator and denominator. Using a rectangle diagram may help.

Numerator: $x^2 + 2x - 24$ Denominator: $x^2 + 7x + 6$

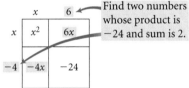 Find two numbers whose product is -24 and sum is 2.

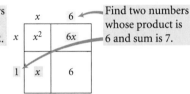 Find two numbers whose product is 6 and sum is 7.

So, $x^2 + 2x - 24 = (x + 6)(x - 4)$ and $x^2 + 7x + 6 = (x + 6)(x + 1)$. Now reduce the rational expression. Be sure to state any restrictions on the variable.

$$\frac{x^2 + 2x - 24}{x^2 + 7x + 6} = \frac{(x + 6)(x - 4)}{(x + 6)(x + 1)}$$
$$= \frac{\cancel{(x + 6)}(x - 4)}{\cancel{(x + 6)}(x + 1)}$$
$$= \frac{x - 4}{x + 1}, \text{ where } x \neq -6 \text{ and } x \neq -1$$

You can check your work by graphing $y = \frac{x^2 + 2x - 24}{x^2 + 7x + 6}$ and $y = \frac{x - 4}{x + 1}$. If the expressions are equivalent the graphs should be the same, except for any points that may be undefined in one graph, but defined in the other.

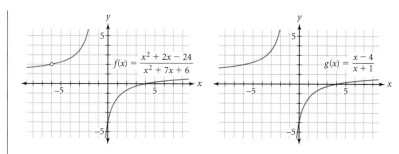

$$f(x) = \frac{x^2 + 2x - 24}{x^2 + 7x + 6}$$

$$g(x) = \frac{x - 4}{x + 1}$$

The only difference in the graphs is that the first graph is missing a point at $(-6, 2)$. So the reduced expression is equivalent to the original expression.

EXERCISES

You will need your graphing calculator for Exercises **2, 3, 9, 12,** and **16.**

▶ Practice Your Skills

1. Use the zero-product property to solve each equation.

   a. $(x + 4)(x + 3.5) = 0$ @
   b. $2(x - 2)(x - 6) = 0$
   c. $(x + 3)(x - 7)(x + 8) = 0$
   d. $x(x - 9)(x + 3) = 0$

2. Graph each equation and then rewrite it in factored form.

   a. $y = x^2 - 4x + 3$ @ $y = (x - 3)(x - 1)$
   b. $y = x^2 + 5x - 24$ $y = (x + 8)(x - 3)$
   c. $y = x^2 + 12x + 27$ $y = (x + 3)(x + 9)$
   d. $y = x^2 - 7x - 30$ $y = (x - 10)(x + 3)$

3. Name the x-intercepts of the parabola described by each quadratic equation. Then check your answers with a graph.

   a. $y = (x - 7)(x + 2)$ @ $x = 7$ and $x = -2$
   b. $y = 2(x + 1)(x + 8)$ $x = -1$ and $x = -8$
   c. $y = 3(x - 11)(x + 7)$ $x = 11$ and $x = -7$
   d. $y = (0.4x + 2)(x - 9)$ $x = -5$ and $x = 9$

4. Write an equation of a quadratic function that corresponds to each pair of x-intercepts. Assume there is no vertical stretch or shrink.

   a. 2.5 and -1 @   **b.** -4 and -4 **c.** -2 and 2 $y = (x + 2)(x - 2)$ **d.** r_1 and r_2 $y = (x - r_1)(x - r_2)$
   $y = (x - 2.5)(x + 1)$ $y = (x + 4)(x + 4)$, or $y = (x + 4)^2$

5. Consider the equation $y = (x + 1)(x - 3)$.

   a. How many x-intercepts does the graph have? two intercepts, $x = -1$ and $x = 3$
   b. Find the vertex of this parabola. $(1, -4)$
   c. Write the equation in vertex form. Describe the transformations of the parent function, $y = x^2$. $y = (x - 1)^2 - 4$; there is a translation right 1 unit and down 4 units.

▶ Reason and Apply

6. Is the expression on the left equivalent to the expression on the right? If not, change the right side to make it equivalent. No; change to $(x - 6)(x - 5)$.

   a. $x^2 + 7x + 12 \overset{?}{=} (x + 3)(x + 4)$ yes   **b.** $x^2 - 11x + 30 \overset{?}{=} (x + 6)(x + 5)$
   c. $2x^2 - 5x - 7 \overset{?}{=} (2x - 7)(x + 1)$ @ yes   **d.** $4x^2 + 8x + 4 \overset{?}{=} (x + 1)^2$ No; change to $4(x + 1)^2$.
   e. $x^2 - 25 \overset{?}{=} (x + 5)(x - 5)$ yes   **f.** $x^2 - 36 \overset{?}{=} (x - 6)^2$ No; change to $(x + 6)(x - 6)$.

▶ **Helping with the Exercises**

1a. $x + 4 = 0$ or $x + 3.5 = 0$, so $x = -4$ or $x = -3.5$

1b. $x - 2 = 0$ or $x - 6 = 0$, so $x = 2$ or $x = 6$

1c. $x + 3 = 0$ or $x - 7 = 0$ or $x + 8 = 0$, so $x = -3$ or $x = 7$ or $x = -8$

1d. $x = 0$ or $x - 9 = 0$ or $x + 3 = 0$, so $x = 0$ or $x = 9$ or $x = -3$

2a.
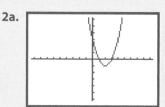
$[-9.4, 9.4, 1, -6.2, 6.2, 1]$

2b.
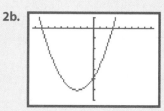
$[-9.4, 9.4, 1, -35, 5, 5]$

2c.
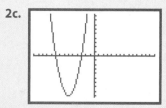
$[-14.1, 14.1, 1, -9.3, 9.3, 1]$

2d.
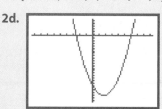
$[-20, 20, 2, -50, 10, 2]$

3a.
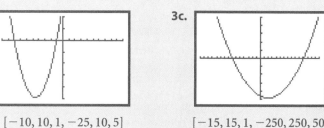
$[-10, 10, 1, -25, 10, 5]$

3b.
$[-10, 10, 1, -25, 10, 5]$

3c.
$[-15, 15, 1, -250, 250, 50]$

3d.
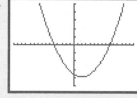
$[-15, 15, 1, -25, 25, 5]$

Exercise 4 Because there's no vertical stretch or shrink, $a = 1$. For 4b, -4 is a *double root*.

7a. $(x + 6)(x + 1)$

	x	6
x	x^2	$6x$
1	x	6

7b. $(x + 5)(x + 2)$

	x	5
x	x^2	$5x$
2	$2x$	10

7c. $(x + 7)(x - 6)$

	x	7
x	x^2	$7x$
-6	$-6x$	-42

7d. $(x - 6)(x + 3)$

	x	-6
x	x^2	$-6x$
3	$3x$	-18

7e. $(x - 4)(x - 6)$

	x	-4
x	x^2	$-4x$
-6	$-6x$	24

7f. $(x + 12)(x - 4)$

	x	12
x	x^2	$12x$
-4	$-4x$	-48

---

7. Use a rectangle diagram to factor each expression.

　a. $x^2 + 7x + 6$ @ 　　**b.** $x^2 + 7x + 10$ 　　**c.** $x^2 + x - 42$ @
　d. $x^2 - 3x - 18$ 　　**e.** $x^2 - 10x + 24$ @ 　**f.** $x^2 + 8x - 48$

8. The sum and product of the roots of a quadratic equation are related to b and c in $y = x^2 + bx + c$. The first row in the table below will help you to recognize this relationship.

　a. Complete the table.

Factored form	Roots	Sum of roots	Product of roots	General form
$y = (x + 3)(x - 4)$	-3 and 4	$-3 + 4 = 1$	$(-3)(4) = -12$	$y = x^2 - 1x - 12$
$y = (x - 5)(x + 2)$	5 and -2	$5 - 2 = 3$	$5(-2) = -10$	$y = x^2 - 3x - 10$
$y = (x + 2)(x + 3)$	-2 and -3	-5	6	$y = x^2 + 5x + 6$
$y = (x - 5)(x + 5)$	5 and -5	0	-25	$y = x^2 - 25$

　b. Use the values of b and c to find the roots of $0 = x^2 + 2x - 8$.
The sum of the roots needs to be -2, and the product needs to be -8; 2 and -4 satisfy these requirements.

9. *Mini-Investigation* In this exercise you will discover whether knowing the x-intercepts determines a unique quadratic equation. Work through the steps in 9a–e to find an answer. Graph each equation to check your work.

　a. Write an equation of a parabola with x-intercepts at $x = 3$ and $x = 7$.　$y = (x - 3)(x - 7)$

　b. Name the vertex of the parabola in 9a.　$(5, -4)$

　c. Modify your equation in 9a so that the graph is reflected across the x-axis. Where are the x-intercepts? Where is the vertex?　$y = -(x - 3)(x - 7)$; x-intercepts: $x = 3$ and $x = 7$; vertex: $(5, 4)$

　d. Modify your equation in 9a to apply a vertical stretch with a factor of 2. Where are the x-intercepts? Where is the vertex? @　$y = 2(x - 3)(x - 7)$; x-intercepts: $x = 3$ and $x = 7$; vertex: $(5, -8)$

　e. How many quadratic equations do you think there are with x-intercepts at $x = 3$ and $x = 7$? How are they related to one another?

10. Write a quadratic equation of a parabola with x-intercepts at -3 and 9 and vertex at $(3, -9)$. Express your answer in factored form. @　$y = 0.25(x + 3)(x - 9)$

11. APPLICATION The school ecology club wants to fence in an area along the riverbank to protect endangered wildflowers that grow there. The club has enough money to buy 200 feet of fencing. It decides to enclose a rectangular space. The fence will form three sides of the rectangle, and the riverbank will form the fourth side.

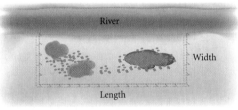

　a. If the width of the enclosure is 30 feet, how much fencing material is available for the length? Sketch this situation. What is the area? @　length: 140 ft; area: 4200 ft²

　b. If the width is w feet, how much fencing material remains for the length, l?　$l = 200 - 2w$

　c. Use your answer from 11b to write an equation for the area of the rectangle in factored form. Check your equation with your width and area from 11a.

　d. Which two different widths would give an area equal to 0? @　$w = 0$ ft and $w = 100$ ft

　e. Which width will give the maximum area? What is that area?　width: 50 ft; maximum area: 5000 ft²

Exercise 8 You can extend this exercise by making a game of giving other sums (such as 8) and products (such as 7) and asking students to find the two numbers with that sum and product (1 and 7).

9e. Possible answer: There are infinitely many quadratic equations with roots 3 and 7. Each is created by substituting a unique value of a into $y = a(x - 3)(x - 7)$. Hence, all are vertical stretches or shrinks and/or reflections across the x-axis. The x-coordinate of each vertex is always 5, but the y-coordinate depends on the value of a.

Exercise 10 Especially if students have worked on Exercise 9, they may wonder whether there's only one quadratic equation satisfying these conditions. Encourage thought about this question. Help them realize that any three noncollinear points lie on only one parabola.

Exercise 11 Students may use guess-and-check to find the maximum, but try to get them all to realize that they can answer the question by finding the vertex of the graph of $A = w(200 - 2w)$.

11c. $A = w \cdot l = w(200 - 2w)$; $30(200 - 2 \cdot 30) = 30(140) = 4200$

12. Mini-Investigation Consider the equation $y = x^2 - 9$.

    a. Graph the equation. What are the x-intercepts?

    b. Write the factored form of the equation. $y = (x - 3)(x + 3)$

    c. How are the x-intercepts related to the original equation?

    d. Write each equation in factored form. Verify each answer by graphing.

        i. $y = x^2 - 49$ $y = (x + 7)(x - 7)$ **ii.** $y = 16 - x^2$ $y = (4 + x)(4 - x)$

        iii. $y = x^2 - 47$ $y = (x + \sqrt{47})(x - \sqrt{47})$ **iv.** $y = x^2 - 28$ $y = (x + \sqrt{28})(x - \sqrt{28})$

    e. An expression in the form $a^2 - b^2$ is called a **difference of two squares.** Based on your work in 12a–d, make a conjecture about the factored form of $a^2 - b^2$. $a^2 - b^2 = (a + b)(a - b)$

    f. Graph the equation $y = x^2 + 4$. How many x-intercepts can you see?

    g. Explain the difficulty in trying to write the equation in 12f in factored form.

13. Kayleigh says that the roots of $0 = x^2 + 16$ are 4 and -4 because $(4)^2 = 16$ and $(-4)^2 = 16$. Derek tells Kayleigh that there are no roots for this equation. Who is correct and why?

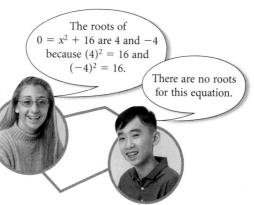

The roots of $0 = x^2 + 16$ are 4 and -4 because $(4)^2 = 16$ and $(-4)^2 = 16$.

There are no roots for this equation.

14. Reduce the rational expressions by dividing out common factors from the numerator and denominator. State any restrictions on the variable. Ⓗ

    a. $\dfrac{(x - 2)(x + 2)}{(x + 2)(x + 3)}$ @   **b.** $\dfrac{x^2 + 3x + 2}{(x - 4)(x + 2)}$

    c. $\dfrac{x^2 - 3x - 10}{x^2 - 5x}$ @   **d.** $\dfrac{x^2 + 2x - 3}{x^2 + 5x + 6}$

    e. $\dfrac{x^2 + x - 6}{x^2 + 6x + 9}$

▶ Review

9.3 **15.** Multiply and combine like terms.

    a. $(x - 21)(x + 2)$ **b.** $(3x + 1)(x + 4)$ **c.** $2(2x - 3)(x + 2)$

        $x^2 - 19x - 42$ $3x^2 + 13x + 4$ $4x^2 + 2x - 12$

9.2 **16.** Edward is responsible for keeping the stockroom packed with the best-selling merchandise at the Super Store. He has collected data on sales of the new video game "Math-a-Magic."

Week	1	2	3	4	5	6	7	8	9	10
Games sold	0	186	366	516	636	727	789	821	825	798

[Data sets: GMWK, GMSLD]

    a. Find a quadratic model in vertex form that fits the data. Let w represent the week number and let s represent the number of games sold. possible answer: $s = -14.5(w - 8.6)^2 + 827$

    b. If the pattern continues, in what week will people stop buying the game? week 16 or 17

    c. How many total games will have been sold when people stop buying the game? Ⓗ approximately 8282 or 8283 games

    d. There are 1000 games left in the stockroom at the start of week 11. How many more should Edward buy? approximately 1619 games

13. Answers will vary. Possible answer: Derek is correct because substituting 4 or -4 for x gives $0 = 16 + 16$, or 32, and not zero; the roots should satisfy the equation.

14a. $\dfrac{x - 2}{x + 3}$, where $x \neq -2$ and $x \neq -3$

14b. $\dfrac{x + 1}{x - 4}$, where $x \neq 4$ and $x \neq -2$

14c. $\dfrac{x + 2}{x}$, where $x \neq 0$ and $x \neq 5$

14d. $\dfrac{x - 1}{x + 2}$, where $x \neq -3$ and $x \neq -2$

14e. $\dfrac{x - 2}{x + 3}$, where $x \neq -3$

Exercise 12 This is the only place where the factoring of the differences of squares is introduced, so be sure to assign this problem if this topic is important to your curriculum.

In 12d, students can think of ii as $y = -1(x^2 - 16)$ and then factor the expression inside the parentheses.

In 12g, the imaginary roots are $2i$ and $-2i$, where $i^2 = -1$. Many students find this idea intriguing, so you may choose to introduce it. (Imaginary numbers are the subject of Take Another Look at the end of the chapter.) Historically, imaginary numbers were first used in solving cubic, not quadratic, equations.

12a. two x-intercepts: $x = 3$ and $x = -3$

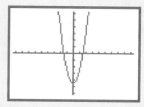

$[-18.8, 18.8, 2, -12.4, 12.4, 2]$

12c. The x-intercepts are the positive and negative square roots of the number subtracted from x^2.

12f. There are no x-intercepts. The graph is above the x-axis.

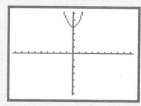

$[-9.4, 9.4, 1, -6.2, 6.2, 1]$

12g. Because there are no x-intercepts, there are no roots, and hence there is no factored form of the equation.

PLANNING

LESSON OUTLINE

One day:

45 min   Activity

5 min   Closing

MATERIALS

- motion sensors
- Calculator Note 9A
- Data and Programs CD, *optional*

Experiment 2

- empty coffee can
- long table

TEACHING

Quadratic equations can model motion of various sorts.

Guiding the Activity

If you don't have the resources to collect data for these experiments, provide students with sample data from the Data and Programs CD.

If your students are collecting data, try to give each student a chance both to control the motion (jumping or rolling the can) and to run a motion sensor.

EXPERIMENT 1

The plotted data points will not lie on a parabola, because the motion sensor is not following the jump. Instead, the graph will consist of three horizontal line segments from which students determine the root values to substitute, in Step 3, into a quadratic equation for motion.

Activity Day

Projectile Motion

You have already learned that quadratic equations model projectile motion. In this lesson you'll do an experiment with projectile motion and find a quadratic function to model the data. If you choose the first experiment, you'll collect data for the *x*-intercepts of a parabola and then find an equation in factored form that matches the graph. If you choose the second experiment, you'll collect parabolic data and then find an equation in vertex form that matches the graph. Read the steps of each experiment and then choose one experiment for your group to do.

Activity

Jump or Roll

You will need

- a motion sensor
- an empty coffee can
- a long table

Each experiment in this activity requires a calculator program. Be sure you have this program in your calculator before you begin. [▸ 🖳 See **Calculator Note 9A** for the required programs. ◂] In the first experiment you will collect data for the zeros of a projectile motion function.

Experiment 1: How High?

The object of this experiment is to find how high you jump.

Step 1

Set up the program to collect data. Jump straight up, without bending your knees while you're in the air. Be sure to land in front of the sensor again. This way, the sensor records the times your feet left the ground and landed.

> **Procedure Note**
>
> Place the motion sensor on the floor. The jumper stands 2 ft or 0.5 m in front of it. There should be a wall or another object about 4 ft or 1 m from the sensor. When the jumper's feet leave the ground, the motion sensor should register a change in distance at a specific instant in time.

LESSON OBJECTIVES

- Use data-collection devices to collect real-world data that can be modeled by quadratic equations
- Write quadratic equations to model real-world data

NCTM STANDARDS

CONTENT		PROCESS	
	Number	✓	Problem Solving
✓	Algebra	✓	Reasoning
	Geometry	✓	Communication
	Measurement	✓	Connections
	Data/Probability	✓	Representation

Step 2

Step 2 Sample answer: Feet left the ground at 0.09 s and landed at 0.57 s.

The data measured by the motion sensor have the form (*time, distance*), where the distance is that between the motion sensor and the nearest object to it. At first this distance is from the sensor to the jumper's feet. Then during the jump the sensor measures the distance to the wall behind the jumper. After the jumper lands, the sensor reads the distance to the jumper's feet again. Look at the graph and use the trace feature to determine the instant the feet left the ground. Do this by finding the sharp change in *y*-values on the graph. Likewise, determine the instant in time when the feet landed back on the ground.

Step 3 Let *t* represent the time in seconds and *h* represent the height in inches (or centimeters) above the ground. Answer from sample data is given below.

If you want to graph the height of your jump over time, what are the variables for the quadratic function in this situation? Substitute the two roots you found in Step 2 for r_1 and r_2 into the equation $h = -192(t - r_1)(t - r_2)$. Use it to calculate the height of your jump in inches. (Or use the equation $h = -490(t - r_1)(t - r_2)$ to find this height in centimeters.) At what time did you reach this height? Explain how you got your answer.

Step 4 Repeat the experiment with each member of your group as a jumper.

Distance for the sample data is not height. Step 2 explains what distance is being measured.

The value $-\frac{1}{2}g$ in Newton's motion equation $h(t) = \frac{1}{2}(-g)t^2 + v_0 t + h_0$ is usually given as -4.9 m/s^2 or -16 ft/s^2. For the jumper, however, it's more convenient to work in inches or centimeters. For inches, this value is $\frac{1}{2} \cdot \frac{-32 \text{ ft}}{s^2} \cdot \frac{12 \text{ in.}}{1 \text{ ft}}$, or -192 in./s^2. For centimeters, it is $\frac{1}{2} \cdot \frac{-9.8 \text{ m}}{s^2} \cdot \frac{100 \text{ cm}}{1 \text{ m}}$, or -490 cm/s^2.

If the motion didn't start when *t* was 0—as is probably the case for the jumper—then Newton's equation no longer holds. The value of *a* in the factored form $h = a(t - r_1)(t - r_2)$ is $-\frac{1}{2}g$, as you can see from expanding $h = a(t - r_1)(t - r_2)$ to get $h = at^2 - a(r_1 + r_2)t + ar_1 r_2$ and comparing the result to Newton's form. But the other coefficients no longer represent the initial velocity and position. For example, if the roots are $r_1 = 0.09$ and $r_2 = 0.57$, then $-192(t - 0.09)(t - 0.57) = -192t^2 + 126.72t - 9.8496$. You can't conclude that the student jumped from a position 9.8496 in. below the ground with initial velocity 126.72 in./s, because the student jumped from ground level. You can use calculus to find the initial velocity of this sample jump.

Experiment 2: Rolling Along

The object of this experiment is to write a quadratic equation from experimental data.

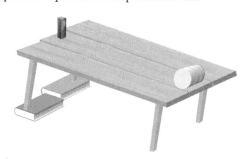

Procedure Note

Prop up one end of the table slightly. Position the motion sensor at the high end of the table and aim it toward the low end.

Step 1 Practice rolling the can up the table directly in front of the sensor. The can should roll up the table, stop about 2 feet from the sensor, and then roll back down. Give the can a short push so that it rolls up the table on its own momentum. Then the force of gravity should cause the can to reverse direction as it rolls back down the slanted table.

Step 2 Set up the program to collect the data. When the sensor begins, gently roll the can up the table. Catch it as it falls off the table.

Step 3 The data collected by the sensor will have the form (*time, distance*). If you do the experiment correctly, the graph should show a parabolic pattern. Sketch this graph.

Step 4 Find the equation of a parabola that fits your data. Which points did you use to find the equation? In which form is it? Sketch a parabola for this equation onto the graph from Step 3.
Equation for sample data: $y = 0.85(x - 3.2)^2 + 2.74$; graph is given below.

EXPERIMENT 2

The motion of the can along the table is not projectile motion, so the coefficients will not look familiar. Students can best represent the parabola by an equation in vertex form. By now, some students may have discovered that their calculators will do quadratic regression to find the parabola of best fit. Have them compare the calculator's equation to their own.

Results for sample data:
Experiment 1
roots at $t = 0.09$ and $t = 0.57$ s;
$h = -192(t - 0.09)(t - 0.57)$
or $h = -490(t - 0.09) \cdot (t - 0.57)$; the vertex is at (0.33, 11.06), so the height of the jump is about 11 in. (or 28.2 cm).

[0, 1, 0.1, −1, 15, 1]

Experiment 2

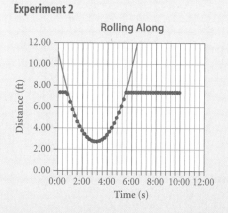

Rolling Along

SHARING IDEAS

One group doing each experiment might describe the procedure and another group the results.

Assessing Progress

Look for students' ability to find the vertex form of a quadratic equation from its roots and to adjust an equation to match a graph.

Closing the Lesson

The motion of rising or falling bodies, along ramps as well as in free fall, can be modeled with quadratic equations.

Using Sketchpad for the Project

A full parabola that will allow you to explore the effect of moving the focus can be drawn in The Geometer's Sketchpad by using this property: When you form an envelope for a parabola by folding tracing paper, the point on the crease that actually lies on the parabola is on the perpendicular to the directrix through the point the focus was placed over to make the crease. After constructing the focus A and directrix, construct a point D on the directrix; construct segment AD and its midpoint E; construct the line (the crease) perpendicular to this segment through point E; construct a perpendicular to the directrix through point D; and construct the intersection point F of this line with the crease. Then select F, D, and the directrix and choose Locus from the Construct menu. You get the locus of F as D moves along the directrix— a parabola.

project

PARABOLA BY DEFINITION

$\mathbf{Y}$ou have learned that the graph of a quadratic equation is a parabola. One definition of a parabola is the set of all points whose distance from a fixed point, the *focus*, is equal to its distance from a fixed line, the *directrix*. (Use the shortest possible distance for the distance between a point and a line.)

You can use The Geometer's Sketchpad or tracing paper to draw a parabola in various ways based on this definition. Start by drawing a line and a point not on the line. Then locate several points equally distant from the focus and the directrix by using the tools in Sketchpad or by folding tracing paper. On tracing paper, fold the focus to lie on the directrix and crease the paper. Repeat to make many creases. The creases will outline a parabola. If you make a similar set of lines in Sketchpad, you can test what happens to the parabola if the focus moves closer to (or farther from) the directrix.

Your project should include

▶ A drawing of the lines with the parabola's focus, directrix, and vertex labeled.

▶ An explanation of how you constructed the lines.

▶ A discussion of how the distance between the focus and the directrix affects the shape of the parabola.

Find more information about parabolas with the Internet links at **www.keymath.com/DA** .

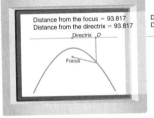 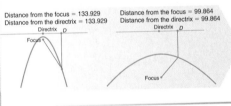

keymath.com/DA

[▶ You can further explore the relationship between the graph of a parabola and the locations of its focus and directrix using the **Dynamic Algebra Exploration** at **www.keymath.com/DA** . ◀]

Supporting the project

MOTIVATION

A parabola can be defined as the set of points equidistant from a fixed point (its *focus*) and a fixed line (its *directrix*).

The dynamic sketch at www.keymath.com/DA can help students explore the geometric definition of a parabola.

OUTCOMES

▶ The report includes some representation of the parabola, such as drawings or sheets of folded tracing paper.

▶ There is a clear description of how the representation was created.

▶ The report describes accurately how the distance between the focus and the directrix affects the shape of the parabola.

• The report includes where the vertex is with respect to the focus and directrix.

• The report includes the fact that the distance from the vertex to the focus is $\frac{1}{4a}$, where a is the coefficient of x^2 in the equation of the parabola.

Completing the Square

Quadratic equations, such as those modeling projectile motion, are often in the form $y = ax^2 + bx + c$. And, often you'll want to find the zeros—the times when the object hits the ground. You can always find approximate zeros of quadratic equations by using tables and graphs. If you can convert the equation to the factored form, $y = a(x - r_1)(x - r_2)$, or the vertex form, $y = a(x - h)^2 + k$, then you can use symbolic methods to find exact zeros. In this lesson you'll learn a symbolic method to find exact zeros of equations in the general form, $y = ax^2 + bx + c$.

Recall that rectangle diagrams help you factor some quadratic expressions.

Perfect-square trinomial

$x^2 + 6x + 9$

	x	3
x	x^2	$3x$
3	$3x$	9

Factorable trinomial

$x^2 + x - 6$

	x	3
x	x^2	$3x$
-2	$-2x$	-6

In the first diagram the sum of the rectangular areas, $x^2 + 3x + 3x + 9$, is equal to the area of the overall diagram, $(x + 3)^2$. So -3 is the root of the equation $x^2 + 6x + 9 = 0$. In the second diagram the sum is $x^2 + 3x + (-2x) + (-6)$, which equals $(x - 2)(x + 3)$. Both 2 and -3 are the roots of $x^2 + x - 6 = 0$.

How do you find the roots of an equation such as $0 = x^2 + x - 1$? It is not a perfect-square trinomial, nor is it easily factorable. For these equations you can use a method called **completing the square.**

Investigation
Searching for Solutions

You will need

- graph paper

To understand how to complete the square with quadratic equations, you'll first work with rectangle diagrams.

Step 1 Complete each rectangle diagram so that it is a square. How do you know which number to place in the lower-right corner?

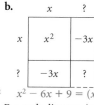

a.

	x	$?$
x	x^2	$2x$
$?$	$2x$	$?$

$x^2 + 4x + 4 = (x + 2)^2$

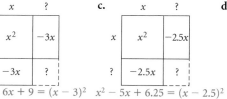

b.

	x	$?$
x	x^2	$-3x$
$?$	$-3x$	$?$

$x^2 - 6x + 9 = (x - 3)^2$

c.

	x	$?$
x	x^2	$-2.5x$
$?$	$-2.5x$	$?$

$x^2 - 5x + 6.25 = (x - 2.5)^2$

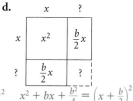

d.

	x	$?$
x	x^2	$\frac{b}{2}x$
$?$	$\frac{b}{2}x$	$?$

$x^2 + bx + \frac{b^2}{4} = \left(x + \frac{b}{2}\right)^2$

Step 2 For each diagram in Step 1, write an equation in the form $x^2 + bx + c = (x + h)^2$. On which side of the equation can you isolate x by undoing the order of operations? the right side, $(x + h)^2$

NCTM STANDARDS

CONTENT		PROCESS	
✔	Number		Problem Solving
✔	Algebra	✔	Reasoning
	Geometry	✔	Communication
	Measurement	✔	Connections
	Data/Probability	✔	Representation

LESSON OBJECTIVES

- Review how to solve quadratic equations in vertex form
- Solve quadratic equations in general form by completing the square

PLANNING

LESSON OUTLINE

One day:

20 min	Investigation
5 min	Sharing
10 min	Examples
5 min	Closing
10 min	Exercises

MATERIALS

- graph paper
- Fun Training (T or W), *optional*

TEACHING

To change a quadratic equation from general form to vertex form, or to solve the general form when it's not clear how to factor, you can complete the square.

Guiding the Investigation

One Step
Show the Fun Training transparency, or distribute it as a handout. Encourage those who approximate the solutions graphically to solve the problem exactly. Some students may want to solve the equation $x(50 - x) = 400$ by saying that $x = 400$ or $50 - x = 400$. Others will struggle to find the vertex form. Suggest that students use rectangle diagrams to help them complete the square, getting $(x - 25)^2 = 225$, so that $x = 10$ or $x = 40$. Encourage students to see how the symmetry about the line $x = 25$ is represented by the expression $25 \pm \sqrt{225}$.

Step 1 If students are having difficulty, ask what number should replace the top question mark to be multiplied by x to get the result in the top right box.

Step 6 As needed, remind students that finding the x-intercepts is the same as finding the roots of the equation.

Step 6

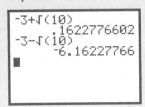

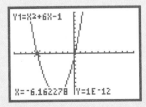

$[-10, 10, 1, -10, 10, 1]$

The x-intercepts are approximately 0.16 and -6.16.

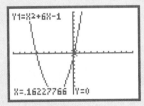

Step 3
a. $(x + 2)^2 = 100$
b. $(x - 3)^2 = 100$
c. $(x - 2.5)^2 = 100$

Step 4 a. $x + 2 = \pm 10$,
$x = 8$ or $x = -12$
b. $x - 3 = \pm 10$,
$x = 13$ or $x = -7$
c. $x - 2.5 = \pm 10$,
$x = 12.5$ or $x = -7.5$

Step 6
$x \approx 0.1622776602$ or
$x \approx -6.16227766$

Step 3

Suppose the area of each diagram in Step 1a–c is 100 square units. For each square, write an equation that you can solve for x by undoing the order of operations.

Step 4

Solve each equation in Step 3 symbolically. You will get two values for x.

The solutions for x in the equations from Step 4 are rational numbers. This means you could have factored the equations with rational numbers. However, the method of completing the square works for other numbers as well. Next you'll consider the solution of an equation that you cannot factor with rational numbers.

Step 5

Consider the equation $x^2 + 6x - 1 = 0$. Describe what's happening in each stage of the solution process.

Stage	Equation	Description
1	$x^2 + 6x - 1 = 0$	Original equation.
2	$x^2 + 6x = 1$	Add 1 to both sides.
3	$x^2 + 6x + 9 = 1 + 9$	Make a perfect-square trinomial by adding 3^2, or 9.

	x	3
x	x^2	$3x$
3	$3x$	9

4	$(x + 3)^2 = 10$	Rewrite the trinomial as a squared binomial.
5	$x + 3 = \pm\sqrt{10}$	Take the square root of both sides.
6	$x = -3 \pm\sqrt{10}$	Subtract 3 from both sides.

Step 6

Use your calculator to find decimal approximations for $-3 + \sqrt{10}$ and $-3 - \sqrt{10}$. Then enter the equation $y = x^2 + 6x - 1$ into Y1. Use a calculator graph or table to check that your answers are the x-intercepts of the equation.

Step 7

Repeat the solution stages in Step 5 to find the solutions to $x^2 + 8x - 5 = 0$.
$x = -4 \pm \sqrt{21}$; $x \approx 0.5826$ or $x \approx -8.5826$

The key to solving by completing the square is to express one side of the equation as a perfect-square trinomial. In the investigation the equations are in the form $y = 1x^2 + bx + c$. Note that the coefficient of x^2, called the **leading coefficient**, is 1. However, there are other perfect-square trinomials. An example is shown at right.

In these cases, the leading coefficient is a perfect-square number. In Example A, you'll learn to complete the square for any quadratic equation in general form.

$4x^2 + 12x + 9$

	$2x$	3
$2x$	$4x^2$	$6x$
3	$6x$	9

$(2x + 3)^2$

SHARING IDEAS

Have groups share ideas for Steps 4 and 7.

[Ask] "Why is the method called *completing the square*?" Encourage students to draw squares when they can't remember the method.

You might challenge students to solve the equation $x^3 + 12x(x + 4) = 274$ by completing a cube. [A cube can be broken down into a cube with edge length x, a diagonally opposite cube with edge length 4, and three 4-by-x-by-$(x + 4)$ slabs. Completing the cube requires adding the volume of the 4-by-4-by-4 cube to both sides of the equation.]

Assessing Progress

Students will demonstrate their ability to solve quadratic equations in vertex form symbolically and to graph and trace equations on a calculator.

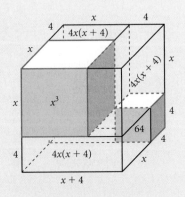

EXAMPLE A | Solve the equation $3x^2 + 18x - 8 = 22$ by completing the square.

▶ **Solution** | First, transform the equation so that you can write the left side as a perfect-square trinomial in the form $x^2 + 2hx + h^2$.

$3x^2 + 18x - 8 = 22$	Original equation.
$3x^2 + 18x = 30$	Add 8 to both sides of the equation.
$x^2 + 6x = 10$	Divide both sides by 3.

Now you need to decide what number to add to both sides to get a perfect-square trinomial on the left side. Use a rectangle diagram to make a square. When you decide what number to add, you must add it to both sides to balance the equation.

$x^2 + 6x + 9 = 10 + 9$	Add 9 to both sides to complete the square.
$(x + 3)^2 = 19$	Write the perfect-square trinomial as a squared binomial and combine any like terms.
$x + 3 = \pm\sqrt{19}$	Take the square root of both sides.
$x = -3 \pm\sqrt{19}$	Add -3 to both sides.

The two solutions are $-3 + \sqrt{19}$, or approximately 1.36, and $-3 - \sqrt{19}$, or approximately -7.36.

You can also complete the square to convert the general form of a quadratic equation to the vertex form.

EXAMPLE B | Find the vertex form of the equation $y = 2x^2 + 12x + 21$. Then identify the vertex and any x-intercepts of the parabola.

▶ **Solution** | To convert $y = 2x^2 + 12x + 21$ to the form $y = a(x - h)^2 + k$, complete the square.

$y = 2x^2 + 12x + 21$	Original equation.
$y = 2(x^2 + 6x) + 21$	Factor the 2 from the coefficients.

Now you can complete the square on the expression inside the parentheses.

The coefficient of x is 6, so divide that by 2 to get 3.

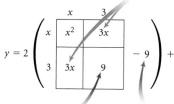

Then add 3^2, or 9, to make a perfect-square trinomial.

You must also subtract 9 inside the parentheses to keep the equation balanced.

▶ **EXAMPLE A**

This example illustrates how to complete the square to solve an equation in which the leading coefficient is not 1.

▶ **EXAMPLE B**

In this example, students also complete the square for an equation in which the leading coefficient is not 1. This time they're transforming an equation from general form to vertex form. Because the x-intercepts involve square roots of negative numbers, they are not real numbers, so the parabola doesn't cross the x-axis. Even roots of negative numbers (including square roots, 4th roots, 6th roots, and so on) are examples of imaginary numbers, with no representation on the number line.

Complex numbers are the subject of Take Another Look at the end of the chapter.

To change a quadratic equation from general form to vertex form or to solve the general form when it's not clear how to factor, you can use a method called **completing the square.** To do so, you factor, if necessary, to be sure the coefficient of x^2 is 1 and then add the square of half the coefficient of the x-term to get a perfect square. Compensate in the rest of the expression or equation for what you have factored and added.

BUILDING UNDERSTANDING

Students practice solving equations by completing the square.

ASSIGNING HOMEWORK

Essential	**1, 2, 4, 6, 7**
Performance assessment	**5, 8, 10**
Portfolio	**9**
Journal	**7**
Group	**3, 9**
Review	**11–13**

▶ Helping with the Exercises

3a. $\left(\dfrac{18}{2}\right)^2$;

$x^2 + 18x + 81 = (x + 9)^2$

3b. $\left(\dfrac{-10}{2}\right)^2$;

$x^2 - 10x + 25 = (x - 5)^2$

3c. $\left(\dfrac{3}{2}\right)^2$; $x^2 + 3x + \dfrac{9}{4} = \left(x + \dfrac{3}{2}\right)^2$

3d. $\left(\dfrac{-1}{2}\right)^2$; $x^2 - x + \dfrac{1}{4} = \left(x - \dfrac{1}{2}\right)^2$

3e. $\left(\dfrac{1}{2} \cdot \dfrac{2}{3}\right)^2$;

$x^2 + \dfrac{2}{3}x + \dfrac{1}{9} = \left(x + \dfrac{1}{3}\right)^2$

3f. $\left(\dfrac{-1.4}{2}\right)^2$;

$x^2 - 1.4x + 0.49 = (x - 0.7)^2$

$$y = 2[(x + 3)^2 - 9] + 21 \qquad \text{Rewrite the expression with a squared binomial.}$$
$$y = 2(x + 3)^2 + 2(-9) + 21 \qquad \text{Distribute the 2.}$$
$$y = 2(x + 3)^2 + 3 \qquad \text{Combine like terms to get the vertex form.}$$

So the vertex is $(-3, 3)$. To find any x-intercepts, you can set $y = 0$ in the vertex form of the equation, then solve symbolically.

$$2(x + 3)^2 + 3 = 0 \qquad \text{Substitute 0 for } y \text{ in the original equation.}$$

$$(x + 3)^2 = \frac{-3}{2} \qquad \text{Subtract 3 and then divide both sides by 2.}$$

$$x = -3 \pm \sqrt{\frac{-3}{2}} \qquad \begin{array}{l}\text{Take the square root and then subtract 3} \\ \text{from both sides.}\end{array}$$

If you try to evaluate $-3 \pm \sqrt{\frac{-3}{2}}$, your calculator may give you an error message about a nonreal answer. These roots are not real numbers because the number under the square root sign is negative, and no real number can be squared to produce a negative number. The set of numbers that includes real numbers and numbers containing even roots of negative numbers is the **complex numbers.** The number-set diagram at the end of Lesson 9.1 can be expanded to include the complex numbers.

Only real numbers appear on a number line, so $y = 2(x + 3)^2 + 3$ has no x-intercepts. The graph confirms this result. Note that the vertex is above the x-axis and the parabola opens upward. So the graph does not cross the x-axis.

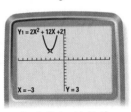

$[-10, 10, 1, -10, 10, 1]$

You can now solve any quadratic equation in general form by completing the square. This process leads to a general formula that you will learn in the next lesson.

EXERCISES

You will need your graphing calculator for Exercises **7, 8, 10, 11,** and **12.**

▶ Practice Your Skills

1. Solve each quadratic equation.
   a. $2(x + 3)^2 - 4 = 0$ @ $x = -3 \pm \sqrt{2}$
   b. $-2(x - 5)^2 + 7 = 3$ @ $x = 5 \pm \sqrt{2}$
   c. $3(x + 8)^2 - 7 = 0$ $\quad x = -8 \pm \sqrt{\dfrac{7}{3}}$
   d. $-5(x + 6)^2 - 3 = -10$ $\quad x = -6 \pm \sqrt{\dfrac{7}{5}}$

2. Solve each equation.
   a. $(x - 5)(x + 3) = 0$ @ $x = 5$ or $x = -3$
   b. $(2x + 6)(x - 7) = 0$ $\quad x = -3$ or $x = 7$
   c. $(3x + 4)(x + 1) = 0$ $\quad x = -\dfrac{4}{3}$ or $x = -1$
   d. $x(x + 6)(x + 9) = 0$ $\quad x = 0$ or $x = -6$ or $x = -9$

3. Decide what number must be added to each expression to make a perfect-square trinomial. Then rewrite the trinomial as a squared binomial.
   a. $x^2 + 18x$ @
   b. $x^2 - 10x$
   c. $x^2 + 3x$
   d. $x^2 - x$
   e. $x^2 + \dfrac{2}{3}x$
   f. $x^2 - 1.4x$

4. Solve each quadratic equation by completing the square. Leave your answer in radical form.

a. $x^2 - 4x - 8 = 0$ @

b. $x^2 + 2x - 1 = -5$

c. $x^2 + 10x - 9 = 0$ $\quad x = -5 \pm \sqrt{34}$

d. $5x^2 + 10x - 7 = 28$ @ $\quad x = -1 \pm \sqrt{8}$

▶ Reason and Apply

5. If you know the vertex and one other point on a parabola, you can find its quadratic equation. The vertex (h, k) of this parabola is $(2, -31.5)$, and the other point is $(5, 0)$. $\qquad y = a(x - 2)^2 - 31.5$

a. Substitute the values for h and k into the equation $y = a(x - h)^2 + k$.

b. To find the value of a, substitute 5 for x and 0 for y. Then solve for a.

c. Use the a-value you found in 5b to write the equation of the graph in vertex form. $\quad y = 3.5(x - 2)^2 - 31.5$

d. Use what you learned in 5a–c to write the equation of the graph whose vertex is $(2, 32)$ and that passes through the point $(5, 14)$. $\quad y = -2(x - 2)^2 + 32$

6. The length of a rectangle is 4 meters more than its width. The area is 12 square meters.

a. Define variables and write an equation for the area of the rectangle in terms of its width. @

b. Solve your equation in 6a by completing the square.

c. Which solution in 6b makes sense for the width of the rectangle? What is the corresponding length? $\quad$ The width cannot be negative, so it must be 2 m. The length is 4 m more than the width, so the length is 6 m.

7. Consider the equation $y = x^2 + 6x + 10$.

a. Convert this equation to vertex form by completing the square.

$7a. \quad y = x^2 + 6x + \left(\dfrac{6}{2}\right)^2 - 3^2 + 10$

$y = x^2 + 6x + 9 - 9 + 10$

$y = (x + 3)^2 + 1$

b. Find the vertex. Graph both equations.

c. Find the roots of the equation $0 = x^2 + 6x + 10$. What happens and why?

8. APPLICATION A professional football team uses computers to describe the projectile motion of a football when punted. After compiling data from several games, the computer models the height of an average punt with the equation

$$h(t) = \frac{-16}{3}(t - 2.2)^2 + 26.9$$

where t is the time in seconds and $h(t)$ is the height in yards. The punter's foot makes contact with the ball when $t = 0$.

a. When does the punt reach its highest point? How high does the football go? @ $\quad$ 2.2 s; 26.9 yd (80.7 ft)

b. Find the zeros of $h(t) = \frac{-16}{3}(t - 2.2)^2 + 26.9$. Which solution is the hang time—that is, the time it takes until the ball hits the ground? $\quad$ 4.446 s

c. How high is the ball when the punter kicks it? @

d. Graph the equation. What are the real-world meanings of the vertex, the y-intercept, and the x-intercepts? @ See page 530.

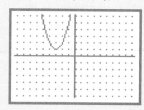

Brad Maynard punts for the New York Giants.

$7c. \quad x^2 + 6x + 10 = 0$

$x^2 + 6x = -10$

$x^2 + 6x + 9 = -10 + 9$

$(x + 3)^2 = -1$

$x + 3 = \pm\sqrt{-1}$

$x = -3 \pm\sqrt{-1}$

Sample answer: There are no real roots because the graph doesn't cross the x-axis.

Exercise 8 The coefficient $-\frac{16}{3}$ results from converting the gravitational constant -16 ft/s² to yd/s².

$8b. \quad t = 2.2 \pm \sqrt{-26.9 \cdot \dfrac{3}{-16}}$,

$t \approx -0.046$ or $t \approx 4.446$

$8c.$ The general form is $\frac{-16}{3}t^2 + 23.4\overline{6}t + 1.08\overline{6}$, so the football is about 1 yd high.

$4a. \quad x^2 - 4x - 8 = 0$

$x^2 - 4x = 8$

$x^2 - 4x + 4 = 12$

$(x - 2)^2 = 12$

$x - 2 = \pm\sqrt{12}$

$x = 2 \pm\sqrt{12}$

$4b. \quad x^2 + 2x - 1 = -5$

$x^2 + 2x = -4$

$x^2 + 2x + 1 = -3$

$(x + 1)^2 = -3$

$x + 1 = \pm\sqrt{-3}$

$x = -1 \pm\sqrt{-3}$

There are no real roots.

Exercise 5b Some students may have difficulty understanding that the equation is satisfied by coordinates of any point that lies on the parabola.

5b. Solve the equation $0 = a(5 - 2)^2 - 31.5$; $a = 3.5$.

6a. Let w represent the width in meters. Let l represent the length in meters. Then $l = w + 4$. The area equation is $w(w + 4) = 12$.

6b. $\qquad w^2 + 4w = 12$

$w^2 + 4w + 4 = 12 + 4$

$(w + 2)^2 = 16$

$w + 2 = \pm 4$

$w = -2 \pm 4$

$w = -6$ or $w = 2$

7b. vertex: $(-3, 1)$;

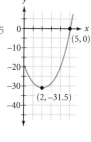

$[-9.4, 9.4, 1, -6.2, 6.2, 1]$

Exercise 7c Students might answer the "why" question in a variety of ways. For example, some may refer to translations (seen from the vertex form of the equation) and others to square roots of negative numbers.

8d. The vertex is the maximum height of the ball. The y-intercept is the height of the ball when the punter kicks it. The positive x-intercept is the hang time. The other x-intercept has no real-world meaning.

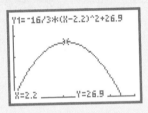

$[0, 5, 1, 0, 40, 10]$

Exercise 9 Some students might benefit from making a chart with various sizes of groups.

9a. $p = 2500 - 5x$, where p represents the price in dollars of a single ticket and x represents the number of tickets sold.

9c. Let C represent the total price of the group package. $C = -5(x - 250)^2 + 312{,}500$

Exercise 10 Students may miss the fact that $P(b)$ represents a rate of growth rather than the bear population itself, which is given by b. The rate of change is zero when the population achieves a maximum or minimum. 10d might especially confuse students: They might say, "When there are 101 bears, the growth rate is negative, but that doesn't mean there can't be 101 bears." That argument is valid even though the mathematical model has a maximum at $b = 100$.

10a. $P(10) = 0.9$; this means that when there are 10 bears in the park, the population grows at a rate of 0.9 bear per year.

10b. $P(b) = 0$ when $b = 0$ or $b = 100$; when there are no bears, the population does not grow, and when there are 100 bears, the population does not grow but remains at that level.

10c. The vertex lies halfway between the roots, 0 and 100, so the population is growing fastest when there are 50 bears.

---

9. **APPLICATION** The Cruisin' Along Company is determining prices for its Caribbean cruise packages. The basic price is $2,500 per person. However, business is slow. To attract corporate clients, the company reduces the price of each ticket by $5 for each person in the group. The larger the group, the less each person pays.

  a. Define variables and write an equation for the price of a single ticket. ⓐ

  b. Write an equation for the total price the company charges for a group package. ⓐ $C = xp = x(2500 - 5x)$

  c. Convert the equation in 9b to vertex form.

  d. What is the total price of a cruise for a group of 20 people? $C(20) = 20(2{,}500 - 100) = 48{,}000;\ \$48{,}000$

  e. The company accountant reports that the cost of running a cruise is $200,000. Solve the equation
$$x(2500 - 5x) = 200{,}000$$
by completing the square. See below.

  f. What limitations on group size should the cruise company use in order to make a profit? ⓗ   To earn a profit, the cruise company should only allow between 100 and 400 people.

10. **APPLICATION** The rate at which a bear population grows in a park is given by the equation $P(b) = 0.001b(100 - b)$. The function value $P(b)$ represents the rate at which the population is growing in bears per year, and b represents the number of bears.

  a. Find $P(10)$ and provide a real-world meaning for this value. ⓐ

  b. Solve $P(b) = 0$ and provide real-world meanings for these solutions. ⓐ

  c. For what size bear population would the population grow fastest?

  d. What is the maximum number of bears the park can support?

  e. What does it mean to say that $P(120) < 0$?
It means that if 120 bears were brought in, the population would shrink, due to overpopulation.

> ## Review

9.3   **11.** Find each product. Check your answers by using calculator tables or graphs.

  a. $(x + 1)(2x^2 + 3x + 1)$ $2x^3 + 5x^2 + 4x + 1$ **b.** $(2x - 5)(3x^2 + 2x - 4)$
$$6x^3 - 11x^2 - 18x + 20$$

9.3   **12.** Combine like terms in these polynomials. Check your answers by using calculator tables or graphs.

  a. $(x + 1) + (2x^2 + 3x + 1)$ $2x^2 + 4x + 2$ **b.** $(2x - 5) + (3x^2 + 2x - 4)$ $3x^2 + 4x - 9$

  c. $(x + 1) - (2x^2 + 3x + 1)$ ⓐ $-2x^2 - 2x$ **d.** $(2x - 5) - (3x^2 + 2x - 4)$ $-3x^2 - 1$

9.4   **13.** Solve each equation by converting to the form $ax^2 + bx + c = 0$ if necessary, then factoring and using the zero-product property. Verify your answers using substitution.

  a. $x^2 - 4x = 0$ $x = 0$ or $x = 4$ **b.** $x^2 + 2x - 3 = 0$ $x = 1$ or $x = -3$

  c. $x^2 - 3x = 4$ $x = 4$ or $x = -1$ **d.** $2x^2 - 11x + 15 = 0$ $x = 3$ or $x = \dfrac{5}{2}$

  e. $5x^2 - 13x + 8 = 0$ $x = 1$ or $x = \dfrac{8}{5}$ **f.** $3x^2 - 8 = -5x$ ⓐ $x = 1$ or $x = -\dfrac{8}{3}$

10d. Because the population does not grow when there are 100 bears, this value must be the maximum population.

Exercise 11 Making a 2-by-3 rectangle can help with each of these products.

9e.
$$2{,}500x - 5x^2 = 200{,}000$$
$$500x - x^2 = 40{,}000$$
$$x^2 - 500x = -40{,}000$$
$$x^2 - 500x + 250^2 = 250^2 - 40{,}000$$
$$(x - 250)^2 = 22{,}500$$
$$x - 250 = \pm 150$$
$$x = 100 \text{ or } x = 400$$

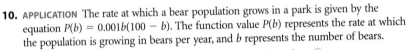

*Most people are more
comfortable with old problems
than with new solutions.*

ANONYMOUS

The Quadratic Formula

You have learned several methods for solving quadratic equations symbolically. Completing the square is particularly useful because it can be used for any quadratic equation. But if your equation is something like $y = 0.2x^2 + \frac{365}{17}x + \frac{2}{19}$, completing the square will be very messy! In this lesson you'll find a formula that solves any quadratic equation in the form $ax^2 + bx + c = 0$ directly, using only the values of a, b, and c. It is called the **quadratic formula.**

Recall that you can solve some quadratic equations symbolically by recognizing their forms:

Vertex form	$-4.9(t - 5)^2 + 75 = 0$
Factored form	$0 = w(200 - 2w)$
Perfect-square trinomial	$x^2 + 6x + 9 = 0$

You can also undo the order of operations in other quadratic equations when there is no x-term, as in these:

$$x^2 = 10$$
$$(x + 5)^2 = 0$$
$$x^2 - 0.36 = 0$$

If the quadratic expression is in the form $x^2 + bx + c$, you can complete the square by using a rectangle diagram.

	x	$\frac{b}{2}$
x	x^2	$\frac{b}{2}x$
$\frac{b}{2}$	$\frac{b}{2}x$	$\left(\frac{b}{2}\right)^2$

In the investigation you'll use the completing-the-square method to derive the quadratic formula.

Investigation
Deriving the Quadratic Formula

You'll solve $2x^2 + 3x - 1 = 0$ and develop the quadratic formula for the general case in the process.

Step 1	Identify the values of a, b, and c in the general form, $ax^2 + bx + c = 0$, for the equation $2x^2 + 3x - 1 = 0$. $a = 2, b = 3, c = -1$
Step 2	Group all the variable terms on the left side of your equation so that it is in the form $$ax^2 + bx = -c \quad 2x^2 + 3x = 1$$

PLANNING

LESSON OUTLINE

One day:

25 min	Investigation
5 min	Sharing
5 min	Example
5 min	Closing
10 min	Exercises

MATERIALS

• The Quadratic Formula (T), *optional*

TEACHING

Because completing the square can be labor-intensive, especially when the coefficient of x^2 is not 1, we often use a shortcut called the *quadratic formula.*

 Guiding the Investigation

One Step
Ask students to solve the general-form quadratic equation $ax^2 + bx + c = 0$ by completing the square. For those having difficulty, suggest that they solve a problem with numbers along with the generalization.

Step 1 There is again great potential for students to confuse letters representing constant coefficients (a, b, c) with the letter x representing the independent variable.

NCTM STANDARDS

CONTENT		PROCESS	
	Number		Problem Solving
✔	Algebra	✔	Reasoning
	Geometry	✔	Communication
	Measurement	✔	Connections
	Data/Probability	✔	Representation

LESSON OBJECTIVES

• Study the derivation of the quadratic formula

• Learn to use the quadratic formula

• Use the discriminant to determine the nature of the roots of a quadratic equation

Steps 3–5 Some students may want to imitate what they did earlier by factoring out a, but not dividing through by it, to get $a\left(x^2 + \frac{b}{a}x\right) = -c$ and then $a\left(x^2 + \frac{b}{a}x + \frac{b^2}{4a^2}\right) - \frac{b^2}{4a} = -c$, or $a\left(x + \frac{b}{2a}\right)^2 = -c + \frac{b^2}{4a}$. Continuing with this approach will yield the standard quadratic formula, though with somewhat more difficult computations than those in the student text.

Step 4

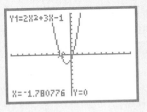

$\frac{9}{16}; \quad x^2 + \frac{3}{2}x + \left(\frac{3}{4}\right)^2 = \left(\frac{3}{4}\right)^2 + \frac{1}{2}$

Step 9 $x \approx -1.7870776406$ or $x \approx 0.2807764064$

Y1=2X²+3X−1

X=-1.780776 Y=0

X	Y1
-1.719	-.2462
-.7192	-2.123
.2808	0
1.2808	6.1231
2.2808	16.246
3.2808	30.369
4.2808	48.492

X=.2807764064044

Step 10 Besides answering that $b^2 - 4ac$ must not be negative, students may point out that a cannot be zero. Ask when that would be the case, but save the answer for Sharing.

SHARING IDEAS

Point out that in solving equations with letters instead of numbers, students should develop the habit of being especially careful not to divide by zero. From Step 3 onward in the investigation, a is in the divisor. Ask if that could lead to difficulties. Indeed, none of these steps hold if $a = 0$, but in that case the equation would be linear, not quadratic.

Step 3 $x^2 + \frac{3}{2}x = \frac{1}{2}$ **Step 3**

Step 4

Step 5 $\left(x + \frac{3}{4}\right)^2 = \frac{9}{16} + \frac{8}{16}$ **Step 5**

Step 6   **Step 6**
$x + \frac{3}{4} = \pm\frac{\sqrt{9+8}}{\sqrt{16}}$

Step 7   **Step 7**
$x = -\frac{3}{4} \pm \frac{\sqrt{17}}{4}$

Step 8   **Step 8**
$x = \frac{-3 + \sqrt{17}}{4}$ or
$x = \frac{-3 - \sqrt{17}}{4}$

Step 10 To avoid   **Step 9**
dividing by
zero, $a \neq 0$.   **Step 10**
To avoid square roots of
negative numbers, $b^2 - 4ac \geq 0$.

Step 3 It's easiest to complete the square when the coefficient of x^2 is 1. So divide your equation by the value of a. Write it in the form

$$x^2 + \frac{b}{a}x = \frac{-c}{a}$$

Step 4 Use a rectangle diagram to help you complete the square. What number must you add to both sides? Write your new equation in the form

$$x^2 + \frac{b}{a}x + \left(\frac{b}{2a}\right)^2 = \left(\frac{b}{2a}\right)^2 - \frac{c}{a}$$

Step 5 Rewrite the trinomial on the left side of your equation as a squared binomial. On the right side, find a common denominator. Write the next stage of your equation in the form

$$\left(x + \frac{b}{2a}\right)^2 = \frac{b^2}{4a^2} - \frac{4ac}{4a^2}$$

Step 6 Take the square root of both sides of your equation, like this:

$$x + \frac{b}{2a} = \pm\frac{\sqrt{b^2 - 4ac}}{\sqrt{4a^2}}$$

Step 7 Rewrite $\sqrt{4a^2}$ as $2a$. Then get x by itself on the left side, like this:

$$x = -\frac{b}{2a} \pm \frac{\sqrt{b^2 - 4ac}}{2a}$$

Step 8 There are two possible solutions given by the equations

$$x = \frac{-b + \sqrt{b^2 - 4ac}}{2a} \quad \text{or} \quad x = \frac{-b - \sqrt{b^2 - 4ac}}{2a}$$

Write your two solutions in radical form.

Step 9 Write your solutions in decimal form. Check them with a graph and a table.

Step 10 Consider the expression $\frac{-b \pm \sqrt{b^2 - 4ac}}{2a}$. What restrictions should there be so that the solutions exist and are real numbers?

The quadratic formula gives the same solutions that completing the square or factoring does. You don't need to derive the formula each time. All you need to know are the values of a, b, and c. Then you substitute these values into the formula.

> ### Quadratic Formula
>
> If a quadratic equation is written in the general form, $ax^2 + bx + c = 0$, the roots are given by $x = \frac{-b \pm \sqrt{b^2 - 4ac}}{2a}$.

In the next example you'll learn how to use the formula for quadratic equations in general form. You can even use it when the values of a, b, and c are decimals or fractions.

[Ask] "What would happen if $b^2 - 4ac$ equaled zero?" [There would be only one root, a double root. The parabolic graph would have its vertex on the x-axis.]

Ask about the quotation opening the lesson. Are your students more comfortable completing the square than using the quadratic formula?

If your students must memorize the quadratic formula at this point, you might teach them a song. Many students like the one to the tune of *Pop Goes the Weasel*, starting "x equals opposite of b . . . ."

Assessing Progress
Watch for students' skill at substituting numbers for letters, completing the square, and using calculator graphs and tables.

EXAMPLE | Use the quadratic formula to solve $3x^2 + 5x - 7 = 0$.

▶ **Solution** | The equation is already in general form, so identify the values of a, b, and c. For this equation, $a = 3$, $b = 5$, and $c = -7$. Here is one way to use the formula:

$$x = \frac{-b \pm \sqrt{b^2 - 4ac}}{2a}$$

The quadratic formula.

$$= \frac{-(\ ) \pm \sqrt{(\ )^2 - 4(\ )(\ )}}{2(\ )}$$

Replace each letter in the formula with a set of parentheses.

$$= \frac{-(5) \pm \sqrt{(5)^2 - 4(3)(-7)}}{2(3)}$$

Substitute the values of a, b, and c into the appropriate places.

$$= \frac{-5 \pm \sqrt{25 - (-84)}}{6}$$

Do the operations.

$$= \frac{-5 \pm \sqrt{109}}{6}$$

Subtract.

The two exact roots of the equation are $\frac{-5 + \sqrt{109}}{6}$ and $\frac{-5 - \sqrt{109}}{6}$.

You can use your calculator to calculate the approximate values, 0.907 and -2.573, respectively.

To make the formula simpler, think of the expression under the square root sign as one number. This expression, $b^2 - 4ac$, is called the **discriminant.** In the example the discriminant is 109. So let $d = b^2 - 4ac$. Then the formula becomes

$$x = \frac{-b \pm \sqrt{d}}{2a}$$

If you store these values into your calculator as shown, then you can use the formula directly on your calculator.

EXERCISES

You will need your graphing calculator for Exercises **4** and **13**.

▶ Practice Your Skills

1. Without using a calculator, evaluate the expression $b^2 - 4ac$ for the values given. Then check your answers with a calculator.

   a. $a = 3, b = 5, c = 2$ ⓐ $25 - 24 = 1$ **b.** $a = 1, b = -3, c = -3$ $9 - (-12) = 9 + 12 = 21$

   c. $a = -2, b = -6, c = -3$ ⓐ $36 - 24 = 12$ **d.** $a = 9, b = 9, c = 0$ $81 - 0 = 81$

▶ **EXAMPLE**

Encourage students to use parentheses as illustrated in the first step after the formula statement. Doing so helps them avoid errors such as writing -3^2 for b^2 if $b = -3$.

The calculator button $\boxed{\text{STO}}$ is used here to store values for a, b, and c. You may need to review this with your students. Also, you might have students write a calculator program that solves quadratic equations using the quadratic formula.

Closing the Lesson

The **quadratic formula** can be used instead of completing the square. It's derived by completing the square on the general quadratic equation. It yields two solutions, $y = \frac{-b \pm \sqrt{b^2 - 4ac}}{2a}$, though they're the same if the square root has the value 0. **[ELL]** *Derive* means to obtain a result from an original true statement by means of step-by-step reasoning.

BUILDING UNDERSTANDING

Students solve quadratic equations using the quadratic formula.

ASSIGNING HOMEWORK

Essential	**1–4, 6, 7**
Performance assessment	**6, 9**
Portfolio	**5**
Journal	**7, 8**
Group	**5, 8, 10, 11**
Review	**12, 13**

2d. $-4.9x^2 + 47x + 18 = 0$;
$a = -4.9, b = 47, c = 18$

3a. $x = \dfrac{3 \pm \sqrt{-23}}{4}$; there are no

real solutions.

3c. Complete the square.

$x^2 - 6x - 8 = 0$

$\quad x^2 - 6x = 8$

$x^2 - 6x + 9 = 17$

$\quad (x - 3)^2 = 17$

$\quad\quad x - 3 = \pm\sqrt{17}$

$\quad\quad\quad x = 3 \pm\sqrt{17}$

Exercise 4 Students should conclude that the sign of the discriminant (the value under the square root) is the key to this determination. This exercise is similar to Lesson 9.6, Exercise 7, but the solution is different now that students know the quadratic formula.

4a. The graph does not cross the x-axis.

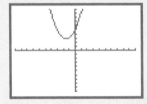

$[-10, 10, 1, -10, 10, 1]$

4b. To use the quadratic formula, $a = 1$, $b = 3$, and $c = 5$;
$x = \dfrac{-3 \pm \sqrt{-11}}{2}$.

There are no real square roots of negative numbers, so there are no real roots.

5a. $-4.9t^2 + 6.2t + 1.9 = 0$;
$t \approx -0.255$ s or $t \approx 1.52$ s; the ball hits the ground 1.52 s after Brandi heads it.

5b. $-4.9t^2 + 6.2t + 1.9 = 3$;
$t \approx 0.21$ s or $t \approx 1.05$ s; the ball is 3 m above the ground after 0.21 s (on the way up) and after 1.05 s (on the way down).

5c. $-4.9t^2 + 6.2t + 1.9 = 4$;
$t \approx \dfrac{-6.2 \pm \sqrt{-2.72}}{-9.8}$; this equation has no real solution, so the ball is never 4 m high.

2. Rewrite each quadratic equation in general form if necessary. For each equation, identify the values of a, b, and c.

a. $2x^2 + 3x - 7 = 0$ $\quad a = 2, b = 3, c = -7$

b. $x^2 + 6x = -11$ ⓐ $\quad$ $x^2 + 6x + 11 = 0; a = 1, b = 6, c = 11$

c. $-3x^2 - 4x + 12 = 0$ $\quad a = -3, b = -4, c = 12$

d. $18 - 4.9x^2 + 47x = 0$ ⓐ

e. $-16x^2 + 28x + 10 = 57$
$-16x^2 + 28x - 47 = 0; a = -16, b = 28, c = -47$

f. $5x^2 - 2x = 7 + 4x$
$\quad 5x^2 - 6x - 7 = 0; a = 5, b = -6, c = -7$

3. Solve each quadratic equation. Which equation can you solve readily by completing the square? Which equation has no real solutions?

a. $2x^2 - 3x + 4 = 0$ ⓐ

b. $-2x^2 + 7x = 3$ $\quad$ Use the quadratic equation or complete the square; $x = \frac{1}{2}$ or $x = 3$.

c. $x^2 - 6x - 8 = 0$

d. $3x^2 + 2x - 1 = 5$ $\quad$ Use the quadratic formula; $x = \dfrac{-2 \pm \sqrt{76}}{6} = \dfrac{-1 \pm \sqrt{19}}{3}$.

▶ **Reason and Apply**

4. Graph the equation $y = x^2 + 3x + 5$. Use the graph and the quadratic formula to answer these questions.

a. How many x-intercepts does the graph have?

b. Use the quadratic formula to try to find the roots of $0 = x^2 + 3x + 5$. What happens when you take the square root?

c. Without looking at a graph, how can you use the quadratic formula to tell if a quadratic equation has any real roots? ⓐ $\quad$ If the discriminant is negative, there are no real roots. If it is positive or zero, there are real roots.

5. The equation $h = -4.9t^2 + 6.2t + 1.9$ models the height of a soccer ball after Brandi hits it with her head. The t-values represent the time in seconds, and the h-values represent the height in meters. Write an equation that describes each event in 5a–c. Then use the quadratic formula to solve it. Explain the real-world meanings of your solutions.

a. The ball hits the ground. ⓐ

b. The ball is 3 meters above ground. ⓐ

c. The ball is 4 meters above ground. ⓐ

6. Find an equation whose solutions as x-intercepts are shown. Evaluate each expression to the nearest tenth. Make a sketch showing a parabola that has these solutions as x-intercepts. ⓗ

a. $\dfrac{14 \pm \sqrt{(-14)^2 - 4(1)(49)}}{2(1)}$ ⓐ

b. $\dfrac{3 \pm \sqrt{(-3)^2 - 4(2)(2)}}{2(2)}$

c. $\dfrac{3 \pm \sqrt{(-3)^2 - 4(2)(-2)}}{2(2)}$

Brandi Chastain of the USA team heads a soccer ball during the 1999 Women's World Cup at Stanford Stadium.

6a. Sample equation: $0 = x^2 - 14x + 49$. The x-intercept is 7.

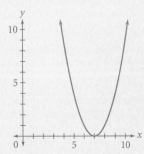

6b. Sample equation: $0 = 2x^2 - 3x + 2$. There are no x-intercepts.

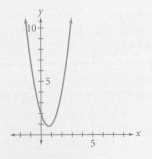

7. Match each quadratic equation with its graph. Then explain how to use the discriminant, $b^2 - 4ac$, to find the number of x-intercepts.

a. $y = x^2 + x + 1$

b. $y = x^2 + 2x + 1$

c. $y = x^2 + 3x + 1$

i.   **ii.**   **iii.**

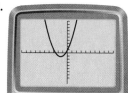

8. *Mini-Investigation* The quadratic formula gives two roots of an equation:

$$x = \frac{-b + \sqrt{b^2 - 4ac}}{2a} \quad \text{and} \quad x = \frac{-b - \sqrt{b^2 - 4ac}}{2a}$$

What is the average of these two roots? How does averaging the roots help you find the vertex? The average of the roots is $\frac{-b}{2a}$; it is the x-coordinate of the vertex of the parabola.

9. The equation $h = -4.9t^2 + 17t + 2.2$ models the height of a stone thrown into the air, where t is in seconds and h is in meters. Use the quadratic formula to find how long the stone is in the air. ⓗ

10. APPLICATION A shopkeeper is redesigning the rectangular sign on her store's rooftop. She wants the largest area possible for the sign. When she considers adding an amount to the width, she subtracts that same amount from the length. Her original sign has width 4 m and length 7 m.

a. Complete the table. ⓗ

Increase (x) (m)	Width (m)	Length (m)	Area (m²)	Perimeter (m)
0	4	7	28	22
0.5	4.5	6.5	29.25	22
1.0	5	6	30	22
1.5	5.5	5.5	30.25	22
2.0	6	5	30	22

b. How do the changes in width and length affect the perimeter? The perimeter does not change.

c. How do the changes in width and length affect the area? The area increases and then decreases.

d. Write an equation in factored form for the area A of the rectangle in terms of x, the amount she adds to the width. $A = (4 + x)(7 - x)$

e. What are the dimensions of the rectangle with the largest area?

11. Algebraically find the intersection points, if any, of the graphs of $y = x^2 + 4x + 2$ and $y = 0.5x + 4$. ⓐ $(0.5, 4.25)$ and $(-4, 2)$

7. When $b^2 - 4ac$ is negative, there are no real roots. When it's zero, there is one root. When it's positive, there are two roots.

7a. i; $1^2 - 4(1)(1) = -3$; no x-intercept

7b. iii; $2^2 - 4(1)(1) = 0$; one x-intercept

7c. ii; $3^2 - 4(1)(1) = 5$; two x-intercepts

Exercise 8 Students might find the averaging here to be a challenge.

9. You need to know the t-value when $h = 0$.

Solve the equation $0 = -4.9t^2 + 17t + 2.2$ with $a = -4.9$, $b = 17$, $c = 2.2$ to get $t \approx -0.125$ or $t \approx 3.59$. The positive solution, 3.59 s, makes sense in this situation.

10e. The largest area occurs at the vertex of the parabola, which is at $x = 1.5$. At this point the rectangle has dimensions 5.5 m by 5.5 m, which means the rectangle is a square.

6c. Sample equation: $0 = 2x^2 - 3x - 2$. The x-intercepts are -0.5 and 2.

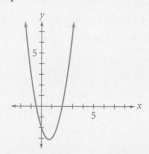

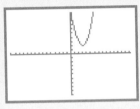
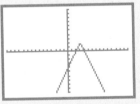
▶ **Review**

9.4 **12.** Reduce each rational expression by factoring, then canceling common factors. State any restrictions on the variable.

a. $\dfrac{x^2 - 5x + 6}{x - 3}$ @

b. $\dfrac{x^2 + 7x + 6}{x + 1}$

c. $\dfrac{2x^2 - x - 1}{2x + 1}$

d. $\dfrac{x^2 - 2x - 15}{x^2 - 3x - 10}$

e. $\dfrac{x^2 + 10x + 24}{x^2 + 2x - 24}$

8.4 **13.** On your graph paper, sketch graphs of these equations. Then use your calculator to check your sketches.

a. $y - 2 = (x - 3)^2$

b. $y - 2 = -2|x - 3|$

IMPROVING YOUR REASONING SKILLS

In Chapter 2, you may have done the project The Golden Ratio. Now you have the tools to calculate this number. One way to calculate the golden ratio is to add 1 to square it. The symbolic statement of this rule is $x^2 = x + 1$ $\left(\text{or } x = \sqrt{x + 1}\right)$.

You can approximate this value using a recursive routine on your calculator.

This is the same as calculating $\sqrt{1 + \sqrt{1 + \sqrt{1 + \sqrt{1 + \ldots}}}}$

You can also divide both sides of $x^2 = x + 1$ by x to get $x = 1 + \frac{1}{x}$.

You can use another recursive routine to approximate x this time.

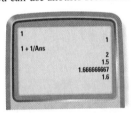

This is the same as calculating $1 + \cfrac{1}{1 + \cfrac{1}{1 + \cfrac{1}{1 + \ldots}}}$

Try different starting values for these recursive routines. Do they always result in the same number? Use one of the methods you learned in this chapter to solve $x^2 = x + 1$ symbolically. What are the answers in radical form? Can you write a recursive routine for the negative solution?

IMPROVING REASONING SKILLS

Students can begin with any number that avoids dividing by zero or taking the square root of a negative. For example, for the square root recursion, they might type 17 (ENTER). The recursive step is given by $\sqrt{}$ (1 + ANS) (ENTER). Repeatedly typing (ENTER) gives the sequence. For the

continued fraction, they could type −3 (ENTER), and then 1 + 1/ANS (ENTER). Repeatedly typing (ENTER) again gives the sequence.

Actually, students had the tools to approximate the value of the Golden Ratio some time ago. Now they can calculate it exactly,

using the quadratic formula. The solutions to the equation $x^2 = x + 1$ are $x = \dfrac{1 \pm \sqrt{5}}{2}$, with approximations 1.618033989 and −0.6180339887. The negative value can be approximated through a routine whose recursive step is −1/(1 − ANS).

Cubic Functions

In this lesson you'll learn about cubic equations, which are often used to model volume. You'll see that some of the techniques you've used with quadratic equations can be applied to cubic equations, too.

The area of the square at right is 16 square meters (m^2), so you can cover the square using 16 smaller squares, each 1 m by 1 m. The sides of a square are equal, so you can write its area formula as *area* $= side^2$. The squaring function, $f(x) = x^2$, models area. Each side length, or input, gives exactly one area, or output.

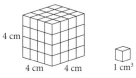

The volume of the cube at right is 64 cubic centimeters (cm^3), so you can fill the cube using 64 smaller cubes, each measuring 1 cm by 1 cm by 1 cm. The edges of a cube have equal length, so you can write its volume formula as *volume* $= (edge\ length)^3$. The **cubing function,** $f(x) = x^3$, models volume. Each edge length, or input, gives exactly one volume, or output.

What is the volume of a Rubik's cube?

The edge length of a cube with a volume of 64 is 4. So you can write $4^3 = 64$. You call 4 the **cube root** of 64 and the number 64 a **perfect cube** because its cube root is an integer. Then you can express the equation as $4 = \sqrt[3]{64}$. You can evaluate cubes and cube roots with your calculator. [▶ 🖳 See **Calculator Note 9B.** ◀]

Graphs of cubic functions have different and interesting shapes. In the window $-5 \le x \le 5$ and $-4 \le y \le 4$, the parent function $y = x^3$ looks like the graph shown.

EXAMPLE A

Write an equation for each graph.

a.

b.

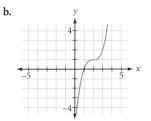

PLANNING

LESSON OUTLINE

One day:

5 min	Introduction
5 min	Example A
15 min	Investigation
5 min	Sharing
10 min	Examples B and C
5 min	Closing
5 min	Exercises

MATERIALS

- Stunt Flying (T or W), *optional*
- Calculator Note 9B
- Fathom demonstration When Is It Safe to Drive?, *optional*

TEACHING

The relationships among roots, x-intercepts, and the factored form of a cubic equation are like those of a quadratic equation.

INTRODUCTION

You might introduce the word *prism.* Just as a square is a special kind of rectangle where $l = w$, a cube is a special case of a right rectangular prism where $l = w = h$.

Besides the method described in Calculator Note 9B, students might find cube roots by guess-and-check or by graphing and tracing $y = x^3$.

NCTM STANDARDS

CONTENT		PROCESS	
✔	Number	✔	Problem Solving
✔	Algebra	✔	Reasoning
✔	Geometry	✔	Communication
	Measurement		Connections
	Data/Probability	✔	Representation

LESSON OBJECTIVES

- Explore general patterns and characteristics of cubic functions
- Learn formulas that model the areas of squares and the volumes of cubes
- Explore the graphs of cubic functions and transformations of these graphs
- Write the equation of a cubic function from its graph

► **EXAMPLE A**

This example helps students review transformations. **[Ask]** "What are the similarities between transformations of $y = x^2$ and those of $y = x^3$?" If you discussed the Take Another Look activity in Chapter 7, you might review inverses by asking whether students think the inverse of $y = x^3$ is a function. They might benefit from solving to get $x = y^{1/3}$ and then seeing its graph.

Guiding the Investigation

One Step
Pose the problem on the Stunt Flying transparency or work-sheet. Students may be baffled at first. Keep assuring them that they have the ability to think through difficult problems. Some will try to graph the path of the stunt plane. Remind them that the question is about the plane's rate equation. (In fact, not enough information is given to determine the flight path.) Focus attention on the main information given: the times at which the plane changed direction—that is, the times at which its velocity was actually zero. Then ask whether a parabola could cross the x-axis three times, and encourage students to think of equations with an x^3 term. Finally, if necessary, suggest that they use a factored form. Even after they graph the rate function, they may be confused because it is decreasing at first, when the plane is rising. Keep reminding them that the cubic equation is a rate equation and that when it's positive the height is increasing.

► **Solution**

a. Each graph is a transformation of the graph of $y = x^3$. The graph shows a translation of the parent function down 1 unit. So the equation is $y = x^3 - 1$.

b. The graph of $y = x^3$ is translated right 2 units and up 1 unit. So the equation is $y - 1 = (x - 2)^3$.

Not all cubic equations and graphs are transformations of $y = x^3$, as you'll see in the investigation.

Investigation
Rooting for Factors

In this investigation you'll discover a relationship between the factored form of a cubic equation and its graph.

Step 1 | List the x-intercepts for each of these graphs.

Graph A

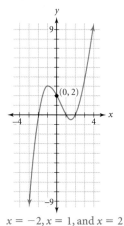

$x = -2, x = 1,$ and $x = 2$

Graph B

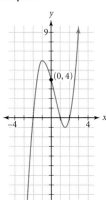

$x = -2, x = 1,$ and $x = 2$

Graph C

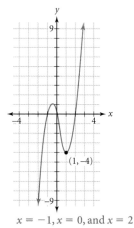

$x = -1, x = 0,$ and $x = 2$

Graph D

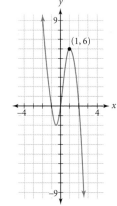

$x = -1, x = 0,$ and $x = 2$

Graph E

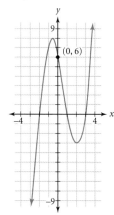

$x = -2, x = 1,$ and $x = 3$

Graph F

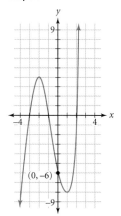

$x = -3, x = -1,$ and $x = 2$

Step 2
a. Graph F
b. Graph C
c. Graph A
d. Graph D
e. Graph B
f. Graph E

Step 2 | Each equation below matches exactly one graph in Step 1. Use graphs and tables to find the matches.

a. $y = (x + 3)(x + 1)(x - 2)$ **b.** $y = 2x(x + 1)(x - 2)$
c. $y = (x + 2)(x - 1)(x - 2)$ **d.** $y = -3x(x + 1)(x - 2)$
e. $y = 0.5(x + 2)(x - 1)(x - 2)$ **f.** $y = (x + 2)(x - 1)(x - 3)$

Step 3 | Describe how the x-intercepts you found in Step 1 relate to the factored forms of the equations in Step 2.

Now you'll write an equation from a graph.

Step 4 | Use what you discovered in Steps 1–3 to write an equation with the same x-intercepts as the graph shown. Graph your equation; then adjust your equation to match the graph.

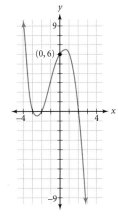

(0, 6)

When you can identify the zeros of a function, you can write its equation in factored form.

EXAMPLE B | Find an equation for the graph shown.

▶ **Solution** | There are three x-intercepts on the graph. They are $x = 0$, -1, and 2. Each intercept helps you find a factor in the equation. These factors are x, $x + 1$, and $x - 2$. Graph the equation $y = x(x + 1)(x - 2)$ on your calculator. The shape is correct, but you need to reflect it across the x-axis. You also need to vertically stretch the graph. Check the y-value of your graph at $x = 1$. The y-value is -2. You need it to be 4, so multiply by -2. The correct equation is $y = -2x(x + 1)(x - 2)$. Check this equation by graphing it on your calculator.

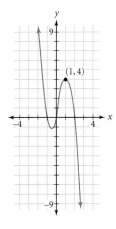

(1, 4)

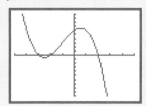

▶ EXAMPLE B

This example helps students see how to find the equation of a cubic function given the *x*-intercepts of its graph and a point to determine the stretch factor.

A parabola that touches the *x*-axis at one point also has a double root. A sample equation is $y = (x - 1)^2$.

Students have seen that a quadratic equation can have zero, one, or two real roots. **[Ask]** "How many real roots can a cubic equation have?" [One or three.] You might have students sketch the possibilities. A cubic graph always crosses the *x*-axis at least once, so a cubic equation will never have zero real roots. The double root at $x = 1$ in this example would count as two real roots.

▶ EXAMPLE C

This example shows how to find all the roots of a cubic function by factoring if you know one of the roots. Students will see the simplification of radicals such as $\sqrt{12}$ in Lesson 11.5, which you can visit immediately after this lesson if you wish.

For another example, you might use the Fathom demonstration When Is It Safe to Drive?, in which students model real-world data with a cubic function.

You can also use what you know about roots to convert cubic equations from general form to factored form. Look at the graph of $y = x^3 - 3x + 2$ at right. It has *x*-intercepts $x = -2$ and $x = 1$. However, most cubic equations you've explored have had three roots. Where is the third one? Notice that the graph just touches the axis at $x = 1$. It doesn't actually pass through the axis. The root at $x = 1$ is called a *double root,* and the factor $x - 1$ is squared. Graph the factored form $y = (x + 2)(x - 1)^2$. It matches the graph shown. If it didn't, you would need to look at a specific point to find the scale change required to make it match.

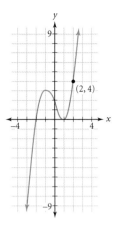

How can you find the roots of an equation when you can't identify the exact *x*-intercepts on a graph? Example C will show you a way to factor a cubic expression if you know only one *x*-intercept.

EXAMPLE C | Find the exact *x*-intercepts of $y = x^3 + 2x^2 - 7x - 2$.

▶ **Solution**

The graph shows that 2 is an *x*-intercept of the function. This means that $(x - 2)$ is a factor. You can approximate the other two roots by tracing, but to find exact algebraic solutions you need to factor. You can do this using a rectangle diagram.

$[-10, 10, 1, -15, 15, 5]$

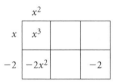

Enter the factor $x - 2$ on the left. Enter the cubic component of the cubic expression in the upper-left rectangle, and the number component in the lower-right rectangle.

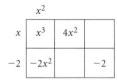

You can now determine that x^2 is the width of the first rectangles, because $x \cdot x^2 = x^3$. Next, $-2 \cdot x^2 = -2x^2$, so enter $-2x^2$ in the lower-left rectangle.

The original equation contains $2x^2$. Because there is already $-2x^2$ in the rectangle diagram, another rectangle must have an area of $4x^2$, so that their areas add to $2x^2$. Enter $4x^2$ in the upper-middle rectangle.

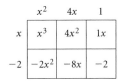

You can now determine that $4x$ is the width of the middle rectangles, because $x \cdot 4x = 4x^2$. Next, $-2 \cdot 4x = -8x$, so enter $-8x$ in the lower-middle rectangle.

The original equation contains $-7x$. Because there is already $-8x$ in the rectangle diagram, another rectangle must have an area of $1x$, so that their areas add to $-7x$. Enter $1x$ in the upper-right rectangle. You can now determine that the width of the right rectangles is 1.

This rectangle diagram shows that $x^2 + 4x + 1$ is another factor of the cubic equation. The values that make this expression equal to zero are the remaining two x-intercepts. The expression doesn't easily factor, so use the quadratic formula to solve $x^2 + 4x + 1 = 0$.

$$\frac{-4 \pm \sqrt{(4^2 - 4 \cdot 1 \cdot 1)}}{2 \cdot 1} = \frac{-4 \pm \sqrt{12}}{2} \approx -0.268 \text{ and } -3.732$$

So the exact x-intercepts are 2, $\frac{-4 + \sqrt{12}}{2}$, and $\frac{-4 - \sqrt{12}}{2}$. You can use the approximate values of the radical expressions to confirm the x-intercepts on the graph.

EXERCISES

You will need your graphing calculator for Exercises **1, 2, 4, 6, 7, 9, 12,** and **13.**

▶ Practice Your Skills

1. Determine whether each number is a perfect square, a perfect cube, or neither.

   a. 2,209   **b.** 5,832   **c.** 1,224 neither   **d.** 10,201
   perfect square; $47^2 = 2,209$ perfect cube; $18^3 = 5,832$ perfect square; $101^2 = 10,201$

2. Write and solve an equation to find the value of x in each figure.

   a.
   @
   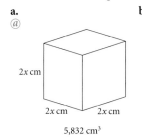
   $2x$ cm
   $2x$ cm $2x$ cm
   5,832 cm³

   b.
   3.5x cm
   3.5x cm   3.5x cm
   21,952 cm³

   c.
   @
   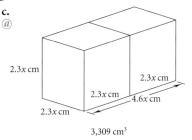
   2.3x cm
   2.3x cm   2.3x cm
   2.3x cm   2.3x cm
   4.6x cm
   3,309 cm³

3. Sometimes you can spot the factors of a polynomial expression without a graph of the equation. The easiest factors to see are those called *common monomial factors*. If you can divide each term by the same expression, then there is a common factor. Factor each expression by removing the largest possible common monomial factor.

   a. $4x^2 + 12x$ @ $4x(x + 3)$

   b. $6x^2 - 4x$ $2x(3x - 2)$

   c. $14x^4 + 7x^2 - 21x$ @ $7x(2x^3 + x - 3)$

   d. $12x^5 + 6x^3 + 3x^2$ $3x^2(4x^3 + 2x + 1)$

Exercise 6 Any integer n raised to the 6th power will be both a perfect square (of n^3) and a perfect cube (of n^2).

6a. Answers will vary. Three possibilities are $0^2 = 0^3 = 0$, $1^2 = 1^3 = 1$, $8^2 = 4^3 = 64$.

6b. Answers will vary. $(a^3)^2 = (a^2)^3$ for any integer a. For example, $(4^3)^2 = (4^2)^3 = 4096$, which is both a perfect cube and a perfect square. Or enter $Y_1 = x^3, Y_2 = x^2$, and $Y_3 = x^6$ into your calculator and look at the table. Y_3 will be Y_1 squared and Y_2 cubed.

7a. If the width is w, the length is $w + 6$ and the height is $w - 2$, so the volume is given by the equation $V = w(w + 6)(w - 2)$.

7b. Three solutions to the equation $47 = w(w + 6)(w - 2)$ are shown on the graph. However, only one solution is a positive value of w. A table gives the answer: $w \approx 3.4$. Widths greater than about 3.4 cm give volumes greater than 47 cm³.

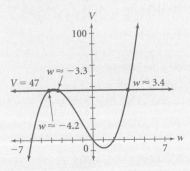

4. Determine whether each table represents a linear function, an exponential function, a cubic function, or a quadratic function. ⓗ

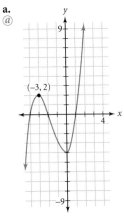

a.

x	y
2	4
5	25
8	64
11	121
14	196

quadratic

b.

x	y
2	7
5	11
8	15
11	19
14	23

linear

c.

x	y
2	4
5	32
8	256
11	2,048
14	16,384

exponential

d.

x	y
2	8
5	125
8	512
11	1,331
14	2,744

cubic

5. Write an equation in factored form for each graph.

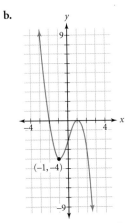

a. ⓐ

$(-3, 2)$

$y = 0.5(x + 4)(x + 2)(x - 1)$

b.

$(-1, -4)$

$y = -(x + 2)(x - 1)^2$

Reason and Apply

6. *Mini-Investigation* Some numbers are both perfect squares and perfect cubes.
   a. Find at least three numbers that are both a perfect square and a perfect cube. ⓗ
   b. Define a rule that you can use to find as many numbers as you like that are both perfect squares and perfect cubes.

7. A box is made so that its length is 6 cm more than its width. Its height is 2 cm less than its width.
   a. Use the width as the independent variable, and write an equation for the volume of the box. ⓐ
   b. Suppose you want to ensure that the volume of the box is greater than 47 cm³. Use a graph and a table to describe all possible widths, to the nearest 0.1 cm, of such boxes.

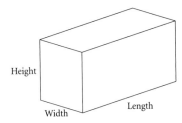

Height

Width

Length

8. Determine whether each statement about the equation $0 = 2x^3 + 4x^2 - 10x$ is true or false.

   a. The equation has three real roots. true

   b. One of the roots is at $x = 2$. false

   c. There is one positive root. true

   d. The graph of $y = 2x^3 + 4x^2 - 10x$ passes through the point $(1, -4)$. true

9. To convert from factored form to general form when there are more than two factors, first multiply any pair of factors. Then multiply the result by the other factor. For example, to rewrite the expression $(x + 1)(x + 3)(x + 4)$ in general form, first multiply the first two factors.

$$(x + 1)(x + 3) = x^2 + 1x + 3x + 3 = x^2 + 4x + 3$$

Then multiply the result by the third factor. You might want to use a rectangle diagram to do this.

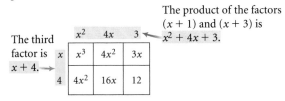

Next, combine like terms to find the sum of the regions.

$$x^3 + 4x^2 + 3x + 4x^2 + 16x + 12 = x^3 + 8x^2 + 19x + 12$$

Convert each expression below from factored form to general form. Use a graph or a table to compare the original factored form to your final general form.

   a. $(x + 1)(x + 2)(x + 3)$ @ $x^3 + 6x^2 + 11x + 6$ **b.** $(x + 2)(x - 2)(x - 3)$ $x^3 - 3x^2 - 4x + 12$

10. The *girth* of a box is the distance completely around the box in one direction—that is, the length of a string that wraps around the box. Shippers put a maximum limit on the girth of a box rather than trying to limit its length, width, and height. Suppose you must ship a box with a girth of 120 cm in one direction and 160 cm in another direction.

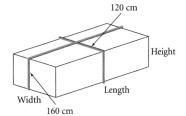

   a. If the height of the box is 10 cm, what is the width of the box? @ 50 cm

   b. If the height of the box is 10 cm, what is the length of the box? 70 cm

   c. What is the volume of the box described in 10a and b? $10 \cdot 50 \cdot 70 = 35{,}000$ cm³

   d. If the height is 15 cm, what are the other two dimensions and what is the volume of the box? The width is 45 cm, and the length is 65 cm; the volume is $15 \cdot 45 \cdot 65$, or 43,875 cm³.

   e. If the height is x cm, find an expression for the width of the box. @ $w = \frac{120 - 2x}{2} = 60 - x$

   f. If the height is x cm, find an expression for the length of the box. $l = \frac{160 - 2x}{2} = 80 - x$

   g. Using your answers to 10e and f, find an equation for the volume of the box. @ $V = x(60 - x)(80 - x)$

   h. What are the roots of the equation you found in 10g, and what do they tell you?

   i. Find the dimensions of a box with a volume of 48,488 cm³. height 22 cm, width 38 cm, and length 58 cm, or height 23.265 cm, width 36.735 cm, and length 56.735 cm

Exercise 10 Some students may think that the information given doesn't specify which girth is related to length and which to width. Point out that in this situation, length is assumed to be longer than width.

10h. $x = 0$ cm, $x = 60$ cm, $x = 80$ cm; these x-values make boxes with no volume.

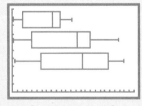
11. Use rectangle diagrams to find the missing expressions.
  a. $(3x - 4)(x^2 + 4x + 5) = (?)$
  b. $(3x + 5)(?) = 6x^2 - 2x - 20$ $2x - 4$
  c. $(x - 5)(?) = 2x^2 - 7x - 15$ @ $2x + 3$
  d. $(x + 5)(?) = 2x^3 + 14x^2 + 17x - 15$

▶ Review

9.3 **12.** Perform the operations, then combine like terms. Check your answers by using tables or graphs.
  a. $(8x^3 - 5x) + (3x^3 + 2x^2 + 7x + 12)$
  b. $(8x^3 - 5x) - (3x^3 + 2x^2 + 7x + 12)$ @
  c. $(2x^2 - 6x + 11) + (-8x^2 - 7x + 9)$
  d. $(2x^2 - 6x + 11)(-8x^2 - 7x + 9)$

8.6, 9.4 **13.** Perform the indicated operation and write the result in lowest terms. State any restrictions on the variable. Verify your answers by using your calculator to compare graphs or tables of values.
  a. $\dfrac{x + 4}{x + 2} \cdot \dfrac{x^2 + 4x + 4}{x^2 - 16}$ @
  b. $\dfrac{x^2 + 2x}{x^2 - 4} \div \dfrac{x^2}{x^2 - 6x + 8}$
  c. $\dfrac{x}{x^2 + 6x + 9} + \dfrac{1}{x + 3}$ @
  d. $\dfrac{x - 1}{x^2 - 1} - \dfrac{4}{x + 1}$

1.3 **14.** The table shows hourly compensation costs in 15 countries for 1980, 1990, and 2000. Use the list commands on your calculator to do this statistical analysis.
  a. Choose at least three countries and graph the hourly compensation costs for those countries over time. Write a paragraph describing the trends you notice and the conclusions you draw. Answers will vary.
  b. Which of the 15 countries had the largest increase in compensation costs from 1980 to 2000? Which country had the least?
  c. Create three box plots that compare the compensation costs for the three years. Write a brief paragraph analyzing your graph.

These production workers are inspecting automobile bodies at an American factory.

Hourly Compensation Costs (in U.S. dollars) for Production Workers

Country	1980	1990	2000
Australia	8.47	13.24	14.47
Canada	8.67	15.95	16.05
Denmark	10.83	18.04	21.49
France	8.94	15.49	15.66
Germany	12.21	21.81	22.99
Hong Kong	1.51	3.23	5.63
Israel	3.79	8.55	12.86
Italy	8.15	17.45	14.01
Japan	5.52	12.80	22.00
Luxembourg	11.54	16.04	17.70
Mexico	2.21	1.58	2.08
Spain	5.89	11.38	10.78
Sri Lanka	0.22	0.35	0.48
Taiwan	1.02	3.90	5.85
United States	9.87	14.91	19.72

(U.S. Bureau of Labor Statistics, in *The New York Times Almanac 2004*, p. 510) [Data Sets: **HCC80, HCC90, HCC00**]

In this chapter you learned about **quadratic functions.** You learned that they model **projectile motion** and the acceleration due to **gravity.** You discovered important connections between the **roots** and the ***x*-intercepts** of quadratic equations and graphs. You learned how to use the three different forms of quadratic equations:

General form	$y = ax^2 + bx + c$
Vertex form	$y = a(x - h)^2 + k$
Factored form	$y = a(x - r_1)(x - r_2)$ or
	$y = ax(x - r_2)$ if $r_1 = 0$

The expression $ax^2 + bx + c$ is a type of **polynomial** because it is the sum of many **terms** or **monomials.** The vertex form gives you information about the **line of symmetry** of the parabola. The factored form shows you the roots of the equation. The **zero-product property** tells you that if the polynomial equals zero, then one of the **binomial** factors, $(x - r_1)$ or $(x - r_2)$, must equal 0. The roots r_1 and r_2 are also called **zeros** of the quadratic function. You learned to expand the vertex and factored forms to the general form by combining like terms.

You first learned to locate solutions to quadratic equations using calculator tables and graphs. You then learned to solve equations symbolically by one of three methods—factor with rectangle diagrams, **complete the square,** or use the **quadratic formula.**

To use the quadratic formula, $x = \frac{-b \pm \sqrt{b^2 - 4ac}}{2a}$, you identified the values of *a, b,* and *c* for the **trinomial** $ax^2 + bx + c$. You also learned to calculate the **discriminant,** $b^2 - 4ac$, and saw that it gives information about the number of solutions to the equation.

You saw that solutions to quadratic equations often contain **radical expressions.** You learned that the square root of a negative number does not result in a **real number.** You also learned how to find **cube roots, perfect cubes,** and **perfect squares.** In the last lesson you studied cubic functions.

EXERCISES

You will need your graphing calculator for Exercise **9.**

@ Answers are provided for all exercises in this set.

1. Tell whether each statement is true or false. If it is false, change the right side to make it true, but keep it in the same form. That is, if the statement is in factored form, write your corrected version in factored form.

a. $x^2 + 5x - 24 \stackrel{?}{=} (x + 3)(x - 8)$
   false; $(x - 3)(x + 8)$

b. $2(x - 1)^2 + 3 \stackrel{?}{=} 2x^2 + x + 1$ false; $2x^2 - 4x + 5$

c. $(x + 3)^2 \stackrel{?}{=} x^2 + 9$
   false; $x^2 + 6x + 9$

d. $(x + 2)(2x - 5) \stackrel{?}{=} 2x^2 - x - 10$ true

▶ Helping with the Exercises

Exercise 6a Students might substitute the coordinates $(3, 0)$ for x and y in the vertex-form equation $y = a(x - 1)^2 - 4$ and solve for a. Or they might cite symmetry to note that the other x-intercept will be at $(-1, 0)$, derive the factored-form equation $y = a(x - 3)(x + 1)$, and solve for a after substituting the coordinates of the vertex.

6b. sample answers:

$y = (x + 1.5)\left(x - \dfrac{1}{3}\right)$,

$y = (2x + 3)(3x - 1)$

7a. $x^2 + 6x - 9 = 13$

$x^2 + 6x = 22$

$x^2 + 6x + 9 = 22 + 9$

$(x + 3)^2 = 31$

$x + 3 = \pm\sqrt{31}$

$x = -3 \pm\sqrt{31}$

7b. $3x^2 - 24x + 27 = 0$

$3x^2 - 24x = -27$

$x^2 - 8x = -9$

$x^2 - 8x + 16 = -9 + 16$

$(x - 4)^2 = 7$

$x - 4 = \pm\sqrt{7}$

$x = 4 \pm \sqrt{7}$

---

2. The equation of the graph at right is

$$y = -2(x + 5)^2 + 4$$

Describe the transformations on the graph of $y = x^2$ that give this parabola.

Sample response: There is a reflection across the x-axis $\left(y = -x^2\right)$ and a vertical stretch by a factor of 2 $\left(y = -2x^2\right)$. Finally, there is a translation left 5 units and up 4 units $\left(y = -2(x + 5)^2 + 4\right)$.

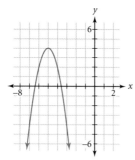

3. Write an equation for each graph below. Choose the form that best fits the information given.

a.

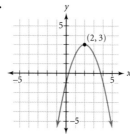

$y = -(x - 2)^2 + 3$; vertex form

b.

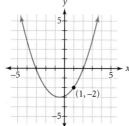

$y = 0.5(x - 2)(x + 3)$; factored form

4. Write an equation in the form $y = a(x - h)^2 + k$ for each graph below.

a.

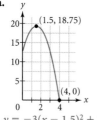

$y = -3(x - 1.5)^2 + 18.75$

b.

$y = -1.6(x - 5)^2 + 30$

5. Use the zero-product property to solve each equation.

a. $(2w + 9)(w - 3) = 0$
$2w + 9 = 0$ or $w - 3 = 0$; $w = -4.5$ or $w = 3$

b. $(2x + 5)(x - 7) = 0$
$2x + 5 = 0$ or $x - 7 = 0$; $x = -2.5$ or $x = 7$

6. Write an equation of a parabola that satisfies the given conditions.

a. The vertex is $(1, -4)$, and one of its x-intercepts is 3. $y = (x - 1)^2 - 4$

b. The x-intercepts are -1.5 and $\dfrac{1}{3}$.

7. Solve each equation by completing the square. Show each step. Leave your answers in radical form.

a. $x^2 + 6x - 9 = 13$

b. $3x^2 - 24x + 27 = 0$

8. Solve each equation by using the quadratic formula. Determine whether there are real number solutions. Leave your answer in radical form.

a. $5x^2 - 13x + 18 = 0$ $x = \dfrac{13 \pm \sqrt{-191}}{10}$; no real number solutions

b. $-3x^2 + 7x + 9 = 0$ $x = \dfrac{-7 \pm \sqrt{157}}{-6}$

9. APPLICATION The function $f(x) = 0.0015x(150 - x)$ models the rate at which the population of fish grows in a large aquarium. The x-value is the number of fish, and the $f(x)$-value is the rate of increase in the number of fish per week.

a. Find $f(60)$, and give a real-world meaning for this value.

b. For what values of x does $f(x) = 0$? What do these values represent?

c. How many fish are there when the population is growing fastest?

d. What is the maximum number of fish the aquarium has to support?

e. Graph this function.

10. A toy rocket blasts off from ground level. After 0.5 s it is 8.8 ft high. It hits the ground after 1.6 s. Write an equation in factored form to model the height of the rocket as a function of time.

11. Name values of c so that $y = x^2 - 6x + c$ satisfies each condition below. Use the discriminant, $b^2 - 4ac$, or translate the graph of $y = x^2 - 6x$ to help you.

a. The graph of the equation has no x-intercepts.

b. The graph of the equation has exactly one x-intercept.

c. The graph of the equation has two x-intercepts.

12. Use the quadratic formula to find the roots of each equation.

a. $x^2 + 10x - 6 = 0$
$x = -5 + \sqrt{31}$ and $x = -5 - \sqrt{31}$

b. $3x^2 - 8x + 5 = 0$ $x = 1$ and $x = \dfrac{5}{3}$

13. For each graph, identify the x-intercepts and write an equation in factored form.

a.

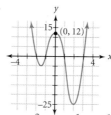

$x = -2, x = -1, x = 1$, and $x = 3$;
$y = 2(x - 3)(x + 2)(x + 1)(x - 1)$

b.

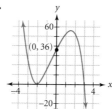

$x = -2$ (double root) and $x = 3$;
$y = -3(x + 2)^2(x - 3)$

14. Make a rectangle diagram to factor each expression.

a. $x^2 + 7x + 12$ $(x + 3)(x + 4)$

b. $x^2 - 14x + 49$ $(x - 7)^2$

c. $x^2 + 3x - 28$ $(x + 7)(x - 4)$

d. $x^2 - 81$ $(x - 9)(x + 9)$

9a. $f(60) = 8.1$; when there are 60 fish in the tank, the population is growing at a rate of about 8 fish per week.

9b. $f(x) = 0$ for $x = 0$ and $x = 150$; when there are no fish, the population does not grow; when there are 150 fish, the number of fish hatched is equal to the number of fish that die, so the total population does not change.

9c. There are 75 fish when the population is growing fastest.

9d. The population no longer grows once there are 150 fish, so that is the maximum number of fish the tank has to support.

9e.

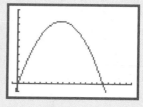

$[-10, 200, 10, -1, 10, 1]$

10. The roots are at 0 s and 1.6 s, so start with the equation $y = x(x - 1.6)$. Then reflect the graph across the x-axis. When $x = 0.5, y = 0.55$. You need the value of y to be 8.8, so apply a vertical stretch with a factor of $\dfrac{8.8}{0.55}$, or 16. The final equation is $y = -16x(x - 1.6)$.

11a. No x-intercepts means taking the square root of a negative number. So $(-6)^2 - 4(1)(c) < 0$; $-4c < -36$; $c > 9$. Or translate the graph of $y = x^2 - 6x$ vertically to see that for $c > 9$, the parabola does not cross the x-axis.

11b. One x-intercept implies a double root, so $x^2 - 6x + c$ must be a perfect-square trinomial. Make a rectangle diagram to find $\left(\dfrac{-6}{2}\right)^2 = 9$, so $x^2 - 6x + 9$ is a perfect-square trinomial, and $c = 9$. The graph touches the x-axis once. You can also solve $b^2 - 4ac = 36 - 4c = 0$ to get $c = 9$.

11c. For $c < 9$, $b^2 - 4ac > 0$, so there are two real roots, and therefore two x-intercepts. The parabola $y = x^2 - 6x + c$ crosses the x-axis twice for values of c less than 9.

14a.

x		3
x	x^2	$3x$
4	$4x$	12

14b.

x		-7
x	x^2	$-7x$
-7	$-7x$	49

14c.

x		-4
x	x^2	$-4x$
7	$7x$	-28

14d.

x		-9
x	x^2	$-9x$
9	$9x$	-81

► Take Another Look

1. Many graphing calculators can operate on imaginary numbers, at least enough to generate the patterns here: $i^2 = -1$; $i^3 = (-1)i = -i$; $i^4 = 1$; $i^5 = i$. This pattern repeats every four powers so that $i^{10} = i^8 \cdot i^2$ (or -1); $i^{25} = i$; and $i^{100} = 1$.

2. See below.

TAKE ANOTHER LOOK

1. In this chapter you have encountered many equations, such as $x^2 = -4$, that have no real solutions. The solutions to these equations exist in another set of numbers called **imaginary numbers.** To find the solution to $x^2 = -4$, mathematicians write $x = 2i$ or $x = -2i$. The symbol i represents the imaginary unit.

Express i as a square root of a negative number. (*Hint:* If $2i = \sqrt{-4}$ and $3i = \sqrt{-9}$, what does $1i$ equal?) What happens if you multiply i by itself to find i^2? Use this result to find i^3 and i^4. What happens if you keep multiplying by i?

Use the pattern you discovered to calculate i^{10}, i^{25}, and i^{100}.

Learn more about imaginary numbers with the links at **www.keymath.com/DA** .

2. On page 499, you saw a Venn diagram that showed relationships among several sets of numbers. In Take Another Look activity 1, you were introduced to imaginary numbers, which are numbers that can be written in the form bi, where b is a real number and $i = \sqrt{-1}$. On page 528, you learned about complex numbers, which are numbers that can be written in the form $a + bi$, where a and b are real numbers. Create a Venn diagram that includes these number sets and all other number sets that you can think of.

Assessing What You've Learned

WRITE IN YOUR JOURNAL Add to your journal by answering one of these prompts:
► There are many ways to solve quadratic equations—calculator tables and graphs, factoring, completing the square, and the quadratic formula. Which method do you like best? Do you always use the same method?
► Compare each form of a quadratic equation—general, vertex, and factored. What information does each form tell you? How can you convert an equation from one form to another?

ORGANIZE YOUR NOTEBOOK Choose your best graph of a parabola from this chapter. Label the vertex, roots, line of symmetry, and y-intercept. Show the equation for the graph in each quadratic form—general, vertex, and factored.

GIVE A PRESENTATION Work with a partner or in a group to create your own problem about projectile motion. It can be about the height of a ball, the path of a rocket, or some other object. If possible, conduct an experiment to collect data. Decide which information will be given and which form of quadratic equation to use. Make up a question about your problem. Put the problem and its solution on a poster and make a presentation to the class.

PERFORMANCE ASSESSMENT Show a classmate, a family member, or your teacher that you can solve any quadratic equation. Demonstrate how to find solutions with a calculator (graph or table) and by hand (factoring, completing the square, or using the quadratic formula).

2. Here is one possibility for a Venn diagram of all complex numbers:

Complex Numbers

Reals

2 + 3i

Irrational — Rational

Imaginary numbers
2i
−4i

π

√7

3 − √2

3/4

Integers
−2   −4

Whole
0   10

2.5

4 − 7i

Students might also include sets such as decimals and natural numbers. Note that the real numbers are a subset of the complex numbers $a + bi$ where $b = 0$.

10

Probability

Overview

In Chapters 0–9, students approached the ideas of elementary algebra while handling data and graphing (analytic geometry). In Chapter 10, the data theme is extended to probability. Chapter 11 will expand on the analytic geometry ideas.

In preparation for a definition of probability, **Lesson 10.1** introduces relative frequency circle and bar graphs. In **Lesson 10.2,** students see the idea of probability as a ratio, and then explore both experimental and theoretical probabilities in **Lesson 10.3.** To calculate the numerator and denominator of a probability fraction, students often need to be able to do complex counting; counting techniques are the subject of **Lesson 10.4. Lesson 10.5** provides a shortcut to counting as students see how to multiply probabilities to find the probability of a path in a tree diagram. **Lesson 10.6** uses probabilities to find expected values.

The Mathematics

Probability

Mountains and clouds are not modeled well by circles and polygons; the fractals of Chapter 0 do a better job. Similarly, real data aren't modeled perfectly by the functions in previous chapters; probability, the subject of this chapter, helps make predictions in uncertain situations.

A **trial** is a real-world activity, such as rolling a die or making a sale, that produces an **outcome,** such as a 3 on a die or a revenue of $29.35. An **event** is a set of outcomes, such as rolling an even number on a die (consisting of the outcomes 2, 4, and 6) or making a sale over $25.00. The **probability** of an event is a number between 0 and 1 associated with the event. Technically, probability is a function mapping the set of all events to the real number interval [0, 1].

For such a function to be a probability function, it must meet several criteria. For example, it must assign the number 0 to the empty set, an event consisting of no outcomes—that is, something that is impossible. It must assign the number 1 to the entire set of all outcomes—that is, something that is certain.

We've referred to probabilities of sales and probabilities of rolling dice and flipping coins. The former probabilities are based on observed data and are called **experimental probabilities.** The latter are based on theory and are called **theoretical probabilities.** In either case, the probability of an event can be defined by a fraction,

$P(A) = \frac{number\ of\ equally\ likely\ outcomes\ in\ A}{total\ number\ of\ equally\ likely\ outcomes}$. If the

event falls into one of several possible categories, this ratio is the **relative frequency** of that category, often represented by a relative frequency circle or bar graph. In some situations the probability of several outcomes is the product of their probabilities. For example, the probability of getting two heads when flipping two coins is $\frac{1}{4}$, the product of $\frac{1}{2}$ and $\frac{1}{2}$. In rolling a die, however, the probability of getting a 2 $\left(\frac{1}{6}\right)$ is not the product of the probabilities of getting a prime $\left(\frac{1}{2}\right)$ and getting an even number $\left(\frac{1}{2}\right)$. That's because there are fewer even primes than odd primes. The event "being prime" is not independent of the event "being even." Only in the case of **independent events** is the product of the probability of two events together the product of their individual probabilities.

Successive events occur on paths through **tree diagrams.** The **multiplication principle** says that the probabilities of events on a path can be multiplied to find the probability of the path as a whole. In this context the notation $P(A \mid B)$, read **the probability of A given B,** means the probability of going to event A if you've arrived at event B on some path. The notation $P(A \mid B)$ is shorthand for $\frac{P(A\ and\ B)}{P(B)}$, so $P(A\ and\ B) = P(B)\ P(A \mid B)$ even if events A and B are dependent.

Counting

The mathematical branch called *combinatorics* concerns methods of counting in complex situations. One of the simplest of these methods is the **counting principle** for counting ways of making a sequence of choices.

An arrangement, or **permutation,** is a special case in which each stage of the sequence has one less choice than the stage before. The symbol $_nP_r$ refers to the number of permutations of n things taken r at a time. Note that it refers to a number, not to the permutations themselves.

A technique for counting subsets, or **combinations,** is to group the permutations into equal subsets and divide $_nP_r$ by the size of the subsets. The symbol $_nC_r$ refers to this number of combinations.

Although the field of combinatorics is distinct from the field of probability, these counting methods are often used to determine the numerator or denominator of a probability fraction.

Expected Value

Another topic that often appears with probability is **expected value,** also called expectation or mean value. The expected value of a trial is the mean outcome of that trial. For example, if you rolled a die 600 times, on average you'd get 100 of each possible outcome. The average outcome, then, would be $\frac{100(1) + 100(2) + \cdots + 100(6)}{600}$, or 3.5. Equivalently, you could use the fact that the probability of each outcome is $\frac{1}{6}$ to write the weighted average $\frac{1}{6}(1) + \frac{1}{6}(2) + \cdots + \frac{1}{6}(6)$.

Using This Chapter

Check your state or district standards to determine how much probability you need to cover in your course. For an introduction to basic probability concepts, covering Lessons 10.1–10.3 might suffice.

Resources

Discovering Algebra Resources

Teaching and Worksheet Masters
Lessons 10.1, 10.4, 10.5

Calculator Notes 0H, 10A, 10B, 10C, 10D, 10E, 10F, 10G, 10H, 10I

Fathom Demonstrations
Lessons 10.2, 10.3, 10.5, 10.6

Dynamic Algebra Explorations online
Lesson 10.3

Assessment Resources
Quiz 1 (Lessons 10.1, 10.2)
Quiz 2 (Lessons 10.3, 10.4)
Quiz 3 (Lessons 10.5, 10.6)
Chapter 10 Test
Chapter 10 Constructive Assessment Options

More Practice Your Skills for Chapter 10

Condensed Lessons for Chapter 10

Other Resources

Probability Activities by Robert Lovell.

Probability Simulations by Mary Jean Winter and Ronald J. Carlson.

For complete references to these and other resources, see www.keypress.com/DA.

Pacing Guide

	day 1	day 2	day 3	day 4	day 5	day 6	day 7	day 8	day 9
standard	10.1	10.2	quiz, 10.3	10.4	10.5	10.5	10.6, quiz	review	assessment
enriched	10.1	10.2, project	quiz, 10.3	10.4, project	10.5	10.5	10.6	quiz, review, TAL	assessment
block	10.1, 10.2	quiz, 10.3, 10.4	10.5	10.6, quiz, review	assessment				

10 Probability

Japanese artist Yutaka Sone
(b. 1965) creates art that deals
with chance and randomness.
He rolled these giant dice down
the steps of the central plaza
during the EXPO 2000 World
Exposition in Hannover, Germany.

CHAPTER 10 OBJECTIVES

- Draw and interpret relative frequency graphs
- Determine experimental and theoretical probabilities, and see how the former approximate the latter
- Use probabilities to describe patterns when outcomes are random
- Count numbers of permutations and combinations to help determine probabilities
- Determine the probabilities of different outcomes for a multiple-stage experiment
- Calculate the expected value of a random event

OBJECTIVES

In this chapter you will
- create and interpret relative frequency graphs
- learn about randomness and the definition of probability
- learn methods of calculating probabilities
- count numbers of possibilities to help determine probabilities
- determine the expected value of a random event

Yutaka Sone is a Japanese-born artist who resides in Los Angeles. His videos, sculptures, and drawings explore Western culture and chance and uncertainty. In a video he produced titled *Double Six,* a cowboy on a horse chases a helicopter that is carrying two large dice like the ones shown here. The dice are released to roll across the ground. **[Ask]** "What different rolls are possible? What is the chance that the roll will be a double six?" [36 different rolls are possible, from 1-1 to

6-6. There is only one way to roll a double six.] "What is the artist attempting to express through his work?" Encourage all ideas. Sone's art encourages the exploration of different possibilities and different interpretations of everyday events. Students may be interested to know that Yutaka Sone has a master's degree in architecture. **[ELL]** The expression "rolling the dice" is used to mean "taking a chance" in English.

L E S S O N
10.1

Relative Frequency Graphs

In this world nothing is certain but death and taxes.

BENJAMIN FRANKLIN

Ⓗow certain are you that your math teacher will assign homework tomorrow? How sure are you that your next report card will show better results than the previous one? What is the chance that your school's track team will be in the state finals? How certain can you really be about anything? Much of life involves uncertainty. In this chapter you'll explore how you can make predictions about uncertain events.

Collecting data can help you determine the likelihood of an event. In Chapter 1, you learned to display categorical data (data that are sorted into categories) in bar graphs. **Relative frequency graphs** also summarize data in categories, but instead of including the actual number for each category, they compare the number in that category to the total for all the categories. Relative frequency graphs can be bar graphs or circle graphs, and they show fractions or percents, not values.

In the investigation and Example A, you'll learn to make relative frequency graphs. In Example B you'll see how relative frequency graphs can be used to determine the chance of an event occurring.

Investigation
Circle Graphs and Bar Graphs

You will need

- graph paper
- a protractor
- a compass or circle template
- a ruler

The bar graph shows the approximate land area of the seven continents.

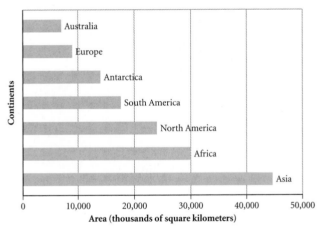

Continental Land Areas

Step 1 | Determine from the bar graph the approximate area of each continent and the total land area.

Step 2 | Convert the data in the bar graph to a circle graph. Use the fact that there are 360 degrees in a circle. Write proportions to find the number of degrees in each sector of the circle graph. Then use a protractor to accurately draw each sector.

Step 3 | Convert the data in the bar graph to a relative frequency circle graph. Instead of showing the land area, the graph will show percents of total land area.

PLANNING

LESSON OUTLINE

One day:

20 min   Investigation

5 min   Sharing

15 min   Examples

5 min   Closing

5 min   Exercises

MATERIALS

- graph paper
- protractors
- compasses, circle templates, or Circle Graphs (W)
- rulers
- Protractors (T, from Chapter 6), *optional*
- Calculator Note 10I for TI-73 only, *optional*

TEACHING

Circle graphs, or pie charts, are good for showing the size of each category relative to the whole. Like histograms and bar graphs, they organize data by categories or intervals. With the help of proportions, circle graphs and bar graphs can be relabeled as *relative frequency graphs* that show the fraction or percent in each category.

 Guiding the Investigation

One Step

Display a relative frequency circle graph and ask students to make one representing the data given by the bar graph in the investigation. As you circulate, encourage students to use calculator lists to convert frequencies to degrees all at once.

Step 1 Approximate answers in millions of square kilometers: Australia 7; Europe 9; Antarctica 14; South America 18; North America 24; Africa 30; Asia 45; Total 147.

Steps 3 and 4 As needed, point out that these steps require only changing the labels from numbers to percents.

Step 3   Continental Land Areas

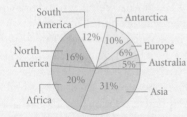

See page 729 for answers to Steps 2 and 4.

| Step 4 | Convert the data in the bar graph to a relative frequency bar graph that shows percents rather than land areas. |
| Step 5 | Compare the graphs you made with the original graph. What advantages are there to each kind of graph? |

EXAMPLE A

Randy has been asked to create a graphical display showing the distribution of the library's collection in six categories. His boss has asked him to create two rough drafts. Together they will decide which one to finalize for the display.

Here are the data:

Library Collection

Category	Number of items
Children's fiction	35,994
Children's nonfiction	28,106
Adult fiction	48,129
Adult nonfiction	69,834
Media	11,830
Other	5,766
Total	199,659

▶ Solution

Randy decides to first create a circle graph. He puts the number of items in each category into list L1. He wants the calculator to determine in list L2 the number of degrees needed for each sector. He writes a proportion to find the number of degrees in the sector for a particular category.

Items in the category → Degrees in the sector →

$$\frac{L_1}{199,659} = \frac{L_2}{360}$$

Total items in all categories → Total degrees in a circle →

By multiplying by 360, he finds the formula to enter into list L2.

$$L_2 = L_1 \cdot \frac{360}{199,659}$$

His calculator quickly determines the number of degrees for each sector of the circle graph. Using a protractor to measure the angles, Randy creates the graph.

L1	L2
35994	65
28106	51
48129	87
69834	126
11830	21
5766	10

L2 = L1 * 360/199659

LESSON OBJECTIVES

• Learn about circle graphs

• Become familiar with relative frequency circle and bar graphs

• Use relative frequency graphs to find the chance of occurrence

---

Step 5 Relative frequency graphs are good for showing ratios, but they don't report actual amounts.

SHARING IDEAS

Select students to present the graphs of Steps 3 and 4. Lead a discussion of ideas about Step 5.

Some graphs display all data items, and others give only a visual summary.

[Ask] "Why do you think relative frequency graphs are called that?" **[Language]** Help students connect the phrase *relative frequency* with the meanings of the words: *frequency* (how often) and *relative* (compared to the whole). Students will encounter this phrase in the next lesson as well.

[Ask] "What types of graphs are visual summaries and which display the actual data?" [Box plots are visual summaries, histograms summarize data in intervals (bins), and dot plots and scatter plots display actual data.] "Are circle graphs visual summaries, or do they display actual data?" [They display the data unless they are relative frequency circle graphs.] "Are relative frequency graphs visual summaries, or do they display actual data?" [Actual data values are not shown on relative frequency graphs.]

Assessing Progress

You can assess students' skill at solving proportions, working with ratios, measuring carefully, drawing angles of given sizes, and seeing similarities and differences.

▶ EXAMPLE A

This example shows how to use a calculator to convert data to degrees for a circle graph and to relative frequencies. Have students enter the lists into their calculators. If there's time, have them apply the same techniques to the data of the investigation.

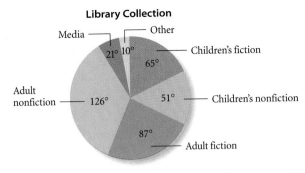

Library Collection

Media — 21° 10° — Other

Children's fiction 65°

Children's nonfiction 51°

Adult fiction 87°

Adult nonfiction 126°

To make a relative frequency graph, Randy finds the percent of the total each category represents. He uses list L1 again and the proportion

$$\frac{L1}{199{,}659} = \frac{L3}{100}$$

He solves for L3 and enters the formula that will give him the percents.

L₁	L₂	L₃
35994	65	18
28106	51	14
48129	87	24
69834	126	35
11830	21	6
5766	10	3

L₃ = L₁ * 100/199659

He makes a relative frequency circle graph by putting these percents in his circle graph. He then uses the same percents to create a relative frequency bar graph.

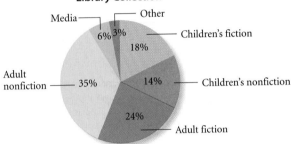

Library Collection

Media — 6% 3% — Other

Children's fiction 18%

Children's nonfiction 14%

Adult fiction 24%

Adult nonfiction 35%

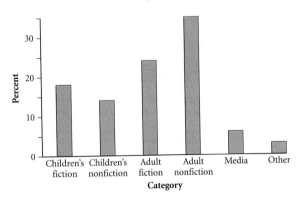

Library Collection

(bar graph: Percent vs. Category — Children's fiction, Children's nonfiction, Adult fiction, Adult nonfiction, Media, Other)

In Example A, do you think the relative frequency circle graph or bar graph shows the data most clearly?

Like the box plots you studied in Chapter 1, relative frequency graphs give a visual summary of the data but don't show actual data values.

Relative frequency graphs can help you predict the chance that something will happen, as shown in Example B.

EXAMPLE B

If you choose a title at random from the library in Example A, what is the chance that it will be children's fiction? What is the chance that it will be fiction, either adult or children's?

▶ Solution

The relative frequency circle graph and relative frequency bar graph tell you that 18% of the library's collection is children's fiction. So there is an 18% chance that a randomly chosen title will be children's fiction.

Eighteen percent of the collection is children's fiction and 24% is adult fiction. Combined, 42% of the collection is fiction. So there is a 42% chance that a randomly chosen title will be fiction.

As you progress through this chapter, you will learn several ways to determine the chance, or *probability*, of an event happening.

EXERCISES

▶ Practice Your Skills

1. **APPLICATION** There are four basic blood types. The distribution of these types in the general population is shown in the relative frequency circle graph. In a city of 75,000 people, about how many people with each blood type would you expect to find? @

Blood Types

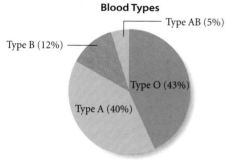

type AB = 3,750; type B = 9,000; type A = 30,000; type O = 32,250

2. Use the relative frequency circle graph in Exercise 1 to answer these questions.

   a. What is the chance that a person chosen at random has type A blood? @ 40%

   b. What is the chance that a person chosen at random has type O blood? 43%

   c. What is the chance that a person chosen at random does not have type AB blood? 95%

▶ Helping with the Exercises

Exercise 1 The circle graph shows visually the percents listed in the labels.

▶ EXAMPLE B

The word *chance* previews the introduction of probability in Lesson 10.2 and randomness in Lesson 10.3. **[Language]** Ask students for words that mean 100% chance, such as *certain, definite,* and *always,* and for words that mean 0% chance, such as *impossible* and *never.*

Direct students to the opening quote. Ask students whether they agree with the quote or whether they can think of other things in life that are certain. You might return to this quote after students have more experience with probability.

Closing the Lesson

Review the important new ideas of this lesson. Circle graphs are circles divided into sectors whose areas represent the relative sizes of different categories of data. Like some bar graphs, they give **relative frequencies.** If your class is using the TI-73, you might want to use Calculator Note 10I to show how to construct circle graphs on the calculator.

BUILDING UNDERSTANDING

In the exercises students practice constructing and interpreting circle graphs and relative frequency graphs.

ASSIGNING HOMEWORK

Essential	1–3, 5, 6, 8
Performance assessment	8, 9
Portfolio	6
Journal	4
Group	6, 7, 12
Review	10–12

5.

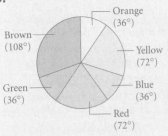

Brown (108°)
Orange (36°)
Yellow (72°)
Green (36°)
Blue (36°)
Red (72°)

Exercise 6 Help students understand that when two bar graphs are constructed on one set of axes, each bar graph has its own color bar.

6. See bottom of page 555.

Exercise 7b As needed, remind students to use the techniques of Chapter 2 and Lesson 6.1 for calculating percent increase and decrease. Neither the total nor the mean of the percent changes of the classes will give the percent change for the school, because the classes have different sizes. Remind students that the mean of means of parts doesn't usually give the mean of the whole. The mean of the changes (2%, −1.5%, 2.5%, −2%) is 0.5%, but because there are different numbers of students in each grade, the change in total population is 0.3%.

7c.

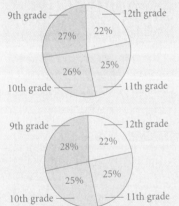

9th grade — 27%
12th grade — 22%
10th grade — 26%
11th grade — 25%

9th grade — 28%
12th grade — 22%
10th grade — 25%
11th grade — 25%

The ninth grade increased to 28% and the tenth grade decreased to 25%.

---

3. Which data set matches the relative frequency circle graph at right? *(h)* c

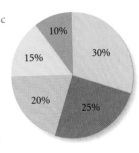

10%
30%
15%
20%
25%

  a. {15, 18, 22, 25, 28}

  b. {20, 24, 30, 36, 45}

  c. {12, 18, 24, 30, 36}

  d. {9, 12, 18, 20, 24}

4. In the relative frequency bar graph of the library's collection created in Example A, the bar for adult fiction represents 24%. Could there be a situation where all the bars represented 24%? Explain your thinking. *@*

No; the total height of all the bars must be 100%.

▶ Reason and Apply

5. A manufacturer states that it produces colored candies according to the percents listed in this table. Create a circle graph to show this information. Label the degree measure of each sector.

Colored Candies Manufactured

Orange	Yellow	Blue	Red	Green	Brown
10%	20%	10%	20%	10%	30%

6. Chloe bought a small package of the candies described in Exercise 5, and counted the number of each color. Her count is shown in the table at right.

Chloe's Colored Candies

Orange	Yellow	Blue	Red	Green	Brown
11	10	4	12	7	14

  a. Construct a relative frequency bar graph for Chloe's package of candies.

  b. Construct a relative frequency bar graph that shows on one graph both Chloe's small package of candies and the percents stated by the candy manufacturer. Use one color for the bar representing Chloe's candies and a different color for the bar representing the manufacturer's. Include a key showing what the two bar colors mean. What conclusions can you make? *@*

7. This table shows the number of students in each grade at a high school.

Class Size

Ninth grade	Tenth grade	Eleventh grade	Twelfth grade
185	175	166	150

  a. What percent of the school is represented in each grade? *(h)* 9th: 27%; 10th: 26%; 11th: 25%; 12th: 22%

  b. At semester break, the student population is counted again. The ninth grade has increased by 2%, the tenth grade has decreased by 1.5%, the eleventh grade has increased by 2.5%, and the twelfth grade has decreased by 2%. How many students are in each grade at the beginning of the second semester? By what percent has the total school population changed? What is the actual change in the number of students? 9th: 189; 10th: 172; 11th: 170; 12th: 147; 0.3%; 2 students

  c. Make a relative frequency circle graph for the situation at the beginning of the year and another circle graph for the situation at the beginning of the second semester. How has the distribution of students changed?

8. Match each bar graph with its corresponding circle graph. Try to do this without calculating the actual percents.

iii **a.**
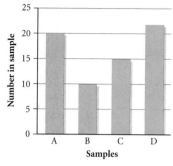
Number in sample vs. Samples (A, B, C, D)

i **b.**
ⓐ
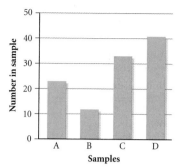
Number in sample vs. Samples (A, B, C, D)

iv **c.**
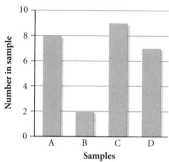
Number in sample vs. Samples (A, B, C, D)

ii **d.**
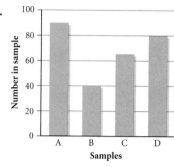
Number in sample vs. Samples (A, B, C, D)

i.

ii.

iii.

iv.

9. What is a reasonable estimate of the chance that a randomly thrown dart will land in the circle if you know the dart always hits the board? ⓗ $\frac{16\pi}{64} \approx 79\%$

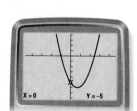
4 in.

▶ **Review**

9.3 **10.** Write an equation in general form for the parabola shown, with x-intercepts -1 and 2.5 and y-intercept -5. ⓐ
$y = 2x^2 - 3x - 5$

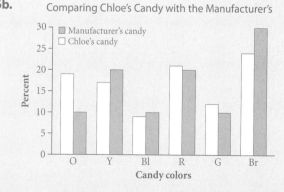
X = 0   Y = −5
[−4.7, 4.7, 1, −8.2, 4.2, 1]

6a.
Chloe's Candy Distribution
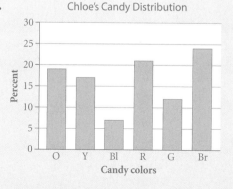
Percent vs. Candy colors (O, Y, Bl, R, G, Br)

6b.
Comparing Chloe's Candy with the Manufacturer's
▪ Manufacturer's candy
▫ Chloe's candy
Percent vs. Candy colors (O, Y, Bl, R, G, Br)

Chloe's bag of candy had the same dominant color as the graph from the manufacturer, and her least common color was one of the least manufactured. But the distributions are not very close.

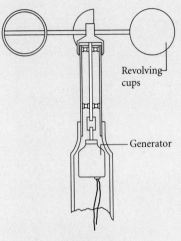

Revolving cups

Generator

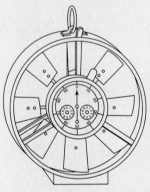

11a. 180 pulses per second

12b. Los Angeles County grew by 118,156, a change of 1.2%.

12c. Los Angeles County grew by over 4.9 times more people than did Douglas County, but it increased by only 1.2% rather than 13.6%. The population growth of Los Angeles County was more manageable from the point of view of the stress on the infrastructure, such as roads, schools, and utilities.

2.3 **11.** Astrid works as an intern in a windmill park in Holland. She has learned that the anemometer, which measures wind speed, gives off electrical pulses and that the pulses are counted each second. The ratio of pulses per second to wind speed in meters per second is always 4.5 to 1.

    a. If the wind speed is 40 meters per second, how many pulses per second should the anemometer be giving off?

    b. If the anemometer is giving off 84 pulses per second, what is the wind speed? 18.6̄ m/s

6.1 **12.** **APPLICATION** In 2001 there were 3141 counties in the United States. Here are data on five counties:

Fastest-Growing Counties between 2000 and 2001

County	2000 population	2001 population	Change from 2000 to 2001	Percent growth
Douglas County, CO	175,766	199,753	23,987	13.6
Loudoun County, VA	169,599	190,903	21,304	12.6
Forsyth County, GA	98,407	110,296	11,889	12.1
Rockwall County, TX	43,080	47,983	4,903	11.4
Williamson County, TX	249,967	278,067	28,100	11.2

(U.S. Census Bureau, *www.census.gov*)

    a. For each county, calculate the change in population from 2000 to 2001, and use it to calculate the percent of growth. Which county had the largest percent of growth in this time period? @ Douglas County had the largest percent of growth.

    b. Los Angeles County in California is the largest county in the country. Its population was 9,637,494 in 2001 and 9,519,338 in 2000. By what percent did the population of Los Angeles County grow?

    c. How does the growth of Los Angeles County compare to the population growth of the fastest-growing county? Which do you think is a better representation of the growth of a county, the percent of change or the actual number by which the county grew?

San Fernando Valley, part of Los Angeles County

LESSON 10.2

Probability Outcomes and Trials

The theory of probability is at bottom only common sense reduced to calculation.

PIERRE SIMON DE LAPLACE

This technician is testing blood types. Most people have blood type A, B, AB, or O, further categorized as either + or −. To learn more about blood types and blood donation, see the links at www.keymath.com/DA .

The chance that the next person you meet has a particular blood type can be determined from this relative frequency circle graph, which you saw in Exercise 1 of the previous lesson. The four possible results, called **outcomes,** are type O, type A, type B, and type AB. The chance that something will happen is called its **probability.** The probability of an outcome is the ratio of the number of ways or times that an outcome will occur to the total number of ways or times under consideration.

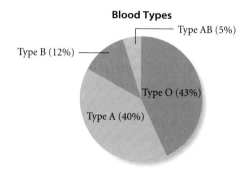

Blood Types

Type AB (5%)
Type B (12%)
Type O (43%)
Type A (40%)

So, what is the probability that the next person you meet will have blood type O? You can see in the circle graph that 43%, or 43 out of every 100 people, have blood type O. So, the probability that the next person has blood type O is $\frac{43}{100}$, or 0.43. Probabilities can be expressed as a percent, but more often they are expressed as a fraction or decimal.

In the example, you'll practice calculating some probabilities.

EXAMPLE

As part of her job with the forest service, Shandra tagged a total of 1470 squirrels last year. She tagged 820 black male squirrels, 100 black female squirrels, 380 gray male squirrels, and 170 gray female squirrels. If this distribution accurately reflects the squirrel population, what is the probability that the next squirrel she tags will be a gray male squirrel? A female squirrel? A red squirrel?

▶ Solution

The probability that the next squirrel tagged is a gray male squirrel can be expressed as the ratio

$$\frac{number\ of\ gray\ male\ squirrels\ tagged}{total\ number\ of\ squirrels\ tagged} = \frac{380}{1470} \approx 0.26$$

The probability that the next squirrel tagged is female is

Black female squirrels   Gray female squirrels

$$\frac{number\ of\ female\ squirrels\ tagged}{total\ number\ of\ squirrels\ tagged} = \frac{100 + 170}{1470} \approx 0.18$$

PLANNING

LESSON OUTLINE

One day:
5 min   Example
25 min   Investigation
5 min   Sharing
5 min   Closing
10 min   Exercises

MATERIALS

• packets of colored candies (or small colored markers)
• paper bags
• protractors
• Calculator Notes 10A, 10B
• Fathom demonstration Candy Colors, *optional*

TEACHING

In this lesson students calculate both experimental and theoretical probabilities.

▶ EXAMPLE

Point out that to be useful for calculating probabilities about the squirrel population, the distribution must be accurate, or representative.

NCTM STANDARDS

CONTENT		PROCESS	
✔	Number		Problem Solving
✔	Algebra	✔	Reasoning
✔	Geometry	✔	Communication
✔	Measurement	✔	Connections
✔	Data/Probability	✔	Representation

LESSON OBJECTIVES

• Define the basic terms and concepts of probability
• Find experimental probabilities
• Calculate theoretical probabilities

Guiding the Investigation

One Step

Start with this problem: "How many ways can you find the probability of drawing a red candy from the bag?" As students work, assist those who need help with the notion of probability, encourage them to find both experimental and theoretical probabilities, and urge groups to extend the question to other colors.

You can use the Fathom demonstration Candy Colors to replace or supplement this investigation.

During the last year Shandra hasn't tagged any red squirrels. Based on that information, the probability that the next squirrel tagged is red is 0.

$$\frac{number\ of\ red\ squirrels\ tagged}{total\ number\ of\ squirrels\ tagged} = \frac{0}{1470} = 0$$

In the example, each time a squirrel is tagged is a **trial.** Shandra conducted 1470 individual trials.

An **event** is any set of desired outcomes. For the squirrel example, you found the probabilities of the events "gray male," "female," and "red." You can use the notation P(gray male), P(female), and P(red) to indicate these probabilities.

Probabilities calculated using collected data, as in the example, are called **experimental probabilities,** or **observed probabilities.** Experimental probabilities generally become more accurate as larger amounts of data are collected, or more trials are performed.

Shandra can't know for sure the exact numbers of each kind of squirrel in the forest. But if she did, she could calculate **theoretical probabilities.** For example, the theoretical probability that the next squirrel tagged is gray would be

$$P(\text{gray squirrel}) = \frac{number\ of\ gray\ squirrels\ in\ the\ forest}{total\ number\ of\ squirrels\ in\ the\ forest}$$

The probability of an event is always between 0 and 1, inclusive. An impossible event has a probability of 0. An event that will definitely occur has a probability of 1. Can you think of an event with a probability of 0? An event with a probability of 1?

Investigation
Candy Colors

You will need

- a packet of colored candies
- a paper bag

In the previous lesson you learned about **relative frequency.** This investigation will show you why the experimental probability is sometimes also called the relative frequency. You will also work with known quantities to calculate theoretical probabilities.

You'll start with a packet of colored candies, and you'll conduct an experiment to determine the experimental probabilities of randomly selecting each color.

Step 1 | Use a table like this one to record the results of each trial. List the candy colors across the top.

	Experimental Outcomes						Total trials
	Red	Orange					
Tally							40
Experimental frequency							
Experimental probability (relative frequency)							/////

Put the candies in the paper bag, then randomly select a candy by reaching into the bag without looking and removing a candy. Record the color as a tally mark, then replace the candy into the bag before the next person reaches in. Take turns removing, tallying the color, and replacing pieces of candy for a total of 40 trials. Your total for each color category is called its **experimental frequency.**

Record the experimental frequency for each outcome (color) in your table.

Step 2 | From the experimental frequencies and the total number of trials (40), you can calculate the relative frequency, or experimental probability, of each color. For instance, the experimental probability of removing a red candy will be

$$\frac{number\ of\ red\ candies\ drawn}{total\ number\ of\ trials}$$

Record the experimental probability in the bottom row of the table. Do you see why experimental probability is also called relative frequency? How can you show these numbers as percents? What should the sum of the percents be?

When all the candies are put into a bag, drawing one candy from the bag has several possible outcomes—the different colors listed on your table. Each individual candy has an equal probability of being drawn, but some colors have a higher probability of being drawn than others.

Step 3 | Make a second table, listing the candy colors across the top.

	Outcomes						Total
	Red	Orange					
Number of candies counted							
Theoretical probability							

Dump out all the candies and count the number of candies of each color. Record this information in the top row.

Step 4 | Use the known quantities in the first row to calculate the theoretical probability of drawing each candy color. For example,

$$P(R) = \frac{number\ of\ red\ candies\ in\ the\ bag}{total\ number\ of\ candies\ in\ the\ bag}$$

Record the results in the bottom row of the table.

Step 2 **[ELL]** The word *draw* has several meanings in English. In this situation, to "draw from" the bag means "pull out of" the bag.

Step 2 It is called *relative frequency* because the number of outcomes in each event is considered in relation to the total number of trials. To show the results as percents, divide the experimental frequency by 40 and write the answer as a percent. The sum should be 100%.

Step 5 Sample answer: When there is a larger quantity of one color, the probability that it will be drawn is higher. The sum of all the probabilities should be 1.

SHARING IDEAS

Have students show (on transparencies) their tables from Steps 1 and 3. **[Ask]** "How would you describe the difference between experimental and theoretical probabilities? When are they the same?" [The experimental probabilities get closer to the theoretical probabilities as the number of trials increases.] This idea provides more preparation for the concept of mathematical limit and leads into Lesson 10.3.

Assessing Progress

Look for skill at finding relative frequencies, organizing data collection, and contributing to a group.

Outcomes may be the result of trials and have **experimental probabilities,** or they may be the result of theory and have **theoretical probabilities,** as symbolized by P(outcome). If there are n outcomes and they're all **equally likely,** the probability of each is $\frac{1}{n}$.

BUILDING UNDERSTANDING

These exercises give students practice at calculating experimental and theoretical probabilities.

ASSIGNING HOMEWORK

Essential	**1–3, 5, 6**
Performance assessment	**7, 11**
Portfolio	**8**
Journal	**7**
Group	**4, 6, 9, 10**
Review	**12, 13**

▶ Helping with the Exercises

Exercise 2b The notation P(S or C) is new. As needed, help students see why the probabilities of the outcomes S and C must be summed to find the probability of "either S or C."

Step 5	Is one color most likely to be drawn? Least likely? Explain the differences you found in the theoretical probabilities of drawing the different colors from the bag. What should their total be?
Step 6	Write a paragraph comparing your results for the theoretical probabilities you just calculated to the relative frequencies you calculated from your experiment.

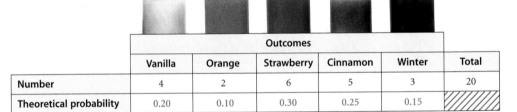

When looking at the probability of a particular outcome, first ask yourself, "What outcomes are possible?" and "Are the outcomes equally likely?" If a packet of candy has exactly the same number of each color of candy, outcomes for each individual color, such as "green," are **equally likely.**

EXERCISES

You will need your graphing calculator for Exercise **10.**

▶ Practice Your Skills

1. For each trial, list the possible outcomes.

  a. tossing a coin heads or tails

  b. rolling a die with faces numbered 1–6 1, 2, 3, 4, 5, or 6

  c. the sum when rolling 2 six-sided dice @ 2, 3, 4, 5, 6, 7, 8, 9, 10, 11, or 12

  d. spinning the pointer on a dial divided into sections A–E A, B, C, D, or E

2. The table below shows the distribution by fragrance of candles in a 20-candle assortment pack.

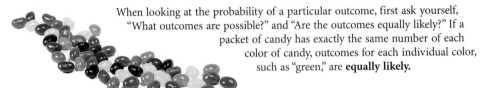

	Outcomes					
	Vanilla	Orange	Strawberry	Cinnamon	Winter	Total
Number	4	2	6	5	3	20
Theoretical probability	0.20	0.10	0.30	0.25	0.15	////

  a. Copy the table and record in the bottom row the probability of selecting at random that type of candle.

  b. Suppose these 20 candles are put into a box. If you reach into the box without looking, what is the probability that you will pull out either a strawberry or a cinnamon candle? In other words, what is P(S or C)? @ 0.55

  c. What is P(W or S or V)? @ 0.65

  d. Suppose all 20-candle assortment packs made by this company have the same number of each type of candle listed above. If you empty ten assortment packs into a huge box, what is P(C) for the huge box? Explain why this is so.

  P(C) = 0.25. All probabilities would be the same as for the original pack because the ratios wouldn't change.

3. One hundred tiny cubes were dropped onto a circle like the one at right, and all 100 cubes landed inside the circle. Twenty-seven cubes were completely or more than halfway inside the shaded region.

   a. Based on what happened, what is the observed probability of a cube landing in the shaded area? $\frac{27}{100} = 0.27$

   b. What is the theoretical probability in this situation? Explain your answer. ⓗ

4. Igba-ita ("pitch and toss") is a favorite recreational game in Africa. In one version of Igba-ita, four cowrie shells are thrown in an effort to get a favorable outcome of all four up or all four down. Now coins are often used instead of cowrie shells, and the name has changed to Igba-ego ("money toss"). Using four coins, what are the chances for an outcome in which all four land heads up or all four land tails up? (Claudia Zaslovsky, *Africa Counts*, 1973, p. 113) ⓐ $\frac{1}{8}$

   You can learn about more games from other countries with the links at 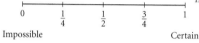 **www.keymath.com/DA** .

5. Draw and label a segment like this one. Answers will vary. The probability of 5f is 0 or very nearly 0; the probability of 5g is 1.

   0   $\frac{1}{4}$ $\frac{1}{2}$ $\frac{3}{4}$ 1

   Impossible   Certain

   Plot and label points on your segment to represent the probability for each situation.

   a. You will eat breakfast tomorrow morning.

   b. It will rain or snow sometime during the next month in your hometown.

   c. You will be absent from school fewer than five days this school year.

   d. You will get an A on your next mathematics test.

   e. The next person to walk in the door will be under 30 years old.

   f. Next Monday every teacher at your school will give 100 free points to each student.

   g. Earth will rotate once on its axis in the next 24 hours.

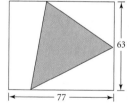

Reason and Apply

6. Suppose that 350 beans are randomly dropped on the rectangle shown at right and that 136 beans lie either totally inside the shaded region or more than halfway inside. Use this information to approximate the area of the shaded region.

   Total area:

   $77 \cdot 63 = 4851$; $\frac{a}{4851} = \frac{136}{350}$; $a = 1885$; the area is about 1900 square units.

Exercise 3 Exercise 3 leads into Exercise 6, in which students calculate the area of a region by finding the portion of randomly distributed objects that fall inside the region. Lesson 10.3 contains a similar exercise.

3b. P(landing in shaded area) = 0.25 because the shaded area is $\frac{1}{4}$ of the circle.

Exercise 5 Encourage students to use a mixture of fraction, decimal, and percent labels for points.

7a. Finding and counting a litter is a trial; an outcome may be having one cub (or two or three or four).

7b. No; if outcomes were equally likely, then the number of litters of each size would have been almost the same, with about nine litters of each size.

Exercise 9 To calculate the probabilities of the categories, students will need to find numerical data for each category by estimating or measuring the angles. Be prepared to lend protractors.

Exercise 10 To select categories with a calculator's random number generator, students must label the categories with intervals of numbers. Students can also use calculators to sort their lists.

7. Dr. Lynn Rogers of the North American Bear Center does research on bear cub survival. He observed 35 litters in 1996. The distribution of cubs is shown in this table.

Bear Litter Study

Number of cubs	1	2	3	4
Number of litters	2	8	22	3

(*The North Bearing News,* July 1997)

a. Describe a trial for this situation. Name one outcome. ⓐ

b. Is each outcome equally likely? Explain. ⓐ

c. Based on the given information, what is the probability that a litter will have exactly three cubs? ⓐ $\frac{22}{35} \approx 0.63$

8. Twenty randomly chosen high school students were asked to estimate the percent of students in their school who are planning to attend college. Base your answers to the questions on their responses.

a. Draw a dot plot to organize the data.

b. What are the chances that the next student asked will give an estimate of at least 75%? $\frac{5}{20}$, or $\frac{1}{4}$

c. If there are 4500 students in this high school, how many students do you think will give an estimate greater than or equal to 50%? $0.75 \cdot 4500$, or 3375

Student Responses

25	45	60	90
70	75	50	33
35	20	65	65
55	80	85	70
65	50	75	60

9. In the Wheel of Wealth game, contestants spin a large wheel like the one at right to see how much money each question is worth. ⓗ

a. What is the probability that a contestant will have a question worth $500? $\frac{1}{8}$

b. What is the probability that a contestant will have a question worth less than $500? ⓐ $\frac{90 + 180}{360} = \frac{270}{360}$, or $\frac{3}{4}$

c. If one contestant spins the wheel and it lands in the $400 section, what is the probability that the next contestant will spin the wheel and have a question worth more than $400? ⓐ $\frac{45 + 45}{360} = \frac{90}{360}$, or $\frac{1}{4}$

10. The Candy Coated Carob Company produces six different-colored candies with colors distributed as shown in the circle graph.

a. You could use the numbers between 1 and 100 to represent all the candies and choose numbers in this range to represent the percent of each color. For example, because P(red) = 12%, let the numbers from 1 to 12 represent a red candy. The next interval, which will represent orange, has to have 18 numbers because P(orange) = 18%. Therefore, let this interval be the numbers from 13 to 30. Identify intervals to represent the yellow, green, light-blue, and dark-blue candies. Make a table like the one on the next page and fill in the intervals.

Carob Candy Colors

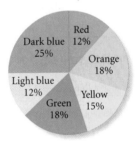

8a.

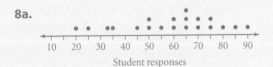

Student responses

	Outcomes						
	Red	Orange	Yellow	Green	Light blue	Dark blue	Total
Interval	1 to 12	13 to 30	31 to 45	46 to 63	64 to 75	76 to 100	/////
Number of candies							50
Probability							/////

b. Answers will vary. A routine that works for some calculators is randInt(1,100,50).

b. Enter a calculator routine that will generate a list of 50 random integers from 1 to 100. These numbers will represent 50 candies. [▶ 🖩 See **Calculator Note 10A.** ◀]

c. Determine how many of each color you have in your collection. You may want to sort, or order, your list first. [▶ 🖩 See **Calculator Note 10B.** ◀] Record the results in your table.

c. Answers will vary. Sorting the list in ascending order is suggested.

d. Enter your experimental probabilities in the last row of your table.
Answers will vary.

11. If you flip a paper cup into the air, what are the possible outcomes? Do you think the outcomes are equally likely? How can you test your conjecture?

▶ **Review**

1.6 **12.** Give four pairs of coordinates that would create a shape like this when connected. ⓗ

1.2 **13.** APPLICATION The star hitter on the baseball team at City Community College had a batting average of .375 before the start of a three-game series. (*Note:* Batting average is calculated by dividing hits by times at bat; sacrifice bunts and walks do not count as times at bat.) During the three games, he came to the plate to bat eleven times. In these eleven plate appearances, he walked twice and had one sacrifice bunt. He either got a hit or struck out in his other plate appearances. If his batting average was the same at the end of the three-game series as at the beginning, how many hits did he get? 3

project

PROBABILITY, GENES, AND CHROMOSOMES

How are we or how are we not like our parents? In this project you will use probabilities to describe how an individual's gender, eye color, color blindness, blood type, or other trait can be traced to his or her parents.

The number of girls and boys is not equal in every family. However, every child born has about an equal chance of being a boy or a girl. So if you consider the children of hundreds of families, about half would be girls and half boys. The same relationship does not hold for eye color. Parents who both have brown eyes may have a child with blue eyes. Or a father with blue eyes and a mother with brown eyes may not be able to have a child with blue eyes.

Research the difference between the way gender and the way eye color, or another human trait, is determined. Write a paper or give a presentation that describes these probabilities.

Exercise 11 You might take this opportunity to mention that flipping the cup is a *trial*.

11. Outcomes: Cup lands on its bottom, cup lands on its top, cup lands on its side; answers will vary, but the outcomes are probably not equally likely; flip or toss a cup many times, record the results, and calculate the experimental probability of each outcome.

12. Answers could be any parallelogram with horizontal sides; one answer might be $(-4, 1), (-1, 3), (4, 3), (1, 1)$.

Exercise 13 Solving this problem requires a good understanding of the game of baseball, which some students may not have.

Supporting the **project**

MOTIVATION

The first experiments to see how parents are like offspring were done on plants in the nineteenth century by Gregor Mendel before genes had been discovered. Now we are beginning to map the genetic codes of many forms of life, including humans. Students can focus on traits that they or their parents have. Students who are adopted or in foster care may prefer to study inheritance in plants.

OUTCOMES

▶ Clear explanations are given of how the gender of human children is determined.
▶ The heredity patterns of one or two other traits are described.
• Additional information about the history and science of genetics is included.
• Heredity for more than three traits is described.

PLANNING

LESSON OUTLINE

One day:

5 min   Example

25 min   Investigation

5 min   Sharing

5 min   Closing

10 min   Exercises

MATERIALS

- Calculator Notes 10A, 10B, 10C
- Fathom demonstration Closer and Closer, *optional*

TEACHING

[Language] *Random* is a relative term. Traffic patterns are random relative to an observer, even though the drivers know where they are going. Although the bees' behavior is determined by instinct and communication with other bees, it is random relative to a person looking at the beehive.

EXAMPLE

[Language] Ask students for examples of predictions to help explain the meaning of *predict*.

Prediction is difficult, especially of the future.

NIELS BOHR

Random Outcomes

Mario is an entomologist who studies the behavior of bees. He videotapes bees leaving a hive for one day and counts 247 bees flying east and 628 bees flying west. Can he predict what the next bee will do? Can he use the results of his study to predict approximately how many of the next 100 bees will fly east? Will the videotape counts be the same if he repeats the study a few days later? Is there a pattern to the bees' flying direction, or does it appear that the bees fly randomly either east or west?

An outcome is **random** when you can't be sure what will happen on the next trial. If three bees always fly west after each eastbound bee, then this action is not random. When a bee leaves a hive, it is following instinct and instructions from other bees. To the bee, its actions are not random. But unless an observer can see a pattern and predict the direction of the next bee, the pattern is random to the observer.

EXAMPLE

Use the results of Mario's study, described above, to predict approximately how many of the next 100 bees will fly east.

▶ Solution

The experimental probability that a bee will fly west is

$$\frac{number\ of\ bees\ that\ flew\ west}{all\ bees\ observed} = \frac{628}{628 + 247} = \frac{628}{875}$$

The experimental probability that a bee will fly east is

$$\frac{number\ of\ bees\ that\ flew\ east}{all\ bees\ observed} = \frac{247}{628 + 247} = \frac{247}{875}$$

Mario can calculate the *probability* of what the next bee will do, but he can't predict its *actual direction*. From Mario's perspective the outcome is random.

The probability ratio $\frac{247}{875}$ is about 0.28, or 28%. So he can expect about 28 out of 100 bees to fly east.

However, this is a probability, not a fact. He should not be surprised by 26 or 30 bees flying east. But if 50 or more of the bees fly east, he might conclude that the conditions have changed and his observations of yesterday no longer help him determine the probabilities for today.

When you toss a coin, you cannot predict whether it will show heads or tails because the outcome is random. You do know, however, that there are two equally likely outcomes—heads or tails. Therefore, the theoretical probability of getting a head is $\frac{1}{2}$, and the theoretical probability of getting a tail is $\frac{1}{2}$. What happens when you toss a coin many times?

LESSON OBJECTIVES

- Understand the difference between random and nonrandom outcomes
- See how experimental probabilities approach theoretical probabilities as the number of trials increases

NCTM STANDARDS

CONTENT		PROCESS
✔ Number		Problem Solving
Algebra		✔ Reasoning
✔ Geometry		✔ Communication
✔ Measurement		✔ Connections
✔ Data/Probability		✔ Representation

Investigation
Calculator Coin Toss

In this investigation you will compare a theoretical probability with an experimental probability from 100 trials. You will look at how the experimental probability is related to the number of trials.

You could do this investigation by tossing coins 100 times, or you can use your calculator to simulate tossing many coins in a very short time.

Step 1 To number your tosses, enter the sequence of numbers from 1 to 100 into list L1 on your calculator. [▶ 🖳 See **Calculator Note 10B.** ◀]

Step 2 If a calculator randomly chooses 0 or 1, that's just like flipping a coin and getting tails or heads. Let 0 represent tails and 1 represent heads. Enter 100 randomly generated 0's and 1's into list L2. [▶ 🖳 See **Calculator Note 10A.** ◀]

Step 3 Display the cumulative sum of list L2 (number of heads) in list L3. [▶ 🖳 See **Calculator Note 10B.** ◀]

The table below shows an example in which the result of nine tosses was T, H, T, H, H, T, T, H, T. The numeral 1 in list L2 indicates heads. What does it mean if the eighth and ninth values in list L3 are both 4? *The ninth flip gave a 0 (tails) and added nothing to the cumulative sum of heads.*

Step 4 Calculate the ratio of heads to total number of tosses by entering $\frac{L3}{L1}$ into list L4. What does this ratio represent? *the experimental probability of tossing heads*

Number of flips (L1)	Result of last flip (L2)	Total number of heads (L3)	Total heads / Total tosses (L4)
1	0	0	0
2	1	1	0.50
3	0	1	0.33
4	1	2	0.50
5	1	3	0.60
6	0	3	0.50
7	0	3	0.43
8	1	4	0.50
9	0	4	0.44
⋮	⋮	⋮	⋮

Step 5	Create a scatter plot using list L1 as the *x*-values and list L4 as the *y*-values. Name an appropriate graphing window for this plot. possible answer: [0, 100, 10, 0.2, 0.8, 0.1]
Step 6	Enter the theoretical probability of tossing a head in Y1 on the Y= screen. Graph your equation on the same screen as your scatter plot from Step 5.
Step 7	Compare your plot to that of other members of your group. Describe what appears to happen after 100 trials. What would you expect to see if you continued this experiment for 150 trials? Make a sketch of your predicted graph of 150 trials. Run the calculator simulation. [▶ 🖥 See **Calculator Note 10C.** ◀] Compare the results to your prediction.
Step 8	Explain what happens to the relationship between the theoretical probability and the experimental probability as you do more and more trials. The larger the number of trials, the closer the experimental probability will be to the theoretical probability.

Step 6 The theoretical probability 0.5 gives a horizontal straight line that the curve from Step 5 should approach.

Steps 7 and 8 By making this comparison as more and more trials are conducted, students should come to realize that experimental probabilities approach theoretical probabilities as the number of trials increases. The graph provides a picture of a curve getting closer and closer to a line. Students again encounter the concept of limit.

SHARING IDEAS

Good results for groups to present are those from Steps 4, 6, and 7. To help students appreciate the notion that more trials yield better results, ask them to imagine what the world would be like if that weren't the case. So much of what we learn is from estimating probabilities on the basis of trials!

Ask students to pretend they've flipped a fair coin seven times and gotten tails each time. **[Ask]**, "What's the probability that the eighth flip will also produce tails?" Some students may say it's very small, because the probability of getting eight tails in a row is tiny. This reasoning is called the "gambler's fallacy." Others may say that the probability of getting tails on the eighth flip is pretty high, because the coin is "running in tails." Actually, the coin has no memory of what has happened to it before; the eighth outcome is independent of all previous outcomes. So the probability of tails on the eighth flip is $\frac{1}{2}$.

Assessing Progress

As students work through the investigation and present results, you can assess their ability to enter and manipulate calculator lists, their understanding of experimental and theoretical probabilities, and their intuition about limits.

If you tossed a coin many times, you would expect the ratio of the number of heads to the number of tosses to be close to $\frac{1}{2}$. The more times you toss the coin, the closer the ratio of heads to total tosses will be to $\frac{1}{2}$. With random events, patterns often emerge in the long run, but these patterns do not help predict a particular outcome.

When flipping a coin, you know what the theoretical probabilities are for heads and tails. However, in some situations you cannot calculate the theoretical probability of an outcome. After performing many trials, you can determine an experimental probability based on your experimental results.

EXERCISES

You will need your graphing calculator for Exercises **5, 7,** and **8.**

▶ Practice Your Skills

1. **APPLICATION** Suppose there are 180 twelfth graders in your school, and the school records show that 74 of them will be attending college outside their home state. You conduct a survey of 50 twelfth graders, and 15 tell you that they will be leaving the state to attend college. What is the theoretical probability that a random twelfth grader will be leaving the state to attend college? Based on your survey results, what is the experimental probability? What could explain the difference? @

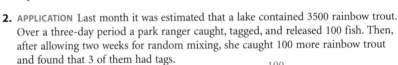

2. **APPLICATION** Last month it was estimated that a lake contained 3500 rainbow trout. Over a three-day period a park ranger caught, tagged, and released 100 fish. Then, after allowing two weeks for random mixing, she caught 100 more rainbow trout and found that 3 of them had tags.
   a. What is the probability of catching a tagged trout? $\frac{100}{3500} \approx 0.0286$
   b. What assumptions must you make to answer 2a? @
   c. Based on the number of tagged fish she caught two weeks later, what is the park ranger's experimental probability? $\frac{3}{100}$, or 0.03

Closing the Lesson

The primary idea of this lesson is that experimental probabilities approach theoretical probabilities as the number of trials increases. Thus, probabilities can help predict the long-term results of many **random** outcomes.

BUILDING UNDERSTANDING

These exercises help strengthen the differences and relationships between experimental and theoretical probabilities.

See page 567 for answers to Exercises 1 and 2b.

3. Suppose 250 people have applied for 15 job openings at a chain of restaurants.

   a. What fraction of the applicants will get a job? $\frac{15}{250}$

   b. What fraction of the applicants will not get a job? $\frac{235}{250}$

   c. Assuming all applicants are equally qualified and have the same chance of being hired, what is the probability that a randomly selected applicant will get a job? $\frac{15}{250}$, or 0.06

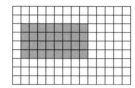

and full-time. Low stress work environment. Excellent benefits package. Call 555-7231, M-F, 9 to 5.

Restaurant Workers

Many positions open at new restaurant chain in desirable downtown location, from entry level to management. Excellent benefits. Apply in person to Dave Lee, 2100 Buena Vista Avenue. No phone calls or emails please.

▶ Reason and Apply

4. If 25 randomly plotted points landed in the shaded region shown in the grid, about how many points do you estimate were plotted? ⓗ $\frac{32}{126}x = 25; x \approx 98$

5. In a random walk, you move according to rules with each move being determined by a random process. The simplest type of random walk is a one-dimensional walk where each move is either one step forward or one step backward on a number line.

   a. Start at 0 on the number line and flip a coin to determine your move. Heads means you take one step forward to the next integer, and tails means you take one step backward to the previous integer. What sequence of six tosses will land you on the number-line locations +1, +2, +1, +2, +3, +2? ⓐ H, H, T, H, H, T

   b. Explore a one-dimensional walk of 100 moves using a calculator routine that randomly generates +1 or −1.

   In list L1, generate random numbers with 1 representing a step forward and −1 representing a step backward. Describe what you need to do with list L1 to show your number-line location after every step. [▶ ▦ See **Calculator Notes 10A** and **10B.** ◀]

   c. Describe the results of your simulation. Is this what you expected?

   After many steps, you may still be close to 0.

ASSIGNING HOMEWORK

Essential	1–4
Performance assessment	3
Portfolio	7
Journal	2, 4, 11
Group	5, 6
Review	8–11

▶ Helping with the Exercises

1. Theoretical probability: $\frac{74}{180} \approx 0.411$; experimental probability: $\frac{15}{50}$, or 0.30. Possible answers: You can expect a wide variation in survey results. Perhaps your method of selecting students was not random. For example, your results could be biased because you talked only to students who were participating in after-school activities or only to students in a particular class. Perhaps the question was worded in such a way that students were biased in their response or reluctant to answer it honestly.

2b. You have to assume that the population is 3500, it remains stable (no fish die and no new fish hatch), and the fish are well mixed.

Exercise 5 As needed, remind students how they found cumulative sums in the investigation. Although students' intuition may say correctly that the walk will probably stay close to the starting point, you might point out that the walk might land on any point if enough steps are taken.

5b. Find the cumulative sum of list L1.

```
2randInt(0,1,100
)-1→L₁
{1 -1 1 1 -1 -1…
cumSum(L₁)
{1 0 1 2 1 0 -1…
```

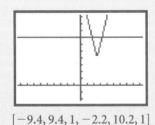

$[-9.4, 9.4, 1, -2.2, 10.2, 1]$

6. A thumbtack can land "point up" or "point down."

   a. When you drop a thumbtack on a hard surface, do you think the two outcomes will be equally likely? If not, what would you predict for $P(\text{up})$? @ Answers will vary.

   b. Drop a thumbtack 100 times onto a hard surface, or drop 10 thumbtacks 10 times. Record the frequency of "point up" and "point down." What are your experimental probabilities for the two responses?

   c. Make a prediction for the probabilities on a softer surface like a towel. Repeat the experiment over a towel. What are your experimental probabilities? In one actual experiment, there was no change between a hard surface and a soft one.

7. APPLICATION A teacher would like to use her calculator to randomly assign her 24 students to 6 groups of 4 students each. Create a calculator routine to do this. One possible routine is randInt(1,6). Assign students in order to groups 1 to 6, skipping a number once that group is full.

▶ Review

7.5   **8.** Use algebraic techniques to solve 8a and b. Then use calculator graphs to help you solve 8c and d.

   a. $2\left|2x - 5\right| + 4 = 7$

   b. $-0.5(x - 2)^2 + 7 = 4$

   c. $2\left|2x - 5\right| + 4 \leq 7$

   d. $-0.5(x - 2)^2 + 7 < 4$

2.2   **9.** APPLICATION Zoe is an intern at Yellowstone National Park. One of her jobs is to estimate the chipmunk population in the campground areas. She starts by trapping 60 chipmunks, giving them a checkup, and banding their legs. A few weeks later, Zoe traps 84 chipmunks. Of these, 22 have bands on their legs. How many chipmunks should Zoe estimate are in the campgrounds? @ 229

0.3   **10.** For 10a–f, if the number has an exponent, write it in standard form. If the number is in standard form, write it with an exponent other than 1.

   a. 4^3 64   **b.** $\left(\frac{1}{6}\right)^2$ $\frac{1}{36}$ **c.** $\left(\frac{3}{4}\right)^2$ $\frac{9}{16}$

   d. 27 3^3 **e.** $\frac{1}{125}$ $\left(\frac{1}{5}\right)^3$ **f.** $\frac{4}{81}$ $\left(\frac{2}{9}\right)^2$, or $\frac{2^2}{3^4}$

10.2   **11.** Explain how to use probability to find the area of the irregular shape in the rectangle.

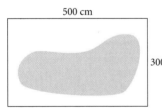

500 cm

300 cm

keymath.com/DA

Answers will vary. You could cover the rectangle with a grid, count the squares in the shaded area, and compare that number to the total number of squares in the rectangle. Or you could cover the area with beans and compare the number of beans inside the shaded area to the total number of beans. Multiply the ratio $\frac{number\ of\ beans\ in\ shaded\ area}{total\ number\ of\ beans}$ by 150,000 cm².

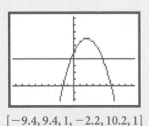

$[-9.4, 9.4, 1, -2.2, 10.2, 1]$

LESSON

10.4

Counting Techniques

A small error in the beginning is a great one in the end.
SAINT THOMAS AQUINAS

When calculating probabilities, you often need to count to find the number of outcomes that go in the numerator or denominator. When there are a lot of possible outcomes, this can get difficult. In this lesson you'll learn some techniques to make counting outcomes easier and faster.

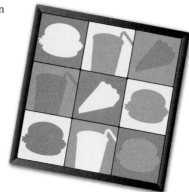

Suppose you take your little brother out to a fast-food restaurant for dinner. The kids' meal allows him to choose between four burgers, three drinks, and two desserts. How many different meal possibilities are there?

Each set of choices can be represented by a path through a **tree diagram.** This tree diagram shows four choices of burgers, then three choices of drink for each burger choice, then two choices of dessert for each burger-drink pair. The complete tree shows 24 paths that represent the 24 different possibilities. Drawing all 24 paths or listing all the sets of choices is a bit messy, but tree diagrams can help you visualize possible choices.

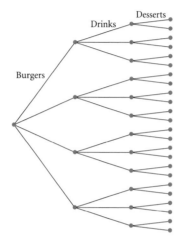

Desserts
Drinks
Burgers

Investigation
Prizes!

As a group, choose four people in your class. You will use their names throughout the investigation. Feel free to abbreviate names.

Step 1 | Suppose one of these four people is going to receive a free CD. Write down all possible prize winners. How many possibilities are there? A, B, C, D; 4

Step 2 | Now suppose that two of these four people will receive prizes. One of the four will receive a free CD and another will receive a free movie ticket. Write down all of the possible sets of two winners. Keep your list organized so that you are sure you don't miss anyone. You might list all the possible ticket winners to go with each possible CD winner, perhaps guided by a tree diagram. How many sets of winners are there? (*Note:* Person A winning a CD and Person B winning a movie ticket is different from Person A winning a movie ticket and Person B winning a CD.) AB, AC, AD, BA, BC, BD, CA, CB, CD, DA, DB, DC; 12

NCTM STANDARDS

CONTENT		PROCESS	
✔	Number	✔	Problem Solving
✔	Algebra	✔	Reasoning
✔	Geometry	✔	Communication
	Measurement		Connections
✔	Data/Probability	✔	Representation

LESSON OBJECTIVES

- Use a tree diagram to represent possible paths or choices
- Learn the definitions of and notations for permutations and combinations, and distinguish between them
- Use the counting principle to count arrangements
- Count permutations, combinations, or other arrangements to determine probabilities

---

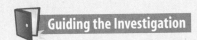
Steps 2 and 3 Students may have difficulty making systematic lists, even with the help of tree diagrams. **[Ask]** "What approach are you taking to be systematic?"

Step 5 You can display the Casting Arrangements transparency and ask students to help complete the tree.

SHARING IDEAS

You might have students present their ideas about Step 5. Encourage students to justify their answers. To preview Example A, **[Ask]** "How many casting arrangements would there be if all five students got parts?" To foreshadow Example C, **[Ask]** "How many ways could three of the five students be chosen for the play without regard to their roles?"

Assessing Progress

You can check students' understanding of probability and randomness and their ability to think systematically.

▶ **EXAMPLE A**

This example motivates the counting principle as a means of counting permutations. Although part a could be answered using the terminology of factorials, that topic is postponed until Exercise 9. **[Alert]** Students may think of permutations as numbers; permutations are the actual arrangements that are being counted.

Step 3
ABC, ABD, ACB, ACD, ADB, ADC, BAC, BAD, BCA, BCD, BDA, BDC, CAB, CAD, CBA, CBD, CDA, CDB, DAB, DAC, DBA, DBC, DCA, DCB; 24

Step 4 4; 4 · 3; 4 · 3 · 2. Multiply decreasing numbers starting with the total number of students and using as many factors as students you want to choose.

Step 3
Now suppose that three of the original four people receive prizes. One person receives a free CD, the second person receives a free movie ticket, and the third person receives a free meal at a local restaurant. Write down all of the possible sets of winners. How many sets of winners are there?

Step 4
Look at your lists and number totals in Steps 1–3. Describe how to calculate the number totals without listing all possible sets.

Step 5
Try your method from Step 4 on this problem: Suppose you have a group of five students, and three of them will be cast in a play as the hero, the villain, and the fool. How many different casting arrangements are possible? To arrange three students from five, multiply 5 · 4 · 3 to get 60.

Arrangements like those in the investigation and in the next example are called **permutations.** The *order* in a permutation is significant, and once a choice is made that choice cannot be used again in the same sequence.

EXAMPLE A

You are redecorating your room and have five pictures to arrange in a row along one wall. The pictures are labeled A, B, C, D, and E.

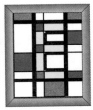

a. How many different ways can you arrange the five pictures?

b. If you arrange the pictures in a random order, what is the probability of any one outcome?

c. How many different ways can you arrange any three of the five pictures along a wall? If you arrange the pictures in a random order, what is the probability that the arrangement will be ABC?

▶ Solution

Tree diagrams will help you analyze this situation.

a. Visualize a tree diagram. There are five choices for the first picture. After you've chosen one, there are four remaining choices for the second picture. This makes 5 · 4, or 20, different paths so far. For each of the twenty arrangements, you can then choose one of the remaining three pictures, and then choose one of the remaining two pictures. Then choose the last remaining picture. The tree diagram will have 5 · 4 · 3 · 2 · 1, or 120, different paths, meaning the pictures can be arranged in 120 ways.

b. Because the arrangement is made at random, all 120 paths are equally likely. So the probability of any one path or arrangement is $\frac{1}{120}$.

c. Imagine a tree now with a sequence of three selections. For the first picture, you have five choices. For the second picture, you have four choices remaining. And for the third picture, you have three choices. So the tree diagram has 5 · 4 · 3, or 60, different paths, meaning three of five pictures can be arranged in 60 ways. The paths are equally likely, so the probability of any one path, such as ABC, is $\frac{1}{60}$.

In Example A you *permuted,* or arranged, all five of the five pictures, and then you permuted three of the five pictures. The numbers of these permutations can be written $_5P_5 = 120$ and $_5P_3 = 60$. The notation $_nP_r$ is read "the number of permutations of *n* things chosen *r* at a time."
[▶ 💻 See **Calculator Note 10D** to learn how to compute numbers of permutations on your calculator. ◀]

In Example B you'll compute the number of outcomes for an arrangement that is not a permutation.

EXAMPLE B

How many different student identification (ID) numbers can be assigned if an ID number consists of any two letters from the alphabet followed by any three digits?

▶ EXAMPLE B

In this example students apply the counting principle to count arrangements that are not permutations.

This arrangement is not a permutation because the ID numbers can have repeated use of letters and digits. Any of the 26 letters A–Z can be used in each of the first two spaces, and any of the 10 digits 0–9 can be used in the next three spaces.

You can imagine a tree diagram, but you certainly wouldn't want to draw one! However, you can figure out the total number of paths, or arrangements, by multiplying the number of choices for each entry.

26 choices	26 choices	10 choices	10 choices	10 choices
↓	↓	↓	↓	↓
_____	_____	_____	_____	_____

So there are 26 · 26 · 10 · 10 · 10, or 676,000, different ID numbers possible.

In the investigation and Examples A and B, you multiplied to find the number of possible outcomes. This procedure is called the **counting principle.**

> ## Counting Principle
>
> Suppose there are *a* ways to make a choice, and for each of these there are *b* ways to make a second choice, and for each of these there are *c* ways to make a third choice, and so on. The product $a \cdot b \cdot c \cdot \cdots$ is the number of possible outcomes.

The counting principle can help you identify the number of possible arrangements without having to make a list and count them. The counting principle works for permutations as well as situations like Example B.

In some situations the arrangements ABC and BCA are counted as the same outcome. For example, the committee of Alan, Benito, and Claire is identical to the committee of Benito, Claire, and Alan, and should not be counted more than once. In fact, the six permutations ABC, ACB, BAC, BCA, CAB, and CBA make up only one combination. A **combination** is an arrangement in which the order is not important. But again, an object can be selected or used only once in any combination (so you can't have a committee of Claire, Claire, and Alan). The notation $_nC_r$ is read "the number of combinations of *n* things chosen *r* at a time."

EXAMPLE C

A piggy bank contains six coins: dollar, half-dollar, quarter, dime, nickel, and penny. If you turn the bank upside down and shake it, one coin will fall out at a time.

a. If you shake the bank until three coins fall out, how many different sets of coins can you get?

b. What is the probability that you will get exactly 40¢?

A puggy bank!

▶ **Solution** This situation is a combination because once the coins fall out, you have a collection—the order is not important. If you have a dime, a nickel, and a penny, that's the same as if you have a nickel, a penny, and a dime.

a. The number of combinations of six things combined three at a time is written $_6C_3$. To calculate this number, start by finding the number of permutations, $_6P_3 = 6 \cdot 5 \cdot 4 = 120$. But this includes all possible orders for any three coins to fall from the bank. Say you have a dime, a nickel, and a penny. Abbreviate these as D, N, and P. The permutations of D, N, and P are

DNP, DPN, NDP, NPD, PDN, PND

So each combination of three objects contains six permutations. (This is equivalent to $_3P_3 = 3 \cdot 2 \cdot 1 = 6$.) So divide the number of permutations by 6 to get the number of combinations, $_6C_3 = \frac{120}{6} = 20$. You can check this result with your calculator. [▶ ▦ See **Calculator Note 10E** to learn how to compute numbers of combinations on your calculator. ◀]

b. You'll have 40¢ only if the quarter, dime, and nickel fall out. So the probability of getting 40¢ is $\frac{1}{20}$.

As you use tree diagrams, the counting principle, and your calculator to find numbers of arrangements, think carefully about each exercise. It is important to determine correctly whether a situation is represented by combinations, permutations, or neither.

EXERCISES

▶ **Practice Your Skills**

1. At a restaurant, you select three different side dishes from eight possibilities. Is this situation a permutation, a combination, or neither? Explain. ⓐ
   combination, because the order doesn't matter and no dish can be chosen more than once
2. Identify each situation as a permutation, a combination, or neither. If neither, explain why.
   a. The number of different committees of 10 students that can be chosen from the 50 members of the freshman class. ⓐ combination
   b. The number of different ice-cream cones if all three scoops are different flavors and a cone with vanilla, strawberry, then chocolate is different from a cone with vanilla, chocolate, then strawberry. permutation
   c. The number of different ice-cream cones if all three scoops are different flavors and a cone with vanilla, chocolate, then strawberry is considered the same as a cone with vanilla, strawberry, then chocolate. combination
   d. The number of different three-scoop ice-cream cones if you can choose multiple scoops of the same flavor. neither, because repeats are allowed

Closing the Lesson

Restate the main ideas of this lesson. To find the numerator and denominator of a probability, we often need to do complex counting. Often a **tree diagram** can help with that counting. When tree diagrams get too messy, we use a shortcut, the **counting principle.** One special case of counting is counting **permutations,** in which each choice can be made in one less way than the previous choice. We can think of collections, or **combinations,** as groups of permutations and count them by dividing the number of permutations by the size of each group.

BUILDING UNDERSTANDING

These exercises give students practice in identifying and counting permutations and combinations and in applying the counting principle, often to calculate probabilities.

ASSIGNING HOMEWORK

Essential	1–4, 9
Performance assessment	5–8, 10
Portfolio	9
Journal	5, 7, 11
Group	5, 12
Review	13–17

▶ **Helping with the Exercises**

Exercises 1 and 2 Students may need to be reminded that in permutations and combinations, an object cannot be selected more than once.

3b. $\dfrac{{}_5P_3}{{}_3P_3} = \dfrac{5 \cdot 4 \cdot 3}{3 \cdot 2 \cdot 1} = 10$

Exercise 4e **[Alert]** Many students have difficulty with the conditional reasoning required here. If needed, **[Ask]** "What paths does the part of the question that follows the phrase *If you know* restrict your attention to?" Representing those paths as DTT, TDT, TTD, and TTT can help students see that the D can occur in any of three places (or not at all).

4a and b.

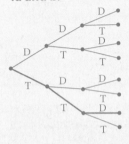

4c. neither, because repetition of the objects is allowed

Exercise 5 Encourage creative stories!

5a. Possible answer: I own eight pairs of shoes and am deciding which two pairs to take. I will wear one pair and pack the other. There are 56 ways to do this.

5b. Possible answer: I have 12 pairs of socks and am deciding which 4 pairs to take. The order in which I pack them doesn't matter. There are 495 ways to do this.

5c. Possible answer: I have six pairs of pants and am deciding which two pairs to take. I can pack them in either order. There are 15 ways to do this.

6c. $\dfrac{1}{6} \approx 0.167$

Exercise 6d As needed, **[Ask]** "In how many of the outcomes are the books in the order of publication? In how many of the outcomes are they not in that order?"

---

3. Evaluate each number of permutations or combinations without using your calculator. Show your calculations.

   a. ${}_5P_3$ @   **b.** ${}_5C_3$ @   **c.** ${}_5P_4$ **d.** ${}_5C_4$

   $5 \cdot 4 \cdot 3 = 60$ $5 \cdot 4 \cdot 3 \cdot 2 = 120$ $\dfrac{5 \cdot 4 \cdot 3 \cdot 2}{4 \cdot 3 \cdot 2 \cdot 1} = 5$

▶ Reason and Apply

4. This tree diagram shows possible results for the first two games in a three-game series between the Detroit Tigers and Texas Rangers.

   a. Copy and extend the diagram on your paper to show all outcomes of a three-game series.

   b. Highlight the path indicating that Texas won the first two games and Detroit won the final game.

   c. Does your diagram model permutations, combinations, or neither? Explain.

   d. If each outcome is equally likely, what is the probability that Texas won the first two games and Detroit won the third? @ $\frac{1}{8}$, or 0.125

   e. If you know Texas wins more than one game, what is the probability that the sequence is TTD? $\frac{1}{4}$, or 0.25

5. You are packing your suitcase for a weekend trip. Create a scenario for each expression. (For example, for $9 \cdot 8 \cdot 7 = 504$, you might answer: I have 9 shirts and I pack 3 in the order I will wear them. There are 504 ways to do this.)

   a. ${}_8P_2 = 56$ **b.** $\dfrac{12 \cdot 11 \cdot 10 \cdot 9}{4 \cdot 3 \cdot 2 \cdot 1} = 495$ @   **c.** ${}_6C_2 = 15$

6. Sydney has one copy of each of the six Harry Potter books.

   a. In how many ways can Sydney's six books be arranged on a shelf? 720

   b. How many ways can the books be arranged so that *Harry Potter and the Chamber of Secrets* will be the rightmost book? 120

   c. Use the answers from 6a and b to find the probability that *Harry Potter and the Chamber of Secrets* will be the rightmost book if the books are arranged at random.

   d. What is the probability that the books will be in the exact order in which they were published? @ $\frac{1}{720} \approx 0.001$

   e. What is the probability that the books will *not* be in the exact order in which they were published? ℎ $\frac{719}{720} \approx 0.999$

J. K. Rowling, author of the Harry Potter series, talks with Queen Elizabeth II at a book signing.

7. *Mini-Investigation* What is the relationship between your answers to 6d and e? These sorts of probabilities are called **complementary outcomes**—one is the chance that something happens and the other is the chance that the same thing *doesn't* happen. What conjecture can you make about complementary outcomes? The answer to 6e can be found by subtracting the answer to 6d from 1. (That is, the answers to 6d and e sum to 1.) The probabilities of complementary outcomes always sum to 1.

8. Five students are to be seated in a row of five chairs.

   a. How many different arrangements are possible? ⓐ 120

   b. If Jon always has to be first, how many arrangements are possible? 24

   c. Are these seating arrangements permutations or combinations? permutations

9. *Mini-Investigation* A product like $3 \cdot 2 \cdot 1$ or $5 \cdot 4 \cdot 3 \cdot 2 \cdot 1$ is called a **factorial** expression and is written with an exclamation point, like this: $3 \cdot 2 \cdot 1 = 3!$ and $5 \cdot 4 \cdot 3 \cdot 2 \cdot 1 = 5!$.

   a. How can you calculate 8!? $8! = 8 \cdot 7 \cdot 6 \cdot 5 \cdot 4 \cdot 3 \cdot 2 \cdot 1 = 40{,}320$

   b. How can you use factorial notation to calculate the number of permutations of 10 objects chosen 10 at a time? [▶ 🖳 See **Calculator Note 10F** to learn how to compute $n!$ with your calculator. ◀] $10! = 3{,}628{,}800$

   c. Write an expression in factorial notation that can be used to calculate $_nP_n$. $_nP_n = n!$

10. You have purchased 4 tickets to a school music department raffle. Three prizes will be awarded, and 150 tickets were sold.

   a. How many ways can the three prizes be assigned to the 150 tickets if the prizes are different? ⓐ 3,307,800

   b. How many ways can the three prizes be assigned to the 150 tickets if the prizes are the same? ⓐ 551,300

11. Evaluate $_6C_2$ and $_6C_4$. Create a context involving students to explain why $_6C_2$ is the same as $_6C_4$.

12. There are 20 students in a class, and every day the teacher randomly selects 6 students to present a homework problem. Noah and Rita wonder what the chance is that they will both present a homework problem on the same day.

   a. How many different ways are there of selecting a group of 6 students? ⓐ $_{20}C_6 = 38{,}760$

   b. How many of these groups include both Noah and Rita? $_{18}C_4 = 3060$

   c. What is the probability that Noah and Rita will both be called on to give their reports? $\frac{3{,}060}{38{,}760}$, or 0.08

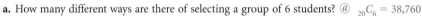

▶ Review

10.2 **13.** Here are the results for 100 rolls of a six-sided die.

Number rolled	1	2	3	4	5	6
Tally	16	15	19	18	14	18

   a. Based on the results of the experiment, what is the experimental probability of rolling a 6? $\frac{18}{100}$, or 0.18

   b. What is the theoretical probability of rolling a 6? $\frac{1}{6}$, or 0.17

   c. What is the experimental probability of rolling an even number? $\frac{51}{100}$, or 0.51

   d. What is the theoretical probability of rolling an even number? $\frac{1}{6} + \frac{1}{6} + \frac{1}{6} = \frac{1}{2}$, or 0.5

   e. Are the experimental and theoretical probabilities in 13a–b and 13c–d close to each other? Based on these results, do you think the die is fair?
     Yes, the results are close; the die is probably fair.

Exercise 8b If students have difficulty seeing that they are to count permutations of the other four students, you might have them either make up some names and draw diagrams or act out the situation.

Exercise 9 The term *factorial* and its notation are introduced in this exercise. Refer students to Calculator Note 10F as needed.

11. $_6C_2 = {_6C_4} = 15$; possible answer: Every time you select a group of four students from six students, you are also selecting a group of two students who are left out.

Exercise 12c If students are having difficulty, focus again on the outcomes. **[Ask]** "What can you say about those collections of six students that include Noah and Rita?" [They contain four other students.]

Exercise 13e This exercise gives you a chance to review the idea that experimental probabilities are close to theoretical probabilities over the long run. **[ELL]** Make sure that students understand the meaning of *fair* in this context. A die is fair if all rolls are equally likely. A coin is fair if heads and tails are equally likely. This term comes up again in Lesson 10.5, Example A.

9.4 **14.** Perform each operation and combine like terms.

    a. $(x^2 + 5x - 4) - (3x^3 - 2x^2 + 6)$ $-3x^3 + 3x^2 + 5x - 10$

    b. $(x + 7)(x^4 - 4x)$ $x^5 + 7x^4 - 4x^2 - 28x$

    c. $3x + 7(x + y) - 4y(x - 8)$ $10x + 39y - 4xy$

15. Find the area of each figure.

    a.
    @   5   4   10
    20 units²

    b.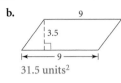
    9   3.5   9
    31.5 units²

    c.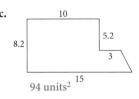
    10   5.2   8.2   3   15
    94 units²

5.3 **16.** Find the solution to each system, if there is one.

    a. $\begin{cases} y = 0 \\ y = 2 + 3x \end{cases}$ $x = -\frac{2}{3}, y = 0$

    b. $\begin{cases} y = 0.25x - 0.25 \\ y = 0.75 + x \end{cases}$ @ $x = -1.\overline{3}, y = -0.58\overline{3}$

    c. $\begin{cases} 2y = x - 2 \\ 3y = x - 3 \end{cases}$ $x = 0, y = -1$

0.1 **17.** At right, what is the ratio of the total area of shaded triangles to the area of the largest triangle? $\frac{6}{16}$, or $\frac{3}{8}$

Exercise 17 This exercise reviews Lesson 0.1 but can be done even if Chapter 0 was omitted.

Pascal's Triangle II Project

Students will return to the study of Pascal's triangle when they study the binomial theorem in advanced algebra. Encourage students to pick a specific row or pair of rows to use in their explanations. It may help to number the rows, with the top row being row 0. Sophisticated reasoning is needed to use combinations to explain why each row entry is the sum of the two entries diagonally above it. For example: $_4C_2$ is the number of combinations of two objects taken from four objects. If one object is definitely included, there are $_3C_1$ combinations available. If the same object is definitely excluded, there are $_3C_2$ combinations available. So $_4C_2 = {_3C_1} + {_3C_2}$.

project

PASCAL'S TRIANGLE II

In the project on page 177, you learned about Pascal's triangle, and you explored the connection between Pascal's triangle and the Sierpiński triangle. Shown below are the first six rows of Pascal's triangle. The first and last numbers in each row are 1, and each number inside the triangle is the sum of the two diagonally above it.

```
            1
          1   1
        1   2   1
      1   3   3   1
    1   4   6   4   1
  1   5   10   10   5   1
```

There is also a connection between Pascal's triangle and numbers of combinations. Can you figure out what it is? Why might this be the case? Present your findings in a paper or a poster.

Supporting the project

MOTIVATION

Students may be surprised to learn that the patterns in Pascal's triangle can be applied to the study of probability. The following outcomes are based on numbering the top row as row 0. Student explanations will vary.

OUTCOMES

▶ Students find that each row, r, contains the values of $_rC_0, {_rC_1}, {_rC_2}, \ldots, {_rC_r}$. In row 4, the numbers 1, 4, 6, 4, and 1 correspond to $_4C_0, {_4C_1}, {_4C_2}, {_4C_3},$ and $_4C_4$.

▶ Students use combinations to explain why the first number and last number of each row are 1. $_4C_0$ and $_4C_4$ both equal 1, because there is one combination containing none of the four choices, and one combination containing four of the four choices.

▶ Students use combinations to explain why the second and second to last numbers of each row equal the row number.

• Students give an argument for why $_rC_n$ is equal to the sum of the two numbers above it, $_{r-1}C_{n-1}$ and $_{r-1}C_n$.

Multiple-Stage Experiments

There are many questions which fools can ask that wise men cannot answer.

GEORGE PÓLYA

In the previous lesson you used lists and diagrams to help determine numbers that could be used in calculating probabilities. For instance, making a list or drawing a tree diagram can help you to see the possible outcomes when rolling two dice. In this lesson you will learn some procedures for calculating more complicated probabilities.

Investigation
Pinball Pupils

You will need
- one die per person

In this investigation you'll simulate a pinball-type game. You and your classmates will start at the back of the room. Then, instead of bouncing off obstacles to determine motion, you'll each roll a die to determine your path to the front of the room.

San Francisco artist Lee Walton wrote detailed instructions for how to create drawings determined entirely by the events in a baseball game. He then drew a representation of every game in a major league season. This one is called *Baseball Drawing from the 2004 Season.*

Steps 1–4 The theoretical totals are shown for 4 trials of a class of 30. Your class results will vary.

Step 1 Roll a die. If you roll a perfect square (1 or 4), go to the sign labeled "Square." Otherwise, go to the sign labeled "Round." When everyone has completed the move, count the number at each sign and record it on the game log at the sign. The total of the two choices should match the total number of students in the class.

Step 2 Roll the die again and use these rules to move to the five signs at the front of the room.

At Square

Roll is an even number:
Go to "Even"
Roll is an odd number:
Go to "Odd"

At Round

Roll is 1: Go to "Unit"
Roll is a prime number (2, 3, or 5):
Go to "Prime"
Roll is a composite number (4 or 6):
Go to "Composite"

When everyone has completed the move, count the number of people at each sign and record it on the game log. The total of these five groups should be the same as the total number of students in the class.

PLANNING

LESSON OUTLINE

First day:

| 40 min | Investigation |
| 10 min | Sharing |

Second day:

20 min	Examples
5 min	Closing
25 min	Exercises

MATERIALS

- dice (1 die per student)
- signs posted around room, with game log at each
- Pinball Game Sheet (W), *optional*
- Pinball Pupils (W), *optional*
- Calculator Note OH, *optional*
- Fathom demonstration Pinball Probabilities, *optional*

TEACHING

One Step

Follow the instructions for the setup and data gathering in the investigation. Then challenge students: "On each branch of the tree diagram write the probability that a student chosen randomly from the group at the beginning, or left end, of that branch will go to the group at the right end of the branch. Can you use these probabilities to determine the number in each circle in the right-hand column?" From the ensuing discussion extract a review of experimental versus theoretical probability and formalize the ideas of conditional probability, independent events, and the multiplication principle.

NCTM STANDARDS

CONTENT		PROCESS	
✔	Number	✔	Problem Solving
✔	Algebra	✔	Reasoning
✔	Geometry	✔	Communication
	Measurement		Connections
✔	Data/Probability	✔	Representation

LESSON OBJECTIVES

- Calculate experimental and theoretical probabilities for multiple-stage experiments
- Distinguish between independent and dependent outcomes
- Learn the multiplication rule and use it to calculate probabilities of sequences of events

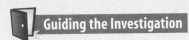

Place signs labeled "Square" and "Round" at each side of the classroom. Also place five signs labeled "Even," "Odd," "Unit," "Prime," and "Composite" along the front of the room.

Each sign should have a game log where students can record the number of students at the sign during each round. You might draw a table on the sign:

Round	1	2	3	4	5
# Students					

As an alternative, students might simulate dice rolls by using randInt() on their calculators (see Calculator Note 0H). If your classroom does not have enough space for students to move around, you can give each group the Pinball Game Sheet worksheet, have them record their results for four rounds, and then report their data for Step 4. As an extension, you might use the Fathom demonstration Pinball Probabilities to simulate this activity.

Steps 4 and 8 You might hand out the Pinball Pupils worksheet, which has the blank diagrams for these steps.

SHARING IDEAS

You might ask students to present their ideas about Steps 5 and 10–12. Emphasize the sense-making parts of the questions. For Step 10, **[Ask]** "What does each product tell you?" [the probability that a randomly chosen student will go along that path]

Assessing Progress

You can assess students' understanding of probability and of tree diagrams.

Step 3 Return to the back of the room and repeat Steps 1 and 2 until you have at least four values on each of the game logs.

Step 4 Calculate the total at each log and enter the totals on a diagram like the one pictured here. If you did this experiment four times, then the Start Total will equal four times the class size.

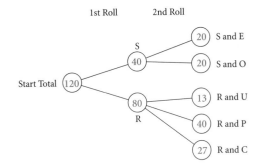

Experiment Totals

Step 5 What is the sum of the numbers of students at the five ending points? Why does this make sense? The sum is equal to the start total; this makes sense because everyone who starts has to end in one of the final five positions.

Steps 6–9 The theoretical probabilities are shown. Your class results will vary.

Step 6 Calculate the experimental probabilities of being "Square" and of being "Round" by using the totals listed on your diagram from Step 4.

Step 7 Use the totals from your diagram to determine the experimental probability of going from "Square" or "Round" to each of the next signs. (You will be dividing by the "Square" and "Round" values.)

Step 8 Use your answers to Steps 6 and 7 to create a tree diagram showing your experimental probabilities for moving through this game. Write the experimental probabilities for the first and second rolls in a tree diagram as shown.

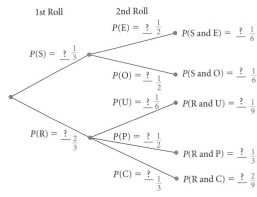

Experimental Probabilities

Step 9 Calculate the experimental probability of being a "Square Even," a "Round Prime," and each of the other outcomes by dividing the ending totals by your starting total.

Step 10

$P(S) \cdot P(E) = P(S \text{ and } E)$; you can calculate the probability of a path on a tree diagram by multiplying the probabilities of each branch of the path.

Step 10 | Multiply the two probabilities on each path ($P(S) \cdot P(E) =$ ___, and so on). What do you notice? Make a conjecture about how to calculate the probability of any path on a tree diagram (for example, S then E).

Step 11 | What is the sum of the probabilities of the five final outcomes? Why does this make sense? The sum is 1; this makes sense because the probability that one of these five outcomes happens is 100%, or 1.

Step 12 | Create another tree diagram for the same game using the theoretical probabilities for each event. How do these values compare to the experimental probabilities?

The examples and exercises in this lesson explore multiple-stage experiments, where probabilities of an outcome involve considering the probabilities of a sequence of two or more events. The following example is a theoretical look at flipping a coin multiple times.

EXAMPLE A

Dian wants to determine the probabilities of various outcomes when flipping a coin.

a. If she flips a fair coin two times, what is the probability that she will get exactly one head?

b. If she flips a fair coin three times, what is the probability that she will get exactly two heads?

▶ **Solution**

When you flip a fair coin, the probabilities of getting a head or a tail are each $\frac{1}{2}$, or 0.5.

a. This tree diagram shows all of the possibilities from two flips: HH, HT, TH, and TT. Two of the four paths contain exactly one head. So the probability of getting exactly one head is $\frac{2}{4}$, or 0.5.

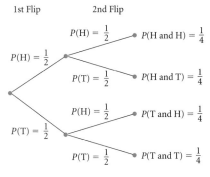

1st Flip   2nd Flip

$P(H) = \frac{1}{2}$ $P(H) = \frac{1}{2}$ $P(H \text{ and } H) = \frac{1}{4}$

$P(T) = \frac{1}{2}$ $P(H \text{ and } T) = \frac{1}{4}$

$P(T) = \frac{1}{2}$ $P(H) = \frac{1}{2}$ $P(T \text{ and } H) = \frac{1}{4}$

$P(T) = \frac{1}{2}$ $P(T \text{ and } T) = \frac{1}{4}$

Note that the probability of the final outcome of any path could be obtained by multiplying the probability of each event along the path. For example, the probability of the second path is $P(H \text{ and } T) = \frac{1}{2} \cdot \frac{1}{2} = \frac{1}{4}$.

▶ **EXAMPLE A**

This example analyzes the probabilities in another multiple-stage experiment. **[Ask]** "If Dian flipped a fair coin eight times and always got heads, what would be the probability of heads on the ninth flip?" Students might argue versions of the "gambler's fallacy," that is, that the run was more than 50% likely either to fail or to continue. To motivate the idea of independent outcomes, ask if the coin has a memory. You might also **[Ask]** "Can you always multiply the probabilities of two outcomes to get the probability of both happening?"

b. This tree diagram shows all of the possibilities from three consecutive flips. Three of the eight paths provide exactly two heads. Because each path is equally likely, the probability of flipping exactly two heads is $\frac{3}{8}$.

Note that the probability of any one path is $\frac{1}{8}$, which is equal to the product of the probabilities of each event along the path, $\frac{1}{2} \cdot \frac{1}{2} \cdot \frac{1}{2}$.

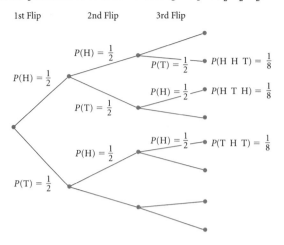

1st Flip   2nd Flip   3rd Flip

$P(H) = \frac{1}{2}$

$P(H) = \frac{1}{2}$ $P(T) = \frac{1}{2}$ $P(H \ H \ T) = \frac{1}{8}$

$P(T) = \frac{1}{2}$ $P(H) = \frac{1}{2}$ $P(H \ T \ H) = \frac{1}{8}$

$P(H) = \frac{1}{2}$ $P(H) = \frac{1}{2}$ $P(T \ H \ T) = \frac{1}{8}$

$P(T) = \frac{1}{2}$

When you are flipping coins, the probability of getting a head on the second or third flip is not influenced by what happened before. That is, your probability of flipping a head is 0.5, regardless of the number of heads flipped in previous tosses. Events are **independent** when the occurrence of one event has no influence on the occurrence of another.

The probabilities of some events are influenced by, or dependent on, the outcome of a previous event, such as in the experiment you did in the investigation. These events are called **dependent,** or **conditional.** Regardless of whether the events in a series are independent or dependent, the probability of an outcome can always be found by multiplying the probability of each event along the path.

EXAMPLE B | Cheryl makes 75% of her first tries at the free throw line. However, her records indicate that her success on the second throw depends on whether her first throw was good (G) or a miss (M). Cheryl makes 80% of her second throws when she makes her first shot, but only 50% of her second throws when she misses her first shot. What is the probability of Cheryl making two consecutive good shots?

▶ **Solution** | The tree diagram shows the probability of each event. The notation $P(G_2 \mid G_1)$ is read, "The probability of a good second shot *given* a good first shot." For Cheryl, $P(G_2 \mid G_1) = 0.8$. So the probability of Cheryl making two consecutive good shots is $P(G_1) \cdot P(G_2 \mid G_1) = 0.75 \cdot 0.8 = 0.6$, or 60%.

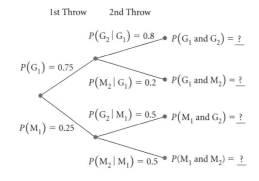

As you saw in the investigation and examples, you multiply to find the probability of a sequence of events.

The Multiplication Rule

If a, b, c, and so on, represent events along a path, then the probability that this sequence of events will occur can be found by multiplying the probabilities of the events:

$$P(a \text{ and } b \text{ and } c \text{ and } \ldots) = P(a) \cdot P(b) \cdot P(c) \cdot \cdots$$

or

$$P(a \text{ and } b \text{ and } c \text{ and } \ldots) = P(a) \cdot P(b \mid a) \cdot P(c \mid (b \text{ and } a)) \cdot \cdots$$

Be thoughtful when determining the probability of a dependent event. For example, consider drawing marbles without replacement from a bag containing one blue and two red marbles. The probability that the second marble is blue depends on the color of the first marble. If the first marble is blue, then the probability of $P(\text{blue}_2 \mid \text{blue}_1) = 0$.

EXERCISES

▶ **Practice Your Skills**

1. Use the information from Example B about Cheryl shooting baskets.
   a. What is the probability that Cheryl misses both shots? ⓐ $\frac{1}{8}$
   b. Explain, in words, the meaning of $P(G_2 \mid M_1)$. ⓐ This is the probability that Cheryl makes the second shot if she misses the first shot.
2. The tree diagram shown here is incomplete.
   a. Find the values for the probabilities a–g on this tree. ⓗ
   b. What is the sum of the final outcome probabilities at d–g? Does this seem reasonable? Why? 1; the sum of the probabilities of all the outcomes should be 1, because the probability that one of the outcomes happens is 100%, or 1.
3. Create a tree diagram with probabilities showing outcomes when drawing two marbles *without replacement* from a bag containing one blue and two red marbles. (You do not replace the first marble drawn from the bag before drawing the second.) ⓐ

Exercise 3 [Ask] "Are drawing a red marble and drawing a blue marble independent or dependent events?" [The probabilities on the second draw are dependent on the outcome of the first draw.]

3.
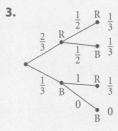

THE MULTIPLICATION RULE

You might point out that the counting principle described in Lesson 10.4 involved multiplying whole numbers, but the multiplication rule is about multiplying probabilities.

[Ask] "Does the multiplication rule say that the probability of n_1 and n_2 and n_3 is always the product of their probabilities?" [no; only if the events are independent]

Closing the Lesson

Emphasize the main idea of this lesson: To calculate the probability of a path through a tree diagram, the **multiplication rule** says that you can multiply the probabilities along the branches. In this context the notation $P(A \mid B)$, *the probability of A given B,* means the probability of going to event A if you've arrived at event B on some path.

BUILDING UNDERSTANDING

Students work with tree diagrams and conditional probabilities.

ASSIGNING HOMEWORK

Essential	1–5
Performance assessment	6–11
Portfolio	11
Journal	8
Group	11
Review	12–14

▶ **Helping with the Exercises**

Exercise 2 As needed, remind students that the probabilities on the branches leading from each point must sum to 1.

Exercise 4 [Ask] "Are drawing a red marble and drawing a blue marble independent or dependent events?" [In this case the probabilities on the second draw are independent of the outcome of the first draw.]

Exercise 7 If students start drawing a tree diagram with 21 initial branches, challenge them to do less work by focusing on probabilities.

8. Dependent; the first student selected affects the probabilities for the second choice.

Exercise 9 [Alert] Students may not understand the subscript notation, which refers to the spin number.

Exercise 10 For 10b and e, once the specified slot is filled, which can only be done in one way out of seven, any order of the remaining six ingredients is allowed. The arrangements of the remaining ingredients do not need to be considered.

Exercise 11 This exercise foreshadows Lesson 10.6.

11c.
$P(W) = \dfrac{1}{158,907} \approx 0.000006$;
$P(L) = \dfrac{158,906}{158,907} \approx 0.999994$

4. Create a tree diagram with probabilities showing outcomes when drawing two marbles *with replacement* from a bag containing one blue and two red marbles. (You *do* replace the first marble drawn from the bag before drawing the second.)

5. State whether each pair of events is dependent or independent.
   a. Roll a die, then roll the same die again. independent
   b. Remove one card from the deck, then draw a second card. @ dependent
   c. Flip a coin, then flip a second coin. independent

▶ **Reason and Apply**

6. Apply the multiplication rule to find the unknown probabilities in the tree diagram at right.

7. A class has 7 male students and 14 female students. One student is selected at random from the class, and then a second student is selected from the class. Draw a tree diagram that shows the events "male" and "female" for the two consecutive selections. Write probabilities on the branches. @

8. Are the events "select a student from a class" and "select another student from the same class" independent or dependent? Explain. @

9. The spinner shown at right is equally likely to land on any of the four colors. The spinner is spun twice. Evaluate each probability.
   a. $P(\text{Blue}_2 \mid \text{Red}_1)$ $\frac{1}{4}$
   b. $P(\text{Blue}_2 \mid \text{Blue}_1)$ $\frac{1}{4}$
   c. $P(\text{Blue}_1) \cdot P(\text{Blue}_2 \mid \text{Blue}_1)$ $\frac{1}{16}$

10. A chili recipe calls for seven ingredients: ground beef, onions, beans, tomatoes, peppers, chili powder, and salt. There are no directions about the order in which the ingredients should be combined. You decide to add the ingredients in a random order.
   5040 **a.** How many different arrangements are there? @
   b. What is the probability that onions are first? $\frac{1}{7}$
   c. What is the probability that the order is exactly as listed above? $\frac{1}{5040}$
   d. What is the probability that the order isn't exactly as listed above? $\frac{5039}{5040}$
   e. What is the probability that beans are third? $\frac{1}{7}$

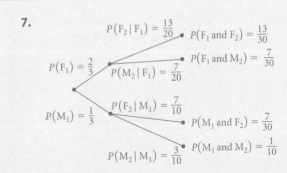

11. Tom Fool wants to make his fortune playing the state lottery. To win the big prize, he must select the six winning numbers, which are drawn from the numbers 1 to 50. He can select exactly six numbers for each ticket.
   a. How many sets of six different numbers from 1 to 50 are there? 15,890,700
   b. What is the probability that any one ticket will be a winner? $\frac{1}{15,890,700} \approx 0.00000006$
   c. If Tom buys 100 tickets each week, what is the probability that he wins in any one week? What is the probability that he loses in any one week?

4.

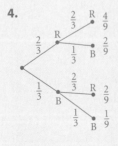

7.

$P(F_1) = \frac{2}{3}$ $P(F_2 \mid F_1) = \frac{13}{20}$ $P(F_1 \text{ and } F_2) = \frac{13}{30}$

$P(M_2 \mid F_1) = \frac{7}{20}$ $P(F_1 \text{ and } M_2) = \frac{7}{30}$

$P(M_1) = \frac{1}{3}$ $P(F_2 \mid M_1) = \frac{7}{10}$ $P(M_1 \text{ and } F_2) = \frac{7}{30}$

$P(M_2 \mid M_1) = \frac{3}{10}$ $P(M_1 \text{ and } M_2) = \frac{1}{10}$

d. Draw a partial tree diagram of four weeks, and use the probability from 11c to determine the probability that he will lose all four weeks.

e. Determine the probability that he will lose every week for one year (52 weeks).

f. At $1 a ticket, 100 tickets a week, 52 weeks a year, what is his cost? $5,200

Review

4.5, **12.** This table shows the average diameter of the pupil of human eyes
5.2   at different ages, in daylight and in darkness.

Pupil Diameters

Age (yr)	Pupil diameter in daylight (mm)	Pupil diameter in darkness (mm)
20	4.7	8.0
30	4.3	7.0
40	3.9	6.0
50	3.5	5.0
60	3.1	4.1
70	2.7	3.2

When it gets dark, the pupil opens wider in order to allow more light to enter the eye. This helps the eye to see better.

a. Without graphing, what patterns do you observe in the data?

b. Plot data in the forms (*age, daylight diameter*) and (*age, darkness diameter*) on the same graph, with a different type of mark for each plot.

c. Write the equation of a line of fit, such as a line through the Q-points, for each of the data sets.

d. Use the substitution method to find the points of intersection of your two lines from 12c. Give a real-world interpretation of your solution. (77.37, 2.41); at about age 77, a person's pupil diameter stays the same in daylight and darkness, about 2.41 mm.

10.2 **13.** Arrange the following events from most likely to least likely. Explain your thinking.

a. being born right-handed

b. flipping a single head if you flip a coin four times

c. not watching any television this week

d. being taller than the average class height

e. no one being late to your math class this week

10.1 **14.** In April 2004, the faculty at Princeton University voted that each department could give A grades to no more than 35% of their students. Japanese teacher Kyoko Loetscher felt that 11 of her 20 students deserved A's, as they had earned better than 90% in the course. However, she could give A's to only 35% of her students. How many students is this? Draw two relative frequency circle graphs: one that shows the grades (A's versus non-A's) that Loetscher would like to give and one that shows the grades she is allowed to give. (*Newsweek*, February 14, 2005, p. 8) @

12a. Possible answers: Pupil diameter decreases as a person gets older. Pupils are larger in the dark. Pupil diameter decreases faster in darkness than in daylight. As a person ages, daylight and darkness pupil diameters get closer.

12b.

[0, 80, 10, 0, 10, 1]

12c. lines through Q-points:
for daylight,
$d = 4.3 - 0.04(a - 30)$;
for darkness,
$d = 7.0 - 0.097(a - 30)$

13. Answers will vary. About 90% of the population is right-handed. The theoretical chance of a single head is four in sixteen, or $\frac{1}{4}$.

14. She can give A's to seven students.

11d.

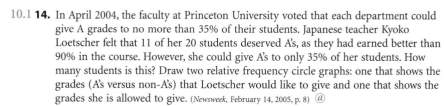

$$P(\text{L for four weeks}) = \left(\frac{158,906}{158,907}\right)^4 \approx 0.999975$$

11e. $P(\text{L for 52 weeks}) = \left(\frac{158,906}{158,907}\right)^{52} \approx 0.999673$

LESSON
10.6

Expected Value

Tad Minor is burning CDs for his band on an old CD burner. Unfortunately, only $\frac{1}{3}$ of the CDs the machine makes are good, and $\frac{2}{3}$ are bad. After five failed attempts in a row, Tad wonders about the average number of CDs used for each good copy.

Chance favors
prepared minds.

LOUIS PASTEUR

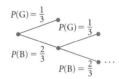

This average number is called the **expected value.** It can be found by calculating probabilities. In the next investigation you will use the multiplication rule to calculate an expected value.

Investigation
Road Trip

In this investigation each member of your group will simulate taking a trip. You'll each roll a die to choose your destinations randomly among six cities.

You will need

- one die per student

Steps 1–5 Answers will vary. The theoretical mean number of cities visited is about 2.775. More trials should result in an experimental mean closer to this value.

Step 1 There are six cities, City 1 through City 6. Each group member should choose a different city in which to begin. Record the city number. Then roll a die to decide which city to travel to next. If you roll the city you are already in, your trip is done. If not, record the city you are traveling to.

Step 2 If your trip is not already done, roll again to determine your next destination. Record the city number. Again, if you roll the number of a city you are in or have already visited, your trip is over.

Step 3 Repeat Step 2 until your trip comes to an end. Be sure to record each city visited along the way.

Step 4 What is the average number of cities visited by members of your group? How does this average compare to the results of other groups?

Step 5 Run the simulation CITIES on your calculator. [▶ 🖥 See **Calculator Note 10G.** ◀] How does the average number of cities visited in the simulation compare to the averages obtained by members of your class?

Step 6 You can use a tree diagram to represent this situation. Instead of making a branch for each city, you can simply have two branches each time—previously visited cities and new cities, as shown at right. Create a complete tree diagram, and write the theoretical probability of each path.

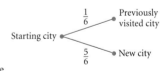

LESSON OBJECTIVE

- Determine the expected value of a trial

NCTM STANDARDS

CONTENT		PROCESS	
✓	Number	✓	Problem Solving
✓	Algebra	✓	Reasoning
✓	Geometry	✓	Communication
	Measurement		Connections
✓	Data/Probability	✓	Representation

Step 7	Use your tree diagram to determine the probability that you will visit one city, two cities, three cities, and so on. Verify that these probabilities sum to 1.
Step 8	To calculate the average number of cities you can expect to visit, multiply each of the probabilities in Step 7 by the number of city visits it represents. Then add these values. How does this number compare to the averages you found in Steps 4 and 5?

$1(0.167) + 2(0.278) + 3(0.278) + 4(0.185) + 5(0.077) + 6(0.015) = 2.775$ cities (if probabilities are used unrounded); this is close to the simulation average.

A randomly determined road trip and making CDs on an unreliable burner are two random situations in which you might want to find the "average" outcome. The next example also involves an average or expected amount.

EXAMPLE A

At the Berkeley City Animal Shelter there are 25 dogs with litters of puppies. The sizes of the litters are shown in the dot plot below. Each day the veterinarian randomly selects a mother dog and checks the health of each of her puppies. What is the expected number of puppies to be checked tomorrow?

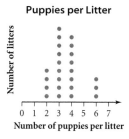

Puppies per Litter

Number of litters

0 1 2 3 4 5 6 7
Number of puppies per litter

Millions of dogs, cats, and other animals end up in animal shelters in the United States every year. About 64% of these are euthanized. Spaying and neutering your pets can greatly decrease the number of animals without homes.

▶ **Solution**

There are four possible outcomes, and each has a known probability. This table shows the probability of each outcome. If you multiply the value of each possible outcome (2, 3, 4, or 6 puppies) by its probability, and sum the results, you get the expected value of the number of puppies the veterinarian will check tomorrow.

Outcome	2 puppies	3 puppies	4 puppies	6 puppies	
Probability	$\frac{4}{25}$	$\frac{10}{25}$	$\frac{8}{25}$	$\frac{3}{25}$	**Sum**
Product	0.32	1.20	1.28	0.72	3.52

The expected value is 3.52 puppies.

For the situation in Example A, note that the mean number of puppies in a litter is also 3.52.

$$\frac{4 \cdot 2 + 10 \cdot 3 + 8 \cdot 4 + 3 \cdot 6}{25} = \frac{88 \text{ puppies}}{25 \text{ litters}} = 3.52$$

Step 6

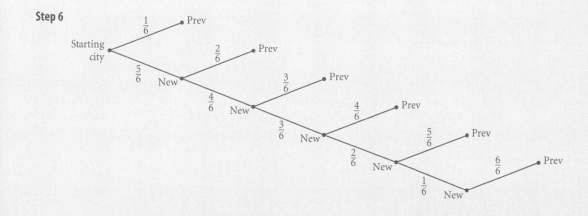

Step 7 $P(\text{one city}) = \frac{1}{6} \approx 0.167$;
$P(\text{two cities}) = \frac{10}{36} \approx 0.278$;
$P(\text{three cities}) = \frac{60}{216} \approx 0.278$;
$P(\text{four cities}) = \frac{240}{1296} \approx 0.185$;
$P(\text{five cities}) = \frac{600}{7776} \approx 0.077$;
$P(\text{six cities}) = \frac{720}{46,656} \approx 0.015$.
The probabilities sum to 1.

Guiding the Investigation

To help students become engaged, you might go through the procedure as a class and then ask for conjectures about how long the simulated trips will be. If you have time, students can name their cities.

Step 1 There may be competition among students to take long trips, and some students may want to take more than one trip. Students whose trip ends right away might record results for other students in their group.

If students aren't sure how to tell when their tree diagram is complete, **[Ask]** "What is the maximum number of cities that can be visited?" [six] There will be six branchings in the tree.

As a follow-up to this investigation, you might use the Fathom demonstration Road Trip.

SHARING IDEAS

You might have students present solutions to Steps 4, 6, and 7. Bring out the idea that probabilities are being used to find a mean, or average.

Assessing Progress

You can check students' comfort level with tree diagrams and with the counting principle, as well as their ability to follow directions and to work within a group.

▶ **EXAMPLE A**

This example applies the probability method of calculating an expected value. **[Ask]** "Why might a veterinarian want to calculate this expected value?" [Knowing the expected number of puppies can help in scheduling.]

The expected value is another name for the mean value. In Example A, the veterinarian doesn't actually expect to examine exactly 3.52 puppies, but if she did this over and over again she should average 3.52 puppies per day.

> **Expected Value**
>
> The **expected value** is an average value that can be found by multiplying the value of each event by its probability and then summing all of the products.

▶ **EXAMPLE B**

In this example students see an infinite sum. You might remind them of the sums for the areas and perimeters of fractals in Chapter 0.

EXAMPLE B

What is the expected number of CDs used to make one good copy if the probability of success is $\frac{1}{3}$?

▶ **Solution**

The probability of success on the first try is $\frac{1}{3}$, but the probability of success on the second attempt requires that two conditions be met: the first CD fails and the second succeeds. From the tree diagram, you can see that this probability is $\frac{2}{3} \cdot \frac{1}{3} = \frac{2}{9} \approx 0.222$.

To determine the probability of success on the third try, you would calculate $\frac{2}{3} \cdot \frac{2}{3} \cdot \frac{1}{3}$, or $\left(\frac{2}{3}\right)^2 \cdot \frac{1}{3} \approx 0.066$.

To find the expected value, you'll multiply each possible number of attempts by its probability and then sum these products. However, it might take 5, 10, or even 100 attempts to make one good CD. But the probability that it will take 100 attempts is very small, far less than 1%. This table shows the probability of success in 1, 2, 3, 4, and 5 CDs.

Outcome	1 CD	2 CDs	3 CDs	4 CDs	5 CDs
Probability	$\frac{1}{3}$	$\frac{2}{3} \cdot \frac{1}{3}$	$\left(\frac{2}{3}\right)^2 \cdot \frac{1}{3}$	$\left(\frac{2}{3}\right)^3 \cdot \frac{1}{3}$	$\left(\frac{2}{3}\right)^4 \cdot \frac{1}{3}$
Product	0.333	0.444	0.148	0.099	0.066

To find the expected value, you'll compute this never-ending sum:

$$1 \cdot \left(\frac{1}{3}\right) + 2 \cdot \left(\frac{2}{3}\right)\left(\frac{1}{3}\right) + 3 \cdot \left(\frac{2}{3}\right)^2\left(\frac{1}{3}\right) + 4 \cdot \left(\frac{2}{3}\right)^3\left(\frac{1}{3}\right) + 5 \cdot \left(\frac{2}{3}\right)^4\left(\frac{1}{3}\right) + \cdots$$

That may seem impossible, but as the pattern continues, the terms get smaller; the 26th term is less than 0.0005. Your calculator can help you compute this sum. [▶ See **Calculator Note 10H.** ◀] If you add enough terms, you'll find that the expected value is 3 CDs.

Expected value is used frequently in business and industry. Businesses write models to determine expected outcomes in manufacturing, as well as associated costs and profits. If a model is correct, a business can predict what will happen in the long run, even if what happens from day to day is not predictable.

EXERCISES

▶ Practice Your Skills

1. Copy and complete this table to determine the expected value of the spinner game shown. The expected value is $4.83.

Outcome	$2	$5	$10	
Probability	$\frac{1}{3}$	$\frac{1}{2}$	$\frac{1}{6}$	**Sum**
Product	$0.\overline{6}$	2.5	$1.\overline{6}$	$4.8\overline{3}$

2. A bag contains one blue marble and two red marbles.

   a. Draw a tree diagram picturing all possible outcomes and probabilities if you draw two marbles without replacement.

   b. Complete a table like that in Exercise 1 to determine the number of red marbles you can expect to draw if you draw two marbles. @

3. The sponsors of an outdoor concert will earn $200,000 if it does not rain the day of the concert. They will lose $30,000 if it does rain. The forecast shows a 25% probability of rain. Complete a table like the one in Exercise 1 to determine the expected value for the concert income. @

4. The heights of students in an algebra class are pictured in the histogram below.

Student Heights

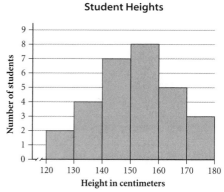

   a. How many students are in the class? @ 29

   b. What is the probability that a randomly chosen student's height is in the first bin? $\frac{2}{29}$, or 0.07

   c. Use the middle value of each bin to find the expected height of a randomly selected student from this class. 151.6 cm

2a. 1st draw   2nd draw

$P(R_1) = \frac{2}{3}$

$P(R_2 \mid R_1) = \frac{1}{2}$ • $P(R_1 \text{ and } R_2) = \frac{1}{3}$

$P(B_2 \mid R_1) = \frac{1}{2}$ • $P(R_1 \text{ and } B_2) = \frac{1}{3}$

$P(B_1) = \frac{1}{3}$

$P(R_2 \mid B_1) = \frac{2}{2}$ • $P(B_1 \text{ and } R_2) = \frac{1}{3}$

$P(B_2 \mid B_1) = \frac{0}{2}$ • $P(B_1 \text{ and } B_2) = 0$

2b. The expected number of red marbles drawn is $\frac{4}{3}$, or about 1.3.

Outcome	0	1	2	
Probability	0	$\frac{2}{3}$	$\frac{1}{3}$	Sum
Product	0	$\frac{2}{3}$	$\frac{2}{3}$	$\frac{4}{3}$

3. The expected value for concert income is $142,500.

Outcome	$200,000	−$30,000	
Probability	0.75	0.25	Sum
Product	150,000	−7,500	142,500

Exercise 5b This is an unusual game in that the player pays less to play than the expected winning value. Lotteries and games in carnivals and casinos depend on expected winnings being less than the amount a player pays.

Exercise 6 **[Ask]** "What would you say to someone who claimed that the probability of each sum is $\frac{1}{11}$, because there are 11 possible sums of two dice, from 2 through 12?" Remind students that probabilities depend on counting equally likely outcomes.

Exercise 7 This exercise extends Lesson 10.5, Example B.

7a. $P(G_1 \text{ and } G_2) = 0.6$

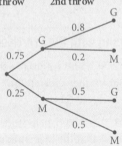

Reason and Apply

5. The game spinner shown is equally likely to land on any of the four sections.
   a. What is the expected value of this game? $5.50
   b. Is it a good deal if you're expected to pay $5 to spin? Explain. Yes, it is a good deal, because over the long run you'll come out $0.50 ahead per spin.

6. The tree diagram of outcomes for rolling two dice would have 36 equally likely paths. It is easier to look at a situation like this using a *two-way table* instead of a tree diagram.
   a. Complete a table like this showing the sums of two six-sided dice.

Second Die

First Die	1	2	3	4	5	6
1	2	3	4	5	6	7
2	3	4	5	6	7	8
3	4	5	6	7	8	9
4	5	6	7	8	9	10
5	6	7	8	9	10	11
6	7	8	9	10	11	12

   b. Calculate the expected sum of rolling two dice. ⓗ 7

7. Cheryl plays on the school basketball team. When shooting free throws, she makes 75% of her first shots, and 80% of her second shots provided she makes the first one. However, if she misses the first shot, she makes only half of her second shots. Each free throw is worth one point.
   a. Draw a tree diagram of a two-shot attempt. What is the probability that she will make both shots? @
   b. What is the expected number of points that Cheryl will make in a two-shot free throw attempt? @ 1.475
   c. If Cheryl has five chances to shoot two free throws in a game, how many points can she expect to make? @ 7.375

8. The Square Deal Electronics store is having a sale. If you buy a TV, you can get a DVD player for a special price. You roll a die and pay the square of the number rolled for the DVD player (a $50 value).
   a. If you roll a 3, how much will you pay for the DVD player? $9
   b. What is the probability that you will roll a 3? $\frac{1}{6}$
   c. What is the expected payment for the DVD player? $15.17
   d. What does this number mean to the store?
      The store will receive a mean payment of $15.17 for each DVD player sold.

9. Taya is a contestant on a television quiz show. If she answers the next question correctly, she will win $16,000. If she misses the question, she will receive only $1,000. The question is multiple choice, and Taya has no idea what the correct answer is, so she will randomly choose one of the four answers.

a. What is the expected value of Taya's earnings for the next question? ⓐ $4,750

b. If Taya can eliminate one answer and her probability of answering correctly is now one-third, what is the expected value? $6,000

10. A local restaurant offers a free music CD with each Extraordinary Value Meal. Two different CDs are available, and you want both. There are equal numbers of the two CDs, and they are randomly distributed with each meal.

a. Create the first few branches of a tree diagram showing the probabilities of getting two different CDs when you purchase Extraordinary Value Meals. End each path once it contains both CDs. ⓗ

b. This tree diagram can be extended indefinitely. (It's unlikely, but it might take 50 or more meals to get both CDs!) Use the pattern in the probabilities from 10a to help you calculate the expected number of Extraordinary Value Meals you will need to purchase to receive both CDs. 3

Exercise 10b This exercise is challenging, as there is no limit to the number of meals that might need to be purchased. Have students make an expected value table for up to 8 meals and look for patterns.

▶ **Review**

10.2 **11.** The diagram shows the algebra students at a local school and indicates their gender and whether they participate in band.

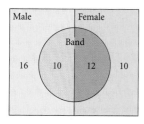

a. How many algebra students are there? 48

b. What is the probability that a randomly chosen student is a male in the band? $\frac{10}{48} \approx 0.208$

c. What is the probability that a randomly chosen student is female and not in the band? ⓐ $\frac{10}{48} \approx 0.208$

d. What is the probability that a randomly chosen male student is not in the band? $\frac{16}{26} \approx 0.615$

10.5 **12.** At this point in the season, Jackson has made 35 out of his 50 free throw attempts, so he's been successful on 70% of his free throws. He wants to improve his rate to 80% as soon as possible.

a. How many consecutive free throws must he make to reach this goal? ⓐ 25

b. If his probability of making any one shot is 70%, what is the probability that he will perform the number of consecutive free throws you found in 12a? ⓐ $(0.7)^{25} \approx 0.00013$

10a.

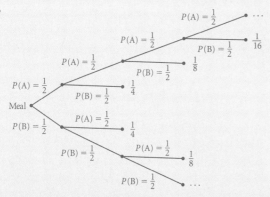

CHAPTER
10
REVIEW

PLANNING

LESSON OUTLINE

One day:

10 min   Introduction

15 min   Exercises

10 min   Checking work

15 min   Student self-assessment

REVIEWING

Pose this problem: "A bag contains one blue marble and two red marbles. You pull out two marbles. What's the probability that you've picked a red marble and a blue marble?" Students may recognize that the problem doesn't say whether you replace the first marble before drawing the second one. Consider the problem both with and without replacement. The problem is also ambiguous about whether the pair RB is to be considered the same as or different from the pair BR. Again, consider the problem both ways. You can review calculating probabilities as fractions, the counting principle, counting permutations and combinations, using tree diagrams, and applying the multiplication principle. You can also ask whether this probability is experimental or theoretical. Then [Ask] "What is the expected number of red marbles?" Students may be surprised to find that the expected value is the same with or without replacement. Ask for explanations, which may vary. One explanation is that the portion of red marbles to start with was the same, so the mean number chosen will be the same in each case.

In this chapter you learned to analyze situations that involve uncertainty. You began by constructing **relative frequency graphs,** which allow you to compare different categories in a data set proportionally. You used these graphs to determine the chance, or **probability,** of an **outcome** or **event.**

You learned that the probability of a given event is a ratio between 0 and 1 that compares the number of successful outcomes of that event to the total number of trials. You learned that the more **trials** you do in an experiment, the closer the **experimental probability** will be to the **theoretical probability.** You investigated **random** outcomes, and you saw that probability values can help you predict what will happen if you do many trials, but they will not help you determine the next outcome.

In order to determine some probabilities, you learned to visualize and count possible outcomes using a **tree diagram.** You also were introduced to the **counting principle,** which states that if there are a ways to make a first choice, b ways to make a second choice, c ways to make a third choice, and so on, the product $a \cdot b \cdot c \cdot \cdots$ represents the total number of different ways in which the entire sequence of choices can be made. Arrangements of choices in which repetition is not allowed and the order is important are called **permutations.** Arrangements in which repetition is not allowed and the order is *not* important are called **combinations.**

You learned that some sequential events are **independent,** meaning that the outcome of the first event has no impact on the probability of the next event. Some sequential events, like drawing marbles from a bag without replacement, are **dependent**—the probability of the second event depends on what happens in the first event. Tree diagrams help you organize the probabilities of each event in situations like these, and the **multiplication rule** allows you to calculate the probability of multiple-stage events.

Using what you learned about theoretical probability, you were able to calculate **expected value** by multiplying the value of each event by its probability and then summing all the products.

EXERCISES

▶ @ Answers are provided for all exercises in this set.

1. A ball is randomly selected from a bin that contains balls numbered from 1 to 99.
   a. What is the probability that the number is even? $\frac{49}{99}$
   b. What is the probability that the number is divisible by 3? $\frac{33}{99}$, or $\frac{1}{3}$
   c. What is the probability that the number contains at least one 2? $\frac{19}{99}$
   d. What is the probability that the number has only one digit? $\frac{9}{99}$, or $\frac{1}{11}$

ASSIGNING HOMEWORK

You might assign evens for homework and have students work individually or in groups on the odds in class.

2. A group of 350 students were surveyed, and their eye colors are shown in the graph at right. Approximately how many students have each eye color?

3. This table shows the approximate populations of the five most populous countries in the world in 2000. The total world population at that time was 6,080,142,000.

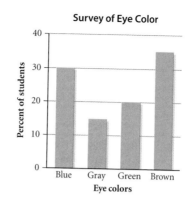

Survey of Eye Color

Country	Population
China	1,261,832,000
India	1,014,004,000
United States	275,563,000
Indonesia	224,784,000
Brazil	172,860,000

Create a relative frequency circle graph of this information with six categories—one for each country listed and one labeled "Other." Label your graph with category names and percentages. List the degree measure of each sector.

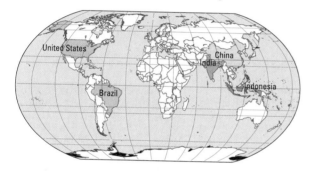

4. Each year the Spanish Club has a fund-raising raffle. First, second, and third prizes are $525, $125, and $25. The net gain is how much money you actually win if you deduct the cost of the ticket. Net gains and their respective probabilities are shown in the table.

a. What is the cost of one raffle ticket? $25

b. If you buy one ticket, what is the probability that you will win more than $50? 6%, or 0.06

c. If only 100 tickets are sold, what would be the net winnings or losses for the group of 100 buyers?

One person is $500 ahead, 5 people are $100 ahead, 10 people are even, and 84 people are $25 behind. This is a net loss of $1,100, or $11 per person.

Raffle Chances

Won	Net gain	Probability
$525	$500	1%
$125	$100	5%
$25	$0	10%
$0	−$25	84%

3. Degrees for each sector, rounded to the nearest degree: China 75°, India 60°, United States 16°, Indonesia 13°, Brazil 10°, Other 185°; degrees add up to less than 360° because of rounding.

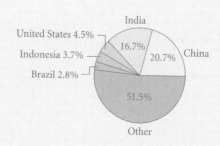

2. 105 students have blue eyes, about 52 or 53 have gray eyes, 70 have green eyes, and about 122 or 123 have brown eyes.

Exercise 3 Students will need a protractor for this exercise.

5. Find the area of each shaded region. Then determine the probability of a random point landing in the shaded region of each figure.

a.
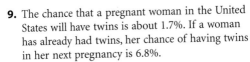
5 cm   5 cm   1.5 cm   2.5 cm

12.5 cm²; $\frac{12.5}{40}$, or 0.3125

b.

9 cm   5 cm   5 cm

32.5 cm²; $\frac{32.5}{45}$, or 0.7$\overline{2}$

6. Standard California license plates have one number (1–9), followed by three letters (A–Z), followed by three numbers (0–9). Repeated numbers or letters are allowed. How many license plates of this type are possible? 158,184,000

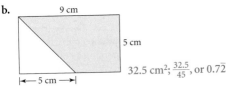

7. A group of four students must assign among themselves the roles of director, timekeeper, recorder, and reporter.

a. If roles are assigned randomly, how many different arrangements are possible? $4 \cdot 3 \cdot 2 \cdot 1$, or 24

b. Is this situation a combination, a permutation, or neither? Explain.

c. If Jesse refuses to be the recorder, how many arrangements are possible? 18

8. A class of 32 students is randomly divided into groups of four. Jenny is hoping to be in a group with her friend Yoana.

a. How many possible arrangements of three other people might be in a group with Jenny? 4495

b. What is the probability that Jenny and Yoana will be in a group together? $\frac{435}{4495} \approx 0.097$

9. The chance that a pregnant woman in the United States will have twins is about 1.7%. If a woman has already had twins, her chance of having twins in her next pregnancy is 6.8%.

a. Draw a tree diagram representing two pregnancies.

b. What is the probability that a woman will have two sets of twins in two pregnancies? 0.001156

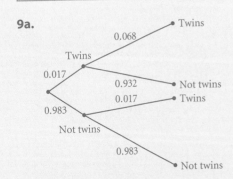

10. Nozomi and Chase are playing a dice game. In each round, each person rolls a die. If the sum of the two dice is greater than 5, Nozomi scores 3 points. Otherwise, Chase scores 6 points. ⓗ

a. What is the probability that Nozomi earns points in any one round? $\frac{26}{36}$, or 0.7$\overline{2}$

b. What is the probability that Chase earns points in any one round? $\frac{10}{36}$, or 0.2$\overline{7}$

c. What is Nozomi's expected point value for any one round? $\frac{26}{36}(3) + \frac{10}{36}(0) = 2.1\overline{6}$

d. If they play ten rounds, what is Nozomi's expected point total? 21.$\overline{6}$

e. If they play ten rounds, who is expected to win, and by how many points? Nozomi, by 5 points

7b. permutation, because the order is important and no person can have more than one role

Exercise 8b If students are struggling, [Ask] "How many groups of four include both Jenny and Yoana?" [If two slots in the group are filled, then there are $_{30}C_2$, or 435 combinations of students to fill the other two slots. So there are 435 different groups of four that contain both Jenny and Yoana.]

Exercise 9 The probability of 1.7% is for any pregnant woman who has not already had twins. [Alert] Students may be confused by the wording of 9b. The question asks for the probability that a woman will have one pair of twins, and then another pair of twins in her next pregnancy.

9a.
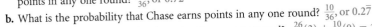
Twins
0.068
Twins
0.017
0.932   Not twins
0.017   Twins
0.983
Not twins
0.983
Not twins

TAKE ANOTHER LOOK

▶ In Lesson 10.4, Exercise 9, you learned about factorial notation, and you probably determined that $_nP_n$ can be calculated using the expression $n!$. Figure out general expressions involving n, r, and factorial notation that can be used to evaluate $_nP_r$ and $_nC_r$. Test your formulas to ensure that you get $_6P_3 = 120$ and $_6C_3 = 20$. Check that you also get $_9P_4 = 3024$ and $_9C_4 = 126$. It may help to look back at Lesson 10.4, Example C.

Assessing What You've Learned

 UPDATE YOUR PORTFOLIO Choose a couple of investigations or exercises from this chapter that you are particularly proud of. Write a paragraph about each piece of work. Describe the objective of the problem, how you demonstrated understanding in your solution, and anything you might have done differently.

 WRITE IN YOUR JOURNAL You have learned several methods for counting possible outcomes. Describe a few situations in which you might need to count outcomes, and state which method would be most appropriate in each case.

 GIVE A PRESENTATION By yourself or with a group, present the results of a probability experiment. Describe the experiment and what probability you were testing. (You might want to use a graphing calculator or computer to perform the experiment.) Show your results in a tree diagram or table. If possible, calculate the theoretical probabilities, and compare them to your experimental probabilities.

▶ **Take Another Look**

$$_nP_r = \frac{n!}{(n-r)!};$$

$$_nC_r = \frac{_nP_r}{r!} = \frac{n!}{r!(n-r)!}$$

ASSESSING

Use the test generator or Assessment Resources to create a written test that is appropriate for your class. You might also choose some of the Constructive Assessment items to give as a group assessment a few days before giving individual assessments. Students can review the concepts of the chapter and deepen their understanding by working together on more challenging questions than you might include on an individual assessment. Circulate during the assessment so that you can hear students' discussions, but let groups work as independently as possible. You can grade one paper from each group or one problem from each student's paper, or you can have each group present a problem or a part of a problem to the class.

FACILITATING SELF-ASSESSMENT

To help students complete the portfolio described in Assessing What You've Learned, suggest that they consider for evaluation their work on Lesson 10.1, Exercise 6; Lesson 10.2, Exercise 8; Lesson 10.3, Exercise 7; Lesson 10.4, Exercise 9; Lesson 10.5, Exercise 11; and Lesson 10.6, Exercise 10.

11

Introduction to Geometry

Overview

Chapters 0–9 of the student text emphasized algebra, with a graphing-calculator approach that included analytic geometry and analysis of data. Chapter 10 extended the data analysis into the area of probability. In Chapter 11, students extend the analytic geometry to solve algebraic problems such as finding the midpoint, finding the length of a segment or the distance between two points, and solving for the unknown side lengths or angle measures of right triangles. Through a study of different polygons, **Lesson 11.1** reviews the slopes of parallel lines and shows how the slopes of perpendicular lines are related. In **Lesson 11.2,** students see how to find the coordinates of a segment's midpoint. In **Lesson 11.3,** students prepare for deriving the Pythagorean Theorem by learning how to draw line segments whose lengths represent radical quantities. The Pythagorean Theorem and its applications are the focus of **Lesson 11.4.** **Lesson 11.5** has students rewrite radical expressions in different forms, using rules for operating on radicals. In **Lesson 11.6,** students derive and learn to apply the distance formula. Trigonometry is the focus of the last two lessons. In **Lesson 11.7,** students study similar triangles and learn the basic trigonometric ratios. Applications of inverse trigonometric ratios are featured in **Lesson 11.8.**

The Mathematics

Approaches to geometry are usually classified as analytic (coordinate) and synthetic. Most geometry associated with algebra is analytic, as is the case in the student text.

Synthetic Geometry

In about 300 B.C.E., the Greek mathematician Euclid wrote 13 books called the *Elements,* the culmination of all mathematics known in the Western world at that time. Because of paradoxes, Euclid was wary of measurement, so Euclid worked only with synthetic geometry. As a whole, the *Elements*

encompasses number theory, ratios, and geometry. The climax of the first book, which lays the groundwork for them all and focuses on triangles, is the Pythagorean Theorem.

Euclid states this theorem in terms of square figures: The square on the hypotenuse of a right triangle equals the sum of the squares on the other two sides. We, more comfortable with associating numbers with shapes, would insert the word *area:* The area of the square on the hypotenuse equals the sum of the areas of the squares on the other two sides. Even more commonly, in this algebraic age, we tend to abandon the consideration of areas of squares altogether and work with the lengths of the triangle's sides. We usually write $c^2 = a^2 + b^2$, although there's no reason why we can't use other letters for the three lengths. Indeed, we often need to do so in applying the theorem.

Analytic Geometry

In this text students have already worked with analytic geometry. They have plotted points and graphed equations. In this chapter they consider polygons, which are not graphs of equations $y = f(x)$.

They already know that two lines with the same slope are parallel. Here they learn that two lines whose slopes are opposite reciprocals $\left(\text{such as } \frac{3}{4} \text{ and } -\frac{4}{3}\right)$ are perpendicular.

The idea of midpoint of a line segment is also familiar. What's new in this chapter is that the coordinates of the midpoint can be found by averaging (finding the mean of) the coordinates of the segment's endpoints.

The reason the Pythagorean Theorem, which is a part of synthetic geometry, is introduced is to derive the formula for the distance between two points whose coordinates are known.

Trigonometry

Trigonometry, which comes from the Greek meaning "triangle measure," relates angles of triangles to

the lengths of their sides. The text uses ratios of sides of right triangles to introduce students to trigonometry for acute angles only. Trigonometry can be extended to obtuse angles, angles with measures more than 180°, and even negative angles, but the right triangle context must be stretched significantly to do so. The extensions tend to be more effective if approached through periodic (circular) functions, in which angles are measured by radians, the number of radii they sweep out on a circle. Periodic functions are useful in modeling various kinds of waves as well as phenomena such as mean daily temperatures.

Using This Chapter

Check your district's standards to see how much analytic geometry and trigonometry must be included in the course. This chapter is good for courses that have some time for exploration at the end. For an abbreviated approach, consider only the highlights of Lessons 11.1, 11.3, 11.4, and 11.6. If students are familiar with right triangles, you might cover only the trigonometry in Lessons 11.7 and 11.8.

Resources

Discovering Algebra Resources

Teaching and Worksheet Masters
  Lessons 11.1–11.3, 11.5–11.8

Calculator Notes 1H, 6B, 11A, 11B, 11C

Sketchpad Demonstrations
  Lessons 11.2, 11.4, 11.7

Dynamic Algebra Explorations online
  Lessons 11.4, 11.6, 11.7

Assessment Resources
  Quiz 1 (Lessons 11.1–11.3)
  Quiz 2 (Lessons 11.4 and 11.5)
  Quiz 3 (Lessons 11.6–11.8)
  Chapter 11 Test
  Chapter 11 Constructive Assessment Options
  Chapters 8 to 11 Exam
  Final Exam

More Practice Your Skills for Chapter 11

Condensed Lessons for Chapter 11

Other Resources

Pythagoras Plugged In by Dan Bennett.

The Ambitious Horse by Lawrence W. Swiencicki.

Mathematical Quilts by Diane Venters and Elaine Krajenke Ellison.

For complete references to these and other resources, see www.keypress.com/DA.

Pacing Guide

	day 1	day 2	day 3	day 4	day 5	day 6	day 7	day 8	day 9	day 10
standard	11.1	11.2	11.3	quiz, 11.4	11.5	11.5	quiz, 11.6	11.6	11.7	11.7
enriched	11.1	11.2	11.3	quiz, 11.4, project	11.5	11.5, project	quiz, 11.6	11.6	11.7	11.7
block	11.1, 11.2	11.3, quiz, 11.4	11.5	quiz, 11.6	11.7	11.8	quiz, review	assessment	mixed review	exam

	day 11	day 12	day 13	day 14	day 15	day 16	day 17	day 18	day 19	day 20
standard	11.8	review	assessment	mixed review	exam					
enriched	11.8	review, TAL	assessment	mixed review	exam					

- Extend knowledge about slopes of parallel lines to perpendicular lines and extend knowledge of midpoints to coordinates

- Learn the definitions of various quadrilaterals defined by their parallel and perpendicular sides

- Learn to distinguish between deductive and inductive reasoning

- Learn to find the areas of polygons by decomposing the figures into triangles and rectangles and by removing triangles from larger rectangles

- See the Pythagorean Theorem and its applications both geometrically and algebraically

- Work with radical expressions: squaring, distributing, simplifying, and applying to quadratic equations and parabolas, and solve radical equations

- See how the Pythagorean Theorem leads to the distance formula and its applications in coordinate geometry

- Use similar triangles to express the definitions of the sine, cosine, and tangent as ratios

- Learn to find an acute angle in a real-world situation when one of its trigonometric ratios is known

These brightly colored wall paintings are a traditional art form of South Africa's Ndebele tribe. Ndebele women paint murals like these to celebrate special occasions such as weddings and harvests. Learning and continuing the ancient art form is an important part of training for young girls. The painters' use of universally recognized geometric shapes helps these murals transcend time and cultural boundaries.

OBJECTIVES

In this chapter you will

- learn definitions and symbols important in geometry
- use algebra to describe geometric relationships
- discover some properties of parallel and perpendicular lines
- learn about inductive and deductive reasoning
- find the coordinates of a line segment's midpoint
- calculate the distance between two points
- learn more about square roots
- explore important relationships between the sides of a right triangle

As you look at these designs with students, you can talk about patterns and transformations. **[Ask]** "What polygons do you see?" [triangles, trapezoids, rectangles, hexagons, dodecagons, ...] "How are the shapes of the painting related to the shape of the fence?" [Both contain parts that are symmetric, lines are parallel, angles are repeated, designs are aligned and so on.] "Where do you see transformations?" [translations: along the top borders, shapes under these borders repeat; reflection: any of the elements that have bilateral symmetry; 2-fold rotation]

The Ndebele art style has come into international recognition through the work of the South African artist Esther Mahlangu. In 1991, she was the first woman to contribute to BMW's Art Car Collection—a series of automobiles that have been painted by notable artists (including Alexander Calder and Andy Warhol). In 1994, she was commissioned by the National Museum of Women in the Arts (Washington, D.C.) to paint a mural for an exhibition in her honor.

Parallel and Perpendicular

When you draw geometric figures on coordinate axes, you are doing **analytic geometry.** You use the axes to identify points and write the equations of lines, which you can use to describe relationships and properties of the figures. In this lesson you will discover some interesting connections between algebra and geometry.

The Russian artist Wassily Kandinsky (1866–1944) used parallel and perpendicular line segments in his 1923 work titled *Circles in a Circle.*

Parallel lines are lines in the same plane that never intersect. They are always the same distance apart. You draw arrowheads on the middle of each line to show that they are parallel. You may have noticed a relationship between the slopes of parallel lines earlier in this course.

Perpendicular lines are lines that meet at a **right angle,** that is, at an angle that measures 90°. In fact, four right angles are formed where perpendicular lines intersect. You draw a small box in one of the angles to show that the lines are perpendicular.

Investigation
Slopes

You will need

- graph paper
- a straightedge

A rectangle has two pairs of parallel line segments and four right angles. When you draw a rectangle on the coordinate plane and notice the slopes of its sides, you will discover how the slopes of parallel and perpendicular lines are related.

Step 1 | Draw coordinate axes centered on graph paper. Each member of your group should choose one of the following sets of points. Plot the points and connect them, in order, to form a closed polygon. You should have formed a rectangle.

  a. $A(6, 20)$, $B(13, 11)$, $C(-5, -3)$, $D(-12, 6)$
  b. $A(3, -1)$, $B(-3, 7)$, $C(9, 16)$, $D(15, 8)$
  c. $A(-11, 21)$, $B(17, 11)$, $C(12, -3)$, $D(-16, 7)$
  d. $A(3, -10)$, $B(-5, 22)$, $C(7, 25)$, $D(15, -7)$

NCTM STANDARDS

CONTENT	PROCESS
Number	Problem Solving
✔ Algebra	✔ Reasoning
✔ Geometry	Communication
Measurement	Connections
Data/Probability	✔ Representation

LESSON OBJECTIVES

- Discover how slopes of parallel and perpendicular lines are related
- Learn the definitions of various quadrilaterals defined by their parallel and perpendicular sides
- Learn the definitions of inductive and deductive reasoning

PLANNING

LESSON OUTLINE

One day:

  5 min   Introduction
  20 min   Investigation
  5 min   Sharing
  10 min   Examples
  5 min   Closing
  5 min   Exercises

MATERIALS

- graph paper
- straightedges
- Surveying (T or W), *optional*
- Quadrilaterals (T), *optional*
- Calculator Notes 1H, 11A

TEACHING

Further study of analytic (coordinate) geometry begins by extending students' knowledge of slopes of parallel lines to geometric figures and learning about slopes of perpendicular lines in those figures.

INTRODUCTION

Remind students what a *plane* is. Work so far with a coordinate plane has included plotting individual points or graphing lines or other functions. Now we turn to other geometric figures composed of line segments.

Any pair of parallel lines will lie in a single plane, but in space three lines each parallel to the other two might not be in the same plane. **[Ask]** "Must a pair of lines either meet or be parallel?" [No; there are lines in space that never meet and are not parallel; they are called *skew.*]

See pages 729–730 for answers to Step 1.

For a tool used to draw line segments, the name *straightedge* (rather than *ruler*) is used to point out that any measurement markings on the tool are irrelevant.

One Step

Display the Surveying transparency and **[Ask]** "What can you say about the shape of this plot of land? Are any of its edges parallel or perpendicular?" As you circulate, keep asking students how they can know for certain whether two lines are parallel or perpendicular. As needed, suggest that they check the slopes of known cases. If they check only the case of horizontal and vertical lines, suggest that they try a rotation of the lines about the origin. In Sharing, discuss the assumptions needed to have two of the edges parallel. (Is the measurement really 637.5 ft?) Students might solve the problem with any of the four vertices at the origin and may begin a discussion of whether a plane is a good representation of this part of the earth.

Step 1 Each student in the group can choose a different set of points. As needed, point out that the notation $A(6, 20)$ means that the point named A has coordinates $(6, 20)$. As needed, help students see that the rectangle is slanted. Students can add "perpendicular boxes."

[Language] A line over the top of other symbols, as used to designate a line segment, is called a *vinculum*. Technically, part of the standard square root symbol is a vinculum. Vincula used to be employed in many places where we now use parentheses.

Step 2 slope of $\overline{AD}$ and $\overline{BC}$: — Step 2
a. $\frac{7}{9}$ b. $\frac{3}{4}$ c. $\frac{14}{5}$ d. $\frac{1}{4}$
Step 3 slope of $\overline{AB}$ and $\overline{DC}$: — Step 3
a. $-\frac{9}{7}$ b. $-\frac{4}{3}$ c. $-\frac{5}{14}$ d. -4
Step 4 Parallel lines have — Step 4
the same slope.

Step 7 Perpendicular — Step 7
lines have opposite reciprocal slopes; their product is -1. Any pair of perpendicular lines should reinforce — Step 8
this conclusion.

These street intersections in New York City are a real-world example of perpendicular lines.

The slope of a line segment is the same as the slope of the line containing the segment. You can write the segment between A and D as $\overline{AD}$.

Find the slopes of $\overline{AD}$ and $\overline{BC}$.

Find the slopes of $\overline{AB}$ and $\overline{DC}$.

What conjecture can you make about the slopes of parallel lines based on your answers to Steps 2 and 3?

The ties underneath these railroad tracks in British Columbia are a real-world example of parallel segments.

The tracks are also parallel as long as they don't curve; they only seem to converge as they recede from view.

To find the **reciprocal** of a number, you write the number as a fraction and then invert it (exchange the numerator and denominator). For example, the reciprocal of $\frac{2}{3}$ is $\frac{3}{2}$. The product of reciprocals is 1.

Step 5 | Express the slope values of $\overline{AB}$ and $\overline{BC}$ as reduced fractions.

Step 6 | Express the slope values of $\overline{AD}$ and $\overline{DC}$ as reduced fractions.

What conjecture can you make about the slopes of perpendicular lines? What is their product? Check your conjecture by finding the slopes of any other pair of perpendicular sides in your rectangle.

On the coordinate plane, draw two new pairs of parallel lines that have the slope relationship you discovered in Step 7. What figure is formed where the two pairs of lines intersect?

Step 4 The idea that slopes of parallel lines are equal will be remembered by many students from the several times it appeared in Chapter 4.

Step 7 [Alert] Students might need help in seeing the relationship here, because both "taking a reciprocal" and "finding the opposite" are needed. If students are having trouble, have them graph another set of lines

with slope -2 and $+\frac{1}{2}$. Or ask them to draw perpendicular lines and find the slope.

Step 8 Try to help students realize that the relationship works both ways. **[Alert]** For students having difficulty understanding the slope relationships, you might suggest that they draw slope triangles on the rectangle's sides.

See page 730 for answers to Steps 5, 6, and 8.

In Steps 4 and 7 of the investigation, you made conjectures based on studying examples. When you do this, you are using **inductive reasoning.**

You can draw any polygon on a graph and assign coordinate pairs to its vertices. Then you can use these points to calculate slopes, lengths of sides, perimeters, areas, and even the sizes of angles. You can use this information to draw conclusions about the polygon.

A **right triangle** has one right angle. The sides that form the right angle are called **legs,** and the side opposite the right angle is called the **hypotenuse.**

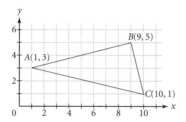

EXAMPLE A

Triangle *ABC* (written as △*ABC*) is formed by connecting the points (1, 3), (9, 5), and (10, 1). Is it a right triangle?

▶ **Solution**

The slope of $\overline{AB}$ is $\frac{1}{4}$, the slope of $\overline{AC}$ is $\frac{-2}{9}$, and the slope of $\overline{BC}$ is -4. The slopes $\frac{1}{4}$ and -4 are opposite reciprocals of each other, so the sides with these slopes are perpendicular. That means angle *B* is a right angle. So these three points define a right triangle.

Did you notice that the product of the two slopes, $\frac{1}{4}$ and -4, is -1?

In Example A you used the fact that perpendicular lines have opposite reciprocal slopes to determine that △*ABC* is a right triangle. The process of showing that certain statements or conclusions follow logically from an initial assumption or fact is called **deductive reasoning.**

A deductive argument starts with a general statement that is assumed to be true, called the **hypothesis,** and shows how that statement leads to a specific result, called the **conclusion.** Each step of the argument is supported by a **premise**—a definition, property, or proven fact.

Inductive and deductive reasoning are used extensively in mathematics and in life. You have been doing both forms of reasoning throughout this course. You used inductive reasoning every time you made a conjecture—for example, when you observed that $3^4 \cdot 3^2 = 3^6$ and $x^3 \cdot x^6 = x^9$, you concluded that $b^m \cdot b^n = b^{m+n}$. When you solved an equation and justified each step, you were doing deductive reasoning. For example, you started with the equation $\frac{3x+4}{6} - 5 = 7$ and followed steps to show that this was equivalent to $x = 22\frac{2}{3}$. In this case, you solved an equation by using deductive reasoning to prove that two equations are equivalent.

The △ symbol is customarily and frequently used in geometry to mean *triangle*. Students should not confuse this with delta, introduced in Lesson 4.1 to help represent a line's slope $\left(\frac{\Delta\,y}{\Delta\,x}\right)$. Quadrilaterals and other polygons do not generally have symbols, although some textbooks use symbols for frequently occurring quadrilaterals such as the square or parallelogram. You may want to introduce the symbol ∠ for "angle." That is, ∠*B* is read "angle *B*." "Angle *B*" means ∠*ABC* (or ∠*CBA*).

[Language] *Inductive* reasoning is the process of investigating specific examples and drawing general conclusions from the patterns observed. *Deductive* reasoning uses general principles, such as definitions or algebraic properties, to work from a hypothesis to a conclusion about a specific example. Exercise 16 asks students to categorize examples of reasoning as inductive or deductive and to identify the hypothesis and conclusion.

Have students present ideas about Step 4 only if there was confusion as they worked. You may want to introduce the symbol ∥ to mean "is parallel to." For example, writing $\overline{AD} \parallel \overline{BC}$ means segment *AD* is parallel to segment *BC*.

Focus class discussion on Steps 7 and 8. Although the term *negative reciprocals* is often used to describe the relationship between, say, $\frac{2}{3}$ and $-\frac{3}{2}$, the term *opposite reciprocals* is preferable because it better captures the fact that each is related to the other in the same way. $\left(\text{That is, } \frac{2}{3} \text{ is the opposite reciprocal of } -\frac{3}{2}, \text{ but only } -\frac{3}{2} \text{ is a negative number.}\right)$ Students encountered opposites in the introduction of absolute values in Lesson 7.5.

Ask whether the slopes of a horizontal and a vertical line are opposite reciprocals of each other or, equivalently, if their product is -1. Because the slope of a vertical line is undefined, these kinds of lines, though perpendicular, contradict the claim that "if two lines are perpendicular, then their slopes are opposite reciprocals." The converse of that claim is true, however: If their slopes are opposite reciprocals, then two lines are perpendicular.

You may want to introduce the symbol ⊥ to mean "is perpendicular to." For example, $\overline{AD} \perp \overline{DC}$ means segment *AD* is perpendicular to segment *DC*.

Assessing Progress

Through your observations of group work and presentations, you can assess students' ability to plot points, find slopes of line segments, and reduce fractions.

▶ **EXAMPLE A**

This example shows how the relationship between slopes of perpendicular lines can be applied to find out whether a triangle has a right angle. As needed, remind students that -4 can be written as $-\frac{4}{1}$.

▶ EXAMPLE B

This example illustrates how the relationships between both parallel and perpendicular lines can be applied to classify geometric figures.

Be sure to sketch pictures when introducing the term *trapezoid*. With this definition of trapezoid, no parallelogram is a trapezoid. Therefore, to verify that the given figure is a trapezoid, the student must verify that the slope of $\overline{CD}$ is indeed different from the slope of $\overline{AB}$. (The term *trapezoid* is often defined without the condition that one pair of edges is nonparallel. With that definition, every parallelogram is a trapezoid, and this additional step isn't needed.)

Closing the Lesson

Slopes of parallel lines are equal. Slopes of **perpendicular lines** are opposite reciprocals. These two facts can be applied to find out something about geometric figures whose vertices are given by coordinates. For example, a triangle can be checked to determine if it's a **right triangle,** and a quadrilateral can be checked to determine whether it's a **trapezoid,** a **parallelogram,** or a **rectangle.**

If you know properties of geometric shapes, you can use deductive reasoning to prove that a figure is a particular shape. A **trapezoid** is a quadrilateral with one pair of opposite sides that are parallel and one pair of opposite sides that are not parallel. A trapezoid with one of the nonparallel sides perpendicular to both parallel sides is a **right trapezoid.**

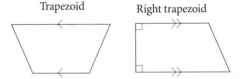

Trapezoid   Right trapezoid

EXAMPLE B | Classify as specifically as possible the polygon formed by the points $A(-4, 1)$, $B(-2, 4)$, $C(4, 0)$, and $D(-1, -1)$.

▶ **Solution** | To graph this shape on your calculator, enter the *x*-coordinates into list L1 and the *y*-coordinates into list L2 (repeat the first value at the end of each list). Set your calculator to graph a connected line plot. [▶ See **Calculator Note 1H.** ◀] Set the graphing window large enough to see all the points, then square the window. [▶ See **Calculator Note 11A.** ◀]

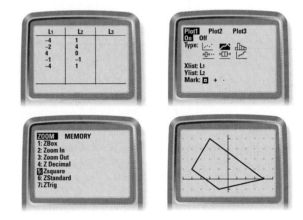

Calculate the slopes of the sides. Notice equal slopes (parallel sides) and opposite reciprocal slopes (perpendicular sides).

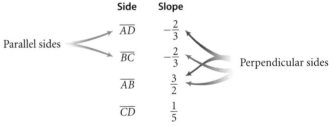

Side	Slope
$\overline{AD}$	$-\dfrac{2}{3}$
$\overline{BC}$	$-\dfrac{2}{3}$
$\overline{AB}$	$\dfrac{3}{2}$
$\overline{CD}$	$\dfrac{1}{5}$

Parallel sides: $\overline{AD}$, $\overline{BC}$

Perpendicular sides

Quadrilateral *ABCD* has one set of parallel sides and one side perpendicular to that pair. So *ABCD* is a right trapezoid.

In Example B you used deductive reasoning to start with the hypothesis "$(-4, 1)$, $(-2, 4)$, $(4, 0)$, and $(-1, -1)$ are the vertices of a polygon," and end with the conclusion, "The polygon is a right trapezoid." Here are several other special quadrilaterals that you may be familiar with.

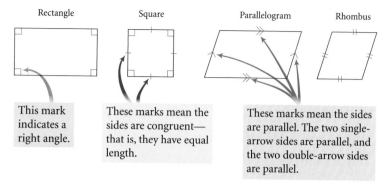

Rectangle   Square   Parallelogram   Rhombus

This mark indicates a right angle.

These marks mean the sides are congruent—that is, they have equal length.

These marks mean the sides are parallel. The two single-arrow sides are parallel, and the two double-arrow sides are parallel.

A **rectangle** has four right angles. Its opposite sides are parallel and congruent. A **square** is a rectangle with four congruent sides. A **parallelogram** has two pairs of opposite sides that are parallel. Its opposite sides are also congruent. A **rhombus** is a quadrilateral with four congruent sides. Opposite sides are also parallel.

Note the marks used to indicate right angles, congruent sides, and parallel sides.

EXERCISES

You will need your graphing calculator for Exercise **2**.

▶ Practice Your Skills

1. Find the slope of each line.
   a. $y = 0.8(x - 4) + 7$ 0.8
   b. $y = 5 - 2x$ -2
   c. $y = -1.25(x - 3) + 1$ ⓐ -1.25
   d. $y = -4 + 2x$ 2
   e. $6x - 4y = 11$ ⓐ $\frac{3}{2}$
   f. $3x + 2y = 12$ $-\frac{3}{2}$
   g. $-9x + 6y = -4$ ⓐ $\frac{3}{2}$
   h. $10x - 15y = 7$ $\frac{2}{3}$

2. Determine whether each pair of lines is parallel, perpendicular, or neither. Verify by graphing on your calculator using a square window. [▶ See **Calculator Note 11A**. ◀] ⓗ
   a. $y = 0.8(x - 4) + 7$
       $y = -1.25(x - 3) + 1$ perpendicular
   b. $y = 5 - 2x$
       $y = -4 + 2x$ neither
   c. $6x - 4y = 11$
       $-9x + 6y = -4$ parallel
   d. $3x + 2y = 12$
       $10x - 15y = 7$ perpendicular

3. Line ℓ has slope 1.2. What is the slope of line p that is parallel to line ℓ? 1.2

4. Line ℓ has slope 1.2. Line m is perpendicular to line ℓ.
   a. What is the slope of line m? ⓐ $\frac{-1}{1.2} = -\frac{5}{6} = -0.8\overline{3}$
   b. What is the product of the slopes of line ℓ and line m? ⓐ -1

5. Find the equation in point-slope form of the line that passes through $(8, -2)$ and is perpendicular to $y = 3x + 7$. $y = -\frac{1}{3}(x - 8) - 2$

BUILDING UNDERSTANDING

The exercises give students practice in working with slopes of parallel and perpendicular lines.

ASSIGNING HOMEWORK

Essential	1, 2–5, 7–11
Performance assessment	6, 15
Portfolio	15
Journal	4, 15
Group	7–15
Review	17, 18

▶ **Helping with the Exercises**

Exercise 1 [Ask] "Is there a quick way to find the slope from the three coefficients of the equation $Ax + By = C$?" Help students solve the general equation once to see that the slope will be $-\frac{A}{B}$. Then, for example, they can see quickly that the slope in 1e is $-\frac{6}{-4}$, or $\frac{3}{2}$.

Exercise 2 This exercise uses the same equations as Exercise 1, so students can use their answers to Exercise 1 to complete this problem.

Exercises 3 and 4 This is the first use of single letters as names for lines. If students are confused, you might have them write out the equations of the lines.

2a.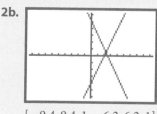
$[-9.4, 9.4, 1, -6.2, 6.2, 1]$

2b.
$[-9.4, 9.4, 1, -6.2, 6.2, 1]$

2c.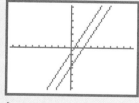
$[-9.4, 9.4, 1, -6.2, 6.2, 1]$

2d.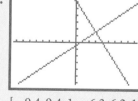
$[-9.4, 9.4, 1, -6.2, 6.2, 1]$

Exercise notes (left column)

Exercise 6 As needed, remind students of the notation for parallel sides and for segments with equal lengths. You might mention the term *congruent*, which was introduced in Chapter 0 and will be used again later.

Exercises 7–14 Students might use graphing calculators or geometry software to graph these polygons. If students need a review of terms, you might go over the Quadrilaterals transparency before they begin work on these exercises. If students are working individually, you might assign only Exercises 7–11. Or you might assign two of Exercises 7–14 to each member of a group of four.

Exercise 15 [Alert] Students may not recall the term *counterexample*, which was introduced in Lesson 7.2. In this context it's a synonym for *exception*. Encourage students to plot their quadrilaterals on graph paper.

16a. deductive; hypothesis: *Tyrannosaurus rex* had sharp teeth; conclusion: *Tyrannosaurus rex* was a carnivore.

16b. inductive; hypothesis: two consecutive numbers are added; conclusion: the result is an odd number.

Exercise 17 Allow students to use rectangle diagrams.

Exercise 18 This exercise will help prepare students for calculating midpoints in Lesson 11.2.

Reason and Apply

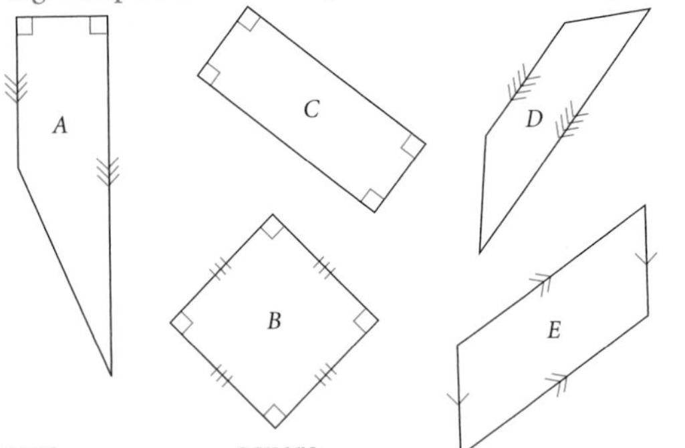

6. Name each quadrilateral using the most specific term that describes it: square, rectangle, parallelogram, right trapezoid, or trapezoid.

For Exercises 7–14, plot each set of points on graph paper and connect them to form a polygon. Classify each polygon using the most specific term that describes it. Use deductive reasoning to justify your answers by finding the slopes of the sides of the polygons.

7. $(-5, 0), (1, 4), (6, 3), (-3, -3)$ @

8. $(-3, -2), (3, 1), (5, -3), (-1, -6)$

9. $(-3, 4), (0, 4), (3, 0), (3, -4)$

10. $(-1, 4), (2, 7), (5, -2), (2, -5)$ @

11. $(-4, -1), (-2, 7), (2, 6), (3, 3)$

12. $(0, 4), (2, 8), (6, -2), (2, -1)$

13. $(-8, -2), (-4, 4), (5, -2), (1, -8)$ @

14. $(-2, 2), (1, 5), (4, 2), (1, -3)$

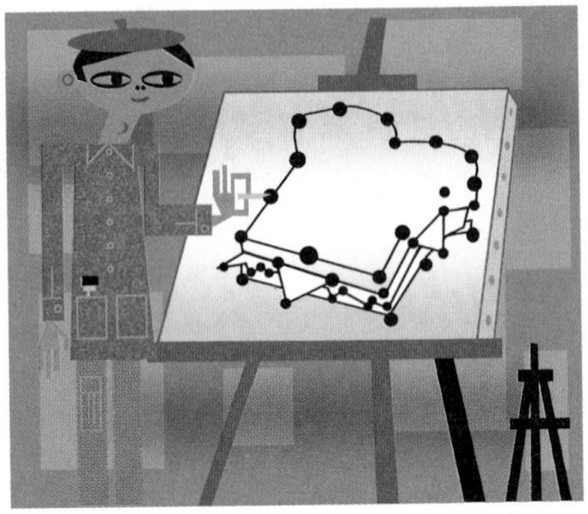

15. Al says you can define a right trapezoid as a quadrilateral with exactly two right angles. Provide a counterexample by naming four points for the vertices of a quadrilateral that has two right angles but is not a right trapezoid. Draw a sketch of your figure.

16. For each situation, identify whether inductive or deductive reasoning is used. Then state the hypothesis and conclusion.

a. The dinosaur *Tyrannosaurus rex* had sharp teeth. Animals with sharp teeth eat meat. Meat-eating animals are called carnivores. Therefore, *Tyrannosaurus rex* was a carnivore.

b. Krystal adds $5 + 6$ and gets 11. Then she adds $13 + 14$ and gets 27. Then she adds $92 + 93$ and gets 185. Krystal concludes that the sum of any two consecutive integers is odd.

c. Kendra uses the properties of numbers to show that $2(x - 3) = 10$ is equivalent to $x = 8$. deductive; hypothesis: $2(x - 3) = 10$; conclusion: $x = 8$.

Review

9.3 **17.** Multiply and combine like terms.

a. $x(x + 2)(2x - 1)$ @ $2x^3 + 3x^2 - 2x$

b. $(0.1x - 2.1)(0.1x + 2.1)$ @ $0.01x^2 - 4.41$

1.2 **18.** Find the value halfway between

a. 3 and 11 7

b. -4 and 7 1.5

c. -12 and -1 -6.5

d. 2 and 47 24.5

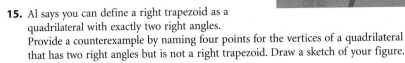
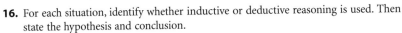

right trapezoid   rectangle   trapezoid
A   C   D
B
square   parallelogram

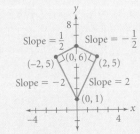

---

7. right trapezoid; slopes: $\frac{2}{3}, -\frac{1}{5}, \frac{2}{3}, -\frac{3}{2}$

8. rectangle; slopes: $\frac{1}{2}, -2, \frac{1}{2}, -2$

9. trapezoid; slopes: $0, -\frac{4}{3}$, undefined, $-\frac{4}{3}$

10. parallelogram; slopes: $1, -3, 1, -3$

11. quadrilateral; slopes: $4, -\frac{1}{4}, -3, \frac{4}{7}$

12. trapezoid; slopes: $2, -\frac{5}{2}, -\frac{1}{4}, -\frac{5}{2}$

13. rectangle; slopes: $\frac{3}{2}, -\frac{2}{3}, \frac{3}{2}, -\frac{2}{3}$

14. quadrilateral; slopes: $1, -1, \frac{5}{3}, -\frac{5}{3}$

15. possible answer:

Slope $= \frac{1}{2}$ Slope $= -\frac{1}{2}$
$(-2, 5)$ $(0, 6)$ $(2, 5)$
Slope $= -2$ Slope $= 2$
$(0, 1)$

Finding the Midpoint

In analytic geometry you can use the algebraic concept of slope to identify parallel and perpendicular lines. That helps you recognize and draw geometric figures like rectangles and right triangles. Another geometric feature is the **midpoint,** or middle point, of a line segment. Midpoints are used, for example, to draw these two geometric figures.

Balance is beautiful.
MIYOKO OHNO

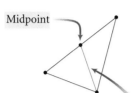

Midpoint

A **median** of a triangle is a segment that connects a vertex to the midpoint of the opposite side.

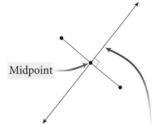

Midpoint

A **perpendicular bisector** is a line that divides a segment in half and that passes through the segment at a right angle.

Investigation
In the Middle

In this investigation you will discover a method for finding the coordinates of the midpoint of a segment. As you work through the steps, think about which algebra concepts help you find a midpoint.

You will need
- graph paper
- a straightedge

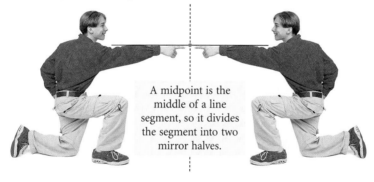

A midpoint is the middle of a line segment, so it divides the segment into two mirror halves.

Step 2 (3, 2); some students will find this by visual inspection; others may average the *x*-coordinates of the endpoints.

Step 3 (5, 4.5); some students will find this by inspection; others may average the *y*-coordinates of the endpoints.

Step 1 Plot the points $A(1, 2)$, $B(5, 2)$, and $C(5, 7)$ and connect them.

Step 2 Find the midpoint of $\overline{AB}$. How did you find this point?

Step 3 Find the midpoint of $\overline{BC}$. How did you find this point?

Step 4 Find the midpoint of $\overline{AC}$. How does the midpoint's *x*-coordinate compare to the *x*-coordinates of *A* and *C*? How does its *y*-coordinate compare to the *y*-coordinates of *A* and *C*? (3, 4.5); the *x*-coordinate is halfway between the *x*-coordinates of *A* and *C*. The *y*-coordinate is halfway between the *y*-coordinates of *A* and *C*.

of the four edges. What do you think of the suggestion?" As students work, suggest as needed that they try a variety of approaches to finding the midpoints. Some students may use graph paper and find areas by counting squares.

Step 1

y

6
C

4

2
A   B
      2   4   6   x

Step 2 You may want to define the points at the ends of a segment as *endpoints*.

Step 4 If students have been answering the questions by measuring, estimating, or counting grid lines, they may find this task difficult. Encourage them to draw horizontal and vertical lines through the midpoint of $\overline{AC}$.

Step 6 As needed, suggest that students think about how finding the midpoint of a line segment relates to previous concepts studied in this book. Specifically, a midpoint can be found by calculating the mean of the *x*- and *y*-coordinates of the endpoints of the segment.

SHARING IDEAS

Have students share their methods from Step 6. Then ask them to state the rule symbolically, aiming for the midpoint formula. Encourage all students to assist with this derivation, which many might find difficult to articulate. Keep a balance between supporting students and challenging them to think.

Point out the quotation opening the lesson. *Design News* called Miyoko Ohno "the first ranking bridge designer in Japan." Ask students what *balance* means. They may discuss the physical, the visual, the emotional, and other realms. **[Ask]** "Is physical balance always achieved at the midpoint?" [Thinking of a beam whose mass is uniformly distributed, they may say yes. Or they may think of the beam balance of Lesson 2.5, with weights placed in various locations, and say no.]

Assessing Progress

Watch for students' ability to plot points and find the mean of two numbers. Also check their understanding of midpoint.

▶ EXAMPLE

In this example students see an application of the midpoint formula to medians of triangles and perpendicular bisectors of line segments. Have students draw the triangle before going through the solution. As necessary, refer students to the pictures of a median and a perpendicular bisector on page 601. The diagram might also be drawn using geometry software.

Step 6 One answer: Find the distance between the *x*-coordinates and add half this distance to the leftmost *x*-coordinate; then find the distance between the *y*-coordinates and add half this distance to the lowest *y*-coordinate. Another answer: Average the *x*-coordinates and average the *y*-coordinates.

Step 5

Step 6

Step 7

Step 8

Consider the points $D(2, 5)$ and $E(7, 11)$. Find the midpoint of $\overline{DE}$. $(4.5, 8)$

Explain how to find the coordinates of the midpoint of a line segment between any two points.

Find the midpoint of the segment between each pair of points.

a. $F(-7, 42)$ and $G(2, 14)$ $(-2.5, 28)$

b. $H(2.4, -1.8)$ and $J(-4.4, -2.2)$ $(-1, -2)$

Make a conjecture about a formula for the midpoint of the segment connecting (a, b) and (c, d). $\left(\dfrac{a+c}{2}, \dfrac{b+d}{2}\right)$

There are several ways to find the midpoint of a segment. However, the midpoint is always halfway between the two endpoints, so its *x*-coordinate will be the mean of the *x*-coordinates of the endpoints. Likewise, its *y*-coordinate will be the mean of the *y*-coordinates of the endpoints.

In the next example you'll combine your knowledge of midpoints and slopes.

EXAMPLE

A triangle has vertices $A(-4, 3)$, $B(5, 9)$, and $C(0, -3)$.

a. Write the equation of the median from vertex B.

b. Write the equation of the perpendicular bisector of $\overline{AB}$.

▶ **Solution**

First, plot $\triangle ABC$.

a. The median from vertex B connects to the midpoint of $\overline{AC}$. Find the midpoint of $\overline{AC}$, then sketch the median.

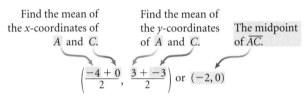

Find the mean of the *x*-coordinates of A and C. Find the mean of the *y*-coordinates of A and C. The midpoint of $\overline{AC}$.

$\left(\dfrac{-4+0}{2}, \dfrac{3+-3}{2}\right)$ or $(-2, 0)$

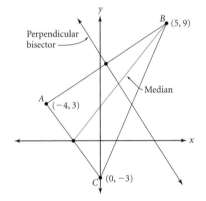

LESSON OBJECTIVES

- Discover the coordinates of the midpoint of a segment in terms of those of its endpoints
- Use coordinates of the midpoint of a segment and knowledge of slope to write equations of lines in polygons

NCTM STANDARDS

CONTENT		PROCESS	
	Number	✔	Problem Solving
✔	Algebra	✔	Reasoning
✔	Geometry	✔	Communication
✔	Measurement		Connections
	Data/Probability	✔	Representation

Now use the coordinates of vertex B and the midpoint of $\overline{AC}$ to find the slope of the median.

Find the slope between
vertex B and the midpoint.

$$\text{Slope} = \frac{9 - 0}{5 - (-2)} = \frac{9}{7}$$

Use the coordinates of the midpoint and the slope to write the equation of the median in point-slope form.

$$y = 0 + \frac{9}{7}(x - (-2)) \quad \text{or} \quad y = \frac{9}{7}(x + 2)$$

b. Look back at the sketch on the previous page. The perpendicular bisector passes through the midpoint of $\overline{AB}$ and is perpendicular to $\overline{AB}$. To find the equation, first find the midpoint of $\overline{AB}$.

$$\left(\frac{-4 + 5}{2}, \frac{3 + 9}{2}\right) \text{ or } \left(\frac{1}{2}, 6\right)$$

The slope of $\overline{AB}$ is $\frac{9 - 3}{5 - (-4)}$, which equals $\frac{6}{9}$, or $\frac{2}{3}$. The slope of the perpendicular bisector is the opposite reciprocal, or $\frac{-3}{2}$.

The equation of the perpendicular bisector of $\overline{AB}$ in point-slope form is

$$y = 6 + \frac{-3}{2}\left(x - \frac{1}{2}\right)$$

You can verify the answers to parts a and b by plotting the triangle and lines on your calculator. If you square the calculator window, the perpendicular lines will appear perpendicular.

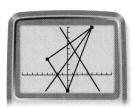

$[-9.4, 9.4, 1, -3.1, 9.3, 1]$

What you have learned about finding the midpoint of a segment is summarized by this formula.

Midpoint Formula

If the endpoints of a segment have coordinates (x_1, y_1) and (x_2, y_2), the midpoint of the segment has coordinates

$$\left(\frac{x_1 + x_2}{2}, \frac{y_1 + y_2}{2}\right)$$

Closing the Lesson

The coordinates of the **midpoint** of a line segment are the means (averages) of the respective coordinates of the segment's endpoints. The midpoint can be used to find **medians** of triangles and **perpendicular bisectors** of line segments.

Students practice finding coordinates of midpoints.

ASSIGNING HOMEWORK

Essential	1–5, 7
Performance assessment	6–8
Portfolio	9
Journal	4–6
Group	2, 8–10
Review	11–13

▶ Helping with the Exercises

Exercise 5 Even if students can answer the question by calculation, encourage them to sketch the triangle.

5. Yes. Possible answer: The slope of $\overline{AB}$ is 5 and the slope of $\overline{BC}$ is $-\frac{1}{5}$, so angle B is a right angle.

Exercise 6 If students aren't thinking of horizontal and vertical lines, you might suggest that they try the standard problem-solving strategy of considering extreme cases. Because the slope of a vertical line is undefined, the product of its slope with that of a horizontal line (0) is also undefined.

6. One line is horizontal and the other is vertical. A horizontal line has slope 0 and a vertical line has an undefined slope, so the product is also undefined.

Exercise 8 You can use the Sketchpad demonstration Quadrilateral Midpoints to replace this exercise.

8a. midpoint of $\overline{AB}$: (10, 3); midpoint of $\overline{BC}$: (15, 8); midpoint of $\overline{CD}$: (9, 10); midpoint of $\overline{DA}$: (4, 5)

8b. Parallelogram; the opposite sides are parallel because the slopes are 1, $-\frac{1}{3}$, 1, and $-\frac{1}{3}$.

EXERCISES

▶ Practice Your Skills

1. Find the midpoint of the segment between each pair of points.
   a. $(4, 5)$ and $(-3, -2)$ @ $(0.5, 1.5)$ **b.** $(7, -1)$ and $(5, -8)$ $(6, -4.5)$

2. Find the midpoint of a segment with endpoints (a, b) and (c, d). @ $\left(\frac{a + c}{2}, \frac{b + d}{2}\right)$

3. For the points $A(4, 7)$, $B(28, 11)$, and $C(-3, -1)$, find the
   a. Midpoint of $\overline{AB}$. @ $(16, 9)$ **b.** Midpoint of $\overline{BC}$. $(12.5, 5)$ **c.** Midpoint of $\overline{AC}$. $(0.5, 3)$

4. For the points $A(4, 7)$, $B(28, 11)$, and $C(-3, -1)$, find the equation in point-slope form of the
   a. Perpendicular bisector of $\overline{AB}$. @ possible answer: $y = 9 - 6(x - 16)$
   b. Median of $\triangle ABC$ from point B. possible answer: $y = 3 + \frac{16}{55}(x - 0.5)$

▶ Reason and Apply

5. The vertices of $\triangle ABC$ are $A(0, 0)$, $B(1, 5)$, and $C(6, 4)$. Is it a right triangle? Explain how you know.

6. There is a situation in which two lines are perpendicular but the product of their slopes is not -1. Describe this situation. ⓗ

7. The points $A(2, 1)$ and $B(4, 6)$ are the endpoints of a segment.
   a. Find the midpoint of $\overline{AB}$. @ $(3, 3.5)$
   b. Write the equation of the perpendicular bisector of $\overline{AB}$. $y = 3.5 - \frac{2}{5}(x - 3)$

8. Sketch this quadrilateral on your paper.
   a. Find the midpoint of each side. @
   b. Connect the midpoints in order. What polygon is formed? How do you know? @
   c. Draw the diagonals of the polygon formed in 8b. Are the diagonals perpendicular? Explain how you know. @ No; the slopes of the diagonals are $\frac{3}{11}$ and -7.

9. *Mini-Investigation* On graph paper or your calculator, draw a triangle with vertices $A(11, 6)$, $B(4, -8)$, and $C(-6, 6)$.
   a. Find the midpoint of each side. Label the midpoint of $\overline{AB}$ point D, the midpoint of $\overline{BC}$ point E, and the midpoint of $\overline{CA}$ point F.
   b. Find the slope of the segment from each vertex to the midpoint of the side opposite that vertex. slope of median $\overline{AE}$: $\frac{7}{12}$; slope of median $\overline{BF}$: $-\frac{28}{3}$; slope of median $\overline{CD}$: $-\frac{14}{27}$
   c. Write an equation for each median. @
   d. Solve a system of equations to find the intersection of median $\overline{AE}$ and median $\overline{BF}$. $\left(3, \frac{4}{3}\right)$

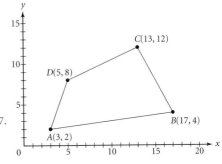

The starting position of the game Cat's Cradle shows triangles, parallel lines, and midpoints. What other geometric shapes do you see?

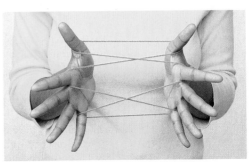

9a. $D(7.5, -1)$, $E(-1, -1)$, $F(2.5, 6)$

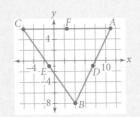

9c. possible answers:
median $\overline{AE}$: $y = 6 + \frac{7}{12}(x - 11)$;
median $\overline{BF}$: $y = 6 - \frac{28}{3}\left(x - \frac{5}{2}\right)$;
median $\overline{CD}$: $y = 6 - \frac{14}{27}(x + 6)$

e. Solve a system of equations to find the intersection of median $\overline{AE}$ and median $\overline{CD}$. $\left(3, \frac{4}{3}\right)$

f. What conjecture can you write, based on your answers to 9d and e?

g. Did you use inductive or deductive reasoning to write your conjecture in 9f?   inductive

10. In 10a–c, you are given the midpoint of a segment and one endpoint. Find the other endpoint.

   a. midpoint: (7, 4)   endpoint: (2, 4) ⓐ (12, 4)

   b. midpoint: (9, 7)   endpoint: (15, 9) (3, 5)

   c. midpoint: (−1, −2) endpoint: (3, −7.5) (−5, 3.5)

▶ **Review**

11.1 **11.** The equation of line ℓ has the form $Ax + By = C$. What is the slope of a line

   a. Perpendicular to line ℓ? $\dfrac{B}{A}$ **b.** Parallel to line ℓ? $-\dfrac{A}{B}$

5.3, **12.** Two intersecting lines have the equations $2x - 3y + 12 = 1$ and $x = 2y - 7$.
8.2
   a. Find the coordinates of the point of intersection. ⓐ $(-1, 3)$

   b. Write the equations of two other lines that intersect at this same point.

   c. Write the equation of a parabola that passes through this same point. ⓐ Possible answer: $y = (x + 1)^2 + 3$;
   any parabola of the form $y = a(x + 1)^2 + 3$ will have its vertex at this point.

11.1 **13.** Draw four congruent rectangles—that is, all the same size and shape.

   a. Shade half the area in each rectangle. Use a different way of dividing the rectangle each time.

   b. Which of your methods in 13a divide the rectangle into congruent polygons?

   c. Ripley divided one of her rectangles like this? Is the area divided in half? Explain.

IMPROVING YOUR GEOMETRY SKILLS

This puzzle was created by the English mathematician Charles Dodgson (1832–1898). You may know him better as Lewis Carroll, the author of *Alice's Adventures in Wonderland.*

Cut an 8-by-8 square into pieces like this: Reassemble them like this:

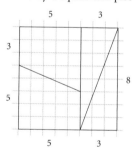
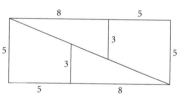

What is the area of the square? What is the area of the rectangle? Why aren't they equal?

9f. Possible answer: The medians of a triangle meet at a single point.

Exercise 11 This exercise relies on the insight obtained from Exercise 1e–h in Lesson 11.1. Students may need to rederive that slope from the standard form $Ax + By = C$.

Exercise 12 [Ask] "Is the student text correct in saying that these are equations of lines?" Students may not have realized that equations of lines can be written like this, especially with x isolated.

12b. possible answer: $x + y = 2$ and $y = 2x + 5$ or any line of the form $y = 3 + m(x + 1)$, where m is any number, or $x = -1$

13a. possible answers:

13b. Answers will vary. Any method that uses only one line segment will form congruent polygons. Some other methods may also produce congruent polygons.

13c. Yes; if you imagine a vertical segment through the upper vertex of the triangle, you can see that the triangles on either side of the vertical line are congruent.

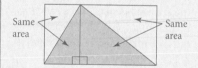

Same area   Same area

IMPROVING GEOMETRY SKILLS

The area of the square is 64 square units, and the area of the rectangle is 65 square units. The slope of each triangle's hypotenuse is $-\frac{2}{5}$, or -0.4. The slope of each right trapezoid's nonperpendicular side is $-\frac{3}{8}$, or -0.375. The slopes of these segments are close enough to fool the eye, but the segments do not lie on the same line. Instead, they create a parallelogram whose area is 1 square unit. This and 59 other puzzles and paradoxes are collected in *One Equals Zero and Other Mathematical Surprises* by Nitsa Movshovitz-Hadar and John Webb (Emeryville, CA: Key Curriculum Press, 1998).

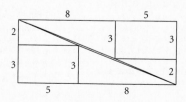

LESSON
11.3

Squares, Right Triangles, and Areas

Triangles, squares, rectangles, and other polygons are essential to design and construction. Finding the areas of farms, lots, floors, and walls is important for city planners, architects, building contractors, interior designers, and people in building trades and other occupations. An architect designs space for the people who will use a building. A contractor must be able to determine an approximate price per square foot to bid a job.

In this lesson you will use graph paper to practice finding the areas of squares and the lengths of their sides. You'll look for a pattern to find the lengths of the sides of a right triangle.

Framing a house requires many parallels, perpendiculars, and area calculations.

EXAMPLE A | Find the area of each shape on the grid at right.

▶ **Solution** | The rectangle has an area of 3 square units. The area of the triangle is half the area of the rectangle, so it has an area of 1.5 square units.

You can often draw or visualize a rectangle or square related to an area to help you find the area.

EXAMPLE B | Find the area of square *ABCD*.

▶ **Solution** | Using the grid lines, draw a square around square *ABCD*. The outer square, *MNOP*, has an area of 9 square units. Each triangle, *MAD*, *ANB*, *CBO*, and *DPC*, has an area equal to half of 2 square units, or 1 square unit.

Area of square ABCD = Area of square MNOP − 4(1)

So the area of square *ABCD* is 9 − 4, or 5, square units.

LESSON OBJECTIVES

- Learn how areas of figures can be found by decomposing the figures into triangles and rectangles or by removing triangles from larger rectangles
- Lay the groundwork for understanding the Pythagorean Theorem by learning that if the area of a square is s, then its side length is $\sqrt{s}$

NCTM STANDARDS

CONTENT		PROCESS	
✓	Number		Problem Solving
✓	Algebra	✓	Reasoning
✓	Geometry		Communication
✓	Measurement		Connections
	Data/Probability	✓	Representation

Investigation
What's My Area?

You will need
- graph paper
- a straightedge

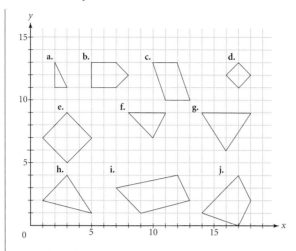

Step 1a 1 unit²

Step 1b 5 units²

Step 1c 6 units²

Step 1d 2 units²

Step 1e 8 units²

Step 1f 3 units²

Step 1g 6 units²

Step 1h 5 units²

Step 1i 10.5 units²

Step 1j 8 units²

Step 1   Copy these shapes onto graph paper. Work with a partner to find the area of each figure.

If you know the side length, *s*, of a square, then the area of the square is s^2. Likewise, if you know that the area of a square is s^2, then the side length is $\sqrt{s^2}$, or *s*. So the square labeled d in Step 1, which has an area of 2, has a side length of $\sqrt{2}$ units.

Step 2 area: 8 units²; side length: $\sqrt{8}$ units

Step 2   What are the area and side length of the square labeled e in Step 1?

Step 3   What are the area and side length of each of these squares?

Step 3a area: 9 units²; side length: 3 units

Step 3b area: 10 units²; side length: $\sqrt{10}$ units

a.   **b.**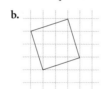

Step 4 Squares with area 2, 5, 8, 10, 13, and 17 can be constructed by tilting the square relative to the grid; squares with area 1, 4, 9, 16, and 25 are possible by following grid lines. Side lengths will be the square root of the area.

Step 4   Shown below are the smallest and largest squares with grid points for vertices that can be drawn on a 5-by-5 grid. Draw at least five other different-size squares on a 5-by-5 grid. They may be tilted, but they must be square, and their vertices must be on the grid. Find the area and side length of each square.

► **EXAMPLE B**

Here students see how to find the area of a figure by subtracting the areas of pieces around the figure. The area can be found in other ways as well. Some students may be able to "count" the area of square *ABCD* by piecing together whole grid squares.

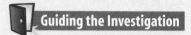 **Guiding the Investigation**

This investigation is written for students working in pairs. Copying the figures onto their own graph paper, or perhaps even a geoboard, provides excellent visualization practice for students. If you are short on time, however, you can give each pair a copy of the What's My Area? worksheet.

Step 1 Encourage students to use both addition and subtraction in finding these areas.

Step 2 Lengths are always positive, so we do not use the symbol $\pm\sqrt{}$ when expressing them.

Step 3 [Ask] "Is the second figure really a square? How can you tell?" [Justifications should mention that the slopes of adjacent edges are opposite reciprocals.] Two ways students can find the area are by adding areas of an interior square and four triangles or by subtracting areas of four triangles from the area of a larger square.

SHARING IDEAS

Students might report results of Step 1 (especially if there is disagreement) and show their ideas from Step 4.

[Ask] "How many different squares can be drawn with vertices at grid points on a 5-by-5 grid?" If "different" is interpreted as "different in size," then help students find a systematic method to show that there are 11 (6 tilted). If "different" includes the placement, then again try to derive a systematic method to count all 105 (50 tilted).

This example shows how to construct a segment whose length is the (positive) square root of an integer. Students may recognize this particular square from Step 3 of the investigation, but being able to think through the process in reverse will be very important for the next lesson.

If you have not done so in earlier chapters, you may want to show the shorthand for "square units" as "units²." Specifically, you can show ft², in.², m², and so on.

Assessing Progress

Watch for the ability to see shapes as what's left over when something else is removed as well as a composite of smaller shapes. You can also assess students' understanding of squares of numbers and their square roots.

Closing the Lesson

Areas of many figures can be found by considering the figures as composites of smaller rectangles and triangles or as the remainder when triangles are removed from a larger rectangle. For many integers, a segment whose length is the square root of that integer can be constructed by drawing a square whose area is that integer.

BUILDING UNDERSTANDING

Students work with finding areas and square root lengths.

ASSIGNING HOMEWORK

Essential	1, 3, 4, 6–9
Performance assessment	7, 8
Portfolio	5, 9
Journal	6
Group	2, 9
Review	10, 11

EXAMPLE C | Draw a line segment that is exactly $\sqrt{10}$ units long.

► **Solution** | A square with an area of 10 square units has a side length of $\sqrt{10}$ units. Ten is not a perfect square, so you will have to draw this square tilted. Start with the next largest perfect square—that is, 16 square units (4-by-4)—and subtract the areas of the four triangles to get 10. Here are two ways to draw a square tilted in a 4-by-4 square. Only the square on the left has an area of 10 square units.

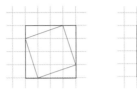

So a line segment with a length of $\sqrt{10}$ units looks like this:

This red segment has a length of $\sqrt{10}$ units.

This fabric quilt, *Spiraling Pythagorean Triples*, shows several tilted squares. It was made by Diana Venters, a mathematician who uses mathematical themes in her quilts. You will learn about the Pythagorean Theorem in Lesson 11.4.

See more mathematical quilts with the links at **www.keymath.com/DA** .

If a 4-by-4 square had not worked in this example, you could have tried a larger square.

You can draw segments on graph paper with lengths equal to many square root values, but you may have to guess and check!

EXERCISES

You will need your graphing calculator for Exercises **2, 10,** and **11.**

► **Practice Your Skills**

1. Find an exact solution to each equation. (Leave your answers in radical form.)
   a. $x^2 = 47$ $\pm\sqrt{47}$
   b. $(x - 4)^2 = 28$ @ $4 \pm \sqrt{28}$
   c. $(x + 2)^2 - 3 = 11$ @ $-2 \pm\sqrt{14}$
   d. $2(x - 1)^2 + 4 = 18$ $1 \pm \sqrt{7}$

2. Calculate decimal approximations for your solutions to Exercise 1. Round your answers to the nearest thousandth. Check each answer by substituting it into the original equation.

► **Helping with the Exercises**

Exercise 2 When checking with decimal approximations, students will not get the exact value on the right side of the equation. For instance, for 2a, $(6.856)^2$ equals 47.004736, not 47. You may need to remind students of the difference between exact values and decimal approximations.

2a. ± 6.856

2b. $-1.292, 9.292$

2c. $-5.742, 1.742$

2d. $-1.646, 3.646$

3. Find the area of each figure at right.

4. Find the side length of the square in 3f.
$\sqrt{18}$ units

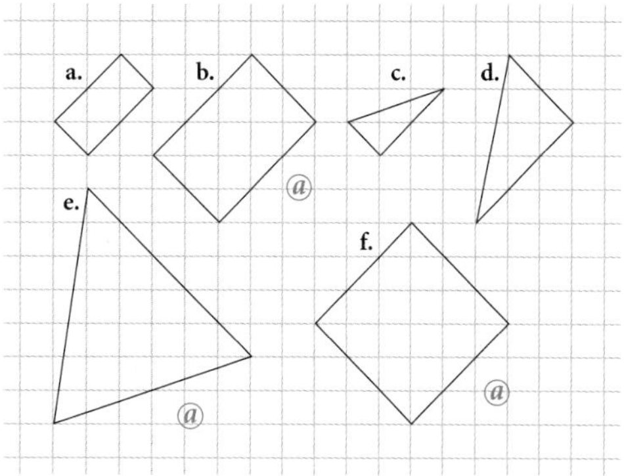

► **Reason and Apply**

5. Find the side lengths of the polygons in 3a, b, and e. ⓐ

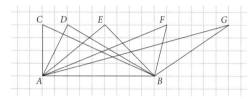

a.   b.   c.   d.

ⓐ

e.

f.

ⓐ   ⓐ

6. Find the area of each triangle below. You may want to draw each triangle separately on graph paper. ⓗ   Each triangle has area 18 units².

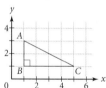

a. $\triangle ABC$ **b.** $\triangle ABD$ **c.** $\triangle ABE$ **d.** $\triangle ABF$ **e.** $\triangle ABG$

7. In the figure at right, $\triangle ABC$ is a right triangle. 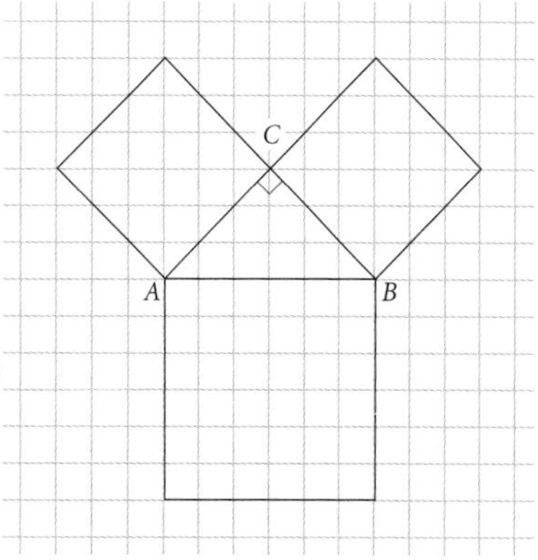
  a. Find the area of each of the squares built on the sides of this triangle. ⓐ   36 units², 18 units², 18 units²
  b. Find the lengths of $\overline{AB}$, $\overline{BC}$, and $\overline{AC}$. ⓐ
length of $\overline{AB}$: 6 units; length of $\overline{BC}$: $\sqrt{18}$ units; length of $\overline{AC}$: $\sqrt{18}$ units

8. A square is drawn on graph paper. One side of the square is the segment with endpoints (2, 5) and (8, 1). Find the other two vertices of the square. There are two possible solutions. Can you find both? (6, 11) and (12, 7), or (−2, −1) and (4, −5)

9. *Mini-Investigation* Below is a right triangle.

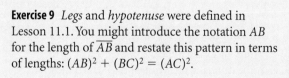

$\overline{AC}$ is the hypotenuse; $\overline{AB}$ and $\overline{BC}$ are the legs.
  a. Which side is the hypotenuse of $\triangle ABC$? Which sides are the legs?
  b. Draw this triangle on graph paper and draw a square on each side, as in Exercise 7.
  c. Find the area of each square you drew in 9b. ⓐ 20 units², 16 units², 4 units²
  d. Find the lengths of $\overline{AB}$, $\overline{BC}$, and $\overline{AC}$. ⓐ length of $\overline{AB}$: 2 units; length of $\overline{BC}$: 4 units; length of $\overline{AC}$: $\sqrt{20}$ units
  e. What is the relationship between the areas of the three squares?
    The areas of the two smaller squares sum to the area of the larger square.

Exercise 9 *Legs* and *hypotenuse* were defined in Lesson 11.1. You might introduce the notation AB for the length of $\overline{AB}$ and restate this pattern in terms of lengths: $(AB)^2 + (BC)^2 = (AC)^2$.

9b.

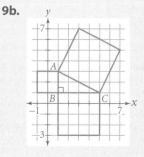

Exercise 3 Some students will find it difficult to find areas by subtracting from the area of a circumscribed rectangle, the preferred method for 3e and perhaps 3d. Encourage them by saying that once they can find area by this method, they will find it easier than trying to piece together parts of little squares.

3a. 4 units²

3b. 12 units²

3c. 2 units²

3d. 6 units²

3e. 20 units²

3f. 18 units²

Exercises 4, 5a and 5b Students are not expected to reduce radical form at this point. For instance, they may leave the answer as $\sqrt{18}$ rather than rewriting it as $3\sqrt{2}$. Reducing radicals will be addressed in Lesson 11.5. However, these exercises offer a chance to preview reducing radicals. You might encourage students to view the side lengths as made up of short segments, each $\sqrt{2}$ units in length. For example, the square in Exercise 4 has three short segments of length $\sqrt{2}$ on each side. From that, students can see that $\sqrt{18}$ equals $3\sqrt{2}$.

5. polygon 3a: $\sqrt{8}$ units and $\sqrt{2}$ units

polygon 3b: $\sqrt{8}$ units and $\sqrt{18}$ units

polygon 3e: $\sqrt{50}$ units, $\sqrt{50}$ units, and $\sqrt{40}$ units

Exercise 6 Encourage students to generalize that triangles with equal bases and equal heights have the same area.

Exercise 7 Again, encourage generalization to a pattern.

Exercise 8 Encourage creative thinking. **[Alert]** Suggest to any students having difficulty that they use their knowledge of slope.

6.6 **10.** The population of City A is currently 47,000 and is increasing at a rate of 4.5% per year. The population of City B is currently 56,000 and is decreasing at a rate of 1.2% per year.

 a. What will the populations of the two cities be in 5 years? ⓐ City A: 58,571; City B: 52,720

 b. When will the population of City A first exceed 150,000? ⓐ in 27 years

 c. If the population decrease in City B began 10 years ago, how large was the population before the decline started? ⓐ 63,186

9.4 **11.** Use all these clues to find the equation of the one function that they describe. ⓗ

 ▶ The graph of the equation is a parabola that crosses the x-axis twice.

 ▶ If you write the equation in factored form, one of the factors is $x + 7$.

 ▶ The graph of the equation has y-intercept 14.

 ▶ The axis of symmetry of the graph passes through the point $(-4, -2)$.
 $y = 2(x + 7)(x + 1)$

IMPROVING YOUR VISUAL THINKING SKILLS

The Chokwe people of northeastern Angola, Africa, are respected for their mat-weaving designs. They weave horizontal white strands with vertical brown strands. In the design below, the first brown strand passes over one white strand and then under four white strands; the next brown strand to the right repeats the weaving pattern, but the design is translated down 2 units.

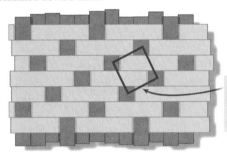

The exposed brown strands could be connected to create tilted squares throughout the design.

Notice that the Chokwe design creates tilted squares similar to those you saw in this lesson. These tilted squares are repeated throughout the design. Paulus Gerdes (b. 1952), a Mozambican mathematician, calls this design a "$(1, -2)$-solution" for finding a pattern of tilted squares (*Geometry from Africa,* 1999, p. 75). That means if you move 1 unit right and 2 units down from any brown square, you hit another brown square. Is this the only design that could be called a $(1, -2)$-solution?

Does every "over-under" design result in tilted squares? For example, what happens if you pass each brown strand over one white strand and then under three white strands? How about over one, under two? How about over one, under five? Describe the results.

What over-under designs result in tilted squares? What design creates a $(1, -3)$-solution?

IMPROVING VISUAL THINKING SKILLS

Weaving over one, under four is the only way to get a $(1, -2)$-solution. (It might be called a $(1, 3)$-solution as well.) Over one, under three either creates diagonal stripes or creates rhombuses, which leave alternating white strands with no brown strands over them, causing the mat to fall apart. Over one, under two creates diagonal stripes, not squares. Over one, under five creates stripes or parallelograms that fall apart. Over one, under nine is the $(1, -3)$-solution. Students may conjecture that the $(1, -k)$-solution must go over one, under k^2. This is indeed true. The $(1, -4)$-solution goes over one, under sixteen. The $(1, -1)$-solution goes over one, under one. In general, imagine one square A in which a brown strand appears. In the next column to the right, the brown strand to which the first one is connected in a tilted square is k white strands lower. So the next appearance of a brown strand below A must be connected to a point k units to the right and one unit up. This will be a brown strand only if each brown strand passes under k^2 white strands.

The Pythagorean Theorem

There can be no mystery in a result you have discovered for yourself.

W. W. SAWYER

In Lesson 11.3, you learned that geometric figures are important in design and building and in many related activities. You saw how to find areas and some side lengths of squares and right triangles, and you noticed that the area of a right triangle is half the area of the rectangle drawn around it. Is this true for all triangles?

The area of each of these triangles is half the area of the rectangle.

Based on these two triangles, you might use inductive reasoning to write the conjecture "The area of any triangle is half the area of the rectangle drawn around it." Can you find a counterexample?

The area of this triangle is less than half the area of the rectangle around it. Can you see why?

The three triangles shown above have the same base and the same height. You might have figured out that all three triangles have the same area. This is true whether or not the triangles all fit inside the same rectangle. The area formula for a triangle is

$$Area = \frac{base \cdot height}{2} \quad \text{or} \quad A = \frac{1}{2}bh$$

You can use the formula to find the area of a triangle without adding grid squares or subtracting areas.

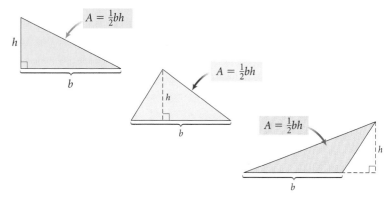

You'll remember a formula more easily if you discover it yourself. In this lesson you will discover a right triangle formula that planners and builders have used for thousands of years.

NCTM STANDARDS

CONTENT		PROCESS	
	Number		Problem Solving
✓	Algebra	✓	Reasoning
✓	Geometry		Communication
✓	Measurement	✓	Connections
	Data/Probability	✓	Representation

LESSON OBJECTIVES

- Discover the Pythagorean Theorem by exploring right triangles and the squares built on each side
- Apply the Pythagorean Theorem to real-world problems

PLANNING

LESSON OUTLINE

One day:

5 min	Introduction
20 min	Investigation
5 min	Sharing
10 min	Examples
5 min	Closing
5 min	Exercises

MATERIALS

- graph paper
- straightedges
- Sketchpad demonstration The Pythagorean Theorem, *optional*

TEACHING

The Pythagorean Theorem is a statement about areas of geometric figures as well as an algebraic claim about lengths of line segments.

One Step

Pose the problem of Example A, insisting on an exact answer. As needed, encourage students to experiment with measurements of smaller right triangles and to look for patterns.

INTRODUCTION

In earlier classes, students may have derived the formula for area of a triangle by dividing a rectangle in half along the diagonal. In this book, they have seen this as the basis for area of a triangle in Lesson 11.3, Example A, and they may have chosen this as a way to divide a rectangle in Lesson 11.2, Exercise 13a. The fact that some triangles do make up half a rectangle and others do not could be illustrated with Lesson 11.3, Exercise 6. Obtuse triangles form half-rectangles only if one edge of

the rectangle coincides with the longest edge of the triangle. All triangles form half-parallelograms, which themselves can be modified into rectangles.

Lesson 11.3, Exercise 6, illustrated that triangles with the same base and height have equal area. You may want to revisit this idea.

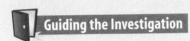
Guiding the Investigation

Step 1 Be sure each member of a group draws a different right triangle.

Step 2 The full extent of each leg or hypotenuse should be used as an edge of a square.

Step 3 If time permits, have each student repeat Steps 1, 2, and 3 for a second, different right triangle.

Step 4 If students find that some data points don't fit their conjecture, have them go back and check for mistakes in their drawings or calculations.

Step 6 You may want to encourage students to repeat the investigation with their own, different triangles.

SHARING IDEAS

Have students share whatever variety of conjectures they derived. Some may refer to areas and others to lengths or squares of numbers.

Point out the student text's statement of the Pythagorean Theorem. Ask how students' own conjectures are the same or different. Following history, the investigation led to a statement about areas: "The square *on* the hypotenuse equals (in area) the sum of the squares *on* the other two sides." The statement in Step 6 and in the box on page 613 is more numerical and algebraic: "The square *of* the (length of the) hypotenuse equals the sum of the squares *of* the (lengths of) the other two sides."

Investigation
The Sides of a Right Triangle

You will need
- graph paper
- a straightedge

This investigation will help you discover a very useful formula that relates the lengths of the sides of a right triangle.

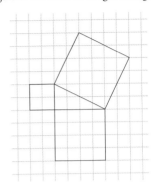

This is only a sample. Your right triangle should be larger or smaller.

Step 1 Draw a right triangle on graph paper with its legs on the grid lines and its vertices at grid intersections.

Step 2 Draw a square on each side of your triangle.

Step 3 Find the area of each square and record it.

Step 4 As a group or as a class, combine your results in a table like this one. Look for a relationship between the numbers in each row of the table.

Step 3 Using the sample triangle in the book:

	Area of square on leg 1	Area of square on leg 2	Area of square on hypotenuse
Trisha's triangle	4	16	20
Joe's triangle			

Step 5 Calculate the lengths of the legs and the hypotenuse for each triangle based on the areas you calculated in Step 3.

Step 5 Using the sample triangle in the book:

	Length of leg 1	Length of leg 2	Length of hypotenuse
Trisha's triangle	2	4	$\sqrt{20}$
Joe's triangle			

Step 6 Use what you discovered about the areas of the squares to write a rule relating the lengths of the legs to the length of the hypotenuse.
(length of leg 1)^2 + (length of leg 2)^2 = (length of hypotenuse)^2

Although the theorem is often stated using the letters *a*, *b*, and *c*, there's no reason why the edges of the triangle should have those names. In fact, students will be working with right triangles whose edges have other names.

You can use the Sketchpad demonstration The Pythagorean Theorem to replace or supplement the investigation.

Assessing Progress

During the investigation and presentations, note students' ability to calculate areas of tilted squares and to record data systematically.

In the investigation you used inductive reasoning to discover the famous **Pythagorean Theorem.** A *theorem* is a mathematical formula or statement that has been proven to be true. This theorem is named after Pythagoras, a Greek mathematician who lived around 500 B.C. This relationship was discovered and used by people in cultures before Pythagoras, but the theorem is usually given his name.

The Pythagorean Theorem

The sum of the squares of the lengths of the legs a and b of a right triangle equals the square of the length of the hypotenuse c.

$$a^2 + b^2 = c^2$$

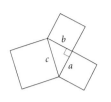

There are many deductive proofs of the Pythagorean Theorem. To learn more about them, see the links at **www.keymath.com/DA** .

The next examples show how you can use what you learned in the investigation to find the missing length of a side of a right triangle.

EXAMPLE A

A baseball diamond is a square with 90 ft between first and second base. What is the distance from home plate to second base?

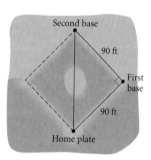

Second base
90 ft
First base
90 ft
Home plate

▶ **Solution**

The distance between home plate and second base is the hypotenuse of a right triangle. Call it c. This means that the area of a square on c equals the sum of the areas of the squares on each leg. The legs a and b are equal in this case.

$c^2 = a^2 + b^2$ Pythagorean Theorem.

$c^2 = 90^2 + 90^2$ Each leg is 90 ft.

$c^2 = 8{,}100 + 8{,}100$ Square each leg length.

$c^2 = 16{,}200$ Add.

$c = \sqrt{16{,}200} \approx 127.3$ Find the square root.

The distance from home plate to second base is approximately 127.3 ft.

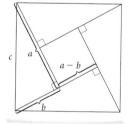

In this example students see another illustration of indirect measurement. Although the ramp could be measured directly after it is built, knowledge of its length is needed for planning.

[Ask] "Do you think Martin will be able to build the ramp as a straight ramp?" [Probably not, because it would need to reach 30 ft horizontally from the building. Students may have seen wheelchair ramps that wind around a building or switch back.]

As an extension, turn the problem around. [Ask] "How much would a horizontal 30 ft walkway that is fixed at one end have to rise at the other end if 1 in. was added to its length?" [The answer, more than 2 ft, might be surprising.] If you leave the problem open, students may want to check and recheck the arithmetic. Be sensitive to how, for many students, changing their intuition is threatening because they see it as changing who they are.

Closing the Lesson

The **Pythagorean Theorem** claims that the square drawn on the hypotenuse of a right triangle is equal in area to the sum of the areas of the squares drawn on the legs. In algebraic terms, $a^2 + b^2 = c^2$, where a and b are the lengths of the legs and c is the length of the hypotenuse.

EXAMPLE B

Martin Weber is building a wheelchair ramp at the Town Hall. The ramp will start at ground level and rise to meet a door that is 30 in. off the ground. Building codes in his area require an exterior ramp to have a slope of 1:12, meaning 1 in. of rise for every horizontal 12 in. What will be the length of the ramp's surface? Give your answer in exact form and as an approximation to the nearest inch.

Ralph Hotchkiss, shown above in his Oakland, California, workshop, is a designer of wheelchairs and an advocate for physical independence. He founded Whirlwind Wheelchair International, an organization that provides wheelchairs to people in developing countries. For a mobility designer like Hotchkiss, handrail dimensions, seat angles, and the slope of wheelchair ramps are important issues.

► **Solution**

The ratio of the rise to the horizontal distance must be equal to $\frac{1}{12}$.

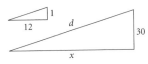

Write a proportion and solve.

$$\frac{1}{12} = \frac{30}{x} \qquad \text{Original equation.}$$

$$\frac{12}{1} = \frac{x}{30} \qquad \text{Invert both sides of the proportion.}$$

$$30 \cdot 12 = x \qquad \text{Multiply by 30 to undo the division.}$$

$$x = 360 \qquad \text{Multiply.}$$

The horizontal length of the ramp is 360 in., or 30 ft. To find the length of the ramp's surface, use the Pythagorean Theorem.

$$d = \sqrt{(30^2 + 360^2)} = \sqrt{130{,}500} \approx 361$$

The ramp's length is $\sqrt{130{,}500}$ inches, or about 30 ft 1 in.

The two triangles shown in the solution to Example B are **similar.** In similar shapes, the corresponding sides are proportional.

EXERCISES

You will need your graphing calculator for Exercise **11**.

Practice Your Skills

In Exercises 1–4, *a* and *b* are the legs of a right triangle and *c* is the hypotenuse.

1. Suppose the square on side *c* has an area of 2601 cm² and the square on side *b* has an area of 2025 cm². What is the area of the square on side *a*? @ 576 cm²

2. Using the areas from Exercise 1, find each side length, *a*, *b*, and *c*. $a = 24$ cm, $b = 45$ cm, $c = 51$ cm

3. Suppose $a = 10$ cm and $c = 20$ cm. Find the exact length of side *b* in radical form. @ $b = \sqrt{300}$ cm

4. Suppose the right triangle is isosceles (two equal sides).
   a. Which two sides are the same length: the two legs or a leg and the hypotenuse? the two legs
   b. If the two equal sides are each 8 cm in length, what is the exact length of the third side in radical form? $c = \sqrt{128}$ cm

Reason and Apply

5. **APPLICATION** Triangles that are similar to a right triangle with sides 3, 4, and 5 are often used in construction. The roof shown here is 36 ft wide. The two halves of the roof are congruent. Each half is a right triangle with sides proportional to 3, 4, and 5. (The shorter leg is the vertical leg.)

   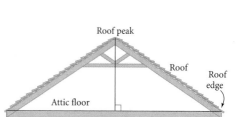
   Roof peak
   Roof
   Roof edge
   Attic floor
   36 ft

   a. How high above the attic floor should the roof peak be? (h) 13.5 ft
   b. How far is the roof peak from the roof edge? @ 22.5 ft
   c. What is the shingled area of the roof if the building is 48 ft long? (h) 2160 ft²

6. Cal and Al are trying to solve the problem $\sqrt{x + 4} = 5$. Cal says that $\sqrt{x + 4} = \sqrt{x} + \sqrt{4}$. Al disagrees but can't explain why. Who is right? Explain your reasoning.

   $\sqrt{x + 4} = \sqrt{x} + \sqrt{4}$
   I disagree.

7. You will need a centimeter ruler for this problem.
   a. Measure the length and width of your textbook cover in centimeters. approximately 21.6 cm by 27.6 cm
   b. Use the Pythagorean Theorem to calculate the diagonal length using the length and width you measured in 7a. approximately 35.0 cm
   c. Measure one of the diagonals of the cover.
   d. How close are the values you found in 7b and c? Should they be approximately the same? Answers will vary. The two results should be approximately the same.

8. Miya was trying to solve the problem $x^2 + 4^2 = 5^2$. She took the square root of both sides and got $x + 4 = 5$, which means *x* equals 1. Explain why her answer is wrong, and show how to find the correct answer. Answers will vary. If $x = 1$, then Miya is claiming that $1^2 + 4^2 = 5^2$, but 17 does not equal 25. You have to isolate *x* before you take the square root: $x^2 + 16 = 25 \Rightarrow x^2 = 9 \Rightarrow x = \pm3$.

Exercise 9 As needed, remind students that 1 mi = 5280 ft.

As an extension, ask students how much a mile of road pavement will buckle if it expands 1 ft, all pushed to the same place. The hypotenuse is barely longer than one leg, yet the other leg is almost 103 ft long.

Exercise 10 The reverse of a theorem is called its *converse*. Evidence by measurement shows that the theorem's converse *seems* to be true, but it does not prove it. [Ask] "Does the truth of a theorem imply the truth of its converse?" Have students examine statements like "If it's a dog, then it has a tail," whose converse is "If it has a tail, then it's a dog." Although converses differ in meaning and often in truth, the converse of the Pythagorean Theorem can be proved to be true.

10a. right triangles: i, ii, iv; not a right triangle: iii

Exercise 11 This exercise is long and challenging. You might want to use it as a group problem or for extra credit. TVs are not actually manufactured to maximize area as indicated in 11g. Instead, there are two standard aspect ratios—4-by-3 for a standard TV and 16-by-9 for a widescreen TV. A standard TV is therefore based on a 3-4-5 triangle, so the actual dimensions of a 27 in. TV would be 21.6 by 16.2 in. Theatrical movies generally have one of three aspect ratios: 1.33 (4-by-3), 1.85, or 2.35. Students may be familiar with these ratios from DVDs that maintain the widescreen aspect ratios.

11a. $L_1 = \{1, 2, 3, \ldots, 26\}$

11b. approximately 26.98 in.

11c. $L_2 = \sqrt{(27^2 - L_1{}^2)}$

11e. $L_3 = L_1 * L_2$, or $L_3 = L_1 * \sqrt{(27^2 - L_1{}^2)}$

9. The launching pad for a hot-air balloon is 1.2 miles away from where you're standing. If the balloon rises vertically 3000 feet into the air, how far (in feet) will it be from you? @
   approximately 7010 ft

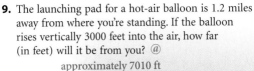
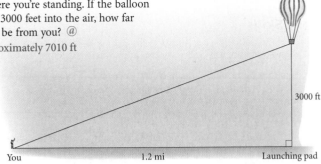

You   1.2 mi   Launching pad

3000 ft

10. *Mini-Investigation* Strips of graph paper may help in 10a.

   a. Draw or make triangles with the side lengths that are given in i–iv. Then use a protractor or the corner of a sheet of paper to find whether each triangle is a right triangle.

      i. 5, 12, 13 @   **ii.** 7, 24, 25
      iii. 8, 10, 12   **iv.** 6, 8, 10

   b. Based on your results from 10a, does the Pythagorean Theorem seem to work in reverse? In other words, if the relationship $a^2 + b^2 = c^2$ is true, is the triangle necessarily a right triangle?
      Yes, the theorem works in reverse.

11. A 27-inch TV has a screen that measures 27 inches on its diagonal. Complete the following steps and use the Pythagorean Theorem to find the **dimensions** of the screen with maximum area for a 27-inch TV.

   a. Enter the positive integers from 1 to 26 into list L_1 on your calculator to represent the possible screen widths.

   b. Imagine a screen 1 inch wide. Calculate the length of a 27-inch TV screen with a width of 1 inch, and enter your answer into the first row of list L_2.

   c. Define list L_2 to calculate all the possible screen lengths.

   d. What is the area of a 27-inch screen with a width of 2 inches? approximately 53.85 in.²

   e. Define list L_3 to calculate all possible screen areas.

   f. Plot points in the form (*width, area*) and find an equation that fits these points.

   g. What screen dimensions give the largest area for a 27-inch TV? Trace the graph or use a table to find that a 19-by-19 in. square gives maximum area.

27 in.

The size of a television is measured on its diagonal.

27-inch TV

Width (L1)	Length (L2)	Area (L3)
1		
2		
3		
⋮		
26		

12. In Exercise 10, you showed that a triangle with side lengths of 5, 12, and 13 units is a right triangle.

   a. Explain why a triangle with side lengths of 10, 24, and 26 units is similar to this triangle. ⓗ

   b. Is the triangle in 12a a right triangle? Explain.
      Yes. Possible answer: Similar figures have congruent angles. Another possible answer: The numbers satisfy the Pythagorean Theorem.

11f. A model that works is $y = x\sqrt{27^2 - x^2}$, where x is the width and y is the area.

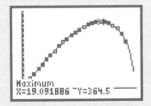

Maximum
X=19.091886 Y=364.5

$[0, 27, 5, -50, 450, 50]$

Exercise 12a [Language] Make sure that students are thinking of the mathematical meaning of the term *similar*, which is reviewed on page 614.

12a. Possible answer: The ratios $\frac{10}{5}$, $\frac{24}{12}$, and $\frac{26}{13}$ all equal 2, so the sides are proportional and the triangles are similar.

13. APPLICATION When objects block sunlight, they cast shadows, and similar triangles are formed. On a sunny day, Sunanda and Chloe measure the shadow of the school flagpole. It is 8.5 m long. Chloe is 1.7 m tall and her shadow is 2.1 m long.

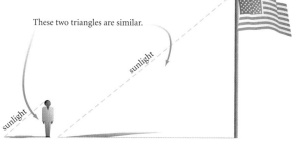

These two triangles are similar.

a. Sketch and label your own diagram to represent this situation.

b. Using the similar triangles in your diagram, write a proportion and find the height of the flagpole. @ $\frac{1.7}{2.1} = \frac{x}{8.5}$; $x \approx 6.88$ or 6.9 m high

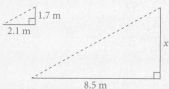

keymath.com/DA

c. Explain how you could use this method to find the height of a very tall tree. Measure the length of the tree's shadow and write a proportion using a person's height and the length of his or her shadow.

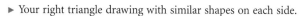

► Review

9.4 **14.** Ibrahim Patterson is planning to expand his square deck. He will add 3 feet to the width and 2 feet to the length to get a total area of 210 square feet. Find the dimensions of his original deck. Show your work.
$(x + 3)(x + 2) = 210, x^2 + 5x + 6 = 210,$
$x^2 + 5x - 204 = 0, x = -17$ or $x = 12;$
the original deck is 12 ft on a side.

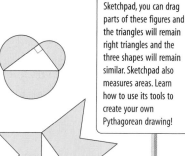

project

PYTHAGORAS REVISITED

You know that the Pythagorean Theorem says that the sum of the areas of the squares on the two legs of a right triangle is equal to the area of the square on the hypotenuse.

But if the shapes aren't squares, does the sum of the areas on the legs still equal the area on the hypotenuse?

Design your own similar shapes on the sides of a right triangle. Carefully measure or calculate their areas. Then report on your results. Your project should include

► Your right triangle drawing with similar shapes on each side.

► Your measurements and calculations.

► A written explanation of how you drew the similar shapes, how you calculated the areas, and a conjecture about whether a Pythagorean-like relationship holds for any shape.

Dot paper, graph paper, a computer drawing program, and The Geometer's Sketchpad software are useful tools for this project.

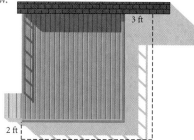

THE GEOMETER'S SKETCHPAD

In The Geometer's Sketchpad, you can drag parts of these figures and the triangles will remain right triangles and the three shapes will remain similar. Sketchpad also measures areas. Learn how to use its tools to create your own Pythagorean drawing!

LESSON
11.5

Operations with Roots

When you use the Pythagorean Theorem to find the length of a right triangle's side, the result is often a radical expression. You can always find an approximate value for a radical expression with a calculator, but sometimes it's better to leave the answer as an exact value, in radical form. However, there is more than one way to write an exact value or a radical expression. In this lesson you'll discover ways to rewrite radical expressions so that you can recognize solutions in a variety of forms.

EXAMPLE A | Draw a segment that is $\sqrt{13} + \sqrt{13}$ units long.

▶ **Solution** | First think of two perfect squares whose sum is 13, such as $4 + 9 = 13$. Then draw a right triangle on graph paper using the square roots of your numbers, 2 and 3, for the leg lengths. By the Pythagorean Theorem, the hypotenuse of your triangle is $\sqrt{13}$ (because $2^2 + 3^2 = (\sqrt{13})^2$).

Now draw a second congruent triangle so that the hypotenuses form a single segment. This pair of hypotenuses is $\sqrt{13} + \sqrt{13}$, or $2\sqrt{13}$, units long.

The combined length is $\sqrt{13} + \sqrt{13}$, or $2\sqrt{13}$.

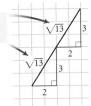

The segment with length $2\sqrt{13}$ from the example can also be drawn as the hypotenuse of a triangle with side lengths 4 and 6.

You can use the Pythagorean Theorem to find that the length of this hypotenuse is also $\sqrt{52}$.

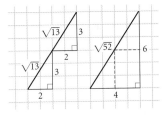

$$h^2 = 4^2 + 6^2$$

$$h^2 = 52$$

$$h = \sqrt{52}$$

So $2\sqrt{13}$ must be equal to $\sqrt{52}$.

In the investigation you'll explore more equivalent radical expressions.

PLANNING

LESSON OUTLINE

First day:

10 min   Example A

40 min   Investigation

Second day:

15 min   Investigation

10 min   Sharing

10 min   Examples B, C

5 min   Closing

10 min   Exercises

MATERIALS

- graph paper
- Pyramid Net (W), *optional*
- Calculator Note 6B

TEACHING

In some cases radical expressions can be rewritten with fewer occurrences of the square root sign.

▶ **EXAMPLE A**

This example introduces the idea of different radical names for the same number. Before students consider the solution, ask if they can think of another way to write $\sqrt{13} + \sqrt{13}$. Some students might claim that the sum equals $\sqrt{26}$. Have them test that conjecture on their calculators. It may come as a slight surprise to some students that the sum equals $2\sqrt{13}$. They may believe easily enough that "1 apple plus 1 apple equals 2 apples," but they might understandably see the multiplication by 2 in $2\sqrt{13}$ as different from the use of 2 as an adjective in "2 apples."

LESSON OBJECTIVES

- Recognize and create equivalent radical expressions
- Square binomials with radical terms
- Use the distributive property with radicals
- Simplify expressions under a radical by factoring out a perfect square
- Revisit quadratic equations and parabolas

NCTM STANDARDS

CONTENT		PROCESS	
	Number		Problem Solving
✔	Algebra	✔	Reasoning
✔	Geometry		Communication
✔	Measurement		Connections
	Data/Probability	✔	Representation

Investigation
Radical Expressions

You will need
- graph paper

How can you tell if two different radical expressions are equivalent? Is it possible to add, subtract, multiply, or divide radical expressions? You'll answer these questions as you work through this investigation.

Step 1 On graph paper, draw line segments for each length given below. You may need more than one triangle to create some of the lengths.

a. $\sqrt{18}$ **b.** $\sqrt{40}$ **c.** $\sqrt{20}$

d. $2\sqrt{5}$ **e.** $3\sqrt{2}$ **f.** $2\sqrt{10}$

g. $\sqrt{10} + \sqrt{10}$ **h.** $\sqrt{2} + \sqrt{2} + \sqrt{2}$ **i.** $\sqrt{5} + \sqrt{5}$
     same as 1f   same as 1e   same as 1d

> **Steps 2 and 3** a, e, and h are equivalent; b, f, and g are equivalent; c, d, and i are equivalent.

Step 2 Do any of the segments seem to be the same length? If so, which ones?

Step 3 Use your calculator to find a decimal approximation to the nearest ten thousandth for each expression in Step 1. Which expressions are equivalent?

Step 4 Make a conjecture about another way to write each expression below. Choose positive values for the variables, and use your calculator to test whether your expression is equivalent to the original expression.

a. $\sqrt{x} + \sqrt{x} + \sqrt{x} + \sqrt{x}$ $4\sqrt{x}$

b. $\sqrt{x} \cdot \sqrt{y}$ $\sqrt{xy}$

c. $\sqrt{x \cdot x \cdot y}$ $x\sqrt{y}$ or $\sqrt{x^2 y}$

d. $\left(\sqrt{x}\right)^2$ x or $\sqrt{x^2}$

e. $\dfrac{\sqrt{xy}}{\sqrt{y}}$ $\sqrt{x}$

> **Step 5** Possible answers: Radical expressions with the same numbers under the square root symbol may be added by adding the coefficients; radical expressions are multiplied (or divided) by multiplying (or dividing) the numbers under the square root symbols and then putting the answer under a single square root symbol.

Step 5 Summarize what you've discovered about adding, multiplying, and dividing radical expressions.

Step 6 Use what you've learned to find the area of each rectangle below. Give each answer in radical form as well as a decimal approximation to the nearest hundredth.

a.
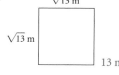
$\sqrt{13}$ m (top), $\sqrt{13}$ m (left), 13 m² (inside)

b.
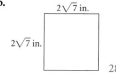
$2\sqrt{7}$ in. (top), $2\sqrt{7}$ in. (left), 28 in.² (inside)

c.

$5\sqrt{3}$ ft (top), $3\sqrt{10}$ ft (left)
$15\sqrt{30}$ ft²; approximately 82.16 ft²

d.
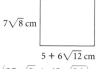
$7\sqrt{8}$ cm (left), $5 + 6\sqrt{12}$ cm (bottom)
$\left(35\sqrt{8} + 42\sqrt{96}\right)$ cm², or $\left(70\sqrt{2} + 168\sqrt{6}\right)$ cm²; approximately 510.51 cm²

---

than the numbers themselves. All have very simple names that involve radicals.

Assessing Progress
Students can demonstrate their ability to draw line segments of radical lengths using appropriate right triangles, to approximate values of square roots, and to find areas of squares and other rectangles.

▶ **EXAMPLE B**

In this example students can see how to simplify a radical name for a number. As needed, encourage students to sketch diagrams.

See page 730 for answers to Steps 1a–f.

Because radical expressions are often irrational numbers (whose decimal names are infinite and nonrepeating), students might think it is impossible to add, subtract, multiply, or divide with them.

Step 1 If students are having difficulty, suggest that they think in reverse: Make a list of perfect squares and then try various sums.

Step 3 Emphasize that although the decimal approximations are helpful for determining equivalence, they are not exact answers. Hence, 4.1234567891 and 4.1234567892 are both 4.1235 when rounded to the ten-thousandths place, yet the original numbers are *not* equal.

Step 4 Students may want to refer to Calculator Note 6B, which shows how to use the calculator to test whether expressions are equivalent. As needed, remind students of the meaning of square root.

Step 6 Remind students that rectangles have four right angles (as originally stated in the investigation in Lesson 11.1). Hence, all of these figures are rectangles, perhaps squares.

SHARING IDEAS

Ask students to present, in writing, their rules from Step 5. After they've presented a variety of rules, you might say that the square root symbol is a *radical* and the number or expression under a radical is the *radicand*. Then help them rephrase their rules using these terms. (Symbols for cube roots and other roots are also radicals.)

Point out that the numbers in Step 6 are irrational: They can't be written as ratios of integers. Ask whether these irrational numbers are "infinite," or "go on forever." Some students will say so, thinking of the decimal names rather

EXAMPLE B

Rewrite this expression with as few square root symbols as possible and no parentheses. Use your calculator to check your answer.

$$2\sqrt{3} + 5\sqrt{3}$$

▶ **Solution**

Add the terms using the distributive property. The distributive property allows you to factor out $\sqrt{3}$.

$$2\sqrt{3} + 5\sqrt{3} = (2 + 5)\sqrt{3} = 7\sqrt{3}$$

The decimal approximations that your calculator gives support the idea that $2\sqrt{3} + 5\sqrt{3}$ is equivalent to $7\sqrt{3}$.

```
2√(3) + 5√(3)
                    12.12435565
7√(3)
                    12.12435565
```

The investigation and Example B have illustrated several rules for rewriting radical expressions.

Rules for Rewriting Radical Expressions

For $x \geq 0$ and $y \geq 0$, and any values of a or b, these rules are true:

Addition of Radical Expressions
$$a\sqrt{x} + b\sqrt{x} = (a + b)\sqrt{x}$$

Multiplication of Radical Expressions
$$a\sqrt{x} \cdot b\sqrt{y} = a \cdot b\sqrt{x \cdot y}$$

For $x \geq 0$ and $y > 0$, this rule is true:

Division of Radical Expressions
$$\frac{\sqrt{x}}{\sqrt{y}} = \sqrt{\frac{x}{y}}$$

EXAMPLE C

Rewrite each expression with as few square root symbols as possible and no parentheses.

a. $3\sqrt{5} \cdot 2\sqrt{7}$ **b.** $\dfrac{\sqrt{15}}{\sqrt{3}}$ **c.** $\sqrt{3}\left(5\sqrt{2} + 3\sqrt{3}\right)$

▶ **EXAMPLE C**

This example illustrates simplifying radical names for numbers. In part c, some students may need to see or write the intermediate step

$$\sqrt{2} \cdot \sqrt{3} = \sqrt{2 \cdot 3} = \sqrt{6}$$

[Ask] "Can you simplify the expression $5\sqrt{6} + 9$ any further?" These unlike terms can't be combined. You might draw an analogy to the expression $5x + 9$.

▶ **Solution**

a. All of the numbers are multiplied. So use the commutative property of multiplication to group coefficients together and radical expressions together.

First the commutative property allows you to swap $\sqrt{5}$ and 2.

$$3\sqrt{5} \cdot 2\sqrt{7} = 3 \cdot 2 \cdot \sqrt{5} \cdot \sqrt{7}$$

Then to multiply two radical expressions, you multiply the numbers under the square root symbols.

$$3 \cdot 2 \cdot \sqrt{5} \cdot \sqrt{7} = 6\sqrt{5 \cdot 7} = 6\sqrt{35}$$

Check this result with your calculator. Do the decimal approximations support the idea that $3\sqrt{5} \cdot 2\sqrt{7}$ is equivalent to $6\sqrt{35}$?

b. To divide radical expressions, you can combine the numbers under one square root symbol and divide.

$$\frac{\sqrt{15}}{\sqrt{3}} = \sqrt{\frac{15}{3}} = \sqrt{5}$$

c. $\sqrt{3}\left(5\sqrt{2} + 3\sqrt{3}\right) = 5\sqrt{2} \cdot \sqrt{3} + 3\sqrt{3} \cdot \sqrt{3}$ Distribute $\sqrt{3}$.

$\qquad\qquad\qquad\qquad = 5\sqrt{6} + 3\sqrt{9}$ Multiply the radical expressions.

$\qquad\qquad\qquad\qquad = 5\sqrt{6} + 3 \cdot 3$ $\sqrt{9}$ is equal to 3.

$\qquad\qquad\qquad\qquad = 5\sqrt{6} + 9$ Multiply.

EXERCISES

You will need your graphing calculator for Exercises **1, 3,** and **6.**

▶ **Practice Your Skills**

1. Rewrite each expression with as few square root symbols as possible and no parentheses. Use your calculator to support your answers with decimal approximations.

a. $2\sqrt{3} + \sqrt{3}$ @ $3\sqrt{3}$

b. $\sqrt{5} \cdot \sqrt{2} \cdot \sqrt{5}$ @ $5\sqrt{2}$

c. $\sqrt{2}\left(\sqrt{2} + \sqrt{3}\right)$ @ $2 + \sqrt{6}$

d. $\sqrt{5} - \sqrt{2} + 3\sqrt{5} + 6\sqrt{2}$ @ $4\sqrt{5} + 5\sqrt{2}$

e. $\sqrt{3}\left(\sqrt{2}\right) + 5\sqrt{6}$ $6\sqrt{6}$

f. $\sqrt{2}\left(\sqrt{21}\right) + \sqrt{3}\left(\sqrt{14}\right)$ $2\sqrt{42}$

g. $\dfrac{\sqrt{35}}{\sqrt{7}}$ $\sqrt{5}$

h. $\sqrt{5}\left(4\sqrt{5}\right)$ 20

Closing the Lesson

Three important rules allow rewriting of radical expressions. For nonnegative (or positive for divisors) values of x and y:

$$a\sqrt{x} + b\sqrt{x} = (a + b)\sqrt{x}$$

$$\sqrt{x} \cdot \sqrt{y} = \sqrt{xy}$$

$$\frac{\sqrt{x}}{\sqrt{y}} = \sqrt{\frac{x}{y}}$$

You can use these rules from left to right to reduce the number of radicals. You can also use them from right to left. For example, $\sqrt{20} = \sqrt{4} \cdot \sqrt{5} = 2\sqrt{5}$. (This idea appears in Exercise 10.)

BUILDING UNDERSTANDING

Many of the exercises review the Pythagorean Theorem or quadratic equations while providing practice in operating on radicals.

ASSIGNING HOMEWORK

Essential	1–6, 9–11
Performance assessment	11, 14, 15
Portfolio	12, 15, 17
Journal	12, 18
Group	10–16
Review	7, 8, 19, 20

► Helping with the Exercises

Exercise 3 [Alert] Students may need to be advised that they are being asked to change quadratic equations from factored to general form. If they still need to, allow them to use rectangle diagrams for the distributivity. They should write $x\sqrt{3}$ rather than $\sqrt{3}x$ and $x\sqrt{5}$ instead of $\sqrt{5}x$ to make it easier to see that the x is not under the radical.

3a. $y = x^2 - 3$

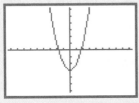

$[-9.4, 9.4, 1, -6.2, 6.2, 1]$

X	Y₁	Y₂
-3	6	6
-2	1	1
-1	-2	-2
0	-3	-3
1	-2	-2
2	1	1
3	6	6

X = -3

Exercise 4b There is no positive root because each factor is $(x + \sqrt{5})$.

Exercises 7 and 8 These exercises use radical expressions and review Chapter 9.

7c. $-3 - \sqrt{2} \approx -4.414$ and $-3 + \sqrt{2} \approx -1.586$

8a. vertex: $(0, -112)$

8b. $\left(\dfrac{-\sqrt{6}}{2}, -75\right)$ or $\approx (-1.225, -75)$

8c. $(-3, -2)$

See pages 730–731 for answers to Exercises 3b and 6.

2. Find the exact length of the missing side for each right triangle.

a.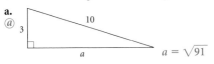

$a = \sqrt{91}$

b.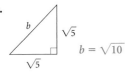

$b = \sqrt{10}$

c.

$c = 4$

d.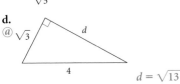

$d = \sqrt{13}$

3. Write the equation for each parabola in general form. Use your calculator to check that both forms give the same graph or table.

a. $y = \left(x + \sqrt{3}\right)\left(x - \sqrt{3}\right)$

b. $y = \left(x + \sqrt{5}\right)\left(x + \sqrt{5}\right)$

4. Name the x-intercepts for each parabola in Exercise 3. Give both the exact value and a decimal approximation to the nearest thousandth for each x-value.
   a. $x = \pm\sqrt{3} \approx \pm 1.732$ **b.** $x = -\sqrt{5} \approx -2.236$

5. Name the vertex for each parabola in Exercise 3. Give both exact values and decimal approximations to the nearest thousandth for the coordinates of each vertex. ⓗ
   a. $(0, -3)$ **b.** $\left(-\sqrt{5}, 0\right) \approx (-2.236, 0)$

► Reason and Apply

6. Write the equation for each parabola in general form. Use your calculator to check that both forms have the same graph or table.

a. $y = \left(x + 4\sqrt{7}\right)\left(x - 4\sqrt{7}\right)$

b. $y = 2\left(x - 2\sqrt{6}\right)\left(x + 3\sqrt{6}\right)$

c. $y = \left(x + 3 + \sqrt{2}\right)\left(x + 3 - \sqrt{2}\right)$

7. Name the x-intercepts for each parabola in Exercise 6. Give both the exact values and a decimal approximation to the nearest thousandth for each x-value. ⓗ
   a. $\pm 4\sqrt{7} \approx \pm 10.583$ **b.** $2\sqrt{6} \approx 4.899$ and $-3\sqrt{6} \approx -7.348$

8. Name the vertex for each parabola in Exercise 6. Give both exact values and decimal approximations to the nearest thousandth for the coordinates of each vertex. ⓗ

9. *Mini-Investigation* A radical expression with a coefficient can be rewritten without a coefficient. Here's an example:

$2\sqrt{5}$	Original expression.
$\sqrt{4} \cdot \sqrt{5}$	$\sqrt{4}$ is equivalent to 2.
$\sqrt{20}$	Multiply.

Use this method to rewrite each radical expression.

a. $4\sqrt{7}$ $\sqrt{112}$

c. $18\sqrt{3}$ $\sqrt{972}$

b. $5\sqrt{22}$ ⓐ $\sqrt{550}$

d. $30\sqrt{5}$ $\sqrt{4500}$

Exercise 9 Some students may need to see or write the intermediate step

$\sqrt{4} \cdot \sqrt{5} = \sqrt{4 \cdot 5} = \sqrt{20}$

Students can use decimal approximations to roughly check their answers.

10. **Mini-Investigation** You can rewrite some radical expressions using the fact that they contain perfect-square factors. Here's an example:

$\sqrt{125}$ Original expression.

$\sqrt{25 \cdot 5}$ 25 is a perfect-square factor of 125.

$\sqrt{25} \cdot \sqrt{5}$ Rewrite the expression as two radical expressions.

$5\sqrt{5}$ Find the square root of 25.

Use this method to rewrite each radical expression.

a. $\sqrt{72}$ @ $6\sqrt{2}$ **b.** $\sqrt{27}$ $3\sqrt{3}$ **c.** $\sqrt{1800}$ $30\sqrt{2}$ **d.** $\sqrt{147}$ $7\sqrt{3}$

11. **Mini-Investigation** You can use the method from Exercise 10 to rewrite expressions like $\frac{-4 \pm \sqrt{12}}{2}$, which result when you use the quadratic formula. For example, $\frac{-4 \pm \sqrt{12}}{2} = \frac{-4 \pm 2\sqrt{3}}{2} = \frac{2(-2 \pm \sqrt{3})}{2} = -2 \pm \sqrt{3}$. Rewrite each expression.

a. $\frac{25 \pm \sqrt{75}}{15}$ @ $\frac{5 \pm \sqrt{3}}{3}$

b. $\frac{21 \pm \sqrt{98}}{7}$ $3 \pm \sqrt{2}$

c. $\frac{-2\sqrt{5} \pm \sqrt{180}}{4\sqrt{5}}$ @ $1, -2$

12. **APPLICATION** The Great Pyramid of Cheops in Egypt has a square base with a side length of 800 ft. Its triangular faces are almost equilateral. These diagrams show an unfolded and a folded scale model of the pyramid.

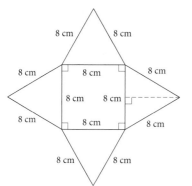

12a. The red line creates two right triangles, each with leg length $\frac{1}{2}(8)$ cm, or 4 cm, and hypotenuse length 8 cm. By the Pythagorean Theorem, the length of the other leg is $4\sqrt{3}$ cm.

a. Note the model's measurements. Explain how to find the distance from the center of the side of the base to the tip of each triangle. (That is, find the length of the segment shown in red.)

b. Find the height of the model. (That is, find the length of the segment shown in blue.) $4\sqrt{2}$ cm

c. Use your result from 12b to find the approximate height of the Great Pyramid. approximately 566 ft

The Great Pyramid of Cheops was built using over 2,300,000 blocks of stone weighing 2.5 tons each.

Exercise 10 Ideally, students will become comfortable moving between the two types of radical expressions in Exercises 9 and 10.

Students need to identify the largest perfect square. Some students can do this more easily if they use several steps. For example, in 10c,

$\sqrt{1800} = \sqrt{18 \cdot 100}$
$= \sqrt{9 \cdot 2 \cdot 100}$
$= \sqrt{9} \cdot \sqrt{100} \cdot \sqrt{2}$
$= 3 \cdot 10 \cdot \sqrt{2}$
$= 30\sqrt{2}$

Because simplifying expressions under a radical by factoring out a perfect square is a new skill for students, you may want them to work through this problem in groups.

Exercise 11c Part c illustrates how a complicated expression can simplify to integer values. The expression would arise from using the quadratic formula to solve the quadratic equation $2\sqrt{5}x^2 + 2\sqrt{5}x - 4\sqrt{5} = 0$, which could more easily be solved by factoring out $2\sqrt{5}$ to get $2\sqrt{5}(x^2 + x - 2) = 0$, and then factoring and using the zero-product property.

Exercises 12, 15 These challenging applications of the Pythagorean Theorem may be assigned for extra credit or review or as group work.

Exercise 12 You might want to ask students to create a net for a scale model of the Great Pyramid of Cheops, or they could cut out the model provided on the Pyramid Net worksheet and make a pyramid. The length being asked for, an altitude of a triangular face, is called the *slant height* or *lateral height* of the pyramid.

To give students practice in simplifying radical expressions, the text approximates the faces with equilateral triangles. The actual sides have lengths 800 ft, 743 ft, and 743 ft, making the height 482 ft instead of 510 ft.

13. The steps below demonstrate that $6 + \sqrt{20}$ is a solution to the equation $0 = 0.5x^2 - 6x + 8$. Fill in the missing expressions and justifications.

$0 = 0.5x^2 - 6x + 8$ 　　　Original equation.

$0 \overset{?}{=} 0.5\left(6 + \sqrt{20}\right)^2 - 6\left(6 + \sqrt{20}\right) + 8$ 　　Substitute $6 + \sqrt{20}$ for x.

$0 \overset{?}{=} 0.5\left(6 + \sqrt{20}\right)^2 \underline{\;-36 - 6\sqrt{20}\;} + 8$ 　　Distribute the -6 over $6 + \sqrt{20}$.

$0 \overset{?}{=} 0.5\left(\underline{}\right) - 36 - 6\sqrt{20} + 8$ 　　Use a rectangle diagram to square the expression $6 + \sqrt{20}$.
$\underline{36 + 6\sqrt{20} + 6\sqrt{20} + 20}$

Distribute the 0.5 over the expression in parentheses.

$0 \overset{?}{=} 18 + 3\sqrt{20} + 3\sqrt{20} + 10 - 36 - 6\sqrt{20} + 8$

$0 \overset{?}{=} \underline{18 + 10 - 36 + 8}$ 　　Combine the radical expressions.

$0 = 0$ 　　Add and subtract.

14. Show that $6 - \sqrt{20}$ is a solution to the equation $0 = 0.5x^2 - 6x + 8$. ⓗ

15. A rectangular box has the dimensions shown in the diagram.

   a. What is the length of the diagonal $\overline{BD}$? ⓐ 5 cm

   b. What is the length of the diagonal $\overline{BH}$? 13 cm

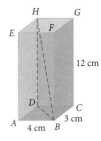

16. Roots can be written as fractional exponents. For example, $\sqrt{x} = x^{1/2}$, $\sqrt[3]{x} = x^{1/3}$, and so on. The exponent rules you learned in Chapter 6 apply not only to integer exponents, but also to fractional exponents. For 16a–c, evaluate the expression. For 16d–e, write an equivalent expression in simplest form.

   a. $9^{1/2} \cdot 8^{1/3} \cdot 2^{-1}$ 3 　　b. $(2^{1/3})^3 + (3^4)^{1/4}$ 5

   c. $2^{1/2} \cdot 8^{1/2}$ 4 　　　　　d. $(m^2)^{1/4} \cdot \sqrt{m}$ m

   e. $(x^4 y^{1/2})^6 \sqrt{x^2 y^2}$ $x^{25} y^4$

17. Find the exact lengths of sides a, b, and c in the figure at right. ⓐ

   $a = 2\sqrt{2}$ cm, $b = 2\sqrt{3}$ cm, $c = \sqrt{8\sqrt{3} + 12}$ cm

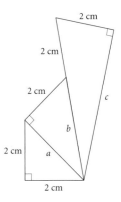

---

14. $0 = 0.5x^2 - 6x + 8$ 　　The original equation.

$0 \overset{?}{=} 0.5\left(6 - \sqrt{20}\right)^2 - 6\left(6 - \sqrt{20}\right) + 8$ 　　Substitute $6 - \sqrt{20}$ for x.

$0 \overset{?}{=} 0.5\left(6 - \sqrt{20}\right)^2 - 36 + 6\sqrt{20} + 8$ 　　Distribute the -6 over $6 - \sqrt{20}$.

$0 \overset{?}{=} 0.5\left(36 - 6\sqrt{20} - 6\sqrt{20} + 20\right) - 36 + 6\sqrt{20} + 8$ 　　Square the expression.

$0 \overset{?}{=} 18 - 3\sqrt{20} - 3\sqrt{20} + 10 - 36 + 6\sqrt{20} + 8$ 　　Distribute the 0.5 over the expression in parentheses.

$0 \overset{?}{=} 18 + 10 - 36 + 8$ 　　Combine the radical expressions.

$0 = 0$ 　　Add and subtract.

18. APPLICATION A factory makes square tiles with a side length of $\sqrt{93}$ mm.

   a. What is the area of the top face of one tile?   93 mm²

   b. If you evaluate $\sqrt{93}$ and round to the nearest tenth, you get $\sqrt{93} \approx 9.6$. Use this value to find the area of one tile. How does this compare to your answer in 18a?

   c. Each tile is 8 mm thick. Find the volume of clay needed to make one tile, using both $\sqrt{93}$ mm and 9.6 mm as values for the side length of a tile. How do your results compare?

   d. The factory needs to make 1000 tiles to satisfy a special order. Calculate how much clay is needed using both $\sqrt{93}$ mm and 9.6 mm as values for the side length of a tile. How do your results compare?

   e. Calculate the volume of clay needed for 1000 tiles if you estimate $\sqrt{93}$ to be 9.64.   743,436.8 mm³

   f. What can you conclude based on your results in 18a–e?   When you estimate a square root value and then use that value in calculations, if you estimate with more precision, the errors in the calculated values are smaller.

 Review

8.4   **19.** Write an equation for each transformation of the graph of $y = x^2$.

   a. a translation up 3 units and right 2 units $y = (x - 2)^2 + 3$

   b. a reflection across the x-axis and then a translation up 4 units $y = -x^2 + 4$

   c. a vertical stretch by a factor of 3 and then a translation right 1 unit $y = 3(x - 1)^2$

9.2   **20.** How many x-intercepts does the graph of each equation in 19a–c have?   **a.** no x-intercept   **b.** two x-intercepts   **c.** one x-intercept

---

SHOW ME PROOF

Throughout history, many different civilizations have used the right triangle relationship $a^2 + b^2 = c^2$. The people of Babylonia, Egypt, China, Greece, and India all found this relationship useful and fascinating.

Along the way, there also have been many different deductive proofs of this theorem. Drawing squares on each side of a right triangle is only one of them. Research the history of the Pythagorean Theorem and locate a proof you find interesting. Prepare a paper or a presentation of the proof.

Your project should include

▶ A clear and accurate presentation of the proof. Include diagrams and mathematical equations when appropriate.

▶ A written or verbal explanation of why the proof works. (You may need to do some research to fully understand what a proof is.)

▶ The history associated with the proof.

▶ A list of the resources you used.

Exercise 18 [Language] Students may not be familiar with the term *face*. Students may have trouble with this exercise if they haven't previously calculated volumes of rectangular prisms. If possible, bring in a tile and discuss why volume, rather than area, must be used to determine how much clay to use to make one tile.

18b. 92.16 mm²; this is about 1 mm² too low.

18c. 744 mm³ and 737.28 mm³; the first volume calculation is accurate, while the second is almost 7 mm³ too low.

18d. 744,000 mm³ and 737,280 mm³; the first volume calculation is accurate, while the second is 6,720 mm³ too low.

Supporting the project

MOTIVATION

Students learn something about the structure of a proof and that a theorem can have more than one proof.

OUTCOMES

▶ Diagrams and mathematics support and explain the proof.

▶ The history of the proof is discussed.

▶ Resources are cited accurately.

• More than one proof is presented, and proofs are compared and contrasted.

• The presentation shows deep understanding of what constitutes a proof, as opposed to isolated examples.

• Ancient peoples (such as the Babylonians) are mentioned; they had knowledge of the Pythagorean relation but, as far as we know, did not have a formal proof.

A Distance Formula

If you hike 2 kilometers east and 1 kilometer north from your campsite, do you know how far you are from camp? Often you are not able to measure distances directly. In this lesson you will use coordinate geometry and the Pythagorean Theorem to find the distance between any two points.

The shortest distance between two points is under construction.
NOELIE ALTITO

PLANNING

LESSON OUTLINE

First day:

10 min   Example A

40 min   Investigation

Second day:

15 min   Investigation

10 min   Sharing

10 min   Examples B, C

 5 min   Closing

10 min   Exercises

MATERIALS

- graph paper
- Surveying (T), *optional*
- Amusement Park (W), *optional*

TEACHING

Using the Pythagorean Theorem with analytic geometry gives a formula for calculating the distance between two points.

One Step

Display the Surveying transparency from Lesson 11.1. Say that to write up a description of the property, you need to find the length of each edge of the plot. Encourage students to draw right triangles and, as they finish, to derive a general formula. As they find the distance formula, ask them to determine the lengths of the plot's diagonals and to check all results by measuring and adjusting for the scale of the drawing.

▶ EXAMPLE A

This example shows how to use the Pythagorean Theorem to calculate a distance. Because *d* is a distance, only the positive square root is considered.

EXAMPLE A

If you start at your campsite at the point (0, 0) and walk 2 km east and 1 km north to the point (2, 1), how far are you from your campsite?

▶ **Solution**

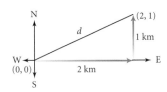

The east-west leg of the right triangle is 2 km in length, and the north-south leg of the triangle is 1 km in length. Let *d* be your distance from camp, the distance between points (0, 0) and (2, 1). By the Pythagorean Theorem, $d^2 = 2^2 + 1^2$, so $d = \sqrt{2^2 + 1^2}$. So your distance from camp is $\sqrt{5}$ km, or approximately 2.24 km.

keymath.com/DA

The four thunderbirds in the center of this Eastern Sioux buckskin pouch (ca. 1820) stand for the four cardinal directions—north, east, south, and west.

LESSON OBJECTIVES

- Learn how to calculate the distance between two points on a grid using right triangles
- Learn to apply the symbolic form of the distance formula
- Solve equations using radicals

NCTM STANDARDS

CONTENT		PROCESS	
	Number	✔	Problem Solving
✔	Algebra	✔	Reasoning
✔	Geometry		Communication
✔	Measurement	✔	Connections
	Data/Probability	✔	Representation

Investigation
Amusement Park

You will need
- graph paper

In this investigation you will discover a general formula for the distance between two points.

Step 1 Copy the map of amusement park attractions and assign coordinates to each attraction on the map.

Step 2 Find the distance between each pair of attractions in a–e. When appropriate, draw a right triangle. Use what you know about right triangles and the Pythagorean Theorem to find the exact distance between each pair of attractions.

Step 2a 6 units
Step 2b $\sqrt{10}$ units
Step 2c 2 units
Step 2d 5 units

a. Bumper Cars and Sledge Hammer
b. Ferris Wheel and Hall of Mirrors
c. Mime Tent and Hall of Mirrors
d. Refreshment Stand and Ball Toss
e. Bumper Cars and Mime Tent
   $\sqrt{85}$ units

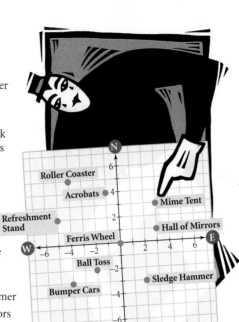

Step 3 Which pair of attractions is farthest apart? If each grid unit represents 0.1 mile, how far apart are these attractions?
Roller Coaster and Sledge Hammer; 10 units, or 1 mi

Step 4 Chris parked his car at the coordinates $(17, -9)$. If each grid unit represents 0.1 mile, how far is it from the Refreshment Stand to his car? (Try to do this without plotting the location of his car.) $11\sqrt{5}$ units, or approximately 2.5 mi

Two new attractions are being considered. The first attraction, designated P_1, will be located at the coordinates (x_1, y_1) as shown at right, and the second building, designated P_2, will be located at the coordinates (x_2, y_2).

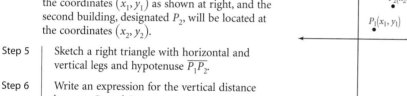

Step 5 Sketch a right triangle with horizontal and vertical legs and hypotenuse $\overline{P_1P_2}$.

Step 6 Write an expression for the vertical distance between P_1 and P_2. $y_2 - y_1$

Step 7 Write an expression for the horizontal distance between P_1 and P_2. $x_2 - x_1$

Step 8 Write an expression for the distance between these two points. (This formula should work for any two points.) $\text{distance between } P_1 \text{ and } P_2 = \sqrt{(x_2 - x_1)^2 + (y_2 - y_1)^2}$

Step 9 Verify that your formula works by using it to find the distance between the Bumper Cars and the Mime Tent.
$\text{distance} = \sqrt{(-4-3)^2 + (-3-3)^2} = \sqrt{(-7)^2 + (-6)^2} = \sqrt{49 + 36} = \sqrt{85}$ units

square root of a sum is the sum of the square roots. If you can challenge them to determine why the data conflict with their belief, they may correct their misconception in a deeper way than if you just tell them they're mistaken.

Assessing Progress

Look for the ability to assign coordinates to points, draw right triangles, and use notation to write a general expression representing a sequence of steps.

Guiding the Investigation

Step 2 You might pass out copies of the Amusement Park worksheet so that students aren't tempted to write in their books.

Some students may have difficulty deciding what right triangle to draw. You might suggest that they think of slope triangles. And when the triangle is drawn, they may not see how to find the lengths of the legs. Suggest that they drop perpendiculars to the axes.

Students also may find it challenging to work with general units rather than feet or meters. As needed, encourage them to think about appropriate length in feet or meters for each unit (in Step 3, they're asked to assume that each unit is 0.1 mi), but have them try to get results in units first.

Steps 5–9 Some students may have difficulty working in the abstract. You might ask them to write out the steps for finding one specific distance in a column and then write the general approach in an adjacent column, using variables.

SHARING IDEAS

Have students present any variety of ideas they came up with in Step 8. Work with the class to derive the distance formula. In the process, ask if the order of subtraction of the x- and y-coordinates matters. Elicit the idea that the squaring operation will yield the same positive radicand either way.

Ask students to calculate distances, assuming that the grid lines are roads along which they must travel. Ask what the distance formula would be in that case. The use of absolute values makes the distance simple to express: $|x_1 - x_2| + |y_1 - y_2|$. Ask if this is the same as the standard distance formula. Some students may think so, believing that the

The Pythagorean Theorem is an efficient way to solve many problems involving distance.

▶ EXAMPLE B

Whereas Example A shows how to find a distance given some points, this example shows how to find a point given a distance.

For this triangle you might want to introduce the terminology of a 1-1-$\sqrt{2}$ triangle or a 45°-45°-90° triangle.

If students reduce the radicals, the location would be written as $\left(2 + 3\sqrt{2}, 1 + 3\sqrt{2}\right)$.

EXAMPLE B | If you walk 6 km northeast from (2, 1), at a compass reading of 45°, what is your new location?

▶ **Solution** | First you find the horizontal and vertical change from your starting position. If you walk northeast, you walk just as far to the east as you walk to the north. Your path creates an isosceles right triangle. Use the Pythagorean Theorem to find a in the sketch below.

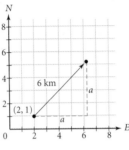

$a^2 + b^2 = c^2$	Pythagorean Theorem.
$a^2 + a^2 = 6^2$	Substitute 6 for c, and substitute a for b because both legs are the same length.
$2a^2 = 36$	Add $a^2 + a^2$.
$a = \sqrt{18}$	Divide by 2 and take the square root of both sides.

To get the coordinates of your new location, add $\sqrt{18}$ to each coordinate of your starting location, (2, 1). Your new location is exactly $\left(2 + \sqrt{18}, 1 + \sqrt{18}\right)$, or about 6.2 km east and 5.2 km north of the campsite.

Note that, as you learned in Lesson 11.5, Exercise 10, you can rewrite $\sqrt{18}$ by removing the perfect-square factor of 9.

$$\sqrt{18} = \sqrt{9 \cdot 2} = \sqrt{9} \cdot \sqrt{2} = 3\sqrt{2}$$

Sometimes equations from distance problems have variables within a square root. Example C shows how to work with these situations.

▶ EXAMPLE C

This example shows how solving an equation with radicals may produce a number that does not check as a solution. Such a root is called an *extraneous root*. Here −3.4 is an extraneous root.

EXAMPLE C | Solve the equation $\sqrt{15 + x} = x$.

▶ **Solution** |

$\sqrt{15 + x} = x$	Original equation.
$\left(\sqrt{15 + x}\right)^2 = x^2$	Square both sides to undo the square root.
$15 + x = x^2$	The result of squaring.
$0 = x^2 - x - 15$	Subtract 15 and x from both sides to get a trinomial set equal to 0.
$x \approx -3.4$ and $x \approx 4.4$	Use the quadratic formula, a graph, or a table to approximate the two possible solutions.

Check:

$$\sqrt{15 + (-3.4)} \neq -3.4$$

The square root of a number can't be negative. So -3.4 is not a solution.

$$\sqrt{15 + 4.4} = \sqrt{19.4} \approx 4.4$$

This solution checks.

So $x = 4.4$ is the only solution to the equation.

Whenever you solve a square root equation, be sure to check whether each solution satisfies the original equation. Often you'll find that one or more of your solutions doesn't work!

In the second part of the investigation you used the Pythagorean Theorem to derive the **distance formula.** When you know the coordinates of two points, this formula allows you to find the distance between the points even without plotting them.

Distance Formula

The distance d between $P_1(x_1, y_1)$ and $P_2(x_2, y_2)$ is given by the formula

$$d = \sqrt{(x_2 - x_1)^2 + (y_2 - y_1)^2}$$

Look back at Example A. Can you show how to use the distance formula to solve this problem without graphing?

The length of a segment is the same as the distance between the endpoints of the segment. So the distance formula has many applications in analytic geometry.

EXERCISES

You will need your graphing calculator for Exercises **6** and **8**.

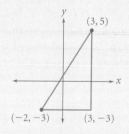

▶ Practice Your Skills

1. Is a triangle with side lengths of 9 cm, 16 cm, and 25 cm a right triangle? Explain. ⓐ no, because $9^2 + 16^2 \neq 25^2$

2. Plot these points on graph paper.

  a. Draw the segment between the two points. Then draw a horizontal segment and a vertical segment to create a right triangle.

  b. Find the lengths of the horizontal and vertical segments.

  c. Find the exact distance between the two points.
    $\sqrt{89}$ units

3. Find the distance between each pair of points.

  a. $(0, 0)$ and $(3, 4)$ **b.** $(1, 2)$ and $(-3, -5)$ **c.** $(2, 0)$ and (s, t)
    5    $\sqrt{65} \approx 8.06$ $\sqrt{(2 - s)^2 + t^2}$, or $\sqrt{(s - 2)^2 + t^2}$

4. On his homework, Matt wrote that the distance between two points was

$$\sqrt{(6 - 1)^2 + (3 - 7)^2}$$

What two points was Matt working with? ⓐ possible answer: $(6, 3)$ and $(1, 7)$

2b. horizontal length: 5 units; vertical length: 8 units

Exercise 4 Be open to two possible solutions here, because the x- and y-coordinates can be subtracted in either order.

Closing the Lesson

The **distance formula** for calculating the distance between points (x_1, y_1) and (x_2, y_2) is derived by applying the Pythagorean Theorem to a triangle with a right angle at a point in line horizontally with one of the given points and vertically with the other. The result is that the distance is $\sqrt{(x_2 - x_1)^2 + (y_2 - y_1)^2}$.

BUILDING UNDERSTANDING

Students work with the distance formula.

ASSIGNING HOMEWORK

Essential	**1–6**
Performance assessment	**7, 8, 11**
Portfolio	**8**
Journal	**4, 9**
Group	**9**
Review	**10–12**

▶ Helping with the Exercises

Exercise 2b If students are having difficulty finding the lengths of these segments, suggest that they drop perpendiculars from the endpoints to the axes.

2a. possible answer:

Exercise 5 You may want to ask
students to make a conjecture
about the lengths of opposite
sides of any parallelogram and to
test it on other parallelograms.

5a. slope of $\overline{AB}$ and $\overline{DC}$: $\frac{4}{5}$;
slope of $\overline{AD}$ and $\overline{BC}$: $-\frac{2}{3}$

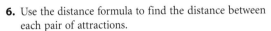

▶ Reason and Apply

5. Quadrilateral *ABCD* is pictured at right.

   a. What is the slope of each side?

   b. What type of quadrilateral is it? parallelogram

   c. Find the length of each side. length of $\overline{AB}$ and $\overline{DC}$:
      $\sqrt{41}$ units; length of $\overline{AD}$ and $\overline{BC}$: $\sqrt{13}$ units

For Exercises 6 and 7, refer to the Amusement Park
investigation on page 627.

6. Use the distance formula to find the distance between
   each pair of attractions.

   a. Refreshment Stand and Bumper Cars ⓐ $\sqrt{26}$ units, or approximately 0.5 mi

   b. Acrobats and Hall of Mirrors 5 units, or 0.5 mi

7. Jake's sawdust spreader is on its way from the Sledge Hammer to the Roller Coaster.
   When he has gone 0.6 mi, it breaks down. See the graph in the investigation on
   page 627. Each unit on the graph is 0.1 mi, so 0.6 mi is equal to 6 units.

   a. Find the equation of the line connecting the Roller Coaster and the Sledge
      Hammer. ⓐ possible answer: $y = -3 - \frac{4}{3}(x - 2)$

   b. Write the distance formula using (x, y) as the breakdown point and the location
      of the Sledge Hammer as the second point. ⓐ $d = \sqrt{(x - 2)^2 + (y + 3)^2}$

   c. Replace y in your distance formula with the expression equal to y that you
      found in 7a. ⓐ

   d. Set the distance equal to 6 units (0.6 mi) and use a calculator graph to solve
      for x.

   e. Give the coordinates of the breakdown point. $(-1.6, 1.8)$

Exercise 8 This exercise assumes
that the pole will not bend. As
needed, encourage students to
draw an auxiliary line.

Solutions should involve two
triangles. You might want to have
a box available as well as a dowel
or straw that students can place
inside the box to help them
visualize the situation.

8. **APPLICATION** The longest pole that fits in a rectangular
   box goes from one corner to the corner farthest from
   it. Find the longest pole that fits a 30-cm-by-50-cm-
   by-20-cm box. Show all your work. Give the
   answer as an exact value. $10\sqrt{38}$ cm

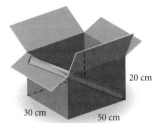

30 cm   50 cm   20 cm

7c. $d = \sqrt{(x - 2)^2 + \left[-3 - \frac{4}{3}(x - 2) + 3\right]^2} = \sqrt{(x - 2)^2 + \left[-\frac{4}{3}(x - 2)\right]^2}$

7d. $6 = \sqrt{(x - 2)^2 + \left[-\frac{4}{3}(x - 2)\right]^2}$; $x = -1.6$ or $x = 5.6$

9. Mini-Investigation Consider the equation
$$\sqrt{20 - x} = x$$

a. Solve the equation symbolically.

b. Solve the equation using a graph or a table.

c. Explain why you get two possible solutions when you solve the equation symbolically and only one solution when you look at a graph or table. Substitute both possible solutions into the original equation, and describe what happens.
$x = 4$ is a solution; $x = -5$ is not a realistic solution because a square root cannot be negative.

► Review

11.5 **10.** Solve each equation.

a. $\frac{3}{5} = \frac{a}{105}$ $a = 63$

b. $\frac{1}{\sqrt{2}} = \frac{b}{7\sqrt{2}}$ $b = 7$

c. $\frac{\sqrt{3}}{2} = \frac{c}{\sqrt{12}}$ @ $c = 3$

11.4 **11.** APPLICATION Nadia Ferrell wants to build an awning over her porch. She wants the slope of the awning to be $\frac{5}{12}$. The porch is 8 ft deep, and the roof line is 14 ft above the porch. She draws this sketch to help her plan.

a. How long will the awning be from the roof line to the porch support posts? Show your work. @

b. How tall will the posts be that hold up the front of the awning? Show your work.
$\frac{5}{12} = \frac{14 - b}{8}$, $b = 10\frac{2}{3}$; 10 ft 8 in. tall

11.5 **12.** Rewrite each radical expression so that it contains no perfect-square factors.

a. $\sqrt{200}$ @ $10\sqrt{2}$

b. $\sqrt{612}$ $6\sqrt{17}$

c. $\sqrt{45}$ $3\sqrt{5}$

d. $\sqrt{243}$ $9\sqrt{3}$

Two Tibetan Buddhist monks create a mandala from colored sand. The delicate geometric design will take days to create and will then be dismantled in a special ceremony.

Learn more about the cultural significance of mandalas and how geometry is used in the making of mandalas with the Internet links at **www.keymath.com/DA** .

Exercise 9c As students compare the solutions they get using these two methods, they see again that some apparent solutions to a square root equation may be extraneous. If students are able to explain that the extraneous solution results when the original equation is squared, they are more likely to remember how important it is to verify solutions. If the symbolic solution is difficult for too many students for you to help individually, you might rely on groups.

Exercise 11 Students may need to be told that a slope of $\frac{5}{12}$ creates a right triangle with legs 5 and 12. Therefore, the hypotenuse is 13. The awning triangle will be similar to this 5-12-13 triangle.

[Alert] If students are having difficulties with 11b, help them see the length of the posts when projected against the house and ask how to find that length by subtracting.

11a. $\frac{13}{12} = \frac{a}{8}$, $a = 8.\overline{6}$; 8 ft 8 in. long

9a. $\sqrt{20 - x} = x$
$$20 - x = x^2$$
$$0 = x^2 + x - 20$$
$$0 = (x + 5)(x - 4)$$
$$x = -5 \text{ or } x = 4$$

9b. Possible answer: The intersection of the graphs of $Y_1 = \sqrt{(20 - x)}$ and $Y_2 = x$ occurs once, at $x = 4$.

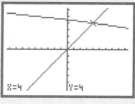

$[-9.4, 9.4, 1, -6.2, 6.2, 1]$

LESSON
11.7

Similar Triangles and Trigonometric Functions

LESSON OUTLINE

First day:

10 min   Example A

40 min   Investigation

Second day:

15 min   Investigation

10 min   Sharing

10 min   Example B

5 min   Closing

10 min   Exercises

MATERIALS

• graph paper

• straightedges

• protractors

• Earth and Moon (T), *optional*

• Protractors (T, from Chapter 6), *optional*

• Calculator Note 11B

• Sketchpad demonstration Right Triangle Ratios, *optional*

TEACHING

Trigonometry can replace similar triangles for finding distances. The concepts of ratio and proportion were first introduced in Chapter 2.

One Step

Display the Earth and Moon transparency. Challenge students to calculate the radius of the moon (*RM*) given that the distance to the moon (*EM*) is 240,000 mi, that the angle at *R* is a right angle, and that the angle at *E* is 0.26°. As you circulate, encourage them to draw scale models and to look for ratios. During Sharing, lead students to the idea that the ratios of corresponding side lengths of all similar right triangles are the same.

Similar figures have corresponding angles that are equal and corresponding side lengths that are proportional. So the figures have the same shape, but one is an enlargement of the other. You can use ratios and proportions to compare and calculate length measurements for similar figures.

These Japanese cat figurines, called Maneki Neko, are near examples of three-dimensional similar figures. In what ways are they not mathematically similar?

EXAMPLE A

Elene is walking to school. From where she stands, she can see the 5 m flagpole on top of her school. She holds her centimeter ruler approximately 50 cm from her eye. Against the ruler, the flagpole looks 25 cm tall. How far is she from school?

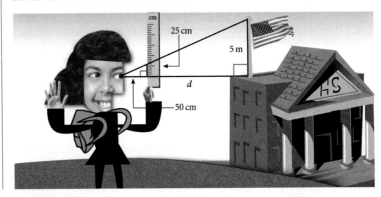

▶ Solution

This situation creates two similar triangles. One triangle is formed by Elene's eye and the 0 cm and 25 cm marks on her ruler. The other triangle is formed by Elene's eye and the ends of the flagpole. Elene's eye is a common vertex.

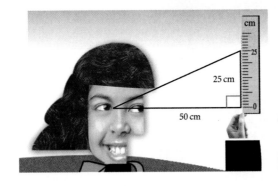

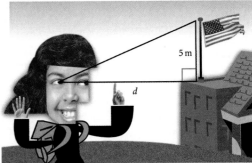

LESSON OBJECTIVES

• Review the basic properties of similar triangles

• Review (or learn) how to measure acute angles using a protractor

• Discover the definitions of the sine, cosine, and tangent ratios

• Write and solve equations involving trigonometric ratios

NCTM STANDARDS

CONTENT		PROCESS	
	Number		Problem Solving
✔	Algebra	✔	Reasoning
✔	Geometry	✔	Communication
✔	Measurement		Connections
	Data/Probability	✔	Representation

Use the ratios of adjacent sides to write the proportion

$$\frac{d \text{ m}}{5 \text{ m}} = \frac{50 \text{ cm}}{25 \text{ cm}}$$

Here, $d = 10$, so Elene is 10 meters from school.

Look back at the similar right triangles in Example A. Notice the ratios compare the vertical legs to the horizontal legs. Both ratios, $\frac{25 \text{ cm}}{50 \text{ cm}}$ and $\frac{5 \text{ m}}{10 \text{ m}}$, equal 0.5.

If another triangle similar to those has a horizontal leg of 7 m, then the vertical leg would be 3.5 m in length. The angles in all of these triangles are about 26.6°, 63.4°, and 90°. Any other right triangle with a value of 0.5 for the ratio of its vertical leg to its horizontal leg also has angles with these measures.

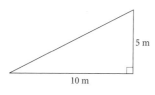
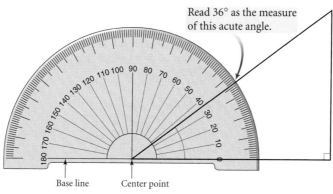

5 m

10 m

In each of these similar triangles, the ratio of the vertical leg to the horizontal leg is 0.5. All three have angles measuring approximately 26.6°, 63.4°, and 90°.

3.5 m

7 m

25 cm

50 cm

Likewise, if a right triangle has these angle measures, the ratio of its vertical leg to its horizontal leg is 0.5. There is a connection between the angle measures of a triangle and the ratios of its sides. You'll explore this connection in the investigation.

The angle below measures 36°. You already know that an angle that measures 90° is called a right angle. An angle that measures less than 90° is called an **acute angle.** An angle that measures more than 90° but less than 180° is called an **obtuse angle.**

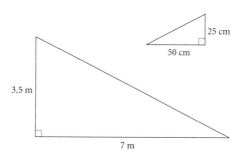

Read 36° as the measure of this acute angle.

Base line   Center point

▶ **EXAMPLE A**

This example shows how to determine a length using similar triangles and points out that corresponding angles of similar triangles have the same measure. Students may need reminding that similar figures are dilations of each other. Saying that "similar" means "same shape" leads some students to think that, for example, all rectangles are similar to each other but not to any triangles.

You might use the Protractors transparency to review measuring angles with a protractor.

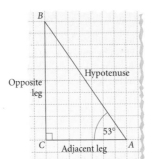

Guiding the Investigation

Step 1 Each member of the group should draw a different right triangle.

Step 3 As needed, remind students that a *leg* of a right triangle is a side that isn't the hypotenuse. In stating the Pythagorean Theorem, the leg called *a* was opposite the angle called *A*, whereas in trigonometry, the leg called *a* is adjacent to angle *A*. The letter *a* stands for *adjacent*, just as *o* stands for *opposite* and *h* stands for *hypotenuse*.

Students should use radicals to express lengths exactly.

Investigation
Ratio, Ratio, Ratio

You will need

- graph paper
- a straightedge
- a protractor

In this investigation you'll learn about some very important ratios in right triangles.

This is only a sample. Your triangle should look different.

Procedure Note

Measuring Angles
Place the center point of your protractor on the vertex of the angle. Line up the base line with one side of the angle. Notice the mark that the other side of the angle passes through. See the example at the bottom of page 633.

Step 1 On graph paper, use a straightedge to draw a right triangle. Use the grid lines of the graph paper to make sure the legs are perpendicular. Make the triangle large enough for you to measure its angles accurately.

Step 2 Label one of the acute angles *A*. Measure it.

If you look at one acute angle in a right triangle, the **adjacent leg** is the leg of the triangle that is part of the measured angle. The **opposite leg** is the leg of the triangle that is not part of the angle you are looking at.

Step 3 Make a table like this one and record the information for each triangle drawn by a member of your group.

	Tony's triangle	Alice's triangle
Measure of angle A		
Length of adjacent leg (a)		
Length of opposite leg (o)		
Length of hypotenuse (h)		

Step 4 Make a new table like this one and calculate the ratios for each triangle drawn by a member of your group.

	Tony's triangle	Alice's triangle
Measure of angle A		
$\frac{o}{h}$		
$\frac{a}{h}$		
$\frac{o}{a}$		

Step 5 | With your calculator in degree mode, find the value of the **sine,** the **cosine,** and the **tangent** of angle A. [▶ 🖳 See **Calculator Note 11B** to learn about evaluating these functions on your calculator. ◀] Record these values to the nearest hundredth in a table like this one.

	Tony's triangle	Alice's triangle
Measure of angle A		
sine (A)		
cosine (A)		
tangent (A)		

Step 6 The results for Steps 4 and 5 should be about the same;

$$\text{sine} = \frac{\text{opposite leg}}{\text{hypotenuse}},$$

$$\text{cosine} = \frac{\text{adjacent leg}}{\text{hypotenuse}},$$

$$\text{tangent} = \frac{\text{opposite leg}}{\text{adjacent leg}}.$$

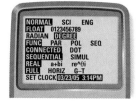 

Step 6 | Compare your results for Steps 4 and 5. Define each function—sine, cosine, and tangent—in terms of a ratio of the lengths of the adjacent leg, the opposite leg, and the hypotenuse.

Step 7 | Draw a larger right triangle with an acute angle D equal to your original angle A.

Step 8 | Measure the side lengths and calculate the sine, the cosine, and the tangent of angle D. What do you find? Students should find that the ratios are the same for any pair of similar right triangles.

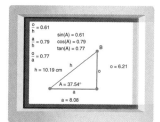 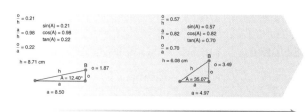

keymath.com/DA

[▶ You can use the **Dynamic Algebra Exploration** at **www.keymath.com/DA** to further explore the topics of the investigation. ◀]

In the investigation you learned that some ratios of the sides of a right triangle have special names: sine, cosine, and tangent. Sine, cosine, and tangent are all called **trigonometric functions.** They are fundamental to the branch of mathematics called **trigonometry.** Learning to identify the parts of a right triangle and to evaluate these functions for particular angle measures are important problem-solving tools.

SHARING IDEAS

Have at least one group share its results from Step 6, and summarize the results by pointing out the box on page 636 of the student text. You might draw a large triangle and then a bunch of line segments within it parallel to one of its legs to point out the equality of the ratios corresponding to the angle shared by the triangles formed.

Students might be helped by the mnemonic SOHCAHTOA (pronounced "soh-cah-toh-ah"), standing for "sine: opposite over hypotenuse, cosine: adjacent over hypotenuse, tangent: opposite over adjacent."

[Ask] "Are there any other ratios of the three sides of a right triangle?" [Sine, cosine, and tangent are only three of six trigonometric functions. The other three are secant $\frac{h}{a}$, cosecant $\frac{h}{o}$, and cotangent $\frac{a}{o}$.]

[Ask] "Do you think that trigonometric ratios apply to nonright triangles?" Challenge students to find two nonright triangles that have an angle in common but different ratios of, say, opposite to adjacent. [Like the Pythagorean Theorem, trigonometric ratios are valid only for right triangles.]

Some students might reasonably ask why we need trigonometry. Similar triangles seem to suffice, as in Elene's finding the distance to the flagpole. Often it's impossible to draw similar triangles, as when you're trying to measure distance in space (as in the One Step problem) or surveying.

Point out the History Connection. Pitiscus was born in Silesia, now part of Poland. Trigonometric ratios (and tables for many angles) were developed 1700 years before Pitiscus for the purpose of measuring such distances.

Assessing Progress

Check for student understanding of right triangles and the ability to collect data systematically.

History
CONNECTION

The word *trigonometry* comes from the Greek words for triangle and measurement. Its first use in English was in a 1614 translation of *Trigonometry: Doctrine of Triangles* by the Silesian mathematician Bartholmeo Pitiscus (1561–1613).

Trigonometric Functions

For acute angle A in a right angle, the trigonometric functions are

sine of angle $A = \dfrac{length\ of\ opposite\ leg}{length\ of\ hypotenuse}$ or $\sin A = \dfrac{o}{h}$

cosine of angle $A = \dfrac{length\ of\ adjacent\ leg}{length\ of\ hypotenuse}$ or $\cos A = \dfrac{a}{h}$

tangent of angle $A = \dfrac{length\ of\ opposite\ leg}{length\ of\ adjacent\ leg}$ or $\tan A = \dfrac{o}{a}$

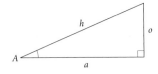

In this lesson you will practice writing ratios associated with the trigonometric functions. You will also practice using ratio, proportion, and similarity. In the next lesson you will apply the ratios to solve problems.

▶ **EXAMPLE B**

You might have students find all three ratios for both angle A and angle B and look for relationships between the ratios. Angles A and B are complements because together they make up a right angle. The word *cosine* stands for *complement's sine,* so $\cos A$ equals $\sin B$, and vice versa.

[Ask] "Do the ratios hold for the right angle?" [Although the sine, opposite over hypotenuse, will be 1, since the opposite *is* the hypotenuse, it's not clear which leg is adjacent. Trigonometric ratios are extended for right angles by other means.]

You might use the Sketchpad demonstration Right Triangle Ratios to investigate values of sine, cosine, and tangent for angle measures close to 90° and 0°.

EXAMPLE B

Find these ratios for this triangle.

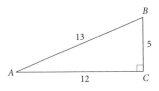

a. $\sin A$

b. $\cos A$

c. $\tan B$

▶ **Solution**

For angle A, the side length values are $a = 12$, $o = 5$, and $h = 13$.

a. $\sin A = \dfrac{o}{h} = \dfrac{5}{13}$

b. $\cos A = \dfrac{a}{h} = \dfrac{12}{13}$

Using angle B changes which leg is opposite and which is adjacent. For angle B, the side length values are $a = 5$, $o = 12$, and $h = 13$.

c. $\tan B = \dfrac{o}{a} = \dfrac{12}{5}$

Note that identifying the opposite and adjacent legs depends on which angle you are using. Be careful to identify the correct sides and angles when using trigonometric functions.

Closing the Lesson

Trigonometry is useful for finding distances that are lengths of sides of right triangles, especially when you know an angle measure and another length. The major **trigonometric functions** are **sine, cosine,** and **tangent.**

This fascinating sketch by Leonardo da Vinci (1452–1519) explains why moonlight is less bright than sunlight. A diverse genius, Leonardo was a painter, draftsman, sculptor, architect, and engineer. The triangles used in this sketch show that he was also knowledgeable about geometry and trigonometry. Learn more about Leonardo da Vinci at www.keymath.com/DA .

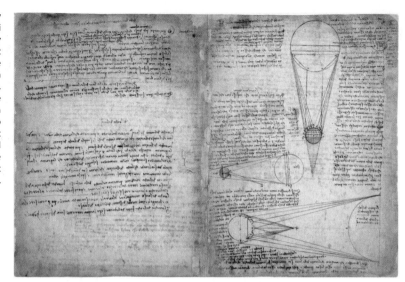

EXERCISES

You will need your graphing calculator for Exercise **8.**

▶ **Practice Your Skills**

1. Solve each equation for x.

   a. $\frac{2}{3} = \frac{18}{x}$ $x = 27$ **b.** $\frac{7}{8} = \frac{x}{40}$ $x = 35$ **c.** $\frac{1}{4} = \frac{\sqrt{10}}{\sqrt{x}}$ ⓐ $x = 160$ **d.** $\frac{2}{x} = \frac{x}{8}$ ⓐ $x = \pm 4$

2. **APPLICATION** One inch on a road map represents 50 miles on the ground. Two cities are 3.6 inches apart on a map. What is the actual distance between the cities?   180 mi

3. Find these ratios for the triangle at right.

   a. $\sin D$ ⓐ $\sin D = \frac{7}{25}$

   b. $\cos E$ $\cos E = \frac{7}{25}$

   c. $\tan D$

      $\tan D = \frac{7}{24}$

4. The diagram at right shows $\triangle ABC$ and $\triangle ADE$.

   a. Are the triangles similar? Why or why not? ⓗ

   b. Find the ratio of corresponding side lengths of $\triangle ADE$ to $\triangle ABC$. ⓐ $\frac{8}{4} = 2$

   c. Find the lengths of $\overline{AD}$ and $\overline{AE}$.   6 cm and 10 cm

   d. Find the areas of $\triangle ADE$ and $\triangle ABC$.   24 cm² and 6 cm²

   e. What is the ratio of the area of $\triangle ADE$ to the area of $\triangle ABC$?
      $\frac{24}{6} = 4 = (2)^2$

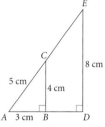

4a. Yes. Possible answer: Angle A is common to both triangles and angles B and D are both right angles, so angles C and E must also be congruent. Because all three angles are congruent, the triangles are similar.

Exercise 5 The proportions in 5a and 5b are easily solved when *x* is in the numerator of each side.

For 5a use the proportion $\frac{x}{6} = \frac{x+2}{7}$.

For 5b use the proportion $\frac{x+1}{5} = \frac{x-2}{4}$.

6a. $\sqrt{60}$ m, or approximately 7.75 m

Exercise 7 Here's an application of trigonometry. You may point out how the angle and one leg of a right triangle are being used in 7e to find a length that's not otherwise easily available. If students ask, however, be ready to acknowledge that indeed the height could be found by using similar triangles, such as those cast by shadows.

7d. $\cos 65° \approx 0.4226$; $\sin 65° \approx 0.9063$; $\tan 65° \approx 2.1445$

5. Find *x* in each pair of similar triangles.

a.

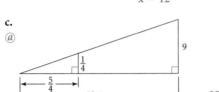

$x = 12$

b.

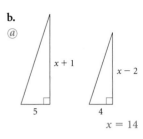

$x = 14$

c.

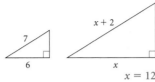

$x = 35$

6. APPLICATION An 8-meter ladder is leaning against a building. The bottom of the ladder is 2 meters from the building.

   a. How high on the building does the ladder reach?

   b. A windowsill is 6 meters high on the building. How far from the building should the bottom of the ladder be placed to meet the windowsill? $\sqrt{28}$ m, or approximately 5.29 m

7. The wire attached to the top of a telephone pole makes a 65° angle with the level ground. The distance from the base of the pole to where the wire is attached to the ground is *d*. The height of the pole is *h*. The length of the wire is *w*.

   a. What trigonometric function of 65° is the same as $\frac{d}{w}$? @ cosine

   b. What trigonometric function of 65° is the same as $\frac{h}{w}$? @ sine

   c. What trigonometric function of 65° is the same as $\frac{h}{d}$? tangent

   d. Use your calculator to approximate the values in 7a–c to the nearest ten thousandth.

   e. If the wire is attached to the ground 2.6 meters from the pole, how high is the pole? approximately 5.6 m

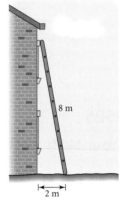

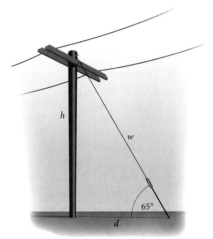

8. Consider this right triangle with a 28° angle.

a. Write an equation that relates x and y, the legs of the right triangle. @ $\tan 28° = \frac{y}{x}$, or $y = x \cdot \tan 28°$

b. Graph your equation on your calculator. Make a sketch of the graph on your paper. Describe the graph.

c. Find y if $x = 100$. $y \approx 53.2$

d. If $y = 80$, find x. $x \approx 151$

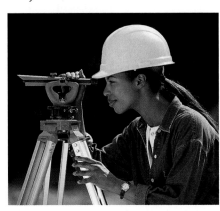

Surveyors use a tool called a theodolite, or transit, to measure angles. The angles are sometimes used with trigonometry to measure distances.

9. *Mini-Investigation* Sketch a right triangle that is isosceles (two equal sides). Label each acute angle 45°.

a. Label one of the legs of your isosceles right triangle "1 unit." Calculate the exact lengths of the other two sides.

b. Make a table like this one on your paper. First write each ratio using the lengths you found in 9a. Then use your calculator to find a decimal approximation for each exact value to the nearest ten thousandth. Finally, find each ratio using the trigonometric function keys on your calculator. Check that your decimal approximations and the values using the trigonometric function keys are the same.

Trigonometric Functions for a 45° Angle

	Sine	Cosine	Tangent
Exact value of ratio	$\frac{1}{\sqrt{2}}$	$\frac{1}{\sqrt{2}}$	$\frac{1}{1}$
Decimal approximation of exact value	0.7071	0.7071	1.0000
Value by trigonometric function keys	0.7071	0.7071	1.0000

10. *Mini-Investigation* Sketch an equilateral triangle (three equal sides). Label each angle 60°.

a. Draw a segment from one vertex to the midpoint of the opposite side. You should have two triangles with angles measuring 30°, 60°, and 90°. @

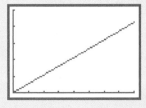
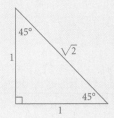
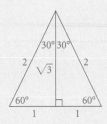

b. Label one side of your equilateral triangle "2 units." Calculate the exact lengths of the other two sides of your 30°-60°-90° triangles.

c. Make tables like these on your paper. First write each ratio using the lengths you found in 10b. Then use your calculator to find a decimal approximation for each exact value to the nearest ten thousandth. Finally, find each ratio using the trigonometric function keys on your calculator. Check that your decimal approximations and the values using the trigonometric function keys are the same.

Trigonometric Functions for a 30° Angle

	Sine	Cosine	Tangent
Exact value of ratio	$\frac{1}{2}$	$\frac{\sqrt{3}}{2}$	$\frac{1}{\sqrt{3}}$
Decimal approximation of exact value	0.5000	0.8660	0.5774
Value by trigonometric function keys	0.5000	0.8660	0.5774

Trigonometric Functions for a 60° Angle

	Sine	Cosine	Tangent
Exact value of ratio	$\frac{\sqrt{3}}{2}$	$\frac{1}{2}$	$\frac{\sqrt{3}}{1}$
Decimal approximation of exact value	0.8660	0.5000	1.7321
Value by trigonometric function keys	0.8660	0.5000	1.7321

▶ Review

11a. rectangle

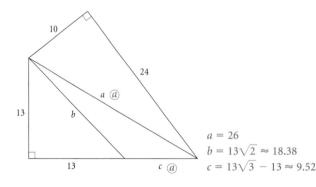

5.2, 11.1 **11.** Here are four linear equations.

$$y = 2x - 1 \qquad x + 2y = 4$$
$$y = 3 + 2x \qquad x = -2y + 10$$

a. Graph the four lines. What polygon is formed?

b. Find the coordinates of the vertices of the polygon. @ $(1.2, 1.4), (2.4, 3.8), (0.8, 4.6), (-0.4, 2.2)$

c. Find the linear equations for the diagonals of the polygon. $y = 11 - 8x, y = \frac{17}{7} + \frac{4}{7}x$

d. Find the coordinates of the point where the diagonals intersect. $(1, 3)$

11.4 **12.** Find the missing side lengths in this figure.

$a = 26$
$b = 13\sqrt{2} \approx 18.38$
$c = 13\sqrt{3} - 13 \approx 9.52$

LESSON 11.8

Trigonometry

In Lesson 11.7, you learned about trigonometric ratios in right triangles. The trigonometric functions allow you to find the ratios of side lengths when you know the measure of an acute angle. So, if you know the length of one side and the measure of one acute angle, you can solve for the lengths of the other sides.

EXAMPLE A

Consider this triangle.

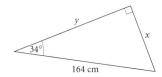

a. Find the length of the side labeled x.
b. Find the length of the side labeled y.

► **Solution**

a. The variable x represents the length of the side opposite the 34° angle. The length of the hypotenuse is 164 cm.

$$\sin A = \frac{o}{h}$$ Definition of sine.

$$\sin 34° = \frac{x}{164}$$ Substitute 34° for the measure of the angle and 164 for the length of the hypotenuse.

$$164 \sin 34° = x$$ Multiply both sides by 164.

$$91.7 \approx x$$ Multiply and round to the nearest tenth.

The side labeled x is approximately 91.7 cm.

b. The variable y represents the length of the side adjacent to the 34° angle. The length of the hypotenuse remains 164 cm.

$$\cos A = \frac{a}{h}$$ Definition of cosine.

$$\cos 34° = \frac{y}{164}$$ Substitute the measure of the angle and the length of the hypotenuse.

$$164 \cos 34° = y$$ Multiply both sides by 164.

$$136.0 \approx y$$ Multiply and round to the nearest tenth.

The side labeled y is approximately 136.0 cm.

What if you know the lengths of the sides but want to know the measure of an acute angle? You can use the inverses of the trigonometric functions to find the angle measure when you know the ratio. The inverses of the trigonometric functions are inverse sine, inverse cosine, and inverse tangent. They are written $\sin^{-1}$, $\cos^{-1}$, and $\tan^{-1}$.

NCTM STANDARDS

CONTENT	PROCESS
Number	✔ Problem Solving
✔ Algebra	✔ Reasoning
✔ Geometry	✔ Communication
✔ Measurement	✔ Connections
Data/Probability	✔ Representation

LESSON OBJECTIVES

- Become familiar with the concept of inverse trigonometric functions
- Learn to interpret topographic maps by using inverse tangent ratios
- Solve real-world problems using trigonometric ratios

▶ **EXAMPLE B**

This example introduces the notion of the inverse sine. Point out that the −1 is not an exponent but part of the symbol for the inverse trig ratio.

You might ask whether this approach will always work. Elicit the idea that $\sin^{-1} x$ is not defined for values of x greater than 1 or less than −1. Indeed, it's not a function, because many angles have the same sine. For this reason, mathematicians have defined $\sin^{-1} x$, $\cos^{-1} x$, and $\tan^{-1} x$, which have restricted domains and are always functions.

 Guiding the Investigation

Step 1 Students who are not familiar with topographic maps (often called *topo sheets*) may find this very difficult. Stress that if you walk around the hill on a contour line, your elevation doesn't change.

You may want to distribute the Contour Map worksheet.

EXAMPLE B   Find the measure of angle A.

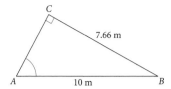

▶ **Solution**   Because you know the length of the side opposite angle A and the length of the hypotenuse, you can find the sine ratio.

$$\sin A = \frac{7.66}{10} = 0.766$$

You find the measure of the angle with the inverse sine of 0.766.

[▶ 🖳 See **Calculator Note 11C** to learn about evaluating the inverses of the trigonometric functions. ◀]

$$A = \sin^{-1}(0.766) \approx 50°$$

So the measure of angle A is approximately 50°. Check your answer using the sine function.

$$\sin 50° \approx 0.766$$

You use an inverse to undo a function. Note that sin and $\sin^{-1}$ undo each other the same way that squaring and finding the square root undo each other.

 Investigation
Reading Topographic Maps

A **topographic map,** or contour map, reveals the shape of the land surface by showing different levels of elevation. The map below shows the elevation of a hill. In this investigation you will take an imaginary hike over the summit and use the map to calculate the steepness of the hill at different points along the way. You can learn more about topographic maps with the links at **www.keymath.com/DA** .

You will need
• a centimeter ruler
• a protractor

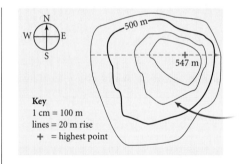

Key
1 cm = 100 m
lines = 20 m rise
+ = highest point

Each of these rings is called a **contour line,** or isometric line. There is a 20 m rise between each contour line.

Step 1 The climb would be easier from the west. From the east the same elevation changes take place in a shorter horizontal distance, so the climb is steeper. Some students may prefer a steep climb to a steep descent and choose to start at the east.

Step 1

Step 1 If you want to hike over the summit, will it be easier to hike up from the west or the east? How can you tell?

Step 3

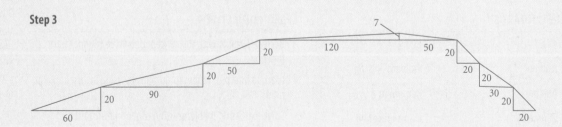

Step 2 | Suppose you want to go from the west side of the hill, over the summit, and down the east side along the dashed-line trail shown on the map. You begin your hike at the edge of the hill, which has an elevation of 480 m above sea level, and travel east. By the contour lines and the peak on the map, your hike will be divided into 8 sections. Find the horizontal and vertical distance traveled for each section of your hike.

Step 3 See bottom of page 642.

Step 3 | Draw a slope triangle representing each section of the hike. On graph paper, draw a right triangle with a base representing the horizontal distance and a leg representing the vertical distance. Find the slope of each hypotenuse.

Step 4 | Use the Pythagorean Theorem to calculate the actual distance you hiked in each section.

Step 5 | Find the angle of the climb for each section of the hike. Use an inverse trigonometric function.

Step 6 Answers should be close to the answers for Step 5.

Step 6 | Use a protractor to measure the angle of the climb in each of your slope triangles in Step 3. How do these answers compare to your answers in Step 5?

Step 7 With a calculator, trigonometry might be more convenient. If only a protractor is available, measuring the angle would be best.

Step 7 | You have used two methods for finding the angle of the climb:

1. Drawing triangles and using a protractor to find angle measures.

2. Using trigonometry to calculate angle measures.

Are there times when one method of finding angle measures is more convenient than the other? Explain your thinking.

EXAMPLE C | Consider this triangle.

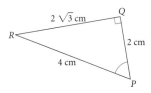

a. Name the lengths of the sides opposite angle *P* and adjacent to angle *P*.

b. Use the side lengths to find exact ratios for sin *P*, cos *P*, and tan *P*.

c. Find the measure of angle *P* using each of the inverse trigonometric functions.

▶ **Solution** | **a.** The length of the side opposite angle *P* is $2\sqrt{3}$ cm, and the length of the side adjacent to angle *P* is 2 cm.

b. $\sin P = \dfrac{2\sqrt{3}}{4} = \dfrac{\sqrt{3}}{2}$ $\cos P = \dfrac{2}{4} = \dfrac{1}{2}$ $\tan P = \dfrac{2\sqrt{3}}{2} = \sqrt{3}$

c. $\sin^{-1}\left(\dfrac{\sqrt{3}}{2}\right) = 60°$ $\cos^{-1}\left(\dfrac{1}{2}\right) = 60°$ $\tan^{-1}\left(\sqrt{3}\right) = 60°$

Each of the inverse trigonometric functions gives the measure of angle *P* as 60°.

Step 2 Again, students without experience may find it difficult to determine the elevations involved. Remind them that there's a 20 m rise between contour lines. It is positive 20 m between contour lines in sections 1 through 3 and negative 20 m in sections 6 through 8. You might need to point out that the topo sheet is a view from above. The distances are horizontal, not along the surface. Help students use the key to determine horizontal distances.

Step 5 The "angle of the climb" is the acute angle between the horizontal leg (the base) and the hypotenuse. Encourage students to discuss which inverse function they should use. It doesn't matter. Students should not forget to use parentheses around the fractions on their calculators. The answer chart, using a negative rise for downward slopes, gives a negative ratio and a negative angle measure.

Step 6 Help students visualize the negative angles as measured down from the horizontal.

SHARING IDEAS

If student answers or approaches vary, have them share their results from Steps 5 and 6. Some students may be confused, even after a presentation by either you or other students. People's filters often keep them from seeing things that are clear to others.

You might mention that in the days before calculators, people would use a table to find the angle with a given trigonometric ratio.

[Ask] "How does the overall angle of climb upward relate to the angles over the sections in which you're climbing upward?" Let students discuss whether it's the mean.

Assessing Progress

Through your observations of group work and pre-sentations, you can assess students' ability to draw slope triangles, calculate slopes, apply the Pythagorean Theorem, and use trigonometric ratios.

▶ EXAMPLE C

This example shows that either $\sin^{-1}$, $\cos^{-1}$, or $\tan^{-1}$ can be used to find the measure of an angle of a right triangle when all three side lengths are known.

[Link] Students will become very familiar with the 30°-60°-90° triangle when they study geometry.

Closing the Lesson

You can work backward from finding trigonometric ratios of angles by using the $\sin^{-1}$, $\cos^{-1}$, and $\tan^{-1}$ buttons on a calculator to find the measures of angles corresponding to ratios of a right triangle's side lengths.

See page 731 for answers to Steps 2–5.

BUILDING UNDERSTANDING

These exercises involve trigonometric ratios and their inverses.

ASSIGNING HOMEWORK

Essential	1–6
Performance assessment	6
Portfolio	8, 10
Journal	9
Group	7–11
Review	12, 13

Helping with the Exercises

A calculator that can calculate trigonometric functions and inverse trigonometric functions is required for Exercises 2–11.

Exercise 1 You may want to mention that the side marked with a lowercase letter is usually opposite the angle marked by the corresponding uppercase letter.

2a.

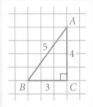

2b. Possible answer:

$A = \sin^{-1}\left(\frac{3}{5}\right) \approx 37°$,

$B = \sin^{-1}\left(\frac{4}{5}\right) \approx 53°$

Exercise 6e Students may already know that the sum of the angle measures in any triangle is 180°. This fact will arise in a geometry course.

EXERCISES

Practice Your Skills

1. Use the triangle at right as a guide. Fill in the correct angle, side, or ratio.

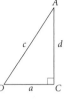

a. $c^2 - a^2 = \boxed{d}^2$ @ **b.** $\tan \boxed{A} = \frac{a}{d}$ **c.** $\cos \boxed{A} = \frac{d}{c}$ @

d. $\sin^{-1}\boxed{} = D$ @ $\frac{d}{c}$ **e.** $\sin D = \cos \boxed{A}$ @ **f.** $\sin \boxed{A} = \frac{a}{c}$

2. You will need a straightedge and a protractor for this exercise.

a. On graph paper, draw a right triangle with legs exactly 3 and 4 units long.

b. Write trigonometric ratios and use inverse functions to find the angle measures.

c. Measure the angles to check your answers to 2b. The angles should measure approximately 37° and 53°.

3. Use a trigonometric ratio to find the length of side x in the triangle at right. @ $x \approx 44.6$ m

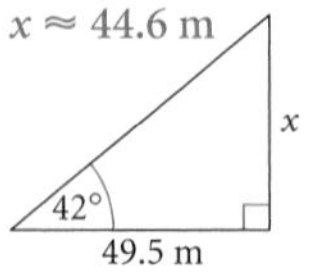

4. Sketch a right triangle to illustrate the ratio

$\tan 25° = \frac{6.8}{b}$

Then find the length of side b. $b \approx 14.6$

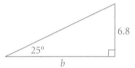

Reason and Apply

5. Find the measure of each labeled angle or side to the nearest tenth of a degree or centimeter.

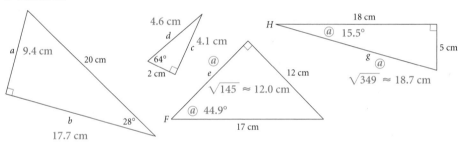

6. The legs of $\triangle PQR$ measure 8 cm and 15 cm.

a. Find the length of the hypotenuse. 17 cm

b. Find the area of the triangle. 60 cm^2

c. Find the measure of angle P. approximately 28°

d. Find the measure of angle Q. approximately 62°

e. What is the sum of the measures of angles P, Q, and R? 180°

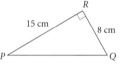

7. APPLICATION The **angle of elevation** is the angle between the horizontal and the line of sight. The angle of elevation of the roof of this building is 31°. Use a trigonometric ratio to find the height of the building. @ approximately 81.1 m

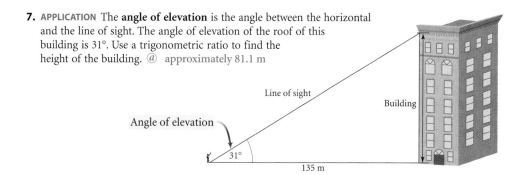

Line of sight

Building

Angle of elevation

31°

135 m

8. You will need to find an actual stairway to do this exercise. Use the diagram below as a guide.

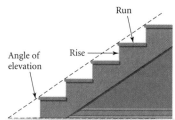

Run

Rise

Angle of elevation

Answers will vary. An average rise-to-run ratio for stairs is $\frac{7}{12}$. The answers provided are based on this ratio.

approximately 30°

a. Estimate the angle of elevation of the stairs.
b. Measure the rise and run of several steps. rise: 7; run: 12
c. Find the slope of the line going up the stairs. $\frac{7}{12}$
d. Calculate the angle of elevation of the stairs.
e. Find the tangent of the angle of elevation. $0.58\overline{3}$, or $\frac{7}{12}$

9. APPLICATION The grade of a road is a percent calculated from the ratio

$$\frac{vertical\ distance\ traveled}{horizontal\ distance\ traveled}$$

The road in the sketch below has a 5% grade.

A sextant is a tool used to measure the angle of elevation of the Sun or a star, thereby allowing one to determine latitude on Earth's surface. Here, Richard Byrd (1888–1957) checks his sextant before a historical 1926 flight over the North Pole. Learn how to use a sextant with the links at **www.keymath.com/DA** .

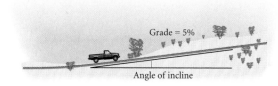

Grade = 5%

Angle of incline

a. Find the angle of incline of the road. @ approximately 2.86°
b. A very steep street has a grade of 15%. If you drive 1000 feet on this street, how much has your elevation changed? @ about 148 ft

Exercise 10 There are several ways to find the areas. Encourage students to share their methods. For 10b, students might find the altitude of the triangle by drawing a median from the 30° angle and then determining its length.

10. Find the area of each figure to the nearest 0.1 cm².

a.

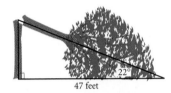

5 cm

68.7 cm²

b.

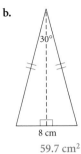

30°

8 cm

59.7 cm²

11. A tree is struck by lightning and breaks as shown. The tip of the tree touches the ground 47 feet from the stump and makes a 22° angle with the ground.

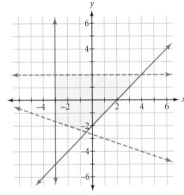

22°

47 feet

a. How high is the part of the trunk that is still standing?   approximately 19 ft

b. How long is the portion of the tree that is bent over?   approximately 51 ft

c. How tall was the tree originally? @   approximately 70 ft

▶ Review

Exercise 12 If you did not cover systems of inequalities in Chapter 5, do not assign this exercise.

5.7 **12.** Write the system of inequalities whose solution is shown here.

$$\begin{cases} y < 2 \\ x \geq -3 \\ y > -\dfrac{8}{3} - \dfrac{1}{3}x \\ y \geq -2 + x \end{cases}$$

9.3 **13.** Give the equation in general form for a parabola with vertex $(1, -6)$ and x-intercepts -1 and 3. @ $y = 1.5x^2 - 3x - 4.5$

Yοu began this chapter by exploring relationships between algebra and geometry. You used **analytic geometry** and **inductive reasoning** to discover properties related to the slopes of **parallel** and **perpendicular lines.** You also used analytic geometry to find the **midpoint** of a segment. And you learned the difference between **inductive** and **deductive reasoning.**

Then you explored area and side relationships for squares drawn on graph paper. You learned how to draw segments whose lengths are equal to many different square roots. You also found ways to rewrite radical expressions.

You discovered the **Pythagorean Theorem,** an important relationship between the lengths of the **legs** and **hypotenuse** of a **right triangle.** This relationship is useful in many professions and has been valuable to many civilizations for thousands of years. You used analytic geometry and the Pythagorean Theorem to find a formula for the distance between any two points.

Finally, you reviewed ratio and proportion, and you learned that **similar** figures have corresponding angles that are equal and corresponding side lengths that are proportional. Similar right triangles introduced you to **trigonometric functions—sine, cosine,** and **tangent.** For an **acute angle** in a right triangle, these functions are defined by ratios between the **opposite leg, adjacent leg,** and **hypotenuse.**

EXERCISES

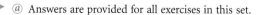

@ Answers are provided for all exercises in this set.

1. Rewrite each expression with as few square root symbols as possible.

   a. $4\sqrt{5} + 4\sqrt{5}$ $8\sqrt{5}$ **b.** $10\sqrt{17} - 6\sqrt{17}$ $4\sqrt{17}$ **c.** $138\sqrt{3} + 21\sqrt{3} - 36\sqrt{3}$ $123\sqrt{3}$

   d. $\sqrt{5} \cdot \sqrt{3}$ $\sqrt{15}$ **e.** $4\sqrt{5} \cdot 4\sqrt{5}$ 80 **f.** $\left(10\sqrt{17}\right)^2$ 1700

   g. $\sqrt{6} \cdot \sqrt{15}$ $3\sqrt{10}$ **h.** $4\sqrt{25} \cdot 4\sqrt{5}$ $80\sqrt{5}$ **i.** $\sqrt{2} + \sqrt{3}$ $\sqrt{2} + \sqrt{3}$

   j. $\sqrt{2} + \sqrt{8}$ $3\sqrt{2}$ **k.** $\dfrac{\sqrt{18}}{\sqrt{3}}$ $\sqrt{6}$ **l.** $\sqrt{3} + \sqrt{27}$ $4\sqrt{3}$

2. Find the area of the tilted square at right. Use two different strategies to check your answer.

3. Use analytic geometry and deductive reasoning to show that the sides of the square in Exercise 2 are perpendicular. What are the hypothesis and conclusion?

4. Explain how to draw a square with a side length of $\sqrt{29}$ units.

PLANNING

LESSON OUTLINE

One day:

  5 min   Introduction

 15 min   Exercises and helping individuals

 15 min   Checking work and helping individuals

 15 min   Student self-assessment

REVIEWING

Direct students' attention to Lesson 11.1, Exercise 7. Ask which pairs of sides, if any, are parallel or perpendicular. Have students find the lengths of all four sides and the diagonals. (Because the two parallel bases are perpendicular to one of the legs, you can review the Pythagorean Theorem to find the lengths of the diagonals.) Ask if the diagonals intersect at their midpoints. You can also ask students to find the angle measures, which they can find using inverse trigonometric ratios.

ASSIGNING HOMEWORK

If students can complete Exercises 6–9 on their own, they will have a good understanding of the chapter.

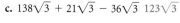

▶ **Helping with the Exercises**

Exercise 1 Decimal approximations may be used to check the exact answers in radical form.

2. The area is 5 square units. Here are two possible strategies:

i. Draw a square around the tilted square using the grid lines. Subtract the area of the outer triangles from the area of the larger square: $9 - 4(1) = 5$.

ii. Find the length of the side between $(1, 0)$ and $(3, 1)$: $\sqrt{(3-1)^2 + (1-0)^2} = \sqrt{5}$. Square the side length to find the area: $\left(\sqrt{5}\right)^2 = 5$.

3. The slopes of the sides are $\frac{1}{2}$, -2, $\frac{1}{2}$, and -2. The slopes of each pair of adjacent sides are opposite reciprocals, so the sides are perpendicular. Answers will vary. Possible hypothesis: The given figure is a square. Possible conclusion: Its sides are perpendicular.

4. Possible answer: Draw a 7-by-7 square on graph paper and remove triangles with areas of 5 square units (legs 2 units and 5 units) from each corner. The area of the remaining square is $49 - 4 \cdot 5$, or 29 square units.

Exercise 5 This procedure in construction is sometimes called "squaring up."

5. Possible answer: Sides of length 5 ft, 12 ft, and 13 ft satisfy the Pythagorean Theorem and form a right triangle. Side lengths of 10 ft, 24 ft, and 26 ft, which sum to 60 ft, also form a right triangle. Stretch 10 ft of the rope along one wall and 24 ft of the rope along the adjacent wall; the remaining 26 ft of rope should exactly fit along the hypotenuse if the foundation corners are right angles.

6b. slope of $\overline{AB}$: $\frac{3}{4}$;

slope of $\overline{BC}$: $-\frac{4}{3}$;

slope of $\overline{CD}$: $\frac{3}{4}$;

slope of $\overline{AD}$: $-\frac{4}{3}$

6c. It is a rectangle; the product of the slopes of adjacent sides is -1, so each pair of adjacent sides is perpendicular.

6d.

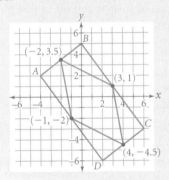

6e. Each side length is $\sqrt{31.25}$ units, or approximately 5.59 units.

8a. sample answer:

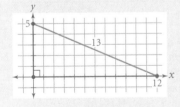

---

5. APPLICATION Is a triangle with side lengths 5 ft, 12 ft, and 13 ft a right triangle? Explain how you know. Then explain how a construction worker could use a 60 ft piece of rope to make sure that the corners of a building foundation are right angles.

6. Draw this quadrilateral on graph paper.
   a. Name the coordinates of the vertices of this quadrilateral. $A(-4, 2), B(0, 5), C(6, -3), D(2, -6)$
   b. Find the slope of each side.
   c. What kind of quadrilateral is this? Explain how you know.
   d. Find the coordinates of the midpoint of each side. Mark the midpoints on your drawing. Connect the midpoints in order.
   e. Use the distance formula to find the lengths of each side of the figure formed by connecting the midpoints in 6d.
   f. Find the slope of each side of the figure formed in 6d. The slopes are $-0.5, -5.5, -0.5,$ and $-5.5.$
   g. What kind of figure is formed in 6d? Explain how you know. It is a rhombus; the sides are all the same length and opposite sides have equal slope, so they are parallel.

7. Find the approximate lengths of the legs of this right triangle.

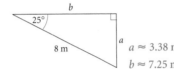

$a \approx 3.38$ m
$b \approx 7.25$ m

8. You will need a straightedge and a protractor for this exercise.
   a. Carefully draw a right triangle with side lengths 5, 12, and 13 units on graph paper.
   b. Measure the angle opposite the 5-unit side. approximately 23°
   c. Find the measure of the angle opposite the 5-unit side using $\sin^{-1}$, $\cos^{-1}$, and $\tan^{-1}$. $\sin^{-1}\left(\frac{5}{13}\right) \approx 23°, \cos^{-1}\left(\frac{12}{13}\right) \approx 23°,$ and $\tan^{-1}\left(\frac{5}{12}\right) \approx 23°$
   d. Explain how you can find the measure of the angle opposite the 12-unit side. What is the measure of this angle? Possible answer: Subtract 23° from 90°; approximately 67°.

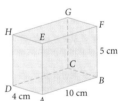

9. A rectangular box has the dimensions shown in the diagram at right. $\sqrt{116}$ cm, or approximately 10.77 cm
   a. What is the length of the diagonal $\overline{AC}$?
   b. What is the length of the diagonal $\overline{AG}$? $\sqrt{141}$ cm, or approximately 11.87 cm

10. *Mini-Investigation* If the sides of a triangle are enlarged by a factor of k, then its area is enlarged by a factor of k^2. Check that this is true using an example. Then explain why it will be true for any triangle.

Exercise 9 This is the third diagonal exercise of this sort in the student text. You may encourage students to extend the Pythagorean Theorem to three dimensions: $a^2 + b^2 + c^2 = d^2$, or $d = \sqrt{a^2 + b^2 + c^2}$.

10. Possible answer: If a triangle has base 8 cm and height 4 cm, its area is 16 cm². If the triangle is enlarged by a factor of 3, its base will be 24 cm, its height will be 12 cm, and its area will be 144 cm², which equals $3^2 \cdot 16$ cm³. For any triangle, the area is given by $A = \frac{1}{2}bh$. If the sides are enlarged by a factor of k, the area is enlarged by k^2: $A = \frac{1}{2}(kb)(kh)$, or $A = \frac{1}{2}bh \cdot k^2$.

MIXED REVIEW

▶ **11.** This table gives the normal minimum and maximum January temperatures for
4.6 18 U.S. cities.

January Temperatures Across the United States

City	Minimum temp. (°F)	Maximum temp. (°F)	City	Minimum temp. (°F)	Maximum temp. (°F)
Mobile, AL	40	61	Helena, MT	10	31
Little Rock, AK	31	49	Atlantic City, NJ	23	41
Denver, CO	15	43	New York, NY	26	38
Jacksonville, FL	42	64	Cleveland, OH	19	33
Honolulu, HI	66	80	Pittsburgh, PA	20	35
Indianapolis, IN	19	35	Rapid City, SD	11	34
New Orleans, LA	43	62	Houston, TX	41	62
Boston, MA	22	37	Richmond, VA	28	45
Minneapolis, MN	4	22	Lander, WY	9	32

(National Climatic Data Center, in *The World Almanac and Book of Facts 2004*, p. 697) [Data sets: JTMIN, JTMAX]

a. Let x represent the normal minimum temperature, and let y represent the normal maximum temperature. Use the Q-point method to find an equation for a line of fit for the data. $y = 61 + 1.08(x - 40)$ or $y = 34 + 1.08(x - 15)$

b. The normal minimum January temperature for Memphis, Tennessee, is 31°F. Use your equation to predict the normal maximum January temperature. approximately 51°F

c. The normal maximum January temperature for Charleston, South Carolina, is 59°F. Use your equation to predict the normal minimum January temperature. approximately 38°F

5.3 **12.** The HealthyFood Market sells dried fruit by the pound. Jan bought 3 pounds of dried apricots and 1.5 pounds of dried papaya for $13.74. Yoshi bought 2 pounds of dried apricots and 3 pounds of dried papaya for $16.32.

a. Write a system of equations to represent this situation.

b. How much does a pound of dried apricots cost? How much does a pound of dried papaya cost?   apricots: $2.79; papaya: $3.58

10.5 **13.** The integers -3 to 16, inclusive, are written on cards and put in a hat. The cards are then drawn from the hat without looking.

a. What is the probability of drawing 0 on the first draw? $P(0) = \frac{1}{20}$, or 0.05

b. What is the probability of drawing a number less than 0 on the first draw? $P(\text{less than zero}) = \frac{3}{20}$, or 0.15

c. What is the probability of drawing an odd number three times in a row, if you replace the card after each draw? $\frac{1}{8}$, or 0.125

d. What is the probability of drawing an odd number three times in a row, if you do not replace the card after each draw? $\frac{2}{19}$, or about 0.105

14a. Inverse variation. Possible explanation: The product of x and y is constant; $xy = 2$ or $y = \frac{2}{x}$.

14b. Neither. Possible explanation: The product is not constant, so it is not an inverse variation. The y-value for $x = 0$ is not 0, so it is not a direct variation.

14c. Direct variation. Possible explanation: The ratio of y to x is constant; $y = 0.25x$.

14d. Neither. Possible explanation: The graph is not a curve, so the relationship is not an inverse variation. The line does not pass through the origin, so it is not a direct variation.

14e. Inverse variation. Possible explanation: The product of the x- and y-coordinates for any point on the curve is 8; $xy = 8$ or $y = \frac{8}{x}$.

14f. Direct variation. Possible explanation: The graph is a straight line through the origin; $y = 1.5x$.

15a. Possible answer: For $0 < x < 3$, f is nonlinear and increasing at a slower and slower rate. For $3 < x < 5$, f is linear and decreasing. For $5 < x < 7$, f is linear and increasing. For $7 < x < 9$, f is linear and constant (neither increasing nor decreasing). For $9 < x < 12$, f is nonlinear and decreasing at a slower and slower rate.

17b. five-number summary: 82, 99, 105, 112, 179

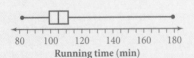

2.5 **14.** Tell whether the relationship between x and y is direct variation, inverse variation, or neither, and explain how you know. If the relationship is direct or inverse variation, write its equation.

a.

x	y
0.2	10
0.8	2.5
1	2
4	0.5
5	0.4

b.

x	y
0.3	6
0	3
1	13
3	33
10.0	103

c.

x	y
0.8	0.2
1	0.25
3	0.75
12	3
28.0	7

d.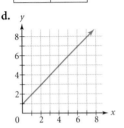

e.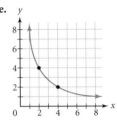

f.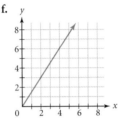

7.3 **15.** Here is a graph of a function f.

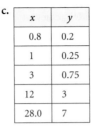

  a. Use words such as *linear, nonlinear, increasing,* and *decreasing* to describe the behavior of the function.

  b. What is the range of this function? $0 \le y \le 5$

  c. What is $f(3)$?   3

  d. For what x-values does $f(x) = 2$?   1, 5, 12

  e. For what x-values does $f(x) = 5$? $7 \le x \le 9$

6.6 **16.** Use the properties of exponents to rewrite each expression. Your answers should have only positive exponents.

  a. $\left(3x^2y\right)^3$ $27x^6y^3$ **b.** $\dfrac{5^2p^7q^3}{5p^3q}$ $5p^4q^2$ **c.** $x^{-4}y^{-2}x^5$ $\dfrac{x}{y^2}$ **d.** $m^2\left(n^{-4} + m^{-6}\right)$ $\dfrac{m^2}{n^4} + \dfrac{1}{m^4}$

1.4 **17.** Here are the running times in minutes of 22 movies in the new-release section of a video store.

  120   116   93   108   134   90   112   99   93   104   110

  105   97   115   100   82   102   105   104   105   112   179

  a. Find the mean, median, and mode of the data.   mean: 108.4; median: 105; mode: 105

  b. Find the five-number summary of the data and create a box plot.

  c. Create a histogram of the data. Use an appropriate bin width.

  d. Make at least three observations about the data based on your results from 17a–c.
Sample answers: (1) About 75% of the new releases have running times of 112 min or less. (2) None of the new releases have running times between 140 and 169 min. (3) Most of the running times are between 90 and 119 min.

17c. Bin widths may vary.

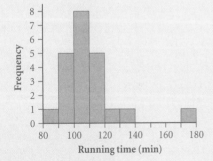

9.4 **18.** Write the equation for this parabola in

    a. Factored form. $y = (x + 3)(x - 1)$

    b. Vertex form. $y = (x + 1)^2 - 4$

    c. General form. $y = x^2 + 2x - 3$

6.5 **19.** **APPLICATION** Six years ago, Maya's grandfather gave her his baseball card collection. Since then, the value of the collection has increased by 8% each year. The collection is now worth $1,900.

    a. How much was the collection worth when Maya first received it? approximately $1,197

    b. If the value of the collection continues to grow at the same rate, how much will it be worth 10 years from now? approximately $4,102

7.6 **20.** If $f(x) = x^2 + |x| - 4$, find

    a. $f(-5)$ 26   **b.** $f(2)$ 2   **c.** $f(-7) - f(4)$ 36

    d. $f(-7 - 4)$ 128   **e.** $-3 \cdot f(3)$ -24

2.1 **21.** **APPLICATION** The Galaxy of Shoes store is having a 22nd anniversary sale. Everything in the store is reduced by 22%.

    a. Anita buys a pair of steel-toed boots originally priced at $79.99. What is the discounted price of the boots? $62.39

    b. The sales tax on Anita's boots is 5%. What total price will Anita pay for the boots? $65.51

8.4 **22.** The image of the black rectangle after a transformation is shown in red.

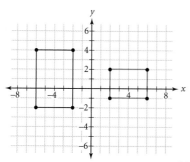

    a. Describe the transformation.   possible answer: a reflection across the y-axis and a vertical shrink by a factor of 0.5

    b. Define the coordinates of any point in the image using (x, y) as the coordinates of any point in the original figure. $(-x, 0.5y)$

Exercise 22 Students might see this as a translation right and a vertical shrink, described by $(x + 8, 0.5y)$.

9.4 **23.** Solve for x.

    a. $0 = (x + 5)(x - 2)$ $x = -5$ or $x = 2$

    b. $0 = x^2 + 8x + 16$ $x = -4$

    c. $x^2 - 5x = 2x + 30$ $x = -3$ or $x = 10$

    d. $x^2 = 5$ $x = \pm\sqrt{5}$

8.4 **24.** Give the equation for each graph, written as transformations of a parent function.

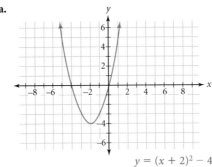

a.

$y = (x + 2)^2 - 4$

b.

$y = -0.5\,|x + 3|$

3.4 **25.** APPLICATION Zoe Kovalesky visits companies and teaches the employees how to use their computers and software. She charges a fixed fee to visit a company, plus an amount for each employee in the training class. This table shows the number of employees trained and the total bill for the last five companies she visited.

Computer Training

Employees trained	Total bill ($)
5	400
11	610
17	820
3	330
25	1100

    a. How much does Zoe charge for each employee in a training class? $35

    b. What fixed fee does Zoe charge to visit a company? $225

    c. Write a recursive routine to find the total bill for any number of employees. $\{0, 225\}$ `ENTER` ; $\{\text{Ans}(1) + 1, \text{Ans}(2) + 35\}$ `ENTER` , `ENTER` , ...

    d. Write an equation to calculate the total bill, y, for any number of employees, x. $y = 225 + 35x$

    e. ACME, Inc., has hired Zoe to train 12 employees. How much will the total bill be? $645

    f. Last week, Zoe taught a training class at the Widget Company. The total bill was $505. How many employees were in the class? 8

11.2 **26.** The vertices of $\triangle ABC$ are $A(-6, 1)$, $B(2, 7)$, and $C(10, 1)$. Do 26a–d before you graph the triangle.

    a. Find the length and slope of each side.

    b. What kind of triangle is $\triangle ABC$? Explain how you know. Isosceles triangle; two sides have equal length.

    c. Find the midpoint of $\overline{AC}$ and call it D. $D(2, 1)$

    d. If points B and D are connected, they form $\overline{BD}$. That creates two triangles. What kind of triangles are $\triangle ABD$ and $\triangle BCD$? Explain how you know.

    e. Draw $\triangle ABC$ on graph paper and draw $\overline{BD}$. Does your drawing support your results from 26a–d?

Exercise 26 Some students may conjecture that the triangle has a right angle, but though the slopes of $\overline{AB}$ and $\overline{BC}$ are opposite, they are not reciprocals.

26a.

Segment	Length	Slope
$\overline{AB}$	10	$\dfrac{3}{4}$
$\overline{BC}$	10	$-\dfrac{3}{4}$
$\overline{AC}$	16	0

26d. Right triangles. Possible explanation: $\overline{BD}$ has an undefined slope, so it is vertical; $\overline{AC}$ has slope 0, so it is horizontal.

26e. A drawing should confirm 26a–d.

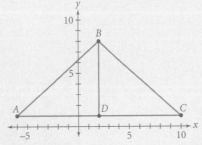

TAKE ANOTHER LOOK

You have seen that the Pythagorean Theorem, $a^2 + b^2 = c^2$, holds true for right triangles. What about triangles that don't have a right angle? Is there a relationship between the side lengths of any triangle?

If a triangle is not a right triangle, you can classify it as one of two other types of triangles, based on its angles. An **acute triangle** has three angles that are all acute. An **obtuse triangle** has one angle that is obtuse.

Use a straightedge and protractor to draw an acute triangle. Label the longest side c, and label the shorter sides a and b. Find the square of the length of each side and compare them. Does the relationship $a^2 + b^2 = c^2$ still hold true? If not, state an equation or inequality that does hold true.

Make a conjecture about the squares of the side lengths for an obtuse triangle. Then draw an obtuse triangle and measure the sides. What relationship do you find this time?

Summarize your results.

You can learn how trigonometry is used in acute and obtuse triangles with the Internet links at www.keymath.com/DA .

Assessing What You've Learned

UPDATE YOUR PORTFOLIO Geometry is the study of points, lines, angles, and shapes, so you have drawn and graphed a lot of figures for this chapter. Choose several pieces of work that illustrate what you have learned, and show how you can use algebra and geometry together. For each piece of work, make a cover sheet that gives the objective, the result, and what you might have done differently.

ORGANIZE YOUR NOTEBOOK Make sure your notebook contains notes and examples of analytic geometry. Your notes should give you quick reference to important concepts like the slope of parallel and perpendicular lines, the Pythagorean Theorem, finding a midpoint of a segment, and finding the distance between two points. In your math class next year you may be studying more advanced concepts of geometry, so your notes can help you in the future too.

PERFORMANCE ASSESSMENT Show a classmate, a family member, or your teacher that you understand how analytic geometry combines algebra and geometry. Show both the geometric and algebraic methods of finding the midpoint of a segment or the distance between two points. Compare and contrast the geometric method and the algebraic method. Explain which method you prefer and why. You may also want to show a geometric proof of the Pythagorean Theorem and the algebraic formula that results.

▶ Take Another Look

The Pythagorean relationship doesn't hold for sides opposite and adjacent to nonright angles in triangles, but students can find inequalities by measurement. If c is opposite an angle with measure less than 90° (an acute angle), then c^2 is less than $a^2 + b^2$. If c is opposite an angle with measure more than 90° (an obtuse angle), then c^2 is greater than $a^2 + b^2$.

You may want to mention that the difference between $a^2 + b^2$ and c^2 is actually $2ab\cos C$. This relationship is called the *Law of Cosines.* When $\angle C$ is acute, this difference is positive, so c^2 is less than $a^2 + b^2$. When $\angle C$ is obtuse, you're subtracting a negative number from $a^2 + b^2$ to get a larger c^2. **[Link]** Students will see why the Law of Cosines holds when they study advanced algebra.

ASSESSING

Use the form of written assessment you have found best for your class. For your end-of-year written assessment, you can use the unit exam or final exam from Assessment Resources. You might choose to use some of the Constructive Assessment items for a take-home final exam. Combine your written assessment with portfolios, projects, and other performance assessments.

FACILITATING SELF-ASSESSMENT

To help students complete the portfolio described in Assessing What You've Learned, suggest that they consider for evaluation their work on Lesson 11.1, Exercise 15; Lesson 11.2, Exercise 9; Lesson 11.3, Exercise 5 or 9; Lesson 11.4, Exercise 10; Lesson 11.5, Exercise 12, 15, or 16; Lesson 11.6, Exercise 8; Lesson 11.7, Exercise 7; and Lesson 11.8, Exercise 8 or 10.

Selected Hints and Answers

This section contains hints and answers for exercises marked with ⓗ or ⓐ in each set of Exercises.

LESSON 0.1

1a. $\frac{1}{8}$; $\frac{1}{16} + \frac{1}{16}$ or $2 \times \frac{1}{16}$

1d. $\frac{7}{625}$; $\frac{1}{625} + \frac{1}{625} + \frac{1}{625} + \frac{1}{625} + \frac{1}{625} + \frac{1}{625} + \frac{1}{625}$ or $7 \times \frac{1}{625}$

2a. $\frac{1}{4} + \frac{1}{16} = \frac{5}{16}$ **2c.** $9 \times \frac{1}{81} = \frac{1}{9}$

3a.

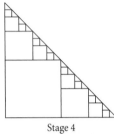

Stage 4

3b. *Hint:* The length of the side of the square is half the length of the base. The area of a triangle is $\frac{1}{2}b \cdot h$, or $\frac{1}{2}b^2$, because $b = h$ in this case.

3c. 48

5b. *Hint:* The smallest triangle shown is $\frac{1}{64}$. Shade only triangles that are $\frac{1}{16}$ of the area.

8a. $8 \div 4 = 2$ **8b.** $8 \times \frac{1}{4} = 2$

8c. Essentially, they are the same.

8d. $8 \times \frac{3}{4} = 6$

11a. $\frac{1}{4} \times \frac{1}{4} \times 32 = \frac{32}{16} = 2$

12. *Hint:* Draw a picture.

LESSON 0.2

1a. 5^4

2a. $3 \times 3 \times 3 \times 3$; $3 \cdot 3 \cdot 3 \cdot 3$; $3(3)(3)(3)$

3a. 3^3

6a. 25 or 5^2

7c. 8^2; 8^3

8a. 10

8d. *Hint:* Look at the number of branches in each stage.

12b. $\frac{29}{64}$

LESSON 0.3

1b. $\frac{25}{9}$; 2.78

5a. *Hint:* For Stage 1, the length is the total number of segments, 5, times the length of each segment, $\frac{1}{4}$. Continue this pattern recursively.

11a. 4

LESSON 0.4

5b. Subtract the number with the smaller absolute value from the number with the larger absolute value. The sign of the answer is the sign of the number with the larger absolute value.

6a. In the first recursion, he should get $-0.2 \cdot 2 = -0.4$, not $+0.4$. His arithmetic when evaluating $0.4 - 4$ was correct. In the second recursion, he used the wrong value (-3.6 instead of -4.4) because of his previous error. His arithmetic was also incorrect, because $-0.2 \cdot -3.6 = +0.72$, not -0.72. His arithmetic when evaluating $-0.72 - 4$ was correct.

7a.

Starting value	2	-1	10
First recursion	-1.8	-2.1	-1
Second recursion	-2.18	-2.21	-2.1
Third recursion	-2.218	-2.221	-2.21
⋮			

7b. yes; about -2.222

8c. The result is $\frac{1}{3}$. The value $\frac{1}{3}$ is a fixed point for this expression.

9a. i. 12

9b. When the coefficient of the box is 0.5, the attractor value is twice the constant. In general the attractor value is $\dfrac{\textit{constant term}}{1 - \textit{coefficient of the box}}$.

12b. 0.2   **12d.** 3

LESSON 0.5

1a. 8.0 cm

5d. The resulting figure should slightly resemble a right-angle Sierpiński triangle.

6c. *Hint:* When you run the calculator program, select 4=SQUARE, then enter 2/3 as your fraction.

7a. This game fills the entire square.

10a. i. 2

10b. The attractor is two-thirds of the constant.

1a. iii   **1b.** v   **1c.** ii

1d. iv   **1e.** i

2a. 72   **2b.** 290   **2c.** -10

2d. 312   **2e.** $2.1\bar{6}$ **2f.** -34

3a. $\frac{1}{3} \times \frac{1}{3} \times \frac{1}{3}$

3b. $\frac{2}{3} \times \frac{2}{3} \times \frac{2}{3} \times \frac{2}{3}$

3c. 1.2×1.2

3d. $16 \times 16 \times 16 \times 16 \times 16$

3e. $2 \times 2 \times 2 \times 2 \times 2 \times 2 \times 2$

4a. $\frac{1}{16} + \frac{1}{16} + \frac{1}{16} = \frac{3}{16}$

4b. $\frac{1}{9} + \frac{1}{9} + \frac{1}{81} + \frac{1}{81} = \frac{20}{81}$

4c. $\frac{1}{4} + \frac{1}{16} + \frac{1}{64} + \frac{1}{64} = \frac{11}{32}$

5a.

Stage 3

A branch is added at the midpoint of each of the newest segments, with half the length, at a 45° clockwise rotation.

5b.

Stage 3

A "bottomless" equilateral triangle is built on the "right" half of segments.

5c.

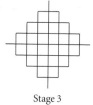

Stage 3

Each new segment is crossed at its midpoint by a centered perpendicular segment of equal length.

5d.

Stage 3

Each unshaded square is divided horizontally and vertically to create four congruent squares; the bottom-right square is shaded.

6a. See below.   **6b.** $\left(\frac{7}{5}\right)^{20} \approx 836.68$

7. The attractor is 5.

LESSON 1.1

1. *Hint:* Begin by ordering the numbers from least to greatest.

4a. Travel Time to School

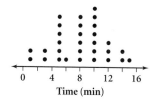

Time (min)

6a. (*Chapter 0 Review*)

Stage number	Total length		
	Multiplication form	Exponent form	Decimal form
0	1	1	1
1	$7 \cdot \left(\frac{1}{5}\right)$	$7^1 \cdot \left(\frac{1}{5}\right)^1 = \left(\frac{7}{5}\right)^1 = \frac{7}{5}$	1.4
2	$7 \cdot 7 \cdot \left(\frac{1}{5}\right) \cdot \left(\frac{1}{5}\right)$	$7^2 \cdot \left(\frac{1}{5}\right)^2 = \left(\frac{7}{5}\right)^2 = \frac{49}{25}$	1.96

4c. *Hint:* Multiply each time value by the number of students.

6d. i

8. a bar graph; because the information falls into categories, is not numerical data, and cannot be scaled on a number line

9a. possible answer: Jonesville's Varsity Basketball Team

11d. −1

12a. 18;

Doubles of 225	450	900	1800	3600	7200
Doubles of 1	2	4	8	16	32

LESSON 1.2

1a. mean and median: 6; mode: 5

1c. mean: 10.25; median: 9; no mode

4a. mean: 262.2 ft; median: 215 ft

7. *Hint:* $\dfrac{53 + 53 + 53 + x + x}{5} = 50$

10a. Multiply the mean by 10; together they weigh approximately 15,274 lb.

10b. Five of the fish caught weigh 1449 lb or less, and five weigh 1449 lb or more.

11a. *Hint:* The data set has five values, with the middle value equal to 12.

12b. mean: 32.65; median: 30; mode: 28

12c. The median is probably best; the mean is distorted by one extremely high value.

13a. A dot plot may be most appropriate for the numeric data. However, if each value was translated into years (divide by 12), you could make a bar graph or pictograph with ages as categories.

LESSON 1.3

1a. 5, 10, 23, 37, 50

1c. 14, 22.5, 26, 41, 47

2b. i. 0, 1, 1.5, 3, 7; ii. 64, 75, 80, 86, 93

5a. Quartiles are the boundaries dividing a data set into four groups, or quarters, with the same number of values.

5b. the range

6b. 23 points

8a. For men, the mean salary is $639.56, and the five-number summary is 342, 495, 629, 718.5, 1001; for women, the mean salary is approximately $466.69, and the five-number summary is 288, 353, 445, 563.5, 708.

Median Weekly Earnings, 2000

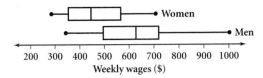

9a. 35 ft

9b. More information is needed. The length is between 11 and 17.5 ft.

9e. No; the units of these data sets are different.

9f. about 47 mi/h

12a. 76 million

12c. $10\frac{1}{2}$ pawprints

LESSON 1.4

1a. *Hint:* Find the sum of the bin heights.

1c. none

3a. 76

3b. Approximately $\frac{1}{4}$ of the countries had a life expectancy between approximately 69 yr and 74 yr.

5b. Ring Finger Length

```
6 | 0  5  5
7 | 0  0  0  5
8 | 5
```

Key

```
6 | 0 means 6.0 cm
```

6a. 240,000 cars

6b. Two models sold between 80,000 and 119,999 cars, inclusive.

6c. [0, 480000, 40000, 0, 9, 1]

6e. An approximate five-number summary is 115000, 131000, 157000, 241000, 434000. The actual five-number summary is 115428, 130650, 157278.5, 240712, 434145.

7a. The bin heights should be about the same, with about 16 or 17 in each of six bins.

8a. *Hint:* The median, Q1, and Q2 are all equal to 7.

8d. *Hint:* The minimum and Q1 are the same value. The maximum and Q3 are the same value.

10a. $1.50

11a. Hospital A's histogram is mounded toward the left. Hospital B's histogram is mounded toward the right. Hospital C's histogram has all bins of equal height. Hospital D's histogram is mounded in the middle.

12a. Ida weighed the apples from the market, which are more uniform in weight, and Mac weighed the backyard apples, whose weights vary more widely.

1.

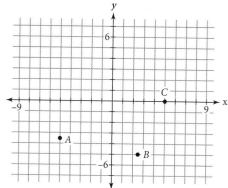

4a. about 2 m

4b. about 5 s

4c. about 2.7 m

4d. between 0 and 1 s, and between 4.5 and 5.5 s

7a. approximate answers (the second coordinates are in millions): (1984, 280), (1985, 320), (1986, 340), (1987, 415), (1988, 450), (1989, 445), (1990, 440), (1991, 360), (1992, 370), (1993, 340), (1994, 345), (1995, 275), (1996, 225), (1997, 175), (1998, 160), (1999, 125), (2000, 75), (2001, 45), (2002, 30), (2003, 15)

8a.   Average Miles per Gallon
       for All U.S. Automobiles

Year	Years elapsed	mpg
1960	0	14.3
1970	10	13.5
1980	20	15.9
1990	30	20.2
1995	35	21.1
1996	36	21.2
1997	37	21.5
1998	38	21.6
1999	39	21.4
2000	40	21.9
2001	41	22.1

(U.S. Department of Transportation, *www.dot.gov*) [Data set: **AMPG**]

8d. 19.5 mpg

10a. 8:06   **10c.** 12 min

1b. $y = x$

3. *Hint:* Plot the points and compare them to the line where *actual temperature = estimated temperature.*

6a. (12, 16)   **6b.** (18, 13)

6d.   **Estimated Prices vs. Actual Prices**

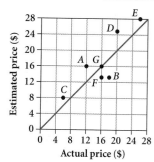

9b. These states also have high verbal scores. The verbal scores are not as high as the math scores.

10a. about 1 m/s, because the distances in meters are about equal to the times in seconds

10b. between 0.5 and 1.0, between 2.5 and 3.0, between 3.5 and 4.0, between 4.0 and 4.5

10d. between 0 and 0.5, between 3.0 and 3.5

11a. Answers will vary. The mean of the values is 125.0 cm, and the median is 125.3 cm.

11c. It means that this measurement is accurate within 0.2 cm.

11d. Answers will vary. The range of measures is 123.3 to 126.5. This could be written 124.9 ± 1.6 cm.

12a. {1, 3, 3, 3, 4, 5, 6}

1. Randall Cunningham threw 19 touchdown passes in 1992.

3. 3 × 4

5. $\begin{bmatrix} 788 & 489 & 35 & 19 \\ 809 & 492 & 53 & 21 \\ 919 & 590 & 61 & 19 \end{bmatrix}$ This matrix gives the totals from the two years.

9b. $\begin{bmatrix} -3 & 4 & -2.5 \\ 2 & -6 & -4 \end{bmatrix}$ **9d.** $\begin{bmatrix} 4 & -2.5 & 2.25 \\ -3 & 4.75 & 2.5 \end{bmatrix}$

12a. Quantity: $\begin{bmatrix} 74 & 25 & 37 \\ 32 & 38 & 16 \\ 120 & 52 & 34 \end{bmatrix}$; profit: $\begin{bmatrix} 0.90 \\ 1.25 \\ 2.15 \end{bmatrix}$;

the number of columns in the quantity matrix must be the same as the number of rows in the profit matrix.

13. *Hint:* Range = Maximum − Minimum

Selected Hints and Answers

1a. Mean: 41.5; divide the sum of the numbers by 14. Median: 40; list the numbers in ascending order and find the mean of the two middle numbers. Mode: 36; find the most frequently occurring number.

1b. 27, 36, 40, 46, 58

Battery Life

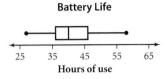

Hours of use

2. possible answer: {9, 11, 14, 16, 19, 21, 22}

3a.

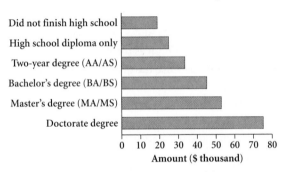

Mean Annual Wages, 1998

3b. greatest jump: from a master's degree to a doctorate; smallest difference: from not finishing high school to a high school diploma

4a.

2003 NCAA Women's Tournament Top Scorers

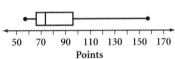

Points

4b. 157 points (Diana Taurasi)

4c. Choices will vary; mean: 83.9; median: 73.5; modes: 66, 74.

5a. Mean: approximately 154; median: 121; there is no mode.

5b. Bin widths may vary.

Pages Read in Current Book

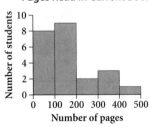

Number of pages

Pages Read in Current Book

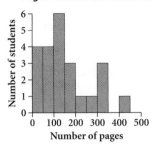

5c. Pages Read in Current Book

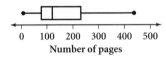

Number of pages

5d. Possible answer: Most of the students questioned had read fewer than 200 pages, with a fairly even distribution between 0 and 200.

6a.

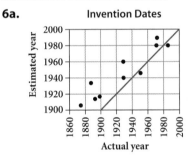

Invention Dates

6b. (1952, 1945), (1985, 1980)

6c. $y = x$, where x represents actual year and y represents estimated year

7a. $\begin{bmatrix} 5.00 & 8.00 \\ 3.50 & 4.75 \\ 3.50 & 4.00 \end{bmatrix}$, $\begin{bmatrix} 0.50 & 0.75 \\ 0.50 & 0.25 \\ 0.50 & 0.25 \end{bmatrix}$, $\begin{bmatrix} 43 & 81 & 37 \end{bmatrix}$

7b. $[A] + [B] = \begin{bmatrix} 5.50 & 8.75 \\ 4.00 & 5.00 \\ 4.00 & 4.25 \end{bmatrix}$

7c. $[C] \cdot ([A] + [B]) = [708.5 \quad 938.5]$; matinee: $708.50, evening: $938.50

8a. between points A and B

8b. Kayo was not moving; perhaps she was resting.

8c. Possible answer: Kayo started out jogging fast but had to rest for a few minutes. Then she jogged much slower until she had to rest again. She finally got the energy to jog all the way home at a steady pace without stopping.

9a. 2,900,000   **9b.** See below.

9c.   The Ten Most Populated
          U.S. Cities, 2000

```
0 | 95
1 | 14 19 22 32 52 95
2 | 90
3 | 69
4 |
5 |
6 |
7 |
8 | 01
```

Key
```
2 | 90  means 2.90 million
```

9d.   The Ten Most Populated
               U.S. Cities, 2000

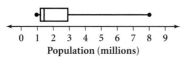

Population (millions)

9e. The bar graph helps show how each city compares
with the others, because they remain identified by
name. The stem plot shows distribution but also shows
actual values. The box plot shows distribution and a
clustering between 1 and 1.4 million but does not show
individual city names or populations.

10a. 416.875 min   **10b.** 425 min

10c. 480 min

CHAPTER 2 • CHAPTER **2** CHAPTER 2 • CHAPTER

LESSON 2.1

2a. $\dfrac{9}{14}$ **2c.** $\dfrac{4}{3}$

3. *Hint:* To write a rate like 9.6 miles per gallon as a
fraction, separate the units. "Per" and "of every" indicate
division. So 9.6 miles per gallon can be written $\frac{9.6\ \text{miles}}{1\ \text{gallon}}$.

3a. $\dfrac{240\ \text{mi}}{1\ \text{h}}$

3b. $\dfrac{10\ \text{parts capsaicin}}{1{,}000{,}000\ \text{parts water}}$, or $\dfrac{1\ \text{part capsaicin}}{100{,}000\ \text{parts water}}$

3c. $\dfrac{350\ \text{women-owned firms}}{1000\ \text{firms}}$, or
$\dfrac{7\ \text{women-owned firms}}{20\ \text{firms}}$

4a. 30   **4c.** 16

5a. *Hint:* Multiply by 30 to undo the division.

5c. $S = 73.5$

6a. *Hint:* Solve the proportion $\frac{1.5}{4} = \frac{55}{x}$.

7a. $\frac{5}{2} = \frac{25}{10}, \frac{2}{10} = \frac{5}{25}, \frac{25}{5} = \frac{10}{2}$

8b. *Hint:* Solve the proportion $\frac{85}{100} = \frac{x}{7.38}$.

9. $\frac{1}{8} = \frac{3000}{P}$; $P = 24{,}000$

11a. 3 carbon, 6 hydrogen, 1 oxygen

11b. You will need 3(470), or 1410 atoms of carbon
and 6(470), or 2820 atoms of hydrogen.

11c. 500 molecules; use all the hydrogen atoms,
1500 atoms of carbon, and 500 atoms of oxygen.

LESSON 2.2

1a. 32% of what number is 24?

2a. $\dfrac{80}{d} = \dfrac{125}{100}$

4a. *Hint:* Solve the proportion $\frac{5}{75} = \frac{250}{x}$.

5a. Marie should win over half the games.

5b. $\dfrac{28\ \text{games won by Marie}}{28 + 19\ \text{total games}} = \dfrac{M}{12}$;

$M = 7.15$ or 7 games

5c. $\dfrac{19}{47} = \dfrac{30}{G}$; $G \approx 74$ games

9b. $\dfrac{5}{8}$

10b. 8

10c. younger than 42, 44, 45, 66, 67, and older
than 69

9b. (*Chapter 1 Review*)

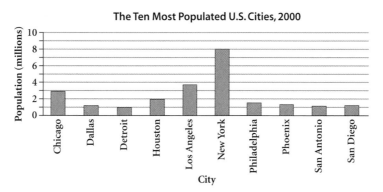

The Ten Most Populated U.S. Cities, 2000

1a. $x = 49.4$

2. *Hint:* First find the total number of seconds in 3 minutes 53.43 seconds.

3a. *Hint:* Multiply: $\dfrac{50\,\text{m}}{1\,\text{s}} \cdot \dfrac{1\,\text{km}}{1000\,\text{m}} \cdot \dfrac{60\,\text{s}}{1\,\text{min}} \cdot \dfrac{60\,\text{min}}{1\,\text{h}}$.

4a. 227 g   **4b.** 1.76 oz

5a. 159 cm   **5c.** 4.72 in.

6a. $\dfrac{3\,\text{lb}}{30\,\text{days}} = 0.1$ lb per day

6c. *Hint:* Find a common denominator and compare ratios.

7b. 90 m

10a. fifteen 12 oz cans to make 960 oz

10c. $\dfrac{\text{number of ounces of concentrate}}{\text{number of ounces of lemonade}} = \dfrac{12}{64}$

12. If the profits are divided in proportion to the number of students in the clubs, the Math Club would get $288, leaving $192 for the Chess Club.

1a. 40

2a. 88

3. The first missing value in the table is 2.8.

4a. Divide by 3.5 to undo the multiplication; $x = 4$.

6b. *Hint:* The cost of corn at Market A can be described by the equation $y = 0.179x$.

7b. $y = 2.2x$ **7c.** 2.95 kg   **7d.** 7920 lb

7e. $100\,\text{lb} = 45.\overline{45}\,\text{kg}$; $100\,\text{kg} = 220\,\text{lb}$

8a. *Hint:* Evaluate the ratio $\frac{150}{93}$.

10a. *Hint:* Solve the proportion $\frac{3\,\text{mi}}{1.5\,\text{h}} = \frac{x}{1\,\text{h}}$.

10e. 2 mi/h; this represents the constant walking speed.

10f. $d = 2t$, where d is distance traveled in miles and t is travel time in hours.

11a. $D = 5t$, where D is the distance traveled in inches and t is the time elapsed in minutes.

11d. 163.2 min, or 2.72 h

12a. 81.25 mi/h

14a. $2.49 per box, 42¢ per bar, $2.99 per box, 25¢ per ounce

14c. 1.495 oz per bar

1a. $y = \dfrac{15}{x}$

2a. *Hint:* Solve $4 = \frac{k}{3}$ for k, then substitute $(4, y)$ and k into $y = \frac{k}{x}$.

5a. 3 h

6a. inverse variation; $y = \dfrac{24}{x}$ or $xy = 24$

7a. $62.\overline{3}$ N, 93.5 N, and 187 N

8a. *Hint:* Solve $65 \cdot 4 = 2.5 \cdot x$.

9b. $15 \cdot M = 20 \cdot 7$; $M \approx 9.3$ kg

10a. The table should include points such as $(100, 100)$, $(200, 50)$, $(250, 40)$, $(400, 25)$.

10b. $y = \dfrac{10,000}{x}$

10c. The graph should stop at $x = 500$ because there are only that many students.

12a. 2 atm   **12c.** 0.1 L

1. 6 Across: $143/42$

1. 10 Down: $40 \cdot 529$

3a. First multiply 16 by 4.5, then add 9.

5a. See bottom of page 661.

5b. At Stages 6 and 7; the original number has been subtracted.

5d. $\dfrac{2(n-3)+4}{2} - n + 4$ or $-3\left[\dfrac{2(n-3)+4}{2} - n\right]$

6a. See bottom of page 661.

1d. 35   **1g.** -19

2a. Subtract 32.

4b. 5

7a. 3

7b. Start with 3 and see if you get the answer 3.

7d. The final result is always the original number no matter what number you choose.

10a. -2.6 **10d.** 75

12a. *Hint:* Substitute $t = 60$.

16a. $1\frac{11}{12}$ cups   **16b.** $13.05

1a. $n = 8.75$

1b. $w = 84.6$

1c. $k = 5\frac{1}{6}$, or $5.1\overline{6}$

2. possible answers:

$\dfrac{7\,bh}{5\,h} = \dfrac{30\,bh}{x\,h}$; $\dfrac{7\,bh}{30\,bh} = \dfrac{5\,h}{x\,h}$; $\dfrac{5\,h}{7\,bh} = \dfrac{x\,h}{30\,bh}$; $\dfrac{30\,bh}{7\,bh} = \dfrac{x\,h}{5\,h}$

3a. Possible points include $(2, 1)$, $(3, 1.5)$, $(4, 2)$, $(5, 2.5)$, $(6, 3)$, $(7, 3.5)$, $(8, 4)$.

3b. All points appear to lie on a line.

Selected Hints and Answers

4a. 75 ft   **4b.** 0.52 ft/mo

5. 1365 shih rice; 169 shih millet

6a. If x represents the weight in kilograms and y represents weight in pounds, one equation is $y = 2.2x$ where 2.2 is the data set's mean ratio of pounds to kilograms.

6b. about 13.6 kg   **6c.** 55 lb

7a. about 7.5 cm

7b. approximately 17 days

7c. $H = 1.5 \cdot D$, where H represents height in centimeters and D represents time in days

8a. Because the product of the x- and y-values is approximately constant, it is an inverse relationship.

8b. One possibility: $y = \frac{45.5}{x}$; the constant 45.5 is the mean of the products.

8c. $y = \frac{45.5}{32}, y \approx 1.4$

9a. directly; $d = 50t$

9b. directly; $d = 1v$, or $d = v$

9c. inversely; $100 = vt$, or $t = \frac{100}{v}$

10a. 2.1875 L   **10b.** $2.\overline{3}$ atm

10c. $y = \frac{1.75}{x}$

5a. (*Lesson 2.7*)

Stage	Picture	Description
1	n	Pick a number.
2	n −1 −1 −1	Subtract 3.
3	n n −1 −1 −1 −1 −1 −1	Multiply your result by 2.
4	n n −1 −1	Add 4.
5	n −1	Divide by 2.
6	−1	Subtract the original number.
7	+1 +1 +1	Add 4 or multiply by −3.

6a. (*Lesson 2.7*)

Description	Jack's sequence	Nina's sequence
Pick the starting number.	5	3
Multiply by 2.	10	6
Multiply by 3.	30	18
Add 6.	36	24
Divide by 3.	12	8
Subtract your original number.	7	5
Subtract your original number again.	2	2

10d.

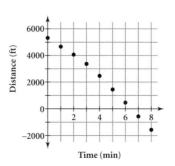

11a. Start with a number. Double it. Subtract 1. Multiply by 3. Add 1.

11b. $x; 2x; 2x - 1; 3(2x - 1); 3(2x - 1) + 1$

11c. $4.5, 9, 8, 24, 25$ **11d.** The starting value is 4.

12. Start with 1. Add 4, to get 5. Multiply by -3, to get -15. Add 12, to get -3. Divide by 6, to get -0.5. Add 5, to get 4.5.

13.

Equation: $\dfrac{12 - 3(x + 4)}{6} + 5 = 4$		
Description	Undo	Result
Pick x.	//////	2
$+ (4)$	$- (4)$	6
$\cdot (-3)$	$/ (-3)$	$- 18$
$+ (12)$	$- (12)$	$- 6$
$/ (6)$	$\cdot (6)$	$- 1$
$+ (5)$	$- (5)$	4

CHAPTER 3 · CHAPTER **3** CHAPTER 3 · CHAPTER

LESSON 3.1

2a.

Figure number	Perimeter
1	5
2	8
3	11
4	14
5	17

2c. 32

3. $-14.2, -10.5, -6.8, -3.1, 0.6, 4.3$

4a. Start with 3, then apply the rule $\text{Ans} + 6$; 10th term = 57.

4b. Start with 1.7, then apply the rule $\text{Ans} - 0.5$; 10th term = -2.8.

6a. Possible explanation: The smallest square has an area of 1. The next larger white square has an area of 4, which is 3 more than the smallest square. The next larger gray square has an area of 9, which is 5 more than the 4-unit white square.

6b. The recursive routine is 1 (ENTER), $\text{Ans} + 2$ (ENTER), (ENTER), and so on.

6c. 17, the value of the 9th term in the sequence

9a. *Hint:* What do you add to get from -4 to 8? What do you multiply by to get from -4 to 8?

10a. $17 \cdot 7$, or 119   **10b.** 14

10c. Possible answer: There are 14 multiples between 100 and 200. There are also 14 multiples of 7 between 200 and 300, but there are 15 between 300 and 400.

10d. Possible answer: The 4th multiple of 7 is $4 \cdot 7$, or 28; the 5th multiple of 7 is $5 \cdot 7$, or 35; and so on. Recursively, you start with 7 and then continue adding 7.

12a. Press 1 (ENTER), $\text{Ans} \cdot 3$ (ENTER), (ENTER) ...; the 9th term is 6561.

12b. Press 5 (ENTER), $\text{Ans} \cdot (-1)$ (ENTER), (ENTER) ...; the 123rd term is 5.

LESSON 3.2

2a. $\{0.5, 1, 1.5, 2, 2.5, 3\}; 0.5, \text{Ans} + 0.5$

2b. $\{4, 3, 2, 1, 0\}; 4, \text{Ans} - 1$

4d. In 4a, the y-coordinates increase by 7. In 4b, the y-coordinates decrease by 6.

7a. Possible answer: $\{1, 1.38\}$ (ENTER), $\{\text{Ans}(1) + 1, \text{Ans}(2) + 0.36\}$ (ENTER), (ENTER),.... The recursive routine keeps track of time and cost for each minute. Apply the routine until you get $\{7, 3.54\}$. A 7 min call costs \$3.54.

9a. *Hint:* The perimeters of the pentagon tile arrangements for 1–10 tiles are 5, 8, 11, 14, 17, 20, 23, 26, 29, 32.

9f. *Hint:* Can you arrange a design with 1.5 tiles?

10a. Answers will vary. The graph starts at $(0, 5280)$. The points $(0, 5280)$, $(1, 4680)$, $(2, 4080)$, and $(3, 3480)$ will appear to lie on a line. From $(3, 3480)$ to $(8, -1520)$, the points will appear to lie on a steeper line. The bicyclist ends up 1520 ft past you.

10b.

12a. $\dfrac{9(C + 40)}{5} - 40$

12b. Add 40, multiply by 5, divide by 9, then subtract 40.

LESSON 3.3
---

1. $\{0, 4.0\}$ and $\{\text{Ans}(1) + 1, \text{Ans}(2) - 0.4\}$

3. Start at the 0.8 m mark and walk away from the sensor at a constant rate of 0.2 m/s.

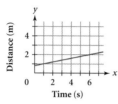

4a. The walker starts 2.5 m away from the motion sensor and walks toward it very slowly at a rate of 1 m in 6 s.

5a. The walker starts 6 m away from the motion sensor and walks toward it at a rate of 0.2 m/s for 6 s.

7. *Hint:* Convert 1 mi/h to ft/s.

8b. away; the distance is increasing

8d. *Hint:* Divide the distance Carol traveled by 4 seconds. Include units in your answer.

8e. $\dfrac{5.5 \text{ m}}{0.6 \text{ m/s}} = 9.1\overline{6}$ s, or approximately 9 s

8f. The graph is a straight line.

10a. The rate is negative, so the line slopes down to the right.

11a. ii

13a. Not possible; the walker would have to be at more than one distance from the sensor at the 3 s mark.

14b. $x = \dfrac{22}{9}$, or $2.\overline{4}$

15a. *Hint:* To find the total number of days, calculate $2 \cdot 365 + 2 \cdot 30.4 + 2$.

16a. *Hint:* Consumption rate is best measured in gallons/mile.

LESSON 3.4

1a. ii

2a. $t \approx 0.18$ h

2c. 24 represents the initial number of miles the driver is from his or her destination.

4a. $x \approx 7.267$

6a. *Hint:* For calories burned per minute, find the common difference between consecutive Y_1 entries.

6b. 400 (ENTER) , Ans + 20.7 (ENTER)

6d. 700 (ENTER) , Ans + 0 (ENTER)

6e. $Y_2 = 700 + 0x$ or $Y_2 = 700$

8a. $s = 5 + 9.8t$ or $s = 9.8t + 5$

8c. 8 s

8d. It doesn't account for air resistance and terminal speed.

9a. *Hint:* The coefficient of x is 0.12.

11a. $\dfrac{8}{n} = \dfrac{15}{100}$, $n \approx 53.3$

14b.

Time (s)	Distance (m)
1	14
2	28
3	42
4	56
5	70
6	84
7	98
8	112
9	126
10	140

15a. The expression equals -4.

Ans $- 8$	-3
Ans $\cdot 4$	-12
Ans/3	-4

15b. $y = 14$

LESSON 3.5

1a.

Input x	Output y
20	100
-30	-25
16	90
15	87.5
-12.5	18.75

2b. $w = 15°\text{F}$

2c. The wind chill temperature changes by 1.4° for each 1° change in actual temperature.

3a. The rate is negative, so the line goes from the upper left to the lower right.

5a. i. 3.5

5b. *Hint:* For table iii, use the rate of change to work backward from the data pair (2, 20.2) to (0, ?).

5b. i. −6   **5c.** i. $y = -6 + 3.5x$

5d. i.

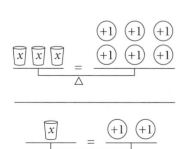

6a. The input variable x is the temperature in °F, and the output variable y is the wind chill in °F.

6b. The rate of change is 1.4°. For every 10° increase in temperature, there is a 14° increase in wind chill.

6c. $y = -28 + 1.4x$

7a. *Hint:* To find the rate of change, calculate $\frac{3 - 3.5}{2 - 0}$ or $\frac{2 - 3}{6 - 2}$.

9a. 990 square units

9b. possible answers: $33x = 990$; $x = \frac{990}{33}$

9c. 30 units

13a. *Hint:* Find the total number of yards in 72 lengths, then convert to feet. How does this compare to the number of feet in a mile, 5280?

14a. $y = 6 + 1.25x$

1a. $2x = 6$

3a. $0.1x + 12 - 12 = 2.2 - 12$

$$0.1x = -9.8$$
$$x = -98$$

5a. $-\dfrac{1}{5}$

6a. $\dfrac{1}{12}$

10a.
$$3 + 2x = 17$$
$$3 - 3 + 2x = 17 - 3$$
$$2x = 14$$
$$\frac{2x}{2} = \frac{14}{2}$$
$$x = 7$$

10e.
$$\frac{4 + 0.01x}{6.2} - 6.2 = 0$$
$$\frac{4 + 0.01x}{6.2} - 6.2 + 6.2 = 0 + 6.2$$
$$\frac{4 + 0.01x}{6.2} = 6.2$$
$$\frac{4 + 0.01x}{6.2} \cdot 6.2 = 6.2 \cdot 6.2$$
$$4 + 0.01x = 38.44$$
$$4 - 4 + 0.01x = 38.44 - 4$$
$$0.01x = 34.44$$
$$\frac{0.01x}{0.01} = \frac{34.44}{0.01}$$
$$x = 3444$$

12a. (*Lesson 3.6*)

Picture	Action taken	Equation
	Original equation.	$2 + 4x = x + 8$
	Subtract $1x$ from both sides.	$2 + 3x = 8$
	Subtract 2 from both sides.	$3x = 6$
	Divide both sides by 3.	$x = 2$

11a. $r = \dfrac{C}{2\pi}$ **11c.** $l = \dfrac{P}{2} - w$

12a. See bottom of page 664.

13. *Hint:* Solve the proportion $\dfrac{90}{2.25} = \dfrac{x}{3}$.

CHAPTER 3 REVIEW

1a. $x = -7$

1b. $x = -23.4$

2a. 1; 3; add 1; $y = 3 + x$

2b. 0.01; 0; add 0.01; $y = 0.01x$

2c. 2; 5; add 2; $y = 5 + 2x$

2d. $-\dfrac{1}{2}$; 3; subtract $\dfrac{1}{2}$; $y = 3 - \dfrac{1}{2}x$

3a. iii   **3b.** i   **3c.** ii

4a. $y = -68.99$ **4b.** $y = 4289.83$

4c. $y = 0.14032$ **4d.** $y = 238{,}723$

5a. $y = x$ **5b.** $y = -3 + x$

5c. $y = -4.3 + 2.3x$ **5d.** $y = 1$

6a. 0 represents no bookcases sold; -850 represents fixed overhead, such as start-up costs; Ans(1) represents the previously calculated number of bookcases sold; Ans(1) + 1 represents the current number of bookcases sold, one more than the previous; Ans(2) represents the profit for the previous number of bookcases; Ans(2) + 70 represents the profit for the current number of bookcases—the company makes $70 more profit for each additional bookcase sold.

6b.

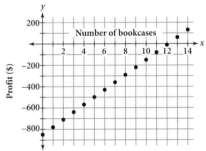

6c. Sample answer: The graph crosses the *x*-axis at approximately 12.1 and is positive after that; the company needs to make at least 13 bookcases to make a profit.

6d. -850, the profit if the company makes zero bookcases, is the *y*-intercept; 70, the amount of additional profit for each additional bookcase, is the rate of change; *y* goes up by $70 each time *x* goes up by one bookcase.

6e. No; partial bookcases cannot be sold.

7a. 3

7b.

Number of sections	1	2	3	4	...	30	...	50
Number of logs	4	7	10	13	...	91	...	151

7c. 4 ⟨ENTER⟩, Ans + 3 ⟨ENTER⟩, ⟨ENTER⟩, ...

7d. 216 m

8a. Let *v* represent the value in dollars and *y* represent the number of years; $v = 5400 - 525y$.

8b. The rate of change is -525; in each additional year, the value of the computer system decreases by $525.

8c. The *y*-intercept is 5400; the original value of the computer system is $5,400.

8d. The *x*-intercept is approximately 10.3; this means that the computer system no longer has value after approximately 10.3 yr.

9a. $50 = 7.7t$ **9b.** $50 = 5 + 6.5t$

$t = \dfrac{50}{7.7} \approx 6.5$ s $t = \dfrac{50 - 5}{6.5} \approx 6.9$ s

9c. Andrei wins; when Andrei finishes, his younger brother is $50 - [5 + 6.5(6.5)] \approx 2.8$ m from the finish line.

10a. $x = 4.5$ **10b.** $x = -4.1\overline{3}$

10c. $x = 0.\overline{6}$ **10d.** $x = 12.8$

10e. $x = 6.\overline{3}$

11a. $L_2 = -5.7 + 2.3 \cdot L_1$

11b. $L_2 = -5 - 8 \cdot L_1$

11c. $L_2 = 12 + 0.5 \cdot L_1$

12a. $y = 1 + \dfrac{1}{2}x$; the output value is half the input value plus 1.

x	y
0	1
1	1.5
2	2
3	2.5
4	3

12b. $y = -x$; the output value is the additive inverse (or opposite) of the input value, or the sum of the input value and the output value is 0.

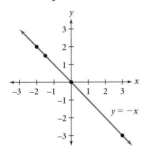

13. No, they won't fit; 210 cm is 6.89 ft.

14a.

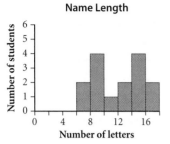

Name Length

14b. 11.6 letters

15a. -54 **15b.** 5 **15c.** 8 **15d.** -18

16a. The starting value is 12; Ans $+ 55$. Possible assumptions: Tom's home is 12 mi closer to Detroit than to Traverse City. He travels at a constant speed. We are measuring highway distance.

16b.

Hours	0	1	2	3	4	5
Distance (mi)	12	67	122	177	232	287

16c. Tom traveled 55 mi each additional hour. The rate of change is 55 mi/h.

17a. approximately 1061 thousand (or 1,0161,000) visitors

17b. 404, 482, 738, 1131, 3379

17c.

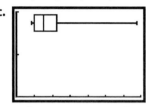

$[0, 3500, 500, 0, 2, 1]$

17d. Yosemite; the number of visitors exceeds 1131 by more than $1.5(1131 - 482)$.

18a. 9 amperes **18b.** 6 ohms

19a. Solution methods will vary; $x = 3.5$.

19b. $2(3.5 - 6) = 2(-2.5) = -5$

20a. $\frac{500}{6} \approx 83.3 \text{ h}$ **20b.** $\frac{500}{0.75 \cdot 6} \approx 111.1 \text{ h}$

CHAPTER 4 · CHAPTER **4** CHAPTER 4 · CHAPTER

LESSON 4.1

1a. 2

2a. $\frac{3}{2}$, or 1.5; one possible point is $(6, 10)$.

3a. $(1, 7), (-1, 1)$

5a. i. The x-values don't change, so the slope is undefined.

5b. i. Using the points $(4, 0)$ and $(4, 3)$, the slope is $\frac{3 - 0}{4 - 4} = \frac{3}{0}$. You can't divide by 0, so the slope is undefined.

5c. i. $x = 4$

7a. Use the slope to move backward from $(40, 16.55)$: $(40 - 10, 16.55 - 0.29 \cdot 10) = (30, 13.65)$, or $\$13.65$ for 30 h; $(30 - 10, 13.75 - 0.29 \cdot 10) = (20, 10.75)$, or $\$10.75$ for 20 h.

7b. Continuing the process in 7a leads to $(0, 4.95)$, or $\$4.95$ for 0 h. This is the flat monthly rate for Hector's Internet service.

8. *Hint:* Find the slope using the given slope triangle.

10b. m/min; the hot-air balloon rises at a rate of 30 m/min.

10d. 254 m

11a. ii. Line 4 is a better choice. Line 3 passes through or is close to a good number of points, but too many points are above this line and too few are below it. Even though line 4 does not intercept any points, it is the better choice because about the same number of points are above the line as below it.

12b. $0.5(18.2)(7.3) = 66.4 \text{ cm}^2$

12d. *Hint:* Subtract the answer to 12a from the answers to 12b and 12c to determine the accuracy component.

14a. $L_2 = 2.5(L_1 + 14); \{27.5, 32.5, 40, 55, 60\}$

14b. $L_3 = \frac{(L_2 - 35)}{2.5}$, or $L_3 = \frac{L_2}{2.5} - 14$

LESSON 4.2

1b. No; although the slope of the line shows the general direction of the data, too many points are below the line.

1d. No; although the same number of points are above the line as below the line, the slope of the line doesn't show the direction of the data.

3a. $y = -2 + \frac{2}{3}x$

4e. A possible equation is $y = 152 + 28x$.

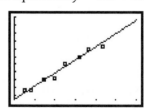

4f. The y-intercept represents the number of quarters Penny's grandmother gave her.

5a. The number of representatives depends on the population.

5b. Let x represent population in millions, and let y represent the number of representatives.

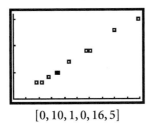

$[0, 10, 1, 0, 16, 5]$

5c. Answers will vary. Two possible points are $(2.8, 4)$ and $(6.1, 9)$. The slope between these points is approximately 1.5. The equation $y = 1.5x$ appears to fit the data with a y-intercept of 0. The slope represents the number of representatives per 1 million people. The y-intercept means that a state with no population would have no representatives.

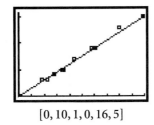

$[0, 10, 1, 0, 16, 5]$

7a. *Hint:* Use the points $(2, 3.4)$ and $(4.5, 4.4)$ to find the slope.

8a. The slope is negative because the distance decreases as the time increases.

8b. The y-intercept represents the start distance for the walk; the x-intercept represents the time elapsed when the walker reaches the detector.

8c. Answers will vary. Quadrant II could indicate walking before you started timing. Quadrant IV could indicate that the walker walks past you; the distances behind you are considered negative.

10a. All lines have a slope of 3; they are all parallel.

11a. neither

11b. inverse variation; $y = \dfrac{100}{x}$

LESSON 4.3

1a. $4; (5, 3)$ **1c.** $-3.47; (7, -2)$

3a. 2   **3b.** $y = -1 + 2(x + 2)$

6. *Hint:* The first of the three equations is $y = 1 + x$.

7b. The slopes are the same; the coordinates of the points are different.

7c. $ABCD$ appears to be a parallelogram because each pair of opposite sides is parallel; the equal slopes in 7b mean that $\overline{AD}$ and $\overline{BC}$ are parallel. $\overline{AB}$ and $\overline{DC}$ are parallel because they both have slope 2.

8b. $\$0.23/oz$; this is the cost per additional ounce after the first.

8e. *Hint:* Think about what the column header for the x-values means. A 3.5 oz letter costs \$1.06 to mail, not \$0.95.

8f. Answers will vary. A continuous line includes points whose x-values are not whole numbers and whose y-values are not possible rates.

10a. $y = 205 + 1.8(x - 1990)$ or $y = 214 + 1.8(x - 1995)$

10b and 10c.

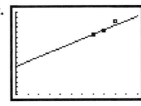

$[1955, 2010, 5, 85, 250, 10]$

The point $(2000, 223)$ is somewhat close to the line, but the predicted value is too low.

10f. *Hint:* Try to adjust the slope value first.

13.

$4x + 3 = 2x + 7$	Original equation.
$4x - 2x + 3 = 2x - 2x + 7$	Subtract $2x$ from both sides.
$2x + 3 = 7$	Combine like terms.
$2x + 3 - 3 = 7 - 3$	Subtract 3 from both sides.
$2x = 4$	Combine like terms.
$\dfrac{2x}{2} = \dfrac{4}{2}$	Divide both sides by 2.
$x = 2$	Reduce.

LESSON 4.4

1a. not equivalent; $-3x - 9$

2b. $y = -15 - 2x$

3b. $-x = 92$; addition property; $x = -92$; multiplication property

5a. *Hint:* Compare the equation to $y = y_1 + b(x - x_1)$. What are the values of x_1 and y_1?

7a. $3(x - 4)$

7b. $-5(x - 4)$

8c. The y_1-value is missing, which means it is zero; $y = 0 + 5(x + 2)$.

8d. $(-2, 0)$; this is the x-intercept.

9a. Equations i and ii are equivalent.

10a. $x = 2$; the point $(2, 0)$ is the x-intercept.

10b. $y = 3$; the point $(0, 3)$ is the y-intercept.

10c.

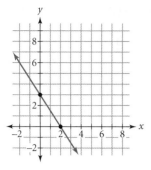

12a. $y = 15.20 + 0.85(x - 20)$

13a. The possible answers are
$y = 568 + 4.6(x - 5)$; $y = 591 + 4.6(x - 10)$;
$y = 614 + 4.6(x - 15)$; $y = 637 + 4.6(x - 20)$.

13c. *Hint:* Use the units in your description of the real-world meaning.

14a. possible answer: $(0, 15)$; $0.45/min

LESSON 4.5

1a. $y = 1 + 2(x - 1)$ or $y = 5 + 2(x - 3)$

2. *Hint:* For the graph in Exercise 1a, you might estimate a y-intercept of -0.5. If you convert the point-slope equation to intercept form, you get $y = -1 + 2x$, so the y-intercept is actually -1.

3a. 3

5a.

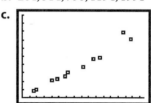

$[10, 45, 5, 40, 120, 20]$

5b. Using the points $(20, 67)$ and $(31.2, 88.6)$, the slope is approximately 1.9 and a possible equation is $y = 67 + 1.9(x - 20)$.

5d. $y = 32 + 1.8(x - 0)$ or $y = 212 + 1.8(x - 100)$

5e. The sample equation in 5b gives $y = 29 + 1.9x$; the equations in 5d both give $y = 32 + 1.8x$.

7d. *Hint:* Subtract the y-intercepts.

8a. $y = 30 + 1.4(x - 67)$

8c. Equations will vary. The graph with a larger y_1-value is parallel but higher, and the graph with a smaller y_1-value is parallel but lower.

9a. *Hint:* Remember that slope is a rate of change. What rate was given in the problem?

10. See below.

LESSON 4.6

1a. 166, 405, 623, 1052, 1483

1b. 204, 514, 756, 1194, 1991

1c.

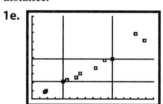

$[0, 1650, 100, 0, 2500, 250]$

1d. The slope will be positive because as the flying distance increases so does the driving distance.

1e.

Q-points: $(405, 514)$, $(1052, 1194)$

1g. approximately 1054 mi

3a. $(5, 4)$, $(10, 9)$

---

10. (*Lesson 4.5*)

Description	Undo	Equation
Pick y.	/////	$y =$
$+ 1$	$- 1$	
$\cdot (-3)$	$/ (-3)$	
$+ 2x$	$- 2x$	

$y = \dfrac{12 - 2x}{-3} - 1$, or $y = -5 + \dfrac{2x}{3}$

$y + 1 = \dfrac{12 - 2x}{-3}$, or $y + 1 = -4 + \dfrac{2x}{3}$

$-3(y + 1) = 12 - 2x$

$2x - 3(y + 1) = 12$

4b.

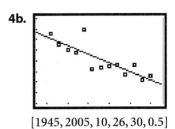

[1945, 2005, 10, 26, 30, 0.5]

5. *Hint:* Separate the coordinates of one point and use each part to make a new point. The point with the smaller x should have the larger y.

7a. $y = 1.3 + 0.625(x - 4)$ or $y = 6.3 + 0.625(x - 12)$

7b. The elevator is rising at a rate of 0.625 s per floor.

7c. 36.3 s after 2:00, or at approximately 2:00:36

7d. almost at the 74th floor

10a. Start with 370, then use the rule Ans $- 54$.

Time (h)	Distance from Mt. Rushmore (mi)
0	370
1	316
2	262
3	208
4	154
5	100
6	46

11. *Hint:* Look at the ratio of cost to size.

LESSON 4.7

2a. $x = 10$

3a. $y = \dfrac{18 - 2x}{5}$, or $y = 3.6 - 0.4x$

4a. Let x represent years, and let y represent distance in meters. The Q-points are (1964, 61.00) and (1992, 68.82). The slope of the line through these points is about 0.28, so the equation is $y = 61.00 + 0.28(x - 1964)$ or $y = 68.82 + 0.28(x - 1992)$. The slope, 0.28, means that the winning distance increases an average of 0.28 m, or 28 cm, each year. The y-intercept, -489 m, is meaningless in this situation because it would indicate that a negative distance was the winning distance in year 0. The model cannot predict that far out from the data range.

CHAPTER 4 REVIEW
---

1. $x_2 = 4$

2a. slope: -3; y-intercept: -4

2b. slope: 2; y-intercept: 7

2c. slope: 3.8; y-intercept: -2.4

3. Line a has slope -1, y-intercept 1, and equation $y = 1 - x$. Line b has slope 2, y-intercept -2, and equation $y = -2 + 2x$.

4a. $y = 13.6x - 25{,}709$ **4b.** $y = -37 - 5.2(x - 10)$

5a. $(-4.5, -3.5)$ **5b.** $y = 2x + 5.5$

5c. $y = 2(x + 2.75)$; the x-intercept is -2.75.

5d. The x-coordinate is 5.5; $y = 16.5 + 2(x - 5.5)$.

5e. Answers will vary. Possible methods are graphing, using a calculator table, and putting all equations in intercept form.

6a. $4 + 2.8 = 51$
$$2.8x = 51 - 4 = 47$$
$$x = \frac{47}{2.8} \approx 16.8$$

6b. $38 - 0.35x = 27$
$$-0.35x = 27 - 38 = -11$$
$$x = \frac{-11}{-0.35} \approx 31.4$$

6c. $11 + 3(x - 8) = 41$
$$3(x - 8) = 41 - 11 = 30$$
$$x - 8 = \frac{30}{3} = 10$$
$$x = 10 + 8 = 18$$

6d. $220 - 12.5(x - 6) = 470$
$$-12.5(x - 6) = 470 - 220 = 250$$
$$x - 6 = \frac{250}{-12.5} = -20$$
$$x = -20 + 6 = -14$$

7a. $y = 12{,}600 - 1{,}350x$

7b. $-1{,}350$; the car's value decreases by \$1,350 each year.

7c. 12,600; Karl paid \$12,600 for the car.

7d. $9\frac{1}{3}$; in $9\frac{1}{3}$ years the car will have no monetary value.

8a. $43 = 30 + 0.375(x - 36)$

8b. $x \approx 71$ s

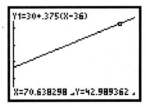

[0, 80, 10, 0, 50, 10]

8c. $x = \dfrac{43 - 30}{0.375} + 36 = 70.\overline{6}$

9a. 1956, 1966, 1980, 1994, 2004; 1.76, 1.875, 1.97, 2.025, 2.06

9b. The Q-points are $(1966, 1.875)$ and $(1994, 2.025)$.

9c. $y = 1.875 + 0.00536(x - 1966)$ or $y = 2.025 + 0.00536(x - 1994)$

9d. Answers will vary. There are more points above the line than below the line.

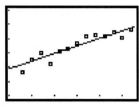

$[1950, 2005, 10, 1.6, 2.2, 0.1]$

9e. Using $y = 1.875 + 0.00536(x - 1966)$, the prediction is 2.12 m.

10a. $y = 2.25 + 0.13(x - 1976.5)$ or $y = 4.025 + 0.13(x - 1990.5)$

10b. The slope means the minimum hourly wage increased approximately \$0.13 per year.

10c. Using the equation $y = 2.25 + 0.13(x - 1976.5)$, the prediction is \$6.61; if the other equation is used, the prediction is \$6.56.

10d. Using either equation from 10a, the prediction is 1967.

11a. In an equation written as $y = a + bx$, b is the slope and a is the y-intercept.

11b. If the points are (x_1, y_1) and (x_2, y_2), then the slope of the line is given by the equation $\frac{y_2 - y_1}{x_2 - x_1} = b$. The equation of the line is $y = y_1 + b(x - x_1)$.

CHAPTER 5 · CHAPTER **5** CHAPTER 5 · CHAPTER

LESSON 5.1

1c. No, because $12.3 \neq 4.5 + 5(2)$; furthermore, the lines are parallel, so the system has no solution.

3a. $(8, 7)$

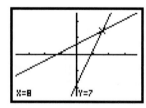

5b. $y = -4 + 0.4x$; $(1, -3.6)$: $2(1) - 5(-3.6) = 20$
The point satisfies both forms of the linear equation.

6a. Let P represent profit in dollars and N represent the number of hits; $P = -12,000 + 2.5N$.

6b. P represents profit, N represents hits. Widget.kom's start-up costs are \$5,000, and its advertisers pay \$1.60 per hit. Because Widget.kom spent less in start-up costs, its website might be less attractive to advertisers, hence the lower rate.

6c. When $N \approx 7778$, $P \approx 7445$ in both equations.

7c. *Hint:* What does it mean if two profit equations have parallel graphs?

8a. $y = 25 + 30x$, where y is tuition for x credits at University College; $y = 15 + 32x$, where y is tuition for x credits at State College

8b. $(5, 175)$; check: $175 = 25 + 30(5)$, $175 = 15 + 32(5)$

8d. When a student takes 5 credit hours, the tuition at either college is \$175.

10d. $\begin{cases} y = 109.2882 - 0.0411x \\ y = 109.289 - 0.0411x \end{cases}$

The graph in 10c appears to show one line; however, the y-values are 0.0008 unit apart. While the two lines are not identical, they are well within the accuracy of the model, so you could say they are the same model.

11c. $a = 2$ and $b = -5$; same slope and y-intercept, lines overlap

14.

$2x + 9 = 6x + 1$	Original equation.
$2x - 2x + 9 = 6x - 2x + 1$	Subtract $2x$ from both sides.
$9 = 4x + 1$	Combine like terms.
$9 - 1 = 4x + 1 - 1$	Subtract 1 from both sides.
$8 = 4x$	Combine like terms.
$\dfrac{8}{4} = \dfrac{4x}{4}$	Divide both sides by 4.
$x = 2$	Reduce.

LESSON 5.2

2. *Hint:* Substitute the point into each equation and check for equality.

3a. $2x + 3x = 4 - 14$
$5x = -10$
$x = -2$

3b. $-2y + y = -3 - 7$
$-y = -10$
$y = 10$

4. *Hint:* Using your calculator with the equations $Y_1 = 25 + 20x$ and $Y_2 = 15 + 32x$, you could check your answer by looking at the intersection point or table values.

5b. $7x - 2(4 - 3x) = 7x - 8 + 6x = 13x - 8$

7a. See below.

7b. The approximate solution, $N \approx 7778$ and $P \approx 7444$, is more meaningful because there cannot be a fractional number of website hits.

9a. $A + C = 200$

9b. $8A + 4C = 1304$

11a. $\begin{cases} d = 35 + 0.8t \\ d = 1.1t \end{cases}$

$1.1t = 35 + 0.8t; \left(116\frac{2}{3}, 128\frac{1}{3}\right)$
The pickup passes the sports car roughly 128 mi from Flint after approximately 117 min.

11d. *Hint:* Write an equation with one distance equal to twice another distance.

12a. women: $y = 71.16 - 0.1715(x - 1976)$ or $y = 67.73 - 0.1715(x - 1996)$; men: $y = 63.44 - 0.142(x - 1976)$ or $y = 60.60 - 0.142(x - 1996)$

12b. $x \approx 2238, y \approx 26.23$

12d. The solution means that in the year 2238 (a little more than 230 years from now), both men and women will swim this race in 26.23 s. This is not likely. The model may be a good fit for the data, but extrapolating that far into the future produces unlikely predictions.

13. 5 lb of sour cherry worms and 15 lb of sour lime bugs

16a. 12.1 ft/s

16b. 50 s

16c. $y = 100 + 12.1x$, where x represents the time in seconds and y represents her height above ground level. To find out how long her ride to the observation deck is, solve the equation $520 = 100 + 12.1x$.

1a. $y = \dfrac{10 - 5x}{2}$, or $y = \dfrac{10}{5} - \dfrac{5x}{2}$

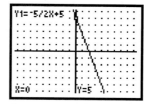

$[-9.4, 9.4, 1, -6.2, 6.2, 1]$

1b. $y = \dfrac{30 - 15x}{6}$, or $y = \dfrac{30}{5} - \dfrac{5x}{2}$

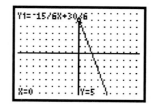

The graph is the same as the graph for 1a. Both equations are equivalent to $y = 5 - \frac{5}{2}x$.

2a. *Hint:* Substitute 6 for x and a for y, then solve for a.

2b. $(-4, -15)$

5a. Multiply the first equation by -5 and the second equation by 3, or multiply the first equation by 5 and the second equation by -3.

6. The solution is $(2, -2)$. You can

(1) solve for y and graph, then look for the point where the lines intersect;
(2) solve for y, create tables, and zoom in to where the y-values are equal;
(3) solve one equation for y (or x) and substitute into the other; or
(4) multiply the equations and add them to eliminate x or y.

8a. $y = -3 + 0.5x$ **8b.** $y = 2 - 0.75x$
8c. $y = 7 - 2x$

8d. The solution of the system is also a solution of the sum of the equations.

7a. (*Lesson 5.2*)

Answers will vary. A sample solution:

$$-12,000 + 2.5N = -5,000 + 1.6N$$ — Set equations equal to each other.
$$-12,000 + 0.9N = -5,000$$ — Subtract $1.6N$ from both sides.
$$0.9N = 7,000$$ — Add 12,000 to both sides.
$$N = \frac{70,000}{9} = 7{,}777\frac{7}{9}$$ — Divide both sides by 0.9.
$$P = -12,000 + 2.5\left(\frac{70,000}{9}\right) = 7{,}444\frac{4}{9}$$

Selected Hints and Answers

9b. $2y = 130, y = 65$

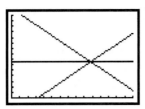

10. *Hint:* The missing equation will be in the form $4x + by = c$.

13a. $\begin{cases} w + p = 10 \\ 3.25w + 10.50p = 61.50 \end{cases}$

14a. Let c represent gallons burned in the city and h represent gallons burned on the highway.
$\begin{cases} c + h = 11 \\ 17c + 25h = 220 \end{cases}$

14b. $(6.875, 4.125)$; 6.875 gal in the city, 4.125 gal on the highway

14c. $\dfrac{17\text{ mi}}{\text{gal}} \cdot 6.875 \text{ gal} \approx 117 \text{ city mi}, \dfrac{25\text{ mi}}{\text{gal}} \cdot$ $4.125 \text{ gal} \approx 103 \text{ hwy mi}$

14d. check: $\begin{cases} 6.875 + 4.125 = 11 \\ 17(6.875) + 25(4.125) = 220 \\ \text{and } 117 + 103 = 220 \end{cases}$

LESSON 5.4

1a. $\begin{cases} 2x + 1.5y = 12.75 \\ -3x + 4y = 9 \end{cases}$

2a. $\begin{bmatrix} 1 & 4 & 3 \\ -1 & 2 & 9 \end{bmatrix}$

3a. $(8.5, 2.8)$

4. *Hint:* Use division to change the first entry to 1.

5a. $\begin{cases} 3x + y = 7 \\ 2x + y = 21 \end{cases}$ **5b.** $\begin{bmatrix} 3 & 1 & 7 \\ 2 & 1 & 21 \end{bmatrix}$

7a.

	Adults	Children	Total (kg)
Monday	40	15	10.8
Tuesday	35	22	12.29

7b. Let x represent the average weight of chips an adult eats and y represent the average weight of chips a child eats. The system is
$\begin{cases} 40x + 15y = 10.8 \\ 35x + 22y = 12.29 \end{cases}$.

9a. *Hint:* The equation for tubas is $5s + 12L = 532$, where s = number of small trucks and L = number of large trucks.

9b. $\begin{bmatrix} 5 & 12 & 532 \\ 7 & 4 & 284 \end{bmatrix}$

11a. $\begin{cases} m + t + w = 286 \\ m - t = 7 \\ t - w = 24 \end{cases}$

11b. $\begin{bmatrix} 1 & 1 & 1 & 286 \\ 1 & -1 & 0 & 7 \\ 0 & 1 & -1 & 24 \end{bmatrix}$

The rows represent each equation. The columns represent the coefficients of each variable and the constants.

13. *Hint:* Find the y-intercept (start value) and rate or change (slope).

15. $\begin{bmatrix} 1 & 3 \\ -2 & 1 \\ 3 & 23 \end{bmatrix} \rightarrow \begin{matrix} 3 & -3 & 0 \\ -6 & -1 \\ 9 & -23 \end{matrix} \rightarrow \begin{matrix} 0 \\ -7 \\ -14 \end{matrix}$
$-7y = -14, y = 2; x = 7$

LESSON 5.5

1a. Multiply by 4; $12 < 28$.

1c. Add -10; $-14 \geq x - 10$.

1e. Divide by 3; $8d < 10\frac{2}{3}$.

2a. Answers will vary, but the values must be > 8.

3a. $x \leq -1$ **3d.** $-2 < x < 1$

4b. $y \geq -2$

6a. $x > 4.34375$, or $\dfrac{139}{32}$

7b. $x < -2$ (number line from -5 to 5, open circle at -2)

8. *Hint:* Will this solution be continuous or discrete?

9a. Add 3 to both sides; $4 < 5$.

11a. The variable x drops out of the inequality, leaving $-3 > 3$, which is never true. So the original inequality is not true for any number x. The graph would be an empty number line, with no points filled in.

13. *Hint:* Consider whether the boundary value makes the statement true. For 13a, if you spend exactly $30, is the statement true?

17a. 0.37 [ENTER]
Ans + 0.23 [ENTER], [ENTER], ...

Weight (oz)	Rate ($)
1	0.37
2	0.60
3	0.83
4	1.06
5	1.29
6	1.52
7	1.75
8	1.98
9	2.21
10	2.44
11	2.67

17b.

Postage Costs

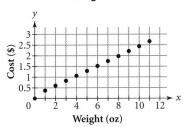

17c. A line would mean that the cost would pass through each amount between the different increments. For example, if a package weighed 0.5 oz, you would pay $0.185. However, the cost increases discretely. To show this, draw segments for each integral ounce. Note the open and closed circles.

Postage Costs

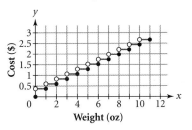

17d. $2.67

LESSON 5.6

1c. i

2a. $y \geq -12x + 10$

3c.

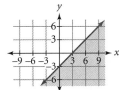

4a–c.

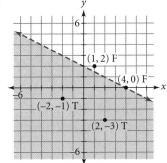

6a.

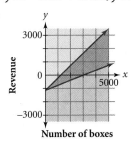

7. *Hint:* First find the equation of the line. Is the line dashed or solid?

7a. $y \leq 1 - 2x$ **7e.** $y \leq 2$

9a.

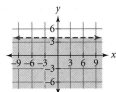

10a. $F + 2S < 84$

10b. $F + 2S = 84$

13. *Hint:* Recall that the distance is equal to the average speed times the time taken.

LESSON 5.7

2a. Yes; $(1, 2)$ satisfies both inequalities.

3a. $y \geq -x + 2; y \geq x - 2$

5. *Hint:* You need three inequalities for this system.

6a. $y \geq -1250 + 0.40x, y \leq -1250 + 1.00x, x \geq 0$

6b.

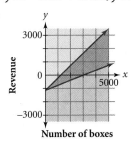

7a. $\begin{cases} A \leq C \\ A + C \leq 75 \\ A \geq 0 \\ C \geq 0 \end{cases}$

8b. $\begin{cases} r \leq 0.90(220 - a) \\ r \geq 0.55(220 - a) \end{cases}$ or $\begin{cases} r \leq 198 - 0.90a \\ r \geq 121 - 0.55a \end{cases}$

8d. $a \geq 14$ and $a \leq 40$

10. *Hint:* The equation for the half-plane below line AB is $y \leq 3 + \frac{2}{3}(x - 2)$.

12. *Hint:* Region 1 is defined by $y \geq 3, y \geq x - 2$, and $y \leq \frac{1}{3}x + \frac{8}{3}$.

13a. $713.15

13b. *Hint:* You don't need to use the 15% for this equation.

CHAPTER 5 REVIEW

1. line *a:* $y = 1 - x$; line *b:* $y = 3 + \frac{5}{2}x$; intersection: $\left(-\frac{4}{7}, \frac{11}{7}\right)$

2. The lines meet at the point $(4, 1)$; the equations $3(4) - 2(1) = 10$ and $(4) + 2(1) = 6$ are both true.

3.

The point of intersection is $(3.75, 4.625)$.

4. See below.

5a. …the slopes are the same but the intercepts are different (the lines are parallel).

5b. …the slopes are the same and the intercepts are the same (the lines coincide).

5c. …the slopes are different (the lines intersect in a single point).

6a. $x > -1$ **6b.** $x < 2$ **6c.** $-2 \le x < 1$

7. $x \le -1$

8. $\begin{cases} y \le x + 4 \\ y \le -1.25x + 8.5 \\ y \ge 1 \end{cases}$

9a. $10\ \mathrm{m^2/min}; 7\ \mathrm{m^2/min}$

9b. No; he will cut $156\ \mathrm{m^2}$, and the lawn measures $396\ \mathrm{m^2}$.

9c. $10h + 7l = 396$ **9d.** $\dfrac{1}{30}\mathrm{L/min}; \dfrac{3}{200}\mathrm{L/min}$

9e. $\dfrac{h}{30} + \dfrac{3l}{200} = 1.2$

9f. $l = 14.4$ min, $h = 29.52$ min; if Harold cuts for 29.52 min at the higher speed and 14.4 min at the lower speed, he will finish Mr. Fleming's lawn and use one full tank of gas.

10. $\begin{bmatrix} 1 & 0 & -3 \\ 0 & 1 & -8 \end{bmatrix}$

CHAPTER 6 · CHAPTER **6** CHAPTER 6 · CHAPTER

LESSON 6.1

1a. starting value: 16; multiplier: 1.25; 7th term: 61.035

3c. $\dfrac{1125}{1000}$, or $\dfrac{112.5}{100}$; $1 + 0.125$

3d. $\dfrac{9,375}{10,000}$, or $\dfrac{93.75}{100}$; $1 - 0.0625$

4b. $1000(1 - 0.18)$, or $1000(0.82)$

4c. $P(1 + r)$

5. *Hint:* To find the constant multiplier, find the ratio of shaded triangles to total triangles in Stage 1.

6a. Start with 20,000, then apply the rule Ans $\cdot (1 - 0.04)$.

6b. 5th term: 16,986.93; $16,982.93 is the selling price of the car after four price reductions.

7a. Start with 7.1, then apply the rule Ans $\cdot (1 + 0.117)$.

9a. 1.7 m

9b. Start with 2, then apply the rule Ans $\cdot 0.85$.

9d. *Hint:* Modify your recursive routine in 9b.

10. *Hint:* $75 + 75(0.02)$ represents an increasing situation that starts with a value of $75 and increases 2% per year.

11a. See below.

12c. *Hint:* The answer is not $7.50.

16a. Let x represent minutes of use and y represent cost; $y = 50$.

16b. $y = 50 + 0.35(x - 500)$

4a. (*Lesson 5 Review*)

$$16 + 4.3(x - 5) = -7 + 4.2x \quad \text{Set the right sides of the two equations equal to each other.}$$
$$16 + 4.3x - 21.5 = -7 + 4.2x \quad \text{Apply the distributive property.}$$
$$-5.5 + 4.3x = -7 + 4.2x \quad \text{Subtract.}$$
$$0.1x = -1.5 \quad \text{Add } -4.2x \text{ and } 5.5 \text{ to both sides.}$$
$$x = -15 \quad \text{Divide both sides by 0.1.}$$
$$y = -7 + 4.2(-15) \quad \text{Substitute } -15 \text{ for } x \text{ to find } y.$$
$$y = -70 \quad \text{Multiply and add.}$$

The solution is $x = -15$ and $y = -70$.

11a. (*Lesson 6.1*)

	Jan	Feb	Mar	Apr	May	June	July	Aug	Sep	Oct	Nov	Dec
Option 1	$50	$25	$25	$25	$25	$25	$25	$25	$25	$25	$25	$25
Option 2	$1	$2	$4	$8	$16	$32	$64	$128	$256	$512	$1,024	$2,048

16d. First plan: $67.50; second plan: $45.00 (she pays only the flat rate of $45.00). She should sign up for the second plan.

16f. The plans cost the same for 800 min of use. A new subscriber who will use more than 800 min should choose the first plan. If she will use 800 min or less, then the second plan is better.

LESSON 6.2

1c. $(1 + 0.12)^4$

2a. $450(1 + 0.2) = 540$ bacteria

5b. $y = 500 \cdot 0.2^x$

8. $100(1 + 0.0175)(1 + 0.0175)(1 + 0.0175) \cdot (1 + 0.0175) = 100(1 + 0.0175)^4$; about $107.19

10c. $2(3)^3$

13a. $y = 5000(1 + 0.05)^x$

13b.
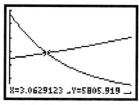
$[0, 10, 1, 0, 12000, 2000]$

The intersection point represents the time and the value of both cars when their value will be the same. By tracing the graph shown, you should see that both cars will be worth approximately $5,800 after a little less than 3 years 1 month.

16a.

Number of steps x	1	2	3	4
Perimeter (cm) y	4	8	12	16

LESSON 6.3

1a. $5x^4$

1d. $-2x^4 - 2x^6$

2b. $(7 \cdot 7 \cdot 7)(7 \cdot 7 \cdot 7 \cdot 7) = 7^7$

5. *Hint:* Student 1 is proposing $(2 \cdot 3)^2$. Student 2 is proposing $2(3^2)$. Does multiplication or exponentiation come first in the order of operations?

10a. 28

12a. $500(1 + 0.015)^6$; $546.72

12b. $46.72

14. *Hint:* a is a constant.

15a. $4.5x - 47$

16b. approximately $(3.095, 0.762)$

LESSON 6.4

1a. 3.4×10^{10}

2a. 74,000

3b. $7y^{16}$

4b. $81y^{12}$

6. 1.674×10^{25}

9a. yes, because they are both equal to 51,800,000,000

9b. Al's answer

9c. possible answer: 518×10^8

9d. Rewrite the digits before the 10 in scientific notation, then use the multiplication property of exponents to add the exponents on the 10's. In this case, $4.325 \times 10^2 \times 10^3 = 4.325 \times 10^5$.

10b. *Hint:* Address why the expression in part ii requires an additional step.

12a. *Hint:* Write a proportion.

14a. 3.8 is the population (in millions) in 1900; 0.017 is the annual growth rate; t is the elapsed time in years since 1900; P is the population (in millions) t years after 1900.

14b. Answers will vary depending on the current year; $0 \le t \le (\text{current year} - 1900)$.

14d. approximately 8.8 million

14e. *Hint:* How many years have passed since 1990? (You may round to the nearest whole year, or give a decimal or fraction value if you wish.) Substitute this value for t.

LESSON 6.5

2a. 7^8 **2c.** $4x^3$

3. *Hint:* Write $\frac{3^6}{3^2}$ using expanded notation, then cancel.

4a. A represents the starting value.

4b. $10,000 = A(1 + 0.1)^{20}$

4c. $10,000 = A(1 + 0.1)^{20}$

$\dfrac{10,000}{(1 + 0.1)^{20}} = A$

$1486.43 \approx A$

The furniture was worth about $1,486 twenty years ago.

5c. $-4x^2$

7a. about 132 people per square mile

8a. 0.25%

9. *Hint:* Recursively work backward from the present by dividing, or create a table for an equation that uses 864 and 3^x.

11a. approximately 61 yr

13. *Hint:* Convert tons to ounces and write a proportion.

15a. *Hint:* Write a proportion for each plant.

LESSON 6.6

1a. $\dfrac{1}{2^3}$

1c. $\dfrac{1.35}{10^4}$

2a. $=$

3a. -5

4a. $45{,}647(1 + 0.028)^0$

4b. the population 12 yr ago

4c. $45{,}647(1 + 0.028)^{-8} \approx 36{,}599$

4d. $\dfrac{45{,}647}{(1 + 0.028)^{12}}; \dfrac{45{,}647}{(1 + 0.028)^8}$

6c. $\dfrac{8x}{3}$

7. *Hint:* This exercise is about inflation, so the constant multiplier is more than 1, but the situation calls for thinking back in time, so the exponent is negative.

9c. false; $\left(10^{-2}\right)^4 = \left(\dfrac{1}{10^2}\right)^4 =$

$\left(\dfrac{1}{10 \cdot 10}\right)\left(\dfrac{1}{10 \cdot 10}\right)\left(\dfrac{1}{10 \cdot 10}\right)\left(\dfrac{1}{10 \cdot 10}\right) = \dfrac{1}{10^8} = 10^{-8}$

10c. *Hint:* Would you use inches, feet, or miles to measure a shoelace?

12a. $1{,}050.63; $1{,}103.81$

12b. $1{,}050; $1{,}102.50$

12c. Possible answer: In the savings account, interest is added at 6 mo, so the interest earns interest. The 1 yr interest is $(1 + 0.025)^2$, or 1.050625; that is more than 5%.

13. *Hint:* A polynomial cannot include a power of x, so $y = x^x + x^2$ is not a polynomial. The equation $y = 3$ *is* a polynomial, because it can be written as $y = 3x^0$, and zero is a nonnegative integer exponent.

LESSON 6.7

1a. $1 + 0.15$; rate of increase: 15%

1c. $1 - 0.24$; rate of decrease: 24%

2a. *Hint:* Is the multiplier more than 1 or less than 1?

3. $B = 250(1 + 0.0425)^t$

4b. $4x^5y^3$

4d. 1

5a. The ratios are 0.957, 0.956, 0.965, 0.964, 0.963, 0.961, 0.959, 0.958, 0.971, and 0.955.

5b. approximately 0.96

5c. $1 - 0.04$

5d. $y = 47(1 - 0.04)^x$

6a. *Hint:* Follow steps similar to those in Exercise 5a–d to help find the equation.

7a. 50%

8a. $y = 2(1 + 0.5)^x$

9a. Possible answer: Let x represent years since 2000 and y represent median price in dollars. An equation is $y = 135{,}500(1 + 0.06)^x$, where 0.06 is derived from the mean ratio of about 1.06.

10. Note 75 above middle C (a D#) would be the highest audible note; note -44 (an E 44 notes below middle C) would be the lowest audible note.

CHAPTER 6 REVIEW

1a. 3^4 **1b.** 3^3 **1c.** 3^2 **1d.** 3^{-1}

1e. 3^{-2} **1f.** 3^0

2a. x^2 **2b.** $\dfrac{2}{x}$ **2c.** $1.23x^5$ **2d.** $\dfrac{1}{3x}$

2e. 3 **2f.** x^7 **2g.** 3^{4x} **2h.** x^2

3a. Possible answer: A $300 microwave depreciates at a rate of 15% per year.

3b. the years (x) for which the depreciating value of the microwave is at least $75

3c. Answers will vary given the context of 3a. $x \le 8$ or $0 \le x \le 8$ (some integers may be excluded by the real-life situation).

4. Answers will vary. Possible answer: $\dfrac{3^x}{3^x} = 3^{x-x} = 3^0$. The result of any number divided by itself is 1.

5a. $y = 200(1 + 0.4)^x$

x	y
0	200
1	280
2	392
3	548.8
4	768.32
5	1075.648
6	1505.9072

5b. $y = 850(1 - 0.15)^x$

x	y
-2	1176.4706
-1	1000.0000
0	850
1	722.5
2	614.125
3	522.00625
4	443.7053

Selected Hints and Answers

6a. $-2{,}400{,}000$

6b. 0.000325

6c. 3.714×10^{10}

6d. 8.011×10^{-8}

7. approximately 1.17×10^0 yr

8. after 24 yr, or in 2028

9a. False; 3 to the power of 3 is not 9; $27x^6$.

9b. False; you can't use the multiplication property of exponents if the bases are different; $9^2 \cdot 8^3$, or 72.

9c. False; the exponent -2 applies only to x; $\frac{2}{x^2}$.

9d. False; the power property of exponents says to multiply exponents; $\frac{x^6}{y^9}$.

10a. Possible answer: $y = 80(1 - 0.17)^x$, where x is the time elapsed in minutes and y is the maximum distance in centimeters; $(1 - 0.17)$ is derived from the mean ratio of approximately 0.83.

10b. approximately 15.0 cm

10c. 15 min

CHAPTER 7 · CHAPTER **7** CHAPTER 7 · CHAPTER

LESSON 7.1

1a. SBOHF

2c. RELATIONSHIP

3a. SECRET CODES

5a. {1:00, 2:00, 3:00, 4:00, 5:00, 6:00, 7:00, 8:00, 9:00, 10:00, 11:00, 12:00} or {1:00 A.M., 1:00 P.M., . . . , 12:00 A.M., 12:00 P.M.}

5b. range: {0100, 0200, 0300, 0400, 0500, 0600, 0700, 0800, 0900, 1000, 1100, 1200, 1300, 1400, 1500, 1600, 1700, 1800, 1900, 2000, 2100, 2200, 2300, 2400}

5c. It is not a function because each standard time designation has two military time designations. If students distinguish A.M. from P.M. times, then it is a function.

7a. $L_1 = \{6, 21, 14, 3, 20, 9, 15, 14, 19\}$
$L_2 = \{15, 30, 23, 12, 29, 18, 24, 23, 28\}$

7b. *Hint:* The letter *A* could be represented by the numbers 1, 27, 53, and so on.

10a. Each input codes to a single output, but each output does not decode to a single input. There are two decoding choices for B.

11a. Domain: $\{0, 1, -1, 2, -2\}$; range: $\{0, 1, 2\}$; the relationship is a function.

13. Yes, it could represent a function even though different inputs have the same output; domain: $\{-2, 0, 1, 3\}$; range: $\{-2, 3\}$.

15a. Subtract the input letter's position from 27 to get the output letter's position.

1a.

Input x	Output y
-4	1
-1	3.4
1.5	5.4
6.4	9.32
9	11.4

4. Answers will vary. In the table, every input value produces exactly one output value. Both graphs in Exercises 2 and 3 pass the vertical line test. Both rules are functions.

5. Sample answer: Start at the 2 m mark and stand still for 2 s. Walk toward the 4 m mark at 2 m/s for 1 s. Stand still for another second. Walk toward the 8 m mark at 4 m/s for 1 s. Then stand still for 3 s. Yes, the graph represents a function.

6c. *Hint:* Notice that the second segment is vertical.

7a. *Hint:* Large cities have multiple ZIP Codes.

7c. No; the same last name will correspond to many different first names.

10. Graphs must pass the vertical line test, have the correct domain and range, and pass through the points $(-2, 3)$ and $(3, -2)$.

12a.

x	2	8	-4	-1	0	5
y	-1	1	-3	-2	$-\frac{5}{3}$	0

The graph is a line. This is a function; each x-value is paired with only one y-value.

13b. domain: $0 \le x \le 360$; range: $-1 \le y \le 1$

14a. *Hint:* The capital letter *A* does not represent a function because it does not pass the vertical line test.

16b. *Hint:* First invert both fractions.

17a. $\left(\dfrac{28}{11}, \dfrac{29}{11}\right) \approx (2.55, 2.64)$

LESSON 7.3

1a.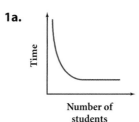

The graph shows an inverse relationship. It is not possible to take 0 hr to decorate, no matter how many students help.

Selected Hints and Answers

2b.

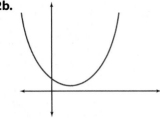

2d.

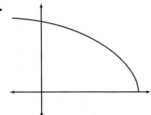

3a. $0 \leq x < 4$

4a.

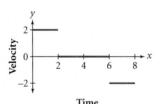

7. *Hint:* Your graph should include three segments.

10a. Erica won in about 13.5 s.

10b. Eileen

10c. They were tied at approximately 3 s, at 5.5 s, from 10 to 10.5 s, and just before the end of the race.

10d. from approximately 0 to 3 s, from 5.5 to 10 s, and from 10.5 to about 13.2 s.

12a. Answers will vary. A sample graph is shown. It should be made up of at least three horizontal segments at heights 0, 2, and -2.

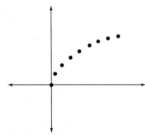

13a. i. moving away　　**13a. ii.** speeding up

LESSON 7.4

1b. $3x + 2 = 2, x = 0; Y_1(0) = 2$

2a. $-2(6) - 5 = -17$

3a. $f(4) = 0$　　　　**3c.** $f(2) = 2, f(5) = 2$

3e. three

4a. The dependent variable, y, is temperature in degrees Fahrenheit; the independent variable, x, is time in hours.

4b. domain: $0 \leq x \leq 24$; range: $5 \leq y \leq 35$

4c. $f(10)$

4d. $f(x) = 10$

5a. $f(x) = 7x + 5$

6. *Hint:* Draw a possible graph of $f(x)$ and use it to look at each situation.

7a. amount of medication in milligrams

7b. time in hours

7c. $0 \leq x \leq 10$; all real numbers x

7d. $53 < y \leq 500, y > 0$

7e. 500

7f. about 4 hr

9a. $f(72) \approx 22.2°C$　　**9c.** $f(x) = 20; x = 68°F$

10a. 6　　　　　　　　　　**10c.** 14

12a. $f(x)$: Independent variable x is time in seconds; dependent variable y is height in meters. $g(x)$: Independent variable x is time in seconds; dependent variable y is velocity in meters per second.

12b. for $f(x)$: domain $0 \leq x \leq 3.2$, range $0 \leq y \leq 50$; for $g(x)$: domain $0 \leq x \leq 3.2$, range $-31 \leq y \leq 0$

12c. Answers will vary. For the graph of $f(x)$, the ball is dropped from an initial height of 50 m. It hits the ground after about 3.2 s. At the moment the ball is dropped, its velocity is 0 m/s. For the graph of $g(x)$, the velocity starts at 0 m/s and changes at a constant rate, becoming more and more negative.

12d. In the 1st second, the ball falls about 5 m, from 50 m at $x = 0$ to about 45 m at $x = 1$.

12f. From the graph of $f(x)$, the ball hits the ground after about 3.2 s. From the graph of $g(x)$, at $x \approx 3.2$ s the velocity is about -31 m/s.

14a. -1

LESSON 7.5

1f. -5

3c. $15 > 9$

4a. 10

4c. 8

7. The solutions are $(2.85, 2.85)$ and $(-2.85, 2.85)$.

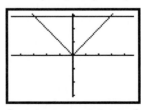

$[-4.7, 4.7, 1, -3.2, 3.2, 1]$

8c. $x = 2$ or $x = -2$

10a. *Hint:* What horizontal line would touch the graph only once?

11a. $g(5) = |5| + 6 = 11$

12b. $-10 \leq x \leq 18$; when $-10 \leq x \leq 18$, the graph of $y = |x - 4| + 3$ is at or below the graph of $y = 17$.

13. *Hint:* You need more than just the range. Compare plots of the data or the set of deviations.

14a. $x = 6$ or $x = -8$

14d. *Hint:* First divide both sides by 3 to isolate the absolute value.

16a. $-1\frac{2}{3} < x$, or $x > -1\frac{2}{3}$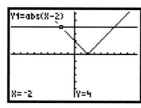

16b. $x \leq -1$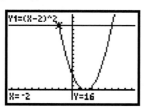

LESSON 7.6

2a. $x = \pm 6$ **2b.** $x = \pm 6$

3b. no real solution

4a. $x = 6$ or $x = -2$

[graph: Y1=abs(X-2), X=-2, Y=4]

$[-9.4, 9.4, 1, -6.2, 6.2, 1]$

4b. $x = 6$ or $x = -2$

[graph: Y1=(X-2)^2, X=-2, Y=16]

$[-9.4, 9.4, 1, -2.2, 18.6, 1]$

6a. $y < 0$

7. $y = |x|$

9c. The sum of the first n positive odd integers is n^2.

11a. sixteen 1-by-1 squares, nine 2-by-2 squares, four 3-by-3 squares, and one 4-by-4 square

12. *Hint:* Why is it impossible for the product of a number multiplied by itself to be negative?

13a. $y = 400(0.75)^x$

14a. $48x^9$

CHAPTER 7 REVIEW

1a. $-2 \leq x \leq 4$

1b. $1 \leq f(x) \leq 3$

1c. 1

1d. -1 and 3

2a. A function; each x-value corresponds to only one y-value.

2b. Not a function; the input $x = 3$ has two different output values, 5 and 7.

2c. A function; each x-value corresponds to only one y-value.

3. The graph is a horizontal line segment at 0.5 m/s.

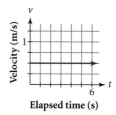

4a. DESCARTES   **4b.** HYPATIA

4c. EUCLID

4d. This code shifts 20 spaces forward, or 6 spaces back, in the alphabet.

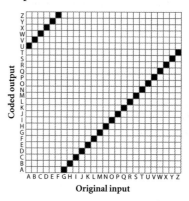

5a. Stories will vary. At the 20 s mark, each girl is moving at the same velocity. Bea's velocity increases steadily in a linear fashion. Caitlin's velocity increases very slowly at first and then becomes faster and faster. Abby's velocity increases very quickly at first and then increases at a slower rate.

5b. No; because Abby starts out moving faster than both Bea and Caitlin, even when she slows down to their speed she stays ahead.

6a. $y = 4.25x + 1.00$

6b.

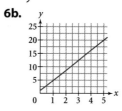

6c. It shifts the graph up 0.50 unit on the y-axis.

6d. $y = 4.25x + 1.50$

7a. Answers will vary. The graph will pass the vertical line test.

7b. Answers will vary. The graph will fail the vertical line test.

8. The domain of the 26 letters is coded to a range of the 13 even-number-positioned letters— {B, D, F, ..., Z}. The code is a function because every original letter is coded to a unique single letter. The rule for decoding is not a function because there are two choices for every letter in the coded message. For example, the letter B could be decoded to either A or N.

9a. $f(-3) = |-3| = 3$ **9b.** $f(2) = |2| = 2$

9c. 10 and -10

10a.

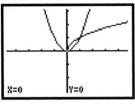

$[-4.7, 4.7, 1, -3.1, 3.1, 1]$

10b. The graph of $y = \sqrt{x}$ looks like half of the graph of $y = x^2$ lying on its side.

10c. The graph of $y = \sqrt{x}$ has only one branch because it gives only positive solutions.

10d. This equation does not represent a function, because a given input can have two different outputs. For example, if $x = 4$, then $y = 2$ or $y = -2$.

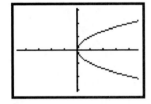

11a. Let t be the number of T-shirts, and let s be the number of sweatshirts.

$t + s = 12$

$6t + 10s = 88$

11b. 8 T-shirts and 4 sweatshirts

12a.   Praying Mantis Length

1	7
2	1 2 6 6
3	4
4	8
5	3 3 3 4 6 6
6	2
7	
8	2
9	4 8
10	
11	
12	1

Key

1 | 7 means 1.7 cm

12b. 10.4 cm

12c. Mean: approximately 5.4 cm; median: 5.3 cm; mode: 5.3 cm. Choice and explanations will vary.

13a. Start with 21, then apply the rule Ans $- 4$; 10th term $= -15$.

13b. Start with -5, then apply the rule Ans $\cdot (-3)$; 10th term $= 98,415$.

13c. Start with 2, then apply the rule Ans $+ 7$; 10th term $= 65$.

14a. $x = 1.875, y = 8.25$

14b. infinitely many solutions

15a. $y = 1.6x$, where x is a measurement in miles and y is a measurement in kilometers

15b. 400 km   **15c.** 3.2 km

15d. approximately 168 m

16. right triangle

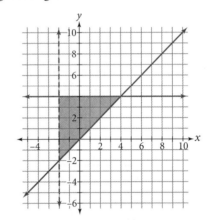

17a. -4 **17b.** 13   **17c.** -12 **17d.** 2

18a. slope: $\dfrac{5}{2}$; y-intercept: $-\dfrac{11}{2}$

18b. slope: undefined; y-intercept: none

18c. slope: $-\dfrac{1}{2}$; y-intercept: $-\dfrac{5}{2}$

19a. $19,777   **19b.** $22,104

19c. $y = 23,039(1 + 0.0225)^{-8} (1 + 0.035)^{-2}$; approximately $18,000

20. Answers will vary depending on the method used. The following possible answers used the Q-point method and a decimal approximation of the slope.

20a. $y = 96 - 5.7(x - 5)$

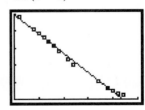

$[0, 25, 5, 0, 125, 25]$

20b. $y = 124.5 - 5.7x$

20c. approximately 16 days

20d. The y-intercept would become 200; $y = 200 - 5.7x$.

20e. 86 g

21a. independent: number of licks; dependent: mass; decreasing, discrete

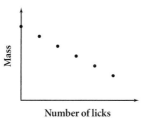

Number of licks

21b. independent: number of scoops; dependent: cost; increasing, discrete

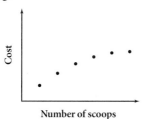

Number of scoops

21c. independent: amount of stretch; dependent: flying distance; increasing, continuous

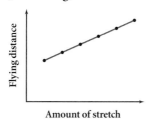

Amount of stretch

21d. independent: number of coins flipped; dependent: number of heads; increasing, discrete

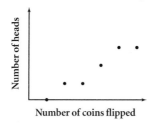

Number of coins flipped

CHAPTER 8 · CHAPTER **8** CHAPTER 8 · CHAPTER

LESSON 8.1

2a. a translation left 5 units

3a. a translation up 4 units

3b. The x-coordinates are unchanged.

4b. $(x - 2, y)$

5c. The signs would change: $L_3 = L_1 - 10$, $L_4 = L_2 + 8$.

7a.

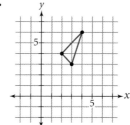

8b. $(x + 12, y + 7)$

8c. *Hint:* Think about recursion: start value and change.

9a. $(4.5, 1.5), (4.5, 2.5), (5.5, 1.5), (5.5, 2.5)$

11b. $x = -4$ **11d.** $-1 + 6x$

LESSON 8.2

1b. 5   **1d.** $2|x + 6| + 1$

3a. $(1, -3)$

4a. a translation of $y = |x|$ right 1.5 units and down 2.5 units

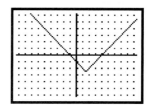

4d. a translation of $y = 3^x$ left 1 unit and up 2 units

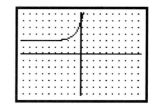

5b. $y = 4^{x-5}$

8. *Hint:* Remember that $Y_1(x)$ does not mean Y_1 times x!

9b. a translation left 2 units

9c. a translation down 2 units

10a. $y = a \cdot b^{x-10}$

10c. *Hint:* Use one point (x, y) and the average ratio to solve for a.

11a. Let x represent time in minutes, and let y represent temperature in degrees Celsius. The scatter plot suggests an exponential function.

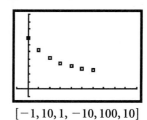

$[-1, 10, 1, -10, 100, 10]$

Time (min)	Temperature (°C)
0	47
1	31
2	20
3	13
4	9
5	6
6	4

A translation down 21 units; the long-run value will now be 0°C.

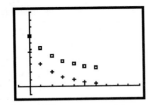

11d. Ratios to the nearest thousandth: 0.660, 0.645, 0.65, 0.692, 0.667, 0.667; the ratios are approximately constant; the mean is approximately 0.66.

11f. a translation up 21 units

13b. $y = b(x - 4) + 8$ **13c.** (H, V)

LESSON 8.3

1b. 37.5   **1e.** $-0.5(x - 3)^2 + 3$

3b. a translation right 6 units or a reflection across the y-axis

3d. a translation left 2 units and a reflection across the x-axis

5c. a reflection across the x-axis followed by a translation up 3 units

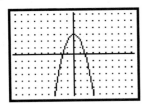

5d. a reflection across the y-axis and a translation up 3 units

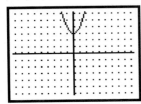

6b. i. Define L3 = −L1 and L4 = L2.

7d. a translation right 2 units and down 4 units

7e. a reflection across the x- and y-axes

7f. *Hint:* Try graphing this.

8b. *Hint:* Try making a sketch of this situation, similar to the one in 8a.

9. $(x + 1, -y)$

10b. possible answer: $y = -f(-(x + 2)) - 4$

11a. i. $y = -x^2 - 4$

ii. $y = -|x| + 7$

iii. $y = 2^{-(x-6)}$

iv. $y = 2(-(x + 8)) + 4$;
$y = (4 + 2(-x)) - 16$;
$y = -(4 + 2x) - 8$; or
$y = -(4 + 2(x + 4))$

11b. i. $y = -2$

ii. $y = 3.5$

iii. $x = 3$

iv. $x = -4$ or $y = -4$

11d. $y = -f(x) + 2b$

13. *Hint:* Use dimensional analysis.

LESSON 8.4

1. $y = |x - 5|$

2a.

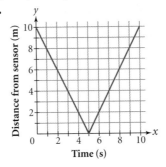

3a. $y = -1.2|x - 5| + 6$

6. *Hint:* Sketch the triangle.

7b. a vertical shrink of $y = |x|$ by a factor of 0.25, then a translation right 2 units and up 1 unit

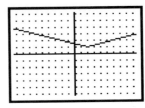

8. The absolute-value graph is stretched vertically by a factor of 3. Its vertex remains at $(0, 0)$.

10a, b. *Hint:* Reflections and dilations can be performed in either order, but both must occur before translations.

13a. possible answer: $f(x) = -25|x - 3.2| + 80$

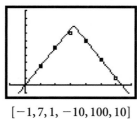

$[-1, 7, 1, -10, 100, 10]$

14. $(x - 1, 0.8y)$

15a. Yes; when you substitute 1 for x, you get $y = a \cdot 1^2 = a$.

16a. $\dfrac{1}{2^9}$

LESSON 8.6

1b. a vertical shrink of the graph of $y = |x|$ by a factor of $\frac{1}{3}$ and a translation right 2 units; $y = \frac{1}{3}|x - 2|$

2. $y = \dfrac{2}{x}$

3. $y = -\dfrac{5}{x}$

5a. a vertical stretch by a factor of 4; domain: $x \neq 0$

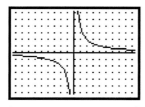

$[-9.4, 9.4, 1, -6.2, 6.2, 1]$

7a. $y = \dfrac{1}{x - 3}$ **7c.** $y = \dfrac{1}{x - 1} + 1$

9. Let x represent the amount of water to add and y represent the concentration of salt. The amount of salt is $0.05(0.5)$.
$y = \dfrac{0.025}{0.5 + x}$; $0.01 = \dfrac{0.025}{0.5 + x}$; $x = 2$; 2 L

11e. $1 - 3x^3$, where $x \neq 0$

12b. $\dfrac{7}{12x}$, where $x \neq 0$

13b. $\dfrac{x + 6}{12}$, where $x \neq 6$

14a. $x < -2$

16b. $\begin{bmatrix} 20.5 & 24.1 \\ 90.25 & 102.75 \end{bmatrix}$; the first row is the total cost for fall and spring this year, and the second row is the total income from sales for fall and spring this year.

LESSON 8.7

1b. $\begin{bmatrix} 0 & 0 & 0 \\ -3 & -3 & -3 \end{bmatrix}$ **1c.** $\begin{bmatrix} -2 & 1 & -2 \\ -1 & -1 & 3 \end{bmatrix}$

2b. $\begin{bmatrix} -4 & -2 & -2 \\ 3 & 5 & 1 \end{bmatrix} + \begin{bmatrix} 9 & 9 & 9 \\ 0 & 0 & 0 \end{bmatrix} = \begin{bmatrix} 5 & 7 & 7 \\ 3 & 5 & 1 \end{bmatrix}$

3a. $[6 \ \ 15]$ **3c.** $[64]$

5a. *Hint:* Graph the four points given. These points are the vertices of what kind of quadrilateral?

5b. Possible answer: For the x-coordinate, multiply row 1 of the transformation matrix by column 2 of the quadrilateral matrix: $[1 \ \ 0] \cdot \begin{bmatrix} 2 \\ -1 \end{bmatrix} = 2$; this goes in row 1, column 2 of the image matrix. For the y-coordinate, multiply row 2 of the transformation matrix by column 2 of the quadrilateral matrix: $[0 \ \ 2] \cdot \begin{bmatrix} 2 \\ -1 \end{bmatrix} = -2$; this goes in row 2, column 2 of the image matrix.

5c. $\begin{bmatrix} -1 & 2 & 1 & -2 \\ 4 & -2 & -4 & 2 \end{bmatrix}$

7a. possible answer: $[Q] = \begin{bmatrix} 2 & 3 & 6 & 7 \\ 2 & 4 & 5 & 1 \end{bmatrix}$

7b. $\begin{bmatrix} 1 & 0 \\ 0 & 0.5 \end{bmatrix} \cdot [Q] = \begin{bmatrix} 2 & 3 & 6 & 7 \\ 1 & 2 & 2.5 & 0.5 \end{bmatrix}$

8c. $\begin{bmatrix} 1 & 2 & 3 & 4 & 5 \\ 6 & 3 & 2 & 3 & 6 \end{bmatrix}$; $y = (x - 3)^2 + 2$

CHAPTER 8 REVIEW

1a. a translation left 2 units and up 1 unit

1b. $(x - 2, y + 1)$

2a. i. a vertical shrink by a factor of 0.5 and a translation left 6 units

2a. ii. possible answer: a reflection across the x-axis, then a translation up 2 units

2a. iii. possible answer: a horizontal stretch by a factor of 2 and a reflection across the y-axis, then a translation right 5 units and down 3 units

2b. i. $L_3 = L_1 - 6, L_4 = 0.5 \cdot L_2$

2b. ii. possible answer: $L_3 = L_1, L_4 = -L_2 + 2$

2b. iii. possible answer: $L_3 = -2 \cdot L_1 + 5, L_4 = L_2 - 3$

3. Answers will vary. For these possible answers, list L_3 and list L_4 are used for the x- and y-coordinates, respectively, of each image.

3a. $L_3 = L_1, L_4 = -L_2$

3b. $L_3 = -L_1, L_4 = L_2$

3c. $L_3 = L_1 + 3, L_4 = -L_2$

4a. a vertical stretch of the graph of $y = |x|$ by a factor of 2, then a translation up 1 unit

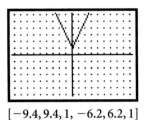

$[-9.4, 9.4, 1, -6.2, 6.2, 1]$

4b. a reflection of the graph of $y = |x|$ across the x-axis, then a translation left 2 units and up 2 units

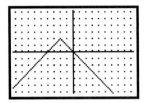

4c. possible answer: a vertical shrink of the graph of $y = x^2$ by a factor of 0.5, then a reflection across the y-axis, then a translation down 1 unit

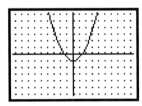

4d. possible answer: a reflection of the graph of $y = x^2$ across the x-axis, then a translation right 2 units and up 1 unit

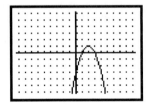

5. $g(x) = f(x - 1) + 2$

6a. $y = -|x| + 3$

6b. $y = (x + 4)^2 - 2$

6c. $y = 0.5x^2 - 5$

6d. $y = -2|x - 3| + 1$

7a. The graph should have the same x-intercept as $f(x)$. The y-intercept should be the opposite of that for $f(x)$.

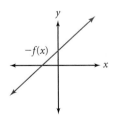

7b. Answers will vary. Possible answer for a friendly window with a factor of 1: If $Y_1 = -x - 2$, then $Y_2 = -Y_1$ reflects the graph across the x-axis (because the calculator interprets $-Y_1$ as $-(-x - 2)$, or $(x + 2)$; this supports the answer to 7a.

8a. a translation right 3 units; asymptotes: $x = 3, y = 0$

8b. a vertical stretch by a factor of 3 and then a translation left 2 units; asymptotes: $x = -2, y = 0$

8c. a translation right 5 units and down 2 units; asymptotes: $x = 5, y = -2$

9a. 5.625 lumens

9b. approximately 2.12 m

10a. a translation of the graph of $y = \frac{1}{x}$ right 3 units and down 2 units; $y = \frac{1}{x - 3} - 2$

10b. a translation of the graph of $y = 2^x$ right 4 units and down 2 units; $y = 2^{(x-4)} - 2$

10c. possible answer: a reflection of the graph of $y = 2^x$ across the x-axis and across the y-axis, followed by a translation up 3 units (or a reflection across the x-axis, followed by a translation up 3 units, followed by a reflection across the y-axis); $y = -2^{(-x)} + 3$

10d. possible answer: a vertical stretch of the graph of $y = \frac{1}{x}$ by a factor of 4 and a reflection across the x-axis, followed by a translation up 1 unit and left 2 units; $y = -\frac{4}{x + 2} + 1$

11a. $\frac{1}{4}$, where $x \neq \frac{3}{2}$

11b. $28x^2$, where $x \neq 3$

12a. possible answer: $[A] = \begin{bmatrix} -1 & 1 & 1 & -1 \\ 1 & 1 & -1 & -1 \end{bmatrix}$

12b. i. Nothing; the image is identical to the original square.

12b. ii. a reflection across the x-axis and across the y-axis, or a rotation through 180°

12b. iii. a vertical stretch by a factor of 3

12b. iv. a translation right 1 unit and up 1 unit

LESSON 9.1

1b. no solution

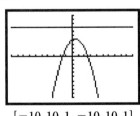

$[-10, 10, 1, -10, 10, 1]$

1d. $x \approx -2.14$ or $x \approx 0.47$

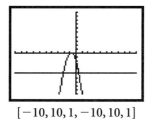

$[-10, 10, 1, -10, 10, 1]$

2b. real, rational, integer

3d. $2(x + 1)^2 = 14$
$(x + 1)^2 = 7$
$x + 1 = \pm\sqrt{7}$
$x = -1 \pm\sqrt{7}$

5d. $t > 5.09$ s

5e. The ball hits the ground when $t \approx 5.48$ s because the positive x-intercept is near the point $(5.48, 0)$.

6d. *Hint:* You could also substitute a known pair of (x, y) values and solve for a.

9a. The x-intercepts indicate when the projectile is at ground level.

9b. 2.63 s and 7.58 s

9c. *Hint:* Think about the symmetry in your parabola.

10a. i. *Hint:* For $y = -16(x - 3)^2 + 20$, the parent graph $y = x^2$ is translated right 3 units, vertically stretched by a factor of 16 and reflected across the x-axis, and translated up 20 units.

11.
$-3x + 4 > 16$	The given inequality.
$-3x > 12$	Subtract 4 from both sides.
$x < -4$	Divide both sides by -3 and reverse the inequality symbol.

LESSON 9.2

1. The average of 3 and -2 is $\frac{3 + (-2)}{2}$, or 0.5. So the axis of symmetry is $x = 0.5$, and the vertex has an x-coordinate of 0.5.

3.
$0 = (x + 1.5)^2 - 7.25$
$7.25 = (x + 1.5)^2$
$\pm\sqrt{7.25} = x + 1.5$
$-1.5 \pm\sqrt{7.25} = x$
$x \approx 1.192582404$ or
$x \approx -4.192582404$

4a. $x \approx -2.732$ and $x \approx 0.732$

---

6. Answers will vary. The graph of $y = (x + 3)^2$ intersects the graph of $y = 7$ at $(-5.646, 7)$ and $(-0.354, 7)$.

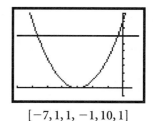

$[-7, 1, 1, -1, 10, 1]$

8b. Starting the table at 3.67 and setting ΔTbl equal to 0.001 gives the answer 3.676 s.

9b. *Hint:* Recall that velocity includes both speed and direction.

9c. When the velocity is negative, the ball is falling.

9d. This is when the ball is at its maximum height and not moving. Its velocity is zero.

10a. *Hint:* Visualize the symmetry of the parabolas.

12. $y = -16(x - 2)^2 + 67$

LESSON 9.3

1b. yes; two terms (binomial)

1d. No; the first term is equivalent to $3x^{-2}$, which has a negative exponent.

1f. *Hint:* Rewrite the first term so that it has only positive exponents.

1h. Not a polynomial as written, but it is equivalent to $3x - 6$, a binomial.

2a. $x^2 + 10x + 25$

3a. $(x + 2)^2 = x^2 + 4x + 4$

4c. $y = -3x^2 - 24x - 47$

5d.

	x
x	x^2
-3	$-3x$

$x(x - 3) = x^2 - 3x$

5e.

	x	2
$2x$	$2x^2$	$4x$
5	$5x$	10

$(x + 2)(2x + 5) = 2x^2 + 9x + 10$

9a. *Hint:* Find the vertex.

9c. The pitcher released the ball at a height of 1.716 m.

11a. meaningful domain: $0 \le x \le 6.5$; meaningful range: $0 \le y \le 897.81$

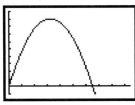

$[0, 9.4, 1, -100, 1000, 100]$

12a.

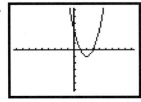

$x^2 + y^2 + 2xy + 6x + 6y + 9$

15c. 12; L   **15h.** 9; I

LESSON 9.4

1a. $x + 4 = 0$ or $x + 3.5 = 0$, so $x = -4$ or $x = -3.5$

2a.

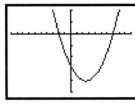

$[-9.4, 9.4, 1, -6.2, 6.2, 1]$

3a. $x = 7$ and $x = -2$

$[-10, 10, 1, -25, 10, 5]$

4a. $y = (x - 2.5)(x + 1)$

6c. yes

7a. $(x + 6)(x + 1)$

	x	6
x	x^2	$6x$
1	x	6

7c. $(x + 7)(x - 6)$

	x	7
x	x^2	$7x$
-6	$-6x$	-42

7e. $(x - 4)(x - 6)$

	x	-4
x	x^2	$-4x$
-6	$-6x$	24

9d. $y = 2(x - 3)(x - 7)$; x-intercepts: $x = 3$ and $x = 7$; vertex: $(5, -8)$

10. $y = 0.25(x + 3)(x - 9)$

11a. length: 140 ft; area: 4200 ft^2

11d. $w = 0$ ft and $w = 100$ ft

14. *Hint:* Factor the numerators and denominators if they are not factored already.

14a. $\frac{x - 2}{x + 3}$, where $x \ne -2$ and $x \ne -3$

14c. $\frac{x + 2}{x}$, where $x \ne 0$ and $x \ne 5$

16c. *Hint:* Sum the numbers for each of the 16 weeks.

LESSON 9.6

1a. $x = -3 \pm \sqrt{2}$

1b. $x = 5 \pm \sqrt{2}$

2a. $x = 5$ or $x = -3$

3a. $\left(\frac{18}{2}\right)^2$; $x^2 + 18x + 81 = (x + 9)^2$

4a.
$$x^2 - 4x - 8 = 0$$
$$x^2 - 4x = 8$$
$$x^2 - 4x + 4 = 12$$
$$(x - 2)^2 = 12$$
$$x - 2 = \pm\sqrt{12}$$
$$x = 2 \pm \sqrt{12}$$

4d. $x = -1 \pm \sqrt{8}$

6a. Let w represent the width in meters. Let l represent the length in meters. Then $l = w + 4$. The area equation is $w(w + 4) = 12$.

8a. 2.2 s; 26.9 yd (80.7 ft)

8c. The general form is $\frac{-16}{3}t^2 + 23.4\overline{6}t + 1.08\overline{6}$, so the football is about 1 yd high.

8d. The vertex is the maximum height of the ball. The y-intercept is the height of the ball when the punter kicks it. The positive x-intercept is the hang time. The other x-intercept has no real-world meaning.

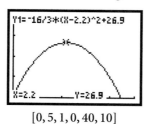

$[0, 5, 1, 0, 40, 10]$

9a. $p = 2500 - 5x$, where p represents the price in dollars of a single ticket and x represents the number of tickets sold. Let C represent the total price of the group package.

9b. $C = xp = x(2500 - 5x)$

9f. *Hint:* Use the equation in 9e.

10a. $P(10) = 0.9$; this means that when there are 10 bears in the park, the population grows at a rate of 0.9 bear per year.

10b. $P(b) = 0$ when $b = 0$ or $b = 100$; when there are no bears, the population does not grow, and when there are 100 bears, the population does not grow but remains at that level.

12c. $-2x^2 - 2x$

13f. $x = 1$ or $x = -\dfrac{8}{3}$

LESSON 9.7

1a. $25 - 24 = 1$

1c. $36 - 24 = 12$

2b. $x^2 + 6x + 11 = 0; a = 1, b = 6, c = 11$

2d. $-4.9x^2 + 47x + 18 = 0; a = -4.9, b = 47, c = 18$

3a. $x = \dfrac{3 \pm \sqrt{-23}}{4}$; there are no real solutions.

4c. If the discriminant is negative, there are no real roots. If it is positive or zero, there are real roots.

5a. $-4.9t^2 + 6.2t + 1.9 = 0; t \approx -0.255$ s or $t \approx 1.52$ s; the ball hits the ground 1.52 s after Brandi heads it.

5b. $-4.9t^2 + 6.2t + 1.9 = 3; t \approx 0.21$ s or $t \approx 1.05$ s; the ball is 3 m above the ground after 0.21 s (on the way up) and after 1.05 s (on the way down).

5c. $-4.9t^2 + 6.2t + 1.9 = 4; t \approx \dfrac{-6.2 \pm \sqrt{-2.72}}{-9.8}$; this equation has no real solution, so the ball is never 4 m high.

6. *Hint:* To sketch the graphs, you can use the x-intercepts, or substitute the values of a, b, and c into the standard form of a quadratic equation.

6a. Sample answers: $y = x^2 - 14x + 49$. The x-intercept is 7.

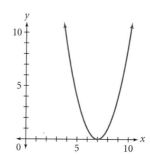

7a. i; $1^2 - 4(1)(1) = -3$; no x-intercept

9. *Hint:* What is the height of the stone when it hits the ground? Substitute this value for h.

10a. *Hint:* For an increase of 0, the area is 28 m² and the perimeter is 22 m. For an increase of 0.5, the width is 4.5 m and the length is 6.5 m.

11. $(0.5, 4.25)$ and $(-4, 2)$

12a. $x - 2; x \neq 3$

LESSON 9.8

2a. $(2x)^3 = 5,832; 2x = 18; x = 9$ cm

2c. $2(2.3x)^3 = 3,309; 2.3x \approx 11.83; x \approx 5.14$

3a. $4x(x + 3)$

3c. $7x(2x^3 + x - 3)$

4. *Hint:* Look at the graphs of each table.

5a. $y = 0.5(x + 4)(x + 2)(x - 1)$

6a. *Hint:* The second-smallest number is 64, which is 4^3 or 8^2.

7a. If the width is w, the length is $w + 6$ and the height is $w - 2$, so the volume is given by the equation $V = w(w + 6)(w - 2)$.

9a. $x^3 + 6x^2 + 11x + 6$

10a. 50 cm

10e. $w = \dfrac{120 - 2x}{2} = 60 - x$

10g. $V = x(60 - x)(80 - x)$

11a. $3x^3 + 8x^2 - x - 20$

11c. $2x + 3$

12b. $5x^3 - 2x^2 - 12x - 12$

13a. $\dfrac{x + 2}{x - 4}; x \neq -2, x \neq 4$, and $x \neq -4$

13c. $\dfrac{2x + 3}{(x + 3)^2}; x \neq -3$

1a. false; $(x - 3)(x + 8)$ **1b.** false; $2x^2 - 4x + 5$

1c. false; $x^2 + 6x + 9$ **1d.** true

2. Sample response: There is a reflection across the x-axis $\left(y = -x^2 \right)$ and a vertical stretch by a factor of 2 $\left(y = -2x^2 \right)$. Finally, there is a translation left 5 units and up 4 units $\left(y = -(x + 5)^2 + 4 \right)$.

3a. $y = -(x - 2)^2 + 3$; vertex form

3b. $y = 0.5(x - 2)(x + 3)$; factored form

4a. $y = -3(x - 1.5)^2 + 18.75$

4b. $y = -1.6(x - 5)^2 + 30$

5a. $2w + 9 = 0$ or $w - 3 = 0$; $w = -4.5$ or $w = 3$

5b. $2x + 5 = 0$ or $x - 7 = 0$; $x = -2.5$ or $x = 7$

6a. $y = (x - 1)^2 - 4$

6b. sample answers:

$$y = (x + 1.5)\left(x - \frac{1}{3} \right),$$

$$y = (2x + 3)(3x - 1)$$

7a.
$$x^2 + 6x - 9 = 13$$
$$x^2 + 6x = 22$$
$$x^2 + 6x + 9 = 22 + 9$$
$$(x + 3)^2 = 31$$
$$x + 3 = \pm\sqrt{31}$$
$$x = -3 \pm \sqrt{31}$$

7b.
$$3x^2 - 24x + 27 = 0$$
$$3x^2 - 24x = -27$$
$$x^2 - 8x = -9$$
$$x^2 - 8x + 16 = -9 + 16$$
$$(x - 4)^2 = 7$$
$$x - 4 = \pm\sqrt{7}$$
$$x = 4 \pm \sqrt{7}$$

8a. $x = \frac{13 \pm \sqrt{-191}}{10}$; no real number solutions

8b. $x = \frac{-7 \pm \sqrt{157}}{-6}$

9a. $f(60) = 8.1$; when there are 60 fish in the tank, the population is growing at a rate of about 8 fish per week.

9b. $f(x) = 0$ for $x = 0$ and $x = 150$; when there are no fish, the population does not grow; when there are 150 fish, the number of fish hatched is equal to the number of fish that die, so the total population does not change.

9c. When there are 75 fish, the population is growing fastest.

9d. The population no longer grows once there are 150 fish, so that is the maximum number of fish the tank has to support.

9e.

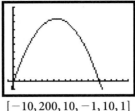

$[-10, 200, 10, -1, 10, 1]$

10. The roots are at 0 s and 1.6 s, so start with the equation $y = x(x - 1.6)$. Then reflect the graph across the x-axis. When $x = 0.5, y = 0.55$. You need the value of y to be 8.8, so apply a vertical stretch with a factor of $\frac{8.8}{0.55}$, or 16. The final equation is $y = -16x(x - 1.6)$.

11a. No x-intercepts means taking the square root of a negative number. So $(-6)^2 - 4(1)(c) < 0$; $-4c < -36$; $c > 9$. Or translate the graph of $y = x^2 - 6x$ vertically to see that for $c > 9$, the parabola does not cross the x-axis.

11b. One x-intercept implies a double root, so $x^2 - 6x + c$ must be a perfect-square trinomial. Make a rectangle diagram to find $\left(\frac{-6}{2} \right)^2 = 9$, so $x^2 - 6x + 9$ is a perfect-square trinomial, and $c = 9$. The graph touches the x-axis once. You can also solve $b^2 - 4ac = 36 - 4c = 0$ to get $c = 9$.

11c. For $c < 9, b^2 - 4ac > 0$, so the discriminant gives two real roots. The parabola $y = x^2 - 6x + c$ crosses the x-axis twice for values of c less than 9.

12a. $x = -5 + \sqrt{31}$ and $x = -5 - \sqrt{31}$

12b. $x = 1$ and $x = \frac{5}{3}$

13a. $x = -2, x = -1, x = 1$, and $x = 3$; $y = 2(x - 3)(x + 2)(x + 1)(x - 1)$

13b. $x = -2$ (double root) and $x = 3$; $y = -3(x + 2)^2(x - 3)$

14a. $(x + 3)(x + 4)$

	x	3
x	x^2	$3x$
4	$4x$	12

14b. $(x - 7)^2$

	x	-7
x	x^2	$-7x$
-7	$-7x$	49

14c. $(x + 7)(x - 4)$

	x	-4
x	x^2	$-4x$
7	$7x$	-28

Selected Hints and Answers

14d. $(x - 9)(x + 9)$

	x	-9
x	x^2	$-9x$
9	$9x$	-81

LESSON 10.1

1. Type AB = 3,750; Type B = 9,000; Type A = 30,000; Type O = 32,250

2a. 40%

3. *Hint:* Find the sum of each data set, then compare each data point to the sum.

4. No; the total height of all the bars must be 100%.

6b.

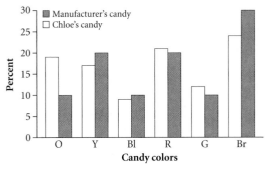

Comparing Chloe's Candy with the Manufacturer's

Chloe's bag of candy had the same dominant color as the graph from the manufacturer, and her least common color was one of the least manufactured. But the distributions are not very close.

7b. i

8a. *Hint:* You must first find the total number of students.

9. *Hint:* Compare the area of the circle to the area of the square.

10. $y = 2x^2 - 3x - 5$

12a. See below.

Douglas County had the largest percent of growth.

LESSON 10.2

1c. 2, 3, 4, 5, 6, 7, 8, 9, 10, 11, or 12

2b. 0.55

2c. 0.65

3b. *Hint:* What percent of the circle is shaded?

4. $\dfrac{1}{8}$

7a. Finding and counting a litter is a trial; an outcome may be having one cub (or two or three or four).

7b. No; if outcomes were equally likely, then the number of litters of each size would have been almost the same, with about nine litters of each size.

7c. $\dfrac{22}{35} \approx 0.63$

9. *Hint:* The central angle of the \$1,000 section is 45°; the \$400 section is 90°; the \$500 section is 60°; and the \$200 section is 165°. Use a protractor to verify these measurements.

9b. $\dfrac{90 + 180}{360} = \dfrac{270}{360}$, or $\dfrac{3}{4}$

9c. $\dfrac{45 + 45}{360} = \dfrac{90}{360}$, or $\dfrac{1}{4}$

12a. (*Lesson 10.1*)

Fastest-Growing Counties between 2000 and 2001

County	2000 population	2001 population	Change from 2000 to 2001	Percent growth
Douglas County, CO	175,766	199,753	23,987	13.6
Loudoun County, VA	169,599	190,903	21,304	12.6
Forsyth County, GA	98,407	110,296	11,889	12.1
Rockwall County, TX	43,080	47,983	4,903	11.4
Williamson County, TX	249,967	278,067	28,100	11.2

(U.S. Census Bureau, *www.census.gov*)

12. *Hint:* The two lower points have the same *y*-coordinate, and the two upper points have the same *y*-coordinate. The slope between the two left-hand points is the same as the slope between the two right-hand points.

LESSON 10.3

1. Theoretical probability: $\frac{74}{180}$, or ≈ 0.411; experimental probability: $\frac{15}{50} \approx 0.30$. Possible answers: You can expect a wide variation in survey results. Perhaps your method of selecting students was not random. For example, your results could be biased because you talked only to students who were participating in after-school activities or only to students in a particular class. Perhaps the question was worded in such a way that students were biased in their response or reluctant to answer it honestly.

2b. You have to assume that the population is 3500, it remains stable (no fish die and no new fish hatch), and the fish are well mixed.

4. *Hint:* Find the ratio of the shaded region to the whole rectangle and write a proportion.

5a. H, H, T, H, H, T

6a. Answers will vary.

9. 229

LESSON 10.4

1. combination, because the order doesn't matter and no dish can be chosen more than once

2a. combination

3a. $5 \cdot 4 \cdot 3 = 60$

3b. $\frac{_5P_3}{_3P_3} = \frac{5 \cdot 4 \cdot 3}{3 \cdot 2 \cdot 1} = 10$

4d. $\frac{1}{8}$, or 0.125

5b. Possible answer: I have 12 pairs of socks and am deciding which 4 pairs to take. The order in which I pack them doesn't matter. There are 495 ways to do this.

6a. 720

6d. $\frac{1}{720} \approx 0.001$

6e. *Hint:* In 6d you counted how many of the possible arrangements *are* in order. So, how many are *not* in order?

8a. 120

10a. 3,307,800   **10b.** 551,300

12a. $_{20}C_6 = 38,760$

15a. 20 units^2

16b. $x = -1.\overline{3}, y = -0.58\overline{3}$

LESSON 10.5

1a. $\frac{1}{8}$

1b. This is the probability that Cheryl makes the second shot if she misses the first shot.

2a. *Hint:* The probabilities of all branches from each vertex must sum to 1.

3.

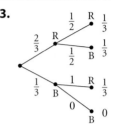

5b. dependent

7.

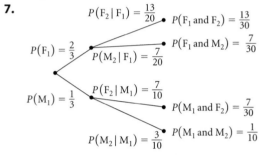

8. Dependent; the first student selected affects the probabilities for the second choice.

10a. 5040

14. She can give A's to seven students.

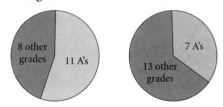

LESSON 10.6

2b. The expected number of red marbles drawn is $\frac{4}{3}$, or about 1.3.

Outcome	0	1	2	
Probability	0	$\frac{2}{3}$	$\frac{1}{3}$	Sum
Product	0	$\frac{2}{3}$	$\frac{2}{3}$	$\frac{4}{3}$

3. The expected value for concert income is $142,500.

Outcome	$200,000	$-$30,000	
Probability	0.75	0.25	Sum
Product	150,000	$-7,500$	142,500

4a. 29

6b. *Hint:* First calculate the probability of each sum. Then complete a table like the one in Exercise 1.

7a. $P(G_1 \text{ and } G_2) = 0.6$

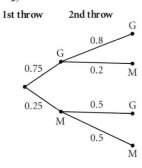

1st throw   2nd throw

7b. 1.475   **7c.** 7.375

9a. $4,750

10a. *Hint:* Your tree diagram should look similar to the one in Example B. Once you get both CDs, that path of the tree diagram ends.

11c. $\frac{10}{48} \approx 0.208$

12a. 25   **12b.** $(0.7)^{25} \approx 0.00013$

CHAPTER 10 REVIEW

1a. $\frac{49}{99}$ **1b.** $\frac{33}{99}$, or $\frac{1}{3}$

1c. $\frac{19}{99}$ **1d.** $\frac{9}{99}$, or $\frac{1}{11}$

2. 105 students have blue eyes, about 52 or 53 have gray eyes, 70 have green eyes, and about 122 or 123 have brown eyes.

3. Degrees for each sector, rounded to the nearest degree: China 75°, India 60°, United States 16°, Indonesia 13°, Brazil 10°, Other 185°; degrees add up to less than 360° because of rounding.

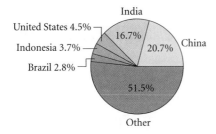

4a. $25   **4b.** 6%, or 0.06

4c. One person is $500 ahead, 5 people are $100 ahead, 10 people are even, and 84 people are $25 behind. This is a net loss of $1,100, or $11 per person.

5a. 12.5 cm²; $\frac{12.5}{40}$, or 0.3125

5b. 32.5 cm²; $\frac{32.5}{45}$, or $0.7\overline{2}$

6. 158,184,000

7a. $4 \cdot 3 \cdot 2 \cdot 1$, or 24

7b. permutation, because the order is important and no person can have more than one role

7c. 18

8a. 4495   **8b.** $\frac{435}{4495} \approx 0.097$

9a.

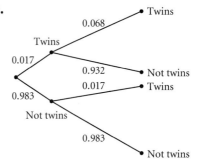

9b. 0.001156

10. *Hint:* Use a two-way table like the one in Exercise 6 with points for Nozomi instead of the sum of the dice. Six points for Chase is −6 points for Nozomi.

10a. $\frac{26}{36}$, or $0.7\overline{2}$

10b. $\frac{10}{36}$, or $0.2\overline{7}$

10c. $\frac{26}{36}(3) + \frac{10}{36}(0) = 2.1\overline{6}$

10d. $21.\overline{6}$

LESSON 11.1

1c. -1.25

1e. $\frac{3}{2}$

1g. $\frac{3}{2}$

2. *Hint:* Make sure that your calculator window is square so that you can identify perpendicular lines.

4a. $\frac{-1}{1.2} = -\frac{5}{6} = -0.8\overline{3}$

4b. -1

7. right trapezoid; slopes: $\frac{2}{3}, -\frac{1}{5}, \frac{2}{3}, -\frac{3}{2}$

10. parallelogram; slopes: $1, -3, 1, -3$

13. rectangle; slopes: $-\frac{2}{3}, \frac{3}{2}, -\frac{2}{3}, \frac{3}{2}$

17a. $2x^3 + 3x^2 - 2x$

17b. $0.01x^2 - 4.41$

LESSON 11.2

1a. $(0.5, 1.5)$

2. $\left(\dfrac{a+c}{2}, \dfrac{b+d}{2}\right)$

3a. $(16, 9)$

4a. possible answer: $y = 9 - 6(x - 16)$

6. *Hint:* Think of an extreme situation.

7a. $(3, 3.5)$

8a. midpoint of $\overline{AB}$: $(10, 3)$; midpoint of $\overline{BC}$: $(15, 8)$; midpoint of $\overline{CD}$: $(9, 10)$; midpoint of $\overline{DA}$: $(4, 5)$

8b. Parallelogram; the opposite sides are parallel because the slopes are 1, $-\frac{1}{3}$, 1, and $-\frac{1}{3}$.

8c. No; the slopes of the diagonals are $\frac{3}{11}$ and -7.

9c. possible answers: median $\overline{AE}$: $y = 6 + \frac{7}{12}(x - 11)$; median $\overline{BF}$: $y = 6 - \frac{28}{3}\left(x - \frac{5}{2}\right)$; median $\overline{CD}$: $y = 6 - \frac{14}{27}(x + 6)$

10a. $(12, 4)$

12a. $(-1, 3)$

12c. Possible answer: $y = (x + 1)^2 + 3$; any parabola of the form $y = a(x + 1)^2 + 3$ will have its vertex at this point.

LESSON 11.3

1b. $4 \pm \sqrt{28}$

1c. $-2 \pm \sqrt{14}$

3b. 12 units^2

3e. 20 units^2

3f. 18 units^2

5. polygon 3a: $\sqrt{8}$ units and $\sqrt{2}$ units
polygon 3b: $\sqrt{8}$ units and $\sqrt{18}$ units
polygon 3e: $\sqrt{50}$ units, $\sqrt{50}$ units, and $\sqrt{40}$ units

6. *Hint:* You must find the height of the triangles.

7a. 36 units^2, 18 units^2, 18 units^2

7b. length of $\overline{AB}$: 6 units; length of $\overline{BC}$: $\sqrt{18}$ units; length of $\overline{AC}$: $\sqrt{18}$ units

9c. 20 units^2, 16 units^2, 4 units^2

9d. length of $\overline{AB}$: 2 units; length of $\overline{BC}$: 4 units; length of $\overline{AC}$: $\sqrt{20}$ units

10a. City A: 58,571; City B: 52,720

10b. in 27 years

10c. 63,186

11. *Hint:* Use your graphing calculator to test various possibilities.

LESSON 11.4

1. 576 cm^2

3. $b = \sqrt{300}$ cm

5a. *Hint:* Write a proportion.

5b. 22.5 ft

5c. *Hint:* What is the shape of a shingled region?

9. approximately 7010 ft

10a. i. right triangle

12a. *Hint:* Triangles are similar if and only if their corresponding sides are proportional.

13b. $\dfrac{1.7}{2.1} = \dfrac{x}{8.5}$; $x \approx 6.88$ or 6.9 m high

LESSON 11.5

1a. $3\sqrt{3}$

1b. $5\sqrt{2}$

1c. $2 + \sqrt{6}$

1d. $4\sqrt{5} + 5\sqrt{2}$

2a. $a = \sqrt{91}$

2d. $d = \sqrt{13}$

5. *Hint:* Where is the line of symmetry?

7. *Hint:* The x-intercepts of $y = a(x - r_1)(x - r_2)$ are r_1 and r_2. The x-intercepts of the parabola in Exercise 6b are $2\sqrt{6}$ and $-3\sqrt{6}$.

8. *Hint:* The x-value of the vertex is midway between the roots. To find the y-value, substitute the x-value into the equation. The vertex of the parabola in Exercise 6b is $\left(\dfrac{-\sqrt{6}}{2}, -75\right)$.

9b. $\sqrt{550}$

10a. $6\sqrt{2}$

11a. $\dfrac{5 \pm \sqrt{3}}{3}$

11c. $1, -2$

14. *Hint:* Substitute and evaluate. Follow steps similar to those in Exercise 10.

15a. 5 cm

17. $a = 2\sqrt{2}$ cm, $b = 2\sqrt{3}$ cm, $c = \sqrt{8\sqrt{3} + 12}$ cm

LESSON 11.6

1. no, because $9^2 + 16^2 \neq 25^2$

4. possible answer: $(6, 3)$ and $(1, 7)$

6a. $\sqrt{26}$ units, or approximately 0.5 mi

7a. possible answer: $y = -3 - \frac{4}{3}(x - 2)$

7b. $d = -3\sqrt{(x - 2)^2 + (y + 3)^2}$

7c. $d = \sqrt{(x - 2)^2 + \left(-3 - \frac{4}{3}(x - 2) + 3\right)^2} = \sqrt{(x - 2)^2 + \left(-\frac{4}{3}(x - 2)\right)^2}$

10c. $c = 3$

11a. $\frac{13}{12} = \frac{a}{8}$, $a = 8.\overline{6}$; 8 ft 8 in. long

12a. $10\sqrt{2}$

1c. $x = 160$ **1d.** $x = \pm 4$

3a. $\sin D = \frac{7}{25}$

4a. *Hint:* The angles in any triangle sum to 180°. Use this information to prove that corresponding angles in the two triangles are equal.

4b. $\frac{8}{4} = 2$

5b. $x = 14$

5c. $x = 35$

7a. cosine

7b. sine

8a. $\tan 28° = \frac{y}{x}$, or $y = x \cdot \tan 28°$

10a.

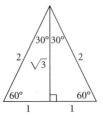

11b. $(1.2, 1.4), (2.4, 3.8), (0.8, 4.6), (-0.4, 2.2)$

12. $a = 26$; $c = 13\sqrt{3} - 13 \approx 9.52$

1a. d

1c. A

1d. $\frac{d}{c}$

1e. A

3. $x \approx 44.6$ m

5. $e = \sqrt{145} \approx 12.0$ cm; $F = 44.9°$; $g = \sqrt{349} \approx 18.7$ cm; $H = 15.5°$

7. approximately 81.1 m

9a. approximately 2.86°

9b. about 148 ft

11c. approximately 70 ft

13. $y = 1.5x^2 - 3x - 4.5$

1a. $8\sqrt{5}$ **1b.** $4\sqrt{17}$

1c. $123\sqrt{3}$ **1d.** $\sqrt{15}$

1e. 80   **1f.** 1700

1g. $3\sqrt{10}$ **1h.** $80\sqrt{5}$

1i. $\sqrt{2} + \sqrt{3}$ **1j.** $3\sqrt{2}$

1k. $\sqrt{6}$ **1l.** $4\sqrt{3}$

2. The area is 5 square units. Here are two possible strategies:

2i. Draw a square around the tilted square using the grid lines. Subtract the area of the outer triangles from the area of the larger square: $9 - 4(1) = 5$.

2ii. Find the length of the side between $(1, 0)$ and $(3, 1)$: $\sqrt{(3 - 1)^2 + (1 - 0)^2} = \sqrt{5}$. Square the side length to find the area: $(\sqrt{5})^2 = 5$.

3. Answers will vary. Possible hypothesis: The given figure is a square. Possible conclusion: Its sides are perpendicular. The slopes of the sides are $\frac{1}{2}$, -2, $\frac{1}{2}$, and -2. The slopes of each pair of adjacent sides are opposite reciprocals, so the sides are perpendicular.

4. Possible answer: Draw a 7-by-7 square on graph paper and remove triangles with areas of 5 square units (legs 2 units and 5 units) from each corner. The area of the remaining square is $49 - 4 \cdot 5$, or 29 units².

5. Possible answer: Sides of length 5 ft, 12 ft, and 13 ft satisfy the Pythagorean Theorem and form a right triangle. Side lengths of 10 ft, 24 ft, and 26 ft, which sum to 60 ft, also form a right triangle. Stretch 10 ft of the rope along one wall and 24 ft of the rope along the adjacent wall; the remaining 26 ft of rope should exactly fit along the hypotenuse if the foundation corners are right angles.

6a. $A(-4, 2), B(0, 5), C(6, -3), D(2, -6)$

6b. slope of $\overline{AB}$: $\frac{3}{4}$; slope of $\overline{BC}$: $-\frac{4}{3}$; slope of $\overline{CD}$: $\frac{3}{4}$; slope of $\overline{AD}$: $-\frac{4}{3}$

6c. It is a rectangle; the product of the slopes of adjacent sides is -1, so each pair of adjacent sides is perpendicular.

6d.

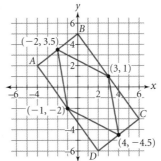

6e. Each side length is $\sqrt{31.25}$ units, or approximately 5.59 units.

6f. The slopes are $-0.5, -5.5, -0.5$, and -5.5.

6g. It is a rhombus; the sides are all the same length and opposite sides have equal slope, so they are parallel.

7. $a \approx 3.38$ m
$\quad b \approx 7.25$ m

8a. sample answer:

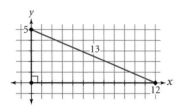

8b. approximately 67°

8c. $\sin^{-1}\left(\frac{12}{13}\right) \approx 67°$, $\cos^{-1}\left(\frac{5}{13}\right) \approx 67°$, and $\tan^{-1}\left(\frac{12}{5}\right) \approx 67°$

8d. Possible answer: Subtract 67° from 90°; approximately 23°.

9a. $\sqrt{116}$ cm, or approximately 10.77 cm

9b. $\sqrt{141}$ cm, or approximately 11.87 cm

10. Possible answer: If a triangle has base 8 cm and height 4 cm, its area is 16 cm². If the triangle is enlarged by a factor of 3, its base will be 24 cm, its height will be 12 cm, and its area will be 144 cm², which equals $3^2 \cdot 16$ cm³. Another possible answer: For any triangle, the area is given by $A = \frac{1}{2}bh$. If the sides are enlarged by a factor of k, the area is enlarged by k^2: $A = \frac{1}{2}(kb)(kh)$ or $A = \frac{1}{2}bh \cdot k^2$.

11a. $y = 61 + 1.08(x - 40)$ or $y = 34 + 1.08(x - 15)$

11b. approximately 51°F

11c. approximately 38°F

12a. $\begin{cases} 3a + 1.5p = 13.74 \\ 2a + 3p = 16.32 \end{cases}$,

where a is the price per pound for dried apricots and p is the price per pound for dried papaya

12b. apricots: \$2.79; papaya: \$3.58

13a. $P(0) = \frac{1}{20}$, or 0.05

13b. $P(\text{less than zero}) = \frac{3}{20}$, or 0.15

13c. $\frac{1}{8}$, or 0.125

13d. $\frac{2}{19}$, or about 0.105

14a. Inverse variation. Possible explanation: The product of x and y is constant; $xy = 2$ or $y = \frac{2}{x}$.

14b. Neither. Possible explanation: The product is not constant, so it is not an inverse variation. The y-value for $x = 0$ is not 0, so it is not a direct variation.

14c. Direct variation. Possible explanation: The ratio of y to x is constant; $y = 0.25x$.

14d. Neither. Possible explanation: The graph is not a curve, so the relationship is not an inverse variation. The line does not pass through the origin, so it is not a direct variation.

14e. Inverse variation. Possible explanation: The product of the x- and y-coordinates for any point on the curve is 8; $xy = 8$ or $y = \frac{8}{x}$.

14f. Direct variation. Possible explanation: The graph is a straight line through the origin; $y = 1.5x$.

15a. Possible answer: For $0 < x < 3$, f is nonlinear and increasing at a slower and slower rate. For $3 < x < 5$, f is linear and decreasing. For $5 < x < 7$, f is linear and increasing. For $7 < x < 9$, f is linear and constant (neither increasing nor decreasing). For $9 < x < 12$, f is nonlinear and decreasing at a slower and slower rate.

15b. $0 \leq y \leq 5$ **15c.** 3

15d. 1, 5, 12   **15e.** $7 \leq x \leq 9$

16a. $27x^6y^3$ **16b.** $5p^4q^2$

16c. $\frac{x}{y^2}$ **16d.** $\frac{m^2}{n^4} + \frac{1}{m^4}$

17a. mean: 108.4; median: 105; mode: 105

17b. five-number summary: 82, 99, 105, 112, 179

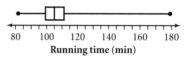
Running time (min)

17c. Bin widths may vary.

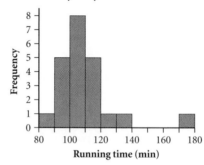
Running time (min)

17d. Sample answers: (1) About 75% of the new releases have running times of 112 min or less. (2) None of the new releases have running times between 140 and 169 min. (3) Most of the running times are between 90 and 119 min.

18a. $y = (x + 3)(x - 1)$

18b. $y = (x + 1)^2 - 4$

18c. $y = x^2 + 2x - 3$

19a. approximately \$1,197

19b. approximately \$4,102

20a. 26   **20b.** 2   **20c.** 36   **20d.** 128

20e. -24

21a. \$62.39   **21b.** \$65.51

22a. possible answer: a reflection across the y-axis and a vertical shrink by a factor of 0.5

22b. $(-x, 0.5y)$

23a. $x = -5$ or $x = 2$ **23b.** $x = -4$

23c. $x = -3$ or $x = 10$ **23d.** $x = \pm\sqrt{5}$

24a. $y = (x + 2)^2 - 4$ **24b.** $y = -0.5\,|\,x + 3\,|$

25a. \$35   **25b.** \$225

25c. $\{0, 225\}$ (ENTER) ; $\{\text{Ans}(1) + 1, \text{Ans}(2) + 35\}$
(ENTER) , (ENTER) , . . .

25d. $y = 225 + 35x$ **25e.** \$645

25f. 8

26a.

Segment	Length	Slope
$\overline{AB}$	10	$\dfrac{3}{4}$
$\overline{BC}$	10	$-\dfrac{3}{4}$
$\overline{AC}$	16	0

26b. Isosceles triangle; two sides have equal length.

26c. $D(2, 1)$

26d. Right triangles. Possible explanation: $\overline{BD}$ has an undefined slope, so it is vertical; $\overline{AC}$ has slope 0, so it is horizontal.

26e. A drawing should confirm 26a–d.

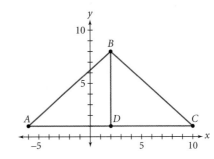

Glossary

The number in parentheses at the end of each definition gives the page where each word or phrase is introduced in the text. Some words and phrases have multiple page numbers listed, either because they have different applications in different chapters or because they first appeared within features such as Project or Take Another Look.

A

abscissa The x-coordinate in an ordered pair (x, y), measuring horizontal distance from the y-axis on a coordinate plane. (70)

absolute value A number's distance from 0 on the number line. The absolute value of a number gives its size, or magnitude, whether the number is positive or negative. The absolute value of a number x is shown as $|x|$. For example, $|-9| = 9$ and $|4| = 4$. (418)

absolute-value function The function $f(x) = |x|$, which gives the absolute value of a number. The absolute-value function is defined by two rules: If $x \geq 0$, then $f(x) = x$. If $x < 0$, then $f(x) = -x$. (420)

accuracy The degree of closeness with which a measurement approaches the actual value. For instance, a rope with actual length 12.2524 inches measured accurate to the nearest 0.01 inch would be measured at 12.25 inches. (78)

acute angle An angle that measures less than 90°. (633)

acute triangle A triangle with three acute angles. (653)

addition expression An expression whose only operation is addition. There are also subtraction expressions, multiplication expressions, and division expressions. See **algebraic expression.** (3)

addition of radical expressions For $x \geq 0$ and $y \geq 0$, and any values of a or b, $a\sqrt{x} + b\sqrt{x} = (a + b)\sqrt{x}$. (620)

addition property of equality If $a = b$, then $a + c = b + c$ for any number c. (243)

additive inverse The opposite of a number. The sum of a number and its additive inverse equals zero. For any value of a, the additive inverse is $-a$, and $a + (-a) = 0$. (196)

adjacent leg If you consider an acute angle of a right triangle, the adjacent leg is the leg that is part of the angle. (634)

algebraic expression A symbolic representation of mathematical operations that can involve both numbers and variables. (138)

analytic geometry The study of geometry using coordinate axes and algebra. (595)

angle of elevation The angle between a horizontal line and the line of sight. (645)

appreciation An increase in monetary value over time. (347)

associative property of addition For any values of a, b, and c, $a + (b + c) = (a + b) + c$. (243)

associative property of multiplication For any values of a, b, and c, $a(bc) = (ab)c$. (243)

asymptote A line that a graph approaches more and more closely, but never actually reaches. (474)

attractor A number that the results get closer and closer to when an expression is evaluated recursively. (24)

average The number obtained by dividing the sum of the values in a data set by the number of values. Formally called the mean. (46)

Avogadro's number The number of molecules in a mole, about 6.02×10^{23}, named in honor of the Italian chemist and physicist Amadeo Avogadro. (358)

axis One of two perpendicular number lines used to locate points in a coordinate plane. The horizontal axis is often called the x-axis, and the vertical axis is often called the y-axis. The plural of axis is axes. (70)

B

balancing method A method of solving an equation that involves performing the same operation on both sides until the variable is isolated on one side. (195)

bar graph A data display in which bars are used to show measures or counts for various categories. (39)

base A number or an expression that is raised to a power. For example, $x + 2$ is the base in the expression $(x + 2)^3$, and 5 is the base in the expression 5^y. (343)

bimodal Used to describe a data set that has two modes. (46)

binary number A number written in base 2. Binary numbers consist only of the digits 0 and 1. Computers store information in binary form. (395)

binomial A polynomial with exactly two terms. Examples of binomials include $-3x + x^4$, $x - 12$, and $x^3 - x^{12}$. (508)

bins Intervals on the horizontal axis of a histogram that data values are grouped into. Boundary values fall into the bin to the right. (59)

box plot A one-variable data display that shows the five-number summary of a data set. A box plot is drawn over a horizontal number line. The ends of the box indicate the first and third quartiles. A vertical segment inside the box indicates the median. Horizontal segments, called whiskers, extend from the left end of the box to the minimum value and from the right end of the box to the maximum value. (53)

box-and-whisker plot See **box plot.**

 C

carbon dating A process that uses the rate of radioactive decay of the carbon isotope carbon-14 to determine the approximate age of any artifact composed of organic matter. (374)

category A group of data with the same attribute. For example, data about people's eye color could be grouped into three categories: blue, brown, and green. (40)

center (of rotation) The point that a figure turns about during a rotation. (488)

chaotic Systematic and nonrandom, yet producing results that look random. Small changes to the input value of a chaotic process can result in large changes to the output value. (30)

coefficient A number that is multiplied by a variable. For example, in a linear equation in intercept form $y = a + bx$, b is the coefficient of x. (179)

collinear A set of points that can be connected by a single straight line. (247)

column matrix A matrix that consists of only one column. (86)

combination An arrangement of objects in which the order is unimportant, but once a choice is made it cannot be used again. For example, there is only one three-letter combination of the letters a, b, and c (abc), but there are three two-letter combinations (ac, ab, and bc). (572)

common denominator A common multiple of the denominators of two or more fractions. For example, 30 is a common denominator of $\frac{7}{10}$ and $\frac{4}{15}$. (6)

common monomial factor A monomial that is a factor of every term in an expression. For example, $3x$ is a common monomial factor of $12x^3 - 6x^2 + 9x$. (541)

commutative property of addition For any values of a and b, $a + b = b + a$. (243)

commutative property of multiplication For any values of a and b, $ab = ba$. (243)

complementary outcomes Two outcomes that combined make up all possible outcomes. For example, the probability that it will rain tomorrow and the probability that it will not rain tomorrow are complementary. (575)

completing the square Adding a constant term to an expression in the form $x^2 + bx$ to form a perfect-square trinomial. For example, to complete the square in the expression $x^2 + 12x$, add 36. This gives $x^2 + 12x + 36$, which is equivalent to $(x + 6)^2$. To solve a quadratic equation by completing the square, write it in the form $x^2 + bx = c$, complete the square on the left side (adding the same number to the right side), rewrite the left side as a binomial squared, and then take the square root of both sides. (525)

complex number A number with a real part and an imaginary part. A complex number can be written in the form $a + bi$, where a and b are real numbers and i is the imaginary unit, $\sqrt{-1}$. (528)

compound inequality A combination of two inequalities. For example, $-5 < x \le 1$ is a compound inequality that combines the inequalities $x > -5$ and $x \le 1$. (307)

conclusion The result of a deductive argument. (597)

conditional See **dependent** (events).

congruent Having the same shape and size. Two angles are congruent if they have the same measure. Two segments are congruent if they have the same length. Two figures are congruent if you can move one to fit exactly on top of the other. (3)

conic section Any curve that can be formed by the intersection of a plane and a double cone. Parabolas, circles, ellipses, and hyperbolas are examples of conic sections. (507)

conjecture A statement that might be true but that has not been proven. Conjectures are usually based on data patterns or on experience. (68)

constant A value that does not change. (115)

constant multiplier In a sequence that grows or decreases exponentially, the number each term is multiplied by to get the next term. The value of $1 + r$ in the exponential equation $y = A(1 + r)^x$. (334)

constant of variation The constant ratio in a direct variation or the constant product in an inverse variation. The value of k in the direct variation equation $y = kx$ or in the inverse variation equation $y = \frac{k}{x}$. (116, 126)

constraint A limitation on the values of the variables in a situation. A system of inequalities can model the constraints in many real-world situations. (320)

continuous function A function that has no breaks in the domain or range. The graph of a continuous function is a line or curve with no holes or gaps. (407)

contour line See **isometric line.**

contour map A map that uses isometric lines to show elevations above sea level, revealing the character of the terrain. Also called a **topographic map.** (211, 642)

conversion factor A ratio used to convert measurements from one unit to another. (109)

coordinate plane A plane with a pair of scaled, perpendicular axes allowing you to locate points with ordered pairs and to represent lines and curves by equations. (70)

coordinates An ordered pair of numbers in the form (x, y) that describes the location of a point on a coordinate plane. The x-coordinate describes the point's horizontal distance and direction from the origin, and the y-coordinate describes its vertical distance and direction from the origin. (70)

cosine If A is an acute angle in a right triangle, $cosine\ of\ angle\ A = \frac{length\ of\ adjacent\ leg}{length\ of\ hypotenuse}$, or $\cos A = \frac{a}{h}$. (635)

counterexample An example that shows that a given conjecture is not true. (401)

counting number See **natural number.**

counting principle When there are a ways to make a first choice, b ways to make a second choice, c ways to make a third choice, and so on, then the product $a \cdot b \cdot c \cdot \cdots$ gives the total number of different ways in which the entire sequence of choices can be made. (572)

cryptography The study of coding and decoding messages. (388)

cube (of a number) A number raised to the third power. The cube of a number x is "x cubed" and is written x^3. For example, the cube of 4 is 4^3, which is equal to 64. (537)

cube root The cube root of a number a is the number b such that $a = b^3$. The cube root of a is denoted $\sqrt[3]{a}$. For example, $\sqrt[3]{64} = 4$ and $\sqrt[3]{-125} = -5$. (537)

cubing function The function $f(x) = x^3$, which gives the cube of a number. (537)

data A collection of information, numbers, or pairs of numbers, usually measurements for a real-world situation. (39)

data analysis The process of calculating statistics and making graphs to summarize a data set. (68)

Glossary

decreasing A term used to describe the behavior of a function. A function is decreasing on an interval of its domain if the y-values decrease as the x-values increase. Visually, the graph of the function goes down as you read from left to right for that part of the domain. (407)

decreasing function A function that is always decreasing. (405)

deductive reasoning Reasoning accepted as logical from agreed-upon assumptions and proven facts. (597)

dependent (events) Events are dependent when the occurrence of one event depends on the occurrence of the other. (580)

dependent variable A variable whose values depend on the values of another variable (called the independent variable). In a graph of the relationship between two variables, the values on the vertical axis usually represent values of the dependent variable. (404)

depreciation A decrease in monetary value over time. (346)

deviation from the mean A data value minus the mean of its data set. The deviations of the data values from the mean give an idea of the spread of the data values. (418)

difference of two squares An expression in the form $a^2 - b^2$, in which one squared number is subtracted from another. A difference of two squares can be factored as $(a + b)(a - b)$. (521)

dimensional analysis A strategy for converting measurements from one unit to another by multiplying by a string of conversion factors. (109)

dimensions (of a matrix) The number of rows and columns in a matrix. If a matrix has 2 rows and 4 columns, its dimensions are 2×4. (83)

dimensions (of a rectangle) The width and length of a rectangle. If a rectangle is 2 units wide and 4 units long, its dimensions are 2-by-4. (616)

direct variation A relationship in which the ratio of two variables is constant. That is, a relationship in which two variables are directly proportional. A direct variation has an equation in the form $y = kx$, where x and y are the variables and k is a number called the constant of variation. (116)

directly proportional Used to describe two variables whose values have a constant ratio. (116)

directrix See **parabola.**

discrete function A function whose domain and range are made up of distinct values rather than intervals of real numbers. The graph of a discrete function is made up of distinct points. (407)

discriminant The expression under the square root symbol in the quadratic formula. If a quadratic equation is written in the form $ax^2 + bx + c = 0$, then the discriminant is $b^2 - 4ac$. If the discriminant is greater than 0, the quadratic equation has two solutions. If the discriminant equals 0, the equation has one real solution. If the discriminant is less than 0, the equation has no real solutions. (533)

distance formula The distance, d, between points (x_1, y_1) and (x_2, y_2) is given by the formula $d = \sqrt{(x_2 - x_1)^2 + (y_2 - y_1)^2}$. (629)

distributive property For any values of a, b, and c, $a(b + c) = a(b) + a(c)$. (241, 243)

division of radical expressions For $x \geq 0$ and $y > 0$, $\frac{\sqrt{x}}{\sqrt{y}} = \sqrt{\frac{x}{y}}$. (620)

division property of equality If $a = b$, then $\frac{a}{c} = \frac{b}{c}$ for any nonzero number c. (243)

division property of exponents For any nonzero value of b and any values of m and n, $\frac{b^m}{b^n} = b^{m-n}$. (362)

domain The set of input values for a function. (390)

dot plot A one-variable data display in which each data value is represented by a dot above that value on a horizontal number line. (40)

double root A value r is a double root of an equation $f(x) = 0$ if $(x - r)^2$ is a factor of $f(x)$. The graph of $y = f(x)$ will touch, but not cross, the x-axis at $x = r$. For example, 3 is a double root of the equation $0 = (x - 3)^2$. The graph of $y = (x - 3)^2$ touches the x-axis at $x = 3$. (540)

 E

elimination method A method for solving a system of equations that involves adding or subtracting the equations to eliminate a variable.

In some cases, both sides of one or both equations must be multiplied by a number before the equations are added or subtracted. For example, to solve $\begin{cases} 3x - 2y = 5 \\ -6x + y = 11 \end{cases}$, you could multiply the first equation by 2 and then add the equations to eliminate x. (289)

engineering notation A notation in which a number is written as a number greater than or equal to 1 but less than 1000, multiplied by 10 to a power that is a multiple of 3. For example, in engineering notation, the number 10,800,000 is written 10.8×10^6. (372)

equally likely Used to describe outcomes that have the same probability of occurring. For example, when you toss a coin, heads and tails are equally likely. (560)

equation A statement that says the value of one number or algebraic expression is equal to the value of another number or algebraic expression. (78, 146)

equilateral triangle A triangle with three sides of the same length. (280, 639)

equivalent equations Equations that have the same set of solutions. (240)

error The difference between a measurement and the actual value. (78)

evaluate (an expression) To find the value of an expression. If an expression contains variables, values must be substituted for the variables before the expression can be evaluated. For example, if $3x^2 - 4$ is evaluated for $x = 2$, the result is $3(2)^2 - 4$, or 8. (22)

even temperament A method of tuning an instrument based on an equal tuning ratio between adjacent notes (that is, an exponential equation). (376)

event A set of desired outcomes in a probability experiment. (558)

excluded value See **restriction on the variable.**

expand (an algebraic expression) To rewrite an expression by multiplying factors and combining like terms. For example, to expand $(x + 8)(x - 2)$, rewrite it as $x^2 + 6x - 16$. (511)

expanded form (of a repeated multiplication expression) The form of a repeated multiplication expression in which every occurrence of each factor is shown. For example, the expanded form of the expression $3^2 \cdot 5^4$ is $3 \cdot 3 \cdot 5 \cdot 5 \cdot 5 \cdot 5$. (343)

expected value A mean, or average, value found by multiplying the value of each possible outcome by its probability, then summing the products. (584)

experimental frequency The number of times a particular outcome occurred during the trials of an experiment. (559)

experimental probability A probability that is calculated based on experience or collected data. (558)

exponent A number or variable written as a small superscript of a number or variable, called the base, that indicates how many times the base is being used as a factor. For example, in the expression y^4, the exponent 4 means four factors of y, so $y^4 = y \cdot y \cdot y \cdot y$. (10)

exponential equation An equation in which a variable appears in the exponent. (343)

exponential form The form of an expression in which repeated multiplication is written using exponents. For example, the exponential form of $3 \cdot 3 \cdot 5 \cdot 5 \cdot 5 \cdot 5$ is $3^2 \cdot 5^4$. (343)

exponential growth A growth pattern in which amounts increase by a constant percent. Exponential growth can be modeled by the equation $y = A(1 + r)^x$, where A is the starting value, r is the rate of growth written as a decimal or fraction, x is the number of time periods elapsed, and y is the final value. (344)

factor One of the numbers, variables, or expressions multiplied to obtain a product. (10)

factored form An expression written as a product of expressions, rather than as a sum or difference. For example, $3(x + 2)$ and $y(4 - w)$ are in factored form. See **factoring.** (335)

factored form (of a quadratic equation) The form $y = a(x - r_1)(x - r_2)$, where $a \neq 0$. The values r_1 and r_2 are the zeros of the quadratic function. (515)

factorial For any integer n greater than 1, n factorial, written $n!$, is the product of all the consecutive integers from n decreasing to 1. For example, $5! = 5 \cdot 4 \cdot 3 \cdot 2 \cdot 1 = 120$. (575)

factoring The process of rewriting an expression as a product of factors. For example, to factor $7x - 28$, rewrite it as $7(x - 4)$. To factor $x^2 + x - 2$, rewrite it as $(x - 1)(x + 2)$. (245)

family of functions A group of functions with the same parent function. For example, $y = |x - 5|$ and $y = -2|x| + 3$ are both members of the family of functions with parent function $y = |x|$. (446)

fault A break in a rock formation caused by the movement of Earth's crust, in which the rocks on opposite sides of the break move in different directions. (446)

feasible region In a linear programming problem, the set of points that satisfy all the constraints. If the constraints are given as a system of inequalities, the feasible region is the solution to the system. (330)

first quartile (Q1) The median of the values below the median of a data set. (52)

first-quadrant graph A coordinate graph in which all the points are in the first quadrant. (72)

five-number summary The minimum, first quartile, median, third quartile, and maximum of a data set. The five-number summary helps show how the data values are spread. (52)

fixed point A number that, when substituted into an expression, results in the same number. For example, -4 is a fixed point for $0.5x - 2$, because $0.5(-4) - 2 = -4$. (24)

focus See **parabola**.

fractal The result of infinitely many applications of a recursive procedure to a geometric figure. The resulting figure has self-similarity. From the Latin word *fractus*, meaning broken or irregular. (2, 4, 5, 15)

frequency The number of times a value appears in a data set. (59, 60)

function A rule or relationship in which there is exactly one output value for each input value. (390)

function notation A notation in which a function is named with a letter and the input is shown in parentheses after the function name. For example, $f(x) = x^2 + 1$ represents the function $y = x^2 + 1$. The letter f is the name of the function, and $f(x)$ (read "f of x") stands for the output for the input x. The output of this function for $x = 2$ is written $f(2)$, so $f(2) = 5$. (412)

G

general equation An equation that represents a whole family of equations. For example, the general equation $y = kx$ represents the family of equations that includes $y = 4x$ and $y = -3.4x$. (155)

general form (of a quadratic equation) The form $y = ax^2 + bx + c$, in which $a \neq 0$. (498)

girth The distance around an object in one direction. The girth of a box is the length of string that wraps around the box. (543)

glyph A symbol that presents information nonverbally. (76)

golden ratio The ratio $\frac{1 + \sqrt{5}}{2}$, often considered an aesthetically "ideal" ratio. Examples of the golden ratio can be found in the environment, in art, and in architecture. (102)

gradient The inclination of a roadway. Also called the **grade** of the road. (194)

gravity The force of attraction between two objects. Gravity causes objects to accelerate toward Earth at a rate of 32 ft/s², or 9.8 m/s². (496)

greatest value See **maximum**.

H

half-life The time needed for an amount of a substance to decrease by one-half. (381)

half-plane The points on a plane that fall on one side of a boundary line. The solution of a linear inequality in two variables is a half-plane. (313)

hexagon A polygon with exactly six sides. (75)

histogram A one-variable data display that uses bins to show the distribution of values in a data set. Each bin corresponds to an interval of data values; the height of a bin indicates the number, or frequency, of values in that interval. (59)

horizontal axis The horizontal number line on a coordinate graph or data display. Also called the **x-axis**. (40, 70)

horizontally reflected See **reflection across the y-axis.**

hypotenuse The side of a right triangle opposite the right angle. (597)

hypothesis The starting statement, which is assumed to be true, in a deductive argument. (597)

image The figure or graph of a function that is the result of a transformation of an original figure or graph of a function. (439)

image function The function that results when a transformation or series of transformations are performed upon an original function. (466)

imaginary number A number that includes the square root of a negative number. In the set of imaginary numbers, $\sqrt{-1}$ is represented by the letter i. For example, the solution to $x^2 = -4$ is the imaginary number $\sqrt{-4}$, or $2i$. (548)

increasing Used to describe the behavior of a function. A function is increasing on an interval of its domain if the y-values increase as the x-values increase. Visually, the graph of the function goes up as you read from left to right for that part of the domain. (407)

increasing function A function that is always increasing. (405)

independent (events) Events are independent when the occurrence of one event has no influence on the occurrence of the other. (580)

independent variable A variable whose values affect the values of another variable (called the dependent variable). In a graph of the relationship between two variables, values on the horizontal axis usually represent values of the independent variable. (404)

inductive reasoning The process of observing data, recognizing patterns, and making conjectures about generalizations. (597)

inequality A statement that one quantity is less than or greater than another. For example, $x + 7 \geq -3$ and $6 + 2 < 11$ are inequalities. (304)

integer Any one of the numbers $\ldots, -3, -2, -1, 0, 1, 2, 3, \ldots$. (499)

intercept form The form $y = a + bx$ of a linear equation. The value of a is the y-intercept, and the value of b, the coefficient of x, is the slope of the line. (179)

interest A percent of the balance added to an account at regular time intervals. (335)

interquartile range (IQR) The difference between the third quartile and the first quartile of a data set. (54)

interval The set of numbers between two given numbers, or the distance between two numbers on a number line or axis. (40)

inverse Reversed in order or effect. In an inverse mathematical relationship, as one quantity increases, the other decreases. (81, 123)

inverse (of a function) The relationship that reverses the inputs and outputs of a function. For example, the inverse of the function $y = x + 2$ is $y = x - 2$. (434, 494)

inverse variation A relationship in which the product of two variables is constant. That is, a relationship in which two variables are inversely proportional. An inverse variation has an equation in the form $xy = k$, or $y = \frac{k}{x}$, in which x and y are the variables and k is a number called the constant of variation. (126)

inversely proportional Used to describe two variables whose values have a constant product. (125, 126)

invert To switch the positions of two objects. For example, to invert the fraction $\frac{3}{4}$, switch the numerator and the denominator to get $\frac{4}{3}$. When you invert a fraction, the result is the reciprocal of the fraction. (97)

IQR See **interquartile range.**

irrational number A number that cannot be expressed as the ratio of two integers. In decimal form, an irrational number has an infinite number of digits and doesn't show a repeating pattern. Examples of irrational numbers include π and $\sqrt{2}$. (99, 499)

isometric line A line on a contour map that shows elevation above sea level. All the points on an isometric line have the same elevation. Also called a **contour line.** (211, 642)

isosceles triangle A triangle with two sides of the same length. (280, 639)

Glossary

key A guide for interpreting the values in a data display. For example, a stem plot has a key that shows how to read the stem and leaf values. (61)

Koch curve A fractal generated recursively by beginning with a line segment and, at each stage, constructing an equilateral triangle on the middle third of each line segment and removing the edge of that triangle on the line segment. (14, 341)

leading coefficient In a polynomial, the coefficient of the term with the highest power of the variable. For example, in the polynomial $3x^2 - 7x + 4$, the leading coefficient is 3. (526)

least value See **minimum.**

leg One of the perpendicular sides of a right triangle. (597)

letter-shift code A method of encryption in which each letter of the alphabet is replaced with a different letter that is shifted by a given amount. (388)

light-year The distance light travels in one year: about 9460 billion kilometers. (359)

like terms Terms that have the same variables raised to the same exponents. For example, $3x^2y$ and $8x^2y$ are like terms. You can add or subtract like terms—this process is sometimes called *combining like terms.* For example, in the expression $4x + 2x^2 - x + 5 + 7x^2$ you can combine the like terms $4x$ and $-x$ and the like terms $2x^2$ and $7x^2$ to get $3x + 9x^2 + 5$. (197)

line of fit A line used to model a set of data. A line of fit shows the general direction of the data and has about the same number of data points above and below it. (225)

line of symmetry A line that divides a figure into mirror-image halves. In a parabola that opens up or down, the line of symmetry is the vertical line through the vertex. (503)

linear In the shape of a line or represented by a line. (166, 404)

linear equation An equation that can be represented with a straight-line graph. A linear equation has variables raised only to the power of 1. For example, $y = 1 + 3x$ is a linear equation. (178)

linear function A function characterized by a constant rate of change—that is, as the x-values change by a constant amount, the y-values also change by a constant amount. The graph of a linear function is a straight line. (404)

linear programming A process that applies the concepts of constraints, points of intersection, and algebraic expressions to solve application problems. (330)

linear relationship A relationship that you can represent with a straight-line graph. A linear relationship is characterized by a constant rate of change—that is, as the value of one variable changes by a constant amount, the value of the other variable also changes by a constant amount. (166)

long-run value The value that the y-values approach as the x-values increase. (451)

lowest terms The form of a fraction or rational expression in which the numerator and denominator have no common factors except 1. (6, 477)

matrix A rectangular array of numbers or expressions, enclosed in brackets. (83)

maximum The greatest value in a data set or the greatest value of a function. (40, 406)

mean The number obtained by dividing the sum of the values in a data set by the number of values. Often called the **average.** (46, 47)

measure of center A single number used to summarize a one-variable data set. The mean, median, and mode are measures of center. (46)

measure of central tendency See **measure of center.**

median (of a data set) If a data set contains an odd number of values, the median is the middle value when the values are listed in order. If a data set contains an even number of values, the median is the mean of the two middle values when the values are listed in order. (46, 47)

median (of a triangle) A segment from the vertex of a triangle to the midpoint of the opposite side. (601)

midpoint The point on a line segment halfway between the endpoints. If a segment is drawn on a coordinate grid, you can use the midpoint formula to find the coordinates of its midpoint. (2, 601)

midpoint formula If the endpoints of a segment are (x_1, y_1) and (x_2, y_2), then the midpoint of the segment is $\left(\frac{x_1 + x_2}{2}, \frac{y_1 + y_2}{2}\right)$. (603)

minimum The least value in a data set or the least value of a function. (40, 406)

mixture problem A problem that involves mixtures and usually requires a system of two or more equations to be solved. (284)

mode The value or values that occur most often in a data set. A data set may have more than one mode or no mode. (46, 47)

mole About 6.02×10^{23} molecules. (358)

monomial A polynomial with only one term. Examples of monomials include $-3x$, x^4, and $7x^2$. (508)

multiplication of radical expressions For $x \geq 0$ and $y \geq 0$, and any values of a or b, $a\sqrt{x} \cdot b\sqrt{y} = a \cdot b\sqrt{x \cdot y}$. (620)

multiplication property of equality If $a = b$, then $ac = bc$ for any number c. (243)

multiplication property of exponents For any values of b, m, and n, $b^m \cdot b^n = b^{m+n}$. (351)

multiplication rule If n_1, n_2, n_3, and so on, represent events along a path, then the probability that this sequence of events will occur can be found by multiplying the probabilities of the events. (581)

multiplicative inverse The product of a number and its multiplicative inverse is 1. For any number a, the multiplicative inverse is $\frac{1}{a}$. (201)

natural number Any one of the numbers $1, 2, 3, 4, \ldots$ (499)

negative exponent For any nonzero value of b and any value of n, $b^{-n} = \frac{1}{b^n}$ and $b^n = \frac{1}{b^n}$. (367)

nonlinear Not in the shape of a line or not able to be represented by a line. In mathematics, a nonlinear equation or expression has variables raised to powers other than 1. For example, $x^2 + 5x$ is a nonlinear expression. (404)

nonlinear function A function characterized by a nonconstant rate of change—that is, as the x-values change by a constant amount, the y-values change by varying amounts. (404)

observed probability See **experimental probability**.

obtuse angle An angle that measures more than $90°$. (633)

obtuse triangle A triangle with an obtuse angle. (653)

one-variable data Data that measure only one trait or quantity. A one-variable data set consists of single values, not pairs of data values. (70)

opposite leg If you consider an acute angle of a right triangle, the opposite leg is the leg that is *not* part of the angle. (634)

order of magnitude A way of expressing the size of an extremely large or extremely small number by giving the power of 10 associated with the number. For example, the number 6.01×10^{26} is on the order of 10^{26} and the number 2.43×10^{-11} is on the order of 10^{-11}. (385)

order of operations The agreed-upon order in which operations are carried out when evaluating an expression: (1) evaluate all expressions within parentheses or other grouping symbols, (2) evaluate all powers, (3) multiply and divide from left to right, and (4) add and subtract from left to right. (5, 135)

ordered pair A pair of numbers named in an order that matters. For example, $(3, 5)$ is different from $(5, 3)$. The coordinates of a point are given as an ordered pair in which the first number is the x-coordinate and the second number is the y-coordinate. (70)

ordinate The y-coordinate in an ordered pair (x, y), measuring vertical distance from the x-axis on a coordinate plane. (70)

origin The point on a coordinate plane where the x- and y-axes intersect. The origin has coordinates $(0, 0)$. (70)

outcome A possible result of one trial of an experiment. (557)

outlier A value that is far outside the range of most of the other values in a data set. As a general rule, a data value is considered an outlier if the distance from the value to the first quartile or third quartile (whichever is nearest) is more than 1.5 times the interquartile range. (48)

parabola The graph of a function in the family of functions with parent function $y = x^2$. The set of all points whose distance from a fixed point, the focus, is equal to the distance from a fixed line, the directrix. (425, 524)

parallel lines Lines in the same plane that never intersect. They are always the same distance apart. (595)

parallelogram A quadrilateral with two pairs of opposite sides that are parallel. In a parallelogram, opposite sides are congruent. (599)

parent function The most basic form of a function. A parent function can be transformed to create a family of functions. For example, $y = x^2$ is a parent function that can be transformed to create a family of functions that includes $y = x^2 + 2$ and $y = 3(x - 4)^2$. (446, 466)

pentagon A polygon with exactly five sides. (32)

perfect cube A number that is equal to the cube of an integer. For example, -125 is a perfect cube because $-125 = (-5)^3$. (537)

perfect square A number that is equal to the square of an integer, or a polynomial that is equal to the square of another polynomial. For example, 64 is a perfect square because it is equal to 8^2, and $x^2 - 10x + 25$ is a perfect-square trinomial because it is equal to $(x - 5)^2$. (428, 510)

permutation An arrangement of choices in which the order is important, and once a choice is made it cannot be used again. For example, the permutations of the letters a, b, and c are *abc*, *acb*, *bac*, *bca*, *cab*, and *cba*. (571)

perpendicular bisector A line that passes through the midpoint of a segment and is perpendicular to the segment. (601)

perpendicular lines Lines that meet at a right angle. (595)

pictograph A data display with symbols showing the number of data items in each category. Each symbol in a pictograph stands for a specific number of data items. (39)

point-slope form The form $y = y_1 + b(x - x_1)$ of a linear equation, in which (x_1, y_1) is a point on the line and b is the slope. (235)

polygon A closed figure made up of segments that do not cross each other. (28)

polynomial A sum of terms that have positive integer exponents. For example, $-4x^2 + x$ and $x^3 - 6x^2 + 9$ are polynomials. (508)

polynomial equation An equation in which a polynomial expression is set equal to a second variable, such as y or $f(x)$. (371)

population density The number of people per square mile. (364)

power properties of exponents For any values a, b, m, and n, $(b^m)^n = b^{mn}$ and $(ab)^n = a^n b^n$. (352)

precision The smallest unit in which a measurement is expressed. For instance, if a measurement is determined as 12.25 inches, then its precision is 0.01 inch, or one-hundredth of an inch. (78)

predict To make an educated guess, usually based on a pattern. (9)

premise A statement, such as a definition, property, or proven fact, used to prove further conclusions in a deductive argument. (597)

probability A number between 0 and 1 that gives the chance that an outcome will happen. An outcome with a probability of 0 is impossible. An outcome with a probability of 1 is certain to happen. (553, 557)

product The result of multiplication. (86)

projectile motion The motion of a thrown, kicked, fired, or launched object—such as a ball— that has no means of propelling itself. (497)

proportion An equation stating that two ratios are equal. For example, $\frac{34}{72} = \frac{x}{18}$ is a proportion. (97)

Pythagorean Theorem The sum of the squares of the lengths of the legs a and b of a right triangle equals the square of the length of the hypotenuse c—that is, $a^2 + b^2 = c^2$. (613)

Q-points On a scatter plot, the vertices of the rectangle formed by drawing vertical lines through the first and third quartiles of the x-values and horizontal lines through the first and third quartiles of the y-values. If the points show an increasing linear trend, then the line through the lower-left and upper-right Q-points is a line of fit. If the points show a decreasing linear trend, then the line through the upper-left and lower-right Q-points is a line of fit. (254)

quadrant One of the four regions that a coordinate plane is divided into by the two axes. The quadrants are numbered I, II, III, and IV, starting in the upper right and moving counterclockwise. (70)

quadratic formula If a quadratic equation is written in the form $ax^2 + bx + c = 0$, then the solutions to the equation are given by $x = \frac{-b \pm \sqrt{b^2 - 4ac}}{2a}$. (531, 532)

quadratic function Any function in the family with parent function $f(x) = x^2$. Examples of quadratic functions are $f(x) = 1.5x^2 + 2$, $f(x) = (x - 4)^2$, and $f(x) = 5x^2 - 3x + 12$. (497)

quadrilateral A polygon with exactly four sides. (237)

quartile Any of the three variables that divide a data set into four equal-sized groups. See also **first quartile** and **third quartile**. (55)

radical expression An expression containing a square root symbol, $\sqrt{}$. Examples of radical expressions are $\sqrt{x + 4}$ and $3 \pm \sqrt{19}$. (499)

radioactive decay The process by which an unstable chemical element loses mass or energy, transforming it into a different element or isotope. (373)

raised to the power A term used to connect the base and the exponent in an exponential

expression. For example, in the expression 7^4, the base 7 is raised to the power of 4. (352)

random Not ordered, unpredictable. (29, 30, 564)

range (of a data set) The difference between the maximum and minimum values in a data set. (41)

range (of a function) The set of output values for a function. (390)

rate A ratio, often with 1 in the denominator. (110, 188)

rate of change The difference between two output values divided by the difference between the corresponding input values. For a linear relationship, the rate of change is constant. (188)

rate problem A problem involving a rate or rates, which is usually solved using the equation $d = rt$. (264)

ratio A comparison of two quantities, often written in fraction form. (96)

rational expression A ratio of two polynomial expressions, such as $\frac{3}{x + 2}$ or $\frac{x + 1}{(x + 3)(x - 1)}$. (477)

rational function A function, such as $f(x) = \frac{3}{x + 2}$ or $f(x) = \frac{x - 1}{(x + 3)(x - 1)}$, that is expressed as the ratio of two polynomial expressions. (475)

rational number A number that can be written as a ratio of two integers. (99, 499)

real number Any number that can be represented on a number line. The real numbers include integers, rational numbers, and irrational numbers. The real numbers do *not* include imaginary numbers. (499)

reciprocal The multiplicative inverse. The reciprocal of a given number is the number you multiply it by to get 1. To find the reciprocal of a number, you can write the number as a fraction and then invert the fraction. For example, the reciprocal of $\frac{3}{4}$ is $\frac{4}{3}$. (97, 596)

rectangle A quadrilateral with four right angles. In a rectangle, opposite sides are parallel and congruent. (599)

recursive Describes a procedure that is applied over and over again, starting with a number or geometric figure, to produce a sequence of numbers or figures. Each stage of a recursive procedure builds

on the previous stage. The resulting sequence is said to be generated recursively, and the procedure is called recursion. (2)

recursive routine A starting value and a recursive rule for generating a recursive sequence. (158)

recursive rule The instructions for producing each stage of a recursive sequence from the previous stage. (3)

recursive sequence An ordered list of numbers defined by a starting value and a recursive rule. You generate a recursive sequence by applying the rule to the starting value, then applying the rule to the resulting value, and so on. (158)

reflection A transformation that flips a figure or graph over a line, creating a mirror image. (454)

reflection across the *x*-axis A transformation that flips a figure or graph across the *x*-axis. Reflecting a point across the *x*-axis changes the sign of its *y*-coordinate. (454)

reflection across the *y*-axis A transformation that flips a figure or graph across the *y*-axis. Reflecting a point across the *y*-axis changes the sign of its *x*-coordinate. (454)

relation Any relationship between two variables. (390)

relative frequency The ratio of the number of times a particular outcome occurred to the total number of trials. Also called **observed probability.** (558)

relative frequency graph A data display (usually a bar graph or a circle graph) that compares the number in each category to the total for all the categories. Relative frequency graphs show fractions or percents, rather than actual values. (550)

repeating decimal A decimal number with a digit or group of digits after the decimal point that repeats infinitely. (96, 211)

restriction on the variable A statement of values that are excluded from the domain of an expression or equation. Any value of a variable that results in a denominator of 0 must be excluded from the domain. (477)

rhombus A quadrilateral with all sides the same length. In a rhombus, opposite sides are parallel. (599)

right angle An angle that measures 90°. (595)

right trapezoid A trapezoid with two right angles. In a right trapezoid, one of the nonparallel sides is perpendicular to both parallel sides. (598)

right triangle A triangle with a right angle. (597)

roots The solutions to an equation in the form $f(x) = 0$. The roots are the *x*-intercepts of the graph of $y = f(x)$. For example, the roots of $(x - 2)(x + 1) = 0$ are 2 and -1. These roots are the *x*-intercepts of the graph of $y = (x - 2)(x + 1)$. (503)

rotation A transformation that turns a figure about a point called the center of rotation. (488)

row matrix A matrix that consists of only one row. (86)

row operations Operations performed on the rows of a matrix in order to transform it into a matrix with a diagonal of 1's with 0's above and below, creating a solution matrix. These are allowable row operations: multiply (or divide) all the numbers in a row by a nonzero number, add (or subtract) all the numbers in a row to (or from) corresponding numbers in another row, add (or subtract) a multiple of the numbers in one row to (or from) the corresponding numbers in another row. (297)

S

sample A part of a population selected to represent the entire population. Sampling is the process of selecting and studying a sample from a population in order to make conjectures about the whole population. (103)

scale (of an axis or a number line) The values that correspond to the intervals of a coordinate axis or number line. (40)

scatter plot A two-variable data display in which values on a horizontal axis represent values of one variable and values on a vertical axis represent values of the other variable. The coordinates of each point represent a pair of data values. (70)

scientific notation A notation in which a number is written as a number greater than or equal to 1 but less than 10, multiplied by an integer power of 10. For example, in scientific notation, the number 32,000 is written 3.2×10^4. (355)

segment Two points on a line (endpoints) and all the points between them on the line. Also called a **line segment.** (3)

self-similar Describes a figure in which part of the figure is similar to—that is, has the same shape as—the whole figure. (6)

shrink A transformation that decreases the height or width of a figure. A vertical shrink decreases the height but leaves the width unchanged. A horizontal shrink decreases the width but leaves the height unchanged. A vertical shrink by a factor of a multiplies the y-coordinate of each point on a figure or graph by a. A horizontal shrink by a factor of b multiplies the x-coordinate of each point on a figure by b. (462)

Sierpiński triangle A fractal created by Waclaw Sierpiński by starting with a filled-in equilateral triangle and recursively removing every triangle whose vertices are midpoints of triangles remaining from the previous stage. You can create a Sierpiński-like fractal design by starting with an equilateral triangle and recursively connecting the midpoints of the sides of each upward-pointing triangle. (3, 337)

similar figures Figures that have the same shape. Similar polygons have proportional sides and congruent angles. (131, 632, 647)

simulate To model an experiment with another experiment, called a *simulation,* so that the outcomes of the simulation have the same probabilities as the corresponding outcomes of the original experiment. For example, you can simulate tossing a coin by randomly generating a string of 0's and 1's on your calculator. (103)

sine If A is an acute angle in a right triangle, $sine\ of\ angle\ A = \frac{length\ of\ opposite\ leg}{length\ of\ hypotenuse}$, or $\sin A = \frac{o}{h}$. (635)

slope The steepness of a line or the rate of change of a linear relationship. If (x_1, y_1) and (x_2, y_2) are two points on a line, then the slope of the line is $\frac{y_2 - y_1}{x_2 - x_1}$. The slope is the value of b when the equation of the line is written in intercept form, $y = a + bx$, and it is the value of m when the equation of the line is written in slope-intercept form, $y = mx + b$. (215, 218)

slope triangle A right triangle formed by drawing arrows to show the vertical and horizontal change from one point to another point on a line. (216)

slope-intercept form The form $y = mx + b$ of a linear equation. The value of m is the slope and the value of b is the y-intercept. (229)

solution The value(s) of the variable(s) that make an equation or inequality true. (146)

solve an equation To determine the value(s) of the variable(s) that make an equation true. (146)

spread A property of one-variable data that indicates how the data values are distributed from least to greatest and where gaps or clusters occur. Statistics such as the range, the interquartile range, and the five-number summary can help describe the spread of data. (40)

square A quadrilateral in which all four angles are right angles and all four sides have the same length. (599)

square (of a number) The product of a number and itself. The square of a number x is "x squared" and is written x^2. For example, the square of 6 is 6^2, which is equal to 36. (424)

square root The square root of a number a is a number b so that $a = b^2$. Every positive number has two square roots. For example, the square roots of 36 are -6 and 6 because $6^2 = 36$ and $(-6)^2 = 36$. The square root symbol, $\sqrt{\ }$, means the positive square root of a number. So, $\sqrt{36} = 6$. (426)

square root function The function that undoes squaring, giving only the positive square root (that is, the positive number that, when multiplied by itself, gives the input). The square root function is written $f(x) = \sqrt{x}$. For example, $\sqrt{144} = 12$. (426)

squaring The process of multiplying a number by itself. See **square** (of a number). (424)

squaring function The function $f(x) = x^2$, which gives the square of a number. (425, 429)

standard deviation A measurement of how widely dispersed a set of data is from its mean. (435)

standard form The form $ax + by = c$ of a linear equation, in which a and b are not both 0. (242)

Glossary

statistics Numbers, such as the mean, median, and range, used to summarize or represent a data set. Statistics also refers to the science of collecting, organizing, and interpreting information. (41)

stem plot A one-variable data display used to show the distribution of a fairly small set of data values. Generally, the left digit(s) of the data values, called the stems, are listed in a column on the left side of the plot. The remaining digits, called the leaves, are listed in order to the right of the corresponding stem. A key is usually included. (61)

stem-and-leaf plot See **stem plot.**

strange attractor A figure that the stages generated by a random recursive procedure get closer and closer to. (30)

stretch A transformation that increases the height or width of a figure. A vertical stretch increases the height but leaves the width unchanged. A horizontal stretch increases the width but leaves the height unchanged. A vertical stretch by a factor of a multiplies the y-coordinate of each point on a figure or graph by a. A horizontal stretch by a factor of b multiplies the x-coordinate of each point on a figure by b. (462)

substitution method A method for solving a system of equations that involves solving one of the equations for one variable and substituting the resulting expression into the other equation. For example, to find the solution to $\begin{cases} y + 2 = 3x \\ y - 1 = x + 3 \end{cases}$ you can solve the first equation for y to get $y = 3x - 2$ and then substitute $3x - 2$ for y in the second equation. (281)

subtraction property of equality If $a = b$, then $a - c = b - c$ for any number c. (243)

symbolic manipulation Applying mathematical properties to rewrite an equation or expression in equivalent form. (284)

symmetric Having a sense of balance, or symmetry. Symmetric is most often used to describe figures with mirror symmetry, or line symmetry— that is, figures that you can fold in half so that one half matches exactly with the other half. (54)

system of equations A set of two or more equations with the same variables. (273)

system of inequalities A set of two or more inequalities with the same variables. (320)

tangent If A is an acute angle in a right triangle, $tangent\ of\ angle\ A = \frac{length\ of\ opposite\ leg}{length\ of\ adjacent\ leg}$, or $\tan A = \frac{o}{h}$. (635)

term (of a polynomial) An algebraic expression that represents only multiplication and division between variables and constants. For example, in the polynomial $x^3 - 6x^2 + 9$, the terms are x^3, $-6x^2$, and 9. (508)

term (of a sequence) Each number in a sequence. (160)

terminating decimal A decimal number with a finite number of nonzero digits after the decimal point. (96, 211)

theoretical probability A probability calculated by analyzing a situation, rather than by performing an experiment. If the outcomes are equally likely, then the theoretical probability of a particular group of outcomes is the ratio of the number of outcomes in that group to the total number of possible outcomes. For example, when you roll a die, one of the six possible outcomes is a 2, so the theoretical probability of rolling a 2 is $\frac{1}{6}$. (558)

third quartile (Q3) The median of the values above the median of a data set. (52)

topographic map See **contour map.**

torque A force that produces rotation. (488)

transformation A change in the size or position of a figure or graph. Translations, reflections, stretches, shrinks, and rotations are types of transformations. (437)

translation A transformation that slides a figure or graph to a new position. (439)

trapezoid A quadrilateral with one pair of opposite sides that are parallel and one pair of opposite sides that are not parallel. (598)

tree diagram A diagram whose branches show the possible outcomes of an event and sometimes probabilities. (569)

trial One round of an experiment. (558)

trigonometric functions The sine, cosine, and tangent functions, which express relationships among the measures of the acute angles in a right triangle and the ratios of the side lengths. (635)

trigonometry The study of the relationships among sides and angles of right triangles. (635)

trinomial A polynomial with exactly three terms. Examples of trinomials include $x + 2x^3 + 4$, $x^2 - 6x + 9$, and $3x^3 + 2x^2 + x$. (508)

two-variable data set A collection of data that measures two traits or quantities. A two-variable data set consists of pairs of values. (70)

undoing method A method of solving an equation that involves working backward to reverse each operation until the variable is isolated on one side of the equation. (146)

value of an expression The numerical result of evaluating an expression. (22)

variable A trait or quantity whose value can change, or vary. In algebra, letters often represent variables. (70, 97, 136)

Venn diagram A diagram of overlapping circles that shows the relationships among members of different sets. (499)

vertex (of an absolute-value graph) The point where the graph changes direction from increasing to decreasing or from decreasing to increasing. (444)

vertex (of a parabola) The point where the graph changes direction from increasing to decreasing or from decreasing to increasing. (447)

vertex (of a polygon) A "corner" of a polygon. An endpoint of one of the polygon's sides. The plural of vertex is vertices. (29)

vertex form (of a quadratic equation) The form $y = a(x - h)^2 + k$, where $a \neq 0$. The point (h, k) is the vertex of the parabola. (505)

vertical axis The vertical number line on a coordinate graph or data display. Also called the **y-axis.** (40, 70)

vertical line test A method for determining whether a graph on the xy-coordinate plane represents a function. If all possible vertical lines

cross the graph only once or not at all, the graph represents a function. If even one vertical line crosses the graph in more than one point, the graph does not represent a function. (397)

vertically reflected See **reflection across the x-axis.**

whole number Any one of the numbers 0, 1, 2, 3, ... (499)

work problem A problem involving a task, a rate of work for the task, and the total time necessary to complete the task. Work problems usually involve the equation *rate of work · time = part of work.* (252)

x-intercept The x-coordinate of a point where a graph meets the x-axis. For example, the graph of $y = x + 2$ has x-intercept -2, and the graph of $y = (x + 2)(x - 4)$ has two x-intercepts, -2 and 4. (205)

y-intercept The y-coordinate of the point where a graph crosses the y-axis. The value of y when x is 0. The y-intercept of a line is the value of a when the equation of the line is written in intercept form, $y = a + bx$, and it is the value of b when the equation for the line is written in slope-intercept form, $y = mx + b$. (179)

zero exponent For any nonzero value of b, $b^0 = 1$. (367)

zero-product property If the product of two or more factors equals zero, then at least one of the factors equals zero. For example, if $x(x + 2)(x - 3) = 0$, then $x = 0$ or $x + 2 = 0$ or $x - 3 = 0$. (518)

zeros (of a function) The values of the independent variable (the x-values) that make the corresponding values of the function (the $f(x)$-values) equal to zero. For example, the zeros of the function $f(x) = (x - 1)(x + 7)$ are 1 and -7 because $f(1) = 0$ and $f(-7) = 0$. See **roots.** (518)

Glossary

Index

Index

Index

Fahrenheit, conversion of, 147, 414, 434
family of functions, 446, 448
Fathom Projects, 67, 82, 260, 380
fault, 446
feasible region, 330
first-quadrant graphs, 72
first quartile (Q1), 52
five-number summary, 52–54
focus, 524
fractals, 4, 5, 15
  drawing of, 2–3, 14
  enclosed shapes formed in, 14
  exponent patterns for, 9–10, 15
  invention of, 21
  Koch curve, 14–15, 19, 341–342
  length of, 14–16, 19, 341–342
  as model, 1
  recursive rules for, 3, 14
  self-similarity of, 6
  Sierpiński triangle, 2–3, 6, 9, 14
  strange attractors, 30
  tree, 11
  weed, 12
fractions
  conversion of decimals into, 212
  conversion into decimals, 96, 212
  reciprocals, 596
  review of operations with, 3–6
frequency, 59, 60
functions
  absolute-value. *See* absolute-value function
  continuous, 407
  counterexamples in testing for, 401
  cubic, 537–541
  decreasing, 405–407
  discrete, 407
  domain, 390–391, 405
  exponential, 446, 447–448
  families of, 446, 448
  graphing of, 396–399, 404–407, 412–413, 418–421
  increasing, 405–407
  inverse of. *See* inverse functions
  inverse variation. *See* inverse variation
  letter-shift codes as, 390–391
  linear, 404
  nonlinear, 404, 405
  notation for, 412–414
  number transformation with, 396
  parent, 446, 474
  quadratic, 497
  range, 390–391, 405
  rational. *See* rational functions
  reflections of, 453–456

representation of, 391, 396
square root, 426, 446
stretching and shrinking of, 464–467, 470
testing for, 396–399
translation of, 444–448
trigonometric. *See* trigonometric functions
See also equations

G

Gauss, Carl Friedrich, 298
GCF (greatest common factor), 245
general form of quadratic equations, 498
  completing the square and, 525–528
  conversion of factored form to, 543
  conversion to vertex form, 527–528
  conversion of vertex form to, 508–511
  expansion to, 511, 517
  information given by, 511, 516
  quadratic formula and, 531–532
general linear equation, 155
The Geometer's Sketchpad Projects, 21, 102, 131, 489, 524, 617
Gerdes, Paulus, 610
girth, 543
glyphs, 76
golden ratio, 102, 536
gradients, 194, 645
graphing
  of absolute-value functions, 420
  as approximate solution of equations, 195, 199
  the constant and effect on, 155
  of cubic functions, 537–541
  of functions, 396–399, 404–407, 412–413
  of inequalities, 306–307, 312–315, 320–322, 330
  of inverse variation, 125–126, 474–475
  of linear equations, 179, 181–182
  of a parabola, 424–425
  of polygons, 597–598
  of quadratic equations, 498–499, 503–505
  of rational functions, 474–475
  as solution to equations, 195, 199, 273–276, 282, 420, 498–499
  of systems of equations, 273–276, 282
  of time-distance relationships, 172–174

graphs
  asymptotes in, 474
  bar graphs, 39–40, 550–553
  box plots, 53–54, 59
  categories, 40
  circle graphs, 550–553
  dependent/independent variables on, 404–405
  dot plots, 40, 46–48, 59
  first-quadrant, 72
  histograms, 59–62
  pictographs, 39
  reflections of, 453–456
  relative frequency, 550–553
  scatter plots, 70–73, 77–78
  stem plots, 61
  stretching and shrinking, 462–467
  translation of, 444–448
  See also coordinate plane; data
gravity, 496
greatest common factor (GCF), 245

H

half-life, 381–382
half-plane, 313
Harriot, Thomas, 304
histograms, 59–62
horizontal axis (*x*-axis), 70
  dot plots and, 40
  independent variable shown on, 404
  reflection across, 454
horizontal lines, slope of, 219
hypotenuse, 597
hypothesis, 597

I

image, 439
imaginary numbers, 548
Improving Your . . . Skills
  Geometry, 280, 411, 605
  Reasoning, 28, 45, 76, 143, 150, 154, 186, 205, 212, 265, 327, 359, 372, 423, 461, 470, 536
  Visual Thinking, 113, 233, 309, 354, 452, 483, 507, 610
inches, conversion of, 108–109
increasing functions, 405–407
independent events, 580
independent variable, 404–405, 412
inductive reasoning, 597
inequalities, 304
  compound, 307, 310
  constraints, 320, 323
  graphing, 306–307, 312–315, 320–322, 330

J

K

L

Index

matrices, use of, 296–299, 303
substitution method, 281–284
three equations in three variables, 319
systems of inequalities, 320–323

Photo Credits

Cover

Background image: Pat O'Hara/DRK Photo; boat image: Marc Epstein/DRK Photo; all other images: Ken Karp Photography

Front Matter

v: Ken Karp Photography; **vi (*t*):** Ken Karp Photography; **vi (*b*):** Ken Karp Photography; **vii (*bl*):** © Tom Bean/CORBIS; **vii (*br*):** © Tom Bean/CORBIS; **viii (*t*):** Cheryl Fenton; **viii (*b*):** Ken Karp Photography; **ix (*t*):** Ken Karp Photography; **ix (*bl*):** © Bettmann/CORBIS; **ix (*br*):** Ken Karp Photography; **x (*b*):** Quilt by Diana Venters/*Mathematical Quilts* by Diana Venters; **xii:** Ken Karp Photography

Chapter 0

1: Copyright 2000 Livesmith Classic Fractals, Palmdale, CA, USA. All rights reserved. http://www.lifesmith.com; **4:** Ken Karp Photography; **5 (*l*):** © Roger Ressmeyer/CORBIS; **5 (*r*):** Ken Karp Photography; **6:** Cheryl Fenton; **12:** © 1995-2002 Sylvie Gallet; **15 (*l*):** © Yann Arthus-Bertrand/CORBIS; **15 (*r*):** Ken Karp Photography; **22:** Ken Karp Photography; **30 (*l*):** © AFP/CORBIS; **30 (*r*):** © Gary Braasch/CORBIS; **33 (*b*):** Ken Karp Photography

Chapter 1

38: © David Robinson/CORBIS; **39:** Ken Karp Photography; **40 (*l*):** © CORBIS; **40 (*r*):** Ken Karp Photography; **43:** © Ted Horowitz/CORBIS; **46:** Cheryl Fenton; **47:** FPG; **49:** Dan Feight; **50:** The Hollow of the Deep-Sea Off Kanagawa by Katsushika Hokusai/Minneapolis Institute of Art Acc. No.74.1.230; **51:** Catherine Noren/Stock Boston; **52:** Jonathan Daniel/Getty Images; **53:** James Amos/Photo Researchers; **57:** Roy Pinney/FPG; **58:** Ken Karp Photography; **60:** Ken Karp Photography; **63 (*tl*):** Sharon Smith/Bruce Coleman Inc.; **63 (*tr*):** © Craig Lovell/CORBIS; **63 (*ml*):** Betty Press/Woodfin Camp & Associates; **63 (*mr*):** Catherine Karnow/Woodfin Camp & Associates; **63 (*bl*):** © Alison Wright/CORBIS; **63 (*br*):** © Craig Lovell/CORBIS; **68:** Ken Karp Photography; **69:** Ken Karp Photography; **72:** © Joseph Sohm ChromoSohm Inc./CORBIS; **73:** Gregg Mancuso/Stock Boston; **75:** John Collier/FPG; **77:** Michael Yamashita/Woodfin Camp & Associates; **83:** Library of Congress; **84:** Ken Karp Photography; **87:** Christian Michaels/FPG; **88:** © Joseph Sohm/ChromoSohm Inc./CORBIS; **89:** © Roger Ball/CORBIS; **90 (*t*):** Ken Karp Photography; **91:** © Mitchell Layton/NewSport/CORBIS

Chapter 2

95: © Morton Beebe/CORBIS; **100:** Ken Karp Photography; **102:** © CORBIS; **103:** Michael Heron/Woodfin Camp & Assoc.; **104 (*l*):** Steve & Dave Maslowski/Photo Researchers Inc.; **104 (*m*):** Mark Stouffer/Animals Animals; **104 (*r*):** Gary Meszaros/Photo Researchers; **106:** Ken Karp Photography; **108:** Robert Fried/Stock Boston; **110 (*l*):** © CORBIS; **110 (*r*):** Cheryl Fenton; **111:** © Dimitri Iundt/CORBIS; **112:** Cheryl Fenton; **113 (*l*):** M. Harvery/DRK Photo; **113 (*ml*):** Anthony Mercieca/Photo Researchers Inc.; **113 (*m*):** Maslowski/Photo Researchers; **113 (*mr*):** © Kevin Schafer/CORBIS; **113 (*r*):** Peter & Beverly Pickford/DRK Photo; **115:** Will & Deni McIntyre/Photo Researchers, Inc.; **118 (*t*):** © Manfred Vollmer/CORBIS; **118 (*b*):** © Archivo Iconografico, SA/CORBIS; **120:** John Carter/Photo Researchers; **121:** Ken Karp Photography; **122 (*l*):** Stephen Simpson/FPG; **122 (*r*):** Telegraph Colour Library/FPG; **124:** Ken Karp Photography; **125:** Cheryl Fenton; **129:** Richard Megna/Fundamental Photographs; **130:** Ken Karp Photography; **131:** Library of Congress; **132:** Ken Karp Photography; **134:** © AFP/CORBIS; **143:** Ken Karp Photography; **149:** © Pete Stone/CORBIS; **149:** Cheryl Fenton; **151:** © Lynda Richardson/CORBIS; **152:** Judith Canty/Stock Boston; **154:** © Burstein Collection/ CORBIS

Chapter 3

157 (*t*): © Alison Wright/CORBIS; **157 (*b*):** Christi's Images; **158:** Rafael Marcia/Photo Researchers Inc.; **159:** Cheryl Fenton; **162:** Photofest; **163:** Jeffry Myers/Stock Boston; **164:** David Falconer/Bruce Coleman Inc.; **170:** D. Burnett/Woodfin Camp & Associates; **172:** Ken Karp Photography; **177:** Courtesy of The Rick Hansen Institute; **179 (*t*):** © Duomo/CORBIS; **179 (*b*):** © Tom and DeeAnn McCarthy/CORBIS; **180:** Anderson/The Image Works; **182:** Hertz Rent-A-Car; **185 (*t*):** © Claude Charlier/CORBIS; **185 (*b*):** Cheryl Fenton; **186:** George D. Lepp/Photo Researchers Inc.; **187:** © Bettmann/CORBIS; **189:** John Eastcott/YVA Momatiuk/Woodfin Camp & Associates; **194:** © Douglas Peebles/CORBIS; **195:** James P. Blair/CORBIS; **204:** Ken Karp Photography; **205:** Cheryl Fenton; **208:** Ken Karp Photography; **210 (*tl*):** Marc Muench/David Muench Photography; **210 (*tr*):** Tom Bean/DRK Photo; **210 (*b*):** © Ted Horowitz/CORBIS; **211:** Bernard Soutrit/Woodfin Camp & Assoc.

Chapter 4

214: Smithsonian American Art Museum, Washington, DC/Art Resource, NY; **215:** Collection of Gretchen and John Berggruen, San Francisco; **219 (*t*):** Ken Karp Photography; **219 (*b*):** Ken Karp Photography; **221:** Ken Karp Photography; **222:** © James Marshall/CORBIS; **224:** The Museum of Modern Art, New York. Gift of Philip Johnson. Digital Image © The Museum of Modern Art/Licensed by SCALA/Art Resource, NY; **225:** © Jonathan Blair/CORBIS; **227 (*t*):** Peter Menzel/Stock Boston; **227 (*b*):** Hamburger (1983) by David Gilhooly, Collection of Harry W. and Mary Margaret Anderson, Photo by M. Lee Fatheree; **231:** © AFP/CORBIS; **232:** Ken Karp Photography; **238:** Ken Karp Photography; **239:** John DeWaele/Stock Boston; **240:** © Burstein Collection/CORBIS; **244:** Interlochen Center for the Arts; **247:** David Weintraub/Stock Boston; **248:** Steven Rubin/The Image Works; **249:** © Morton Beebe, S.F./CORBIS; **250:** © Michael Sedam/CORBIS; **253:** Ken Karp Photography; **255:** Bob Daemmrich/Stock Boston; **259:** Tom Bean/DRK Photo; **264:** AMTRAK; **266:** Ken Karp Photography; **269:** Mike Powell/Getty Images

Chapter 5

272: George Holton/Photo Researchers Inc.; **273:** Ken Karp Photography; **275 (*l*):** © Tom Bean/CORBIS; **275 (*r*):** © Tom Bean/CORBIS; **276:** George Chan/Photo Researchers Inc.; **279:** Gerard Smith/Photo Researchers Inc.; **280:** © Martin Bydalek Photography/CORBIS; **281:** © Philip James/CORBIS; **282:** Cheryl Fenton; **283:** © Royalty-Free/CORBIS; **285 (*t*):** © Tom Bean/CORBIS; **285 (*b*):** © Tom Bean/CORBIS; **286 (*t*):** Photofest; **286 (*l*):** Photofest; **286 (*r*):** Photofest; **287:** © David Gray/Reuters/CORBIS; **288:** © Douglas Mesney/CORBIS; **294 (*l*):** A. Ramey/Stock Boston; **294 (*r*):** © Julian Hirshowitz/CORBIS; **295:** © Don Mason/CORBIS; **296:** © Dan McCoy/Rainbow; **299:** Milton Rand/Tom Stack & Associates; **305:** Ken Karp Photography; **306:** George Olson/Woodfin Camp & Associates; **309:** Ken Karp Photography; **310:** Ken Karp Photography; **311:** NASA; **312:** © Charles Mann/CORBIS; **318:** Ezra Shaw/Getty Images; **320:** Bob Daemmrich/Stock Boston; **322 (*t*):** Ken Karp Photography; **322 (*b*):** Cheryl Fenton; **323:** Cheryl Fenton; **327:** Tom Walker/Stock Boston; **328 (*t*):** George Chan/Photo Researchers Inc.; **328 (*b*):** Ken Karp Photography; **330:** Tony Hawk/Getty Images

Chapter 6

332: © Bettman/CORBIS; **333 (*t*):** Ken Karp Photography; **333 (*bl*):** Cheryl Fenton; **338:** Jose Palaez/CORBIS; **339:** Cheryl Fenton; **340:** Ken Karp Photography; **341:** Courtesy of José Tence Ruiz; **345:** Geoff Tompkinson/Photo Researchers; **346:** Timothy Eagan/Woodfin Camp & Associates; **347:** Cheryl Fenton; **349:** © Tom & Dee Ann McCarthy/CORBIS; **350:** Runk-Schoenberger/Grant Heilman Photography; **355:** Paul Thiessen/Tom Stack & Associates; **356 (*t*):** Mark Godfrey/The Image Works;

356 (*b*): © Bettmann/CORBIS; 357: Cheryl Fenton; 358: © Bettmann/CORBIS; 359 (*t*): Cheryl Fenton; 364: © Lee White/CORBIS; 365: Stephen Dalton/Photo Researchers, Inc.; 369: Peter Arnold Inc.; 371: Ken Karp Photography; 372: Dick Luria/Photo Researchers, Inc.; 373 (*l*): © Chuck Savage/CORBIS; 373 (*m*): © Cydney Conger/CORBIS; 373 (*r*): © Hulton-Deutsch Collection/CORBIS; 374: AP/Wide World; 375: Tom & Therisa Stack/Tom Stack & Associates; 378: Ken Karp Photography; 379: Alexander Tsiaras/Photo Researchers Inc.; 380 (*t*): © Hulton-Deutsch Collection/CORBIS; 380 (*b*): Manfred Cage/Peter Arnold, Inc.; 381: Ken Karp Photography; 383 (*t*): Cheryl Fenton; 384: Image by Man Ray © Man Ray Trust-ADAGP/ARS, 2001

Chapter 7

387: Scala/Art Resource, NY; 388 (*tl*): © Archivo Iconografico, SA/CORBIS; 388 (*tr*): Stuart Craig/ Bruce Coleman, Inc.; 388 (*b*): Ken Karp Photography; 391: Getty Images; 396: Guitare Et Journal by Pablo Picasso/Christie's Images; 399: J. Pickerell/The Image Works; 403: © Tom Stewart/CORBIS; 408 (*t*): Ed Young/Photo Researchers; 412: © Bettmann/CORBIS; 419: A. Ramey/Woodfin Camp & Associates; 422: Bob & Clara Calhoun/Bruce Coleman Inc.; 424: National Museum of Women in Art/Gift of Wallace and Wilhelmina Holladay; 425: Frank Siteman/Stock Boston; 430: © Roy Morsch/CORBIS; 431: Michael Lustbader/Photo Researchers; 432: © T. J. Florian/Rainbow; 433 (*t*): Cheryl Fenton; 433 (*b*): © J. Barry O'Rourke/CORBIS

Chapter 8

436: J.C. Carton/Bruce Coleman Inc.; 437: © 2001 Alias Systems Corp.; 444: Ken Karp Photography; 446 (*t*): National Museum of Women in Art/Gift of Wallace and Wilhelmina Holladay; 446 (*b*): © CORBIS; 450: Jason Luz; 451: Ken Karp Photography; 462: Ken Karp Photography; 462: Ken Karp Photography; 463: Erich Lessing/Art Resource; 464: Erich Lessing/Art Resource; 469: Interlochen Center for the Arts; 471: Ken Karp Photography; 474: Cedar Point Photo by Dan Feicht; 475: © David D. Keaton/CORBIS; 481: Ken Karp Photography; 483: Cheryl Fenton; 484: Phyllis Picardi/Stock Boston; 488: Ken Karp Photography; 490: Phyllis Picardi/Stock Boston; 492: Norman Tomalin/Bruce Coleman Inc.; 494: © Galen Rowell/CORBIS

Chapter 9

495: T.J. Florian/Rainbow; 496 (*t*): Ken Karp Photography; 497: © Bettmann/CORBIS; 502: Lee Foster/Bruce Coleman Inc.; 506: Ken Karp Photography; 512: Getty Images; 513: © Rick Gayle/CORBIS; 515: Ken Karp Photography; 522: Ken Karp Photography; 525: Ken Karp Photography; 529: Ezra Shaw/Getty Images; 530: Stuart Westmorland/Photo Researchers Inc.; 534: Tom Hauck/Getty Images; 537: Jason Luz; 544: © Roger Ball/CORBIS; 545 (*t*): © Bettmann/CORBIS; 545 (*m*): Ken Karp Photography; 545 (*b*): Ken Karp Photography

Chapter 10

549: Courtesy David Zwirner Gallery, New York; 551: Kelly-Mooney Photography; 553: Larry Mulvehill/Photo Researchers; 556 (*t*): David L. Brown/Tom Stack & Associates; 556 (*b*): Cary Wolinsky/Stock Boston; 557: Robert Longuehay, NIBSC/Science Photo Library; 558: Cheryl Fenton; 560 (*t*): Cheryl Fenton; 560 (*b*): Cheryl Fenton; 562: © Royalty-Free/CORBIS; 564: S. Dalton/Animals Animals; 568: Tom Lazar/Animals Animals; 571: Ken Karp Photography; 572: Jason Luz; 574: © Reuters/ CORBIS; 577: Courtesy of Lee Walton; 580: Ken Karp Photography; 582: © Michelle Garrett/CORBIS; 583 (*t*): Adam Hart-Davis/Science Photo Library; 583 (*b*): Adam Hart-Davis/Science Photo Library; 585: Getty Images; 587: Ken Karp Photography; 589: Getty Images; 590 (*t*): Cheryl Fenton; 592: © Dennis Degnan/CORBIS

Chapter 11

594: © Linsay Hebberd/CORBIS; 595: © Philadelphia Museum of Art/CORBIS; 596 (*t*): © Jeff Greenberg/Rainbow; 596 (*b*): © Richard Berenholtz/CORBIS; 601: Ken Karp Photography; 604: Ken Karp Photography; 606: © Coco McCoy/Rainbow; 608: Quilt by Diana Venters/*Mathematical Quilts* by Diana Venters; 614 (*l*): William Johnson/Stock Boston; 614 (*r*): Peter Menzel/Stock Boston; 616: Ken Karp Photography; 623: Will & Deni McIntyre/Photo Researchers, Inc.; 625: © Philadelphia Museum of Art/CORBIS; 626: Founders Society Purchase with funds from Flint Ink Corporation/Photograph © 1991 The Detroit Institute of Art, Accession Number 81.488; 628: Cheryl Fenton; 631: Daniel E. Wray/The Image Works; 632 (*t*): © Robert Holmes/CORBIS; 637: © Seth Joel/CORBIS; 639: © Michael Keller/CORBIS; 645: © Bettmann/CORBIS; 647 (*t*): Richard Berenholtz/CORBIS; 647 (*m*): Quilt by Diana Venters/*Mathematical Quilts* by Diana Venters; 647 (*b*): © Michael Keller/CORBIS; 649: Cheryl Fenton

Additional Answers

Steps 1–6 histogram using sample data

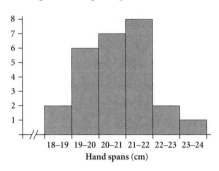

Step 5 sample data results

58 white beans were removed and replaced with red beans.

Number of tagged fish	Total number of fish	Fraction of tagged fish
3	60	$\frac{3}{60}$, or $\frac{1}{20}$
6	67	$\frac{6}{67}$
3	73	$\frac{3}{73}$
4	66	$\frac{4}{66}$, or $\frac{2}{33}$
4	88	$\frac{4}{88}$, or $\frac{1}{22}$
2	72	$\frac{2}{72}$, or $\frac{1}{36}$

The mean of the ratios of tagged to total fish in a sample is 0.052 and the median is 0.048. Because 0.05 is the average of the mean and the median, you might use the fraction $\frac{1}{20}$. Solve the proportion: $\frac{58}{x} = \frac{1}{20}$; $x = 1160$.

Step 1

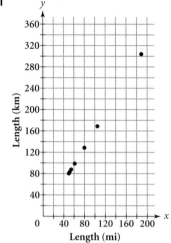

Step 2

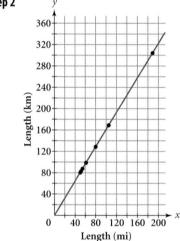

Step 3

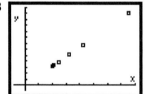

$[-20, 200, 25, -20, 325, 25]$

Step 3

Time (min)	Minivan (mi)	Sports car (mi)	Pickup (mi)
100	100	115	110
120	76	131	132
180	4	179	198
190	−8	187	209
200	−20	195	220
230	−56	219	253
240	−68	227	264

4a.

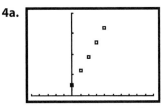

$[−5, 10, 1, 0, 40, 10]$

4b.

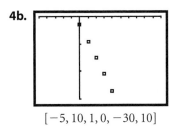

$[−5, 10, 1, 0, −30, 10]$

Step 1a Start at the 2 m mark and walk toward the 4 m mark (away from the motion sensor) at $\frac{1}{3}$ m/s.

Step 1b Start at the 3.5 m mark and walk toward the 0 m mark (toward the motion sensor) at $\frac{1}{4}$ m/s.

Step 1c Start at the 3 m mark and walk toward the 4 m mark (away from the motion sensor) at $\frac{1}{4}$ m/s for 4 s. Then walk toward the 0 m mark (toward the motion sensor) at 1 m/s.

Step 2a

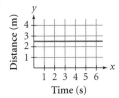

Step 2b

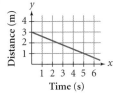

Step 2c

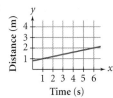

13.

$4x + 3 = 2x + 7$	Original equation.
$4x − 2x + 3 = 2x − 2x + 7$	Subtract 2x from both sides.
$2x + 3 = 7$	Combine like terms.
$2x + 3 − 3 = 7 − 3$	Subtract 3 from both sides.
$2x = 4$	Combine like terms.
$\frac{2x}{2} = \frac{4}{2}$	Divide both sides by 2.
$x = 2$	Reduce.

Step 7 It is reasonable. Although the combined data are not a simple average of male and female, the line should still lie between the two.

Step 8 Answers will vary. The intercept-form method first gives a parallel line that has to be raised or lowered based on estimation (weakness); however, that method involves adjusting the line to a fit (strength). The point-slope method immediately gives you a line (strength), but the line must go through points and could possibly benefit from adjusting (weakness). The point-slope method also increases the chance that different people will get the same equation of best fit.

6d. Graphing windows will vary. The one shown is $[0, 12000, 1000, −15000, 15000, 6000]$.

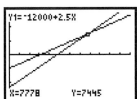

7b.

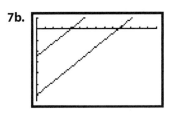

$[0, 7000, 500, −13000, 2000, 2000]$

Additional Answers

LESSON 6.1, PAGE 333

Step 2 See table. The rate of change does not indicate a linear pattern because it is not constant.

Step 3

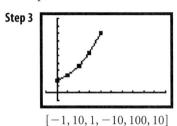

$[-1, 10, 1, -10, 100, 10]$

The slope of the line segments from point to point increases.

LESSON 6.4, PAGE 356

Steps 4 and 5

	Standard notation	Scientific notation
	5,000	5×10^3
a.	250	2.5×10^2
b.	$-5,530$	-5.53×10^3
c.	14,000	1.4×10^4
d.	7,000,000	7×10^6
e.	18	1.8×10^1
f.	$-470,000$	-4.7×10^5

LESSON 6.5, PAGE 360

Step 1a $\dfrac{5^9}{5^6} = \dfrac{5 \cdot 5 \cdot 5 \cdot \cancel{5} \cdot \cancel{5} \cdot \cancel{5} \cdot \cancel{5} \cdot \cancel{5} \cdot \cancel{5}}{\cancel{5} \cdot \cancel{5} \cdot \cancel{5} \cdot \cancel{5} \cdot \cancel{5} \cdot \cancel{5}} = 5^3$

Step 1b $\dfrac{3^3 \cdot 5^3}{3 \cdot 5^2} = \dfrac{3 \cdot 3 \cdot \cancel{3} \cdot 5 \cdot \cancel{5} \cdot \cancel{5}}{\cancel{3} \cdot \cancel{5} \cdot \cancel{5}} = 3^2 \cdot 5^1$

Step 1c $\dfrac{4^4 x^6}{4^2 x^3} = \dfrac{4 \cdot 4 \cdot \cancel{4} \cdot \cancel{4} \cdot x \cdot x \cdot x \cdot \cancel{x} \cdot \cancel{x} \cdot \cancel{x}}{\cancel{4} \cdot \cancel{4} \cdot \cancel{x} \cdot \cancel{x} \cdot \cancel{x}} = 4^2 x^3$

LESSON 6.7, PAGE 374

Steps 1–3, 5 Data will vary. Following is a sample set of data recorded using 201 counters and an angle of 68° on the plate.

"Years" elapsed	"Atoms" remaining	Successive ratios
0	201	
1	147	0.7313
2	120	0.8163
3	94	0.7833
4	71	0.7553
5	52	0.7324
6	42	0.8077
7	32	0.7619
8	28	0.8750
9	22	0.7857
10	18	0.8182
11	15	0.8333
12	12	0.8000
13	10	0.8333
14	9	0.9000

Step 4 Students should notice an exponential pattern. Here is a graph of the sample data (W).

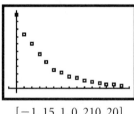

$[-1, 15, 1, 0, 210, 20]$

Step 9 The equation from Step 8 does not fit very well.

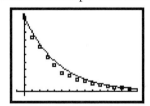

Step 10 Students may find that A seems to adjust the curve's position vertically and r seems to change the steepness of the curve. The equation $y = 201(1 - 0.22)^x$ fits the sample data better.

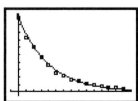

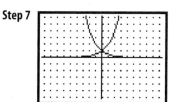

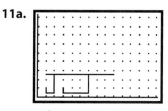

Step 10 Changing the sign of the *x*-coordinates of points, or negating the variable *x* in a function, produces a flip across the *y*-axis; likewise, changing the sign of the *y*-coordinates of points, or negating the variable *y* in a function, produces a flip across the *x*-axis.

11a.

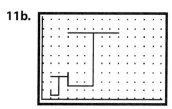

$[0, 28.2, 2, 0, 18.6, 2]$

11b.

11c.

Step 1

$[-9.4, 9.4, 1, -6.2, 6.2, 1]$

Step 4 This graph shows the relationship between the input numbers and their squares.

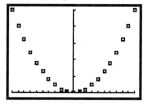

$[-10, 10, 1, 0, 100, 20]$

Step 8 This line is in the middle of the parabola and on top of the *y*-axis. The left and right sides of the parabola are reflection images of each other across this "mirror" line, also called the *line of symmetry*.

Step 9 They are alike in that they are both continuous and symmetric, and they are in Quadrants I and II, with one point at the origin. The absolute-value graph looks like a V, and the parabola is smoothly curved, more like a U.

Step 10 Only points in the first quadrant could represent squares, because both side lengths and areas are positive numbers.

Steps 1 and 2

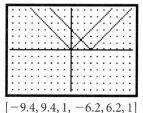

$[-9.4, 9.4, 1, -6.2, 6.2, 1]$

Steps 2 and 3

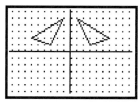

$[-9.4, 9.4, 1, -6.2, 6.2, 1]$

Step 6

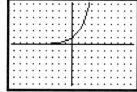

Additional Answers

Step 2 Predictions will vary.

Step 2a a vertical stretch of the graph of $y = \frac{1}{x}$ by a factor of 3 and a reflection across the x-axis

Step 2b a vertical stretch of the graph of $y = \frac{1}{x}$ by a factor of 2, then a translation up 3 units

Step 2c a translation of the graph of $y = \frac{1}{x}$ right 2 units

Step 2d a translation of the graph of $y = \frac{1}{x}$ left 1 unit and down 2 units

---

LESSON 8.7, PAGES 486–488

Step 9

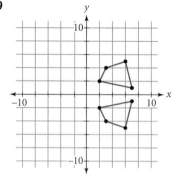

Step 11a
$$\begin{bmatrix} -2 & -3 & -6 & -7 & -x \\ 2 & 4 & 5 & 1 & y \end{bmatrix};$$
a reflection across the y-axis

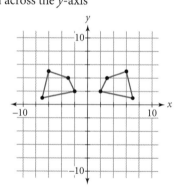

Step 11b
$$\begin{bmatrix} 2 & 3 & 6 & 7 & x \\ 1 & 2 & 2.5 & 0.5 & 0.5y \end{bmatrix};$$
a vertical shrink by a factor of 0.5

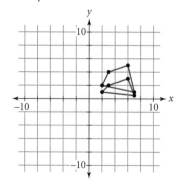

Step 11c
$$\begin{bmatrix} 1 & 1.5 & 3 & 3.5 & 0.5x \\ 4 & 8 & 10 & 2 & 2y \end{bmatrix};$$
a horizontal shrink by a factor of 0.5 and a vertical stretch by a factor of 2

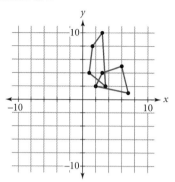

Step 12 If a matrix of the form $\begin{bmatrix} a & 0 \\ 0 & b \end{bmatrix}$ is multiplied by $[B]$, then a affects the x-coordinates of the figure described by $[B]$, and b affects the y-coordinates. If a is negative, the figure reflects across the y-axis; if a is not 1 or -1, there is a horizontal stretch or shrink by a factor of a. If b is negative, the figure reflects across the x-axis; if b is not 1 or -1, there is a vertical stretch or shrink by a factor of b.

1a.

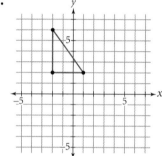

9a. Answers will vary; sample answer: $\begin{bmatrix} 0 & 3 & 4 \\ 0 & 2 & 0 \end{bmatrix}$.

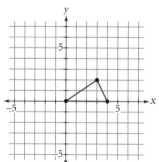

9b. Answers will vary; sample answer:
$$\begin{bmatrix} 0.5 & -0.866 \\ 0.866 & -0.5 \end{bmatrix}\begin{bmatrix} 0 & 3 & 4 \\ 0 & 2 & 0 \end{bmatrix} = \begin{bmatrix} 0 & -0.232 & 2 \\ 0 & 3.598 & 3.464 \end{bmatrix}.$$

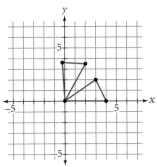

9c. a rotation through 60° about the origin, or the point $(0,0)$

9d. $\begin{bmatrix} -0.500 & -0.866 \\ 0.866 & -0.5 \end{bmatrix}$; sample answer:

$$\begin{bmatrix} -0.500 & -0.866 \\ 0.866 & -0.5 \end{bmatrix}\begin{bmatrix} 0 & 3 & 4 \\ 0 & 2 & 0 \end{bmatrix} = \begin{bmatrix} 0 & -3.232 & -2 \\ 0 & 1.598 & 3.464 \end{bmatrix};$$

a rotation through 120° about the origin

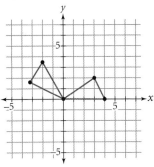

9e. Possible answer: Multiply $\begin{bmatrix} 0.5 & -0.866 \\ 0.866 & -0.5 \end{bmatrix}$ by itself three times $(3 \cdot 60° = 180°)$. Then multiply the result by matrix $[R]$.

9f. Possible answer: Multiply $\begin{bmatrix} 0.5 & -0.866 \\ 0.866 & -0.5 \end{bmatrix}$ by itself six times $(6 \cdot 60° = 360°)$. Then multiply the result by matrix $[R]$ or just multiply $[R]$ by $\begin{bmatrix} 1 & 0 \\ 0 & 1 \end{bmatrix}$.

10a.

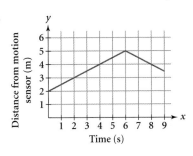

11b. Most Populated Countries, 2004

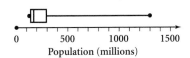

Step 4 sample using window $[-1, 12, 1, -20, 180, 10]$:

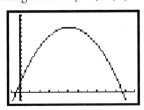

Step 5

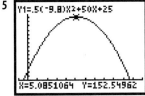

Step 9

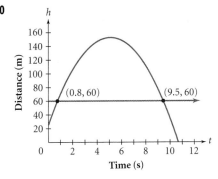

Step 10

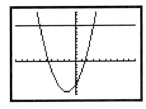

1. Enter one side of the equation into Y₁ and the other into Y₂ on the calculator. Then find the x-coordinate of each intersection point by tracing on the graph or zooming in on the table.

1a. $x = -6$ or $x = 3$

$[-10, 10, 1, -10, 15, 1]$

Additional Answers

1b. no solution

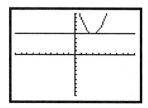

$[-10, 10, 1, -10, 10, 1]$

1c. $x = 3$

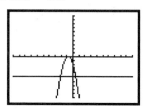

$[-10, 10, 1, -10, 10, 1]$

1d. $x \approx -2.14$ or $x \approx 0.47$

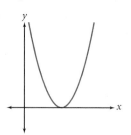

$[-10, 10, 1, -10, 10, 1]$

4. sample answers:

4a.

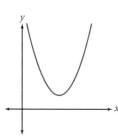

4b.

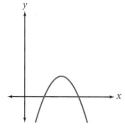

4c.

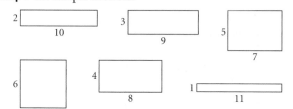

4d.

6d. Start with $h(t) = -t^2$ and a vertical stretch of 108, a horizontal stretch of 4.7, a horizontal translation of $+4.7$, and a vertical translation of $+108$. The equation is $h(t) = -108\left[\frac{1}{4.7}(t - 4.7)\right]^2 + 108 = -4.9(t - 4.7)^2 + 108$.

6f. Answers are $t = 4.7 \pm \sqrt{\frac{61}{4.9}}$. At about 1.17 s and 8.23 s, the flare will be 47 m above the ground.

8a. The graphs intersect at $(3, 4)$, so the solution is $x = 3$.

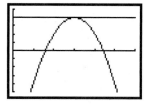

$[0, 6, 1, -5, 5, 1]$

8b. The table shows the solution to be at $x = 3$.

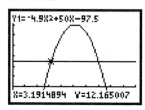

9f. Answers will vary. The horizontal line $y = 12.5$ intersects the parabola twice—when $x \approx 3.2$ s and when $x \approx 7.0$ s.

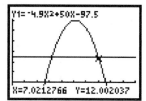

$[0, 10, 1, -5, 35, 5]$

LESSON 9.2, PAGE 502

Step 1 six sample answers:

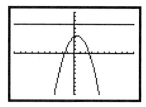

Step 2

Width	Length	Area
1	11	11
2	10	20
3	9	27
4	8	32
5	7	35
6	6	36
7	5	35
8	4	32

Step 3 sample answers:

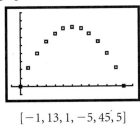

Step 4 sample graph:

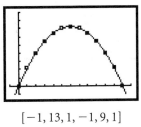

$$[-1, 13, 1, -5, 45, 5]$$

The area increases rapidly at first until the width becomes 6, then it decreases; yes, it makes sense to draw a curve through points to represent decimal widths and areas.

Step 7 $y = x(12 - x)$; the graph shows that a square has the largest area.

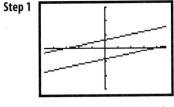

$$[-1, 13, 1, -1, 9, 1]$$

Step 1

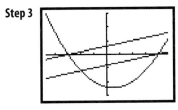

$$[-10, 10, 2, -15, 15, 5]$$

Step 3

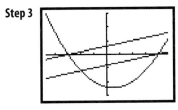

$$[-10, 10, 2, -15, 15, 5]$$

The graph looks like a parabola. The x-intercepts are where the lines $y = x + 3$ and $y = x - 4$ cross the x-axis.

Step 2 Continental Land Areas (millions of km²)

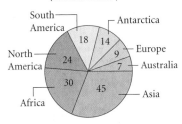

Step 4 Continental Land Areas

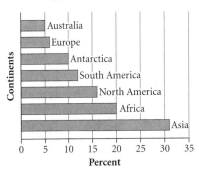

Step 1a

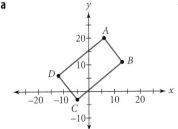

Step 1b

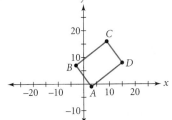

Additional Answers

Step 1c

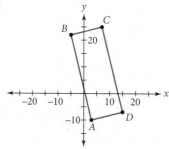

Step 1d

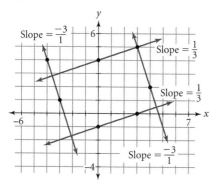

Step 5a slope of $\overline{AB}$: $-\frac{9}{7}$; slope of $\overline{BC}$: $\frac{7}{9}$

Step 5b slope of $\overline{AB}$: $-\frac{4}{3}$; slope of $\overline{BC}$: $\frac{3}{4}$

Step 5c slope of $\overline{AB}$: $-\frac{5}{14}$; slope of $\overline{BC}$: $\frac{14}{5}$

Step 5d slope of $\overline{AB}$: $-\frac{4}{1}$; slope of $\overline{BC}$: $\frac{1}{4}$

Step 6a slope of $\overline{AD}$: $\frac{7}{9}$; slope of $\overline{DC}$: $-\frac{9}{7}$

Step 6b slope of $\overline{AD}$: $\frac{3}{4}$; slope of $\overline{DC}$: $-\frac{4}{3}$

Step 6c slope of $\overline{AD}$: $\frac{14}{5}$; slope of $\overline{DC}$: $-\frac{5}{14}$

Step 6d slope of $\overline{AD}$: $\frac{1}{4}$; slope of $\overline{DC}$: $-\frac{4}{1}$

Step 8 sample answer:

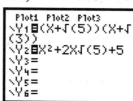

Slope $= \frac{-3}{1}$ Slope $= \frac{1}{3}$ Slope $= \frac{1}{3}$ Slope $= \frac{-3}{1}$

A rectangle is formed.

Step 1a

$\sqrt{18}$ 3   3

Step 1b

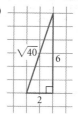

$\sqrt{40}$ 6   2

Step 1c

$\sqrt{20}$ 4   2

Step 1d

$2\sqrt{5}$ $\sqrt{5}$ 2 $\sqrt{5}$ 1   2   1

Step 1e

$3\sqrt{2}$ $\sqrt{2}$ 1 $\sqrt{2}$ 1   1 $\sqrt{2}$ 1   1   1

Step 1f

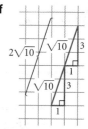

$2\sqrt{10}$ $\sqrt{10}$ 3   1 $\sqrt{10}$ 3   1

3b. $y = x^2 + 2x\sqrt{5} + 5$

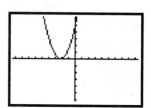

$[-9.4, 9.4, 1, -6.2, 6.2, 1]$

X	Y1	Y2
-3	.58359	.58359
-2	.05573	.05573
-1	1.5279	1.5279
0	5	5
1	10.472	10.472
2	17.944	17.944
3	27.416	27.416

X=-3

Additional Answers

6a. $y = x^2 - 112$

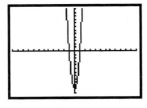

$[-120, 120, 10, -120, 120, 10]$

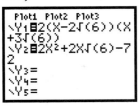

6b. $y = 2x^2 + 2x\sqrt{6} - 72$

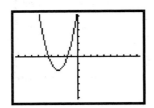

$[-100, 100, 10, -100, 100, 10]$

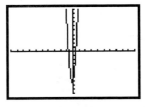

6c. $y = x^2 + 6x + 7$

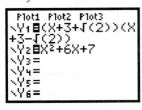

$[-9.4, 9.4, 1, -6.2, 6.2, 1]$

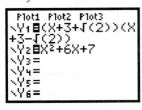

Steps 2–5

Section	Horizontal distance traveled (Step 2)	Slope (Step 3)	Diagonal distance (Step 4)	Angle of climb (Step 5)
1	60 m	$\dfrac{20\text{ m}}{60\text{ m}} = \dfrac{1}{3}$	$20\sqrt{10}$ m ≈ 63.2 m	$\tan^{-1}\left(\dfrac{1}{3}\right)$ $\approx 18.4°$
2	90 m	$\dfrac{20\text{ m}}{90\text{ m}} = \dfrac{2}{9}$	$10\sqrt{85}$ m ≈ 92.2 m	$\tan^{-1}\left(\dfrac{2}{9}\right)$ $\approx 12.5°$
3	50 m	$\dfrac{20\text{ m}}{50\text{ m}} = \dfrac{2}{5}$	$10\sqrt{29}$ m ≈ 53.9 m	$\tan^{-1}\left(\dfrac{2}{5}\right)$ $\approx 21.8°$
4	120 m	$\dfrac{7\text{ m}}{120\text{ m}}$ $= \dfrac{7}{120}$	$\sqrt{14{,}449}$ m ≈ 120.2 m	$\tan^{-1}\left(\dfrac{7}{120}\right)$ $\approx 3.3°$
5	50 m	$\dfrac{-7\text{ m}}{50\text{ m}}$ $= -\dfrac{7}{50}$	$\sqrt{2{,}549}$ m ≈ 50.5 m	$\tan^{-1}\left(-\dfrac{7}{50}\right)$ $\approx -8.0°$
6	20 m	$\dfrac{-20\text{ m}}{20\text{ m}}$ $= -1$	$20\sqrt{2}$ m ≈ 28.3 m	$\tan^{-1}(-1)$ $= -45°$
7	30 m	$\dfrac{-20\text{ m}}{30\text{ m}}$ $= -\dfrac{2}{3}$	$10\sqrt{13}$ m ≈ 36.1 m	$\tan^{-1}\left(-\dfrac{2}{3}\right)$ $\approx -33.7°$
8	20 m	$\dfrac{-20\text{ m}}{20\text{ m}}$ $= -1$	$20\sqrt{2}$ m ≈ 28.3 m	$\tan^{-1}(-1)$ $= -45°$

Additional Answers